# THE OFFICIAL® PRICE GUIDE TO

# FINE ART

## FIRST EDITION

## SUSAN THERAN

THE HOUSE OF COLLECTIBLES
NEW YORK, NEW YORK 10022

*Cover Photograph:* The reproduction on the front cover is entitled *Basket of Apples,* by Levi Wells Prentice, courtesy of Sotheby's, Inc.

Published by:   The House of Collectibles
                201 East 50th Street
                New York, New York 10022

Distributed by Ballantine Books, a division of Random House, Inc., New York and simultaneously in Canada by Random House of Canada Limited, Toronto.

Manufactured in the United States of America

ISBN: 0-87637-589-1

10  9  8  7  6  5  4  3  2  1

# Table of Contents

# ACKNOWLEDGMENTS

The mere "acknowledgment" of the efforts and contributions of the people who participated in bringing this volume into your hands is not enough. This is really a page of warm and heartfelt "thank you's," so

Thank you:

to Dorothy Harris, my editor, for her genuine enthusiasm for this book, her constant support, and for making the entire project a pleasure from start to finish.

to the experts, who were so generous with their time and expertise in the reading of my first drafts: Carolyn Backlund, Janice Chadbourne, William Dane, Peter Fairbanks, Margaret and Charles Godwin, Pamela Hurd, Sam Pennington, Dorothy Polansky, Peter Rathbone, Charlotte Riordan, Sam Robbins.

to those who contributed their expertise and helped to make this book accurate: Laila Abdel-Malek, Gwen Knight, Pat Pierce, Ron Stark, Peter Williams.

to the many libraries throughout the country that generously offered their services, and most especially to the librarians at the Boston Public Library's Fine Arts Department for their ongoing help and support.

to Susan Ebert, who took the thoughts and words in this book and helped turn them into prose.

to Marjorie Adams, whose knowledge as art librarian, dealer, and editor of *Leonard's Index* has been so invaluable.

to my staff, who worked so tirelessly compiling the database and researching artists: Linda Bohannon-Bellamy, Jim Cadorette, Debby Ebert, Jane Fischbein, Karen Fordyce, Betsy Gibbons, J. Ferol Jones, Julie Lane, Rona Leff, Patrizia Mineo, Anne Rouillard.

to Sheldon Fogelman, Esq. who has given me advice and encouragement and guided me through the intricacies of publishing.

to Rich LaChance of The Systems Approach, whose systems allowed this book to come into being.

and, most of all, to my daughters Sally and Rachel.

## AUCTION HOUSE ACKNOWLEDGMENTS

Special appreciation and thanks to all the auction houses who provide catalogs and prices in a timely manner for the Auction Index database. All these auction houses are listed in Appendix C.

And a special thank you to the auction houses who so generously provided the photographs used and some of the stories behind the captions. The citation for each caption lists specific information for the lot sold; the auction house cited has provided the photograph. They are: Barridoff Galleries, Frank H. Boos Gallery, Inc., Richard A. Bourne Co., Inc., Butterfield & Butterfield, Chicago Art Galleries, Inc., Christie, Manson & Woods International, Inc., Christie's East, William Doyle Galleries, Du Mouchelle Art Galleries, Robert C. Eldred Co., Inc., Fine Arts Co. of Philadelphia, Inc., Samuel T. Freeman & Co., Hanzel Galleries, Leslie Hindman Auctioneers, James D. Julia, Mapes Auctioneers and Appraisers, Milwaukee Auction Galleries, Phillips Son & Neale, Inc., Selkirk Galleries, Robert W. Skinner Galleries, C.G. Sloan & Company, Inc., Sotheby's, Inc., Stalker Gallery, Inc., Weschler's, and Wolf's Auction Galleries.

## Where to Start

Nearly everyone buys art.

Some people buy Old Master drawings and others buy preframed posters, but we all buy things to enhance the spaces in which we live and work. It's a natural extension of adorning ourselves. We surround ourselves with paintings, sculpture, posters, photographs, and objects that are aesthetically appealing, and enjoy looking at and living with them.

Choosing and collecting fine art is a continuous adventure. Like most adventures, it has ups and downs, moments of exhilaration, and times of absolute frustration. Collecting art sounds like such a serious undertaking that, at the beginning, it can seem daunting. Collecting means different things to different people. For some, it is an occasional excursion to a gallery, auction, or flea market, while for others it becomes a life-long passion which absorbs time, space, energy, and money. Whether your interest is intense or casual, creating a collection is a realistic, reachable goal.

The media hype that accompanies record-breaking auction prices for artwork obscures the fact that for every million dollar painting there are thousands of works by recognized artists that sell for considerably less than $10,000. In fact, for any given year, statistics drawn from the Auction Index, Inc. database show that 40% of the art sold at auction sold for less than $1,000, and another 25% sold for between $1,000 and $5,000.

Your interest, knowledge, and eagerness to learn will all contribute to your ability to collect. This book will make you an informed purchaser and provide the vital price data that will enable you to buy with confidence.

## Look Before You Leap

You've probably already taken many of the first steps that culminate in collecting. Most of us begin to develop an interest in fine art by visiting museums. There is no better place to start—the phrase "museum quality" denotes the highest standard of workmanship. Museums with extensive collections provide exposure

1

to an encyclopedic variety of styles and artistic media. Smaller museums, especially those with specialized collections, provide an opportunity to study a particular aspect of art in depth.

In every case, museum going will help you develop your own eye for quality. Examine the individual works carefully. Analyze their composition. How does the artist lead you into the work? Are you made to focus on the foreground and then drawn further back? Are you led immediately to a particular point on the canvas? What are the primary lines of composition? How are light and shadow achieved? What did the artist set out to accomplish? Does the painting tell a story? If it is a portrait, does it convey personality? It is the ability of paintings to spark these questions that contributes to their quality. Your ability to respond to them is an indication of your growing understanding of what quality means in art.

At the same time, you will be sharpening your taste and defining your preferences. Is your eye drawn to particular subjects? Do you like still lifes? Landscapes? Animals? Domestic interiors? Abstract shapes? Do you prefer specific color ranges? Do you like looking at pictures of activities you enjoy? What kinds of artistic media attract you? Do you like chalk, pencil, watercolor? Do you like finished paintings, or do you prefer oil sketches? A few leisurely afternoons in a museum will help you make such determinations.

Galleries offer a way of learning about the works of individual artists. Owners are generally knowledgeable and most have chosen to sell art because they love it. Keep in mind, however, that galleries are governed by the realities of the marketplace. Many, but by no means all, are willing to take the time to help educate potential customers and share their frequently specialized and unique information. Most collectors agree that the very best galleries are the ones that will take the time to educate, confident that their investment in time will ultimately show a return in sales.

Classes, courses, lectures, and workshops offered by museums and historical societies afford additional opportunities to learn about art. Frequently, individual lectures are planned to coincide with annual or semi-annual exhibits and shows. Since smaller institutions often cannot afford to advertise, you will have to call for information or watch local newspaper "Calendars" for announcements.

Above all, you must read—art books, magazines, exhibition catalogs, and auction catalogs. When, after conscientious museum going and gallery visits, you determine that you are seriously interested in, for example, the Boston School, and want to begin collecting this late 19th- to early 20th-century group, your next stop is the library. What was the Boston School? Who was associated with it? By doing your own research, you'll pull together the bits of information gleaned from museum labels and dealers, and begin to assemble a composite body of data. You don't need to be an expert before you begin to buy art—the learning process is continuous. If you're like most collectors, once you've been drawn into a subject, you'll want to learn more and more.

Thorough knowledge and study lay the groundwork for serious collecting. Anyone who builds a valuable collection has worked hard, studying and learning.

## Developing Your Taste

The best way to begin is by buying.

Buy what you can afford. Buy in little shops. Buy in junk shops. Buy in antique shops, flea markets, and at low-priced auctions. But buy!

Nothing else shapes your eye so quickly. Nothing sharpens your taste like making a purchase. In making a financial commitment, you make a statement of your likes and dislikes. It is a process subject to constant refinement.

What catches your eye?

Will the first item in your collection be a scene that you recognize, something that evokes a feeling or memory which you want to preserve? For many people, collecting starts with something very specific that is tied to a strong personal interest and then extends and develops. Many real or armchair sailors collect maritime scenes. Gardeners often are drawn to pictures of flowers. Mountain scenes are popular with many collectors.

Discovering what you really like is akin to stripping paint from a piece of old furniture. As you work through to the essence of your taste, you will reveal successive layers of appreciation for different types of work. In the process, you will refine your taste—and you may end up selling some of your early acquisitions.

But, begin by buying. Don't be afraid to make mistakes.

In the course of building a collection you will develop a consistent eye. That is, over time you will find that everything you buy fits together. Buying will enable you to develop a sureness of taste, and the confidence of your own judgments.

## Where to Buy Art

Buying art is somewhat less straightforward than buying a washing machine or an air conditioner, but it's more absorbing and more fun. The sheer variety of places in which you can look for a work of art and the process of looking are at once an education and an activity in themselves.

## Yard Sales, Garage Sales, and Flea Markets

Yard sales, garage sales, and flea markets are a boon to weekend collectors. Someone we know who has a phenomenal memory for artists' names has been very successful (and very lucky) at turning up pictures that others have cleaned out of their attics.

The first rule for getting to any of these sales is—be early. Most flea markets advertise in the classified section of local newspapers and list their hours. (Some open at dawn.) Often dealers will sell right out of their cars to early arrivals—even before they've had a chance to set up their displays. One word of caution—"early birds" aren't always welcome, particularly at garage sales. But it may be worth the risk of a chilly reception on the chance that you'll catch the proverbial worm.

At a flea market you'll find most old paintings and drawings in the antiques section. Check a map of the field when you arrive, since some markets divide dealers' merchandise into old and new, and you can waste a great deal of time trudging past racks of bubble gum and shoelaces before you find the right area. But don't overlook the "junk" area. Some of the best buys may be in the section reserved for sellers who have just cleaned out their attics or garages and don't know what they have.

Some flea markets are held regularly, even weekly. Others are occasional—sponsored by service groups, churches, or fraternal organizations.

The queen of the flea markets is held three times a year (May, July, and September) in Brimfield, Massachusetts. Thousands of dealers set up their displays on acres of fields for this event that attracts purchasers not only from the Northeast but the entire nation and abroad. Some European dealers buy a year's stock of American antiques and paintings at Brimfield.

Our veteran Brimfield connoisseur recommends arriving before dawn. The show opens at 5:00 A.M. and the line begins to form two hours earlier. Carry a flashlight, she advises, so that you can see what's displayed on the tables, and spot the dealers walking around carrying signs that read, "I buy penknives," or "I buy old cameras." Take the time to savor the unique character of this enormous show, which includes the spectacle of pairs of collectors or dealers who race from one display to the next, using walkie-talkies to announce finds to their partners.

Brimfield runs for a week—you may find the very best buys if you're there before first light, but good quality material is on sale all day long. Brimfield is a joy for collectors, and a good place for dealers as well. Many of them save unique pieces to bring to this market, which attracts thousands of sophisticated purchasers.

Flea markets, garage, and yard sales are fun to go to, and great places to buy. They are good sources for watercolors, drawings. . .and fakes. Chances are strong that the painting you find signed "Picasso" wasn't the work of Pablo. Even a name-plaque on the frame does not assure that a piece is actually the work of the designated artist. (You might, however, find an original of a more obscure artist.) Some prints, especially chromolithographs, closely resemble paintings. Also, some prints were painted over, closely following the original lines. They are often very difficult to detect. They turn up at places like Brimfield, but they occasionally also turn up at auction, and are sold as "painted by the artist who did the original work for the print."

When you decide to buy at a flea market, yard, or garage sale, examine the condition of the work carefully. Flea market merchandise is sold "as is." Usually it's helpful to ask where the work came from—that is, attic, basement, or Aunt Gertrude. Most sellers know something about what they're selling, and though there won't be a provenance (history) supplied for a picture at a yard sale, there may well be an interesting story attached to it. Some material could be "hot." Last year a painting stolen from a New England historical society surfaced at a church flea market where it was purchased for under $100. The work was recognized when it was brought in for appraisal.

The rule of purchase at yard sales and flea markets is—make an offer. There is usually little science, knowledge, or reason for the price written on the tag. Be ready to negotiate.

One final note.

Don't go to any of these sales expecting to find a lost masterwork. When you buy, buy because you are drawn to the work, because it appeals to you, because it is consistent with the things you like and own, and because you can afford it.

## Second Hand, Junk and Consignment Stores, and Antique Shops

One step up from garage sales and flea markets (and sometimes a very short step indeed) is browser's paradise—second hand, junk, and consignment shops. These are places where you may find almost anything, but seldom what you are looking for. Often the owners of these emporia will acquire stray pictures or drawings in the process of acquiring an estate or cleaning out a garage or attic. Art may be almost hidden in many of these stores. Ask if there are any pictures. Look under tables and behind furniture.

Antique stores are another good source. It's hard to be knowledgeable about everything. Store owners may be expert about furniture but unaware of the value of a picture they have acquired. They may have purchased a picture in order to acquire an entire estate and be willing to sell at minimal profit to move it, because they specialize in another field.

Wherever you are, look for frames. Good period frames are hard to find. Even if you don't like the picture, the frame may be just what you need for your picture at home.

## Dealing With Dealers

A first trip to a big-city gallery can be intimidating. The imposing front entrance and glacial sales staff can combine to keep beginning collectors at a distance. Yet the same people won't hesitate for a second to get out of the car at a country antiques store and ask if there are any pictures in the back room. It's a mistake to assume that a country dealer in a flannel shirt is any less knowledgeable about value and quality than his Madison Avenue or Newbury Street counterpart, or that his prices will be lower. The overhead will be higher in the city, and that will affect prices, but a higher turnover may enable a city gallery to work on a lower profit margin.

Some collectors who are just starting out may hesitate to visit dealers, for they're convinced that this is the most expensive way to purchase, or concerned that they'll be pushed into something they're not ready for. Others wouldn't begin to look for a work of art without the guidance of a professional.

If, in fact, you end up developing a very serious interest in collecting, you'll become an expert in the area that interests you. When you walk into a tiny up-country store and spot a small dirty canvas that looks promising, you'll have the knowledge you need to examine it carefully and decide if you want to add it to your collection.

Should that happen when you're just starting out, and it's a small purchase, go ahead and buy it. As long as the work really appeals to you, there's no such thing as a $150 error. But imagine a different scenario in which the price tag is substantially higher, and you really don't know whether the work is fairly priced, or even authentic. (Of course, you'll have this book in hand, and that will give you confidence and credibility if you decide to negotiate the price.) That's a compelling reason for making major purchases from dealers. Until, and even when, you develop your own store of knowledge, they are the professionals.

A good dealer knows an artist's work and style, can authenticate it, and can recognize whether it has been altered. Experienced dealers know a great deal about the process of making art, and the scholarly and technical aspects of art history.

There were, for example, artists who painted the major elements of pictures, and then turned to apprentices to fill in the rest. Works completed during certain periods of an artist's life are worth more than others. There are nuances in a painting which will change its value. If there's a glass in a still life by an artist who didn't usually paint glass, the work is more valuable. If the artist worked in a realistic style during much of his career, but later became more impressionistic, the pictures from different periods will have differing values. If, in a particular picture, an artist introduced an element which later became characteristic of his work, the picture will have particular value. Some artists chose not to sign their canvases, or signed them on the back so that they didn't disturb the aesthetic balance of the work. This is the type of specialized information for which you will turn to a dealer.

In addition to being a storehouse of knowledge, a dealer can be extremely helpful in locating the kind of work you find most appealing, particularly if your taste is very specialized. Once you've developed a relationship with a dealer, he or she will buy with you in mind and be able to sell to you with a lower markup because there will be a quicker turnover. An ongoing relationship with a reputable dealer is a good way to assure access to quality work. Every serious collector has a good working relationship with at least a few dealers. It's true that you may pay more when you buy from a dealer than you might at an auction, but you're paying for knowledge and time.

Note, too, that most dealers will generally not sell a painting unless it has been cleaned and, if needed, restored by a competent professional restorer. This can save both time and money for a collector.

The key question is, how do you find a dealer with whom you'll be comfortable? There are literally hundreds of galleries, shops, and dealers in most areas. Consult the *Art in America Gallery Guide*, available on newsstands in August and in many libraries. In larger cities you can begin by looking through the yellow pages, the gallery listings in newspapers and magazines, weekly calendar supplements, and even guidebooks. In smaller areas where galleries are dispersed, dealers often form regional associations and publish a listing of members and a map showing their locations. These are available in the stores, or at local, state-sponsored tourist information centers.

Galleries may specialize. Visit as many as you can until you find those dealers whose taste is very much like your own, and begin to cultivate a working relationship. Put your name on the mailing list so that you will be invited to previews and kept informed about publications.

Networking and talking with other collectors is essential. Talk to people at auctions. You may get to meet dealers you'd never meet otherwise because they don't generally sell to the public.

### Terms

The term *dealer* covers such a broad range of operations that it will be useful to distinguish among the various types who operate at all different levels of the art market. On the very first rung of the ladder are *pickers*, people with good eyes, developed taste, and eternal optimism. They scour flea markets, yard sales, and country auctions, always on the lookout for the underpriced, unrecognized "find." Pickers have established relationships with lawyers representing estates, dealers, galleries, and individual collectors. They buy and sell to their contacts.

Then there are *door knockers*. The name says it all. Door knockers are a variety of picker who go door to door in search of old paintings, rugs, and furniture to resell to dealers or through auction houses.

*Runners* are the matchmakers, the link between dealers, or dealers and collectors. A very few who work the upper end of the market are essentially private dealers who make a handsome commission on costly works of art. Most live a far less glamorous existence, moving individual pieces from one dealer to the next, hoping to make a quick sale and a small profit. *Brokers* are a more elite version of runners, often relying on a large circle of acquaintances to keep up to date about what's for sale and who might be looking. Brokers never actually own any work (although they may take a piece on consignment). They direct their energies instead to bringing buyer and seller together.

*Wholesalers* don't maintain a retail space, but work directly with galleries rather than individual collectors.

*Collector dealers* start as collectors, but become so involved with their interest that they sell parts of their collections in order to "feed their habits" and upgrade or diversify their holdings.

### Strategies

The term *dealer*, as it is usually used, means an individual who owns and runs a shop or gallery. But the word is so inclusive that it covers everything from an exquisitely decorated world famous gallery which commands instant name recognition, to the tiniest, most crowded, backstreet junkstore.

But. . .the range of dealers really runs the gamut from part-time entrepreneurs who do business out of the trunks of their cars, on up. Some limit their activities and only participate in shows. Some will see clients only by appointment.

With this variety, it is clear that no single strategy of dealing with dealers will work in all situations. What follows is the composite of advice from a number of dealers, collectors, and personal experience.

On your first visits to a dealer or gallery, you should make your interests and intentions clear. Establish yourself. Let the owner or salesperson know why you've come in. Are you there to learn or to buy? Do you know what you like? (This can be a particularly important question if you're in a major gallery. Some have enormous inventories, literally hundreds of paintings. It's no time to start trying to define your taste.)

Are you buying for visual and aesthetic pleasure? Are you buying for decoration—a blue painting to hang over the sofa? Or, are you buying for investment?

Know what your price range is, and state it, but don't be afraid to look at things you can't afford. Consider it another step in honing your eye and developing your own standards of taste by correlating quality and price.

### Authenticity

Ask the dealer to show you the painting in a darkened room under a black light, an uncomplicated ultraviolet light which, when it shines on the canvas, will reveal inpainting and overpainting. The former is the precise repainting of a damaged area, the latter, the addition of too much new paint which alters the appearance of the work. Particularly in an older work, a certain amount of restoration is acceptable, and perhaps even desirable. A hundred year old painting can show some signs of wear around the edges. A skilled restorer can repair it, filling in the missing spots, enhancing the painting's appearance, and increasing its value. Inpainting is an absolute necessity when a torn or punctured canvas is repaired.

It's when the restorer's skill is abused and a painting is significantly changed from its original form that inpainting becomes a problem. Among the long list of items that can be added to a painting to make it seem more attractive are: parasols, balloons, American flags, baby carriages, little dogs, long white dresses, flowers, pretty women tending gardens or interiors, butterflies, and by no means least, signatures and dates. It is to discover these abuses that a black light is used.

Under a black light, it's easy to detect changes that would otherwise be impossible to see. Paint that is only a few months or years old looks different from paint applied a century ago. Inpainting will fluoresce under a black light. However, some 20th-century pigments will always fluoresce. Surface cracks and other irregularities, changes in composition and color also become dramatically apparent. Some new techniques, however, do not show up under a black light.

Thus, if you've found a painting you like, ask to see it under a black light. In fact, a reputable dealer will be eager to show a canvas under a black light and quick to point out any alterations in the surface. If, however, he or she is reluctant to have the painting subjected to such scrutiny, you ought to look for another painting...and another dealer. (If you would like to buy your own black light, you can probably find one in a novelty store for less than an art supply store will charge. They're popular with young people because they make fluorescent posters glow.)

If you're looking at paintings in a less formal setting, it may be helpful to carry a magnifying glass so that you can closely examine the surface of the work. With the aid of a lens you can pick out an inscription or signature that would otherwise be difficult to see. You may also be able to tell if a signature or anything else has been added over the varnish that covers the original work.

A final step before making a purchase is to ask to have the picture removed from the frame. If the work is old and hasn't been restored, the canvas shouldn't be taut. The surface of the painting may show some *craquelure*, a web of tiny fine lines caused by the drying out of the canvas. When the canvas is out of the frame, you'll be able to see if the picture has been remounted—if the canvas has been tautened as a result of relining it with another canvas or a board. Ask the dealer why the work was relined. It may not affect the value of the painting, but it's something you should know. At the same time, you can see if the painting has been cropped, or even cut out of a larger work.

## Provenance

Depending on the level at which you are buying, a painting may have a written provenance, a life history from the time it left the artist's easel to its arrival at the gallery, which includes the names of previous owners and the dates on which it changed hands. Obviously, the better known and more costly the painting, the likelier and more necessary the provenance. Not surprisingly, a provenance adds to the value of a painting.

You might begin by asking about the painting's history. If the dealer has the estate, he may have the artist's notebook, preliminary sketches for the work (very collectible), or other information. Has the work been in a catalog? Was it included in an exhibit? This may be pertinent to a given work, or it may not. Quite a number of very fine works have never been shown publicly, and thus, their formal record is quite short. Because dealers' connections in the art world may give them access to works before any private buyers get to see them, the picture you're looking at may have remained in the hands of a single owner or family and be new to the market. It may, for example, have been the gift of the artist to the grandfather of the present owner, or have some similar history.

A less expensive work may have no written history at all, just the statement of the dealer to the effect that ''I bought it from the Smith estate up in Westfield.'' If you're looking at the work of a relative unknown, this is quite an acceptable response. The dealer may be able to fill you in on the family that owned the painting, the general nature of the estate, and the artist as well.

## Negotiating a Price

While the price that a dealer quotes to you is not necessarily the one you'll end up paying, the issue of price negotiations raises questions, eyebrows, and sometimes, tempers.

To negotiate or not to negotiate. Most dealers will insist that they won't. Many buyers will tell you they've tried and sometimes succeeded. If you're embarrassed, don't, but as a general rule of thumb, try. Remember that if you can walk away from a potential purchase, there's a far greater chance of success than if you're caught up in the process and dead set on acquiring a particular work.

The possibilities for negotiation depend very much upon the dealer, the gallery, the painting, and the realities of the marketplace. Galleries at prestigious addresses in major cities carry enormous overheads which are necessarily reflected in the prices of the paintings they sell. There is generally a close relationship between the location and prestige of the gallery, the desirability of the painting, and the readiness of the customer to make an offer and the dealer to accept it. It's complicated by the length of time the picture has been in the dealer's possession, and last, but by no means least, the percentage which it has been marked up.

In other words, if you want to buy a picture which has been in a gallery for only a week, the dealer is not likely to negotiate. If the picture is still on the wall when you come back six months later, there's a much greater likelihood that you'll find some flexibility in the price.

Of course, the whole question of negotiation depends upon who you are talking to and where. We know one very genteel lady who successfully bargains at Cartiers. While small informal stores which carry a mix of paintings and other things seem to invite bargaining more than others, serious collectors will negotiate anywhere.

Remember, too, that when you question a price, you are at least in part asking why it has been set at a certain level. If it seems especially high, there may be a good reason for it—the work may have some unique quality. Keep in mind as well that some dealers will overprice, expecting to be negotiated down.

Dealers maintain that it is not in their own interest to overprice paintings, since most guarantee that they will take a work back in trade for at least the original price. Most dealers will add that they will not try to outbid an individual collector at auction, since they will later have to resell the painting.

Bear in mind, too, that prices in this *Guide* were achieved at auction, a market that is frequently considered wholesale. It is perfectly reasonable for the dealer who has spent time and money acquiring, and possibly restoring, the work to make a profit on it. Your readiness to make an offer, and the dealer's willingness to be somewhat flexible about pricing, will constitute the negotiation.

### Bills of Sale

For major purchases, for purposes of insurance and recordkeeping, it is important to secure a bill of sale. You can be assured of the authenticity of a work of art if the dealer will write out and *sign* the sales slip to read:

"One oil, title, *by* Robert Smith, size, location of signature, and any other significant details."

If the slip reads: "One oil *signed* Robert Smith" or "One oil *inscribed* Robert Smith," or "One oil *attributed* to Robert Smith," then the dealer is not liable should the painting turn out to be a forgery. You can be forceful, or you can be innocent and say that your sister the attorney insisted that you ask for that specific wording, but don't leave the gallery without it.

### Methods of Payment

You may find a greater degree of flexibility in price if you can pay cash; however, most people find it more convenient to make major purchases by check.

If you do pay cash, be sure to save your sales slip, since it is the only proof you will have to present to an insurance company in the event of loss.

Some dealers will permit you to pay for a painting in installments, but unless you are a well-established customer, you should not expect to be able to take the work home until it is completely paid for. (However, if you offer to let the dealer keep the painting until you finish paying for it, he may let you take it home.)

## Auctions

You don't need a course in assertiveness training to bid at an auction. Neither do you need to sit absolutely still while bidding goes on around you, lest an auctioneer mistake some motion as a hidden signal. Auctions are entertaining to attend, and a good way to purchase art.

### Terms

As in all specialized fields, there are specific terms used in auctions which you must understand before you begin. The most important, listed alphabetically, are:

*Auction.* A sale in which the auctioneer, acting as the agent for sellers (called consignors), offers a series of objects to prospective buyers who bid incrementally. The highest bidder buys the object. The auctioneer always encourages bidding to try to get the highest price, since his payment is generally a percentage of the sale.

*Bought-in.* If a lot does not achieve its reserve (see page 14) it is said to be bought-in by the auction house and will be returned to the consignor or be reoffered at a later sale. However, bear in mind that if, on its own momentum, bidding does not reach the reserve, the auction house will bid on behalf of the consignor against bids from the floor. Only if the work still does not reach its reserve is it bought-in. It's not always clear whether there's a reserve on an individual lot. (New York City law requires that all lots with a reserve be marked with a black square or dot in the auction catalog.) Neither is it always clear whether a lot has been bought-in. New laws pending in New York City may require the auction house to announce whether a lot has been bought-in. Terminology will vary—passed, bought-in, or unsold.

*Buyer premium.* At the majority of auctions, a premium amounting to 10% of the hammer price is added to the cost of each item. Sales tax is calculated on the total. An auctioneer who adds a buyer premium will usually indicate this in advertisements or catalogs.

*Catalog sale.* An auction for which a printed listing of lots is prepared and distributed in advance. Catalogs can be mimeographed lists with brief descriptions or beautifully illustrated, carefully researched, book-length publications.

*Consignor.* The individual who has asked the auction house to sell a particular piece or pieces.

*Estimate.* The price range within which an auction house expects to sell a particular lot. The estimate is included in the printed catalog. Reserve is usually two-thirds of the low estimate. For more expensive lots, reserve is usually close to the low estimate. At best, an estimate is the auctioneer's best judgment based on the artist's sales history, and the condition and desirability of the particular piece.

*Hammer price (knockdown).* The price at which a lot is sold.

*Inspection.* See "preview."

*Left bid (including mail bids).* A bid submitted by a prospective buyer who can't attend the auction. These are executed by the auctioneer or a member of his staff during the sale.

*Lot.* An individual work or group of works offered for sale at one time.

*Paddle.* A numbered card which may be anything from an imprinted plastic paddle to a paper plate. It is given to bidders when they register and must be held aloft in order to bid.

*Passed.* If there is no interest from the floor and no bidding on the lot, it is passed over, and the auctioneer goes on to the next.

*Preview (exhibition).* The period before a sale reserved for the inspection or viewing of items to be auctioned. In larger auction houses, the preview period may be as long as a week. At smaller sales, the preview may be only the day of the sale. Generally, lots cannot be viewed after the sale starts. However, if it is really impossible to schedule a pre-sale inspection, call the auction house in advance and arrange to see the item when you arrive.

*Prices realized.* A listing of lots sold and the prices achieved. Some auction houses publish these prices and some do not. They may be published with or without the buyer premium.

*Reserve.* The lowest price which a consignor will accept for a lot. It is ordinarily used only for high-priced works. The reserve is often two-thirds of the low estimate. At the major houses, the reserve for more expensive paintings is frequently close to the low estimate. If reserve is not reached and the lot is bought-in, the piece may be offered again at a later sale. Reserves are rarely set at country sales, so that sparse attendance, or limited interest, may make it possible to pick up a good buy.

*The ring (the pool).* An informal agreement among dealers that they will not bid against each other for a specific lot. After the sale they adjourn to the parking lot for a "knockout" in which the lot is sold to one of the dealers in the pool. Each writes down the figure that he or she is ready to pay. The highest bidder ends up with the merchandise, while the others split the difference between the actual purchase price at the auction and the price reached in the post-auction action. Most merchandise sold in this manner leaves the parking lot at the price it should have fetched at the sale. The losers, clearly, are the auction house and the consignor. These activities amount to restraint of trade and are illegal in most states. Curiously, some members of the ring never actually deal in merchandise but manage to make a small living simply by participating. While the ring can be a potent force in controlling prices at an auction, an independent purchaser can beat it. Just set your price and stick to it.

*Shill.* An individual planted in the crowd by the house or by an individual consignor to bid up the price of a lot. Contracts at most houses forbid the consignor or his agent to bid on the lot he has consigned.

*Telephone bid.* A bid from someone not attending the auction, who makes advance arrangements with the house to bid actively during the auction. Telephone bidding is generally limited to higher priced works, and at important auctions, there may be a bank of telephones in place for long distance participation. (Not all telephone bidding is long distance. Sometimes, bidders use a pay phone in the auction house so that they can bid without being identified.)

*Underbidder.* The losing bidder.

*Withdrawn.* A lot removed before the sale begins.

## Types

Auctions vary widely in the variety and quality of artwork they offer. At country auctions mixed offerings are the rule, and they will include furniture, paintings and drawings, rugs, bric-a-brac, and assorted collectibles. A painting sold at a country auction may have been hanging on the same wall for the past 100 years, or it might be the ten-year-old work of a summer painter. That stained work on paper may be an original watercolor, or clipped from a magazine and hung in a five and dime store frame.

Some auctioneers assemble a collection for a sale by combining lots from many different households or sources. Be aware that some dealers will consign "hard to sell" merchandise at these sales. Such sales are frequently held in halls and lodges, veteran's posts or fraternal organizations and may include some paintings or watercolors.

Some paintings are usually put on the block at estate auctions, where the entire contents of a house are sold on site and often on a weekday. Estate auctions bring fresh, new, and thus particularly desirable material to the market.

## Catalogs

One advantage of buying a work of art at a large auction house is that a great deal of your work has already been done for you. By the time something appears in an auction house catalog, it has already filtered past the first levels of professional assessment.

An auction house catalog, a listing of lots to be sold at a particular auction, can be anything from a mimeographed list to a splendidly printed and illustrated volume that looks a great deal like an expensive art book. A catalog can be a source of valuable information, but it should be read in the context in which it is created. An auction house catalog is a sales tool. It can be glamorous and packed with information, but it is compiled to help the house successfully market a product.

Catalogs, while useful art reference tools, are not definitive sources of information. The fact that a work is listed in a catalog does not legitimize it.

Catalogs are not always scholarly works. They may or may not be written by knowledgeable people. They are not infallible and may contain errors in attribution or authentication.

In reading an art auction catalog, it is important to remember that at the major houses, works are generally arranged chronologically, rather than in order of importance. Color illustrations often draw the reader's attention. Whether a lot is illustrated or not, or in black and white or in color, does not indicate importance. Remember that most auction houses charge consignors for illustrations, and charge more for color than black and white.

Auction houses list the title of the painting, if known. Otherwise they give a descriptive title.

A typical catalog description will include the artist's name; the title (in quotation marks or capital letters); whether and where the work is signed; the medium (oil on canvas, oil on board, pencil on paper, *etc.*); size and condition; and the price estimate. It may also provide information about the provenance of the work, or literature about the artist. (If you buy a picture at an auction, save the catalog, for it becomes part of the provenance.)

The auction house may indicate its confidence in the authenticity of a particular piece in the way it prints the artist's name. For example, if it catalogs a piece by Sir Jacob Epstein, you can be confident that it's by the great 20th-century English sculptor. A little less certainty will shorten the listing to Jacob Epstein. If there's more question, the name may appear as J. Epstein. Dropping a title or abbreviating a first name to an initial usually indicates doubt. If the catalog description says "bears signature" or "apocryphal signature," this is another way of saying the signature is false. If the catalog says "signature is inscribed," this means written by someone other than the artist. When you read the description, be aware that state laws vary, as does the buy back policy or guarantee. Terminology also varies from house to house. Christie's uses the term "cast from a model by" as its guarantee for bronzes. This term has been picked up by auction houses outside of New York state, but does not necessarily mean the same thing.

The same cautions apply to the use of such terms as "school," "school of," "studio of," and "circle of," whether in catalogs or anywhere else. "School of," as in "School of Raphael," is generally applied to the work of students or apprentices who studied with a renowned artist. An individual work by a member of the "school" may actually have been touched in one or two places by the master's brush. "Circle of" covers a broader area—the connection is more tenuous, but the work of art may still be very valuable. "After" means a copy of the work of an artist—perhaps by an art student sitting in a museum—at

**Missing Sense**

*Spanish artist Jiusepe Ribera (1589 - 1652) is known to have painted a series of works on the five senses between 1615 and 1616. The whereabouts of only two works are known. "Sense of Touch" is in the Norton Simon Museum in Pasadena, California, and "Sense of Taste" is in the Wadsworth Athenaeum in Hartford, Connecticut.*

*Early in 1985, Christie's East was consigned an unsigned 17th-century painting depicting a man holding a peeled onion behind a table sparsely decorated with a flower blossom, garlic buds, and an onion in its skin. The auction house staff decided that it was most likely a copy of an original oil, "Sense of Smell," by Ribera, and estimated that it would bring $5,000 - $7,000. The work was cataloged as "School of Ribera," indicating that it was the work of an apprentice who trained in Ribera's studio by copying the work of the master. Two New York dealers thought that this painting was the original and it was bid up to $242,000 at auction. (School of Ribera, "Sense of Smell," oil on canvas, 45 x 35 in., Christie's East, March 14, 1985, $242,000.)*

least a hundred years after the original was completed. "Attributed to" indicates that a work is *most probably* by a particular artist even though it is not signed.

Auction catalogs are compiled and published by the major houses six weeks to a few days before the actual sale. In the United States the art auction market is dominated by two huge New York houses, Sotheby's and Christie's. Together they account for 90% of all catalog lots sold annually and dominate the market. Their specialized sales are scheduled in the same seasons each year: major American paintings sales are traditionally early in December and the last week in May; Latin American sales at the end of May, etc. Both offer catalogs by subscription which assure that you are on the auction house mailing list and will receive their newsletter and notices of forthcoming sales. Most houses also send catalog subscribers lists of the prices realized at sales. Appendix C is a list of the major auction houses. All of them offer some art and sell by catalog or flyer.

Read carefully the "Conditions of Sale" at the front of each catalog, which provides important information on absentee bidding, establishing credit, shipping, insurance, and storage.

### Strategy

One basic ground rule covers all purchasing at all auctions.

**NEVER BID ON SOMETHING YOU HAVEN'T LOOKED AT FIRST.**

Take advantage of the auction preview. Carefully examine the piece you are interested in. Re-examine it just before the sale begins. Sometimes a piece is damaged during the preview.

Inspect carefully. If you've done your reading and research, you'll be aware of the characteristic styles and signatures of the artists you're interested in. Don't be put off by small signs of wear or damage. Don't be afraid to bid on a dirty painting—at least a dirty painting hasn't been damaged by an amateur restorer. Most paintings can be cleaned. Holes can be repaired. Torn canvas can usually be mended. Stains and acid can be removed from paper. Skilled restorers can perform near-miracles.

If you've received a catalog in which a piece is described, but not illustrated, ask the auction house to send a color photograph or transparency for you to examine. After you've looked at the illustration, know that you're interested enough to buy, but can't possibly attend the preview or the sale and don't want to risk a telephone bid on unseen merchandise, there's still hope. You can arrange with a dealer to bid for you. This method provides a built-in advantage—experience. A firsthand examination by a knowledgeable dealer can help a prospective purchaser decide whether or not to bid. The dealer will preview the painting, check authenticity, examine its condition, assess its value, and look at the frame. The dealer will then call you from the auction house and discuss overall values, and you will be able to decide whether and how much to bid.

Dealer's commissions will vary for this service. Some charge 5% of the purchase price if they bid successfully for you. Some won't charge if they don't get the painting, but others will ask for a flat fee for time and effort. Fees vary and should be negotiated in advance.

## Bidding

To bid in an auction you must secure a number by registering and presenting a valid form of identification, usually a driver's license and major credit card, which will enable the auctioneer to accept your check at the end. If you can't establish a line of credit, you will need to leave your merchandise until your check clears.

Bidding strategy is individual. There are as many different strategies as there are bidders. Some people like to be identified as bidders and others do not. Some prefer to get in early and join the action from the opening bid. Others will follow for a while before jumping in. There's no rule that one must begin at the auctioneer's opening figure. However, bidding will occasionally start at that level if the work is very desirable, or if an individual bidder has decided to try to bring action on that particular item to a quick close by getting a psychological jump on others who wanted to start much lower.

Before bidding starts on the lot you are interested in, make sure you know what you think the piece is worth. Keep this guide at hand and remember that there are a number of factors that influence prices. Don't be discouraged by high estimates, for they may be wishful thinking. Write your top price for the lot on your catalog or on a pad of paper. Add 10% to give yourself some flexibility and then add another 10% for the buyer's premium. If there's state sales tax, calculate that as well. Be sure that your opening bid is below what you're finally willing to pay. Be alert for symptoms of "auction fever," a potentially dangerous disease in which a purchaser decides to pay whatever is necessary to own a particular work.

Be prepared to exceed your own limit, if only a little. If you've decided that you'll spend $1250 on a painting, and your last bid of $1200 was followed by someone else's reluctant $1300, go ahead to $1350—you may get what you're after.

If you've left a bid with the auctioneer, make it an odd figure, such as $625, and consider giving instructions that will enable him to go up to the next level on your behalf. In this way you have an advantage, since the bidding normally goes up in round increments.

Don't be reluctant to bid against dealers. Unless a dealer is bidding on behalf of a client, he will have to resell the painting to make a profit, so he must begin by buying at a price that he can mark up.

If you were hesitant, pulled out of the bidding, and the item you wanted was bought-in because it didn't reach its reserve, you may still be able to purchase it after the auction. Most auction house contracts empower the auction house to sell the consigned lot at its reserve price for up to sixty days after the sale. After consulting the consignor, the auction house may sell the lot below the reserve price.

## The Impossible Dream

It happens every year—at least once. The lost work reappears; a locked storage closet is opened in a warehouse; a dusty old canvas is brought out of an.attic; a masterwork surfaces at a garage sale. It is the stuff that dreams are made of.

The odds against making a major find are overwhelming. However, there is always the possibility of turning up something undervalued or unrecognized. But if you succeed, what then?

The first step is to do your basic research. If the picture is signed, perhaps another work by the same artist is listed in this book, or some other art price guide. However, the name alone is not enough to authenticate the work, for the signature may have been added. Or, the painting may have the wrong attribution inscribed on a plaque on the frame, or on the back of the canvas. Don't believe something just because it's written down.

Next, have the work appraised. Take the picture to an established dealer or auction house. Most auction houses will give a free verbal appraisal. Get a second opinion.

Some museums hold appraisal days. Call for information. On a typical appraisal day, a museum will assemble outside experts, art specialists from auction houses and galleries, who will tell you who, what, and when, but will not set a dollar value. Charges vary from $5-$12 for a verbal opinion. Some charitable organizations or schools occasionally sponsor appraisal days.

Auction houses offer free verbal estimates, by appointment, at their main galleries. They will supplement the information provided by the museum by appraising the work for its "auction" value. Sotheby's and Christie's maintain offices around the country, and there are numerous smaller houses listed in Appendix B. If you can't bring the work in, mail a photograph to the appropriate department of your favorite auction house and ask for an unofficial appraisal. Auction houses are responsive to these inquiries, and will follow up immediately if they think you've made a find.

Get a second opinion, for appraisal is a highly subjective process and linked to the constant vagaries of the art market.

For everyone who cherishes the dream of making a find, hope is fed by stories like the one about the William Merrit Chase canvas that was sold at Sotheby's in 1984.

### The Signature in Green

*William Merrit Chase painted many pictures of Prospect Park in Brooklyn, New York. Early in 1984, a small painting of a park turned up at a warehouse auction in Denver. Most dealers, noting that the work was signed in green, turned away saying, "William Merrit Chase wouldn't sign his name in green." A furniture dealer took a chance, and bought the canvas for $550. He quickly mailed transparencies of the picture to Ron Pisano, the acknowledged expert on Chase, and to Peter Rathbone, head of Sotheby's American Paintings Department. Both confirmed that the picture was, indeed, by Chase. The excited dealer flew to New York with the painting on the following day, and Rathbone selected it for the cover of the December sales catalog. The work sold for an astonishing $451,000. (William Merrit Chase, "Prospect Park," oil on board, 10¼ x 16 in., Sotheby's, December 6, 1984, $451,000.)*

# Restoration

Great art is undaunted by wear or time, but it can certainly be damaged. Even if it remains unblemished, a canvas which has hung for a century will have darkened with age. Or, it may have been harmed by too much attention. In most cases, a skilled restorer can make the painting look as it did when it was new.

You should bring exactly the same criteria to deciding whether to purchase a slightly damaged work of art as to one in pristine condition. If the painting moves you, and you can afford it, buy. Overlook *small* physical flaws, because they can be repaired. Restorers can accomplish near miracles with canvases that have holes or tears, or even water damage. Stains, mold, and foxing (chemical impurities in the paper) can be removed from paper; fractured sculpture can be mended. Fire-damaged canvases present a particular problem, however. In some cases, fire damages only the varnish covering the surface paint. It can be removed and fresh varnish applied. Sometimes fire affects the paint and changes it all to a brownish hue which is neither reversible nor restorable. If you choose to buy a damaged work and have it restored, you may be getting a bargain and you'll actually come out ahead. Remember, however, that restoration can affect value, and the line between minor and major restoration may be fine where sensitive areas of the painting are concerned. Get the advice of a restorer or knowledgeable dealer before you purchase a work in poor condition.

A word of caution—restoration is a profession, not a hobby. Cleaning a canvas is not a do-it-yourself job. If you buy a dirty painting and must defer a professional cleaning, leave it alone until you can afford to have a restorer do the work. Don't touch the surface with anything more than a feather duster, and then only occasionally. Continue to give all paintings the care they need. Don't expose them to extremes of temperature (don't hang a painting over a radiator or air conditioner and particularly not over a fireplace or wood stove) or humidity.

Restoration, or conservation as it is also called, is an exceedingly delicate procedure. A restorer has an arsenal of materials and techniques, but the same solvents and materials are available to both highly skilled and inept practitioners. The aim of restoration is to put a painting into good condition. Poor restoration can do more damage than the ravages of time.

Cleaning a canvas can be as simple as removing old varnish, lightly cleaning the surface, and applying a synthetic varnish that won't discolor.* The art and

---

* Restoration can dramatically change the way in which an artist is perceived. Subsequent to the cleaning of the Sistine Chapel, art historians have been forced to re-evaluate Michelangelo, long thought to have painted in muted colors. The cleaned ceiling of the chapel revealed amazingly vibrant colors.

science of restoration combine in the decision of which materials to use, in what quantity, and, of the greatest importance, when to stop. Some artists signed their paintings after applying a preliminary coat of varnish. If a restorer fails to detect this, he may remove the signature. Other artists applied alternating layers of paint and varnish to build up a feeling of depth on the canvas. A restorer who doesn't recognize this technique will cause terrible damage.

Relining may be called for if the painting has lost its tautness. Relining is an absolute necessity to restore a punctured or torn canvas. In this process, the work is removed from its stretcher and adhered to another support (board, canvas, fiberglass, etc.). It is important to photograph or preserve in some manner any inscriptions or labels which are on the back prior to mounting. A modern rule of thumb is that restoration should be reversible so that, if a better technique is developed, it can be employed.

Sometimes all that is required to restore a work is a bit of inpainting, perhaps to touch up the edges where paint has chipped off at the stretcher line. Flaking or cracking paint requires more concerted attention. A variety of techniques can be used, and most often a painting will require a combination to complete the restoration.

Modern art, on the other hand, presents a different challenge to museums and collectors alike. Young artists often don't have the money to buy quality materials and costly pigments. Sometimes they don't prime their canvases. When they do start to sell, they may be tempted to invest in sports cars instead of art supplies. The results are awful—cheap paint on bad canvas can require attention in as little as five years.

Proper restoration is time consuming and expensive, but worth it. It is better to leave a canvas in the condition in which you bought it, than to have the job done poorly.

It must be noted that there is a significant body of opinion that holds that restoration can destroy the value of a work. For clumsy restoration, or restoration that changes the character of the original, that is undoubtedly true. Choosing the right restorer thus becomes vitally important.

Assume that you have purchased an "ancestor portrait" that seems lovely beneath the accumulated dirt, but has a small tear on the left side. How do you go about finding a restorer who will do the job well, but not charge an exorbitant price?

The cost of restoration varies widely, as does the quality. Probably the best source of referrals is a gallery owner, who will share your interest in paying a fair price for quality work. Major museums maintain their own restoration departments, but they will know of outside restorers, who, perhaps, once worked for the museum.

The price of restoration varies depending on the size of the work and its condition. In 1986, a highly skilled Boston restorer would have charged from $350-$500 to clean, reline, and do minor repairs on a 25 x 30 inch ancestor portrait. More elaborate procedures to deal with flaking, fly spots, fire, or water damage would increase the price two or three times or more.

**Restoration**

*A skilled restorer can work apparent miracles. When this fire-damaged painting was brought in to Boston restorer Peter Williams it appeared to be beyond repair. Williams painstakingly removed the varnish and was able to inform the fortunate owner that the fire had done little to hurt the painting itself. He inpainted where necessary and applied new varnish, reclaiming a seemingly destroyed work. (Peter Williams/Museum Services)*

In requesting an estimate for restoration, you may be asking for the impossible. A complex problem may involve x-raying, testing with a variety of solvents, or other preliminary steps to determine what the best approach will be. Once the preliminary work has been done, a conservator will discuss any unforeseen problems before proceeding. For example, a painting may appear to have a firm surface, but when tested, the paint may show a tendency to lift, indicating that it should be relined. Most conservators will give you a verbal listing of the work they will do, but will charge for a written one.

## Art as Investment

Should you buy art as an investment?

"No!" is the resounding answer of dealers, gallery owners, auction house executives, and investment counselors.

Buy art because it moves you, because it is beautiful, because it appeals to you. Buy quality.

If these are your guidelines, it is quite possible that in ten or twenty years your purchases will be worth substantially more than what you first paid for them. Don't ever buy because you think that a currently underpriced field will come back into demand, or because you've read a glowing review of a popular young painter and you've heard that art is a gilt-edged investment.

Collecting art is an investment in the largest sense. It is an investment in time, in aesthetic pleasure, in developing your own eye and your expertise. If, along the way, your collection appreciates, the increase in value is an added benefit. It should never be a starting point.

Beware of a dealer who suggests a particular painting as a good investment. There's a sales pitch in marketing art, sometimes even a hard sell, and the hope that today's modest purchase will both enhance the living room and help send the children to college can be hard to resist.

"But what about those clever connoisseurs who bought the Impressionists in the 1950s?" you ask. "Haven't they sat smiling while prices for Impressionist works increased forty times and more?"

Indeed they have, but those same people who are fortunate enough to own paintings that now sell for millions made a significant investment when they first purchased, paying prices in the $40,000 range thirty or more years ago. (Note that the same $40,000 invested in an account paying 10% interest would have increased to over $1,120,000 in the same time period.)

Remember, too, that while public opinion of the Impressionists has done a complete about-face within a century, time has been less kind to other artists. During the '50s, '60s, and '70s, the paintings of 19th-century academicians William Adolphe Bouguereau and Sir Lawrence Alma-Tadema could be bought very inexpensively. Only recently have works by these artists commanded prices similar to what they sold for in the 19th century.

Similarly, 19th-century American painter Thomas Moran was immensely popular during his lifetime, and his works commanded high prices. He was later eclipsed by other artists, and only recently have his works again begun to sell for close to their original prices.

If, despite all these cautions, you are still intent on assembling your collection as an investment tool, you should bear a number of points in mind.

There is usually a strong correlation between cost and investment. Barring the occasional flukes and finds, investment quality work is expensive. Most works included in museum collections are important examples of an artist's style. A piece in a private collection does not need to be so representative of an artist's work. In general, a work is more valuable if it is a typical rather than atypical example, although this is not always the case. A work that is both decorative and attractive is a safer bet than one that is not. The real trick is to find the museum quality paintings of the future today.

Studies and drawings done in preparation for major works are more valuable than those done for works that may never have been completed. Also, any documentation of a painting, especially if the artist has written about it in letters or in a diary, makes the work more valuable. A solid provenance, or having been part of a major collection, enhances the value of an individual picture. Similarly, if a work has changed hands frequently, or been hawked around from dealer to dealer, it may lose value. Yet another factor that influences the value of an individual work is whether it was from a "good" period in the artist's career, when he was producing his best works.

Where a work is sold can greatly affect its value, for art can be geographically chauvinistic. Scenes of the White Mountains of New Hampshire are popular in New England. Cowboy art is popular in the west. However, there are always exceptions—French Impressionist art is very popular in Japan. And some subjects do better than others—scenes of dead game are generally not sought after in the United States but are popular in Europe.

In general, pleasant subjects are more sought after than troubling ones: country scenes are more appealing than sickbeds; baskets of fresh flowers more attractive than those that are withered. Bright and colorful pictures are more salable than gloomy and drab ones.

The size and shape of the work are of great importance. Some modern artists have produced canvases of heroic proportion, measuring ten by twenty feet. Few homes can accommodate such massive works, rendering them difficult to sell. Some dealers consider horizontal pictures easier to sell than vertical ones. The ratio 2 x 3 is thought to be the "ideal" proportion for a painting.

Assembling a collection of older art is a challenge, but the highest risks for the investor/collector are in contemporary art, for it hasn't stood the test of time. Chroniclers of the art market note that only about 5% of the artists who have their first one-person shows in major cities in any given year ever have another show. Another concern is that in the curious intersection of art and publicity, some young artists may be heavily promoted by a gallery with a healthy public relations budget and good press contacts. The difference between hype and a consistent display of talent may be difficult to ascertain.

There is, of course, another side to all this caution. Some of today's young artists will be tomorrow's masters, and a collector discerning and lucky enough to find this work will be able to combine aesthetic satisfaction with the pleasure of watching it appreciate.

A collector of contemporary work must be carefully attuned to every turn of the market, attend shows, gallery talks, visit artists' studios, and read the art press. While even the experts make mistakes, if you can buy the artists who the curators, collectors, gallery owners, and artists themselves are buying, you're closer to the right track, but there are no guarantees. At best, buying contemporary work is a long-term investment, which may take ten years or more to appreciate, if it ever does. Some collectors think that the best time to buy is 30-40 years after an artist dies, when the sales price for his work hits a low.

One of the few characteristics that art and the traditional financial markets have in common is the tendency to run in cycles, with well-publicized periods of solid growth creating a bandwagon effect of purchases, only to be followed by a sharp decline in prices.

Double-digit inflation fuels speculation in the art market, but there are those who believe that art prices have been rising so much and so long that there could not be much more room for increase for a long time to come.

In short, you're more likely to find success as an investor by staying with more conventional financial instruments. Your investment in art belongs in a personal portfolio under ''A'' for aesthetic and ''L'' for love.

## A Brief Guide to Art Research

This chapter will not make you a skilled art researcher. It will, however, provide you with basic approaches to art research, the names of the standard sources, and an overall method of developing your knowledge about a school or a movement in painting, or about an individual artist. A selective bibliography appears at the end of this chapter.*

---

*The approach assumes that you will begin your research in a library. However, it is also advisable to begin to build your own library of art reference books. An inexpensive, pocket-sized handbook, Ralph Mayer's *Dictionary of Art Terms and Techniques*,

## The Library

### General Art Reference Works and Encyclopedias

Where and how you begin to do art research depends very much on what you want to learn. If, fresh from a foray to a museum, you decide to explore a budding interest in flower painting, start at the main branch of your local library.

Inquire at the reference desk for general art sources; the three prime general reference books on the visual arts are *Encyclopedia of World Art, McGraw-Hill Dictionary of Art,* and *Praeger Encyclopedia of Art.* Each is well illustrated and geared to the general reader and beginning student. Each contains many articles on artists, periods, styles, terms, museums, and countries. Articles vary in length—from very short ones that define terms to more substantial pieces on individual artists that include bibliographies. The five-volume McGraw-Hill work is especially accessible and readable.

Taking this first step and consulting a general reference book may give you all the information that you need or want to know. Should you require more data, there are various additional sources.

### The Card Catalog

The card catalog lists every book in a library's collection. Holdings are indexed by author, subject, and title. If you are checking to see if the library owns a specific work, the author and title listings are the place to turn. If, however, you are pursuing a broader area, track it down in the subject catalog, starting with an inclusive topic, such as "painting," and then working through the subheadings to the one that will lead you to the pertinent titles. Research an artist by looking under his name. (See Appendix D for a detailed explanation of how artists' names are listed.) Types of books listed in a card catalog include:

*Monographs.* Monographs are books about individual artists that provide historical or biographical material and information about his or her more famous works.

*Oeuvre catalogues*. Oeuvre catalogues are systematic lists of each work of art in an artist's entire creative output, or the works in a specific medium.

explains schools, techniques, styles, and art terms. Information is easy to retrieve.

Another very useful book is Lois Swan Jones' *Art Research Methods and Resources: A Guide to Finding Art Information.* This comprehensive guide, geared for more advanced researchers, surveys the basic sources, deals with research methods, and provides practical advice on how to obtain reference material. Of particular value is the inclusion of facsimiles of pages from major reference works and directions for their use. Jones also provides a dictionary of French, German, and Italian art terms.

*Catalogues raisonnés.* Catalogues raisonnés are similar to *oeuvre catalogues*, but provide a more complete citation for each work. (An auction catalog may try to give a particular lot added cachet by noting that it has been or will be listed in the *catalogue raisonné*.)

*Exhibition catalogs.* Exhibition catalogs document the exhibition of an artist's work at a museum or gallery.

Most public libraries will have some, but not all, of these resources. One time-tested way to find additional titles is to review the bibliography of related books and magazines that is usually found at the end of reference works. Librarians will be able to help you locate the more scholarly materials at an art library or in an adjacent larger city.

## General Artist Dictionaries

There are no general dictionaries of artists in English, but there are two outstanding foreign language works that are the basic resources in the field. Many researchers turn first to Emmanuel Bénézit's *Dictionnaire Critique et Documentaire des Peintres, Sculpteurs, Dessinateurs et Graveurs* (Benezit for short). The ten-volume set, written in French, is an alphabetical listing of names with life dates and other basic information about international artists. It may include the names of cities where they studied and worked, and note any honors or awards given to them. Bénézit also provides facsimiles of some artists' signatures and some sales information. Last revised in 1976, the work retains certain idiosyncrasies. The names of some American and English artists, for example, are altered to the French versions—a Henry may be called Henri; a Mary, Marie. You may occasionally hear an auctioneer say that an artist is listed in Benezit—it's nice to know, but it doesn't really confer any value.

Another general reference, in German, is the highly regarded biographical dictionary compiled by Ulrich Thieme and Felix Becker, *Allgemeines Lexikon der bildenden Künstler von der Antike bis zur Gegenwart,* which runs to thirty-seven volumes. Generally preferred by scholars, it is a specialized, alphabetical index that contains material similar to that in Bénézit. At the end of each entry on an individual artist, there is a bibliography from which the data was drawn, with titles in the original language. Thieme-Becker, as it is usually called, was published from 1907 through 1950. Hans Vollmer's *Allgemeines Lexikon der bildenden Künstler des XX Jahrhunderts,* which covers artists born after 1870, is a supplement to Thieme-Becker.

## Artist Indexes and General Indexes

An index can best be used as a jumping-off point for further research. Brief entries, listed alphabetically by the artist's last name, provide the complete name, nationality, life dates, and abbreviated notations of books or articles from which the information was compiled. The abbreviations used in a particular index are explained in the introduction to the individual work. These short listings direct you to longer articles and books about the artist in whom you are interested.

Patricia Havlice's two-volume *Index to Artistic Biography,* published in 1973, is a survey of sixty-four different biographical dictionaries exclusive of Thieme-Becker and Benezit, and thus a valuable source of additional information. A supplement including material in seventy additional sources was published in 1981. Daniel Mallett's *Index of Artists*, first published in 1935, and its supplement which appeared in 1940, are other valuable biographical reference tools.

It is especially difficult to find information on little-known 20th-century artists, or on regional or very contemporary artists. The *Biography and Genealogy Master Index* is a guide to more than 725,000 listings in over fifty current editions of *Who's Who*. It includes the names of many individuals who are not listed anywhere else. *The New York Times Index* and *The New York Times Obituaries Index* are excellent sources of information about 20th-century artists. The latter, particularly, includes information about regional artists that may not be found elsewhere.

Major artists, movements, and periods are the subjects of books; less prominent names may become the special subjects of devoted researchers who publish articles in popular or scholarly periodicals. An index of periodical literature provides easy reference to recent articles on both major and minor artists. There are a number of specialized art indexes. Most libraries subscribe to *Art Index,* a quarterly which covers 230 journals and began publishing in 1929. (A selective list of art periodicals, tabloids, and newsletters appears in Appendix B.) As comprehensively as they survey periodical literature, none of the indexes include the highly respected tabloid *The Maine Antique Digest,* to which many avid collectors subscribe—a serious omission.

## Specialized Artist Dictionaries and Directories

If you already know the basic facts about an artist's nationality and life dates, you may go directly to a specialized dictionary. Mantle Fielding's *Dictionary of American Painters, Sculptors and Engravers,* first published in 1925 and revised in 1974, is one of the better known dictionaries, though it is sometimes at variance with other sources and thus less reliable. Peter Falk's *Who Was*

*Who in American Art,* compiled from the original thirty volumes of *American Art Annual, 1898-1933,* and from four volumes of *Who's Who in Art, 1935-1947,* includes biographical data and information about exhibitions, prizes, and membership in artist societies. Chris Pettey's *Dictionary of Women Artists* is international in scope and an excellent source on women artists born before 1900.

Other sources to check are George C. Groce and David H. Wallace's *New York Historical Society's Dictionary of Artists in America, 1565-1860;* William Young's *A Dictionary of American Artists, Sculptors and Engravers;* and Peggy and Harold Samuels' *Artists of the American West.*

For information about contemporary American artists, consult *Who's Who in American Art;* the *Art in America Annual Guide to Galleries, Museums and Artists;* Samuels' *Contemporary Western Artists;* Paul Cummings' *A Dictionary of Contemporary American Artists;* and Les Krantz's *American Artists.*

If you are looking for information about a European artist, you will be able to turn to a number of standard texts. The basic biographical references for Italian art are Giulio Bolaffi's *Dizionario Enciclopedico Bolaffi dei Pittori e Degli Incisori Italiani: Dall' XI al XX Sècolo,* published in 1972, and A.M. Comanducci's *Dizionario Illustrato dei Pittori, Disegnatori, e Incisori Italiani Moderni e Contemporanei,* last revised in 1962, which covers the 19th and 20th centuries.

Standard biographical references to British art include Christopher Wood's *Dictionary of Victorian Painters,* published in 1971; Grant Waters' *Dictionary of British Artists Working 1900-1950,* 1975; H.L. Mallalieu's *The Dictionary of British Watercolor Artists up to 1920,* 1976; and J. Johnson and A. Greutzner's *Dictionary of British Artists, 1880-1940,* 1976.

## Additional Resources

Additional resources are available to a researcher intent on discovering information about a particular artist. Many are accessible by telephone, greatly easing the research process.

### Archives of American Art

The Archives of American Art is a bureau of the Smithsonian Institution which documents the history of the visual arts in America by collecting and preserving original documents, diaries, letters, photographs, oral histories, and other materials.

The main offices of the Archives are in Washington, D.C., and regional offices are located in New York City, Boston, Detroit, San Francisco, and San Marino.

Records in the Archives include artists' personal papers, letters, diaries, sketches, photographs, exhibition material, financial information, writings, and lectures. The Archives also contains the records of arts organizations and institutions, and the papers of critics, dealers, collectors, and scholars. In addition, the Archives publishes a newsletter which is available by subscription.

The Archives responds to telephone inquiries. If you are interested in a particular artist, call and ask if there is any information on file, and then make an appointment to see the material.

## The National Museum of American Art

*The Inventory of American Painting Executed Before 1914* was begun as a project to celebrate America's bicentennial in 1976. It is a little-known but invaluable source which now has information on over 20,000 artists and 230,000 paintings, indexed by artist, title, owner/location, and subject matter. While the information is maintained on computer, and the database is constantly updated, it is not absolutely accurate and may contain errors of date or spelling. However, up to twenty pages of information will be photocopied free of charge, and nominal charges apply to additional pages.

*The Inventory of American Sculpture,* another National Museum of American Art project, was begun in 1985. This is a new research database on the location, physical characteristics, and subject matter of outdoor monuments as well as sculpture in over 800 public and private collections. Information on each sculpture includes artist, title, medium, foundry identification, cast number, subject matter, location, and other data. Information on both sources is available by calling (202) 357-2941.

## Vertical Files

Many libraries maintain files of special material which is not listed in the card catalog, not shelved with books, and which may not be otherwise publicized. Generally filed under specific artists' names, these files preserve "casual" information that is quickly lost and almost impossible to replicate, and may include press releases, exhibition reviews, newspaper and magazine clippings, and obituaries. Librarians generally concentrate on artists working in the region. Historical societies also maintain excellent vertical files. If you can locate an artist's home town, call the library or museum there and inquire if they have such information and if they will duplicate these materials. Most will comply and charge only a small fee for the service. These ephemera or vertical files are gold mines of information unavailable anywhere else.

## *Associations*

Many dictionaries will refer to the local or regional associations to which an artist belonged. Many of these groups maintained private archives, another resource of valuable information about individual artists. The *American Art Directory* and the *Encyclopedia of Associations* provide the addresses of associations, museums, and art clubs across the nation. The Society of Illustrators may have information on illustrators not found elsewhere. The Guild of Boston Artists, the National Academy of Design in New York, and the National Watercolor Society in Lakewood, California, may all preserve unique resources. Pursue your artist—it's a grown-up treasure hunt.

## Price Guides

An artist's sales history is an invaluable record of information. Auction records are frequently the only source of public information about art prices, since those achieved from gallery sales and purchases from estates or personal collections may remain private. More detailed information about the price histories of artists at auction over the past five years is available in the parent publication of this volume, *Leonard's Price Index of Art Auctions,* published quarterly and annually since 1981 by Auction Index, Inc., Newton, Massachusetts. *Leonard's Index,* listed alphabetically by artist, includes every original work of art (exclusive of multiples) sold at auction at every major auction house in the United States. It appears every ninety days, provides the most current information, and can be found in many libraries. (Some surprising and prominent names turn up in *Leonard's Index.* The paintings of Gloria Swanson, Jimi Hendrix, and Winston Churchill—all better known for other endeavors—have all sold at auction.)

Additional price information is available in Richard Hislop's *The Annual Art Sales Index,* which is published in England and covers international sales, but excludes all lots under $500 and any artists not listed in Benezit.

Another index is Enrique Mayer's *International Auction Records,* translated from the French, which is published annually and includes prints in its price listings.

## A Selective Bibliography

### *General Art Reference Works and Encyclopedias*

*Arts in America: A Bibliography.* 4 vols. Edited by Bernard Karpel. Washington, D.C., Smithsonian Institution Press, 1979.

*Encyclopedia of American Art.* Edited by Milton Rugoff. New York, E.P. Dutton, 1981.

*Encyclopedia of World Art.* 15 vols. New York, McGraw-Hill Book Co., 1958.

Jones, Lois Swan. *Art Research Methods and Resources.* 2nd ed. Dubuque, Iowa, Kendall/Hunt Publishing Co., 1984.

Mayer, Ralph. *A Dictionary of Art Terms and Techniques.* New York, Harper and Row Publishers, 1981.

*McGraw-Hill Dictionary of Art.* 5 vols. Edited by Bernard S. and Shirley D. Meyers. New York, McGraw-Hill Book Co., 1969.

*Phaidon Dictionary of Twentieth-Century Art.* New York, Phaidon Publishers, 1973.

*Praeger Encyclopedia of Art.* 5 vols. New York, Praeger Publishers, Inc., 1971.

## General Artist Dictionaries

Bénézit, Emmanuel. *Dictionnaire Critique et Documentaire des Peintres, Sculpteurs, Dessinateurs et Graveurs.* 10 vols. 3rd ed. Paris, Grund, 1976.

Thieme, Ulrich, and Becker, Felix. *Allgemeines Lexikon der Bildenden Künstler von der Antike bis zur Gegenwart; unter Mitwirkung von 300 Fachgelehrten des In-und Auslandes.* 37 vols. Leipzig, E.A. Seemann, 1907-50; reprint, 37 vols. Leipzig, F. Allmann, 1964.

Vollmer, Hans. *Allgemeines Lexikon der bildenden Künstler des XX. Jahrhunderts.* 6 vols. Leipzig, E.A. Seemann, 1953-62.

## Artist Indexes and General Indexes

*Art Index.* 1 vol. Edited by Bertrum Delli. New York, H.W. Wilson Co., 1929+.

*Biographical Dictionaries Master Index.* Detroit, Michigan, Gale Research Co., 1975+.

Havlice, Patricia Pate. *Index to Artistic Biography.* 2 vols. Metuchen, New Jersey, The Scarecrow Press, Inc., 1973. Suppl. 1981.

Mallett, Daniel Trowbridge. *Mallett's Index of Artists.* New York, R.R. Bowker Co., 1935. Suppl. 1940; reprint, 1948.

*New York Times Index.* Vol. 1-1913. New York, New York Times Co., 1913+.

*New York Times Obituaries Index, 1858-1968.* New York, New York Times Co., 1970. Suppl. 1969-1978, 1980.

## Specialized Artist Dictionaries and Directories

*Art in America Annual Guide to Galleries, Museums, Artists.* Edited by Elizabeth C. Baker. New York, Brant Art Publications, 1986.

Baigell, Matthew. *Dictionary of American Art.* New York, Harper and Row Publishers, 1979.

Comanducci, Agostino Mario. *Dizionario Illustrato dei Pittori, Disegnatori e Incisori Italiani Moderni e Contemporanei.* Milano, Italy, Luigi Patuzzi Editore, 1970.

*Dictionary of Contemporary American Artists.* 4th ed. Edited by Paul Cummings. New York, St. Martin's Press, 1982.

*Dizionario Enciclopedico Bolaffi dei Pittori e Degli Incisori Italiani: Dall' XI al XX Sècolo.* 11 vols. Turin, Italy, Giulio Bolaffi Editore, 1972-76.

Falk, Peter Hastings. *Who Was Who in American Art.* Madison, Connecticut, Sound View Press, 1985.

Fielding, Mantle. *Dictionary of American Painters, Sculptors and Engravers.* Pough-keepsie, New York, Apollo Book, 1983.

Groce, George C., and Wallace, David H. *The New York Historical Society's Dictionary of Artists in America, 1564-1860.* New Haven and London, Yale University Press, 1957.

Harper, J. Russell. *Early Painters and Engravers in Canada.* Toronto, Canada, University of Toronto Press, 1970.

Houfe, Simon. *The Dictionary of British Book Illustrators and Caricaturists.* Baron Publishing, Woodbridge, England, Antique Collectors Club, 1978.

Hughes, Edan Milton. *Artists in California, 1786-1940.* San Francisco, Hughes Publishing Co., 1986.

Johnson, J., and Greutzner, A. *Dictionary of British Artists, 1880-1940: An Antique Collector's Club Research Project Listing 41,000 Artists.* Baron Publishing, Woodbridge, England, Antique Collectors Club, 1976.

Krantz, Les. *American Artists.* New York, Facts on File Publications, 1985.

Krantz, Les. *American Art Galleries.* New York, Facts on File Publications, 1985.

MacDonald, Colin S. *A Dictionary of Canadian Artists.* Ottawa, Canada, Canadian Paperbacks, 1972.

Mallalieu, H.L. *The Dictionary of British Watercolour Artists up to 1920.* Woodbridge, England, Antique Collectors Club, 1976.

Naylor, Colin, and Genesis, P-Orridge. *Contemporary Artists.* New York, St. Martin's Press, 1977; 2nd ed., 1983.

Petteys, Chris. *Dictionary of Women Artists: An International Dictionary of Women Artists Born Before 1900.* Boston, Massachusetts, G.K. Hall Co., 1985.

Samuels, Peggy, and Samuels, Harold. *The Illustrated Biographical Encyclopedia of Artists of the American West.* Garden City, New York, Doubleday, 1976.

Samuels, Peggy, and Samuels, Harold. *Contemporary Western Artists.* New York, Crown Publishing, 1985.

*A Dictionary of American Artists, Sculptors and Engravers; From the Beginning Through the Turn of the Twentieth Century.* Edited by William Young. Cambridge, Massachusetts, William Young and Co., 1968.

## Association Directories

*American Art Directory.* 50th ed. New York, R.R. Bowker Co., 1986.

*Encyclopedia of Associations.* 21st ed. Detroit, Gale Research Co., 1987.

*The Official Museum Directory: United States and Canada.* 1st issue. Washington, D.C., American Association of Museums, 1971+.

## Price Guides

*The Annual Art Sales Index.* 1st ed. Edited by Richard Hislop. Weybridge, Surrey, England, Art Sales Index, Ltd., 1969-70+.

*Leonard's Price Index of Art Auctions.* 1 vol. Edited by Susan Theran. Newton, Massachusetts, Auction Index Inc., 1980+.

Mayer, Enrique. *International Auction Records: Engravings, Drawings, Watercolors, Paintings, Sculpture.* 1st English ed. Paris, Editions Enrique Mayer, 1967+.

## How to Use This Book

The *Official Price Guide to Fine Art* is a compilation of prices of fine art sold at auction throughout the United States from September 1980 through August 1985. Prices of fine art are established in the marketplace—at galleries, private sales, and auctions. Only those established at auction are public record (in most cases governed by state regulations). These are the prices listed in this *Guide*.

The database for this volume consists of 26,321 names. Size limitations have forced us to refine it to 20,689 names, eliminating all artists whose top price was less than $175 at auction during this five-year period. You will find that there are famous artists, especially Old Masters such as Hieronymus Bosch and Leonardo da Vinci, whose works are extremely rare and are not listed because their works have not been offered for sale during this period.

By providing data about the *actual prices* realized at auction for the work of thousands of artists, the *Official Price Guide to Fine Art* presents a baseline of information about the art market. Auction prices are sometimes considered to be wholesale—sometimes retail, depending on location and date of sale. The *Guide* will help you assess comparative price data for individual artists and will help you determine whether a particular work is fairly priced, overvalued or a bargain. The final consideration, however, must be the artistic quality of the painting—condition and other factors being equal.

The price range reflects the low and high prices for a category of work. Identical prices in ''low'' and ''high'' reflect that more than one work by the artist has sold but at the same price. If only one work by an artist was sold, the price will appear in the high column. An asterisk (*) after a price indicates that it was an unusually high price which did not fit into the general price range for the artist's work. (A listing of these atypical prices appears in Appendix E.)

Price ranges are just that. Prices for an artist's work vary for a tremendous variety of reasons, including the importance and quality of the work, its size, and differences in medium. Other factors are the desire of competing bidders, condition, subject matter, framing, provenance, attendance, weather, etc. The price ranges in this book reflect these variables.

For the purpose of this *Guide,* fine art is categorized as paintings, drawings, and sculpture. Prints and etchings, while certainly within the category of fine art, are not included, because they are works that exist in multiples. Paintings include oil, tempera, acrylic, casein, and fresco. Drawings include watercolor, pastel, gouache, crayon, pencil, charcoal, pen and ink, and mixed media. Included in the sculpture category are bronzes, marble statuary, bas reliefs, constructions, mobiles, and assemblages.

Indexing in this *Guide* conforms to the *Anglo-American Cataloging Rules* for names, revised in 1979. For reasons of size, we have not cross-indexed artists' names. Appendix D provides a brief summary of the cataloging rules. If there is any doubt, check all the possibilities.

Nationality and life dates are included for all artists where available. When conflicts have arisen as to their validity, we have been diligent in our research and have made informed decisions.

There is sometimes confusion about the authorship of a particular work. John Herring Sr. and his son, John Jr., are frequently confused. We've done our best to sort through all these problems and present accurate prices.

Prices reflect the popularity of a particular artist or style in a certain region, fads, and fashion in art. Above all they reflect the overall strength of the economy. The years between 1979 and 1982 were a highly speculative period for the entire art market. Prices for American Western art rose notably, spurred by double-digit inflation and other market factors. A sharp drop in oil prices in 1986 heavily impacted the Southwest economy and forced many collectors of western paintings to curtail their purchases. On May 29, 1986, at Sotheby's, Alfred Jacob Miller's watercolor, *Racing at Fort Laramie,* sold for $82,500, a steep decline from the record $101,750 the work sold for in 1982.

Price is not the only index of value of an individual painting. Price will not tell you if a work is authentic. Neither will it tell you the unique characteristics or rarity of a painting. Note, too, that the price an artist sells for at auction is not necessarily what you will receive if you want to sell.

Finally, don't be discouraged by high prices. If you desire a work by a famous artist, it may be possible to buy a minor example for a reasonable sum. Slight sketches and smaller, less typical examples sell well below the prices of major canvases. The works of lesser known, undiscovered, or undervalued artists provide many good buying opportunities.

For more specific information on the works of a particular artist, refer to *Leonard's Price Index of Art Auctions*, the parent volume of this *Guide*, which provides more detailed information on titles of works sold, size, auction house, and date of sale.

| | | Current Price Range | |
| --- | --- | --- | --- |
| | | Low | High |
| **A'BECKET, Maria** ............... *paintings* | | $70 | $1,210 |
| American d. 1904 | | | |
| **AACH, Herbert** ............... *paintings* | | | $495 |
| contemporary | | | |
| **AAGAARD, Carl Frederic** ............... *paintings* | | | $528 |
| Danish 1833-1895 | | | |
| **ABA-NOVAK, Vilmos** ............... *paintings* | | | $660 |
| Hungarian b. 1924 | | | |
| **ABABES, Juan Martinez** ............... *paintings* | | | $1,650 |
| **ABATTUCCI, Pierre** ............... *paintings* | | $400 | $440 |
| Belgian b. 1871 | | | |
| **ABBEING, Louise** ............... *paintings* | | | $330 |
| late 19th cent. | | | |
| **ABBEMA, Louise** ............... *paintings* | | | $352 |
| French 1858-1927 | | | |
| **ABBEY, Edwin Austin** ............... *paintings* | | $137 | $1,430 |
| American 1852-1911 ............... *drawings* | | $330 | $4,950 |
| **ABBIATI, Filippus** ............... *paintings* | | | $2,750 |
| Italian 18th cent. | | | |
| **ABBOTT, A.G.** ............... *paintings* | | | $467 |
| **ABBOTT, Eleanor P.** ............... *drawings* | | | $715 |
| American b. 1875 | | | |
| **ABBOTT, Lemuel Francis** ............... *paintings* | | $275 | $4,840 |
| English 1760-1803 | | | |
| **ABBOTT, Samuel Nelson** ............... *paintings* | | $275 | $2,310 |
| American 1874-1953 ............... *drawings* | | | $935 |
| **ABBOTT, Yarnall** ............... *paintings* | | $110 | $990 |
| American 1870-1938 | | | |
| **ABBRESCIA, Joe** ............... *paintings* | | $137 | $6,500 |
| American 20th cent. | | | |
| **ABDO, Edward** ............... *paintings* | | | $770 |
| **ABDY, Rowena Meeks** ............... *paintings* | | | $440 |
| American 1887-c. 1945 ............... *drawings* | | $192 | $330 |
| **ABEL, Myer** ............... *paintings* | | | $467 |
| American b. 1904 | | | |
| **ABEL-TRUCHET, Louis** ............... *paintings* | | $2,090 | $4,950 |
| French 1857-1918 | | | |
| **ABELA, Eduardo** ............... *paintings* | | | $8,250 |
| Latin American | | | |
| **ABELARD, Gessner** ............... *paintings* | | $192 | $1,430 |
| Haitian b. 1922 | | | |
| **ABELSON, Evelyn** ............... *paintings* | | | $250 |
| **ABERDAM, Alfred** ............... *paintings* | | | $715 |
| **ABEYTA, Narciso** ............... *drawings* | | | $1,100 |
| American (Navajo) b. 1918 | | | |
| **ABLETT, William** ............... *drawings* | | $110 | $462 |
| English 1877-1937 | | | |
| **ABOEIMA, Louise** ............... *paintings* | | | $1,210 |
| **ABORNETS, J.** ............... *paintings* | | | $715 |

| | | Current Price Range | |
|---|---|---|---|
| | | Low | High |

| | | | |
|---|---|---|---|
| ☐ **ABOT, S.** ............................ *paintings* | | | $440 |
| ☐ **ABRAHAM, B.H.** ..................... *paintings* | | | $467 |
| Dutch 19th cent. | | | |
| ☐ **ABRAM, Paul (Jr.)** ............... *drawings* | | | $900 |
| American | | | |
| ☐ **ABRAMOFSKY, Ismael** ......... *paintings* | | $44 | $440 |
| American 20th cent. | | | |
| ☐ **ABRAMOVITZ, Albert** ......... *paintings* | | $66 | $521 |
| Russian/American 1879-1963 | | | |
| ☐ **ABRUZZI** ............................ *paintings* | | | $220 |
| Italian (?) 20th cent. | | | |
| ☐ **ABSOLON, John** ................... *paintings* | | | $165 |
| English 1815-1895 ...................... *drawings* | | $82 | $990 |
| ☐ **ABT, Charles** ...................... *paintings* | | | $2,200 |
| American b. 1933 | | | |
| ☐ **ABULARACH, Rodolfo** ......... *paintings* | | $1,100 | $1,210 |
| Guatemalan b. 1934 .................... *drawings* | | $880 | $1,100 |
| ☐ **ACCARD, Eugene** ................. *paintings* | | $1,540 | $1,650 |
| French 1824-1888 | | | |
| ☐ **ACEVES** ............................ *paintings* | | | $2,090 |
| ☐ **ACHEFF, William** ................. *paintings* | | $10,000 | $56,000 |
| American b. 1947 ....................... *drawings* | | $2,500 | $3,000 |
| ☐ **ACHEN, Georg Nicolaj** ......... *paintings* | | | $1,320 |
| Danish b. 1860 | | | |
| ☐ **ACHENBACH, Andreas** ......... *paintings* | | $1,430 | $36,300 |
| German 1815-1910 ..................... *drawings* | | $33 | $770 |
| ☐ **ACHENBACH, Oswald** ......... *paintings* | | $3,960 | $39,600 |
| German 1827-1905 ..................... *drawings* | | | $275 |
| ☐ **ACHILLE-FOULD, Georges** ...... *paintings* | | | $1,320 |
| French 1865-1951 | | | |
| ☐ **ACHINI, Angiolo** ................. *drawings* | | $880 | $2,860 |
| Italian 1850-1930 | | | |
| ☐ **ACHTENHAGEN, August** ...... *paintings* | | | $935 |
| German b. 1865 | | | |
| ☐ **ACKERMAN, Paul** ............... *paintings* | | $165 | $302 |
| Rumanian/French b. 1908 | | | |
| ☐ **ACKLAND, T.G.** ................... *drawings* | | $495 | $1,430 |
| English 19th cent. | | | |
| ☐ **ACOQUAT, Louise-Marie** ...... *paintings* | | | $1,127 |
| French 19th/20th cent. | | | |
| ☐ **ACOSTA, A.** ....................... *paintings* | | | $440 |
| Spanish 19th cent. | | | |
| ☐ **ACUNA, Louis Alberto** ......... *paintings* | | $550 | $990 |
| Columbian b. 1905 | | | |
| ☐ **ADAM, Albrecht** ................. *paintings* | | $1,870 | $22,000 |
| German 1786-1862 ..................... *drawings* | | $1,100 | $1,155 |
| ☐ **ADAM, Benno** ................... *paintings* | | | $4,400 |
| German 1812-1892 | | | |

## Animal Paintings

*This picture was completed during a time of large-scale industrialization in America, when young people were leaving their family farms to find work in the city. It was a work aimed toward city dwellers that idealized the values of rustic simplicity, although farmers took a less romantic view of rural life. The 19th-century painter Benno Adam was well known for his paintings of animals. (Benno Adam, "Neighbors," oil on cradled panel, 21¾ x 30 in., Skinner, September 13, 1984, $4,400.)*

| | | Current Price Range | |
| --- | --- | --- | --- |
| | | *Low* | *High* |
| ☑ **ADAM, Edouard** .............................. *paintings* | | $330 | $2,250 |
| French 1847-1922 | | | |
| ☐ **ADAM, Emil** ..................................... *paintings* | | $12,100 | $14,300 |
| German 1843-1924 | | | |
| ☐ **ADAM, Emmy** .................................. *paintings* | | $302 | $352 |
| German/American b. 1871 | | | |
| ☐ **ADAM, Eugen** .................................. *paintings* | | | $660 |
| ☐ **ADAM, Heinrich** .............................. *paintings* | | $4,400 | $5,225 |
| German 1787-1886 | | | |
| ☐ **ADAM, Joseph Denovan** ...................... *paintings* | | $550 | $2,640 |
| English 1842-1896 | | | |
| ☐ **ADAM, Julius** ................................... *paintings* | | $1,045 | $19,800 |
| German 1852-1913 | | | |
| ☐ **ADAM, Patrick William** ...................... *paintings* | | $400 | $2,640 |
| English b. 1854 | | | |
| ☐ **ADAM, Richard B.** ............................ *paintings* | | | $550 |
| American 20th cent. | | | |
| ☐ **ADAM, Richard Benno** ...................... *paintings* | | | $2,200 |
| German b. 1873 | | | |

| | | Current Price Range | |
|---|---|---|---|
| | | Low | High |
| ☐ **ADAM, Robert** ................................ *drawings* | | | **$2,310** |
| Scottish 1728-1792 | | | |
| ☐ **ADAM, Wilbur G.** ............................. *paintings* | | | **$264** |
| ☐ **ADAM, William** .................................. *paintings* | **$165** | | **$770** |
| Anglo/American b. 1846 | | | |
| ☐ **ADAM-KUNZ, L.** ............................... *paintings* | | | **$1,045** |
| German 19th/20th cent. | | | |
| ☐ **ADAMI, Pietro** .................................. *drawings* | | | **$880** |
| Italian 18th cent. | | | |
| ☐ **ADAMI, Valerio** ............................... *paintings* | **$4,400** | | **$13,200** |
| Italian b. 1935 | | | |
| ☐ **ADAMOFF, Helena** ............................ *paintings* | | | **$715** |
| Russian b. 1906 | | | |
| ☐ **ADAMS, Catherine Langhorne** .............. *paintings* | | | **$1,870** |
| American 20th cent. | | | |
| ☐ **ADAMS, Charles Partridge** .................. *paintings* | **$385** | | **$3,080** |
| American 1858-1942 .................................. *drawings* | **$137** | | **$1,650** |
| ☐ **ADAMS, Douglas** ............................... *paintings* | | | **$4,200** |
| English 1853-1920 | | | |
| ☐ **ADAMS, John Clayton** ........................ *paintings* | **$1,100** | | **$4,400** |
| British 1840-1906 | | | |
| ☐ **ADAMS, John Otis** ............................. *paintings* | **$2,420** | | **$2,750** |
| American 1851-1927 | | | |
| ☐ **ADAMS, Wayman** ............................... *paintings* | **$110** | | **$1,650** |
| American 1883-1959 | | | |
| ☐ **ADAMS, William** ................................ *paintings* | | | **$250** |
| English 19th cent. | | | |
| ☐ **ADAMS, Willis Seaver** .......................... *paintings* | **$440** | | **$521** |
| American 1842-1921 | | | |
| ☐ **ADAN, L. Emile** ................................. *paintings* | **$880** | | **$71,500** |
| French 1839-1937 .................................... *drawings* | | | **$55** |
| ☐ **ADCOCK, J. Wilton** ............................ *paintings* | | | **$550** |
| British exhib. 1886-1891 ............................ *drawings* | | | **$82** |
| ☐ **ADDAMS, Charles** ............................... *drawings* | | | **$605** |
| American 20th cent. | | | |
| ☐ **ADDY, Alfred** .................................... *paintings* | **$137** | | **$825** |
| 19th/20th cent. ....................................... *drawings* | **$44** | | **$110** |
| ☐ **ADICKES, David** ................................ *paintings* | | | **$356** |
| ☐ **ADICKES, W.** .................................... *drawings* | | | **$550** |
| American | | | |
| ☐ **ADLER, Edmund** ............................... *paintings* | **$2,640** | | **$7,150** |
| German 1871-1957 | | | |
| ☐ **ADLER, Jankel** ................................. *paintings* | **$1,430** | | **$1,870** |
| Polish 1895-1949 ..................................... *drawings* | **$660** | | **$1,210** |
| ☐ **ADLER, Jules** ................................... *paintings* | **$4,400** | | **$33,000** |
| French 1865-1952 .................................... *drawings* | | | **$495** |
| ☐ **ADNET, Francoise** ............................. *paintings* | **$22** | | **$330** |
| French b. 1924 | | | |

|  | | Current Price Range | |
|---|---|---|---|
|  | | Low | High |
| ☐ **ADNET, Jean Jacques** .......................... *sculpture* <br> French early 20th cent. | | | **$8,800** |
| ☐ **ADOLPH, Virginia Hope** ..................... *paintings* <br> American b. 1880 | | **$192** | **$302** |
| ☐ **ADOLPHE, Albert Jean** ........................ *paintings* <br> American 1865-1940 | | **$33** | **$2,970** |
| ☐ **ADOMEIT, George G.** .......................... *paintings* <br> German/American 1879-1967 | | **$138** | **$495** |
| ☐ **ADRIAENSSEN, Alexander** ................. *paintings* <br> Flemish 1587-1661 | | **$1,870** | **$6,600** |
| ☐ **ADRIANI, Camille** ............................. *paintings* | | **$55** | **$605** |
| ☐ **ADRIEDENS, H.** ................................. *paintings* | | | **$550** |
| ☐ **ADRIENNE-GATES, Elaine** ................. *paintings* <br> American 20th cent. | | | **$275** |
| ☐ **ADRION, Lucien** ............................... *paintings* <br> French 1889-1953 ...................................... *drawings* | | **$253** | **$4,400** <br> **$660** |
| ☐ **ADVIER, Victor-Andre** ........................ *paintings* <br> French 20th cent. | | | **$467** |
| ☐ **AEIN, A.** ............................................ *drawings* <br> American 20th cent. | | | **$660** |
| ☐ **AELST, Evert van** .............................. *paintings* <br> Dutch 1602-1657 | | | **$2,200** |
| ☐ **AELST, Willem van** ........................... *paintings* <br> Dutch 1625/26-c. 1683 | | **$2,860** | **$10,450** |
| ☐ **AERNI, Franz Theodor** ....................... *paintings* <br> German 1853-1918 | | | **$2,200** |
| ☐ **AFFLECK, William** ............................ *drawings* <br> British 1869-1909 | | **$330** | **$412** |
| ☐ **AFRO, (Afro BASALDELLA)** .............. *paintings* <br> Italian 1912-1976 ...................................... *drawings* | | **$1,760** <br> **$330** | **$7,975** <br> **$900** |
| ☐ **AFSARY, Cyrus** ............................... *paintings* <br> American | | | **$3,000** |
| ☐ **AGAM, Yaacov** ................................. *sculpture* <br> Israeli b. 1928 | | **$1,210** | **$49,500** |
| ☐ **AGAR, Charles d'** ............................. *paintings* <br> French 1669-1723 | | | **$1,320** |
| ☐ **AGARD, Charles** ............................... *paintings* <br> French b. 1866 | | **$660** | **$682** |
| ☐ **AGASSE, Jacques Laurent** .................... *paintings* <br> Swiss 1767-1849 | | **$4,675** | **$9,350** |
| ☐ **AGENNAI** ......................................... *sculpture* <br> 19th cent. | | | **$192** |
| ☐ **AGENOR, Joceyln** ............................. *paintings* | | | **$880** |
| ☐ **AGLIELLI, G.** ................................... *paintings* <br> 19th cent. | | | **$425** |
| ☐ **AGOSTINI, Max** ............................... *paintings* | | | **$466** |
| ☐ **AGOSTINI, Peter** ............................. *paintings* <br> American b. 1913 | | **$220** | **$385** |

|  | | Current Price Range | |
|---|---|---|---|
|  | | Low | High |
| ☐ **AGOSTINI, Tony** ................................ *paintings* | | $110 | $385 |
| American b.1916 | | | |
| ☐ **AGOSTON, Acs.** ................................ *paintings* | | | $357 |
| Hungarian 20th cent. | | | |
| ☐ **AGRASOT Y JUAN, Joaquin** ............... *paintings* | | $2,750 | $4,675 |
| Spanish 1836-1907 | | | |
| ☐ **AGRESTI** ........................................... *paintings* | | $440 | $495 |
| Italian 19th cent. | | | |
| ☐ **AGRESTI, Livio** ................................. *drawings* | | | $4,125 |
| Italian d. 1580 | | | |
| ☐ **AGRESTI, R.** ...................................... *paintings* | | | $1,600 |
| ☐ **AGUAYO, Fermin** ............................. *paintings* | | | $330 |
| ☐ **AGUILA, A.** ...................................... *paintings* | | | $302 |
| Spanish 19th cent. | | | |
| ☐ **AGUILAR, M.** .................................... *paintings* | | | $660 |
| b. San Salvador 1919 | | | |
| ☐ **AGUIRRE, Ignacio** ............................. *paintings* | | | $1,650 |
| Mexican b. 1902 | | | |
| ☐ **AHEARN, John** ................................. *sculpture* | | $3,575 | $4,125 |
| ☐ **AHGUPUK, George A.** ........................ *drawings* | | $110 | $286 |
| Eskimo 20th cent. | | | |
| ☐ **AHL, Henry Hammond** ....................... *paintings* | | $88 | $825 |
| American 1869-1953 | | | |
| ☐ **AHLBORNE, Emil** ............................. *paintings* | | | $200 |
| American early 20th cent. | | | |
| ☐ **AHLSTROM, Claude** ......................... *sculpture* | | | $1,045 |
| American 19th cent. | | | |
| ☐ **AHLSTROM, Ronald** ......................... *drawings* | | $60 | $440 |
| American b. 1922 | | | |
| ☐ **AHRENDTS, C.E.** ............................... *paintings* | | | $440 |
| ☐ **AHRENS, Carl** .................................. *paintings* | | $44 | $797 |
| Canadian 1863/67-1936 | | | |
| ☐ **AIGEN, Karl** ..................................... *paintings* | | | $1,980 |
| Austrian 1684-1764 | | | |
| ☐ **AIKEN, Charles A.** ............................. *paintings* | | $412 | $495 |
| American 1872-1965 ................................ *drawings* | | | $246 |
| ☐ **AIKEN, James** ................................... *paintings* | | $935 | $2,530 |
| American 19th cent. | | | |
| ☐ **AIKMAN, George** ............................. *paintings* | | $418 | $660 |
| ☐ **AIKMAN, William** ............................. *paintings* | | $440 | $1,650 |
| English 1682-1731 | | | |
| ☐ **AINSLEY, Dennis** ............................. *paintings* | | $252 | $302 |
| American 20th cent. | | | |
| ☐ **AIRY, Anna** ..................................... *paintings* | | | $1,870 |
| English 1882-1964 | | | |
| ☐ **AISELIN, E.** ...................................... *sculpture* | | | $450 |
| ☐ **AIVAZOFFSKI,** | | | |
| **Ivan Constantinowitsch** ......................... *paintings* | | $1,430 | $66,000 |
| Russian 1817-1900 ................................... *drawings* | | $275 | $1,430 |

| | Current Price Range | |
|---|---|---|
| | *Low* | *High* |
| ☐ **AIZELIN, Eugene Antoine** ..................... *sculpture* | $795 | $2,200 |
| French 1821-1902 | | |
| ☐ **AIZENBERG, Roberto** ......................... *drawings* | $1,320 | $1,760 |
| ☐ **AIZPIRI, Paul** ...................................... *paintings* | $770 | $6,600 |
| French b. 1919 ....................................... *drawings* | | $1,100 |
| ☐ **AJAY** .................................................. *paintings* | | $440 |
| ☐ **AJDUKIEWICZ, Sigismund von** ........... *paintings* | $2,310 | $3,850 |
| Austrian b. 1861 | | |
| ☐ **AJDUKIEWICZ, Thaddeus von** ............ *paintings* | | $550 |
| Polish 1852-1916 | | |
| ☐ **AJMONE, Giuseppe** .............................. *paintings* | | $495 |
| Italian b. 1923 | | |
| ☐ **AKDIK, Mehemet Seref** ........................ *paintings* | | $330 |
| ☐ **AKELEY, Carl Ethan** ......................... *paintings* | $3,080 | $11,550 |
| American 1864-1926 | | |
| ☐ **AKEN, Leo van** ................................. *paintings* | | $2,420 |
| Belgian 1857-1904 | | |
| ☐ **AKKERINGA, Johann** ........................ *paintings* | $4,950 | $4,950 |
| Dutch b. 1864 | | |
| ☐ **AKKERSDIJK, Jacob** .......................... *paintings* | $850 | $1,650 |
| Dutch 1815-1862 | | |
| ☐ **AL, Mayer** ....................................... *paintings* | | $325 |
| German 19th cent. | | |
| ☐ **ALAJALOV, Constantin** ...................... *paintings* | | $605 |
| Russian/American b. 1900 ............................. *drawings* | $247 | $1,100 |
| ☐ **ALAJOS, Mayer** ................................. *paintings* | | $550 |
| Hungarian 19th/20th cent. | | |
| ☐ **ALAMANNO, Pietro** ......................... *paintings* | | $27,500 |
| ☐ **ALARCON, Felix** ................................. *paintings* | $1,100 | $3,410 |
| Spanish 19th cent. | | |
| ☐ **ALAUX, Guillaume** ............................. *paintings* | | $1,210 |
| French d. 1913 | | |
| ☐ **ALAUX, Gustave** ............................... *paintings* | | $605 |
| French 1887-1965 | | |
| ☐ **ALAUX, Jean Pierre** ........................... *paintings* | $275 | $600 |
| French b. 1925 | | |
| ☐ **ALBANI, Francesco** ........................... *paintings* | | $8,800 |
| Italian 1578-1660 | | |
| ☐ **ALBANO, Salvatore** ............................ *sculpture* | | $5,500 |
| Italian 1841-1893 | | |
| ☐ **ALBEE, Percy** ..................................... *drawings* | $137 | $412 |
| American 1883-1934 | | |
| ☐ **ALBERS, Josef** ................................... *paintings* | $2,750 | $57,200 |
| American 1888-1976 ................................... *drawings* | $1,000 | $2,090 |
| ☐ **ALBERT, Adolphe** ............................ *paintings* | $352 | $467 |
| French 20th cent. | | |
| ☐ **ALBERT, Ernest** ............................... *paintings* | $110 | $8,250 |
| American 1857-1946 | | |
| ☐ **ALBERT, V.** ........................................ *paintings* | | $605 |

| | | Current Price Range | |
|---|---|---|---|
| | | Low | High |
| ☐ **ALBERTI, Carl** .................................. *paintings* | | **$1,320** | **$1,540** |
| German b. 1800 | | | |
| ☐ **ALBERTI, Henri** ................................ *paintings* | | **$495** | **$1,430** |
| French b. 1868 | | | |
| ☐ **ALBERTINELLI, Mariotto** ................... *paintings* | | **$3,960** | **$10,450** |
| Italian 1474-1515 | | | |
| ☐ **ALBERTIS, Sebastiano de** .................... *paintings* | | **$3,850** | **$4,950** |
| Italian 1828-1897 | | | |
| ☐ **ALBERTS, W.J.** ............................... *paintings* | | | **$330** |
| Dutch 20th cent. | | | |
| ☐ **ALBINO, J.** ....................................... *paintings* | | | **$467** |
| Italian 20th cent. | | | |
| ☐ **ALBOY-REBOUET, Alfred** ................. *paintings* | | | **$1,870** |
| French 1841-1875 | | | |
| ☐ **ALBRIGHT, Adam Emory** ................... *paintings* | | **$880** | **$3,575** |
| American 1862-1957 | | | |
| ☐ **ALBRIGHT, Henry James** ................... *paintings* | | **$191** | **$660** |
| American 1887-1951 | | | |
| ☐ **ALBRIGHT, Ivan Le Lorraine** ............. *paintings* | | | **$8,000** |
| American 1897-after 1982 | | | |
| ☐ **ALBRIZZI, Enrico (or ALBERICI)** ........ *paintings* | | | **$9,350** |
| Italian 1714-1775 | | | |
| ☐ **ALCAY, F.** ....................................... *paintings* | | | **$550** |
| ☐ **ALCOCK, Edward** ............................. *paintings* | | | **$1,100** |
| ☐ **ALDA, T.** ......................................... *paintings* | | | **$550** |
| English 19th cent. | | | |
| ☐ **ALDEN, Edwin** .................................. *paintings* | | | **$550** |
| ☐ **ALDEN, Rebecca B.** ........................... *drawings* | | | **$176** |
| American 19th cent. | | | |
| ☐ **ALDER, Edmund** .............................. *paintings* | | | **$4,950** |
| Austrian 1871-1957 | | | |
| ☐ **ALDERMAN, George P.B.** ................... *drawings* | | **$220** | **$462** |
| American 1862-1942 | | | |
| ☐ **ALDI, Pietro** ....................................... *paintings* | | | **$2,090** |
| Italian 1852-1888 | | | |
| ☐ **ALDIN, Cecil Charles Windsor** ............. *drawings* | | | **$176** |
| English 1870-1935 | | | |
| ☐ **ALDINE, Marc** ................................... *paintings* | | **$330** | **$1,540** |
| French 19th/20th cent. | | | |
| ☐ **ALDRICH, George Ames** ..................... *paintings* | | **$100** | **$6,050** |
| American 1872-1941 | | | |
| ☐ **ALDRIDGE, Frederick James** .............. *paintings* | | **$440** | **$660** |
| English 1850-1933 ..................................... *drawings* | | **$242** | **$467** |
| ☐ **ALDUNATE, Carmen** .......................... *drawings* | | | **$1,320** |
| b. Chile 1940 | | | |
| ☐ **ALECHINSKY, Pierre** ......................... *paintings* | | **$7,700** | **$33,000** |
| Belgian b. 1927 ....................................... *drawings* | | **$660** | **$9,075** |
| ☐ **ALEGIANI, Francesco** ......................... *paintings* | | **$1,210** | **$2,090** |
| Italian 19th cent. | | | |

|                                             | Current Price Range | |
|                                             | Low    | High      |
|---------------------------------------------|--------|-----------|
| ☐ **ALEKSANDROV, Michael** ............... *paintings* | **$220** | **$220** |
| Russian 20th cent.                          |        |           |
| ☐ **ALEX, Kosta** ...................... *paintings* | **$440** | **$1,540** |
| American b. 1925                            |        |           |
| ☐ **ALEXANDER, Clifford Grear** ............... *paintings* | **$220** | **$495** |
| American b. 1870                            |        |           |
| ☐ **ALEXANDER, Francesca**                  |        |           |
| **(Esther Frances)** ...................... *drawings* |        | **$220** |
| American 19th cent.                         |        |           |
| ☐ **ALEXANDER, Francis** ..................... *drawings* |        | **$302** |
| American 1800-1881                          |        |           |
| ☐ **ALEXANDER, G.** ........................ *paintings* |        | **$1,320** |
| ☐ **ALEXANDER, Henry** ..................... *paintings* | **$5,500** | **$6,050** |
| American 1860-1895                          |        |           |
| ☐ **ALEXANDER, John White** ............... *paintings* | **$2,200** | **$24,200** |
| American 1856-1915 ...................... *drawings* |        | **$990** |
| ☐ **ALEXANDER, Robert L.** ............... *paintings* |        | **$605** |
| British 1840-1923                           |        |           |
| ☐ **ALEXANDROVITCH** ..................... *sculpture* |        | **$900** |
| ☐ **ALEXAY(?), E.** ........................ *paintings* |        | **$1,100** |
| ☐ **ALFANI, Domenico** ..................... *paintings* |        | **$550** |
| ☐ **ALFARO, Jose** ........................ *paintings* |        | **$30,800** |
| Mexican 18th cent.                          |        |           |
| ☐ **ALFONSO, J.** ......................... *paintings* |        | **$1,210** |
| Cuban 19th cent.                            |        |           |
| ☐ **ALHORI, V.** .......................... *paintings* |        | **$880** |
| Italian 19th/20th cent.                     |        |           |
| ☐ **ALIGNY, Claude Felix Theodore** ........... *paintings* |        | **$4,950** |
| French 1798-1871                            |        |           |
| ☐ **ALIVEZ** ............................. *paintings* | **$220** | **$660** |
| Spanish 19th/20th cent.                     |        |           |
| ☐ **ALIX, Gabriel** ....................... *paintings* |        | **$550** |
| ☐ **ALIZARD, Jean Paul** ................... *paintings* |        | **$1,650** |
| French 19th cent.                           |        |           |
| ☐ **ALIZON, H.** .......................... *paintings* |        | **$605** |
| French 19th/20th cent.                      |        |           |
| ☐ **ALIZON, Hipolite** .................... *paintings* |        | **$825** |
| French 19th cent.                           |        |           |
| ☐ **ALKEN, Henry Gordon**                   |        |           |
| **(Samuel Henry)** ...................... *paintings* | **$440** | **$16,500** |
| English 1810-1894 ...................... *drawings* | **$522** | **$3,520** |
| ☐ **ALKEN, Henry Thomas** ............... *paintings* | **$1,540** | **$77,000** |
| English 1785-1851 ...................... *drawings* | **$330** | **$7,150** |
| ☐ **ALLAN, Donald F.** ................... *paintings* |        | **$352** |
| American 20th cent.                         |        |           |
| ☐ **ALLAN, Margo** ...................... *sculpture* |        | **$220** |
| American b. 1895                            |        |           |
| ☐ **ALLAN, W.R.** ........................ *paintings* |        | **$550** |
| 20th cent.                                  |        |           |

|  | | Current Price Range | |
|---|---|---|---|
|  | | Low | High |
| □ **ALLBON, Charles F.** ........................... *drawings* | | | $385 |
| British 19th cent. | | | |
| □ **ALLDRIDGE, R. L.** ........................... *paintings* | | | $418 |
| □ **ALLEGRAIN, Christophe Gabriel** ......... *sculpture* | | | $1,650 |
| French 1710-1795 | | | |
| □ **ALLEGRINI, Francesco** ...................... *drawings* | | $550 | $660 |
| □ **ALLEMOND** ..................................... *paintings* | | | $2,090 |
| French 1809-1886 | | | |
| □ **ALLEN, A.C.** ..................................... *paintings* | | | $357 |
| British 19th cent. | | | |
| □ **ALLEN, Barbara** ............................... *paintings* | | | $187 |
| English 20th cent. | | | |
| □ **ALLEN, Charles Curtis** ........................ *paintings* | | $154 | $2,970 |
| American 1886-1950 ................................. *drawings* | | | $99 |
| □ **ALLEN, Courtney** ............................... *paintings* | | $220 | $357 |
| American b. 1896 | | | |
| □ **ALLEN, Douglas** ................................. *paintings* | | | $1,210 |
| American 20th cent. | | | |
| □ **ALLEN, Howard** ............................... *paintings* | | | $605 |
| American 19th/20th cent. | | | |
| □ **ALLEN, Joel D.** .................................. *paintings* | | $110 | $440 |
| American 20th cent. | | | |
| □ **ALLEN, Joseph William** ....................... *paintings* | | | $880 |
| British 1803-1852 | | | |
| □ **ALLEN, Junius** ................................. *paintings* | | $110 | $1,870 |
| American 1898-1962 | | | |
| □ **ALLEN, Marion Boyd** ........................... *paintings* | | $100 | $467 |
| American 1862-1941 | | | |
| □ **ALLEN, Philip** .................................. *paintings* | | | $330 |
| □ **ALLEN, Robert Weir** ........................... *paintings* | | $650 | $1,650 |
| American 1851-1942 ................................. *drawings* | | $150 | $440 |
| □ **ALLEN, Thomas** ............................... *paintings* | | $302 | $770 |
| American 1849-1924 | | | |
| □ **ALLEN, W.** ..................................... *drawings* | | | $385 |
| British 19th cent. | | | |
| □ **ALLERSTON, John Taylor** ..................... *paintings* | | | $330 |
| English 19th cent. | | | |
| □ **ALLINGHAM, Helen** ........................... *drawings* | | $550 | $13,200 |
| English 1848-1926 | | | |
| □ **ALLIOT, Lucien Charles Edouard** ......... *sculpture* | | $1,650 | $3,080 |
| French early 20th cent. | | | |
| □ **ALLIS, C. Harry** ............................... *paintings* | | $105 | $1,650 |
| American d. 1938 ................................. *drawings* | | | $137 |
| □ **ALLISON, David** ............................... *paintings* | | | $363 |
| □ **ALLISON, William Merie** ..................... *drawings* | | | $187 |
| American b. 1880 | | | |
| □ **ALLOM, Thomas** ............................... *drawings* | | $220 | $440 |
| □ **ALLONGE, Auguste** ........................... *paintings* | | $302 | $1,045 |
| French 1833-1898 | | | |

|  | | Current Price Range | |
|---|---|---|---|
|  | | Low | High |
| ☐ **ALLORI, Christofano** ........................... *paintings* | | | $10,450 |
| Italian 1577-1621 | | | |
| ☐ **ALLOU, Gilles** ..................................... *paintings* | | | $5,225 |
| ☐ **ALLOUARD, Henri** ............................... *sculpture* | | $385 | $17,600 |
| French 1844-1929 | | | |
| ☐ **ALLSTON, Washington** ....................... *paintings* | | | $9,900 |
| American 1779-1843 ..................................... *drawings* | | | $4,180 |
| ☐ **ALMA-TADEMA, Lady Laura** | | | |
| **(Laura EPPS)** ...................................... *paintings* | | $4,950 | $8,250 |
| English 1852-1909 | | | |
| ☐ **ALMA-TADEMA, Sir Lawrence** ........... *paintings* | | $6,600 | $330,000 |
| English 1836-1912 ........................................ *drawings* | | $7,150 | $20,900 |
| ☐ **ALMANZA, Cleofas** ............................. *paintings* | | $8,800 | $19,800 |
| Latin American | | | |
| ☐ **ALMONAR, J.** ..................................... *paintings* | | | $330 |
| Haitian | | | |
| ☐ **ALMQUIST, Carl** ............................... *paintings* | | | $1,650 |
| ☐ **ALONZO, Dominique** ........................... *sculpture* | | $220 | $1,650 |
| French 20th cent. | | | |
| ☐ **ALOTT, Robert** ................................... *paintings* | | | $1,430 |
| Austrian 19th cent. | | | |
| ☐ **ALOUX, Jean Pierre** ........................... *paintings* | | | $352 |
| ☐ **ALPERIZ, Nicholas** ............................. *paintings* | | | $1,210 |
| Spanish b. 1869 | | | |
| ☐ **ALPHOND, Georges** ............................. *paintings* | | | $1,100 |
| ☐ **ALPUY, Julio** ..................................... *drawings* | | | $1,100 |
| ☐ **ALSINA, J.** ......................................... *paintings* | | $715 | $1,320 |
| French 19th/20th cent. | | | |
| ☐ **ALSLOOT, Denis van** ........................... *paintings* | | | $31,900 |
| Flemish 1570-1628 | | | |
| ☐ **ALSOP, Frederic** ................................. *paintings* | | | $330 |
| English 19th cent. | | | |
| ☐ **ALT, Franz** ......................................... *drawings* | | $4,180 | $4,400 |
| Austrian 1821-1914 | | | |
| ☐ **ALT, Jacob** ......................................... *paintings* | | | $3,410 |
| German 1789-1872 | | | |
| ☐ **ALT, Rudolf von** ................................. *drawings* | | $4,400 | $24,200 |
| Austrian 1812-1905 | | | |
| ☐ **ALTAMURA,** | | | |
| **Saverio Francesco Raffaele** .................... *paintings* | | | $550 |
| Italian 1826-97 | | | |
| ☐ **ALTEN, Mathias Joseph** ....................... *paintings* | | $247 | $1,760 |
| German/American 1871-1938 ......................... *drawings* | | | $330 |
| ☐ **ALTENKIRCH, Otto** ............................. *paintings* | | | $412 |
| German b. 1875 | | | |
| ☐ **ALTINI, E.** ......................................... *paintings* | | | $385 |
| ☐ **ALTMANN, Aaron** ............................... *paintings* | | | $357 |
| b. 1872 | | | |

|  | | Current Price Range | |
|---|---|---|---|
|  | | Low | High |
| ☐ **ALTMANN, Anton** ............................ *drawings* | | | $660 |
| Austrian 1808-1871 | | | |
| ☐ **ALTOON, John** ................................. *paintings* | | $1,100 | $2,090 |
| American b. 1925 | | | |
| ☐ **ALTSON, Aby** .................................. *paintings* | | $990 | $12,100 |
| British b. 1864 | | | |
| ☐ **ALVAREZ, Gian** ............................... *paintings* | | | $19,800 |
| Spanish 19th cent. | | | |
| ☐ **ALVAREZ, Luis** ............................... *paintings* | | $1,045 | $28,600 |
| Spanish 1841-1901 ................................. *drawings* | | $2,750 | $2,750 |
| ☐ **ALVAREZ-DUMONT, Eugenio** ............. *paintings* | | | $880 |
| Spanish 1864-1927 | | | |
| ☐ **ALVARO, Jorge** ............................... *drawings* | | | $1,100 |
| Argentinian b. 1949 | | | |
| ☐ **ALVARO DI PIERO,** | | | |
| **(IL PORTOGHESE)** ............................ *paintings* | | | $110,000 |
| ☐ **AMADO Y BERNARDET, Ramon** ........ *paintings* | | | $2,310 |
| Spanish 1844-1888 | | | |
| ☐ **AMAN-JEAN, Edmond Francois** ........... *paintings* | | $385 | $9,075 |
| French 1860-1935/36 ................................. *drawings* | | $550 | $3,575 |
| ☐ **AMANS, James** ................................. *paintings* | | | $7,150 |
| American 1801-1888 | | | |
| ☐ **AMARAL, Antonio Henrique Abeu** ....... *paintings* | | $2,200 | $4,400 |
| Brazilian b. 1935 | | | |
| ☐ **AMAT, Jose** ...................................... *paintings* | | $1,650 | $1,760 |
| ☐ **AMBERG, August Wilhelm** .................. *paintings* | | $1,320 | $2,200 |
| German 1822-1899 | | | |
| ☐ **AMBERGER, Christoph** ....................... *paintings* | | | $33,000 |
| German c. 1500-1562/63 | | | |
| ☐ **AMBROGIANI, Pierre** ......................... *paintings* | | | $880 |
| French b. 1907 | | | |
| ☐ **AMBROS, Raphael von** ....................... *paintings* | | | $1,870 |
| Czechoslovakian 19th cent. | | | |
| ☐ **AMEGLIO, Merio** .............................. *paintings* | | $302 | $880 |
| French 1897-1970 | | | |
| ☐ **AMEN, Irving** ................................... *paintings* | | | $302 |
| b. 1918 | | | |
| ☐ **AMERANI, Giovanni** ........................... *drawings* | | | $990 |
| ☐ **AMERLING, Friedrich von** .................. *paintings* | | | $2,420 |
| German 1803-1887 | | | |
| ☐ **AMERO, Emilio** ................................. *drawings* | | $550 | $990 |
| ☐ **AMES** ............................................. *drawings* | | | $385 |
| American 19th cent. | | | |
| ☐ **AMES, B.** ........................................ *paintings* | | | $275 |
| American 19th cent. | | | |
| ☐ **AMES, Blanche** ................................. *paintings* | | | $440 |
| ac.1923 | | | |
| ☐ **AMES, Ezra** ..................................... *paintings* | | $605 | $7,700 |
| American ac. 1768-1836 | | | |

|  | | Current Price Range | |
|---|---|---|---|
|  | | Low | High |
| ☐ **AMES, May** .......................... *paintings* | | $176 | $302 |
| American d. 1946 | | | |
| ☐ **AMESEDER, Edward** ........................... *paintings* | | | $1,430 |
| Austrian 1856-1938 | | | |
| ☐ **AMICK, Robert Wesley** ........................ *paintings* | | $137 | $13,200 |
| American 1879-1969 ................................ *drawings* | | $300 | $522 |
| ☐ **AMICO, E. di** ................................................ *paintings* | | | $605 |
| ☐ **AMIGONI, Jacopo** ............................. *paintings* | | $770 | $9,265 |
| Italian 1675-1752 | | | |
| ☐ **AMOROSI, Antonio** ............................ *paintings* | | | $2,860 |
| Italian 1660-c. 1736 | | | |
| ☐ **AMORSOLO, Fernando** ...................... *paintings* | | $1,320 | $3,850 |
| Phillipino ac. 1925-1935 | | | |
| ☐ **AMOS, G.T.** ................................................. *paintings* | | | $2,420 |
| ☐ **AMSDEN, William King** ....................... *paintings* | | $550 | $605 |
| American 20th cent. | | | |
| ☐ **ANA MARIA** ..................................... *paintings* | | | $880 |
| ☐ **ANASTASI, August** ............................. *paintings* | | | $935 |
| French 1820-1889 ................................ *drawings* | | $110 | $176 |
| ☐ **ANATOLE, Charles** ............................ *paintings* | | | $440 |
| ☐ **ANBURU, Manuel de** ........................... *paintings* | | | $880 |
| Mexican 18th cent. | | | |
| ☐ **ANCILLOTTI** ..................................... *paintings* | | | $412 |
| ☐ **ANDERS, Ernst** .................................. *paintings* | | | $3,300 |
| German 1845-1911 | | | |
| ☐ **ANDERSON, Carolyn A.** ...................... *drawings* | | | $700 |
| American | | | |
| ☐ **ANDERSON, Doris** ............................. *drawings* | | | $500 |
| American | | | |
| ☐ **ANDERSON, E.S.** ............................... *paintings* | | $176 | $357 |
| American 19th/20th cent. | | | |
| ☐ **ANDERSON, Frank** ............................ *paintings* | | | $3,300 |
| American 19th cent. | | | |
| ☐ **ANDERSON, Frederic A.** ...................... *paintings* | | | $770 |
| American 19th/20th cent. | | | |
| ☐ **ANDERSON, Harold Edgerly** ................ *paintings* | | $137 | $1,500 |
| American b. 1899 | | | |
| ☐ **ANDERSON, James Bell** ....................... *paintings* | | $60 | $412 |
| Scottish 1886-1938 | | | |
| ☐ **ANDERSON, John** ............................... *drawings* | | | $220 |
| English 19th/20th cent. | | | |
| ☐ **ANDERSON, Karl** ............................... *paintings* | | $715 | $6,050 |
| American 1874-1956 ................................ *drawings* | | $330 | $440 |
| ☐ **ANDERSON, Lennart** ........................ *paintings* | | | $990 |
| ☐ **ANDERSON, Martinus** ........................ *paintings* | | | $1,100 |
| American b. 1878 | | | |
| ☐ **ANDERSON, Ronald Lee** ...................... *paintings* | | $605 | $1,540 |
| American 1886-1926 | | | |

|                                        |            | Current Price Range |          |
|                                        |            | Low       | High    |
| --- | --- | --- | --- |
| ☐ **ANDERSON, Ruth A.** |  |  |  |
| **(Mrs. Samuel TEMPLE)** ........................ *paintings* | | $300 | $1,320 |
| American 1884-1939 | | | |
| ☐ **ANDERSON, Victor Coleman** ............... *paintings* | | | $1,100 |
| 1882-1937 ................................................ *drawings* | | | $440 |
| ☐ **ANDERSON, W. Livingston** ................. *paintings* | | | $1,540 |
| English ac.1856-1893 ................................ *drawings* | | $66 | $88 |
| ☐ **ANDERTON, C.W.** ............................. *drawings* | | | $176 |
| English 19th cent. | | | |
| ☐ **ANDRADE, Mary F.** ........................... *paintings* | | $522 | $825 |
| American | | | |
| ☐ **ANDRE, Albert** ..................................... *paintings* | | $1,320 | $13,200 |
| French 1869-1954 ....................................... *drawings* | | $220 | $8,250 |
| ☐ **ANDRE, Carl** ..................................... *drawings* | | | $220 |
| American b. 1935 ....................................... *sculpture* | | $660 | $31,900 |
| ☐ **ANDRE, Charles** ................................ *drawings* | | | $12,100 |
| French 19th cent. | | | |
| ☐ **ANDRE, Jules** ....................................... *paintings* | | | $2,640 |
| French 1807-69 | | | |
| ☐ **ANDREA DI NICCOLO** ....................... *paintings* | | | $66,000 |
| Italian | | | |
| ☐ **ANDREENKO, Mikhail** ......................... *paintings* | | | $1,870 |
| Russian b. 1894 | | | |
| ☐ **ANDREIS, Alex de** ............................... *paintings* | | $330 | $2,860 |
| European 19th cent. | | | |
| ☐ **ANDRENS, Sherry** ............................. *drawings* | | $110 | $302 |
| ☐ **ANDREOLI, Andre** .............................. *paintings* | | $192 | $357 |
| American b. 1941 | | | |
| ☐ **ANDREOTTI, Federigo** ........................ *paintings* | | $880 | $20,900 |
| Italian 1847-1930 | | | |
| ☐ **ANDREU, Mariano** ............................. *paintings* | | $275 | $880 |
| Spanish b. 1888/1901 ................................. *drawings* | | | $302 |
| ☐ **ANDREWS, Ambrose** ......................... *paintings* | | $900 | $3,300 |
| American ac. 1824-1859 | | | |
| ☐ **ANDREWS, Benny** ............................. *paintings* | | | $55 |
| American b. 1930 ....................................... *drawings* | | | $473 |
| ☐ **ANDREWS, George Henry** ................. *paintings* | | $550 | $4,950 |
| English 1816-1898 | | | |
| ☐ **ANDREWS, Henry** ............................. *paintings* | | $1,100 | $5,500 |
| English ac. 1830-1860 | | | |
| ☐ **ANDRIEU, Mathuran Arthur** ............... *paintings* | | $325 | $450 |
| French d. 1896 | | | |
| ☐ **ANDRIEU, Pierre** ............................... *drawings* | | | $2,090 |
| French 1821-1892 | | | |
| ☐ **ANDRIEUX, Clement Auguste** ............. *drawings* | | | $330 |
| French b. 1829 | | | |
| ☐ **ANDRINGA, Tjeerd** ............................ *paintings* | | $1,540 | $1,650 |
| Dutch 1806-1827 | | | |
| ☐ **ANDRION, Lucien** ............................... *paintings* | | | $3,300 |

| | Current Price Range | |
|---|---|---|
| | Low | High |

| | | Low | High |
|---|---|---|---|
| ☐ ANDROMID, Sperry ........................... *paintings* | | | $275 |
| ☐ ANEDEE, Vesnus ............................... *paintings* | | | $2,200 |
| French 1831-1909 | | | |
| ☐ ANELAY, Henry ................................. *paintings* | | $330 | $440 |
| English 1817-1883 | | | |
| ☐ ANESI, Paolo ..................................... *paintings* | | $1,100 | $4,400 |
| Italian c. 1700-c. 1761 | | | |
| ☐ ANFRIE, C. ...................................... *sculpture* | | $495 | $770 |
| late 19th cent. | | | |
| ☐ ANGAROLA, Anthony ........................... *paintings* | | $1,980 | $2,310 |
| American 1893-1929 | | | |
| ☐ ANGEL, Felix .................................... *paintings* | | | $880 |
| Colombian | | | |
| ☐ ANGELI, Filippo | | | |
| (called IL NAPOLETANO) ..................... *drawings* | | | $522 |
| Italian c. 1600-c. 1640 | | | |
| ☐ ANGELI, Giuseppe ............................. *paintings* | | | $9,900 |
| Italian c. 1709-1798 | | | |
| ☐ ANGELI, Heinrich von ......................... *paintings* | | | $2,750 |
| Austrian 1840-1925 | | | |
| ☐ ANGELIS, D. de ................................ *drawings* | | $302 | $495 |
| Italian 19th cent. | | | |
| ☐ ANGELIS, Desiderio de ....................... *paintings* | | $2,640 | $4,950 |
| Italian 19th cent. ................................... *drawings* | | $165 | $550 |
| ☐ ANGELIS, Domenico de ....................... *drawings* | | | $660 |
| Italian 1852-1904 | | | |
| ☐ ANGELL, Louise M. ........................... *paintings* | | | $385 |
| American 19th/20th cent. | | | |
| ☐ ANGELO, Valenti ............................... *paintings* | | | $467 |
| ☐ ANGLADA-CANMARASA, Herman ..... *paintings* | | | $1,870 |
| Spanish 1873-1959 | | | |
| ☐ ANGLADE, Gaston ............................. *paintings* | | $220 | $495 |
| French b. 1854 | | | |
| ☐ ANGLES, Joaquin ............................... *sculpture* | | | $412 |
| French | | | |
| ☐ ANGO, Jean Robert ............................. *drawings* | | $385 | $1,320 |
| French late 18th cent. | | | |
| ☐ ANGRAND, Charles ............................. *drawings* | | | $4,620 |
| French 1854-1926 | | | |
| ☐ ANGUIANO, Raul ............................... *paintings* | | $550 | $5,225 |
| Mexican b. 1915 ................................... *drawings* | | $220 | $1,100 |
| ☐ ANISFELD, Boris ............................... *paintings* | | $198 | $1,980 |
| Russian/American 1879-1973 ..................... *drawings* | | $550 | $1,210 |
| ☐ ANIVITTI, Filippo ............................... *drawings* | | | $935 |
| Italian b. 1876 | | | |
| ☐ ANKARCRONA, Alexia ....................... *paintings* | | | $880 |
| Swedish 1825-1901 | | | |
| ☐ ANKARCRONA, Henrik August ........... *paintings* | | $715 | $10,450 |
| Swedish b. 1831 ................................... *drawings* | | | $522 |

| | | Current Price Range | |
| | | Low | High |
| --- | --- | --- | --- |
| ☐ **ANNA, Alessandro d'** ........................ *paintings* | | | $715 |
| Italian | | | |
| ☐ **ANNENKOFF, Georges** ...................... *paintings* | | $440 | $1,045 |
| Russian 1890/94-1971 | | | |
| ☐ **ANNENKOFF, Yuri** ........................... *paintings* | | | $990 |
| ............................................... *drawings* | | | $1,210 |
| ☐ **ANNIGONI, Pietro** ........................... *paintings* | | | $4,675 |
| Italian b.1910 ..................................... *drawings* | | | $467 |
| ☐ **ANNISON, Edward S.** ....................... *paintings* | | | $1,210 |
| ☐ **ANREU, Mariano** ............................. *drawings* | | | $302 |
| ☐ **ANSALDO, Andrea** ........................... *paintings* | | | $3,300 |
| ☐ **ANSDELL, Richard** ........................... *paintings* | | $275 | $18,700 |
| English 1815-1885 | | | |
| ☐ **ANSELMI, Michelangelo** ..................... *paintings* | | | $24,200 |
| Italian 1491-1554 | | | |
| ☐ **ANSHUTZ, Thomas Pollock** ................. *paintings* | | $770 | $19,800 |
| American 1851-1912 ................................ *drawings* | | $165 | $7,700 |
| ☐ **ANSON, M.** ..................................... *paintings* | | | $450 |
| ☐ **ANTAKOLSKY, Markus** ..................... *sculpture* | | | $990 |
| Russian 19th cent. | | | |
| ☐ **ANTES, Horst** ................................ *paintings* | | $1,760 | $9,900 |
| German b. 1936 ................................... *drawings* | | $935 | $1,870 |
| ☐ **ANTHONISSEN, Hendrick van** ............. *paintings* | | | $17,600 |
| Dutch c. 1606-1654/60 | | | |
| ☐ **ANTHONY, Carol** ............................ *paintings* | | $440 | $1,760 |
| American b. 1943 ................................... *drawings* | | | $2,860 |
| ☐ **ANTHONY, Ernest Edwin** ................... *paintings* | | | $220 |
| American b. 1894 | | | |
| ☐ **ANTIGES, E.** ................................... *paintings* | | | $330 |
| American 19th/20th cent. | | | |
| ☐ **ANTIGNA, Alexandre** ........................ *paintings* | | | $192 |
| French 1817-1878 | | | |
| ☐ **ANTIGNA, Marc** .............................. *paintings* | | | $247 |
| French 19th/20th cent. | | | |
| ☐ **ANTOINE, Montas** ............................ *paintings* | | $110 | $605 |
| Latin American 20th cent. | | | |
| ☐ **ANTOMMARCHI, Dr. F.** ..................... *sculpture* | | | $990 |
| ☐ **ANTONIANI, Pietro** .......................... *paintings* | | | $7,370 |
| Italian d. 1805 | | | |
| ☐ **ANTONIO, Christobal de** ................... *paintings* | | | $990 |
| ☐ **ANTONIO VENEZIANO,** | | | |
| **Antonio Francesco da Venezia** .............. *paintings* | | | $16,500 |
| Italian c. 1340-c. 1387 | | | |
| ☐ **ANTONIOLI, A.** ............................... *paintings* | | | $440 |
| 20th cent. | | | |
| ☐ **ANTROBUS** ...................................... *paintings* | | | $301 |
| ☐ **ANTROS, A. van** .............................. *paintings* | | | $990 |
| European 19th cent. | | | |

|                                                          | | *Current Price Range* | |
| --- | --- | --- | --- |
|                                                          | | *Low* | *High* |
| ☐ **ANTUNEZ, Nemesio** ............................ *paintings* | | $1,980 | $3,300 |
| Chilean b. 1918 | | | |
| ☐ **ANTY, Andre d'** ................................. *paintings* | | | $220 |
| French b. 1910 | | | |
| ☐ **ANTY, Henry d'** ................................. *paintings* | | $121 | $550 |
| French b. 1910 | | | |
| ☐ **ANUSZKIEWICZ, Richard** ................... *paintings* | | $660 | $10,450 |
| American b. 1930 | | | |
| ☐ **ANVILLE,** | | | |
| **Hubert Francois Bourguignon d'** ............ *paintings* | | | $275 |
| French 1699-1773 | | | |
| ☐ **APOL, Armand** .................................... *drawings* | | | $825 |
| Belgian 19th cent. | | | |
| ☐ **APOL, Louis** ....................................... *paintings* | | | $330 |
| Dutch b. 1850 | | | |
| ☐ **APOLINAR** ......................................... *paintings* | | | $385 |
| ☐ **APPEL, Charles P.** ............................. *paintings* | | $275 | $3,080 |
| American b. 1857 | | | |
| ☐ **APPEL, Karel** ..................................... *paintings* | | $1,540 | $38,500 |
| Dutch/American b. 1921 ............................. *drawings* | | $5,500 | $6,600 |
| ............................................................... *sculpture* | | $500 | $5,500 |
| ☐ **APPERT, Eugene** ................................ *paintings* | | | $1,650 |
| French 1814-67 | | | |
| ☐ **APPERT, G.** ....................................... *paintings* | | $385 | $1,045 |
| French 19th cent. | | | |
| ☐ **APPIAN, Jacques Bartholomy** | | | |
| **(called Adolphe)** ..................................... *paintings* | | | $1,430 |
| French 1818-1898 ..................................... *drawings* | | | $242 |
| ☐ **APPIANI, Andrea** ................................ *drawings* | | | $990 |
| ☐ **APSHOVEN, Thomas van** ..................... *paintings* | | $1,100 | $6,050 |
| Flemish 1622-1664 | | | |
| ☐ **APT, Charles** ...................................... *paintings* | | | $880 |
| American 20th cent. | | | |
| ☐ **AQUINO, Edmundo** ............................. *paintings* | | | $1,100 |
| Mexican/American b. 1939 | | | |
| ☐ **AQUINO, Humberto** ............................ *paintings* | | $1,100 | $6,600 |
| Peruvian b. 1947 | | | |
| ☐ **ARAI** ................................................. *paintings* | | | $302 |
| French (?) 20th cent. | | | |
| ☐ **ARAKAWA, Shusaku** ........................... *paintings* | | $11,000 | $23,100 |
| Japanese b. 1936 ..................................... *drawings* | | $550 | $2,200 |
| ☐ **ARANGO, Ramiro** ............................... *drawings* | | $715 | $825 |
| ☐ **ARCANGELO, Allan d'** ....................... *paintings* | | $1,760 | $12,100 |
| American b. 1930 | | | |
| ☐ **ARCE, Manuel de** ............................... *paintings* | | $137 | $1,210 |
| ☐ **ARCENZA, Nicola d'** ........................... *drawings* | | | $356 |
| American 19th cent. | | | |
| ☐ **ARCHAINBAUD, P.G.** ......................... *paintings* | | | $2,090 |

| | | | Current Price Range | |
|---|---|---|---|---|
| | | | Low | High |
| ☐ **ARCHER, Edmund** .............................. *paintings* | | | | $247 |
| American 20th cent. | | | | |
| ☐ **ARCHILTA, Clara** .............................. *drawings* | | | | $825 |
| American (Kiowa) | | | | |
| ☐ **ARCHIPENKO, Alexander** .................... *paintings* | | | $825 | $5,500 |
| Russian 1887-1964 ...................................... *drawings* | | | $99 | $2,310 |
| .................................................................. *sculpture* | | | $1,210 | $71,500 |
| ☐ **ARDISSONE, Yolande** .......................... *paintings* | | | $770 | $1,346 |
| French b. 1872 | | | | |
| ☐ **ARELLANO, Juan de** ........................... *paintings* | | | | $30,800 |
| Spanish 1614-1676 | | | | |
| ☐ **AREN, C.L.** ........................................ *paintings* | | | | $632 |
| Continental (?) 19th cent. | | | | |
| ☐ **AREND, G.** ......................................... *paintings* | | | | $385 |
| Dutch 19th/20th cent. | | | | |
| ☐ **ARENTZ, Josef M.** .............................. *paintings* | | | $385 | $1,155 |
| American 1903-1969 | | | | |
| ☐ **ARGIENTO, Nicholas (Duster)** .............. *paintings* | | | | $990 |
| contemporary | | | | |
| ☐ **ARIAS, Miguel** ................................... *paintings* | | | $880 | $4,125 |
| Cuban 19th cent. | | | | |
| ☐ **ARIZA, Gonzalo** ................................. *drawings* | | | | $660 |
| Columbian b. 1912 | | | | |
| ☐ **ARLAUD-JURINE, Louis Ami** .............. *drawings* | | | | $2,860 |
| ☐ **ARLINGTON** ...................................... *paintings* | | | | $253 |
| ☐ **ARMAN, (Arman FERNANDEZ)** .......... *paintings* | | | | $6,600 |
| French b. 1928 ......................................... *drawings* | | | | $935 |
| .................................................................. *sculpture* | | | $174 | $82,500 |
| ☐ **ARMBRUSTER, Francois** ...................... *paintings* | | | | $2,090 |
| ☐ **ARMENISE, R.** .................................... *paintings* | | | | $302 |
| Italian 19th cent. | | | | |
| ☐ **ARMER, Laura Adams** ......................... *paintings* | | | $165 | $302 |
| American 1874-1963 | | | | |
| ☐ **ARMFIELD, Edward** ........................... *paintings* | | | $550 | $6,050 |
| British 19th cent. | | | | |
| ☐ **ARMFIELD, George** ............................ *paintings* | | | $440 | $14,300 |
| British ac. 1840-1875/80 | | | | |
| ☐ **ARMINGTON, Caroline** ....................... *paintings* | | | | $770 |
| ☐ **ARMINGTON, Frank Milton** ................ *paintings* | | | $605 | $2,200 |
| Canadian/Amer. 1876-1941 ...................... *drawings* | | | | $55 |
| ☐ **ARMITAGE, Kenneth** .......................... *sculpture* | | | $1,210 | $4,070 |
| English b. 1916 | | | | |
| ☐ **ARMOR, Charles** ................................. *paintings* | | | $247 | $770 |
| American b. 1844 | | | | |
| ☐ **ARMOUR, George Denholm** ................. *drawings* | | | $121 | $605 |
| British 1864-1949 | | | | |
| ☐ **ARMSTEAD, Henry Hugh** .................... *paintings* | | | $990 | $3,080 |
| ☐ **ARMSTRONG, David Maitland** ............ *paintings* | | | | $1,545 |
| American 1836-1918 | | | | |

| | Current Price Range | |
|---|---|---|
| | *Low* | *High* |
| ☐ **ARMSTRONG, Geoffrey** ................. *paintings* | | $550 |
| ☐ **ARMSTRONG, John** ........................... *paintings* | | $412 |
| English 1893-1973 | | |
| ☐ **ARMSTRONG, Rolf** ........................... *paintings* | | $1,650 |
| American 1881-1960 ................................... *drawings* | $935 | $4,950 |
| ☐ **ARMSTRONG, Thomas** ..................... *paintings* | | $247 |
| English 1835-1911 | | |
| ☐ **ARMSTRONG, William L.** ................. *paintings* | | $220 |
| American | | |
| ☐ **ARMSTRONG, William W.** ................. *paintings* | $605 | $1,980 |
| Irish/American 1822-1914 | | |
| ☐ **ARNAUD, Moise** .................................. *paintings* | | $2,090 |
| ☐ **ARNAUTOFF, Victor Michail** ............. *paintings* | | $357 |
| b. 1896 | | |
| ☐ **ARNEGGER, Alwin** ........................... *paintings* | $330 | $2,200 |
| European 1883-1916 | | |
| ☐ **ARNESEN, Vilhelm** ........................... *paintings* | $935 | $1,500 |
| Danish b. 1865 | | |
| ☐ **ARNESON, Robert** ........................... *drawings* | | $1,980 |
| American b. 1930 ...................................... *sculpture* | $825 | $1,540 |
| ☐ **ARNO, Peter** ...................................... *drawings* | $110 | $411 |
| American 1904-1968 | | |
| ☐ **ARNOLD, G.** ....................................... *paintings* | $638 | $550 |
| Canadian 20th cent. | | |
| ☐ **ARNOLD, James** ................................. *paintings* | $425 | $500 |
| American 20th cent. | | |
| ☐ **ARNOLD, Jay** ..................................... *paintings* | | $467 |
| American 19th/20th cent. | | |
| ☐ **ARNOLD, John Knowlton** ................. *paintings* | $200 | $770 |
| American 1834-1909 | | |
| ☐ **ARNOLD, Reginald Ernst** ................. *paintings* | $550 | $1,540 |
| British ac. 1876-1896 | | |
| ☐ **ARNOLD, S.** ....................................... *paintings* | | $302 |
| British 19th cent. | | |
| ☐ **ARNOLDI, Charles** ........................... *paintings* | | $7,150 |
| American b. 1946 ...................................... *sculpture* | $1,100 | $12,100 |
| ☐ **ARNOULD DE COOL, Delphine** .......... *paintings* | | $4,400 |
| French b. 1830 | | |
| ☐ **ARNOUX, Charles Albert** ................. *paintings* | | $4,730 |
| French 1820-1863 | | |
| ☐ **ARNTZENIUS, H.** ............................... *paintings* | | $357 |
| Dutch 19th cent. | | |
| ☐ **ARNZ, A.** ........................................... *paintings* | | $440 |
| European 19th cent. | | |
| ☐ **ARONS, Philipp** ................................. *paintings* | | $495 |
| German School 1821-1902 | | |
| ☐ **ARONSON, Boris** ............................... *drawings* | $715 | $1,980 |

| | | Current Price Range | |
|---|---|---|---|
| | | Low | High |
| ☐ **ARP, Jean** ............................................ *paintings* | | $28,600 | $35,200 |
| French 1887-1966 ...................................... *drawings* | | $550 | $3,300 |
| .................................................................. *sculpture* | | $770 | $110,000 |
| ☐ **ARRANGO, Ramiro** ............................ *drawings* | | | $990 |
| b. Colombia | | | |
| ☐ **ARRANTS, Shirley** ............................ *drawings* | | | $900 |
| American | | | |
| ☐ **ARRIENS, Franz** ................................ *paintings* | | | $330 |
| ☐ **ARRIOLA, Fortunato** ........................ *paintings* | | | $3,575 |
| American 1827-1872 | | | |
| ☐ **ARTAN, Louis** ..................................... *paintings* | | | $440 |
| ☐ **ARTE, Fontana** ................................... *sculpture* | | | $9,900 |
| Milan | | | |
| ☐ **ARTER, J. Charles** ............................. *paintings* | | | $247 |
| American d. 1923 | | | |
| ☐ **ARTHOIS, Jacques d'** ......................... *paintings* | | $880 | $22,000 |
| Flemish 1613-1686 ...................................... *drawings* | | | $990 |
| ☐ **ARTHUR, Reginald** ............................ *paintings* | | $880 | $3,740 |
| British ac. 1881-1896 | | | |
| ☐ **ARTHUR, Robert** ................................ *paintings* | | | $440 |
| American | | | |
| ☐ **ARTHURS, Stanley Massey** ................. *paintings* | | $33 | $440 |
| American 1877-1950 | | | |
| ☐ **ARTIGES, Emile** ................................. *paintings* | | $500 | $800 |
| American 20th cent. | | | |
| ☐ **ARTS, Dorus** ....................................... *paintings* | | | $192 |
| Dutch 1901-1961 | | | |
| ☐ **ARTSCHWAGER, Richard** ................. *paintings* | | $7,920 | $16,500 |
| American b. 1924 ...................................... *drawings* | | | $1,980 |
| .................................................................. *sculpture* | | | $1,100 |
| ☐ **ARTZ, David Adolf Constant** .............. *paintings* | | $385 | $5,225 |
| Dutch 1837-1890 ...................................... *drawings* | | $162 | $935 |
| ☐ **ARUNDALE, Francis Vyvyan Jago** ........ *drawings* | | $3,850 | $6,050 |
| English 1807-1853 | | | |
| ☐ **ARUS, Jean Marie Joseph** ..................... *paintings* | | $330 | |
| French b. 1846 | | | |
| ☐ **ARUS, Joseph Raoul** ............................ *paintings* | | | $5,225 |
| French 1848-1921 | | | |
| ☐ **ARY-BITTER** ...................................... *sculpture* | | | $990 |
| ☐ **ASANO, Kyoko** ................................... *paintings* | | | $3,300 |
| American b. 1933 | | | |
| ☐ **ASARO, John** ...................................... *paintings* | | | $7,500 |
| American contemporary | | | |
| ☐ **ASCH, Pieter Jansz van** ....................... *paintings* | | | $7,700 |
| Dutch 1603-1678 | | | |
| ☐ **ASCHENBRENNER, Heinrich** .............. *paintings* | | | $1,540 |
| German ac. 1857-1862 | | | |
| ☐ **ASHBAUGH, Dennis** ........................... *paintings* | | | $660 |
| American 20th cent. | | | |

| | *Current Price Range* | |
|---|---|---|
| | Low | High |
| ☐ **ASHBURNER, William F.** .................. *drawings* | | $825 |
| ☐ **ASHE, Edmund M.** ............................. *drawings* | | $522 |
| American 20th cent. | | |
| ☐ **ASHFORD, Leonard** ........................... *paintings* | | $2,090 |
| British 19th/20th cent. | | |
| ☐ **ASHLEY, Clifford Warren** ................. *paintings* | $2,750 | $7,500 |
| American 1881-1947 | | |
| ☐ **ASHLEY, Frank N.** ............................ *paintings* | $55 | $385 |
| American b. 1920 ...................................... *drawings* | $385 | $605 |
| ☐ **ASHLEY, James** ............................... *paintings* | | $176 |
| American 20th cent. | | |
| ☐ **ASHLEY, John** ................................... *paintings* | | $275 |
| ☐ **ASHTON, Julian Howard** ................... *paintings* | | $2,530 |
| Austrialian 1877-1964 | | |
| ☐ **ASHTON, William** ............................. *paintings* | $242 | $330 |
| English 19th cent. | | |
| ☐ **ASHWORTH, L.** ................................. *paintings* | | $495 |
| British 19th cent. | | |
| ☐ **ASILOFF, L.** ..................................... *paintings* | | $825 |
| ☐ **ASOMA, Tadashi** .............................. *paintings* | | $500 |
| ☐ **ASPETTATI, Antonio Mario** ............... *paintings* | $385 | $4,125 |
| Italian b. 1880 | | |
| ☐ **ASPLUND, Nils** ................................. *paintings* | | $385 |
| Swedish 1874-1958 | | |
| ☐ **ASSELIN, Maurice** ............................. *paintings* | | $220 |
| French 1882-1947 ..................................... *drawings* | | $165 |
| ☐ **ASSELYN, Jan** ................................... *paintings* | $2,530 | $6,600 |
| Dutch 1610-1652/60 .................................. *drawings* | | $1,650 |
| ☐ **ASSERETO, Gioacchino** ...................... *paintings* | | $44,000 |
| Italian 1600-1649 | | |
| ☐ **ASSETTO, Franco** ............................. *paintings* | $110 | $192 |
| Italian b. 1911 | | |
| ☐ **ASSIA, Enrico d'** .............................. *drawings* | | $330 |
| ☐ **ASSMUS, Robert** ............................... *paintings* | | $9,350 |
| German b. 1837 | | |
| ☐ **ASSTEYN, Bartholomeus** ..................... *paintings* | | $44,000 |
| Austrian 1628-1662 | | |
| ☐ **AST, Balthasar van der** ......................... *paintings* | $44,000 | $132,000 |
| Dutch c. 1590-c. 1656 | | |
| ☐ **ASTANIERES, S.** ............................... *sculpture* | | $1,980 |
| French 19th cent. | | |
| ☐ **ASTE, Jean Louis** ............................. *drawings* | | $220 |
| French b. 1864 | | |
| ☐ **ASTI, Angelo** ................................... *paintings* | $66 | $2,750 |
| French 1847-1903 | | |
| ☐ **ASTON, G.** ....................................... *paintings* | | $462 |
| ☐ **ASTORI, C.** ...................................... *paintings* | | $357 |
| ☐ **ASTORRI, E.** .................................... *sculpture* | | $3,960 |
| Italian | | |

| | Current Price Range | |
| --- | --- | --- |
| | *Low* | *High* |
| ☐ **ASTUDIN, Nicolai** ............................ *paintings* | | $462 |
| ☐ **ATALAYA, Enrique** ......................... *paintings* | $440 | $550 |
| ☐ **ATAMIAN, Charles Garabed** ............... *paintings* | | $770 |
| Turkish ac. 1913-1945 ................................. *drawings* | | $110 |
| ☐ **ATHERTON, John** ............................ *paintings* | $220 | $880 |
| American, d.Canada 1900-1952 | | |
| ☐ **ATIRNOMIS** ..................................... *paintings* | | $247 |
| American b. 1938 | | |
| ☐ **ATISTRISH, George** .......................... *drawings* | | $660 |
| ☐ **ATKINS, Samuel** ................................ *drawings* | $550 | $15,400 |
| British ac. 1787-1808 | | |
| ☐ **ATKINSON, H.** ................................... *paintings* | | $275 |
| ☐ **ATKINSON, John** ............................... *paintings* | | $385 |
| English 19th/20th cent. | | |
| ☐ **ATKINSON, Robert** ........................... *paintings* | | $660 |
| British 1863-1898 | | |
| ☐ **ATKINSON, William E.** ...................... *paintings* | | $550 |
| ☐ **ATL, Dr. (Geraldo MURILLO)** ............. *paintings* | $3,850 | $44,000 |
| Mexican 1875-1964 ................................... *drawings* | $605 | $2,310 |
| ☐ **ATLAN, Jean Michel** .......................... *paintings* | $2,200 | $7,150 |
| French 1913-1960 ..................................... *drawings* | | $357 |
| ☐ **ATSARA, Vives** ................................. *paintings* | | $302 |
| Mexican 20th cent. | | |
| ☐ **ATTANSIO, Natale** ............................ *paintings* | | $935 |
| ☐ **AUBERT, Jean Ernest** ......................... *paintings* | $550 | $17,050 |
| French 1824-1906 | | |
| ☐ **AUBLET, Albert** ................................. *paintings* | $495 | $99,000 |
| French 1851-1938 | | |
| ☐ **AUBRAY, C.F.** ................................. *paintings* | | $1,045 |
| French 19th cent. | | |
| ☐ **AUBRY, Earl** ..................................... *paintings* | | $2,420 |
| ☐ **AUCLAIR, Andre** ............................... *paintings* | | $687 |
| French 20th cent. | | |
| ☐ **AUCOZI, L.** ...................................... *sculpture* | | $330 |
| European late 19th cent. | | |
| ☐ **AUDGREM, W. Livingstone** ............... *paintings* | $165 | $495 |
| British 19th/20th cent. | | |
| ☐ **AUDRY, Jean** ................................... *drawings* | $3,850 | $4,400 |
| 16th century | | |
| ☐ **AUDUBON, John James** ...................... *drawings* | $1,300 | $93,500 |
| American 1780/85-1851 | | |
| ☐ **AUDY, Jonny** ..................................... *paintings* | | $750 |
| French ac. 1872-1876 ................................. *drawings* | $522 | $660 |
| ☐ **AUER, Robert** .................................... *paintings* | | $605 |
| Austrian 1873-1952 | | |
| ☐ **AUERBACH, Frank** ............................ *paintings* | $4,620 | $27,500 |
| ............................................................ *drawings* | $1,320 | $2,310 |
| ☐ **AUERBACH-LEVY, William** ............... *paintings* | $55 | $770 |
| Russian/American 1889-1964 ......................... *drawings* | | $110 |

| | | Current Price Range | |
|---|---|---|---|
| | | Low | High |

| | | | Low | High |
|---|---|---|---|---|
| ☐ **AUFFRAY, Eugene** | paintings | | | $1,540 |
| French School 19th cent. | | | | |
| ☐ **AUFRAY, Joseph Athanase** | paintings | | $4,290 | $6,600 |
| French b. 1836 | | | | |
| ☐ **AUFSANDAN, F.** | paintings | | $715 | $1,100 |
| German 19th cent. | | | | |
| ☐ **AUGE, Philippe** | paintings | | $660 | $1,760 |
| French b. 1935 | | | | |
| ☐ **AUGE, Pierre** | paintings | | $247 | $350 |
| ☐ **AUGLES** | sculpture | | | $605 |
| ☐ **AUGUSTE, Salnave Philippe** | paintings | | $1,100 | $1,430 |
| Haitian | | | | |
| ☐ **AUGUSTE, Simon** | paintings | | | $330 |
| ☐ **AUGUSTIN, L.** | paintings | | | $1,760 |
| French 20th cent. | | | | |
| ☐ **AUGUSTIN, Ludwig** | paintings | | | $825 |
| German 20th cent. | | | | |
| ☐ **AUGUSTINES, Eduardo** | paintings | | $2,200 | $3,410 |
| Panamanian b. 1956 | | | | |
| ☐ **AUGUSTINO** | sculpture | | | $500 |
| ☐ **AULMAN, Theodore** | paintings | | | $440 |
| ☐ **AULMANN, Theodora** | paintings | | $192 | $440 |
| American b. 1882 | | | | |
| ☐ **AULT, Charles H.** | paintings | | | $308 |
| Canadian 19th cent. | | | | |
| ☐ **AULT, George C.** | paintings | | $495 | $17,050 |
| American 1891-1948 | drawings | | $121 | $2,420 |
| ☐ **AUMONIER, James** | paintings | | $99 | $200 |
| English 1832-1911 | | | | |
| ☐ **AUREL, Naray** | paintings | | $412 | $418 |
| ☐ **AUREL, Suzanne** | paintings | | | $275 |
| ☐ **AURELI, Giuseppe** | paintings | | $2,310 | $3,250 |
| Italian 1858-1929 | drawings | | $352 | $8,250 |
| ☐ **AUSSANDON, Hippolyte** | paintings | | | $3,300 |
| ☐ **AUSTEN, Alexander** | paintings | | $990 | $2,310 |
| British 19th/20th cent. | | | | |
| ☐ **AUSTEN, Anton J.** | paintings | | | $605 |
| Polish b. 1865 | | | | |
| ☐ **AUSTEN, Winifred** | drawings | | | $1,100 |
| ☐ **AUSTIN, Charles Percy** | paintings | | | $825 |
| American 1883-1948 | | | | |
| ☐ **AUSTIN, Darrel** | paintings | | $412 | $4,180 |
| American b. 1907 | drawings | | $264 | $320 |
| ☐ **AUSTIN, David** | paintings | | | $550 |
| American 20th cent. | | | | |
| ☐ **AUSTIN, R.S.** | paintings | | | $341 |
| American 19th cent. | | | | |
| ☐ **AUSTREICHER, H.** | paintings | | | $1,045 |

| | Current Price Range | |
|---|---|---|
| | Low | High |
| ☐ **AUSTRIAN, Ben** ................... *paintings* | $176 | $4,125 |
| American 1870-1921 | | |
| ☐ **AUVREST** ................... *drawings* | | $605 |
| ☐ **AVATA, George F.** ................... *drawings* | | $467 |
| ☐ **AVATRANI, A.** ................... *drawings* | | $522 |
| ☐ **AVEDESIAN, Edward** ................... *paintings* | $440 | $2,200 |
| American b. 1935/36 | | |
| ☐ **AVENDANO, Serafin de** ................... *paintings* | | $7,700 |
| Spanish 1838-1916 | | |
| ☐ **AVERCAMP, Hendrick** ................... *paintings* | | $209,000 |
| Dutch 1585-1663 | | |
| ☐ **AVERY, March** ................... *paintings* | | $330 |
| American | | |
| ☐ **AVERY, Milton** ................... *paintings* | $385 | $115,500 |
| American 1893-1965 ................... *drawings* | $242 | $46,200 |
| ☐ **AVIGDOR, Rene** ................... *paintings* | $550 | $1,540 |
| French b. 1891 | | |
| ☐ **AVINOFF, Andre** ................... *drawings* | | $440 |
| Russian/American 1884-1949 | | |
| ☐ **AVONT, Pieter von** ................... *paintings* | | $3,300 |
| Flemish 1600-1632 | | |
| ☐ **AVRAMIDIS, Joannis** ................... *sculpture* | | $1,430 |
| Greek b. 1922 | | |
| ☐ **AVROLL, James** ................... *paintings* | | $495 |
| English 19th cent. | | |
| ☐ **AVY, Joseph Marius** ................... *paintings* | | $6,600 |
| French b. 1871 | | |
| ☐ **AYDELOTT, Dean** ................... *paintings* | | $440 |
| American 20th cent. | | |
| ☐ **AYLWARD, J.D.** ................... *paintings* | | $330 |
| ☐ **AYLWARD, William James** ................... *paintings* | $880 | $990 |
| 1875-1956 ................... *drawings* | | $330 |
| ☐ **AYRTON, Michael** ................... *sculpture* | $900 | $2,750 |
| English 1921-1975 | | |
| ☐ **AZE, Adolphe** ................... *paintings* | | $467 |
| ☐ **AZEGLIO, Marchese d'** | | |
| (Massimo TAPARELLI) ................... *paintings* | | $825 |
| Italian 1798-1866 | | |
| ☐ **AZEMA, Ernest** ................... *paintings* | | $286 |
| ☐ **BAADE, Knud-Andreassen** ................... *paintings* | | $7,150 |
| Norwegian 1808-1879 | | |
| ☐ **BAADER, Johann** ................... *paintings* | | $1,980 |
| German 1709-1779 | | |
| ☐ **BAAGOE, Carl Emil** ................... *paintings* | $1,100 | $1,650 |
| Danish 1829-1902 | | |
| ☐ **BAARLE, H.M.** ................... *paintings* | | $1,650 |
| Belgium 19th cent. | | |
| ☐ **BABB, Charlotte E.** ................... *drawings* | | $1,100 |
| English c. 1830-1906 | | |

|  | | Current Price Range | |
|---|---|---|---|
|  | | Low | High |
| ☐ **BABBIDGE, James C.** ............................ *paintings* <br> American 19th cent. | | | $5,060 |
| ☐ **BABBIDGE, James Gardner** ................. *paintings* <br> American 1844-1919 | | | $5,720 |
| ☐ **BABCOCK, William P.** ........................ *paintings* <br> American 1826-1899 ..................................... *drawings* | | $302 | $1,100 <br> $176 |
| ☐ **BABER, Alice** ....................................... *paintings* <br> American b. 1928 ....................................... *drawings* | | $220 | $4,400 <br> $660 |
| ☐ **BABOT, Joaquin Canete** ....................... *paintings* <br> Continental 20th cent. | | $330 | $330 |
| ☐ **BABOULENE, Eugene** ......................... *paintings* <br> French b. 1905 | | | $385 |
| ☐ **BABOULET, Francois** ......................... *paintings* <br> French b. 1915 | | | $2,530 |
| ☐ **BABUREN, Theodor van (Dirck)** ............ *paintings* <br> b. c. 1570/90, d. 1623/24 | | | $148,500 |
| ☐ **BAC, Fernand** ..................................... *drawings* <br> French 1859-1952 | | | $1,540 |
| ☐ **BACCANI, Attilio** ............................... *paintings* <br> Italian 19th cent. | | | $5,500 |
| ☐ **BACH, Esther E.** ................................. *drawings* <br> American 20th cent. | | | $200 |
| ☐ **BACH, Florence Julia** ......................... *paintings* <br> American 1887-? | | | $440 |
| ☐ **BACH, Guido** ..................................... *paintings* <br> German 1828-1905 | | | $1,650 |
| ☐ **BACH, M.** ........................................... *paintings* <br> French (?) 19th cent. | | | $1,650 |
| ☐ **BACH, Oscar B.** ................................. *sculpture* <br> American b. 1884 | | | $220 |
| ☐ **BACHELET, Emile Just** ....................... *sculpture* <br> French b. 1892 | | $1,870 | $26,400 |
| ☐ **BACHELIER, Jean Jacques** ................. *paintings* <br> French 1724-1806 | | | $17,600 |
| ☐ **BACHELIN, Auguste** ......................... *paintings* <br> Swiss 1830-1890 | | $1,925 | $6,050 |
| ☐ **BACHER, Otto Henry** ......................... *paintings* <br> American 1856-1909 ..................................... *drawings* | | $4,125 | $47,300 <br> $220 |
| ☐ **BACHMANN, Hans** ............................. *paintings* <br> Swiss b. 1852 | | | $4,180 |
| ☐ **BACHMANN, Max** ............................... *sculpture* <br> American 1862-1921 | | $124 | $5,060 |
| ☐ **BACHMANN, Otto** ............................... *paintings* | | $770 | $3,300 |
| ☐ **BACHRACH-BAREE, Emmanuel** ......... *paintings* | | $385 | $880 |
| ☐ **BACKER, Jacob** ................................... *paintings* <br> Dutch | | $5,500 | $6,600 |
| ☐ **BACKES, Nick** ..................................... *drawings* | | | $1,100 |
| ☐ **BACKHUYSEN, Ludolf (the elder)** ......... *paintings* <br> Dutch 1631-1708 ....................................... *drawings* | | $9,900 | $25,300 <br> $2,640 |

| | | Current Price Range | |
|---|---|---|---|
| | | Low | High |
| ☐ **BACON, Charles Roswell** ...... *paintings* | | | $550 |
| American 1868-1913 | | | |
| ☐ **BACON, Francis** ............... *paintings* | | $104,500 | $517,000 |
| Irish b. 1909 | | | |
| ☐ **BACON, Frank A.** ............... *paintings* | | | $1,100 |
| American 1803-1887 | | | |
| ☐ **BACON, Henry** ................ *paintings* | | $467 | $9,900 |
| American 1839-1912 ................ *drawings* | | $121 | $1,320 |
| ☐ **BACON, I.L.** .................... *paintings* | | $110 | $1,265 |
| American late 19th cent. | | | |
| ☐ **BACON, Irving R.** .............. *paintings* | | $154 | $522 |
| American 1875-1962 ................. *drawings* | | $258 | $786 |
| ☐ **BACON, Peggy** ................. *paintings* | | $1,100 | $3,850 |
| American b. 1895 .................... *drawings* | | $132 | $990 |
| ☐ **BACON, R. S.** ................... *paintings* | | | $450 |
| American 20th cent. | | | |
| ☐ **BACON OF CULFORD,** | | | |
| **Sir Nathaniel J.** ............... *paintings* | | | $4,675 |
| English 17th cent. | | | |
| ☐ **BADEN, Heinz** ................. *paintings* | | $110 | $247 |
| German b.1887 | | | |
| ☐ **BADEN, Jan Juriaensz van** ......... *paintings* | | | $15,400 |
| Dutch b. c. 1604, d. 1663 | | | |
| ☐ **BADGER, Frances** .............. *paintings* | | | $1,540 |
| 19th/20th cent. | | | |
| ☐ **BADGER, Joseph** ............... *paintings* | | | $2,860 |
| American | | | |
| ☐ **BADGER, S.F.M.** ............... *paintings* | | $2,200 | $4,200 |
| American 19th cent. | | | |
| ☐ **BADGER, Thomas** .............. *paintings* | | | $1,000 |
| American 1792-1868 | | | |
| ☐ **BADIA, Juan** .................... *paintings* | | | $275 |
| Mexican b. 1938 | | | |
| ☐ **BADIN, Jean Jules** .............. *paintings* | | | $4,675 |
| French b. 1843 | | | |
| ☐ **BADIN, Jules** ................... *paintings* | | | $550 |
| French 19th/20th cent. | | | |
| ☐ **BADMAN, Stanley Roy L.** ......... *drawings* | | $110 | $880 |
| ☐ **BADUE, Daniel Serra** ........... *paintings* | | | $4,400 |
| Latin American | | | |
| ☐ **BADURA, Bernard** ............. *paintings* | | | $38 |
| American b. 1896 .................... *drawings* | | | $176 |
| ☐ **BAEDER, John** ................. *paintings* | | $15,400 | $22,000 |
| American b. 1938 | | | |
| ☐ **BAEN, Jan de** .................. *paintings* | | | $2,200 |
| Dutch 1633-1702 | | | |
| ☐ **BAER, Martin** ................. *paintings* | | $165 | $1,210 |
| American 1894-1961 | | | |

| | | Current Price Range | |
|---|---|---|---|
| | | Low | High |
| ☐ **BAERDEMAEKER, Felix de** ............... *paintings* | | | $660 |
| Belgian 1836-1878 | | | |
| ☐ **BAERTLING, Olle** ............................ *paintings* | | | $3,850 |
| Swedish b. 1911 | | | |
| ☐ **BAES, Edgar Alfred** ........................... *paintings* | | $1,320 | $2,200 |
| Belgian 1837-1909 | | | |
| ☐ **BAES, Emile** .................................... *paintings* | | | $950 |
| Belgian b. 1879 | | | |
| ☐ **BAES, Lionel Oscar** ........................... *paintings* | | $357 | $385 |
| Belgian 1839-1913 | | | |
| ☐ **BAGANI, T.** ..................................... *paintings* | | | $495 |
| late 19th cent. | | | |
| ☐ **BAGER, Johann Daniel** ..................... *paintings* | | | $16,500 |
| German 1734-1815 | | | |
| ☐ **BAGGALLY, Osborn J.** ....................... *paintings* | | | $550 |
| British 19th cent. | | | |
| ☐ **BAGGE, Magnus Thulstrup von** ........... *paintings* | | | $440 |
| Norwegian 1825-1890 | | | |
| ☐ **BAGLER, T.** ..................................... *paintings* | | | $209 |
| 19th cent. | | | |
| ☐ **BAGLIONE, Carlos** ............................ *paintings* | | | $1,100 |
| ☐ **BAGNELL, Stephen** ............................ *paintings* | | $385 | $522 |
| ☐ **BAHICA, A.** ..................................... *paintings* | | | $880 |
| ☐ **BAHIEU, Jules G.** ............................ *paintings* | | $357 | $1,650 |
| Belgian 19th cent. | | | |
| ☐ **BAHRE, Hans E.** ............................... *paintings* | | | $209 |
| German b. 1882 | | | |
| ☐ **BAHUE, Th.** ..................................... *paintings* | | | $3,850 |
| ☐ **BAHUNEK, Branko** ........................... *paintings* | | | $550 |
| Yugoslavian b. 1935 | | | |
| ☐ **BAIERL, Theodor** ............................. *paintings* | | $715 | $1,540 |
| German 1881-1932 | | | |
| ☐ **BAIGLER, Aristodemo** ........................ *paintings* | | | $700 |
| Italian b. 1928 | | | |
| ☐ **BAIGUEREAU,** | | | |
| **Elizabeth Jeanne Gardner** ................ *paintings* | | | $16,500 |
| American 1851-1922 | | | |
| ☐ **BAIL, Franck Antoine** ........................ *paintings* | | | $12,100 |
| ☐ **BAIL, Joseph** .................................. *paintings* | | $1,760 | $8,800 |
| French 1862-1921 | | | |
| ☐ **BAILEY, Beatrice** ............................. *paintings* | | | $300 |
| American 20th cent. | | | |
| ☐ **BAILEY, Henry V.** ............................. *paintings* | | $302 | $907 |
| English 20th cent. | | | |
| ☐ **BAILEY, James G.** ............................. *paintings* | | | $450 |
| American b. 1870 | | | |
| ☐ **BAILEY, LaForce** ............................. *drawings* | | | $330 |
| ☐ **BAILEY, Malcolm** ............................. *drawings* | | $82 | $715 |
| American b. 1947 | | | |

| | Current Price Range | |
|---|---|---|
| | Low | High |
| ☐ **BAILEY, Merrill A.** ........................ *drawings* | | $330 |
| American b. 1909 | | |
| ☐ **BAILEY, T.** ................................ *paintings* | $49 | $900 |
| American 20th cent. | | |
| ☐ **BAILEY, Thomas** ........................ *paintings* | | $495 |
| American 20th cent. | | |
| ☐ **BAILEY, Vernon Howe** .................. *drawings* | $467 | $770 |
| American 1874-1953 | | |
| ☐ **BAILEY, Walter Alexander** ............... *paintings* | $467 | $1,430 |
| American b. 1894 | | |
| ☐ **BAILEY, William H.** ...................... *paintings* | | $30,800 |
| American b. 1930 | | |
| ☐ **BAILLY, A.** ............................... *paintings* | $165 | $412 |
| French (?) 19th/20th cent. | | |
| ☐ **BAILLY, F.V.** ............................ *paintings* | | $1,100 |
| Dutch 19th/20th cent. | | |
| ☐ **BAIN, Marcel Adolphe** ................... *paintings* | | $4,070 |
| French b. 1878 | | |
| ☐ **BAIRD, Nathaniel Hughes John** .......... *paintings* | | $1,320 |
| Scottish 1865-after 1935 .................... *drawings* | $193 | $550 |
| ☐ **BAIRD, William Baptiste** ................ *paintings* | $274 | $6,050 |
| American b. 1847 | | |
| ☐ **BAIXAS, Juan** ............................ *paintings* | | $2,970 |
| Spanish 19th cent. | | |
| ☐ **BAIZE, Wayne** ........................... *paintings* | | $17,500 |
| American b. 1943 ............................ *drawings* | $2,200 | $6,000 |
| ☐ **BAJ, Enrico** ............................. *paintings* | $440 | $605 |
| Italian b. 1924 .............................. *drawings* | $220 | $3,300 |
| ☐ **BAKALOWICZ, Ladislaus** ................ *paintings* | $1,540 | $6,600 |
| Polish 1833-1904 | | |
| ☐ **BAKALOWICZ,** | | |
| **Stephan Wladislawowitsch** ............... *paintings* | $90 | $2,200 |
| Russian b. 1857 | | |
| ☐ **BAKER, Amos** ........................... *paintings* | | $500 |
| ☐ **BAKER, Charles** ........................ *drawings* | | $220 |
| American 1844-1906 | | |
| ☐ **BAKER, Elisha Taylor** ................... *paintings* | | $550 |
| American 1827-1890 | | |
| ☐ **BAKER, Elizabeth H.** .................... *drawings* | $250 | $300 |
| ☐ **BAKER, Ellen Kendall** ................... *paintings* | | $302 |
| d. 1933 | | |
| ☐ **BAKER, Emilie H.** ....................... *paintings* | | $198 |
| American b. 1876 | | |
| ☐ **BAKER, Ernest** .......................... *paintings* | $605 | $880 |
| American 19th cent. | | |
| ☐ **BAKER, Ernest Hamlin** .................. *paintings* | | $550 |
| American 1889-1975 | | |
| ☐ **BAKER, Francis W.** ...................... *paintings* | | $2,200 |

| | Current Price Range | |
|---|---|---|
| | *Low* | *High* |

☐ **BAKER, G.W.** ................... *paintings* | | **$5,500**
American 19th cent.

☐ **BAKER, George Augustus** ................... *paintings* | **$275** | **$600**
American 1821-1880

☐ **BAKER, George H.** ........................... *paintings* | | **$935**
American

☐ **BAKER, Gladys** ................................ *paintings* | **$330** | **$330**
☐ **BAKER, J. Elder** ............................... *drawings* | **$330** | **$2,860**
American 19th cent.

☐ **BAKER, Jack** ...................................... *paintings* | | **$1,650**
American 20th cent.

☐ **BAKER, K. Siegfried** ........................... *paintings* | | **$500**
German b. 1922

☐ **BAKER, Percy Bryant** ........................ *sculpture* | | **$2,750**
American 1881-1970

☐ **BAKER, Samuel Bortis** ....................... *paintings* | | **$246**
American 1882-1967

☐ **BAKER, Sarah** .................................... *paintings* | | **$467**
American 20th cent.

☐ **BAKER, T.E.** ...................................... *paintings* | | **$6,050**
American 19th/20th cent.

☐ **BAKER, Thomas (of Leamington)** .......... *paintings* | **$1,210** | **$6,600**
British 1809-1869

☐ **BAKER, W.H.** .................................... *paintings* | | **$1,540**
American

☐ **BAKER, William Bliss** ........................ *paintings* | **$935** | **$34,100**
American 1859-1887 ................................. *drawings* | | **$990**

☐ **BAKHUIZEM, W. van de Sande** ........... *paintings* | | **$770**
Dutch 20th cent.

☐ **BAKHUYSEN, G. van de** ..................... *paintings* | | **$440**
Dutch 19th cent.

☐ **BAKHUYZEN, Hendrik van de Sande** ... *paintings* | | **$3,520**
Dutch 1795-1860 ................................. *drawings* | | **$275**
☐ **BAKHUYZEN, Ludolf** ........................ *paintings* | | **$605**
Dutch 1631-1708

☐ **BAKKER-KORFF, Alexander Hugo** ...... *paintings* | | **$2,750**
Dutch 1824-1882

☐ **BAKSHEEN, V.N.** ............................. *paintings* | | **$302**
☐ **BAKST, Leon** .................................. *paintings* | **$440** | **$1,540**
Russian 1866-1924 ................................. *drawings* | **$220** | **$10,175**
☐ **BALACHI, A.** ................................... *sculpture* | | **$880**
☐ **BALAS, M.** ..................................... *drawings* | | **$231**
French 19th cent.

☐ **BALCIAR, Gerald G.** ........................... *sculpture* | | **$850**
American

☐ **BALDO** .............................................. *drawings* | | **$264**
☐ **BALDRY, H.** ..................................... *paintings* | | **$660**
English 19th cent.

## Costume and Set Design

Costume and set designs are
attractive to many collectors. Of
particular interest are the ballet set
and costume designs from the
Ballets Russes, which traveled to
Paris for the first time in 1909. Many
of the costume and set designs
from this period were the work of
Leon Bakst and Alexandre Benois.
Bakst, in particular, turned costume
into a vivid, almost violent display of
color and line. He influenced
couturiers Paul Poiret and Mariano
Fortuny, and jewelry designers such
as Cartier, who then began to
create mixed settings of sapphires
and emeralds. Both Picasso and
Natalia Gontcharova also designed
for the Ballets Russes. (Leon Bakst,
"Costume Design for a Russian
Ballerina, Tamara Karsavina," pencil
and watercolor heightened by gilt,
13 x 10½ in., DuMouchelles,
December 14, 1984, $1,870.)

|  | | *Current Price Range* | |
|---|---|---|---|
|  | | *Low* | *High* |
| ☐ **BALDUCCI, Matteo** ............................ *paintings* | | $3,400 | $8,250 |
| ☐ **BALDWIN, A.A.** .................................. *paintings* | | | $4,675 |
| ☐ **BALDWIN, Albertus H.** ...................... *drawings* | | | $247 |
| American b. 1865 | | | |
| ☐ **BALDWIN, G.B.** ................................. *paintings* | | | $1,650 |
| American 19th cent. | | | |
| ☐ **BALE, Charles Thomas** ....................... *paintings* | | $330 | $3,025 |
| English ac. 1868-1875 | | | |
| ☐ **BALEN, Hendrik van (the elder)** ............ *paintings* | | $990 | $7,700 |
| Flemish 1575-1632 ..................................... *drawings* | | | $2,310 |
| ☐ **BALEN, Jan Van** ................................. *paintings* | | | $1,540 |
| ☐ **BALEN, Mattys** ................................... *paintings* | | | $990 |
| Flemish 1684-1766 | | | |
| ☐ **BALESTRA, Antonio** ........................... *paintings* | | $7,700 | $12,100 |
| Italian 1666-1740 | | | |
| ☐ **BALESTRIERI, Lionello** ...................... *paintings* | | $990 | $1,980 |
| Italian 1872-1958 | | | |
| ☐ **BALFIN, A.** ....................................... *paintings* | | | $330 |
| Dutch 19th cent. | | | |
| ☐ **BALGUET, A.** ..................................... *paintings* | | | $550 |

| | | Current Price Range | |
|---|---|---|---|
| | | Low | High |
| □ **BALINK, Henry C.** ............................. *paintings* <br> Dutch/American 1882-1963 | | $3,575 | $17,000 |
| □ **BALL, Alice Worthington** ..................... *paintings* <br> American d. 1929 | | $440 | $715 |
| □ **BALL, H.** .......................................... *paintings* | | | $301 |
| □ **BALL, James** ..................................... *paintings* <br> American | | | $23,100 |
| □ **BALL, L. Clarence** ........................... *paintings* <br> American 1858-1915 ................................ *drawings* | | $1,320 | $1,320 <br> $247 |
| □ **BALL, Thomas** .................................... *sculpture* <br> American 1819-1911 | | $1,540 | $30,800 |
| □ **BALL, Thomas Watson** ...................... *paintings* <br> American 1863-1934 | | | $187 |
| □ **BALL, Wilfred Williams** ..................... *paintings* <br> English 1853-1917 | | | $209 |
| □ **BALLA, Giacomo** ............................... *paintings* <br> Italian 1871-1958 ........................................ *drawings* <br> ............................................................ *sculpture* | | $907 | $17,600 <br> $4,675 <br> $1,320 |
| □ **BALLANGER, Rene** ........................... *paintings* <br> French 1895-1964 | | | $990 |
| □ **BALLANTYNE, Edith** ......................... *paintings* <br> British ac. 1868-1887 | | | $825 |
| □ **BALLAVOINE, Jules Frederic** ............. *paintings* <br> French ac. 1880-1900 ................................. *drawings* | | $825 | $6,050 <br> $302 |
| □ **BALLESIO, Federico** .......................... *paintings* <br> Italian 19th cent. ...................................... *drawings* | | $275 | $14,300 <br> $17,600 |
| □ **BALLESIO, Giuseppe** ......................... *paintings* <br> Italian 19th cent. | | | $3,850 |
| □ **BALLHEIM, H.** .................................. *paintings* | | | $2,860 |
| □ **BALLIN, Auguste** ............................... *paintings* <br> French b. 1842 | | $660 | $4,180 |
| □ **BALLIN, Hugo** .................................... *paintings* <br> American 1879-1956 | | $165 | $2,200 |
| □ **BALLINGER, Harry Russell** ................. *paintings* <br> American b. 1892 | | $192 | $220 |
| □ **BALLOWE, Marcia** ........................... *drawings* <br> American | | | $700 |
| □ **BALLUE, Pierre Ernest** ....................... *paintings* <br> French 1855-1928 | | | $1,540 |
| □ **BALMETTE, Jules Jean** ...................... *paintings* <br> French 19th cent. | | | $2,860 |
| □ **BALOUZET, A.** ................................... *paintings* <br> French 1858-1905 | | | $660 |
| □ **BALQUET, A.** ..................................... *paintings* | | | $550 |
| □ **BALSCH, A.** ....................................... *paintings* | | $200 | $385 |
| □ **BALTEN, Pieter** ................................... *paintings* <br> Flemish c. 1525-c. 1598 | | | $7,700 |
| □ **BALTHAZAR, Edmund** ........................ *paintings* | | | $715 |

| | | | *Current Price Range* | |
| | | | *Low* | *High* |
|---|---|---|---|---|
| ☐ **BALTHUS, (Count Balthazar** | | | | |
|    **KLOSSOWSKI de Rola)** | *paintings* | | **$154,000** | **$440,000** |
|    Polish/French b. 1908 | *drawings* | | **$6,600** | **$27,500** |
| ☐ **BALTUS, Jean** | *drawings* | | | **$900** |
|    French 19th/20th cent. | | | | |
| ☐ **BALVERO, L.G.** | *paintings* | | | **$715** |
| ☐ **BAMA, James** | *paintings* | | **$660** | **$17,500** |
|    American b. 1926 | *drawings* | | **$4,950** | **$19,800** |
| ☐ **BAMBERGER, Gustave** | *paintings* | | | **$1,210** |
|    German b. 1860 | | | | |
| ☐ **BANCK, John van der** | *paintings* | | | **$1,595** |
|    English 1686-1739 | | | | |
| ☐ **BANCROFT, Milton Herbert** | *paintings* | | **$77** | **$385** |
|    American b. 1867 | *drawings* | | **$220** | **$302** |
| ☐ **BAND, Max** | *paintings* | | **$165** | **$385** |
|    Lithuanian/Amer. b. 1900 | | | | |
| ☐ **BANDEIRA, Antonio** | *paintings* | | | **$2,200** |
|    Brazilian 1922-1967 | | | | |
| ☐ **BANDERA, Mendez** | *paintings* | | | **$220** |
|    Spanish 19th/20th cent. | | | | |
| ☐ **BANDIERI, C.** | *paintings* | | | **$2,750** |
|    Italian 19th cent. | | | | |
| ☐ **BANEROFT, S.T.** | *paintings* | | | **$605** |
|    American mid 19th cent. | | | | |
| ☐ **BANG, L.** | *paintings* | | | **$700** |
| ☐ **BANIER, E.** | *paintings* | | | **$3,080** |
| ☐ **BANKS, Richard** | *paintings* | | **$22** | **$2,750** |
|    American b. 1929 | | | | |
| ☐ **BANKS, Thomas J.** | *paintings* | | | **$330** |
|    English 19th cent. | | | | |
| ☐ **BANNARD, Walter Darby** | *paintings* | | **$330** | **$3,520** |
|    American b. 1931 | | | | |
| ☐ **BANNATYNE, J.J.** | *paintings* | | | **$302** |
|    Scottish 19th cent. | | | | |
| ☐ **BANNER, A.** | *paintings* | | | **$1,430** |
| ☐ **BANNER, Delmar Harmood** | *drawings* | | | **$357** |
|    British b. 1896 | | | | |
| ☐ **BANNER, Joseph** | *paintings* | | | **$424** |
|    English 19th cent. | | | | |
| ☐ **BANNISTER, Edward Mitchell** | *paintings* | | **$990** | **$15,400** |
|    American 1833-1901 | | | | |
| ☐ **BANNISTER, Patti** | *paintings* | | **$110** | **$880** |
|    American 20th cent. | | | | |
| ☐ **BANTA, Weart** | *paintings* | | **$88** | **$660** |
|    American 1826-1892 | | | | |
| ☐ **BANTA, Werter** | *paintings* | | | **$660** |
|    American 19th cent. | | | | |
| ☐ **BANTZER, Carl-Ludwig-Noah** | *paintings* | | | **$1,760** |
|    German b. 1857 | | | | |

| | *Current Price Range* | |
|---|---|---|
| | Low | High |
| ☐ **BAQUERO, Mariano** .................... *paintings* | | $880 |
| Spanish 19th cent. .................... *drawings* | | $11,000 |
| ☐ **BAQUET** .................... *sculpture* | | $2,420 |
| ☐ **BAQUET, J.W.** .................... *drawings* | | $330 |
| American 19th cent. | | |
| ☐ **BAR, Bonaventure de** .................... *paintings* | | $10,450 |
| French 1700-1729 | | |
| ☐ **BARADUC, Jeanne** .................... *paintings* | | $1,430 |
| French 20th cent. | | |
| ☐ **BARATTI, F.** .................... *paintings* | $1,045 | $1,540 |
| Italian 19th/20th cent. | | |
| ☐ **BARBARINI, Emil** .................... *paintings* | $440 | $6,600 |
| Austrian 1855-1930 | | |
| ☐ **BARBARINI, Gustav** .................... *paintings* | $2,420 | $2,750 |
| Austrian 1840-1909 | | |
| ☐ **BARBARO, Giovanni** .................... *drawings* | $88 | $1,100 |
| Italian 19th cent. | | |
| ☐ **BARBATELLI, Bernardino** | | |
| **(called POCCETTI)** .................... *drawings* | | $660 |
| ☐ **BARBEDIENNE, F.** .................... *sculpture* | $192 | $1,650 |
| ☑ **BARBER, Charles Burton** .................... *paintings* | | $11,550 |
| British 1845-1894 | | |
| ☑ **BARBER, John** .................... *paintings* | $220 | $3,410 |
| American 1898-1965 | | |
| ☑ **BARBER, John Warner** .................... *drawings* | | $264 |
| American 1798-1885 | | |
| ☑ **BARBER, M.** .................... *paintings* | | $330 |
| Italian 19th/20th cent. | | |
| ☐ **BARBERINO MASTER** .................... *paintings* | | $8,000 |
| ☐ **BARBERIS, Eugene de** .................... *paintings* | | $3,300 |
| French b. 1851 | | |
| ☐ **BARBEY, Jeanne Marie** .................... *paintings* | | $1,045 |
| French 1882-1960 | | |
| ☐ **BARBIER, Georges** .................... *drawings* | $155 | $522 |
| French 1882-1932 | | |
| ☐ **BARBIERE, C.** .................... *paintings* | | $192 |
| French 20th cent. | | |
| ☐ **BARBIERI, Giovanni** .................... *paintings* | | $330 |
| Italian 1780-1864 | | |
| ☐ **BARBIERI, Giovanni Francesco** | | |
| **(called IL GUERCINO)** .................... *paintings* | | $165 |
| Italian 1591-1666 .................... *drawings* | $770 | $5,500 |
| ☐ **BARBIERS, Pieter (II)** .................... *drawings* | | $1,045 |
| Dutch 1749-1842 | | |
| ☐ **BARBONERO, Jose Moreno** .................... *paintings* | | $715 |
| ☐ **BARBUDO, Salvador Sanchez** .................... *paintings* | $3,300 | $3,630 |
| Spanish 1857-1917 | | |
| ☐ **BARCHUS, Eliza R.** .................... *paintings* | $44 | $2,090 |
| American 1857-1959 | | |

| | | | Current Price Range | |
|---|---|---|---|---|
| | | | Low | High |
| ☐ **BARCLAY, Ada** .............................. *paintings* | | | | $275 |
| ☐ **BARCLAY, Edgar** .............................. *paintings* | | | | $3,080 |
| British ac. 1868-1913 | | | | |
| ☐ **BARCLAY, J. Edward** ......................... *paintings* | | | | $500 |
| British 20th cent. | | | | |
| ☐ **BARCLAY, McClelland** ....................... *paintings* | | $200 | $2,970 |
| American 1891-1943 ................................ *drawings* | | $110 | $231 |
| ................................................................... *sculpture* | | $577 | $1,633 |
| ☑ **BARD, James** ..................................... *paintings* | | $7,150 | $44,000 |
| American 1815-1897 | | | | |
| ☐ **BARDERY, Louis Armand** .................. *sculpture* | | | | $352 |
| French 20th cent. | | | | |
| ☐ **BARDIN, M.** ........................................ *paintings* | | | | $357 |
| Continental 19th cent. | | | | |
| ☐ **BARDONE, Guy** ................................. *paintings* | | $605 | $770 |
| French b. 1927 | | | | |
| ☐ **BARDOU, Paul Joseph** ......................... *drawings* | | | | $2,750 |
| English 1745-1814 | | | | |
| ☐ **BARE, E.** ............................................. *paintings* | | $900 | $1,650 |
| French 19th cent. | | | | |
| ☐ **BAREAU, Georges Marie Valentin** ........ *sculpture* | | | | $2,420 |
| French b. 1866 | | | | |
| ☐ **BARENGER, James** ............................. *paintings* | | $3,300 | $4,400 |
| English 1745-1813 | | | | |
| ☐ **BARENGER, James (Jr.)** ....................... *paintings* | | $660 | $18,700 |
| English 1780-1831 | | | | |
| ☐ **BARENSFELD, H.** ............................... *paintings* | | | | $19,800 |
| ☐ **BARETTI, Andrea** ............................... *paintings* | | | | $550 |
| ☐ **BARGUE, Charles** ............................... *drawings* | | $55 | $550 |
| French d. 1883 | | | | |
| ☐ **BARIAS, E.** ......................................... *sculpture* | | | | $308 |
| ☐ **BARILE, Xavier J.** ............................... *paintings* | | $240 | $1,100 |
| American b. 1891 | | | | |
| ☐ **BARILLARD, J.** .................................... *paintings* | | | | $286 |
| ☐ **BARILLET, M.** ..................................... *paintings* | | $132 | $302 |
| ☐ **BARILLOT, Leon** ............................... *paintings* | | $500 | $1,650 |
| French 1844-1929 | | | | |
| ☐ **BARISON, G.** ....................................... *paintings* | | | | $1,760 |
| British 19th cent. | | | | |
| ☐ **BARKEDIENNE, Ferdinand** ................. *sculpture* | | | | $220 |
| French 1810-1892 | | | | |
| ☐ **BARKER, George** ............................... *paintings* | | $125 | $412 |
| American 1882-1965 | | | | |
| ☐ **BARKER, John Joseph** ......................... *paintings* | | $411 | $16,500 |
| British 1835-1866 | | | | |
| ☐ **BARKER, Samuel H.** ........................... *paintings* | | | | $2,090 |
| ☐ **BARKER, Thomas (of Bath)** ................. *paintings* | | $770 | $2,420 |
| British 1769-1847 ................................... *drawings* | | | | $110 |

| | Current Price Range | |
|---|---|---|
| | *Low* | *High* |
| ☐ **BARKER, Walter** ............................... *paintings* <br> American b. 1921 | | **$440** |
| ☐ **BARKER, Wright** ............................... *paintings* <br> British ac. 1891-1913 | **$385** | **$11,000** |
| ☐ **BARKHOUSE, James E.** ...................... *paintings* <br> American 20th cent. | | **$385** |
| ☐ **BARLACH, Ernst** ............................... *drawings* <br> German 1870-1938 ...................................... *sculpture* | **$440** <br> **$3,080** | **$8,800** <br> **$23,100** |
| ☐ **BARLAG, Isak Philip Hartvig** .............. *paintings* <br> Norwegian 1840-1930 | | **$247** |
| ☐ **BARLAND, Adam** ............................... *paintings* | | **$1,980** |
| ☐ **BARLE, Meurice** ................................ *paintings* <br> French 20th cent. | | **$247** |
| ☐ **BARLEAN, A.** ................................... *paintings* <br> French 20th cent. | | **$385** |
| ☐ **BARLOW, Francis** .............................. *paintings* <br> British 1626-1702 | | **$1,760** |
| ☐ **BARLOW, John Noble** ......................... *paintings* <br> Anglo/American 1861-1917 | **$200** | **$5,225** |
| ☐ **BARLOW, Myron** ............................... *paintings* <br> American 1873-1938 ................................. *drawings* | **$220** <br> **$95** | **$11,000** <br> **$200** |
| ☐ **BARNA (?), P. Delommas** .................... *drawings* | | **$275** |
| ☐ **BARNABA DA MODENA** ...................... *paintings* <br> Italian ac. 1367-1383 | | **$15,400** |
| ☐ **BARNABE, Duilio** ............................... *paintings* <br> Italian 1914-1961 ..................................... *drawings* | **$308** <br> **$275** | **$5,500** <br> **$330** |
| ☐ **BARNAIN, H.** ..................................... *paintings* | | **$880** |
| ☐ **BARNARD, Edward Herbert** ................ *paintings* <br> American 1855-1909 | **$220** | **$1,650** |
| ☐ **BARNARD, George Gray** ...................... *sculpture* <br> American 1863-1938 | | **$4,675** |
| ☐ **BARNES, C.** ..................................... *paintings* | | **$550** |
| ☐ **BARNES, Edward Charles** .................... *paintings* <br> English 19th cent. | **$715** | **$1,650** |
| ☐ **BARNES, Ernest Harrison** ................... *paintings* <br> American b. 1873 | **$137** | **$1,650** |
| ☐ **BARNES, Gertrude Jamison** ................ *paintings* <br> American b. 1865 | | **$1,650** |
| ☐ **BARNES, James** ................................. *paintings* <br> British 19th/20th cent. | **$330** | **$412** |
| ☐ **BARNES, John Pierce** ......................... *paintings* <br> American b. 1893 | **$2,970** | **$3,190** |
| ☐ **BARNES, Robert** ................................ *paintings* <br> English 19th cent. | | **$7,150** |
| ☐ **BARNES, Samuel J.** ............................ *paintings* <br> English 19th cent. | **$150** | **$605** |
| ☐ **BARNES, Will R.** ............................... *drawings* <br> American 19th/20th cent. | **$55** | **$605** |

| | | Current Price Range | |
| | | Low | High |
| --- | --- | --- | --- |
| ☐ **BARNET, Isa** ........................................ *paintings* | | | $330 |
| American 20th cent. | | | |
| ☐ **BARNET, Will** ................................ *paintings* | | $770 | $4,730 |
| American ɔ. 1911 ...................................... *drawings* | | | $660 |
| ☐ **BARNETT, Bion (Jr.)** ............................ *paintings* | | | $770 |
| American b. 1887 ......................................... *drawings* | | | $495 |
| ☐ **BARNETT, Herbert P.** ......................... *paintings* | | $115 | $440 |
| American 1910-1972 | | | |
| ☐ **BARNETT, Rita Wolpe** ......................... *paintings* | | $170 | $374 |
| American contemporary ................................ *drawings* | | | $77 |
| ☐ **BARNETT, Thomas P.** ......................... *paintings* | | $143 | $1,100 |
| American 1870-1929 | | | |
| ☐ **BARNETT, William** ............................... *paintings* | | $90 | $220 |
| American 20th cent. | | | |
| ☐ **BARNEY, Caroline Richmond** .............. *drawings* | | | $301 |
| British 19th cent. | | | |
| ☐ **BARNEY, Frank A.** .............................. *paintings* | | $44 | $750 |
| American b. 1862 | | | |
| ☐ **BARNOIN, Henri Alphonse** ................. *paintings* | | | $440 |
| French 20th cent. ....................................... *drawings* | | | $275 |
| ☐ **BARNSLEY, James MacDonald** ............ *paintings* | | | $110 |
| Canadian 1861-1929 ..................................... *drawings* | | | $412 |
| ☐ **BARNUM, Kay** ....................................... *paintings* | | $176 | $330 |
| American | | | |
| ☐ **BAROCCI, Federico** ............................. *drawings* | | | $16,500 |
| Italian | | | |
| ☐ **BARON, Henri Charles Antoine** ............ *paintings* | | $880 | $1,870 |
| French 1816-1885 | | | |
| ☐ **BARON, Theodore** ............................... *paintings* | | | $2,200 |
| French 1840-1899 | | | |
| ☐ **BARON DE CEDERSTROM,** | | | |
| **Ture Nikolaus** ....................................... *paintings* | | | $2,750 |
| Swedish 1843-1924 | | | |
| ☐ **BARONE, Antonio** ............................... *paintings* | | | $357 |
| American 1889-1907 | | | |
| ☐ **BAROS, T.** ............................................ *paintings* | | | $275 |
| French 20th cent. | | | |
| ☐ **BARR, H.G.** ......................................... *paintings* | | | $302 |
| 20th cent. | | | |
| ☐ **BARR, William** ..................................... *paintings* | | $440 | $550 |
| American 1867-1933 | | | |
| ☐ **BARRAGAN, Julio** ............................... *paintings* | | | $1,760 |
| Argentinian b. 1928 | | | |
| ☐ **BARRALET, John-James** ...................... *drawings* | | $385 | $1,760 |
| Irish 1747-1815 | | | |
| ☐ **BARRATT, George Watson** ................. *paintings* | | | $1,430 |
| American 1894-1963 | | | |
| ☐ **BARRAU, Laureano** ............................. *paintings* | | | $8,800 |
| Spanish b. 1864 | | | |

| | Current Price Range | |
|---|---|---|
| | *Low* | *High* |
| ☐ **BARRAUD, Aime** ............... *paintings* <br> Swiss | | **$1,980** |
| ☐ **BARRAUD, Alfred Thomas** ............... *paintings* <br> Canadian 1849-1925 | **$220** | **$385** |
| ☐ **BARRAUD, Francois** ............... *paintings* <br> English 1811-1874 | | **$1,210** |
| ☐ **BARRAUD, Henry** ............... *paintings* <br> English 1811-1874 | **$1,980** | **$17,000** |
| ☐ **BARRAUD, William** ............... *paintings* <br> English 1810-1850 | **$1,500** | **$13,200** |
| ☐ **BARRAULT, Jean-Louis** ............... *paintings* | | **$770** |
| ☐ **BARRE, Elizabeth** ............... *paintings* <br> French 19th/20th cent. | | **$3,080** |
| ☐ **BARRERA, Antonio** ............... *paintings* <br> Italian b. 1889 | | **$2,310** |
| ☐ **BARRET, George (Jr.)** ............... *paintings* | **$220** | **$286** |
| ☐ **BARRETT, Elizabeth Hunt** ............... *paintings* <br> American b. 1863 | **$132** | **$935** |
| ☐ **BARRETT, Henry** ............... *paintings* | | **$1,045** |
| ☐ **BARRETT, Oliver Glen** ............... *paintings* <br> American 20th cent. | | **$412** |
| ☐ **BARRETT, William** ............... *sculpture* <br> American contemporary | | **$275** |
| ☐ **BARRETT, William S.** ............... *paintings* <br> American 1854-1927 | **$605** | **$2,090** |
| ☐ **BARRIAS, Louis Ernest** ............... *sculpture* <br> French 1841-1905 | **$2,530** | **$6,050** |
| ☐ **BARRIER, Gustave** ............... *paintings* <br> French 20th cent. | **$440** | **$990** |
| ☐ **BARRITT, William A.** ............... *paintings* <br> American ac. 1845-1869 | | **$495** |
| ☐ **BARRON Y CABRILLO, Manuel** ......... *paintings* <br> Spanish 19th cent. | | **$4,675** |
| ☐ **BARROW, John Dobson** ............... *paintings* <br> American 1823-1907 | | **$330** |
| ☐ **BARROW, Julian** ............... *paintings* <br> American 20th cent. | | **$247** |
| ☐ **BARROWS, C.C.** ............... *paintings* | **$302** | **$632** |
| ☐ **BARRUCCI, P.** ............... *paintings* | | **$825** |
| ☐ **BARRY, C.M.** ............... *paintings* <br> British 19th cent. | | **$605** |
| ☐ **BARRY, Edith Cleaves** ............... *paintings* <br> American 19th/20th cent. | **$165** | **$176** |
| ☐ **BARRY, Gerard** ............... *paintings* <br> Irish/American b. 1864 | | **$302** |
| ☐ **BARRY, John** ............... *paintings* <br> British 20th cent. | **$325** | **$400** |
| ☐ **BARRY, W.** ............... *paintings* | | **$250** |

| | | Current Price Range | |
|---|---|---|---|
| | | Low | High |
| ☐ **BARSE, George Randolph (Jr.)** ............. *drawings* | | $770 | $4,950 |
| American 1861-1938 | | | |
| ☐ **BARSTOW, Miss S. M.** ........................ *paintings* | | | $2,000 |
| American 19th cent. | | | |
| ☐ **BART, Sir John MacPherson** .............. *paintings* | | | $302 |
| ☐ **BARTEAU, Andre** ............................... *paintings* | | $192 | $385 |
| French 20th cent. | | | |
| ☐ **BARTELS, Hans von** ........................... *paintings* | | | $770 |
| German b. 1856 ...................................... *drawings* | | | $3,300 |
| ☐ **BARTENBACH, Hans** ......................... *paintings* | | | $2,420 |
| German b. 1908 | | | |
| ☐ **BARTHALOT, Marius** ........................ *paintings* | | $660 | $660 |
| French b. 1861 | | | |
| ☐ **BARTHE, Louis** ............................... *paintings* | | | $330 |
| ☐ **BARTHEL, Paul** ............................... *drawings* | | | $1,760 |
| German b. 1862 | | | |
| ☐ **BARTHELEMY, L.** ........................... *sculpture* | | | $1,650 |
| early 20th cent. | | | |
| ☐ **BARTHINING, L.** .............................. *paintings* | | | $1,100 |
| ☐ **BARTHOLDI, Frederic Auguste** ............ *sculpture* | | $26,400 | $121,000 |
| French 1834-1904 | | | |
| ☐ **BARTHOLOMEW, F.W.** .................... *paintings* | | | $302 |
| English 19th/20th cent. | | | |
| ☐ **BARTHOLOMEW, W. N.** .................... *paintings* | | | $522 |
| American 19th cent. .................................. *drawings* | | $60 | $550 |
| ☐ **BARTLE, Annette** ............................... *paintings* | | | $247 |
| contemporary | | | |
| ☐ **BARTLETT, Charles William** .............. *drawings* | | $308 | $1,045 |
| British 1860-1940 | | | |
| ☐ **BARTLETT, Dana** ............................. *paintings* | | $275 | $1,320 |
| American 1878/82-1957 | | | |
| ☐ **BARTLETT, Jennifer Losch** ................ *drawings* | | $825 | $1,045 |
| American b. 1941 ...................................... *sculpture* | | | $5,775 |
| ☐ **BARTLETT, Jonathan Adams** .............. *paintings* | | | $7,150 |
| 1817-1902 | | | |
| ☐ **BARTLETT, Paul Wayland** ................. *sculpture* | | $466 | $2,420 |
| American 1865-1925 | | | |
| ☐ **BARTOL, William Thompson** .............. *paintings* | | | $880 |
| 1817-1859 | | | |
| ☐ **BARTOLINI, F.** ............................... *paintings* | | | $55,000 |
| ☐ **BARTOLINI, Francesco** ....................... *paintings* | | | $1,650 |
| Italian 1844-1881 | | | |
| ☐ **BARTOLINI, Frederico** ........................ *drawings* | | $1,760 | $18,700 |
| Italian 19th/20th cent. | | | |
| ☐ **BARTOLINI, Lorenzo** ......................... *drawings* | | | $4,400 |
| Italian 1777-1850 | | | |
| ☐ **BARTOLOZZI, Francesco** ................... *drawings* | | $550 | $2,420 |
| Italian 1725/27-1815 | | | |

| | | Current Price Range | |
| --- | --- | --- | --- |
| | | Low | High |
| ☐ **BARTON, Minette** ..................... *paintings*<br>American | | $2,200 | $4,125 |
| ☐ **BARTON, Ralph** ..................... *drawings*<br>American 1891-1931 | | | $187 |
| ☐ **BARTON, Rose** ..................... *drawings*<br>British 19th cent. | | | $440 |
| ☐ **BARTON, Thomas Hart** ..................... *drawings*<br>American 1889-1975 | | | $385 |
| ☐ **BARTONEK, Adalabert** ..................... *paintings*<br>Czechoslovakian b. 1859 | | | $3,520 |
| ☐ **BARTTENBACH, Hans** ..................... *paintings*<br>German b. 1908 | | | $1,705 |
| ☐ **BARUCCI, Pietro** ..................... *paintings*<br>Italian 1845-1917 | | $412 | $4,400 |
| ☐ **BARVITIUS, Victor** ..................... *paintings*<br>Czechoslovakian 1834-1902 | | | $40,700 |
| ☐ **BARWICK, John** ..................... *paintings*<br>English b. 1820 | | $330 | $4,000 |
| ☐ **BARWIG, Franz** ..................... *sculpture*<br>Austrian b. 1868 | | | $2,310 |
| ☐ **BARYE, Alfred** ..................... *sculpture*<br>French 19th cent. | | $330 | $4,400 |
| ☐ **BARYE, Antoine Louis** ..................... *drawings*<br>French 1795-1875 ..................... *sculpture* | | $275<br>$200 | $3,080<br>$11,000 |
| ☐ **BARZAGHI, F.** ..................... *sculpture*<br>Italian | | | $4,400 |
| ☐ **BARZANTI, L.** ..................... *paintings* | | $220 | $330 |
| ☐ **BARZANTI, P.** ..................... *sculpture*<br>Italian 19th/20th cent. | | | $2,750 |
| ☐ **BASALDUA, Hector** ..................... *paintings*<br>Argentinian b. 1895 | | | $1,760 |
| ☐ **BASCHENIS, Evaristo** ..................... *paintings*<br>Italian 1617-1677 | | | $60,500 |
| ☐ **BASCOM, Ruth Henshaw** ..................... *paintings*<br>American 1772-1848 ..................... *drawings* | | $2,750 | $2,090<br>$7,150 |
| ☐ **BASDEN, T.** ..................... *paintings*<br>European 19th/20th cent. | | $165 | $770 |
| ☐ **BASELITZ, Georg** ..................... *paintings*<br>German b. 1938 ..................... *drawings* | | $71,500 | $79,750<br>$2,420 |
| ☐ **BASIENSKI, S.** ..................... *paintings*<br>Russian 19th/20th cent. | | | $191 |
| ☐ **BASILE, Castera** ..................... *paintings*<br>Latin American 20th cent. | | | $935 |
| ☐ **BASING, Charles** ..................... *paintings*<br>American 1865-1933 | | $935 | $1,760 |
| ☐ **BASKE, Yamado** ..................... *paintings*<br>Chinese/American 20th cent. | | | $192 |

| | | | Current Price Range | |
| --- | --- | --- | --- | --- |
| | | | Low | High |
| ☐ **BASKIN, Leonard** | ............................... | *paintings* | | $605 |
| American b. 1922 | ....................................... | *drawings* | $302 | $1,320 |
| | ................................................. | *sculpture* | $330 | $1,045 |
| ☐ **BASQUE, Henri le** | ............................... | *paintings* | | $11,000 |
| French 1865-1937 | | | | |
| ☐ **BASQUIAT, Jean Michel** | ..................... | *paintings* | $18,700 | $23,100 |
| American b. 1960 | ....................................... | *drawings* | $1,045 | $22,000 |
| ☐ **BASSANI, Luigi** | ................................... | *paintings* | | $4,950 |
| Italian b. 1825 | | | | |
| ☐ **BASSANO, (Jacopo da PONTE)** | ............ | *paintings* | $2,200 | $3,850 |
| Italian 1516/18-1592 | | | | |
| ☐ **BASSANO, Leandro da Ponte** | | | | |
| **(called Leandro)** | ..................................... | *paintings* | $4,620 | $13,200 |
| Italian 1557-1622 | | | | |
| ☐ **BASSEN, Bartholomeus van** | ................. | *paintings* | | $4,180 |
| Dutch 1590-1652 | | | | |
| ☐ **BASSETTI, Marcantonio** | ...................... | *paintings* | | $8,250 |
| Italian 1588-1630 | | | | |
| ☐ **BASSLER, Clare K.** | ........................... | *paintings* | | $880 |
| ☐ **BASTERT, Nicholaas** | ........................... | *paintings* | | $330 |
| Dutch 1854-1939 | ......................................... | *drawings* | | $880 |
| ☐ **BASTIANINI, Augusto** | ........................ | *drawings* | | $302 |
| ☐ **BASTIEN, Alfred Theodore Joseph** | ....... | *paintings* | | $605 |
| French 1873-1955 | ........................................ | *drawings* | | $121 |
| ☐ **BASTIEN-LEPAGE, Jules** | .................... | *paintings* | $38,900 | $41,800 |
| French 1848-1884 | | | | |
| ☐ **BASTIN** | ............................................... | *sculpture* | | $330 |
| Belgian 19th/20th cent. | | | | |
| ☐ **BASTON, T.** | ....................................... | *paintings* | | $2,640 |
| ☐ **BATACCHI, A.** | .................................... | *sculpture* | | $2,200 |
| Italian 19th cent. | | | | |
| ☐ **BATCHELDER, M.** | ............................... | *paintings* | | $550 |
| ☐ **BATCHELLER, Frederick S.** | ................ | *paintings* | $660 | $4,675 |
| American 1837-1889 | | | | |
| ☐ **BATCHILLIER** | ..................................... | *paintings* | | $990 |
| American | | | | |
| ☐ **BATE, Louis Robert** | ........................... | *sculpture* | | $467 |
| French b. 1898 | | | | |
| ☐ **BATECCHI, A.** | .................................... | *sculpture* | | $1,980 |
| Italian 19th cent. | | | | |
| ☐ **BATEMAN, James** | ............................... | *paintings* | | $4,950 |
| English 1797-1859/67 | | | | |
| ☐ **BATES, C.C.** | ...................................... | *drawings* | | $528 |
| ☐ **BATES, David** | ..................................... | *paintings* | $550 | $4,180 |
| British 1840-1921 | ....................................... | *drawings* | | $440 |
| ☐ **BATES, Frederick Davenport** | ................ | *paintings* | $440 | $14,850 |
| English b. 1867 | | | | |
| ☐ **BATES, W.E.** | ...................................... | *paintings* | | $880 |
| ☐ **BATH, J. T.** | ........................................ | *paintings* | | $418 |

| | | | *Current Price Range* | |
|---|---|---|---|---|
| | | | *Low* | *High* |
| ☐ **BATONI, Pompeo Girolamo** | ................. | *paintings* | **$26,400** | **$143,000** |
| Italian 1708-1787 ........................................ | | *drawings* | | **$2,200** |
| ☐ **BATT, Arthur** | ................................ | *paintings* | **$110** | **$4,400** |
| English ac. 1879-1892 | | | | |
| ☐ **BATTAGLIA, A.** | ............................ | *drawings* | | **$352** |
| ☐ **BATTAGLIA, C.E.** | ........................... | *drawings* | | **$1,980** |
| Italian 19th cent. | | | | |
| ☐ **BATTAGLIA, Pasquale M.** | ................... | *drawings* | | **$330** |
| American 1905-1959 | | | | |
| ☐ **BATTEM, Gerrit** | ............................. | *drawings* | | **$4,400** |
| Dutch c. 1636-1684 | | | | |
| ☐ **BATTIGLIA, E.** | ............................... | *sculpture* | **$605** | **$1,210** |
| Italian 19th/20th cent. | | | | |
| ☐ **BATTIGNANT** | ................................ | *paintings* | **$528** | **$825** |
| ☐ **BATTISTA, Giovanni** | ........................ | *drawings* | **$154** | **$275** |
| Italian 1858-1925 | | | | |
| ☐ **BATTON, Jean de** | .............................. | *paintings* | | **$605** |
| ☐ **BATURIN, Viktor Pavlovich** | ................. | *paintings* | **$357** | **$1,210** |
| Russian 1863-1938 | | | | |
| ☐ **BAUCHANT, Andre** | .......................... | *paintings* | **$418** | **$22,000** |
| French 1873-1958 | | | | |
| ☐ **BAUCHMANN, C.** | ............................. | *paintings* | | **$363** |
| American late 19th cent. | | | | |
| ☐ **BAUCK, Jeanna Maria Charlotta** | .......... | *paintings* | | **$2,860** |
| Swedish 1840-1926 | | | | |
| ☐ **BAUDER, F.** | ................................... | *paintings* | | **$660** |
| ☐ **BAUDESSON, Nicolas** | ....................... | *paintings* | | **$8,800** |
| French c. 1611-1680 | | | | |
| ☐ **BAUDIN, Jean Baptiste** | ..................... | *paintings* | | **$2,475** |
| French 19th cent. | | | | |
| ☐ **BAUDOIN, Pierre** | ............................ | *paintings* | | **$1,650** |
| French 19th cent. | | | | |
| ☐ **BAUDOUIN, Pierre Antoine** | ................. | *paintings* | | **$2,420** |
| French 1723-1769 ......................................... | | *drawings* | | **$2,200** |
| ☐ **BAUDRY, Paul** | ............................... | *drawings* | | **$198** |
| French 1828-1886 | | | | |
| ☐ **BAUER, Anton** | ............................... | *paintings* | **$2,310** | **$4,400** |
| German 19th cent. | | | | |
| ☐ **BAUER, C.F.** | ................................. | *paintings* | **$220** | **$275** |
| American (?) | | | | |
| ☐ **BAUER, Marius** | .............................. | *paintings* | | **$385** |
| Dutch 1867-1932 ......................................... | | *drawings* | | **$935** |
| ☐ **BAUER, Rudolf** | ............................... | *paintings* | **$7,700** | **$27,500** |
| German 1889-1953 ...................................... | | *drawings* | | **$13,200** |
| ☐ **BAUER, Willi** | ................................ | *paintings* | **$110** | **$770** |
| German b. 1923 | | | | |
| ☐ **BAUER, William C.** | ........................... | *paintings* | **$77** | **$550** |
| American b. 1888 ........................................ | | *drawings* | **$165** | **$330** |

| | | | *Current Price Range* | |
|---|---|---|---|---|
| | | | Low | High |
| ☐ **BAUERMEISTER, Mary** | ...................... | *sculpture* | $165 | $6,050 |
| German b. 1934 | | | | |
| ☐ **BAUERNFEIND, Gustav** | ...................... | *paintings* | | $352,000 |
| Austrian 1848-1904 | | | | |
| ☐ **BAUFFE, Victor** | ..................................... | *paintings* | | $467 |
| Dutch ac. 19th cent. | ..................................... | *drawings* | | $247 |
| ☐ **BAUGH, Sam** | ..................................... | *paintings* | | $900 |
| British 1822-1878 | | | | |
| ☐ **BAUGNIET, Charles** | ........................... | *paintings* | $770 | $15,400 |
| Belgian 1814-1886 | | | | |
| ☐ **BAUM, Carl** | ..................................... | *paintings* | | $700 |
| American 19th cent. | | | | |
| ☐ **BAUM, Charles** | ........................... | *paintings* | | $6,600 |
| American 1812-1877 | | | | |
| ☐ **BAUM, Mark** | ........................... | *paintings* | | $220 |
| American 20th cent. | | | | |
| ☐ **BAUM, Paul** | ..................................... | *paintings* | | $495 |
| German 1859-1932 | | | | |
| ☐ **BAUM, Walter Emerson** | ...................... | *paintings* | $44 | $13,200 |
| American 1884-1956 | ................................. | *drawings* | $66 | $264 |
| ☐ **BAUMANN, Gustave** | ........................... | *paintings* | | $440 |
| German/American 1881-1971 | | | | |
| ☐ **BAUMEISTER, F.** | ..................................... | *paintings* | | $440 |
| ☐ **BAUMEISTER, Willi** | ........................... | *paintings* | | $8,800 |
| German 1889-1955 | ..................................... | *drawings* | $1,540 | $2,860 |
| ☐ **BAUMGARTNER, H.** | ........................... | *paintings* | $77 | $3,080 |
| German 19th cent. | | | | |
| ☐ **BAUMGARTNER, Henry J.** | ................. | *paintings* | $110 | $632 |
| American 19th cent. | | | | |
| ☐ **BAUMGARTNER, Johann Wolfgang** | .... | *paintings* | | $14,300 |
| Austrian 1712-1761 | | | | |
| ☐ **BAUMGARTNER, Peter** | ...................... | *paintings* | | $9,350 |
| German 1834-1911 | | | | |
| ☐ **BAUMGARTNER, Warren** | ................... | *drawings* | $165 | $605 |
| American 1894-1963 | | | | |
| ☐ **BAUMGRAS, Peter** | ........................... | *paintings* | $600 | $632 |
| American 1827-1904 | | | | |
| ☐ **BAUMHOFER, Walter M.** | ...................... | *paintings* | $198 | $770 |
| American b. 1904 | | | | |
| ☐ **BAUR, Ferdinand** | ................................. | *drawings* | | $1,320 |
| Austrian 1760-1826 | | | | |
| ☐ **BAUR, Johann Wilhelm** | ...................... | *paintings* | $2,800 | $6,050 |
| French 1600-1640 | | | | |
| ☐ **BAUR, Theodore** | ................................. | *sculpture* | | $1,000 |
| American 1835-1894 | | | | |
| ☐ **BAUTIS, Charles** | ................................. | *paintings* | | $605 |
| ☐ **BAUWARD** | ........................................... | *paintings* | | $280 |
| ☐ **BAXTER, Charles** | ................................. | *paintings* | | $2,420 |

| | | Current Price Range | |
|---|---|---|---|
| | | *Low* | *High* |
| ☐ **BAYARD, Clifford Adams** .................. *paintings* | | | $990 |
| American 1892-1934 | | | |
| ☐ **BAYARD, Emile Antoine** ..................... *paintings* | | $660 | $18,700 |
| French 1837-1891 | | | |
| ☐ **BAYER, Anton** ................................... *paintings* | | $2,090 | $3,850 |
| Bohemian c. 1850 | | | |
| ☐ **BAYER, Herbert** ................................ *paintings* | | $4,180 | $6,600 |
| Austrian/American b. 1900 ......................... *drawings* | | | $400 |
| .................................................. *sculpture* | | | $1,540 |
| ☐ **BAYER, J.** ........................................... *paintings* | | | $935 |
| Continental 19th cent. | | | |
| ☐ **BAYERLEIN, Fritz** ............................ *paintings* | | $770 | $1,210 |
| German b. 1872 | | | |
| ☐ **BAYES, Gilbert** ................................. *sculpture* | | | $715 |
| English 1872-1953 | | | |
| ☐ **BAYES, Jessie** .................................. *paintings* | | | $247 |
| early 20th cent. | | | |
| ☐ **BAYEU Y SUBIAS, Francisco** .............. *paintings* | | | $13,200 |
| Spanish 1734-1795 | | | |
| ☐ **BAYHA, Edwin F.** ............................... *paintings* | | | $33,880 |
| American | | | |
| ☐ **BAYMA, Edwin F.** .............................. *paintings* | | | $715 |
| American 20th cent. | | | |
| ☐ **BAYNARD, Edward** .......................... *drawings* | | $2,310 | $2,750 |
| American b. 1940 | | | |
| ☐ **BAZAINE, Jean Rene** ......................... *paintings* | | | $16,500 |
| French b. 1904 ...................................... *drawings* | | $242 | $1,760 |
| ☐ **BAZELEY, H.** .................................... *paintings* | | | $770 |
| American 19th cent. | | | |
| ☐ **BAZHIN, Nicolai Nikolaevich** ............... *paintings* | | | $3,740 |
| Russian 1856-1917 | | | |
| ☐ **BAZILE, Alberoi** ................................ *paintings* | | $495 | $605 |
| Haitian | | | |
| ☐ **BAZILE, Castera** ............................... *paintings* | | $2,750 | $27,500 |
| Haitian 1923-1965 | | | |
| ☐ **BAZIN, Francois Victor** ....................... *sculpture* | | | $1,870 |
| French early 20th cent. | | | |
| ☐ **BAZIOTES, William** ........................... *paintings* | | $935 | $253,000 |
| American 1912-1963 ................................ *drawings* | | $1,100 | $29,700 |
| ☐ **BAZZANI, Luigi** ................................. *paintings* | | $1,045 | $9,900 |
| Italian 1836-1926/27 ................................. *drawings* | | | $495 |
| ☐ **BAZZICALUVA, Ercole** ...................... *drawings* | | | $1,760 |
| Italian 1600-1640 | | | |
| ☐ **BEACH, Chester** .............................. *sculpture* | | $209 | $330 |
| American 1881-1956 | | | |
| ☐ **BEACH, E.J.** ..................................... *paintings* | | | $605 |
| British 19th cent. | | | |
| ☐ **BEACH, Thomas** ............................... *paintings* | | $2,750 | $15,400 |
| English 1738-1806 | | | |

| | | *Current Price Range* | |
|---|---|---|---|
| | | *Low* | *High* |
| ☐ **BEAL, Franz de** .................................... *paintings* | | | $2,200 |
| English late 19th cent. | | | |
| ☐ **BEAL, Gifford** .................................... *paintings* | | $247 | $55,000 |
| American 1879-1956 .................................... *drawings* | | $82 | $2,090 |
| ☐ **BEAL, Jack** .................................... *paintings* | | $1,650 | $19,800 |
| American b. 1931 | | | |
| ☐ **BEAL, Reynolds** .................................... *paintings* | | $412 | $13,200 |
| American 1867-1951 .................................... *drawings* | | $110 | $1,870 |
| ☐ **BEALE, Mary** .................................... *paintings* | | $770 | $3,850 |
| English 1632/33-1697/99 | | | |
| ☐ **BEALES, L.F.** .................................... *paintings* | | | $467 |
| ☐ **BEALL, Cecil C.** .................................... *paintings* | | | $137 |
| b. 1892 .................................... *drawings* | | $165 | $187 |
| ☐ **BEALS, Willis H.** .................................... *paintings* | | | $220 |
| American 20th cent. | | | |
| ☐ **BEAMAN, Gamaliel W.** .................................... *paintings* | | $440 | $1,100 |
| American 19th cent. | | | |
| ☐ **BEAME, W.** .................................... *paintings* | | | $220 |
| American 19th cent. | | | |
| ☐ **BEAN, Ainslie** .................................... *drawings* | | | $522 |
| English ac. 1870-1886 | | | |
| ☐ **BEAN, Caroline Van Hook** .................................... *paintings* | | | $550 |
| American 1879/80-1980 | | | |
| ☐ **BEAN, Hannah** .................................... *drawings* | | | $550 |
| American | | | |
| ☐ **BEARD, Adelia Belle** .................................... *paintings* | | | $1,000 |
| American d. 1920 | | | |
| ☐ **BEARD, Alice** .................................... *paintings* | | $385 | $1,870 |
| 19th/20th cent. | | | |
| ☐ **BEARD, Harry** .................................... *paintings* | | | $800 |
| American 19th cent. | | | |
| ☐ **BEARD, James Carter** .................................... *drawings* | | | $467 |
| American 1837-1913 | | | |
| ☐ **BEARD, James Henry** .................................... *paintings* | | $550 | $16,500 |
| American 1812/14-1893 | | | |
| ☐ **BEARD, William Holbrook** .................................... *paintings* | | $528 | $15,950 |
| American 1825-1900 | | | |
| ☐ **BEARDEN, Romare** .................................... *paintings* | | $357 | $17,600 |
| American b. 1914 | | | |
| ☐ **BEARDSLEY, Aubrey** .................................... *drawings* | | $1,760 | $2,750 |
| English 1872-1898 | | | |
| ☐ **BEARDSLEY, J.** .................................... *paintings* | | | $715 |
| American 19th cent. | | | |
| ☐ **BEARDSLEY LIMNER** .................................... *paintings* | | | $22,000 |
| American ac. c. 1785-1805 | | | |
| ☐ **BEATON, Cecil** .................................... *paintings* | | | $770 |
| English 1904-1980 .................................... *drawings* | | $88 | $1,210 |
| ☐ **BEATTIE, Alexander** .................................... *paintings* | | | $246 |
| American 20th cent. | | | |

| | | Current Price Range | |
|---|---|---|---|
| | | Low | High |
| ☐ **BEATTIE-BROWN, William** ............... *paintings*<br>Scottish 1831-1909 | | $495 | $2,310 |
| ☐ **BEATTY, Frank T.** ............................. *drawings*<br>American b. 1899 | | | $2,050 |
| ☐ **BEATTY, John William** ........................ *paintings*<br>American 1851-1924 | | $880 | $1,980 |
| ☐ **BEAUCHAMP, Robert** ..................... *paintings*<br>American b. 1923 ......................................... *drawings* | | $192<br>$605 | $880<br>$715 |
| ☐ **BEAUDIN, Andre** ............................... *paintings*<br>French 1895-1980 ...................................... *drawings* | | $660 | $1,210<br>$2,750 |
| ☐ **BEAUDOUIN, Frank** ........................... *paintings*<br>American 20th cent. | | | $440 |
| ☐ **BEAUDUIN, Jean** ............................... *paintings*<br>Belgian 1851-1916 | | $330 | $3,300 |
| ☐ **BEAUFORT, John** ............................. *paintings*<br>American 19th cent. | | | $8,250 |
| ☐ **BEAUGUREAU, Bety W.** ..................... *paintings*<br>American 20th cent. | | | $302 |
| ☐ **BEAULIEU, Gustave de** ..................... *paintings*<br>French 1801-1860 | | $330 | $412 |
| ☐ **BEAUMONT, Arthur** ........................... *paintings*<br>Anglo/American 1877/79-1956 ...................... *drawings* | | $154 | $1,210<br>$330 |
| ☐ **BEAUMONT, Auguste Bouthillier De** .... *paintings*<br>German 1842-1899 | | $440 | $880 |
| ☐ **BEAUMONT, Charles Edouard de** ........ *paintings* | | | $400 |
| ☐ **BEAUMONT, Hugues de** ..................... *paintings*<br>French 1874-1947 | | | $550 |
| ☐ **BEAUMONT, Jean** ............................... *drawings*<br>French | | $88 | $286 |
| ☐ **BEAUMONT, Lilian Adele** ..................... *paintings*<br>American 1880-1922 | | | $192 |
| ☐ **BEAUMONT, T.D.** ............................... *paintings*<br>English (?) 19th cent. | | | $522 |
| ☐ **BEAUNE, Joseph** ............................... *paintings*<br>French 19th cent. | | | $2,860 |
| ☐ **BEAUQUESNE, Wilfrid Constant** ......... *paintings*<br>French 1847-1913 | | $302 | $4,400 |
| ☐ **BEAUREGARD, C.G.** ........................... *paintings*<br>American 19th cent. | | $385 | $825 |
| ☐ **BEAUREGARD, Le Sourd de** ............... *paintings* | | | $30,800 |
| ☐ **BEAUVERIE, Charles Joseph** ............... *paintings*<br>French 1839-1924 | | $412 | $2,200 |
| ☐ **BEAUX, Cecilia** ................................. *paintings*<br>American 1863-1942 ................................... *drawings* | | $1,760<br>$356 | $3,960<br>$1,320 |
| ☐ **BEAVER, Fred** ................................. *drawings*<br>American (Creek) b. 1911 | | $1,320 | $3,520 |
| ☐ **BEAVIS, Richard** ............................... *paintings*<br>English 1824-1896 ...................................... *drawings* | | $192<br>$400 | $7,700<br>$1,100 |

| | | *Current Price Range* | |
|---|---|---|---|
| | | Low | High |
| ☐ **BEBIE, Henry** ..................... *paintings* | | | $1,980 |
| c. 1824-1888 | | | |
| ☐ **BECHER, Arthur E.** ............. *paintings* | | $110 | $2,860 |
| German/American 1877-1941 .......... *drawings* | | $192 | $660 |
| ☐ **BECHI, Luigi** ..................... *paintings* | | $715 | $11,000 |
| Italian 1830-1919 | | | |
| ☐ **BECHTLE, Robert Alan** ......... *paintings* | | $3,850 | $25,300 |
| American b. 1932 ..................... *drawings* | | | $700 |
| ☐ **BECK, A.T.** ...................... *paintings* | | | $660 |
| ☐ **BECK, Bernard** .................. *paintings* | | $1,045 | $3,080 |
| ..................................... *drawings* | | | $330 |
| ☐ **BECK, Clifford** ................. *drawings* | | | $550 |
| American (Navajo) | | | |
| ☐ **BECK, Corn. F.** .................. *paintings* | | | $198 |
| German 19th cent. | | | |
| ☐ **BECK, H.R.** ...................... *drawings* | | | $209 |
| American 19th cent. | | | |
| ☐ **BECK, J. Augustus** ............. *paintings* | | | $242 |
| American 1831-before 1918 .......... *drawings* | | $82 | $137 |
| ☐ **BECK, Raphael** ................. *paintings* | | | $154 |
| American d. 1947 ..................... *drawings* | | $110 | $385 |
| ☐ **BECKENKAMP, Kaspar Benedikt** ........ *paintings* | | | $9,900 |
| German 1747-1828 | | | |
| ☐ **BECKER, Albert** ................ *paintings* | | $302 | $1,430 |
| German 1830-1896 | | | |
| ☐ **BECKER, August** ............... *paintings* | | | $6,600 |
| German 1822-87 | | | |
| ☐ **BECKER, Carl Ludwig Friedrich** .......... *paintings* | | $880 | $7,700 |
| German 1820-1900 ..................... *drawings* | | | $225 |
| ☐ **BECKER, Charlotte** ............ *paintings* | | $385 | $440 |
| American b. 1907 | | | |
| ☐ **BECKER, Ernst August** .......... *paintings* | | | $3,575 |
| German ac. 1840-1854 | | | |
| ☐ **BECKER, Frederick W.** .......... *paintings* | | $137 | $220 |
| American b. 1888 | | | |
| ☐ **BECKER, J.** ...................... *paintings* | | | $31,900 |
| Continental School 19th cent. | | | |
| ☐ **BECKER, Johann Wilhelm** ........... *paintings* | | | $2,750 |
| German 1744-1782 | | | |
| ☐ **BECKER, Joseph** ................ *paintings* | | | $825 |
| American 1841-1910 | | | |
| ☐ **BECKER, Maurice** .............. *paintings* | | | $247 |
| Russian/American 1889-1975 .......... *drawings* | | | $22 |
| ☐ **BECKER-GUNDAHL** ............. *paintings* | | | $550 |
| ☐ **BECKERATH, Moritz van** ......... *paintings* | | | $1,650 |
| German 1838-1896 | | | |
| ☐ **BECKERS, Frans** ............... *paintings* | | | $495 |
| Dutch b. 1898 | | | |

| | | Current Price Range | |
|---|---|---|---|
| | | Low | High |
| ☐ **BECKETT, Charles E.** *paintings* | | | $357 |
| American ac. 1840-1850 | | | |
| ☐ **BECKHOFF, Harry** *drawings* | | $99 | $440 |
| American 1901-1979 | | | |
| ☐ **BECKINGHAM, A.** *paintings* | | | $1,100 |
| American 19th cent. | | | |
| ☐ **BECKLEY, William** *drawings* | | | $880 |
| ☐ **BECKMAN, Hans** *paintings* | | | $2,640 |
| German 1809-1882 | | | |
| ☐ **BECKMAN, William** *drawings* | | | $4,950 |
| American 20th cent. *sculpture* | | | $13,200 |
| ☐ **BECKMANN, Conrad** *paintings* | | $12,100 | $19,800 |
| German 1846-1902 | | | |
| ☐ **BECKMANN, Max** *paintings* | | $4,125 | $660,000 |
| German/American 1884-1950 *drawings* | | $440 | $74,800 |
| ☐ **BECKOFF, Harry** *paintings* | | $302 | $539 |
| American 1901-1979 | | | |
| ☐ **BECKWITH, Arthur** *paintings* | | $192 | $880 |
| American 1860-1930 | | | |
| ☐ **BECKWITH, James Carroll** *paintings* | | $50 | $18,700 |
| American 1852-1917 *drawings* | | $110 | $357 |
| ☐ **BEDA, Francesco** *paintings* | | $5,500 | $44,000 |
| Italian 1840-1900 | | | |
| ☐ **BEDINI, Giovanni Paolo** *paintings* | | $467 | $8,800 |
| Italian 1844-1924 | | | |
| ☐ **BEECH, M. E.** *paintings* | | | $385 |
| American 19th/20th cent. | | | |
| ☐ **BEECHEY, Richard Brydges** *paintings* | | | $2,970 |
| British 1808-95 | | | |
| ☐ **BEECHEY, Sir William** *paintings* | | $825 | $9,350 |
| English 1753-1839 | | | |
| ☐ **BEEK, Bernardus Antonie van** *paintings* | | | $450 |
| Dutch b. 1875 | | | |
| ☐ **BEELDEMAKER, Adriaen** *paintings* | | | $10,450 |
| Dutch 1625-1701 | | | |
| ☐ **BEELDEMAKER, John** *paintings* | | | $440 |
| ☐ **BEELER, Joe** *paintings* | | $10,000 | $27,000 |
| American b. 1931 *drawings* | | $2,200 | $10,000 |
| *sculpture* | | $10,000 | $20,000 |
| ☐ **BEELT, Cornelis** *paintings* | | $4,125 | $14,300 |
| Dutch 1660-c. 1702 | | | |
| ☐ **BEEMER, Ed** *drawings* | | | $302 |
| ☐ **BEER, Bern A. van** *paintings* | | | $357 |
| ☐ **BEER, Dick** *drawings* | | | $220 |
| Swedish 1893-1938 | | | |
| ☐ **BEER, John** *paintings* | | $660 | $935 |
| British 19th/20th cent. | | | |
| ☐ **BEER, W.A.** *drawings* | | | $935 |

## Portrait Painting

*Portraits, or ancestor pictures, appeal to many buyers. At the end of the 18th century, Sir William Beechey, John Hoppner, and Sir Thomas Lawrence were the leading portrait painters of fashionable London. Beechey's portrait formula appealed to contemporary taste. He created some of his best effects by silhouetting a single figure against a low horizon or dramatic sky.*

*A regular exhibitor at the Royal Academy from 1776 on, Beechey was appointed the official portrait painter to the Crown by Queen Charlotte, whose full-length portrait he completed in 1793. He was knighted and elected to membership in the Royal Academy in 1798. (Sir William Beechey, "Portrait of Harriet Douglas," circa 1831, oil on canvas, 36 x 28 in., Sloan's, April 26, 1985, $8,800.)*

| | Current Price Range | |
| --- | ---: | ---: |
| | *Low* | *High* |
| ☐ **BEERBOHM, Max** .............................. *drawings* | | $330 |
| British b. 1872 | | |
| ☐ **BEERLER, F.** ..................................... *paintings* | | $900 |
| ☐ **BEERS, Jan van** ................................. *paintings* | $660 | $1,320 |
| Belgian 1852-1927 | | |
| ☐ **BEERS, Julia** .................................... *paintings* | $137 | $418 |
| American 1835-1913 | | |
| ☐ **BEERSTRATEN, Anthonie** ................... *paintings* | $16,500 | $42,900 |
| Dutch 17th cent. | | |
| ☐ **BEERSTRATEN, Jan Abrahamsz** ......... *paintings* | $2,750 | $16,500 |
| Dutch 1622-1666 | | |
| ☐ **BEERT, Osias** .................................... *paintings* | $38,500 | $209,000 |
| Flemish | | |
| ☐ **BEERT, Osias (the elder)** ...................... *paintings* | | $30,800 |
| Flemish c. 1570-1624 | | |
| ☐ **BEEST, Albert van** .............................. *paintings* | | $550 |
| Dutch 1820-1860 ...................................... *drawings* | $132 | $3,300 |
| ☐ **BEEST, Sybrand van** .......................... *paintings* | $1,320 | $3,300 |
| Dutch 1610-1674 | | |
| ☐ **BEETHOLME, George Law** .................. *paintings* | | $742 |
| English ac. 1847-1878 | | |

| | | Current Price Range | |
|---|---|---|---|
| | | Low | High |
| ☐ **BEETZ-CHARPENTIER, Elisa** ............. *sculpture* | | | $800 |
| French 19th cent. | | | |
| ☐ **BEGA, Cornelis Pietersz** ........................ *paintings* | | $13,200 | $41,800 |
| Dutch 1620-1664 | | | |
| ☐ **BEGAS, Oskar** .................................... *paintings* | | $55 | $7,700 |
| German 1828-1883 | | | |
| ☐ **BEGAY, Harrison** .............................. *paintings* | | | $1,210 |
| American (Navajo) b. 1917 .......................... *drawings* | | $500 | $506 |
| ☐ **BEGEYN, Abraham Jansz** .................... *paintings* | | $3,300 | $5,500 |
| Dutch 1637-1697 | | | |
| ☐ **BEGUINE, Michel Leonard** ................. *sculpture* | | | $1,760 |
| French 1855-1925 | | | |
| ☐ **BEHELL, T.** ..................................... *paintings* | | | $356 |
| ☐ **BEHRE, F.J.** .................................... *paintings* | | | $1,600 |
| American 19th/20th cent. | | | |
| ☐ **BEHRENS, August Frederick** ............... *paintings* | | | $8,250 |
| Danish b. 1821 | | | |
| ☐ **BEIL, Charles A.** ................................ *sculpture* | | $1,760 | $5,500 |
| Canadian d. 1976 | | | |
| ☐ **BEINKE, Fritz** ................................... *paintings* | | | $440 |
| German 1842-1907 | | | |
| ☐ **BEITL, J.G.** ...................................... *paintings* | | | $550 |
| ☐ **BEJAR, Feliciano** ................................ *paintings* | | $305 | $660 |
| ....................................................... *drawings* | | | $605 |
| ☐ **BEJARANO, Manuel Cabral** ................ *paintings* | | | $770 |
| ☐ **BELANGER, Francois Joseph** .............. *drawings* | | | $1,320 |
| French 1744-1818 | | | |
| ☐ **BELANGER, Louis** .............................. *drawings* | | $715 | $4,950 |
| French 1736-1816 | | | |
| ☐ **BELAY, Pierre de** ............................... *paintings* | | $1,100 | $2,090 |
| French 1890-1947 ....................................... *drawings* | | | $77 |
| ☐ **BELCHER, Hilda** ............................... *paintings* | | | $385 |
| American 1881-1963 ................................... *drawings* | | $154 | $1,320 |
| ☐ **BELIMBAU, Adolfo** ............................ *paintings* | | $605 | $1,320 |
| Italian b. 1845 | | | |
| ☐ **BELIN DE FONTENAY, Jean Baptiste** .. *paintings* | | $4,180 | $8,800 |
| French | | | |
| ☐ **BELKIN, Arnold** ................................ *paintings* | | $1,320 | $3,300 |
| Canadian/American b. 1930 .......................... *drawings* | | | $550 |
| ☐ **BELKNAP, Zedekiah** .......................... *paintings* | | $2,310 | $49,500 |
| American 1781-1858 | | | |
| ☐ **BELL, A.D.** ...................................... *paintings* | | | $264 |
| ☐ **BELL, Cecil C.** .................................. *paintings* | | | $187 |
| American b. 1906 ...................................... *drawings* | | $275 | $770 |
| ☐ **BELL, Charles** ................................... *paintings* | | $25,300 | $35,200 |
| American b. 1935 | | | |
| ☐ **BELL, D.C.** ...................................... *paintings* | | | $400 |
| British 19th cent. | | | |

| | | | Current Price Range | |
| | | | Low | High |
|---|---|---|---|---|
| ☐ **BELL, Edward Auguste** | ........................ | *paintings* | **$1,100** | **$2,750** |
| American 1862- after 1914 | | | | |
| ☐ **BELL, John Clement** | ............................ | *paintings* | **$5,225** | **$31,900** |
| English ac. 1850-1892 | | | | |
| ☐ **BELL, L.** | ........................................ | *paintings* | | **$1,072** |
| English 19th cent. | | | | |
| ☐ **BELL, Larry** | ........................................ | *paintings* | | **$330** |
| American b. 1939 | ........................................ | *drawings* | | **$330** |
| | ........................................ | *sculpture* | **$3,850** | **$6,600** |
| ☐ **BELL, S.H.** | ........................................ | *paintings* | | **$440** |
| ☐ **BELL, William** | ........................................ | *paintings* | | **$770** |
| British 1740-1804 | | | | |
| ☐ **BELL-SMITH, Frederick Marlett** | .......... | *drawings* | | **$605** |
| Canadian 1846-1923 | | | | |
| ☐ **BELLA, Stefano della** | ........................... | *drawings* | **$176** | **$8,800** |
| Italian 1610-1664 | | | | |
| ☐ **BELLANDI, Ernesto** | ........................... | *paintings* | | **$880** |
| Italian b. 1842 | | | | |
| ☐ **BELLANGE, Joseph Louis Hippolyte** | .... | *paintings* | **$275** | **$1,320** |
| French 1800-1866 | ........................................ | *drawings* | **$110** | **$1,650** |
| ☐ **BELLANGER, Camille Felix** | ................ | *paintings* | **$1,650** | **$8,250** |
| French 1853-1923 | | | | |
| ☐ **BELLANTONIO, E.** | ............................. | *paintings* | | **$412** |
| ☐ **BELLARDEL, N.** | ............................. | *paintings* | | **$1,650** |
| ☐ **BELLAVOINE, Claude** | ......................... | *paintings* | | **$577** |
| French 19th cent. | | | | |
| ☐ **BELLE, Alexis Simon** | ......................... | *paintings* | | **$18,700** |
| French 1674-1734 | | | | |
| ☐ **BELLE, Charles Ernest de** | .................. | *drawings* | **$120** | **$247** |
| Hungarian/American 1873-1937 | | | | |
| ☐ **BELLE, Marcel** | .................................. | *paintings* | | **$440** |
| French 19th/20th cent. | | | | |
| ☐ **BELLEI, Gaetano** | ................................. | *paintings* | | **$2,200** |
| Italian 1857-1922 | | | | |
| ☐ **BELLERMANN, Ferdinand** | ................ | *paintings* | | **$66,000** |
| German 1814-1889 | | | | |
| ☐ **BELLET, Pierre** | .................................. | *paintings* | | **$495** |
| French 19th/20th cent. | | | | |
| ☐ **BELLEVOIS, Jacob Adriaensz** | ............. | *paintings* | **$8,250** | **$8,800** |
| Dutch 1621-1675 | | | | |
| ☐ **BELLI, Enrico** | .................................. | *paintings* | | **$467** |
| Italian 19th cent. | | | | |
| ☐ **BELLIAS, Richard** | ............................. | *paintings* | | **$275** |
| French b. 1921 | | | | |
| ☐ **BELLINGER, Margaret T.** | .................. | *paintings* | **$55** | **$192** |
| American b. 1899 | | | | |
| ☐ **BELLINI, Emmanuel** | ........................... | *paintings* | | **$192** |
| b. Monaco 1904 | | | | |

|                                                  | Current Price Range | |
|--------------------------------------------------|-----------|-----------|
|                                                  | Low       | High      |
| ☐ **BELLINI, Giovanni** .............. *paintings* |           | **$484,000** |
| Italian                                          |           |           |
| ☐ **BELLIS, Antonio de** ............. *paintings* |           | **$7,150** |
| Italian d. 1656                                  |           |           |
| ☐ **BELLIS, Hubert** ................... *paintings* | **$242**  | **$770**  |
| Belgian 1831-1902                                |           |           |
| ☐ **BELLMER, Hans** ................... *paintings* | **$1,210** | **$6,050** |
| German/French b. 1902                            |           |           |
| ☐ **BELLONI, Giorgio** .............. *paintings*  | **$137**  | **$1,430** |
| Italian 1861-1944                                |           |           |
| ☐ **BELLOSO, S.** ..................... *paintings* |           | **$271**  |
| ☐ **BELLOTTI, Dina** ................ *paintings*  | **$275**  | **$742**  |
| Italian 19th/20th cent.                          |           |           |
| ☐ **BELLOTTO, Bernardo** .......... *paintings*    |           | **$198,000** |
| Italian 1720/24-1780 ................ *drawings*   | **$2,750** | **$14,300** |
| ☐ **BELLOWS, Albert Fitch** ...... *paintings*     | **$880**  | **$9,900** |
| American 1829-1883 ................ *drawings*     | **$440**  | **$935**  |
| ☐ **BELLOWS, George Wesley** ...... *paintings*    | **$3,850** | **$41,800** |
| American 1882-1925 ................ *drawings*     | **$220**  | **$20,900** |
| ☐ **BELLUCCI, Antonio** .......... *paintings*     |           | **$4,400** |
| Italian 1654-1726                                |           |           |
| ☐ **BELLYNCK, Hubert Emile** ......... *paintings* |           | **$1,870** |
| French b. 1859                                   |           |           |
| ☐ **BELMONT, Ira Jean** ......... *paintings*      |           | **$220**  |
| American,b. Lithu. 1885-1962                     |           |           |
| ☐ **BELMONT, L.V.** ............... *drawings*     |           | **$302**  |
| 20th cent.                                       |           |           |
| ☐ **BELOFF, Angelica** ............ *drawings*     |           | **$880**  |
| Russian b. 1905                                  |           |           |
| ☐ **BELOT** ..................... *paintings*      |           | **$550**  |
| ☐ **BELTRAN-MASSES, Federico** ...... *paintings*  | **$632**  | **$9,625** |
| Spanish b. 1885                                  |           |           |
| ☐ **BELVEDERE, Andrea**                           |           |           |
| **(called Abate Andrea)** ............ *paintings* |           | **$7,700** |
| Italian 1642-1732                                |           |           |
| ☐ **BEMELMANS, Ludwig** ......... *paintings*      | **$165**  | **$770**  |
| Austrian/American 1898-1963 ...... *drawings*     | **$110**  | **$2,750** |
| ☐ **BEMISH, R. Hills** ............ *drawings*     | **$33**   | **$220**  |
| American 19th/20th cent.                          |           |           |
| ☐ **BEMMEL, Karl Sebastian von** ...... *drawings* |           | **$2,090** |
| German 1743-1796                                 |           |           |
| ☐ **BEMMEL, Peter von** ......... *paintings*      | **$2,200** | **$4,400** |
| German 1685-1754                                 |           |           |
| ☐ **BENASCHI, Giovanni Battista** ...... *paintings* |         | **$1,210** |
| Italian 1636-1688                                |           |           |
| ☐ **BENASSIT, Louis Emile** ...... *paintings*    | **$302**  | **$418**  |
| French 1833-1902                                 |           |           |

| | | | *Current Price Range* | |
|---|---|---|---|---|
| | | | *Low* | *High* |

| | | | Low | High |
|---|---|---|---|---|
| ☐ **BENAVENT Y ROCAMORA,** | | | | |
| **Cayetano** ............................................... | *paintings* | | | $2,200 |
| Spanish 19th/20th cent. | | | | |
| ☐ **BENBRIDGE, Henry** ........................... | *paintings* | | | $8,250 |
| American 1744-1812 | | | | |
| ☐ **BENCOVICH, Federico** ........................ | *drawings* | | | $6,600 |
| Italian b. 1677 | | | | |
| ☐ **BENCZUR, Gyula** ............................... | *paintings* | | | $990 |
| Hungarian 1844-1920 | | | | |
| ☐ **BENCZUR, Julius de** ........................... | *paintings* | | | $4,400 |
| Hungarian 1844-1920 | | | | |
| ☐ **BENDER, Bill** ..................................... | *paintings* | | | $1,760 |
| American b. 1920 | | | | |
| ☐ **BENDER, S.H.** .................................... | *paintings* | | $576 | $1,650 |
| ☐ **BENDER, Tony** ................................... | *paintings* | | | $550 |
| ☐ **BENDER, Whitney** ............................. | *paintings* | | | $385 |
| American | | | | |
| ☐ **BENDINER, Alfred** ............................. | *drawings* | | | $220 |
| American b. 1899 | | | | |
| ☐ **BENEDICT, A.C.** ................................ | *paintings* | | | $2,860 |
| American 19th/20th cent. | | | | |
| ☐ **BENEDICTER, Alois Josef** ................. | *paintings* | | | $2,090 |
| German b. 1843 | | | | |
| ☐ **BENEDIT, Luis** ................................... | *drawings* | | | $1,100 |
| b. Argentina 1937 | | | | |
| ☐ **BENEKER, Gerrit Augustus** ................ | *paintings* | | $250 | $2,420 |
| American 1882-1934 ................................ | *drawings* | | | $174 |
| ☐ **BENELLI, Giuseppe** ............................ | *paintings* | | | $1,870 |
| Italian 1819-1861 | | | | |
| ☐ **BENES, Barton Lidice** ........................ | *drawings* | | | $605 |
| American 20th cent. | | | | |
| ☐ **BENES, R.H.** ...................................... | *paintings* | | | $770 |
| French 19th/20th cent. | | | | |
| ☐ **BENESCH, S.** ...................................... | *drawings* | | | $286 |
| ☐ **BENETTI, A.** ...................................... | *paintings* | | | $660 |
| ☐ **BENEZIT, E.C.** .................................... | *paintings* | | | $550 |
| ☐ **BENFORD, Elnora** ............................. | *paintings* | | | $550 |
| French 19th cent. | | | | |
| ☐ **BENGLIS, Linda** ................................. | *drawings* | | | $4,400 |
| American b. 1941 ...................................... | *sculpture* | | $2,750 | $16,500 |
| ☐ **BENGSTON, Billy Al** ........................... | *paintings* | | $3,300 | $10,450 |
| American b. 1934 ...................................... | *drawings* | | $715 | $1,430 |
| ☐ **BENITEZ, Dario** ................................. | *paintings* | | | $440 |
| ☐ **BENJAMIN, Karl** ............................... | *paintings* | | | $1,320 |
| American b. 1925 | | | | |
| ☐ **BENLLIURE Y GIL, Jose** .................... | *paintings* | | $6,875 | $20,900 |
| Spanish 1855-after 1914 | | | | |
| ☐ **BENLLIURE Y GIL, Juan Antonio** ....... | *paintings* | | | $17,050 |
| Spanish 19th cent. | | | | |

| | | | Current Price Range | |
|---|---|---|---|---|
| | | | *Low* | *High* |
| ☐ **BENLLIURE Y GIL, Mariano** | ............. | *drawings* | **$1,540** | **$4,400** |
| Spanish b. 1862 | | | | |
| ☐ **BENN, Ben** | ......................... | *paintings* | **$176** | **$3,740** |
| American 1884-1983 | ............................... | *drawings* | **$110** | **$308** |
| ☐ **BENNER, Emmanuel** | ........................... | *paintings* | **$935** | **$7,150** |
| French 1836-1896 | | | | |
| ☐ **BENNER, Mary** | ................................. | *paintings* | | **$330** |
| ☐ **BENNETT, Arthur** | ............................. | *paintings* | | **$450** |
| English 19th cent. | | | | |
| ☐ **BENNETT, Frank Moss** | ....................... | *paintings* | **$825** | **$18,700** |
| English 1874-1953 | | | | |
| ☐ **BENNETT, Lyle Hatcher** | ...................... | *paintings* | | **$660** |
| American b. 1903 | | | | |
| ☐ **BENNETT, Rainey** | ............................. | *drawings* | **$220** | **$247** |
| American b.1907 | | | | |
| ☐ **BENNETT, William James** | ................... | *drawings* | **$2,420** | **$41,800** |
| American 1787-1844 | | | | |
| ☐ **BENNETTER, Johan Jakob** | ................. | *paintings* | | **$1,320** |
| Norwegian 1822-1904 | | | | |
| ☐ **BENNEY, Robert** | ............................... | *drawings* | | **$220** |
| American b. 1904 | | | | |
| ☐ **BENNI, Endi** | ..................................... | *paintings* | | **$280** |
| Italian 19th cent. | | | | |
| ☐ **BENNICE, V.H.** | ................................. | *paintings* | | **$935** |
| English School 19th cent. | | | | |
| ☐ **BENOIS, Albert Nikolajewitch** | ............. | *drawings* | | **$330** |
| Russian b. 1852 | | | | |
| ☐ **BENOIS, Alexander Nikolaivitch** | .......... | *drawings* | **$38** | **$2,310** |
| Russian 1870-1960 | | | | |
| ☐ **BENOIS, Nicolai** | ............................... | *drawings* | **$110** | **$1,320** |
| Russian b.1902 | | | | |
| ☐ **BENOIST, J.** | ..................................... | *paintings* | **$880** | **$990** |
| French 19th cent. | | | | |
| ☐ **BENOIT, Leon** | ................................... | *paintings* | | **$990** |
| ☐ **BENOIT, Rigaud** | ............................... | *paintings* | **$412** | **$17,600** |
| Haitian 20th cent. | | | | |
| ☐ **BENOLDI, Walter** | ............................. | *paintings* | **$137** | **$275** |
| Italian b. 1914 | | | | |
| ☐ **BENOUVILLE, Jean Achille** | ................. | *drawings* | | **$550** |
| French 1815-1891 | | | | |
| ☐ **BENSA, Ernesto** | ............................... | *paintings* | | **$935** |
| Italian 19th/20th cent. | ............................... | *drawings* | | **$220** |
| ☐ **BENSA, Giuseppe** | ............................. | *paintings* | | **$1,320** |
| ☐ **BENSELL, George F.** | ......................... | *paintings* | **$192** | **$4,125** |
| American 1837-1879 | | | | |
| ☐ **BENSI, Cesare** | ................................. | *paintings* | | **$440** |
| Italian School 19th/20th cent. | | | | |
| ☐ **BENSO, Giulio** | ................................. | *drawings* | **$1,320** | **$1,760** |
| Italian 1601-1668 | | | | |

| | | Current Price Range | |
|---|---|---|---|
| | | Low | High |
| ☐ **BENSON, Ambrosius** ............................ *paintings* | | $18,150 | $30,800 |
| Flemish 1495-1550 | | | |
| ☐ **BENSON, Eugene** ................................ *paintings* | | $220 | $8,800 |
| American 1839-1908 | | | |
| ☐ **BENSON, Frank Weston** ..................... *paintings* | | $2,000 | $93,500 |
| American 1862-1951 ................................ *drawings* | | $412 | $11,000 |
| ☐ **BENSON, John P.** ................................ *paintings* | | $357 | $484 |
| American 1865-1947 | | | |
| ☐ **BENSON, Leslie** .................................. *paintings* | | $55 | $1,540 |
| American b. 1885 ..................................... *drawings* | | | $55 |
| ☐ **BENT, Johannes van der** ..................... *paintings* | | $1,210 | $4,000 |
| Dutch c. 1650-1690 | | | |
| ☐ **BENTABOLE, Louis** ............................ *paintings* | | $1,320 | $17,600 |
| French 1827-1880 | | | |
| ☐ **BENTHAM-DINSDAL, John** ............... *paintings* | | | $990 |
| British b. 1927 | | | |
| ☐ **BENTLEY, Augustus** ............................ *paintings* | | | $466 |
| ☐ **BENTLEY, C.E.** ................................... *drawings* | | | $550 |
| British 1806-1854 | | | |
| ☐ **BENTLEY, John W.** ............................. *paintings* | | $220 | $1,320 |
| American b. 1880 | | | |
| ☐ **BENTOLS, L.** ....................................... *paintings* | | | $825 |
| ☐ **BENTON, Dwight** ................................ *paintings* | | $247 | $880 |
| American b. 1834 | | | |
| ☐ **BENTON, Thomas Hart** ........................ *paintings* | | $700 | $374,000 |
| American 1889-1975 ................................ *drawings* | | $110 | $68,750 |
| ☐ **BENVENUTI, B.** ................................... *drawings* | | | $522 |
| ☐ **BENVENUTI, Edouardo** ....................... *drawings* | | | $247 |
| Italian 20th cent. | | | |
| ☐ **BENVENUTI, Eugenio** ......................... *drawings* | | $220 | $935 |
| Italian 19th cent. | | | |
| ☐ **BENZ, Severin** ................................... *paintings* | | | $660 |
| Swiss 1834-1898 | | | |
| ☐ **BENZING, G.** ....................................... *drawings* | | | $356 |
| ☐ **BERAIN, Jean (the elder)** ...................... *drawings* | | $660 | $6,050 |
| French 1640-1709/11 | | | |
| ☐ **BERANGER, Charles** ............................ *paintings* | | | $5,500 |
| French 1816-1853 | | | |
| ☐ **BERANGER,** | | | |
| **Jean Baptiste Antoine Emile** .................. *paintings* | | | $1,430 |
| French 1814-1883 | | | |
| ☐ **BERARD, Christian** ............................. *paintings* | | | $11,000 |
| French 1902-1949 ..................................... *drawings* | | $385 | $2,640 |
| ☐ **BERATI, Antonio** ................................ *drawings* | | | $1,760 |
| ☐ **BERAUD, Jean** .................................... *paintings* | | $715 | $203,500 |
| French 1849-1936 ................................... *drawings* | | | $25,300 |
| ☐ **BERCHEM, Nicolaes** ........................... *paintings* | | | $17,600 |
| Dutch 1620-1683 | | | |

| | | Current Price Range | |
|---|---|---|---|
| | | Low | High |
| ☐ BERCHERE, Narcisse ........................ *paintings* | | $154 | $2,640 |
| French 1819-1891 ..................................... *drawings* | | | $528 |
| ☐ BERCHMANS, Emile .......................... *paintings* | | | $770 |
| Belgian b. 1867 | | | |
| ☐ BERCKHEYDE, Gerrit Adriaensz. ....... *paintings* | | | $5,500 |
| Dutch 1638-1698 | | | |
| ☐ BERCKHEYDE, Job ........................... *paintings* | | | $10,450 |
| Dutch 1630-1693 | | | |
| ☐ BERCKMANS, Hendrick ..................... *paintings* | | | $1,760 |
| ☐ BERDANIER, Paul F. ......................... *paintings* | | | $363 |
| American b. 1879 | | | |
| ☐ BERDELL .......................................... *sculpture* | | | $411 |
| 19th cent. | | | |
| ☐ BEREA, Dimitri .................................. *paintings* | | $302 | $825 |
| Rumanian/American 1908-1975 | | | |
| ☐ BEREAU, J. ....................................... *paintings* | | | $357 |
| ☐ BEREK, V. ......................................... *paintings* | | | $385 |
| ☐ BERENDT, Moritz ............................. *paintings* | | | $2,640 |
| German b. 1803 | | | |
| ☐ BERENTZ, Christian .......................... *paintings* | | | $8,800 |
| German 1658-1722 | | | |
| ☐ BERG, Albert .................................... *paintings* | | $418 | $495 |
| German 1825-1884 | | | |
| ☐ BERG, George Lewis ......................... *paintings* | | $412 | $1,760 |
| American 1868/70-1941 | | | |
| ☐ BERG, Gijsbertus Johannes van den ...... *drawings* | | | $825 |
| ☐ BERG, Johann van den ....................... *paintings* | | | $330 |
| European | | | |
| ☐ BERG, Ralph ..................................... *sculpture* | | $3,200 | $3,800 |
| American | | | |
| ☐ BERG, Simon van den ........................ *paintings* | | $200 | $1,650 |
| Dutch 1812-1891 | | | |
| ☐ BERG, Willem van den ....................... *paintings* | | | $605 |
| Dutch 1886-1970 | | | |
| ☐ BERGAMINI, Federico ....................... *paintings* | | | $3,300 |
| ☐ BERGAMINI, Francesco ..................... *paintings* | | $1,980 | $8,250 |
| Italian 19th cent. | | | |
| ☐ BERGE, Edward ................................ *sculpture* | | $550 | $4,950 |
| American 1876-1924 | | | |
| ☐ BERGE, Elmar S. .............................. *paintings* | | | $220 |
| American School 20th cent. | | | |
| ☐ BERGEN, Claus ................................. *paintings* | | $1,100 | $1,430 |
| German 20th cent. | | | |
| ☐ BERGEN, Dirck van ........................... *paintings* | | $1,320 | $1,650 |
| Dutch 1645-1690 | | | |
| ☐ BERGEN, George ............................... *paintings* | | | $550 |
| American 19th/20th cent. | | | |
| ☐ BERGENTHAL, A. ............................. *paintings* | | | $715 |
| ☐ BERGER, Claus ................................. *paintings* | | | $275 |

| | | | Current Price Range | |
|---|---|---|---|---|
| | | | Low | High |
| ☐ **BERGER, Edward** | ............................. | *sculpture* | | $700 |
| American 1876-1924 | | | | |
| ☐ **BERGER, Giacomo** | ............................. | *paintings* | | $880 |
| French 1754-1822 | | | | |
| ☐ **BERGER, Hans** | ................................. | *paintings* | $1,331 | $2,750 |
| Swiss b. 1882 | | | | |
| ☐ **BERGERE** | ......................................... | *paintings* | | $301 |
| ☐ **BERGERET, Denis Pierre** | .................... | *paintings* | $440 | $3,300 |
| French 1846-1910 | | | | |
| ☐ **BERGH, Gillis de** | ............................... | *paintings* | | $55,000 |
| Dutch c. 1600-1669 | | | | |
| ☐ **BERGH, Matthys van den** | ...................... | *drawings* | | $440 |
| ☐ **BERGHE, Fritz van den** | ....................... | *paintings* | | $15,950 |
| Belgian 1883-1939 | | | | |
| ☐ **BERGHIUS** | ....................................... | *paintings* | | $192 |
| Dutch 19th cent. | | | | |
| ☐ **BERGMAN, Charles Pierre** | ................. | *paintings* | $302 | $825 |
| French ac. 1900-1905 | | | | |
| ☐ **BERGMAN, Franz** | ............................. | *sculpture* | $242 | $1,540 |
| Austrian | | | | |
| ☐ **BERGMANN, Georg** | ........................... | *paintings* | | $33,000 |
| German 1819-1870 | | | | |
| ☐ **BERGMANN, Otto** | ............................. | *paintings* | | $385 |
| German 19th cent. | | | | |
| ☐ **BERGNER, Yosl** | ................................ | *paintings* | $4,400 | $9,350 |
| Israeli b. 1920 | ....................................... | *drawings* | | $176 |
| ☐ **BERGSLEIN, Knud Larsen** | ................. | *paintings* | | $1,870 |
| Norwegian 1827-1908 | | | | |
| ☐ **BERJON, Antoine** | ............................. | *drawings* | | $605 |
| French 1754-1893 | | | | |
| ☐ **BERKE, Ernest** | ................................. | *paintings* | $1,320 | $15,400 |
| American b. 1921 | | | | |
| ☐ **BERKES, Antal** | ................................. | *paintings* | $605 | $825 |
| ☐ **BERLANDINA, Jane** | ........................... | *paintings* | $88 | $192 |
| American 1898-1962 | ................................ | *drawings* | | $55 |
| ☐ **BERLANT, Tony** | ................................. | *sculpture* | | $1,650 |
| American b. 1941 | | | | |
| ☐ **BERLEWI, Henryk** | ........................... | *drawings* | $143 | $14,300 |
| Polish 1894-1967 | | | | |
| ☐ **BERLIN, F.** | ....................................... | *paintings* | | $1,300 |
| ☐ **BERLINI, Joseph** | ............................. | *sculpture* | | $357 |
| ☐ **BERMAN, Eugene** | ............................. | *paintings* | $605 | $7,700 |
| American 1899-1972 | ................................ | *drawings* | $66 | $3,080 |
| ☐ **BERMAN, Fred** | ................................. | *sculpture* | $825 | $1,100 |
| ☐ **BERMAN, Harry G.** | ........................... | *paintings* | | $825 |
| American 20th cent. | | | | |
| ☐ **BERMAN, Leonid** | ............................. | *paintings* | $110 | $2,420 |
| Russian 1896/98-1976 | ................................ | *drawings* | | $99 |

|  | | Current Price Range | |
| --- | --- | --- | --- |
|  | | Low | High |
| ☐ **BERMAN, Saul** ............................ *paintings* | | | $3,520 |
| Russian/American b. 1899 | | | |
| ☐ **BERMAN, Wallace** ............................ *drawings* | | $522 | $990 |
| American 1926-1976 | | | |
| ☐ **BERMUDEZ, Cundo** ........................ *paintings* | | $880 | $22,000 |
| Cuban b. 1914 ....................................... *drawings* | | $275 | $2,860 |
| ☐ **BERMUDEZ, Jorge** ........................ *paintings* | | | $3,850 |
| Argentinian 20th cent. | | | |
| ☐ **BERNACCHI** ................................ *sculpture* | | | $302 |
| ☐ **BERNAGOZZI, F.** ........................ *paintings* | | | $2,310 |
| Italian 19th cent. | | | |
| ☐ **BERNALDO DE QUIROS, Cesareo** ....... *paintings* | | $660 | $1,760 |
| Argentinian ac. 20th cent. | | | |
| ☐ **BERNAR, J.** ................................ *paintings* | | | $825 |
| ☐ **BERNARD, E.** ............................ *paintings* | | | $66 |
| ................................................ *sculpture* | | | $1,210 |
| ☐ **BERNARD, Emile** ........................ *paintings* | | $275 | $57,200* |
| French 1868-1941 ................................. *drawings* | | | $412 |
| ☐ **BERNARD, Jean Clement** .................... *paintings* | | | $6,050 |
| French b. 1761 | | | |
| ☐ **BERNARD, Jean Joseph** | | | |
| **(called Bernard de Paris)** ..................... *drawings* | | | $1,980 |
| French 1740-1809 | | | |
| ☐ **BERNARD, Joseph** ............................ *paintings* | | $3,850 | $6,050 |
| French 1864-1933 | | | |
| ☐ **BERNARD, Jules Francois** .................... *paintings* | | $660 | $3,300 |
| French 20th cent. | | | |
| ☐ **BERNARD, Louis Michel** ..................... *paintings* | | | $660 |
| French b. 1885 | | | |
| ☐ **BERNARDING, A.** ............................ *paintings* | | | $1,320 |
| ☐ **BERNE-BELLECOUR,** | | | |
| **Etienne Prosper** ............................ *paintings* | | $467 | $44,000 |
| French 1838-1910 ................................. *drawings* | | $412 | $440 |
| ☐ **BERNE-BELLECOUR, Jean Jacques** .... *paintings* | | $715 | $2,420 |
| French b. 1874 | | | |
| ☐ **BERNEKER, Louis Frederick** .............. *paintings* | | $330 | $2,475 |
| American 1876-1937 ................................. *drawings* | | | $330 |
| ☐ **BERNHARDT, Sarah** ........................ *paintings* | | $300 | $1,760 |
| French 1844-1923 ..................................... *sculpture* | | | $9,900 |
| ☐ **BERNI, Antonio** ............................ *paintings* | | | $5,500 |
| Argentinian b. 1905 ................................. *drawings* | | $4,400 | $6,600 |
| ☐ **BERNIER, George** ........................ *paintings* | | | $242 |
| Belgian 1862-1918 | | | |
| ☐ **BERNIEZ, S.** ................................ *paintings* | | | $330 |
| European 19th cent. | | | |
| ☐ **BERNINGER, Edmund** ........................ *paintings* | | $176 | $1,210 |
| German b. 1843 | | | |
| ☐ **BERNINGHAUS, Charles** ..................... *paintings* | | $154 | $522 |
| American 20th cent. | | | |

| | | Current Price Range | |
| | | Low | High |
|---|---|---|---|
| ☐ **BERNINGHAUS, Oscar Edmund** .......... *paintings* | | $1,100 | $209,000 |
| American 1874-1952 ................................ *drawings* | | $6,600 | $14,000 |
| ☐ **BERNSTAMM, Leopold** ...................... *sculpture* | | $286 | $396 |
| Russian 1859-1910 | | | |
| ☐ **BERNSTEIN, Richard** ........................ *paintings* | | | $880 |
| ☑ **BERNSTEIN, Theresa** ........................ *paintings* | | $137 | $302 |
| American 20th cent. | | | |
| ☐ **BEROUD, Louis** ................................ *paintings* | | $1,320 | $8,250 |
| French b. 1852 | | | |
| ☐ **BERRETTONI, Niccolo** ....................... *paintings* | | | $4,620 |
| Italian 1637-1682 | | | |
| ☐ **BERRIO, Gaspar Miguel de** ............... *paintings* | | $1,320 | $17,600 |
| ☐ **BERROCAL, Miguel Oritz** .................. *sculpture* | | $66 | $7,260 |
| Spanish b. 1933 | | | |
| ☐ **BERRY, A.J.** ..................................... *paintings* | | | $525 |
| ☐ **BERRY, Carroll Thayer** ..................... *paintings* | | $44 | $600 |
| American 1886-1978 | | | |
| ☐ **BERRY, Louise M.** ............................. *paintings* | | | $330 |
| American 19th cent. | | | |
| ☐ **BERRY, N.L.** ..................................... *paintings* | | $148 | $1,100 |
| American 19th/20th cent. | | | |
| ☐ **BERRY, Patrick Vincent** ...................... *paintings* | | $174 | $1,650 |
| American 1843-1913 | | | |
| ☐ **BERSCH, F.** ...................................... *paintings* | | | $495 |
| ☐ **BERSON, Adolphe** ............................. *paintings* | | $330 | $550 |
| American 1880-1970 ................................ *drawings* | | | $124 |
| ☐ **BERT, A.P.** ....................................... *paintings* | | | $467 |
| ☐ **BERT, Charles H.** ............................. *paintings* | | | $550 |
| American b. 1873 | | | |
| ☐ **BERTAULT, Paul Seguin** ................... *paintings* | | | $385 |
| ☐ **BERTAUX, H.G.** ................................ *drawings* | | | $1,100 |
| ☐ **BERTEAUX, Rudolph S.** ..................... *paintings* | | | $880 |
| French 19th cent. | | | |
| ☐ **BERTEL, G.** ....................................... *paintings* | | | $350 |
| Italian late 19th cent. | | | |
| ☐ **BERTGIN, A.** ..................................... *paintings* | | | $3,080 |
| ☐ **BERTH (?), L.L.** ............................... *paintings* | | | $521 |
| American 19th cent. | | | |
| ☐ **BERTHELON, Eugene** ........................ *paintings* | | $495 | $5,500 |
| French 1829-after 1914 ............................ *drawings* | | $2,420 | $3,410 |
| ☐ **BERTHELSEN, Johann** ....................... *paintings* | | $330 | $7,700 |
| Danish/American b. 1883 | | | |
| ☐ **BERTHOLD, Joachim** ......................... *sculpture* | | | $1,100 |
| American | | | |
| ☐ **BERTHOT, Jake** ................................ *paintings* | | $990 | $13,200 |
| American b. 1939 ................................... *drawings* | | | $550 |
| ☐ **BERTHOU, P.F.** ................................ *sculpture* | | | $715 |
| French early 20th cent. | | | |

| | | Current Price Range | |
|---|---|---|---|
| | | Low | High |
| ☐ **BERTHOUD, Auguste Henri** ........ *paintings* <br> Swiss 1829-1887 | | | $770 |
| ☐ **BERTI, A.** ................ *paintings* | | $247 | $550 |
| ☐ **BERTIER, Charles Alexandre** ........ *paintings* <br> French 1860-1924 | | | $1,210 |
| ☐ **BERTIER, R.** ................ *paintings* | | | $385 |
| ☐ **BERTIN, Jean Victor** ........ *paintings* <br> French 1775-1842 ................ *drawings* | | | $3,575 <br> $1,980 |
| ☐ **BERTIN, Nicolas** ........ *paintings* <br> French 1668-1736 | | | $8,250 |
| ☐ **BERTIN, Roger** ........ *paintings* <br> French b. 1915 | | | $440 |
| ☐ **BERTINI, L.** ................ *paintings* <br> Italian 20th cent. | | $302 | $935 |
| ☐ **BERTOIA, Harry** ........ *sculpture* <br> Italian/American 1915-1978 | | $660 | $23,100 |
| ☐ **BERTOJA, Jacopo** <br> **(called Jacopo ZANGUIDI)** ........ *drawings* <br> Italian 1544-1574 | | | $495 |
| ☐ **BERTOLD, C.** ................ *paintings* <br> Swiss 20th cent. | | $192 | $522 |
| ☐ **BERTOLD, G.** ................ *paintings* | | | $550 |
| ☐ **BERTON, Armand** ........ *paintings* <br> French 1854-1927 | | | $1,100 |
| ☐ **BERTON, L.** ................ *paintings* | | | $264 |
| ☐ **BERTONCELLI, G.** ........ *paintings* <br> Italian 19th cent. | | | $440 |
| ☐ **BERTRAM, Abel** ........ *paintings* <br> French 1871-1954 ................ *drawings* | | $660 | $2,200 <br> $55 |
| ☐ **BERTRAND, Georges Jules** ........ *paintings* <br> French 1849-1929 | | | $1,760 |
| ☐ **BERTRAND, Jean Baptiste** ........ *paintings* <br> French 19th cent. | | | $550 |
| ☐ **BERTRAND, Paulin** ........ *paintings* <br> French 1852-1940 | | $1,100 | $1,210 |
| ☐ **BERTRAND, Pierre** ........ *paintings* <br> French | | $88 | $770 |
| ☐ **BERTUCCI, Giovanni Battista** ........ *paintings* <br> Italian | | | $6,325 |
| ☐ **BERTUCCI, Giovanni Battista** ........ *paintings* <br> Italian | | | $55,000 |
| ☐ **BERTZIK** ................ *paintings* <br> European 19th cent. (?) | | | $2,310 |
| ☐ **BERTZKI, A.** ................ *paintings* <br> European 19th cent. | | | $330 |
| ☐ **BERUETE, Aureliano de** ........ *paintings* <br> Spanish 1845-1911 | | $275 | $880 |
| ☐ **BESANCON, A.** ................ *drawings* | | | $605 |

| | Current Price Range | |
| --- | --- | --- |
| | *Low* | *High* |
| ☐ **BESCHEY, Balthasar** ............... *paintings* | $935 | $8,800 |
| Flemish 1708-1776 | | |
| ☐ **BESCHEY, Jacob Andries** ......... *paintings* | | $3,740 |
| Flemish 1710-1786 | | |
| ☐ **BESNARD, Paul Albert** ........... *paintings* | $75 | $7,150 |
| French 1849-1934 ......................... *drawings* | | $220 |
| ☐ **BESNUS, Amedee** .................. *paintings* | $1,430 | $2,640 |
| French 1831-1909 | | |
| ☐ **BESS, Forrest** ...................... *paintings* | $1,760 | $9,900 |
| American b. 1911 | | |
| ☐ **BESSE, Raymond** ................. *paintings* | $137 | $412 |
| French 1899-1969 | | |
| ☐ **BESSIRE, Dale Philip** ............ *paintings* | $330 | $1,100 |
| American 1892-1974 | | |
| ☐ **BESSON, Faustin** ................. *paintings* | $143 | $605 |
| French 1821-1882 | | |
| ☐ **BESSON, G.** ........................ *paintings* | | $1,000 |
| ☐ **BESSONOF, Boris** ................ *paintings* | $357 | $880 |
| Russian 20th cent. | | |
| ☑ **BEST, Arthur W.** .................. *paintings* | $192 | $1,540 |
| American b. 1865 | | |
| ☑ **BEST, Hans** ....................... *paintings* | | $495 |
| German 19th/20th cent. | | |
| ☑ **BEST, Harry Cassie** .............. *paintings* | $99 | $1,100 |
| American 1863-1936 ..................... *drawings* | $77 | $137 |
| ☑ **BEST, John** ........................ *paintings* | $7,500 | $14,300 |
| English ac. 1750-1791 | | |
| ☑ **BEST, Mary Ellen** ................ *drawings* | $660 | $19,250 |
| English b. 1809 | | |
| ☐ **BEST Y MAUGARD, Adolfo** ......... *paintings* | | $308 |
| ☐ **BESTI, Prof. G.** ................... *sculpture* | $247 | $990 |
| Italian c. 1900 | | |
| ☐ **BETSBERG, Ernestine** ............ *paintings* | | $1,650 |
| American b. 1909 | | |
| ☐ **BETTERA, Bartolomeo** ............ *paintings* | | $13,200 |
| Italian 1639-1700 | | |
| ☐ **BETTIJAI, G.** ...................... *paintings* | | $2,310 |
| Italian 19th cent. | | |
| ☐ **BETTINGER, Hayland B.** ........ *paintings* | | $300 |
| American 1890-1950 | | |
| ☐ **BETTS, Grace** ..................... *paintings* | | $275 |
| American b. 1883 | | |
| ☐ **BETTS, Harold Harrington** ........ *paintings* | $154 | $2,750 |
| American b. 1881 | | |
| ☐ **BETTS, Louis** ..................... *paintings* | $1,100 | $27,500 |
| American 1873-1961 .................... *drawings* | | $50 |
| ☐ **BETTS, Virginia Battle** .......... *paintings* | | $302 |
| American ac. 1930 | | |

| | | Current Price Range | |
|---|---|---|---|
| | | *Low* | *High* |
| ☐ **BEUGET, Charles** ............... *paintings* <br> French 19th cent. | | $165 | $176 |
| ☐ **BEUL, Frans de** ............... *paintings* <br> Dutch 1849-1919 | | $412 | $2,640 |
| ☐ **BEUL, Henri de** ............... *paintings* <br> Belgian 1845-1900 | | $715 | $4,400 |
| ☐ **BEUL, Laurent de** ............... *paintings* <br> Belgian 19th cent. | | $1,540 | $2,475 |
| ☐ **BEUYS, Josef** ............... *drawings* <br> German b. 1921 ............... *sculpture* | | $385 <br> $302 | $1,870 <br> $550 |
| ☐ **BEWLEY, Murray Percival** ............... *paintings* <br> American b. 1884 | | $165 | $1,870 |
| ☐ **BEYER, Carl** ............... *paintings* <br> 1826-1903 | | | $220 |
| ☐ **BEYER, E.** ............... *paintings* <br> German 19th cent. | | $440 | $825 |
| ☐ **BEYER, Jan de** ............... *paintings* <br> Swiss 1705-1768 | | | $2,420 |
| ☐ **BEYER, M.O.** ............... *paintings* <br> American 19th cent. | | | $220 |
| ☐ **BEYEREN, Abraham Hendricksz van** ... *paintings* <br> Dutch 1620/21-c. 1675/90 | | $4,400 | $44,000 |
| ☐ **BEYLARD, Louis Charles** ............... *paintings* <br> French d. 1925 | | | $880 |
| ☐ **BEYLE, Pierre Marie** ............... *paintings* <br> French 1838-1902 | | $165 | $385 |
| ☐ **BEZARD, Jean Louis** ............... *paintings* <br> French b. 1799 ............... *drawings* | | $242 | $1,540 <br> $308 |
| ☐ **BEZOMBES, Roger** ............... *paintings* <br> ............... *drawings* | | | $467 <br> $330 |
| ☐ **BEZZUOLI, Giuseppe** ............... *drawings* | | | $440 |
| ☐ **BHAVSAR, Natvar** ............... *paintings* <br> Indian/American b. 1934 | | $33 | $990 |
| ☐ **BHY, P.D.** ............... *paintings* | | | $330 |
| ☐ **BIABARON, P.** ............... *paintings* | | | $522 |
| ☐ **BIAGIMI, V.** ............... *sculpture* | | | $660 |
| ☐ **BIALA, Janice** ............... *paintings* <br> Polish/American b. 1903 ............... *drawings* | | $77 | $121 <br> $247 |
| ☐ **BIALNITSKY-BIRULYA,** <br> **Vitold Kaetanovich** ............... *paintings* | | | $550 |
| ☐ **BIANCHI, A.** ............... *paintings* <br> American 20th cent. | | | $247 |
| ☐ **BIANCHI, Ben** ............... *sculpture* | | $220 | $495 |
| ☐ **BIANCHI, C.** ............... *drawings* <br> Italian 20th cent. | | | $264 |
| ☐ **BIANCHI, Mose di Giosue** ............... *paintings* <br> Italian 1840/45-1904 | | | $30,800 |
| ☐ **BIANCHI, Prof. O.** ............... *paintings* <br> Italian 19th cent. | | | $275 |

| | Current Price Range | |
|---|---|---|
| | Low | High |
| ☐ **BIARD, Francois Auguste** ...... *paintings* | | $23,100 |
| French 1799-1882 | | |
| ☐ **BIBIENA, Giuseppe Galli** ...... *drawings* | | $1,760 |
| Italian 1696-1757 | | |
| ☐ **BICCHI, Ferrari** ...... *paintings* | | $990 |
| Italian late 19th/early 20th cent | | |
| ☐ **BICCI, Lorenzo di** ...... *paintings* | $8,800 | $20,900 |
| Italian c. 1350-1427 | | |
| ☐ **BICCI, Neri di** ...... *paintings* | | $93,500 |
| Italian 1419-1491 | | |
| ☐ **BICHAL, A.** ...... *paintings* | | $275 |
| ☐ **BICKERSTAFF** ...... *paintings* | $250 | $522 |
| American 20th cent. | | |
| ☐ **BICKNELL, Albion Harris** ...... *paintings* | $300 | $7,700 |
| American 1837-1915 | | |
| ☐ **BICKNELL, Evelyn M.** ...... *paintings* | $137 | $330 |
| American 19th/20th cent. ...... *drawings* | $55 | $275 |
| ☐ **BICKNELL, Frank Alfred** ...... *paintings* | $330 | $3,850 |
| American 1866-1943 ...... *drawings* | | $154 |
| ☐ **BIDA, Alexandre** ...... *paintings* | | $880 |
| French 1823-1895 ...... *drawings* | $198 | $308 |
| ☐ **BIDAU, Eugene** ...... *paintings* | $3,080 | $16,500 |
| French 19th cent. | | |
| ☐ **BIDAULD, Jean Joseph Xavier** ...... *paintings* | $11,000 | $93,500 |
| French 1758-1846 | | |
| ☐ **BIDDELL, Lawrence** ...... *paintings* | | $605 |
| British 20th cent. | | |
| ☐ **BIDDLE, George** ...... *paintings* | $825 | $6,380 |
| American 1885-1973 ...... *drawings* | $220 | $440 |
| ☐ **BIDDLE, Laurence** ...... *paintings* | $247 | $2,860 |
| English b. 1888 | | |
| ☐ **BIDO, Candido** ...... *paintings* | $220 | $3,850 |
| Latin American | | |
| ☐ **BIDWELL, A.** ...... *paintings* | | $247 |
| American 19th cent. | | |
| ☐ **BIE, Cornelis de** ...... *paintings* | | $5,500 |
| Dutch 1621-1654 | | |
| ☐ **BIEGAS, Boleslas** ...... *sculpture* | | $1,980 |
| French early 20th cent. | | |
| ☐ **BIEGEL, Peter** ...... *paintings* | | $2,420 |
| ☐ **BIEHLE, A.F.** ...... *paintings* | | $1,210 |
| ☐ **BIEL, Joseph** ...... *paintings* | $550 | $1,430 |
| American 1891-1943 | | |
| ☐ **BIELEFELDT, C.** ...... *paintings* | | $275 |
| American 20th cent. | | |
| ☐ **BIENDT, N.** ...... *paintings* | | $700 |
| ☐ **BIERER** ...... *paintings* | | $550 |
| ☐ **BIERHALS, Otto** ...... *paintings* | $330 | $440 |
| German b. 1879 | | |

| | Current Price Range | |
|---|---|---|
| | *Low* | *High* |
| ☐ **BIERMANN, Edouard Karl** ................ *paintings* | | **$1,430** |
| German 1803-1892 | | |
| ☐ **BIERNACKA, Aniela de** ...................... *paintings* | | **$330** |
| Polish 19th cent. | | |
| ☐ **BIERNCHIN, E.** ................................... *sculpture* | | **$300** |
| ☐ **BIERSTADT, Albert** .......................... *paintings* | **$1,100** | **$792,000** |
| German/American 1830-1902 ...................... *drawings* | **$1,210** | **$6,050** |
| ☐ **BIESE, Karl** ....................................... *paintings* | | **$440** |
| German b. 1863 | | |
| ☐ **BIESTER, Anthony** ............................ *paintings* | | **$247** |
| German d. 1917 | | |
| ☐ **BIEVRE, Marie de** ............................. *paintings* | | **$3,080** |
| Belgian b. 1865 | | |
| ☐ **BIGARI, Vittorio** .............................. *drawings* | | **$4,400** |
| Italian 1692-1776 | | |
| ☐ **BIGATTI** ........................................... *drawings* | | **$1,870** |
| ☐ **BIGAUD, Wilson** ............................... *paintings* | **$110** | **$5,500** |
| Haitian b. 1931 | | |
| ☐ **BIGELOW, Daniel Folger** ..................... *paintings* | **$143** | **$825** |
| American 1823-1910 | | |
| ☐ **BIGELOW, Mary** ............................... *paintings* | | **$300** |
| American 20th cent. | | |
| ☐ **BIGELOW, Mrs. James W. (Sophia)** ...... *paintings* | | **$440** |
| American ac. 1852-1857 | | |
| ☐ **BIGELOW, Olive** ............................... *paintings* | | **$412** |
| American b. 1886 | | |
| ☐ **BIGELOW, Thomas** ............................ *paintings* | | **$605** |
| American | | |
| ☐ **BIGG, William Redmore** ....................... *paintings* | **$3,850** | **$4,400** |
| English 1755-1828 | | |
| ☐ **BIGGI, Felice Fortunato** ...................... *paintings* | | **$17,600** |
| Italian 17th cent. | | |
| ☐ **BIGGS, Robert Oldham** ........................ *paintings* | | **$1,430** |
| American b. 1920 | | |
| ☐ **BIGGS, Walter** ................................... *paintings* | | **$3,025** |
| American b. 1886 | | |
| ☐ **BIGOT, Trophime (or Theophisme)** ........ *paintings* | | **$8,800** |
| French ac. 1620-1635 | | |
| ☐ **BILA, Batogh** .................................... *paintings* | | **$357** |
| ☐ **BILBIE, James Lees** ............................ *paintings* | **$700** | **$1,210** |
| English 19th cent. | | |
| ☐ **BILCOQ, Marie Marc Antoine** .............. *paintings* | | **$2,200** |
| French 1755-1838 | | |
| ☐ **BILDERS, Albert Gerard** ..................... *drawings* | **$1,100** | **$1,320** |
| Dutch 1838-1865 | | |
| ☐ **BILDERS, Johannes Wernardus** ............ *paintings* | | **$8,580** |
| Dutch 1811-1890 | | |
| ☐ **BILIBINE, Alexander** .......................... *drawings* | | **$550** |
| ☐ **BILINSKY, Boris** ................................ *drawings* | **$412** | **$1,320** |

|  | | Current Price Range | |
|---|---|---|---|
|  | | Low | High |
| ☐ **BILL, Max** .......................................... *sculpture* | | | **$5,500** |
| Swiss b. 1908 | | | |
| ☐ **BILL, Oliver** ...................................... *paintings* | | | **$880** |
| British 19th cent. | | | |
| ☐ **BILLE, Carl Ludwig** ........................... *paintings* | | **$825** | **$1,210** |
| Danish 1815-1898 | | | |
| ☐ **BILLE, Wilhelm Victor** ........................ *paintings* | | | **$1,870** |
| Danish 1864-1908 | | | |
| ☐ **BILLET, Etienne** ................................. *paintings* | | | **$1,650** |
| French b. 1821 | | | |
| ☐ **BILLET, Pierre** ................................... *paintings* | | **$467** | **$3,575** |
| French 1837-1922 ................................. *drawings* | | | **$1,100** |
| ☐ **BILLET DE FOMBELLE, Suzanne** ....... *paintings* | | | **$495** |
| French 20th cent. | | | |
| ☐ **BILLING, Anna** ................................. *paintings* | | | **$220** |
| American 19th cent. | | | |
| ☐ **BILLOTTE, Leon Joseph** ..................... *paintings* | | | **$2,750** |
| French b. 1815 | | | |
| ☐ **BILTIUS, Jacobus** ............................... *paintings* | | | **$3,300** |
| Dutch 1640?-1679? | | | |
| ☐ **BIMICH** ............................................ *paintings* | | | **$1,870** |
| ☐ **BIMMERMANN, Caesar** ...................... *paintings* | | | **$2,750** |
| German ac.c. 1881 | | | |
| ☐ **BINBECK, A.** ..................................... *drawings* | | | **$440** |
| ☐ **BINCK, Alfred** .................................. *drawings* | | | **$440** |
| ☐ **BINDEMAN, G.** .................................. *paintings* | | | **$357** |
| British 19th cent. | | | |
| ☐ **BINDER, Alois** .................................. *paintings* | | **$275** | **$3,850** |
| German b. 1857 | | | |
| ☐ **BINDER, John** ................................... *paintings* | | **$44** | **$220** |
| 20th cent. | | | |
| ☐ **BINDER, Tony** ................................... *paintings* | | | **$1,980** |
| German 20th cent. | | | |
| ☐ **BINET, Adolphe Gustave** ..................... *paintings* | | | **$5,500** |
| French 1854-1897 | | | |
| ☐ **BINET, Georges** ................................ *paintings* | | | **$2,090** |
| French 1865-1949 | | | |
| ☐ **BINET,** | | | |
| **Victor Jean Baptiste Barthelemy** ............ *paintings* | | **$412** | **$6,875** |
| French 1849-1924 | | | |
| ☑ **BINFORD, Julien** ................................ *paintings* | | | **$935** |
| American b. 1908 | | | |
| ☐ **BINGHAM, George Caleb** ..................... *paintings* | | **$5,500** | **$192,500** |
| American 1811-1879 | | | |
| ☐ **BINKS, Reuben Ward** ......................... *drawings* | | **$1,000** | **$1,600** |
| English exhib. 1934 | | | |
| ☐ **BINOIT, Peter** .................................... *paintings* | | | **$15,400** |
| German 17th cent. | | | |

| | | *Current Price Range* | |
|---|---|---|---|
| | | *Low* | *High* |
| ☐ **BIONDO, Giovanni del** .................... *paintings* Italian 1356-1392 | | | $110,000 |
| ☐ **BIORO, Gustave** ............................ *drawings* French 19th/20th cent. | | | $1,100 |
| ☐ **BIRAM** .......................................... *drawings* British late 19th cent. | | | $275 |
| ☐ **BIRCH, John** ................................. *paintings* British 1807-57 | | | $550 |
| ☐ **BIRCH, Reginald** ........................... *drawings* American 1856-1943 | | $165 | $660 |
| ☐ **BIRCH, S.J. Lamorna** ..................... *drawings* English 1869-1955 | | $220 | $275 |
| ☐ **BIRCH, Thomas** ............................. *paintings* American 1779-1851 | | $3,200 | $181,500 |
| ☐ **BIRCH, William R.** ......................... *drawings* American 1755-1834 | | | $275 |
| ☐ **BIRCHALL, William Minshall** ............. *drawings* American/English b. 1884 | | $137 | $880 |
| ☐ **BIRCHLER, Nicholas** ....................... *paintings* 1800-1857 | | | $440 |
| ☐ **BIRD, A.F.** .................................... *paintings* American 19th cent. | | | $192 |
| ☐ **BIRD, Edward** ............................... *paintings* | | | $440 |
| ☐ **BIRD, Harrington** ........................... *paintings* English 1846-1936 ..................... *drawings* | | $605 $385 | $17,600 $7,150 |
| ☐ **BIRD, Isaac F.** .............................. *drawings* English 1826-1861 | | | $247 |
| ☐ **BIRD, John Alexander Harington** .......... *drawings* British ac. 1870-1893 | | | $15,400 |
| ☐ **BIRD, Samuel** ............................... *paintings* British active 1865-93 | | | $715 |
| ☐ **BIRDICK, H.R.** .............................. *paintings* American 19th/20th cent. | | $125 | $225 |
| ☐ **BIRDSALL, Amos** ........................... *paintings* American b. 1865 | | | $357 |
| ☐ **BIRDSEY** ..................................... *paintings* Bermudian 20th cent. .................... *drawings* | | | $99 $440 |
| ☐ **BIRELLI, A.** .................................. *paintings* | | | $1,100 |
| ☐ **BIRKINGER, Franz Xaver** .................. *paintings* | | | $3,300 |
| ☐ **BIRLEY, Oswald** ............................ *paintings* Australian b. 1880 | | $176 | $825 |
| ☐ **BIRNEY, Frank A.** ........................... *paintings* | | | $850 |
| ☐ **BIRNEY, William Verplanck** ............... *paintings* American 1858-1909 ..................... *drawings* | | $880 $462 | $10,450 $2,860 |
| ☐ **BIRO, Ljubo** ................................. *paintings* Yugoslavian | | | $550 |
| ☐ **BIRREN, Joseph P.** ......................... *paintings* American 1864-1933 | | $250 | $990 |
| ☐ **BIRTLES, Harry** ............................. *drawings* | | | $715 |

| | | Current Price Range | |
|---|---|---|---|
| | | Low | High |
| ☐ **BISBING, Henry Singlewood** ........... *paintings* | | $660 | $2,090 |
| American 1849-1919 | | | |
| ☐ **BISCHOFF, Franz A.** ........... *paintings* | | $275 | $4,675 |
| Austrian/American 1864-1929 | | | |
| ☐ **BISCHOFF, Frederich** ........... *paintings* | | | $300 |
| German 1819-1873 | | | |
| ☐ **BISCHOFF, Theofile** ........... *paintings* | | | $3,300 |
| Swiss 19th cent. | | | |
| ☐ **BISHOP, A.F.** ........... *paintings* | | | $4,730 |
| American 19th/20th cent. | | | |
| ☐ **BISHOP, Alfred S.** ........... *paintings* | | | $1,870 |
| English 19th cent. | | | |
| ☐ **BISHOP, E.W.** ........... *paintings* | | | $302 |
| English 19th cent. | | | |
| ☐ **BISHOP, Harry** ........... *paintings* | | | $357 |
| 20th cent. | | | |
| ☐ **BISHOP, Isabel** ........... *drawings* | | $264 | $1,210 |
| American b. 1902 | | | |
| ☐ **BISHOP, Richard E.** ........... *paintings* | | | $660 |
| American 20th cent. | | | |
| ☐ **BISHOP, William James** ........... *paintings* | | | $660 |
| ☐ **BISON, Giuseppe Bernardino** ........... *paintings* | | $715 | $1,430 |
| Italian 1762-1844 | | | |
| ☐ **BISPHAM, Henry Collins** ........... *paintings* | | $467 | $6,050 |
| American 1841-1882 | | | |
| ☐ **BISSCHOP, Jan de** ........... *drawings* | | $2,200 | $3,575 |
| Dutch 1628-1671 | | | |
| ☐ **BISSELL, Edgar J.** ........... *paintings* | | | $330 |
| American b. 1856 | | | |
| ☐ **BISSELL, George Edwin** ........... *sculpture* | | | $330 |
| American | | | |
| ☐ **BISSIER, Julius (or Jules)** ........... *paintings* | | $2,420 | $15,400 |
| German/Swiss 1893-1965 ........... *drawings* | | $660 | $7,700 |
| ☐ **BISSIERE, Roger** ........... *paintings* | | $247 | $13,200 |
| French 1886/88-1964 | | | |
| ☐ **BISSON, Edouard** ........... *paintings* | | $1,540 | $6,050 |
| French b. 1856 | | | |
| ☐ **BISSON, Pierre** ........... *paintings* | | | $1,870 |
| French 19th cent. | | | |
| ☐ **BISSOT, Andre** ........... *paintings* | | | $440 |
| French 20th cent. | | | |
| ☐ **BISTAGNE, Paul** ........... *paintings* | | | $990 |
| French 1850-1886 | | | |
| ☐ **BISTTRAM, Emil** ........... *drawings* | | | $715 |
| Hungarian/American b. 1895 | | | |
| ☐ **BITNEY, Bye** ........... *paintings* | | | $550 |
| American | | | |
| ☐ **BITTER, Ary** ........... *sculpture* | | $495 | $2,000 |
| French b. 1883 | | | |

|  | | Current Price Range | |
|---|---|---|---|
|  | | Low | High |
| ☐ **BITTINGER, Charles** .............. *paintings* | | $110 | $605 |
| American 1879-1970 | | | |
| ☐ **BIXBEE, William Johnson** ............ *paintings* | | $124 | $1,000 |
| American 1850-1921 ....................... *drawings* | | $110 | $800 |
| ☐ **BIZET, Andree** ............................... *paintings* | | | $250 |
| French b. 1888 | | | |
| ☐ **BJULF, Soren Christian** ................ *paintings* | | | $1,210 |
| Danish b. 1890 | | | |
| ☐ **BLAAS, Carl von** ........................ *paintings* | | $22,000 | $44,000 |
| Austrian 1815-1894 | | | |
| ☐ **BLAAS, Eugen von** ...................... *paintings* | | $4,400 | $52,800 |
| Austrian 1843-1931 ......................... *drawings* | | | $1,210 |
| ☐ **BLAAS, Guilio da** ........................ *drawings* | | | $495 |
| Italian/American 1880-1934 | | | |
| ☐ **BLAAS, Julius von** ...................... *paintings* | | $605 | $27,500 |
| Austrian 1845-1922 ......................... *drawings* | | | $1,045 |
| ☐ **BLACK, Andrew** .......................... *paintings* | | | $330 |
| British 1850-1916 ........................... *drawings* | | | $500 |
| ☐ **BLACK, Eleanor Simms** ............... *paintings* | | | $275 |
| American 19th/20th cent. | | | |
| ☐ **BLACK, LaVerne** ........................ *paintings* | | $2,200 | $55,000 |
| American 1887-1938/39 ..................... *drawings* | | | $7,975 |
| ☐ **BLACK, Olive Parker** .................. *paintings* | | $165 | $3,300 |
| American 1868-1948 | | | |
| ☐ **BLACKBURN, Joseph** .................. *paintings* | | $880 | $7,700 |
| American ac. 1750-1774 | | | |
| ☐ **BLACKBURN, Morris** ................. *drawings* | | | $495 |
| American 20th cent. | | | |
| ☐ **BLACKER, L.** ............................. *drawings* | | | $385 |
| American 19th cent. | | | |
| ☐ **BLACKLOCK, Thomas B.** .............. *paintings* | | | $660 |
| ☐ **BLACKLOCK, William Kay** ............ *paintings* | | | $3,575 |
| English b.1872, exhib.1897-1922 | | | |
| ☐ **BLACKMAN, Walter** .................... *paintings* | | $137 | $8,250 |
| American 1847-1928 | | | |
| ☐ **BLACKMAN, William** ................... *paintings* | | | $247 |
| American 20th cent. | | | |
| ☐ **BLACKMORE, Edward** .................. *paintings* | | | $605 |
| ☐ **BLAGDEN, Allen** ........................ *drawings* | | $770 | $1,870 |
| American | | | |
| ☐ **BLAIN, P.** ................................. *paintings* | | | $522 |
| 19th cent. | | | |
| ☐ **BLAINE, Nell** ............................ *paintings* | | | $2,310 |
| American b. 1922 ........................... *drawings* | | | $302 |
| ☐ **BLAIR, Robert H.** ...................... *paintings* | | | $700 |
| American b. c. 1937 ........................ *drawings* | | | $1,400 |
| ☐ **BLAIR, Streeter** ........................ *paintings* | | $137 | $3,960 |
| American 1888-1966 | | | |
| ☐ **BLAIRAT, Marcel** ........................ *drawings* | | | $275 |

|                                  |          | Current Price Range |          |
|----------------------------------|----------|--------|----------|
|                                  |          | Low    | High     |
| ☐ **BLAIS, B. de** .................................... *paintings* |          |        | $300     |
| ☐ **BLAISE, Saint Louis** ........................... *paintings* |          | $550   | $2,640   |
| ☐ **BLAKE, A.** ......................................... *paintings* |          |        | $357     |
| English 19th cent.               |          |        |          |
| ☐ **BLAKE, Benjamin** ............................ *paintings* |          |        | $1,650   |
| British d. 1830                  |          |        |          |
| ☐ **BLAKE, James** .................................... *paintings* |          |        | $935     |
| ☐ **BLAKE, Leo B.** ................................. *paintings* |          | $192   | $990     |
| American                         |          |        |          |
| ☐ **BLAKE, T.** ......................................... *paintings* |          |        | $35,000  |
| British ac. 1829-1839            |          |        |          |
| ☐ **BLAKE, Thomas C.** ........................... *paintings* |          | $94    | $191     |
| Scottish b. 1890                 |          |        |          |
| ☐ **BLAKE, William** ............................... *drawings* |          |        | $4,730   |
| British 1757-1827                |          |        |          |
| ☐ **BLAKELOCK, Ralph Albert** ............... *paintings* |          | $275   | $33,000  |
| American 1847-1919               |          |        |          |
| ☐ **BLAKESLEE, Frederick** ...................... *paintings* |          | $82    | $275     |
| American 20th cent.              |          |        |          |
| ☐ **BLAKESLEE, W.H.** ............................ *paintings* |          |        | $412     |
| American 19th cent.              |          |        |          |
| ☐ **BLAMANN, M.** .................................... *paintings* |          |        | $1,650   |
| ☐ **BLAMPIED, Edmund** .......................... *paintings* |          | $495   | $1,210   |
| English 1886-1966 .................................... *drawings* |          |        | $825     |
| ☐ **BLANC, J.N. la** .................................. *paintings* |          |        | $440     |
| ☐ **BLANCH, Arnold** .............................. *paintings* |          | $187   | $990     |
| American 1896-1968               |          |        |          |
| ☐ **BLANCH, Ventura** ............................. *paintings* |          |        | $440     |
| Spanish 19th/20th cent.          |          |        |          |
| ☐ **BLANCHARD, Antoine** ....................... *paintings* |          | $165   | $2,750   |
| French 20th cent.                |          |        |          |
| ☐ **BLANCHARD, Blanche** ....................... *paintings* |          |        | $1,100   |
| American 1866-1959               |          |        |          |
| ☐ **BLANCHARD, Carol** .......................... *paintings* |          |        | $264     |
| American                         |          |        |          |
| ☐ **BLANCHARD, Charles** ........................ *paintings* |          |        | $412     |
| 19th cent.                       |          |        |          |
| ☐ **BLANCHARD, Maria** .......................... *paintings* |          | $14,300 | $37,400 |
| Spanish/French 1881-1932         |          |        |          |
| ☐ **BLANCHARD, Sisson** .......................... *paintings* |          | $247   | $412     |
| ☐ **BLANCHE, Jacques Emile** ................... *paintings* |          | $440   | $7,260   |
| French 1861-1942                 |          |        |          |
| ☐ **BLANCHE, V.E.** ................................. *paintings* |          |        | $825     |
| ☐ **BLANCO, Ramos** ............................... *sculpture* |          |        | $1,210   |
| Cuban                            |          |        |          |
| ☐ **BLANCPAIN, Jules** ............................ *paintings* |          |        | $4,675   |
| Swiss b. 1860                    |          |        |          |
| ☐ **BLANDY, L.V.** .................................... *paintings* |          |        | $220     |
| English 19th cent.               |          |        |          |

| | | | Current Price Range | |
|---|---|---|---|---|
| | | | *Low* | *High* |
| ☐ **BLANES, Juan M.** | .............................. *paintings* | | | **$4,675** |
| Uruguayan 1830-1901 | | | | |
| ☐ **BLANEY, Dwight** | ................................ *paintings* | | | **$198** |
| American | | | | |
| ☐ **BLANK, E. Beatrice** | ............................ *paintings* | | | **$352** |
| ☐ **BLANK, J.** | ............................................ *paintings* | | | **$1,650** |
| ☐ **BLANKENSHIP, Roy** | .......................... *paintings* | | **$300** | **$935** |
| American b. 1943 | | | | |
| ☐ **BLANKERHOFF, Jan Theunisz.** | ........... *paintings* | | | **$17,600** |
| Dutch 1628-1669 | | | | |
| ☐ **BLARENBERGHE, Henri Desire van** | .... *drawings* | | | **$1,210** |
| French 1734-1812 | | | | |
| ☐ **BLARENBERGHE, Louis Nicolas van** | ... *paintings* | | **$1,800** | **$14,300** |
| French 1716-1794 | ................................. *drawings* | | **$4,400** | **$8,250** |
| ☐ **BLAS, L. O.** | ...................................... *drawings* | | **$550** | **$1,100** |
| Italian 19th cent. | | | | |
| ☐ **BLASHFIELD, Edwin Howland** | ............ *paintings* | | **$770** | **$39,600** |
| American 1848-1936 | ................................. *drawings* | | **$242** | **$1,100** |
| ☐ **BLASHKI, M.E.** | ................................ *paintings* | | | **$660** |
| American 19th cent. | | | | |
| ☐ **BLASS, Charlotte L.** | ........................... *paintings* | | **$60** | **$275** |
| American b. 1908 | | | | |
| ☐ **BLASSET, E.** | ...................................... *paintings* | | | **$1,000** |
| French 19th cent. | | | | |
| ☐ **BLATAS, Arbit** | ................................. *paintings* | | **$220** | **$3,300** |
| Lithuanian b. 1908 | ...................................... *drawings* | | **$165** | **$356** |
| | ................................................... *sculpture* | | **$1,320** | **$2,640** |
| ☐ **BLATTER, Bruno** | ............................ *paintings* | | **$550** | **$825** |
| German 19th cent. | | | | |
| ☐ **BLATTER, Vincent** | ........................... *drawings* | | | **$385** |
| French (?) b. 1843 | | | | |
| ☐ **BLAU-LANG, Tina** | ........................... *paintings* | | | **$6,325** |
| Austrian 1845-1937 | | | | |
| ☐ **BLAUVELT, Charles F.** | ....................... *paintings* | | **$550** | **$2,750** |
| American 1824-1900 | | | | |
| ☐ **BLAZEBY, James** | ............................. *paintings* | | | **$3,025** |
| British 19th cent. | | | | |
| ☐ **BLECKNER, Ross** | ............................. *paintings* | | | **$2,310** |
| ☐ **BLEECK, Peter de** | ............................ *paintings* | | | **$880** |
| Dutch 1700-1764 | | | | |
| ☐ **BLEIMAN, Max** | ............................... *paintings* | | **$192** | **$495** |
| American 19th/20th cent. | | | | |
| ☐ **BLEIMANN, M.** | ................................ *paintings* | | | **$2,530** |
| ☐ **BLENNER, Carle John** | ........................ *paintings* | | **$220** | **$8,140** |
| American 1864-1952 | | | | |
| ☐ **BLENY, Jacques** | ................................ *paintings* | | | **$247** |
| French 1925-1960 | | | | |

| | | Current Price Range | |
|---|---|---|---|
| | | Low | High |
| ☐ **BLES, Hendrik Met de** (called **CIVETTA in Italy**) ...... *paintings* Flemish c. 1480/1500-after 1550 | | $4,180 | $52,500 |
| ☐ **BLES, Joseph** ............ *paintings* Dutch 1792-1883 | | | $2,420 |
| ☐ **BLEYFUS, Lucien** ......... *paintings* French 20th cent. | | | $605 |
| ☐ **BLIECK, Daniel de** ......... *paintings* Dutch d. 1673 | | | $3,300 |
| ☐ **BLIGNY, Albert** ......... *paintings* French 1849-1908 | | | $605 |
| ☐ **BLIN, Francis** ......... *paintings* French 1827-1866 | | $412 | $440 |
| ☐ **BLINKS, Thomas** ......... *paintings* English 1860-1912 | | $605 | $3,520 |
| ☐ **BLISS, Robert R.** ......... *paintings* American 1925-after 1950's | | $44 | $1,045 |
| ☐ **BLOCH, Albert** ......... *drawings* American 1882-1961 | | | $1,100 |
| ☐ **BLOCH, Alexandre** ......... *paintings* French 20th cent. | | | $275 |
| ☐ **BLOCH, Julius Thiengen** ...... *paintings* German/American 1888-1966 ......... *drawings* | | $412 | $660 $77 |
| ☐ **BLOCK, Eugenius Franz de** ...... *paintings* Belgian 1812-1893 | | | $605 |
| ☐ **BLOCK, Joseph** ......... *paintings* German b. 1863 | | $605 | $4,620 ⸳ |
| ☐ **BLOCKLANDT, Anthonie van Montfoort** ......... *paintings* Dutch 1532/34-1583 | | | $4,950 |
| ☐ **BLODGETT, Walton** ......... *drawings* American b. 1908 | | $220 | $770 |
| ☐ **BLOEM, Mathias** ......... *paintings* Dutch 17th cent. | | | $3,300 |
| ☐ **BLOEMAERT, Abraham** ...... *paintings* Dutch c. 1564-1651 ......... *drawings* | | $660 | $2,090 $4,400 |
| ☐ **BLOEMAERT, Hendrick** ...... *paintings* Dutch 1601-1672 | | | $5,500 |
| ☐ **BLOEMAERT, Matthew** ...... *paintings* | | $3,300 | $4,125 |
| ☐ **BLOEMEN, Jan Frans van** (called **ORIZONTE**) ......... *paintings* Flemish 1662-1749 | | $2,200 | $30,000 |
| ☐ **BLOEMEN, Pieter van** ...... *paintings* Flemish c. 1657-1720 | | $660 | $3,960 |
| ☐ **BLOEMERS, Arnoldus** ......... *paintings* Dutch 1792-1844 | | $17,600 | $19,800 |
| ☐ **BLOK, J.** ......... *paintings* | | | $330 |

| | | Current Price Range | |
|---|---|---|---|
| | | Low | High |

| | | | Low | High |
|---|---|---|---|---|
| ☐ **BLOM,** | | | | |
| **Jan and Johannes LINGLEBACH** | .......... *paintings* | | | $6,600 |
| Dutch 17th cent. | | | | |
| ☐ **BLOMFIELD, Charles** | ....................... *paintings* | | | $2,090 |
| British 19th cent. | | | | |
| ☐ **BLOMFIELD, G.** | ............................... *paintings* | | | $605 |
| American 19th cent. | | | | |
| ☐ **BLOMMERS, Arnoldus** | ....................... *paintings* | | | $9,350 |
| Dutch 19th cent. | | | | |
| ☐ **BLOMMERS, Bernardus Johannes** | ....... *paintings* | | $474 | $13,200 |
| Dutch 1845-1914 | .............................................. *drawings* | | $660 | $1,870 |
| ☐ **BLONDEAU, Paul** | ............................. *paintings* | | | $4,180 |
| French 19th cent. | .................................... *drawings* | | | $357 |
| ☐ **BLONDEL, Georges Francois** | .............. *drawings* | | | $550 |
| French 1730-after 1791 | | | | |
| ☐ **BLONDEL, Jacques Francois** | ................ *drawings* | | | $1,045 |
| Dutch 1705-1774 | | | | |
| ☐ **BLONDELL, Jacob D.** | .......................... *paintings* | | | $880 |
| ☐ **BLONDIN, Charles** | ............................. *paintings* | | $44 | $715 |
| French 20th cent. | | | | |
| ☐ **BLONDIN, Marie Louise** | ....................... *paintings* | | | $247 |
| French 20th cent. | | | | |
| ☐ **BLOODGOOD, M. Seymour** | ................ *paintings* | | | $495 |
| English late 19th cent. | | | | |
| ☐ **BLOODGOOD, Robert F.** | ....................... *drawings* | | $66 | $220 |
| American 19th/20th cent. | | | | |
| ☐ **BLOOM, Hyman** | ................................. *paintings* | | $5,500 | $7,700 |
| American b. 1913 | ................................... *drawings* | | $176 | $715 |
| ☐ **BLOOMER, Hiram Reynolds** | ................ *paintings* | | $192 | $1,100 |
| American 1845-1910/11 | | | | |
| ☐ **BLOOMSTER, E.I.** | ............................. *drawings* | | | $550 |
| ☐ **BLOOT, Pieter de** | ............................... *paintings* | | $8,250 | $41,800 |
| Dutch c. 1602-1658 | | | | |
| ☐ **BLOSSOM, David** | ............................... *paintings* | | $137 | $467 |
| b. 1927 | | | | |
| ☐ **BLOT, Jacques** | ..................................... *paintings* | | | $330 |
| French 1885-1960 | | | | |
| ☐ **BLUEMNER, Oscar F.** | ........................ *paintings* | | $25,000 | $50,600 |
| German/American 1867-1938 | ......................... *drawings* | | $99 | $31,900 |
| ☐ **BLUHM, Norman** | ............................... *paintings* | | $660 | $9,900 |
| American b. 1920 | ................................... *drawings* | | $99 | $880 |
| ☐ **BLUM** | ................................................ *paintings* | | | $467 |
| American 20th cent. | | | | |
| ☐ **BLUM, Camille** | .................................... *paintings* | | | $440 |
| ☐ **BLUM, Jerome** | ................................... *paintings* | | $175 | $550 |
| American 1884-1956 | ................................ *drawings* | | | $143 |
| ☐ **BLUM, Ludwig** | .................................... *paintings* | | | $660 |
| Israeli 20th cent. | | | | |

## Themes

Themes of death and the darker
aspects of man's existence are
expressed in the works of Hyman
Bloom. He was born in Lithuania
and received his early art training at
a settlement house in Boston.
During the Depression, he worked
as a WPA artist, and in the 1950s
he taught at Wellesley and Harvard.
"Harpies," completed in the 1920s,
focuses on Bloom's preoccupation
with death. This painting of the
winged creatures that carry off the
souls of the dead was exhibited in
Venice in 1930, at Harvard's Fogg
Museum, and at the California
Palace of Honor in 1949. (Hyman
Bloom, "The Harpies," oil on
canvas, 36 x 55½ in., Christie's
East, June 26, 1985, $5,500.)

|  | | Current Price Range | |
|---|---|---|---|
|  | | *Low* | *High* |
| ☐ **BLUM, Maurice** ............................. *paintings* | | $467 | $1,650 |
| French b. 1832 | | | |
| ☐ **BLUM, Robert Frederick** .................... *paintings* | | $4,180 | $52,800* |
| American 1857-1903 ............................. *drawings* | | $325 | $104,500 |
| ☐ **BLUMBERG, Yuli** ........................... *paintings* | | | $192 |
| American 20th cent. | | | |
| ☐ **BLUME, Edmund** ........................... *paintings* | | $660 | $2,750 |
| British b. 1844 | | | |
| ☐ **BLUME, Peter** ............................. *drawings* | | $275 | $770 |
| American b. 1906 | | | |
| ☐ **BLUMENSCHEIN,** | | | |
| **Mary Shepard Green** ........................ *paintings* | | $550 | $10,450 |
| American 1869-1958 | | | |

| | | Current Price Range | |
|---|---|---|---|
| | | Low | High |
| ☐ **BLUNT, John S.** ............................... *paintings* | | | **$14,300** |
| American 1798-1835 | | | |
| ☐ **BLYTHE, David Gilmour** ................ *paintings* | | **$4,950** | **$60,000** |
| American 1815-1865 | | | |
| ☐ **BOARDMAN, William G.** .................... *paintings* | | **$550** | **$1,650** |
| American 1815-1895 | | | |
| ☐ **BOBAREWSKI, N.** ............................ *paintings* | | | **$2,750** |
| Russian 19th cent. | | | |
| ☐ **BOBERG, Anna** ................................. *paintings* | | | **$330** |
| Swedish 1864-1935 | | | |
| ☐ **BOCCHI, Faustino** ............................ *paintings* | | | **$7,700** |
| Italian 1659-1742 | | | |
| ☐ **BOCCIA, Edward E.** ........................... *drawings* | | | **$330** |
| American contemporary | | | |
| ☐ **BOCCIONI, Umberto** ......................... *drawings* | | | **$2,860** |
| ☐ **BOCHMANN, Gregor Alexander von** | | | |
| **(Sr.)** ...................................................... *paintings* | | **$770** | **$6,600** |
| German 1850-1930 | | | |
| ☐ **BOCION, Francois Louis David** ............ *paintings* | | **$7,700** | **$8,250** |
| Swiss 1828-1890 | | | |
| ☐ **BOCK, Theophile Emile Achille de** ........ *paintings* | | **$440** | **$9,350** |
| Dutch 1851-1904 ......................................... *drawings* | | | **$715** |
| ☐ **BOCKLIN, Arnold** ............................. *paintings* | | | **$33,000** |
| Swiss 1827-1901 | | | |
| ☐ **BOCKLIN, Carlo** ................................ *paintings* | | | **$1,650** |
| Swiss b. 1870 | | | |
| ☐ **BOCKSBERGER, Johann Melchior** ...... *drawings* | | | **$2,200** |
| German 1540-1589 | | | |
| ☐ **BODAN, Andreas (the younger)** ............. *drawings* | | | **$1,650** |
| Alsatian 1656-1696 | | | |
| ☐ **BODDINGTON, Edwin H.** .................... *paintings* | | **$176** | **$4,400** |
| English 1836-c. 1905 | | | |
| ☐ **BODDINGTON, Henry John** ................. *paintings* | | **$825** | **$10,450** |
| English 1811-1865 | | | |
| ☐ **BODEGONES** ...................................... *paintings* | | | **$440** |
| ☐ **BODENHAUSEN, Cuno Von** ................ *paintings* | | | **$990** |
| German b. 1852 | | | |
| ☐ **BODENMULLER, Friedrich** ................. *paintings* | | **$2,100** | **$3,190** |
| German 1845-1913 | | | |
| ☐ **BODILY, Sherly L.** ............................. *paintings* | | | **$850** |
| American | | | |
| ☐ **BODLEY, Josselin** ............................. *paintings* | | | **$412** |
| British 20th cent. | | | |
| ☐ **BODMER, Karl** ................................. *paintings* | | | **$4,400** |
| Swiss 1809-1893 ......................................... *drawings* | | | **$187** |
| ☐ **BODWELL, A.V.** ................................ *paintings* | | | **$330** |
| American 20th cent. | | | |
| ☐ **BODYGUARD, W.J.** ........................... *paintings* | | | **$357** |
| ☐ **BOECKEL, Pieter van** ........................ *paintings* | | | **$5,280** |

|  | | Current Price Range | |
|---|---|---|---|
|  | | *Low* | *High* |
| ☐ **BOECKHORST, Jan van** ...... *paintings* | | | **$3,300** |
| German 1661-1724 | | | |
| ☐ **BOEHM, E.** ................... *paintings* | | **$160** | **$880** |
| ☐ **BOEHM, H.** ................... *paintings* | | | **$770** |
| ☐ **BOEHN, Wolfgang** ............ *paintings* | | | **$2,310** |
| British 19th cent. | | | |
| ☐ **BOESE, Henry** ............... *paintings* | | **$407** | **$3,520** |
| American 19th cent. | | | |
| ☐ **BOESE, T.** ................... *sculpture* | | | **$968** |
| ☐ **BOESSENECKER, J. Henri** ...... *paintings* | | **$187** | **$440** |
| ☐ **BOEUFF, Pierre le** ........... *paintings* | | | **$770** |
| French School late 19th cent. | | | |
| ☐ **BOEYERMANS, Theodor** ...... *paintings* | | **$7,150** | **$8,800** |
| Flemish 1620-1678 | | | |
| ☐ **BOFILL, Antoine** ............ *sculpture* | | **$110** | **$1,320** |
| Spanish ac. c. 1921 | | | |
| ☐ **BOGAERT, Hendricksz** ........ *paintings* | | | **$3,300** |
| Dutch 1626/7-after 1672 | | | |
| ☐ **BOGAERT, Martin van der** | | | |
| **(called DESJARDINS)** .......... *sculpture* | | | **$1,650** |
| French 19th cent. | | | |
| ☐ **BOGDANOFF-BJELSKI,** | | | |
| **Nikolai Petrowitsch** ........... *paintings* | | **$1,100** | **$12,100** |
| Russian 1868-1945 | | | |
| ☐ **BOGDANOVE, A.J.** ............ *paintings* | | | **$210** |
| Russian/American b. 1877-1941 | | | |
| ☐ **BOGDANY, Jakob** ............ *paintings* | | **$10,450** | **$18,700** |
| Hungarian 1660-1724 | | | |
| ☐ **BOGERT, George Hirst** ........ *paintings* | | **$250** | **$1,760** |
| American 1864-1944 | | | |
| ☐ **BOGGIO, Emilio** ............. *paintings* | | **$4,620** | **$66,000** |
| Venezuelan/French 1857-1920 | | | |
| ☐ **BOGGS, Frank Myers** ......... *paintings* | | **$825** | **$8,525** |
| American/French 1855-1926 ......... *drawings* | | **$240** | **$2,310** |
| ☐ **BOGHOSIAN, Varujan** ........ *drawings* | | | **$192** |
| American b. 1926 ................. *sculpture* | | | **$11,550** |
| ☐ **BOGOLIUBOV, Alexei** ........ *paintings* | | | **$3,190** |
| Russian 1824-1896 | | | |
| ☐ **BOGOMAZOV, Alexander** ...... *paintings* | | | **$15,400** |
| Russian b. 1880 ................. *drawings* | | **$770** | **$880** |
| ☐ **BOHANNON, Joseph S.** ........ *paintings* | | | **$411** |
| ☐ **BOHLER, Hans** ............ *paintings* | | | **$385** |
| American 20th cent. | | | |
| ☐ **BOHLER, Joseph** ............ *drawings* | | | **$1,350** |
| American | | | |
| ☐ **BOHM, F.W.** ................ *paintings* | | | **$522** |
| German (?) 19th cent. | | | |
| ☐ **BOHM, G.** ................... *paintings* | | | **$412** |

| | | *Current Price Range* | |
|---|---|---|---|
| | | *Low* | *High* |
| ☐ **BOHM, Max** ..................... *paintings* | | $522 | $2,640 |
| American 1868-1923 | | | |
| ☐ **BOHME, Karl** ..................... *paintings* | | $715 | $2,640 |
| German 1866-1939 | | | |
| ☐ **BOHR, Rudolf** ..................... *paintings* | | | $1,320 |
| Austrian School 19th cent. | | | |
| ☐ **BOHRMANN** ..................... *sculpture* | | | $330 |
| Austrian 20th cent. | | | |
| ☐ **BOHROD, Aaron** ................. *paintings* | | $385 | $7,700 |
| American b. 1907 ..................... *drawings* | | $192 | $2,090 |
| ☐ **BOICHARD, Georges Lucien** ........ *paintings* | | $605 | $2,530 |
| French 19th cent. | | | |
| ☐ **BOILAUGES, F.** ..................... *paintings* | | | $605 |
| ☐ **BOILAUGES, Fernand** ........... *paintings* | | $605 | $1,540 |
| French b. 1891 ..................... *drawings* | | | $2,640 |
| ☐ **BOILEAU, Philip** ............... *paintings* | | $150 | $1,980 |
| Canadian 1864-1917 ............... *drawings* | | | $850 |
| ☐ **BOILLY, Louis Leopold** ......... *paintings* | | $1,100 | $46,750 |
| French 1761-1845 ..................... *drawings* | | $605 | $16,500 |
| ☐ **BOISGONTIER, Henri** ........... *paintings* | | | $440 |
| French 1850-1940 | | | |
| ☐ **BOISSEAU, Emile Andre** ........ *sculpture* | | $750 | $1,100 |
| French 1842-1923 | | | |
| ☐ **BOISSELIER, Antoine Felix** ...... *drawings* | | | $220 |
| French 1790-1857 | | | |
| ☐ **BOISSIEU, I.I.** ..................... *paintings* | | | $264 |
| ☐ **BOISSIEU, Jean Jacques de** ...... *drawings* | | | $2,750 |
| French 1736-1810 | | | |
| ☐ **BOISSONAS, B.** ..................... *drawings* | | | $550 |
| ☐ **BOIT, Edward Darley** ........... *drawings* | | $352 | $2,000 |
| American 1840-1915 | | | |
| ☐ **BOIT, Julia Overing** ............ *drawings* | | $165 | $467 |
| American 20th cent. | | | |
| ☐ **BOITARD, Francois** ............. *drawings* | | $396 | $660 |
| Dutch c. 1670-c. 1715 | | | |
| ☐ **BOITEL, Maurice** ............... *paintings* | | | $495 |
| French b. 1919 | | | |
| ☐ **BOITTE, Louis** ..................... *drawings* | | | $550 |
| ☐ **BOIZARD, C.U.** ..................... *paintings* | | | $495 |
| American 19th cent. | | | |
| ☐ **BOIZOT, Simon Louis** ........... *drawings* | | | $825 |
| French 1743-1809 | | | |
| ☐ **BOKER, Carl** ..................... *paintings* | | | $17,600 |
| German 1836-1905 | | | |
| ☐ **BOKER, Edmund** ............... *paintings* | | $275 | $577 |
| German 19th cent. | | | |
| ☐ **BOKHORST, H.G.** ............... *paintings* | | | $330 |
| German early 20th cent. | | | |

|  | | *Current Price Range* | |
|---|---|---|---|
|  | | *Low* | *High* |
| ☐ **BOKHUYZEN, Lidolf** ............... *paintings* | | | $550 |
| Dutch 1631-1708 | | | |
| ☐ **BOKS, Evert Jan** ............... *paintings* | | $10,450 | $44,000 |
| Dutch b. 1938 | | | |
| ☐ **BOL, A. (?)** ............... *paintings* | | $275 | $385 |
| Dutch 19th cent. | | | |
| ☐ **BOL, Ferdinand** ............... *paintings* | | $8,800 | $18,700 |
| Dutch 1616-1680 | | | |
| ☐ **BOLAND, Charles H. D.** ............... *paintings* | | | $660 |
| ☐ **BOLDINI, Giovanni** ............... *paintings* | | $11,000 | $198,000 |
| Italian 1842-1931 ............... *drawings* | | $825 | $22,000 |
| ☐ **BOLENDS** ............... *paintings* | | | $220 |
| American 20th cent. | | | |
| ☐ **BOLLES, Enoch** ............... *paintings* | | $1,100 | $1,980 |
| 20th cent. | | | |
| ☐ **BOLLES, Reginald Fairfax** ............... *paintings* | | $350 | $352 |
| American 20th cent. ............... *drawings* | | | $500 |
| ☐ **BOLLES, Robert** ............... *paintings* | | | $330 |
| American 20th cent. | | | |
| ☐ **BOLLONGIER, Hans** ............... *paintings* | | | $11,000 |
| Dutch 1600-1644 | | | |
| ☐ **BOLMER, M. De Forrest** ............... *paintings* | | | $935 |
| American 1854-1910 | | | |
| ☐ **BOLOTOWSKY, Ilya** ............... *paintings* | | $1,045 | $26,950 |
| Russian/American 1907-1981 ............... *drawings* | | $137 | $880 |
| ☐ **BOLPINI, A.** ............... *paintings* | | | $390 |
| ☐ **BOLSI, U.** ............... *paintings* | | | $742 |
| Italian 19th cent. | | | |
| ☐ **BOLSTER, Janette Wheeler** ............... *paintings* | | $250 | $325 |
| American 1821-1883 ............... *drawings* | | | $275 |
| ☐ **BOLTON, A.K.** ............... *paintings* | | $330 | $495 |
| American | | | |
| ☐ **BOMBLED, Karel Frederik** ............... *drawings* | | | $274 |
| Dutch 1822-1902 | | | |
| ☐ **BOMBLED, Louis Charles** ............... *paintings* | | $550 | $1,430 |
| French 1862-1927 ............... *drawings* | | | $275 |
| ☐ **BOMBOIS, Camille** ............... *paintings* | | $1,100 | $23,100 |
| French 1883-1970? | | | |
| ☐ **BOMHALS, Charles** ............... *paintings* | | | $385 |
| ☐ **BOMMEN, E. van** ............... *paintings* | | $880 | $1,100 |
| ☐ **BOMPARD, Maurice** ............... *paintings* | | $110 | $1,870 |
| French 1857-1936 | | | |
| ☐ **BOMPIANA, Antonio** ............... *drawings* | | | $264 |
| ☐ **BOMPIANI, Roberto** ............... *paintings* | | | $2,530 |
| Italian 1821-1908 | | | |
| ☐ **BOMPIANI-BATTAGLIA, Cecelia** ............... *drawings* | | | $450 |
| Italian 1847-1927 | | | |
| ☐ **BONACINO, G.** ............... *paintings* | | | $1,100 |
| Italian 19th cent. | | | |

| | | *Current Price Range* | |
|---|---|---|---|
| | | Low | High |
| ☐ **BONAMICI, A.** ............... *paintings* | | | $550 |
| Italian 20th cent. | | | |
| ☐ **BONAMICI, Louis** ............ *paintings* | | | $412 |
| French ac. 1930 | | | |
| ☐ **BONANNI, E.** ................. *drawings* | | $660 | $1,870 |
| Italian 19th cent. | | | |
| ☐ **BONANNO (?), A.** ............ *paintings* | | | $935 |
| American 19th cent. | | | |
| ☐ **BONAR, James** ............... *paintings* | | | $220 |
| American 20th cent. | | | |
| ☐ **BONASONE, Giulio** ........... *drawings* | | | $1,540 |
| ☐ **BONAVIA, Carlo** ............. *paintings* | | | $10,450 |
| Italian ac. 1740-1756 | | | |
| ☐ **BOND, Douglas** .............. *paintings* | | $605 | $2,420 |
| contemporary ...................... *drawings* | | | $550 |
| ☐ **BOND, Richard Sebastian** ........ *paintings* | | | $412 |
| British 1808-1866 | | | |
| ☐ **BOND, William J.J.C.** ......... *paintings* | | $247 | $440 |
| English 1833-1926/28 | | | |
| ☐ **BONDI** ...................... *paintings* | | | $412 |
| ☐ **BONDOUX, Jules George** ....... *paintings* | | | $2,420 |
| European | | | |
| ☐ **BONE, Sir Muirhead** ........... *drawings* | | $110 | $1,650 |
| Scottish 1876-1953 | | | |
| ☐ **BONELLI, G.** ................ *paintings* | | $990 | $1,100 |
| Italian 19th cent. | | | |
| ☐ **BONEVARDI, Marcelo** .......... *paintings* | | $5,500 | $12,100 |
| Argentinian b. 1929 ................ *drawings* | | $935 | $5,500 |
| ☐ **BONFIELD, George Robert** ........ *paintings* | | $220 | $6,325 |
| American 1802-1898 | | | |
| ☐ **BONFIELD, William van de Velde** ....... *paintings* | | $631 | $880 |
| American 19th cent. ................ *drawings* | | $231 | $350 |
| ☐ **BONFILS, Gaston** ............. *paintings* | | | $2,750 |
| French 19th cent. | | | |
| ☐ **BONGART, Sergei R.** .......... *paintings* | | $220 | $660 |
| Russian/American b. 1918 | | | |
| ☐ **BONGEY, H.** ................. *paintings* | | | $577 |
| French 19th cent. | | | |
| ☐ **BONGHI, A.** ................. *paintings* | | | $330 |
| Italian school 19th cent. | | | |
| ☐ **BONHEUR, Auguste** ........... *paintings* | | $770 | $2,475 |
| French 1824-1884 | | | |
| ☐ **BONHEUR, Ferdinand** ......... *paintings* | | $412 | $990 |
| French 19th cent. | | | |
| ☐ **BONHEUR, Isidore Jules** ....... *sculpture* | | $467 | $22,000 |
| French 1827-1901 | | | |
| ☐ **BONHEUR, Juliette** ........... *paintings* | | | $1,650 |
| French 1830-1891 | | | |

| | | *Current Price Range* | |
|---|---|---|---|
| | | *Low* | *High* |
| ☐ **BONHEUR, Rosa** .............................. *paintings* | | $350 | $11,550 |
| French 1822-1899 ..................................... *drawings* | | $165 | $3,630 |
| ...................................................... *sculpture* | | $467 | $770 |
| ☐ **BONHOMME, Leon** ........................... *drawings* | | $88 | $1,430 |
| French 1870-1924 | | | |
| ☐ **BONI, E.** ............................................ *drawings* | | | $412 |
| Italian 19th cent. | | | |
| ☐ **BONIFANTI, Decoroso** ....................... *paintings* | | | $660 |
| Italian 1860-1941 | | | |
| ☐ **BONIFAZI, Adriano** ........................... *paintings* | | $660 | $1,430 |
| Italian 19th cent. | | | |
| ☐ **BONINGTON, Richard** ........................ *paintings* | | $302 | $330 |
| English 19th cent. | | | |
| ☐ **BONINGTON, Richard Parkes** ............. *paintings* | | $1,500 | $33,000 |
| English 1801-1828 ..................................... *drawings* | | | $1,650 |
| ☐ **BONITO, Giuseppe** ........................... *paintings* | | | $10,450 |
| Italian 1705-1789 | | | |
| ☐ **BONJOUR, David** .............................. *paintings* | | | $467 |
| Swiss 19th cent. | | | |
| ☐ **BONNARD, Pierre** ............................. *paintings* | | $17,600 | $462,000 |
| French 1867-1947 ..................................... *drawings* | | $357 | $50,600 |
| ☐ **BONNAT, Leon Joseph Florentin** .......... *paintings* | | $385 | $8,800 |
| French 1833-1922 | | | |
| ☐ **BONNECHOSE, R.** ............................ *paintings* | | | $935 |
| French 19th cent. | | | |
| ☐ **BONNEFOY, Henri Arthur** ................. *paintings* | | | $1,100 |
| French 1839-1917 | | | |
| ☐ **BONNELLI, C.** .................................... *paintings* | | | $440 |
| contemporary | | | |
| ☐ **BONNENCONTRE, Ernest Courtois** ..... *drawings* | | $330 | $1,320 |
| French 19th/20th cent. | | | |
| ☐ **BONNET, Leon** ................................. *paintings* | | $187 | $935 |
| American late 19th/20th cent.13 | | | |
| ☐ **BONNET, Maurice S. de** ...................... *drawings* | | | $192 |
| b. 1871 | | | |
| ☐ **BONNIER, G.** .................................... *paintings* | | | $3,080 |
| French 19th cent. | | | |
| ☐ **BONOME** ......................................... *sculpture* | | | $550 |
| French | | | |
| ☐ **BONOME, Adolphine** ........................ *paintings* | | | $467 |
| French 19th cent. | | | |
| ☐ **BONPENSTERE, L.** ........................... *paintings* | | | $528 |
| ☐ **BONSALL, Elizabeth F.** ..................... *drawings* | | | $418 |
| American | | | |
| ☐ **BONSI, Giovanni** ............................... *paintings* | | | $41,250 |
| Italian ac. 14th cent. | | | |
| ☐ **BONTE, Paula** .................................. *paintings* | | | $660 |
| ☐ **BONTECOU, Lee** ............................... *drawings* | | $440 | $528 |
| American b. 1931 ..................................... *sculpture* | | $3,740 | $4,950 |

| | | | Current Price Range | |
| --- | --- | --- | --- | --- |
| | | | Low | High |
| ☐ **BONTEMPI, E.** ..................................... | *paintings* | | $209 | $374 |
| 19th/20th cent. | | | | |
| ☐ **BONTOIT, Louis** .............................. | *paintings* | | | $308 |
| ☐ **BONVIN, Francois** ........................... | *paintings* | | $2,310 | $12,100 |
| French 1817-1887 ..................................... | *drawings* | | | $1,760 |
| ☐ **BOOG, Carle Michel** ........................... | *paintings* | | $154 | $1,320 |
| Swiss/American b. 1877 | | | | |
| ☐ **BOOGAARD, Willem Jacobus** .............. | *paintings* | | $660 | $5,775 |
| Dutch 1842-1887 | | | | |
| ☐ **BOOKATZ, Samuel** ............................. | *paintings* | | | $1,980 |
| American 20th cent. | | | | |
| ☐ **BOONE, E.** ......................................... | *paintings* | | | $357 |
| ☐ **BOONEN, Arnold** .............................. | *paintings* | | | $770 |
| Dutch 1669-1729 | | | | |
| ☐ **BOOTH, Cameron** .............................. | *paintings* | | | $352 |
| ☐ **BOOTH, Franklin E.** ........................... | *paintings* | | $110 | $302 |
| American 1874-1948 .................................. | *drawings* | | $550 | $1,320 |
| ☐ **BOOTH, S.L.** ..................................... | *paintings* | | $220 | $715 |
| English 19th/20th cent. .............................. | *drawings* | | | $50 |
| ☐ **BOOTHE** ............................................. | *paintings* | | | $220 |
| American 20th cent. | | | | |
| ☐ **BOPILL (?), A.** ................................... | *sculpture* | | | $605 |
| ☐ **BORACK, Stanley** ............................... | *drawings* | | $165 | $302 |
| ☐ **BORANDA, Lester D.** .......................... | *paintings* | | $165 | $880 |
| American b. 1886 | | | | |
| ☐ **BORBELY, M.** ..................................... | *paintings* | | | $330 |
| ☐ **BORBINO, J.** ..................................... | *paintings* | | | $1,000 |
| Italian/American 1905-1964 | | | | |
| ☐ **BORDENAVE, Pierre** .......................... | *paintings* | | $247 | $550 |
| French 19th/20th cent. | | | | |
| ☐ **BORDONE, Paris** ............................... | *paintings* | | | $1,430 |
| Italian 1500-1571 | | | | |
| ☐ **BOREIN, John Edward (or Edward)** ...... | *paintings* | | $742 | $12,100 |
| American 1872-1943 .................................. | *drawings* | | $137 | $26,400 |
| ☐ **BORELY, Jean Baptiste** ........................ | *paintings* | | | $1,540 |
| French 1776-1823 | | | | |
| ☐ **BOREN, James** ................................... | *paintings* | | $6,050 | $35,000 |
| American b. 1921 ..................................... | *drawings* | | $2,500 | $20,000 |
| ☐ **BOREN, Nancy** ................................... | *paintings* | | | $5,500 |
| American contemporary ............................. | *drawings* | | $450 | $650 |
| ☐ **BORES, Francisco** .............................. | *paintings* | | $660 | $3,025 |
| Spanish 1898-1972 .................................... | *drawings* | | | $385 |
| ☐ **BORG, Axel Leonard** .......................... | *paintings* | | | $550 |
| Swedish b. 1847 ....................................... | *drawings* | | | $33 |
| ☐ **BORG, Carl Oscar** .............................. | *paintings* | | $550 | $13,000 |
| American 1879-1947 .................................. | *drawings* | | $137 | $4,400 |
| ☐ **BORGELLA, Frederic** .......................... | *paintings* | | $528 | $660 |
| French 19th cent. | | | | |

| | | | Current Price Range | |
| | | | Low | High |
|---|---|---|---|---|
| ☐ **BORGES, Jacobo** ............................ *drawings* | | | $1,870 | $2,200 |
| Venezuelan b. 1931 | | | | |
| ☐ **BORGET, Auguste** ........................... *drawings* | | | | $660 |
| ☐ **BORGLUM, Gutzon** .......................... *sculpture* | | | $121 | $8,800 |
| American 1867-1941 | | | | |
| ☐ **BORGLUM, Solon Hannibal** ............... *sculpture* | | | $6,600 | $88,000 |
| American 1868-1922 | | | | |
| ☐ **BORGMANN, Paul** .......................... *paintings* | | | | $1,540 |
| German b. 1851 | | | | |
| ☐ **BORGO, Louis** ................................. *paintings* | | | | $192 |
| American b. 1867 | | | | |
| ☐ **BORGORD, Martin** .......................... *paintings* | | | $225 | $1,540 |
| American 1869-1935 | | | | |
| ☐ **BORGRAF, Diego de** ......................... *paintings* | | | | $3,520 |
| ☐ **BORI, I.** ......................................... *sculpture* | | | | $770 |
| ☐ **BORIE, Adolphe** .............................. *paintings* | | | $308 | $13,200 |
| American 1877-1934 | | | | |
| ☐ **BORIEU, J.** ....................................... *paintings* | | | | $264 |
| ☐ **BORIN, F.** ....................................... *paintings* | | | | $330 |
| ☐ **BORIONE, Bernard Louis** ................... *paintings* | | | $1,320 | $3,850 |
| French b. 1865 ...................................... *drawings* | | | $325 | $605 |
| ☐ **BORNOIN, Henri Alphonse** ................. *paintings* | | | | $1,430 |
| French 20th cent. | | | | |
| ☐ **BORNOZI** ...................................... *paintings* | | | | $385 |
| Italian 19th/20th cent. | | | | |
| ☐ **BOROFSKY, Jon** .............................. *drawings* | | | $4,180 | $14,850 |
| American b. 1942 | | | | |
| ☐ **BORONDA, Lester D.** ......................... *paintings* | | | $247 | $1,045 |
| American 1886-1951 | | | | |
| ☐ **BOROVIKOVSKY, Vladimir Lukitch** ... *paintings* | | | | $1,430 |
| Russian 1757-1825 | | | | |
| ☐ **BORRAS Y ABELLA, Vicente** ............. *paintings* | | | | $1,540 |
| Spanish 19th cent. | | | | |
| ☐ **BORREL, J.B.** ................................. *drawings* | | | | $330 |
| ☐ **BORRERO, R.** ................................. *paintings* | | | $92 | $301 |
| Spanish 19th cent. | | | | |
| ☐ **BORRIS, C.** .................................... *paintings* | | | | $200 |
| 19th cent. | | | | |
| ☐ **BORRMEISTER, Ralph** ....................... *paintings* | | | $357 | $715 |
| ☐ **BORSA** ........................................... *sculpture* | | | | $1,100 |
| ☐ **BORSATO, A. (the elder)** .................... *paintings* | | | | $660 |
| .......................................................... *sculpture* | | | $275 | $440 |
| ☐ **BORSELEN, Jan Willem van** ............... *paintings* | | | | $495 |
| Dutch 1825-1892 | | | | |
| ☐ **BORSTEL, R.A.** ............................... *paintings* | | | | $2,000 |
| ☐ **BORTOLUZZI, Millo** .......................... *paintings* | | | | $1,320 |
| Italian 1868-1933 | | | | |
| ☐ **BOS, Georges van den** ........................ *paintings* | | | $990 | $3,300 |
| Belgian 1835-1911 | | | | |

| | | Current Price Range | |
|---|---|---|---|
| | | Low | High |
| ☐ **BOS, Henk** .......................................... paintings | | $467 | $1,210 |
| Dutch b. 1901 | | | |
| ☐ **BOS, J.** ................................................. paintings | | | $660 |
| American 19th cent. | | | |
| ☐ **BOSA, Louis** ........................................ paintings | | $77 | $1,760 |
| Italian/American b. 1905 .............................. drawings | | $77 | $1,320 |
| ☐ **BOSBOOM, Johannes** ........................ paintings | | $550 | $6,050 |
| Dutch 1817-1891 ....................................... drawings | | | $440 |
| ☐ **BOSCH, Ernst** ..................................... paintings | | | $7,150 |
| ☐ **BOSCH, Hendrick** .............................. paintings | | $990 | $1,650 |
| Dutch 17th cent. | | | |
| ☐ **BOSCHER, Ferdinand Jean Edouard** .... drawings | | $132 | $412 |
| French b. 1888 | | | |
| ☐ **BOSCHETTI, B.** ................................... sculpture | | | $412 |
| Italian 20th cent. | | | |
| ☐ **BOSCHETTO, Giuseppe** ....................... paintings | | $495 | $1,980 |
| Italian 1841-1918 | | | |
| ☐ **BOSCHI, Fabrizio** .............................. paintings | | | $4,400 |
| Italian c. 1570-1642 | | | |
| ☐ **BOSELLI, Felice** ............................... paintings | | | $4,400 |
| Italian 1650-1732 | | | |
| ☐ **BOSER, Karl Friedrich Adolf** .............. paintings | | | $11,000 |
| German 1809-1881 | | | |
| ☐ **BOSHAMER, Jan Hendirk** ................... paintings | | | $1,760 |
| Dutch b. 1775 | | | |
| ☐ **BOSIO, Baron Francois Joseph** ............ sculpture | | $550 | $2,200 |
| French 1768-1845 | | | |
| ☐ **BOSIO, Jean Francois** ......................... paintings | | | $3,300 |
| French 1767-1827 ...................................... drawings | | | $5,775 |
| ☐ **BOSKERCK, Robert Ward van** ............ paintings | | $302 | $7,150 |
| American 1855-1932 ................................... drawings | | | $302 |
| ☐ **BOSMAN, Richard** .............................. paintings | | | $12,650 |
| contemporary | | | |
| ☐ **BOSS, Henry Wolcott** ......................... paintings | | | $675 |
| American 1820-1916 | | | |
| ☐ **BOSS, Homer** ..................................... paintings | | | $385 |
| American b. 1882 | | | |
| ☐ **BOSS, T.** ............................................. paintings | | | $715 |
| American 19th cent. | | | |
| ☐ **BOSSCHAERT, Ambrosius** | | | |
| **(the Elder)** ......................................... paintings | | | $132,000 |
| Flemish 1573-1621 | | | |
| ☐ **BOSSCHAERT, Jan Baptiste** ............... paintings | | $2,970 | $26,400 |
| Flemish 1667-1746 | | | |
| ☐ **BOSSCHE, Balthasar van den** .............. paintings | | $2,750 | $3,300 |
| Flemish 1681-1715 | | | |
| ☐ **BOSSHART, A.A.** ............................... paintings | | $66 | $231 |
| American 20th cent. | | | |

|                                          |            | Current Price Range | |
|------------------------------------------|------------|---------|-----------|
|                                          |            | Low     | High      |
| ☐ **BOSSI, Domenico** .................. *drawings* |            |         | $341      |
| Italian 1765-1853                        |            |         |           |
| ☐ **BOSSONE, Carlo** .................. *paintings* |            | $121    | $302      |
| ☐ **BOSSUET, Francois Antoine** ........ *paintings* |            |         | $11,000   |
| Belgian 1800-1889                        |            |         |           |
| ☐ **BOSTON, F.D.** .................. *paintings* |            |         | $466      |
| American 20th cent.                      |            |         |           |
| ☐ **BOSTON, Frederick James** ......... *paintings* |            | $301    | $2,200    |
| American 1855-1932                       |            |         |           |
| ☐ **BOSTON, Joseph H.** ............ *paintings* |            | $55     | $2,090    |
| American 19th/20th cent.                 |            |         |           |
| ☐ **BOTELLO** .................. *paintings* |            |         | $715      |
| Puerto Rican contemporary                |            |         |           |
| ☐ **BOTERO, Fernando** ............ *paintings* |            | $8,250  | $242,000  |
| Colombian b. 1932 .................. *drawings* |            | $1,375  | $52,250   |
| .................. *sculpture* |            | $3,850  | $82,500   |
| ☐ **BOTH, Jan and Nicolaes BERCHEM** .... *paintings* |            |         | $30,800   |
| Dutch 17th cent.                         |            |         |           |
| ☐ **BOTHUM, J. Shirley** ........... *sculpture* |            | $385    | $770      |
| American 20th cent.                      |            |         |           |
| ☐ **BOTKE, Cornelius** ............ *paintings* |            | $302    | $1,540    |
| American 1887-1954                       |            |         |           |
| ☐ **BOTKE, Jessie Arms** .......... *paintings* |            | $715    | $9,350    |
| American 1883-1971 .................. *drawings* |            |         | $2,475    |
| ☐ **BOTKIN, Henry** ............ *paintings* |            | $110    | $330      |
| American b. 1896 .................. *drawings* |            |         | $330      |
| ☐ **BOTT, E.F.E.V.** ............ *paintings* |            | $825    | $935      |
| American 19th cent.                      |            |         |           |
| ☐ **BOTT, Francis** .................. *paintings* |            |         | $825      |
| German b. 1904                           |            |         |           |
| ☐ **BOTT, R.T.** .................. *paintings* |            | $2,090  | $18,700   |
| British ac. 1847-1862                    |            |         |           |
| ☐ **BOTTEX, Seymour E.** .......... *paintings* |            | $330    | $1,100    |
| ☐ **BOTTHGONG** .................. *paintings* |            |         | $660      |
| ☐ **BOTTI, A.** .................. *paintings* |            |         | $522      |
| Italian 20th cent.                       |            |         |           |
| ☐ **BOTTI, Italo** .................. *paintings* |            |         | $660      |
| Italian 20th cent.                       |            |         |           |
| ☐ **BOTTICELLI, Sandro** .......... *paintings* |            | $35,200 | $308,000  |
| Italian 1444/45-1510                     |            |         |           |
| ☐ **BOTTICINI, Francesco** ......... *paintings* |            |         | $15,400   |
| Italian 1446-1497                        |            |         |           |
| ☐ **BOTTINI, Georges** ........... *paintings* |            |         | $1,320    |
| French 1874-1907 .................. *drawings* |            | $825    | $990      |
| ☐ **BOTTON, Jean Isy de** .......... *paintings* |            | $81     | $2,090    |
| French 1898-1978 .................. *drawings* |            | $242    | $275      |
| ☐ **BOTTONI, E.** .................. *paintings* |            |         | $550      |
| Italian                                  |            |         |           |

| | | Current Price Range | |
|---|---|---|---|
| | | *Low* | *High* |
| ☐ **BOTTUME, George F.** ...... *paintings* | | | $700 |
| American b. 1828, d. after 1878 | | | |
| ☐ **BOUCART, Gaston H.** ...... *paintings* | | $308 | $750 |
| French 20th cent. | | | |
| ☐ **BOUCHARD, Pierre Louis** ...... *paintings* | | | $1,980 |
| French 1831-1889 | | | |
| ☐ **BOUCHARDON, Edme** ...... *drawings* | | $385 | $3,410 |
| French 1698-1762 ...... *sculpture* | | | $53,900 |
| ☐ **BOUCHAUD, P.** ...... *paintings* | | | $357 |
| ☐ **BOUCHE, Alphonse** ...... *paintings* | | | $1,045 |
| ☐ **BOUCHE, Louis** ...... *paintings* | | $660 | $14,300 |
| American 1896-1969 ...... *drawings* | | | $302 |
| ☐ **BOUCHE, Louis Alexandre** ...... *paintings* | | | $4,950 |
| French 1838-1911 | | | |
| ☐ **BOUCHE, Rene** ...... *paintings* | | $220 | $352 |
| ☐ **BOUCHER, Alfred** ...... *sculpture* | | $1,650 | $2,420 |
| French late 19th/early 20th cent | | | |
| ☐ **BOUCHER, Francois** ...... *paintings* | | $35,750 | $220,000 |
| French 1703-1770 ...... *drawings* | | $1,045 | $37,400 |
| ☐ **BOUCHERVILLE, Adrien de** ...... *paintings* | | $11,000 | $11,550 |
| French d. 1912 | | | |
| ☐ **BOUCKHORST, Jan Philipsz. van** ...... *drawings* | | | $3,630 |
| Dutch 1588-1631 | | | |
| ☐ **BOUCQUET, Victor** ...... *paintings* | | | $5,500 |
| Flemish 1619-1677 | | | |
| ☐ **BOUDEWYNS, Adriaen Frans** ...... *paintings* | | $1,320 | $6,600 |
| Flemish | | | |
| ☐ **BOUDEWYNVE, A.** ...... *paintings* | | | $770 |
| Dutch 19th cent. | | | |
| ☐ **BOUDIN, Eugene** ...... *paintings* | | $1,000 | $154,000 |
| French 1824-1898 ...... *drawings* | | $880 | $30,800 |
| ☐ **BOUET, Eutrope** ...... *sculpture* | | | $2,200 |
| French 1839-1906 | | | |
| ☐ **BOUET, Pierre Henri** ...... *paintings* | | $247 | $330 |
| French 1828-1889 | | | |
| ☐ **BOUGANTNER** ...... *paintings* | | | $1,600 |
| ☐ **BOUGH, Samuel** ...... *paintings* | | $176 | $9,900 |
| Scottish 1822-1878 ...... *drawings* | | $132 | $770 |
| ☐ **BOUGHTON, George Henry** ...... *paintings* | | $330 | $19,800 |
| American 1833-1905 ...... *drawings* | | $110 | $418 |
| ☐ **BOUGUEREAU,** | | | |
| **Elizabeth Jane Gardner** ...... *paintings* | | $2,530 | $60,000 |
| American 1851-1922 ...... *drawings* | | | $1,320 |
| ☐ **BOUGUEREAU, William Adolphe** ...... *paintings* | | $770 | $407,000 |
| French 1825-1905 ...... *drawings* | | $247 | $13,200 |
| ☐ **BOUILLATS, B.** ...... *paintings* | | | $1,870 |
| French early 18th cent. | | | |
| ☐ **BOULAN, E.** ...... *paintings* | | | $275 |
| French 19th cent. | | | |

## 19th-Century "Academic" Painting

*A contemporary of the Impressionists, William Adolphe Bouguereau epitomized a style of French painting immensely popular during the 19th century. Bouguereau was a teacher at the Academy, the official government-approved school, and enjoyed the favor of state patronage and broad public acclaim during his lifetime. His reputation has since fluctuated violently, and from the 1950s through the 1970s his paintings sold for very little. Recently, he has again begun to be appreciated for his painterly skills. Bouguereau painted religious and mythological subjects. His paintings idealized women, and his works are noted for the translucent quality of skin tones. (William Adolphe Bouguereau, "L'Amour Désarmé," oil on canvas, 57½ x 38¼ in., Sotheby's, May 23, 1985, $126,500.)*

| | Current Price Range | |
|---|---|---|
| | Low | High |
| ☐ **BOULANGER, Clement** ...... *paintings* <br> French 1805-1842 | | **$880** |
| ☐ **BOULANGER, Francois Jean Louis** ...... *paintings* <br> French 1819-1873 | | **$2,860** |
| ☐ **BOULANGER,** <br> **Gustave Clarence Rodolphe** ...... *paintings* <br> French 1824-1888 | | **$3,520** |
| ☐ **BOULANGER, Louis** ...... *drawings* <br> French 1806-1867 | **$220** | **$330** |
| ☐ **BOULANGER, S.L.** ...... *paintings* <br> French 19th cent. | | **$3,850** |
| ☐ **BOULARD, Auguste (Jr.)** ...... *paintings* <br> French 1852-1927 | | **$990** |
| ☐ **BOULARD, Auguste (Sr.)** ...... *paintings* <br> French 1819-1873 | | **$1,540** |
| ☐ **BOULAVY, C.** ...... *paintings* | | **$1,100** |
| ☐ **BOULAYE, Paul de la** ...... *paintings* <br> French 19th cent. | | **$550** |

| | | Current Price Range | |
|---|---|---|---|
| | | *Low* | *High* |
| ☐ **BOULET, Cyprien Eugene** ............... *paintings*<br>French 1877-1927 | | $330 | $660 |
| ☐ **BOULIARD, Marie Genevieve** ............ *paintings*<br>French 1772-1819 | | | $4,180 |
| ☐ **BOULINEAU, Aristide** ..................... *paintings*<br>French 19th cent. | | | $1,870 |
| ☐ **BOULLOGNE, Louis de** ................... *drawings*<br>French 1654-1733 | | $660 | $3,300 |
| ☐ **BOULT, F. Cecil** ............................ *paintings* | | | $1,100 |
| ☐ **BOULTBEE, John** ........................... *paintings*<br>English ac. 1775-1788 | | $3,300 | $15,400 |
| ☐ **BOUMAN, Adrianus** ........................ *paintings*<br>Dutch 19th/20th cent. | | | $385 |
| ☐ **BOUMAN, Johan** ........................... *paintings*<br>Dutch 1602-1635 | | | $27,500 |
| ☐ **BOUNDEY, Burton Shepard** ............ *paintings*<br>American 1879-1962 | | | $1,650 |
| ☐ **BOUQUET, Andre** .......................... *paintings*<br>French b. 1897 | | $275 | $1,100 |
| ☐ **BOURAINE, A.** ............................... *sculpture*<br>French early 20th cent. | | $550 | $1,980 |
| ☐ **BOURAINE, Marcel** ........................ *sculpture*<br>French ac.1918-1935 | | $550 | $20,900 |
| ☐ **BOURDELLE, Emile Antoine** ............ *drawings*<br>French 1861-1929 ........................ *sculpture* | | $350<br>$1,700 | $1,540<br>$50,600 |
| ☐ **BOURDILLON, F.** ............................ *paintings* | | | $330 |
| ☐ **BOURDON, Sebastien** ...................... *paintings*<br>French 1616-1671 | | | $14,300 |
| ☐ **BOURELLE, P.** ................................ *sculpture*<br>French | | | $550 |
| ☐ **BOURET, Eutrope** .......................... *sculpture*<br>French 1833-1906 | | $125 | $2,640 |
| ☐ **BOURGAIN, Gustave** ...................... *drawings*<br>French b. 1921 | | | $990 |
| ☐ **BOURGEOIS, Eugene** ...................... *paintings*<br>French 1855-1909 | | | $1,540 |
| ☐ **BOURGEOIS, Louise** ....................... *paintings*<br>American b. 1911 ........................... *drawings* | | | $4,400<br>$2,750 |
| ☐ **BOURGEOIS, Sir Francis** ................. *paintings* | | | $935 |
| ☐ **BOURGEOIS DU CASTELET,**<br>**Florent Fidele Constant** ................. *drawings*<br>French 1767-1836 | | | $330 |
| ☐ **BOURGES, Pauline Elise Leonide** ........ *paintings*<br>French 1838-1910 | | $440 | $660 |
| ☐ **BOURGONNIER-CLAUDE, Berthe** ...... *drawings*<br>French d. 1922 | | | $935 |
| ☐ **BOURLARD, Antoine Joseph** .............. *paintings*<br>Belgian 1826-1899 | | $7,700 | $9,900 |
| ☐ **BOURNE, J.** ................................... *paintings* | | $935 | $1,210 |

| | | Current Price Range | |
|---|---|---|---|
| | | Low | High |
| ☐ **BOURRELLY, D.** ............... *paintings* | | | $550 |
| ☐ **BOURSIQUOT, J. David** .......... *paintings* | | $88 | $385 |
| ☐ **BOURY, Forman** ............... *paintings* | | | $660 |
| ☐ **BOUSQUET, Robert** ........... *sculpture* | | $440 | $700 |
| French 1894-1917 | | | |
| ☐ **BOUSSEAU, J.** ............... *sculpture* | | | $3,080 |
| ☐ **BOUT, Peeter** ............... *paintings* | | $1,760 | $4,400 |
| Flemish 1658-1702/19 | | | |
| ☐ **BOUTELLE, De Witt Clinton** ......... *paintings* | | $880 | $5,500 |
| American 1817/20-1884 | | | |
| ☐ **BOUTER, Cornelis Wouter** | | | |
| **(called Cor)** ............... *paintings* | | $550 | $4,950 |
| Dutch 1888-1966 | | | |
| ☐ **BOUTET DE MONVEL, Bernard** ....... *paintings* | | $195 | $2,420 |
| French 1884-1949 | | | |
| ☐ **BOUTET DE MONVEL, Maurice** ...... *drawings* | | | $660 |
| ☐ **BOUTH, G.** ............... *paintings* | | | $935 |
| French 19th cent. | | | |
| ☐ **BOUTIGNY, Paul Emile** ......... *paintings* | | | $2,640 |
| French 1854-1895 | | | |
| ☐ **BOUTON, H.A. von** ............ *paintings* | | | $1,540 |
| ☐ **BOUTT, Pierre de** ............ *paintings* | | | $385 |
| European 19th cent. | | | |
| ☐ **BOUVAL, Maurice** ............ *sculpture* | | | $1,210 |
| French early 20th cent. | | | |
| ☐ **BOUVARD, Antoine** ........... *paintings* | | $1,540 | $4,675 |
| French d. 1956 | | | |
| ☐ **BOUVARD, Auguste** ........... *paintings* | | | $440 |
| French 19th cent. | | | |
| ☐ **BOUVARD, G.** ............ *paintings* | | | $286 |
| ☐ **BOUVARD, Hughes de** ......... *paintings* | | $3,250 | $3,300 |
| Austrian 1879-1959 | | | |
| ☐ **BOUVARD, Noel** ............ *paintings* | | | $715 |
| French 1912-1975 | | | |
| ☐ **BOUVERET,** | | | |
| **Pascal Adolphe Jean Dagnan** ......... *paintings* | | | $990 |
| ☐ **BOUVIER, Armand** ........... *drawings* | | $55 | $242 |
| French 20th cent. | | | |
| ☐ **BOUVIER, Arthur** ........... *paintings* | | | $880 |
| Belgian 1837-1921 | | | |
| ☐ **BOUVIER, Augustus Jules** ...... *drawings* | | | $935 |
| French 1837-1881 | | | |
| ☐ **BOUVY, Firmin Gaston** ......... *paintings* | | $467 | $1,210 |
| Belgian 1822-1891 | | | |
| ☐ **BOUWMAN, W.** ............ *paintings* | | | $264 |
| ☐ **BOUY, Gaston** ............ *drawings* | | | $330 |
| French b. 1866 | | | |
| ☐ **BOUYS, Andre** ............ *paintings* | | | $3,850 |
| French 1656-1740 | | | |

| | | Current Price Range | |
|---|---|---|---|
| | | Low | High |
| ☐ **BOUYSSOU, Jacques** ............ *paintings* | | $660 | $1,650 |
| ☐ **BOVEE, I.A.** ................... *paintings* | | | $220 |
| American 19th/20th cent. | | | |
| ☐ **BOWDOIN, Harriette** ............ *paintings* | | $275 | $825 |
| American d. 1952 | | | |
| ☐ **BOWEN, Owen** ................. *paintings* | | $247 | $1,100 |
| English 1873-1967 | | | |
| ☐ **BOWER, Alexander** ............ *paintings* | | $209 | $2,530 |
| American 1875-1952 ............... *drawings* | | $110 | $550 |
| ☐ **BOWER, Lucy Scott** ............ *paintings* | | | $275 |
| American 1867-1934 | | | |
| ☐ **BOWER, Maurice L.** ............ *paintings* | | $330 | $1,210 |
| American 20th cent. ............... *drawings* | | $44 | $192 |
| ☐ **BOWERS, H.N.** ................. *paintings* | | | $605 |
| late 19th cent. | | | |
| ☐ **BOWERS, Stephen** ............ *drawings* | | | $500 |
| British ac. 1874-1891 | | | |
| ☐ **BOWIE, Frank Louville** ......... *paintings* | | $27 | $220 |
| American 1857-1936 | | | |
| ☐ **BOWKETT, Jane Maria** ......... *paintings* | | $605 | $1,210 |
| English 19th cent. | | | |
| ☐ **BOWMAN, Adrianus M.** ......... *paintings* | | | $357 |
| American 19th cent. | | | |
| ☐ **BOWYER, Alan** ................. *paintings* | | | $495 |
| American 19th/20th cent. | | | |
| ☐ **BOXER, Stanley Robert** ......... *paintings* | | $770 | $2,530 |
| American b. 1926 ................. *drawings* | | $110 | $825 |
| ☐ **BOYD, Rutherford** ............ *drawings* | | $1,045 | $3,300 |
| American 1884-1951 ............... *sculpture* | | | $16,500 |
| ☐ **BOYD, Walter Scott** ............ *paintings* | | | $247 |
| English ac. 1880's | | | |
| ☐ **BOYDEN, Dwight Frederick** ...... *paintings* | | $302 | $357 |
| American 1860-1933 | | | |
| ☐ **BOYE, Abel Dominique** ......... *paintings* | | $2,750 | $4,125 |
| French 1864-1934 | | | |
| ☐ **BOYEA, M.O.** ................. *paintings* | | | $1,100 |
| ☐ **BOYER, Emile** ................. *sculpture* | | | $1,540 |
| French 19th/20th cent. | | | |
| ☐ **BOYER, Emile** ................. *paintings* | | $247 | $350 |
| French b. 1877 | | | |
| ☐ **BOYER, Fred** ................. *sculpture* | | | $850 |
| American | | | |
| ☐ **BOYES, Sidney T.** ............ *sculpture* | | | $396 |
| ☐ **BOYLE, Caleb** ................. *paintings* | | | $6,050 |
| ☐ **BOYLE, Charles Wellington** ...... *paintings* | | | $1,760 |
| American 1864-1925 | | | |
| ☐ **BOYLE, Ferdinand Thomas Lee** ... *paintings* | | | $500 |
| American 1820-1906 | | | |
| ☐ **BOYLE, George** ............... *paintings* | | $385 | $412 |

|  | | | Current Price Range | |
|---|---|---|---|---|
|  | | | Low | High |
| ☐ **BOYLE, John J.** ................................. *sculpture* | | | $3,850 | $6,600 |
| American 1852-1917 | | | | |
| ☐ **BOYLE, Mark** ..................................... *sculpture* | | | | $10,450 |
| Scottish b. 1934 | | | | |
| ☐ **BOYLE, William W.** ........................... *paintings* | | | | $660 |
| ac. 1852-1869 | | | | |
| ☐ **BOYLES, Sidney J.** ............................ *sculpture* | | | | $352 |
| ☐ **BOYNTON, Ray** ................................. *paintings* | | | | $605 |
| American 1883-1951 ................................. *drawings* | | | $220 | $385 |
| ☐ **BOYS, Thomas Shotter** ........................ *drawings* | | | $660 | $18,700 |
| British 1803-1874 | | | | |
| ☐ **BOZNANSKA, Olga** ........................... *paintings* | | | $200 | $4,400 |
| Polish 1865-1945 | | | | |
| ☐ **BOZZARICH, S.** ................................. *paintings* | | | $220 | $660 |
| Greek (?) 19th cent. | | | | |
| ☐ **BRAAKMAN, Anthonie** ....................... *paintings* | | | | $1,650 |
| Dutch b. 1811 | | | | |
| ☐ **BRABAZON, Hercules Brabazon** .......... *drawings* | | | $220 | $495 |
| English 1821-1906 | | | | |
| ☐ **BRACE, Reeves** ................................. *paintings* | | | | $577 |
| American 20th cent. | | | | |
| ☐ **BRACH, Paul** .................................... *paintings* | | | | $605 |
| American b. 1924 | | | | |
| ☐ **BRACHO, Angel** ................................ *paintings* | | | | $1,650 |
| Mexican b. 1911 ................................... *drawings* | | | | $357 |
| ☐ **BRACK, Emil** ................................... *paintings* | | | | $23,100 |
| German 1860-1905 | | | | |
| ☐ **BRACKETT, A. Loring** ....................... *paintings* | | | $165 | $825 |
| American 19th/20th cent. | | | | |
| ☐ **BRACKETT, Sid L.** ............................ *paintings* | | | | $400 |
| ☐ **BRACKETT, Walter M.** ....................... *paintings* | | | $880 | $22,000 |
| American 1823-1919 | | | | |
| ☑ **BRACKMAN, Robert** ........................... *paintings* | | | $110 | $7,700 |
| American 1898-1980 ................................. *drawings* | | | $176 | $1,760 |
| ☐ **BRACQUEMOND** ............................... *sculpture* | | | | $700 |
| ☐ **BRACY, Arthur E.** ............................. *paintings* | | | $150 | $363 |
| ☐ **BRAD, J.** ......................................... *paintings* | | | | $550 |
| American 19th cent. | | | | |
| ☐ **BRADBURY, Bennett** ........................... *paintings* | | | | $247 |
| American 20th cent. | | | | |
| ☐ **BRADE, J.** ........................................ *paintings* | | | | $550 |
| American late 19th cent. | | | | |
| ☐ **BRADER, B.** ...................................... *paintings* | | | | $770 |
| ☐ **BRADFORD, William** .......................... *paintings* | | | $400 | $77,000 |
| American 1823-1892 ................................. *drawings* | | | $440 | $4,000 |
| ☐ **BRADLEY, Anne Cary** ........................ *paintings* | | | | $770 |
| American b. 1884 | | | | |
| ☐ **BRADLEY, John** ................................ *paintings* | | | | $23,100 |
| ac. c. 1830-1874 | | | | |

| | | Current Price Range | |
|---|---|---|---|
| | | Low | High |
| ☐ **BRADLEY, Tom** ............... *drawings* | | | $440 |
| British 19th cent. | | | |
| ☐ **BRADSTREET, Julie E.** ............. *paintings* | | | $770 |
| American 19th cent. | | | |
| ☐ **BRAEDEL, A.L.** ............... *paintings* | | | $825 |
| American 19th cent. | | | |
| ☐ **BRAEKELEER, Ferdinand de** | | | |
| **(the elder)** ............... *paintings* | | $1,430 | $24,200 |
| Belgian 1792-1883 | | | |
| ☐ **BRAEKELEER, Adrien Ferdinand de** ... *paintings* | | | $4,125 |
| Belgian 1818-1904 | | | |
| ☐ **BRAGARD, Charles de** ............. *paintings* | | | $825 |
| French 19th/20th cent. | | | |
| ☐ **BRAGG, Charles** ............... *paintings* | | $880 | $1,452 |
| American 20th cent. | | | |
| ☐ **BRAGG, Charles William** ............. *paintings* | | | $660 |
| British 19th cent. | | | |
| ☐ **BRAHMILL** ............... *paintings* | | | $935 |
| American | | | |
| ☐ **BRAINARD, Ann Elizabeth** ............. *paintings* | | | $466 |
| American | | | |
| ☐ **BRAITH, Anton** ............... *paintings* | | $16,500 | $63,800 |
| German 1836-1905 ............... *drawings* | | | $330 |
| ☐ **BRAKENBURG, Richard** ............. *paintings* | | $1,650 | $12,500 |
| Dutch 1650-1702 | | | |
| ☐ **BRALEY, C.** ............... *paintings* | | | $660 |
| ............... *drawings* | | $55 | $550 |
| ☐ **BRAMER, Leonard** ............. *paintings* | | | $1,100 |
| Dutch 1596-1674 ............... *drawings* | | $352 | $440 |
| ☐ **BRAMHALL, George** ............. *paintings* | | $300 | $474 |
| ☐ **BRAMLEY, Robert** ............. *paintings* | | $165 | $297 |
| 19th cent. | | | |
| ☐ **BRAMMER, R.** ............... *paintings* | | | $1,100 |
| Dutch 19th cent. | | | |
| ☐ **BRANCACCIO, Carlos** ............. *paintings* | | | $2,310 |
| Italian 1861-1920 | | | |
| ☐ **BRANCARD, Raoul** ............. *paintings* | | | $423 |
| ☐ **BRANCHARD, Emile Pierre** ............. *paintings* | | | $880 |
| 1881-1938 | | | |
| ☐ **BRANCUSI, Constantin** ............. *drawings* | | $2,640 | $63,800 |
| Rumanian 1876-1957 ............... *sculpture* | | $137,500 | $1,650,000 |
| ☐ **BRANDAS** ............... *paintings* | | | $385 |
| American 20th cent. | | | |
| ☐ **BRANDEIS, Antonietta** ............. *paintings* | | $770 | $7,700 |
| Czechoslovakian b. 1849 ............. *drawings* | | | $440 |
| ☐ **BRANDEIS, Johann Melchior** ............. *paintings* | | | $2,200 |
| German 18th cent. | | | |

| | | Current Price Range | |
|---|---|---|---|
| | | *Low* | *High* |
| ☐ **BRANDES, Willy** ............................ *paintings* | | | $1,100 |
| German b. 1876 ......................................... *drawings* | | | $440 |
| ☐ **BRANDI, Domenico** ........................... *paintings* | | $1,100 | $6,050 |
| Italian 1683-1736 | | | |
| ☐ **BRANDI, Giacinto** ............................. *paintings* | | | $6,050 |
| Italian 1623-1691 | | | |
| ☐ **BRANDIEN, Carl W.** ........................... *paintings* | | | $550 |
| American 20th cent. | | | |
| ☐ **BRANDIS, August von** ......................... *paintings* | | | $880 |
| German b. 1862 | | | |
| ☐ **BRANDNER, Karl C.** .......................... *paintings* | | $330 | $660 |
| American b. 1898 ...................................... *drawings* | | $44 | $99 |
| ☐ **BRANDRETT, M.** .............................. *paintings* | | | $330 |
| ☐ **BRANDRIFF, George Kennedy** ............. *paintings* | | $110 | $11,000 |
| American 1890-1936 | | | |
| ☐ **BRANDS, Eugene** ............................. *drawings* | | $385 | $715 |
| Dutch b. 1913 | | | |
| ☐ **BRANDT, A.** ................................... *paintings* | | | $412 |
| Continental School 19th/20th cent. | | | |
| ☐ **BRANDT, Carl** ................................. *paintings* | | | $2,420 |
| ☐ **BRANDT, Edgar** .............................. *sculpture* | | | $1,210 |
| French 1880-1960 | | | |
| ☐ **BRANDT, Edgar and Paul MERGIER** ... *sculpture* | | | $18,700 |
| French 20th cent. | | | |
| ☐ **BRANDT, Josef von** .......................... *paintings* | | $1,430 | $28,600 |
| Polish 1841-1915/28 | | | |
| ☐ **BRANDT, Otto** ............................... *paintings* | | $550 | $3,300 |
| ☐ **BRANDT, Paul** ............................... *drawings* | | | $286 |
| ☐ **BRANDT, Warren** ............................. *paintings* | | $247 | $352 |
| American | | | |
| ☐ **BRANGWYN, Sir Frank** ..................... *paintings* | | $110 | $4,620 |
| British 1867-1956 ...................................... *drawings* | | $385 | $4,950 |
| ☐ **BRANNAN, William Penn** .................... *paintings* | | | $2,090 |
| American d. 1866 | | | |
| ☐ **BRANNER, Martin** .......................... *drawings* | | $192 | $302 |
| American 1888-1970 | | | |
| ☐ **BRANQUAR** ................................... *paintings* | | | $825 |
| ☐ **BRANSCOMBE, Charles H.** ................ *paintings* | | | $247 |
| American 20th cent. | | | |
| ☐ **BRANSOM, Paul** .............................. *drawings* | | $330 | $715 |
| American 1885-1981 | | | |
| ☐ **BRANT, S.** ..................................... *paintings* | | | $1,760 |
| German 19th cent. | | | |
| ☐ **BRANWHITE, Charles** ........................ *paintings* | | | $2,090 |
| English 1817-1880 | | | |
| ☐ **BRAPIZZI** ...................................... *paintings* | | | $250 |
| Italian | | | |
| ☐ **BRAQUAVAL, Louis** ........................... *paintings* | | $385 | $825 |
| French d. 1919 | | | |

| | | Current Price Range | |
|---|---|---|---|
| | | Low | High |
| ☐ **BRAQUE, Georges** .............. *paintings* | | $16,500 | $605,000 |
| French 1882-1963 ..................... *drawings* | | $1,320 | $22,000 |
| ................................... *sculpture* | | $5,775 | $23,100 |
| ☐ **BRASCASSAT, Jacques Raymond** ......... *paintings* | | $935 | $16,500 |
| French 1804-1867 | | | |
| ☐ **BRASCH, Morten** .............. *drawings* | | | $770 |
| Danish 17th cent. | | | |
| ☐ **BRASCH, Wenzel Ignaz** ....... *paintings* | | $660 | $1,760 |
| German d. 1761 | | | |
| ☐ **BRASHER, Rex** ..................... *drawings* | | | $325 |
| American 1869-1960 | | | |
| ☐ **BRASILIER, Andre** .............. *paintings* | | $660 | $6,600 |
| French b. 1929 ..................... *drawings* | | | $825 |
| ☐ **BRASSAI, Henri** .............. *sculpture* | | | $1,980 |
| ☐ **BRASSAK** .............. *paintings* | | | $550 |
| ☐ **BRASSAUW, Melchior** ......... *paintings* | | | $7,150 |
| Flemish 1709-1757 | | | |
| ☐ **BRASTOFF, Sascha** ............. *sculpture* | | | $550 |
| American b. 1918 | | | |
| ☐ **BRATBY, John** .............. *paintings* | | $302 | $330 |
| English b. 1928 | | | |
| ☐ **BRAUER, Erich** ................. *drawings* | | | $4,950 |
| Austrian b. 1929 | | | |
| ☐ **BRAUGHTON, Edouard** ......... *sculpture* | | | $605 |
| ☐ **BRAUN, Louis** .............. *paintings* | | | $2,420 |
| German 1836-1916 | | | |
| ☐ **BRAUN, Maurice** .............. *paintings* | | $66 | $5,500 |
| American 1877-1941 ............. *drawings* | | | $192 |
| ☐ **BRAUN, Warren** .............. *paintings* | | | $264 |
| ☐ **BRAUNER, Victor** .............. *paintings* | | $5,500 | $71,500 |
| Rumanian 1903-1966 ............. *drawings* | | $3,300 | $30,800 |
| ☐ **BRAVO, Claudio** .............. *paintings* | | $9,350 | $44,000 |
| Chilean b. 1936 ............. *drawings* | | $1,210 | $12,100 |
| ☐ **BRAVURA, Denyse** ............. *drawings* | | | $2,310 |
| French 20th cent. | | | |
| ☐ **BRAWLEY, William John** ............. *paintings* | | | $220 |
| American | | | |
| ☐ **BRAY, Jan de** .............. *paintings* | | $2,200 | $6,600 |
| Dutch c. 1626/27-1697 | | | |
| ☐ **BRAY, W.L.** .............. *paintings* | | | $495 |
| ☐ **BRAYER, Yves** .............. *paintings* | | $825 | $2,200 |
| French b. 1907 ..................... *drawings* | | | $110 |
| ☐ **BREA** .............. *paintings* | | | $1,210 |
| French 18th cent. | | | |
| ☐ **BREACH, Edward R.** ............. *paintings* | | | $17,600 |
| ☐ **BREACH, John L.** .............. *paintings* | | | $302 |
| English 19th cent. | | | |
| ☐ **BREAKSPEARE, A.** ............. *paintings* | | | $330 |

| | | *Current Price Range* |  |
|---|---|---|---|
| | | *Low* | *High* |
| ☐ **BREAKSPEARE, William A.** ............... *paintings* | | $209 | $4,675 |
| English 1855/56-1914 | | | |
| ☐ **BREANSKI, Alfred Fonteville de (Jr.)** .... *paintings* | | $247 | $6,050 |
| English 1877-c. 1945 | | | |
| ☐ **BREANSKI, Alfred de** ......................... *paintings* | | $220 | $6,050 |
| English | | | |
| ☐ **BREANSKI, Alfred de (Sr.)** .................. *paintings* | | $715 | $4,400 |
| English 1852-1928 | | | |
| ☐ **BREANSKI, Gustave de** ....................... *paintings* | | $350 | $1,540 |
| English c. 1856-1898 | | | |
| ☐ **BREANSKI, William** ........................... *paintings* | | | $2,200 |
| British 19th/20th cent. | | | |
| ☐ **BRECELT** ......................................... *sculpture* | | | $1,650 |
| ☐ **BRECKENRIDGE, Hugh Henry** .......... *paintings* | | $2,750 | $5,775 |
| American 1870-1937 ................................... *drawings* | | | $165 |
| ☐ **BREDAEL, Jan Frans van** .................... *paintings* | | | $4,675 |
| Flemish 1686-1750 | | | |
| ☐ **BREDAEL, Josef van** .......................... *paintings* | | $3,850 | $20,900 |
| Flemish 1688-1739 | | | |
| ☐ **BREDAEL, Peeter van** ........................ *paintings* | | $6,600 | $7,150 |
| Dutch 1629-1719 | | | |
| ☐ **BREDIES, O.** ..................................... *paintings* | | | $495 |
| ☐ **BREDIN, Rae Sloan** ............................ *paintings* | | | $8,000 |
| American 1881-1933 | | | |
| ☐ **BREDT, Ferdinand Max** ....................... *paintings* | | $165 | $13,200 |
| German 1860-1921 | | | |
| ☐ **BREE, C. de** ...................................... *paintings* | | | $605 |
| ☐ **BREEDON, William E.** ......................... *drawings* | | | $400 |
| ☐ **BREEM, Paul** ..................................... *paintings* | | | $715 |
| American 19th cent. | | | |
| ☐ **BREENBERG, Bartholomaus** ............... *paintings* | | $7,700 | $13,200 |
| 1599/1600-1663 | | | |
| ☐ **BREENE, Alexander** ........................... *paintings* | | | $191 |
| American 20th cent. | | | |
| ☐ **BREEVORT, James Renwick** ............... *paintings* | | | $2,475 |
| American 1832-1918 | | | |
| ☐ **BREHM, George** ............................... *paintings* | | $412 | $770 |
| American b. 1878 ...................................... *drawings* | | $357 | $495 |
| ☐ **BREHM, Worth** ................................ *drawings* | | $330 | $450 |
| American 1883-1928 | | | |
| ☐ **BREITBACH, Carl** ............................. *paintings* | | | $1,430 |
| German 1833-1904 | | | |
| ☐ **BREITENBACH, Franz Schmid** ........... *paintings* | | $1,100 | $3,300 |
| German (?) 19th/20th cent. | | | |
| ☐ **BREITENSTEIN, Carl August** ............. *paintings* | | | $660 |
| Dutch b. 1864 | | | |
| ☐ **BREITMAYER** .................................... *paintings* | | | $726 |
| American | | | |

| | | Current Price Range | |
| --- | --- | --- | --- |
| | | Low | High |
| ☐ **BREITNER, Georg Hendrik** ............... *paintings* | | | $605 |
| Dutch 1857-1923 ....................................... *drawings* | | | $495 |
| ☐ **BREKELENKAM,** | | | |
| **Quirihgh Gerritsz van** ................... *paintings* | | $1,980 | $85,250 |
| Dutch after 1620-1668 | | | |
| ☐ **BRELING, Heinrich** ........................... *paintings* | | $1,210 | $11,000 |
| German b. 1849 | | | |
| ☐ **BREMAND, Henri** ........................... *paintings* | | | $1,320 |
| ☐ **BREMER, Anne** ................................. *paintings* | | $247 | $2,200 |
| American 1872-1923 | | | |
| ☐ **BREMOND, Henri** ........................... *paintings* | | | $3,850 |
| French b. 1875 | | | |
| ☐ **BRENAN, J.B.** ................................. *paintings* | | $220 | $495 |
| British 19th cent. | | | |
| ☐ **BRENAN, John J.** .............................. *paintings* | | | $522 |
| British 19th cent. | | | |
| ☐ **BRENDEL, Albert** .............................. *paintings* | | | $660 |
| German 1827-1895 | | | |
| ☐ **BRENNAN, Alfred Laurens** ................. *paintings* | | | $4,400 |
| American 1853-1921 ................................ *drawings* | | $88 | $176 |
| ☐ **BRENNEMAN, George W.** ................... *paintings* | | | $522 |
| American 1856-1906 | | | |
| ☐ **BRENNER, Adam** ........................... *paintings* | | | $1,650 |
| Austrian 1800-1891 | | | |
| ☐ **BRENNER, Carl Christ** ....................... *paintings* | | $990 | $2,860 |
| American 1838-1888 | | | |
| ☐ **BRENNER, F.H.** ................................. *paintings* | | $198 | $330 |
| American 19th cent. | | | |
| ☐ **BRENNER, N.** ................................. *paintings* | | | $385 |
| ☐ **BRENNER, Victor David** ...................... *sculpture* | | $110 | $275 |
| American | | | |
| ☐ **BRENNIR, Carl** ................................. *paintings* | | | $1,430 |
| British 1850-1920 | | | |
| ☐ **BRENTANO, Al** ................................. *paintings* | | | $660 |
| ☐ **BRENTANO, Frans (Anton)** ................. *paintings* | | | $500 |
| German 1840-1888 | | | |
| ☐ **BRENTANO, H.** ................................. *paintings* | | | $770 |
| ☐ **BRENTANO, Patricia** ........................... *drawings* | | $330 | $330 |
| ☐ **BRENTZER, B.** ................................. *paintings* | | | $300 |
| ☐ **BRESCIANINO, Andrea del** ................. *paintings* | | $6,050 | $15,400 |
| Italian ac. 1506-1545 | | | |
| ☐ **BRESLAU, Marie Louise Catherine** ....... *paintings* | | | $7,150 |
| Swiss 1856-1928 | | | |
| ☐ **BRESSAN** ........................................... *drawings* | | | $220 |
| American 19th cent. | | | |
| ☐ **BRESSLER, Emile** .............................. *paintings* | | $2,200 | $2,475 |
| Swiss 20th cent. | | | |
| ☐ **BREST, Germain-Fabius** ...................... *paintings* | | | $275 |
| French 1823-1900 | | | |

| | | | Current Price Range | |
|---|---|---|---|---|
| | | | Low | High |
| □ **BRETLAND, Thomas W.** | ..................... | *paintings* | $1,200 | $14,300 |
| English 1802-1874 | | | | |
| □ **BRETON, Emile Adelard** | ..................... | *paintings* | | $385 |
| French 1831-1902 | | | | |
| □ **BRETON, Jules** | ..................... | *paintings* | $192 | $33,000 |
| French 1827-1906 | ..................... | *drawings* | | $2,750 |
| □ **BRETON, Virginie Demont** | ..................... | *paintings* | | $4,950 |
| French 1859-1935 | | | | |
| □ **BRETT, Dorothy** | ..................... | *paintings* | $770 | $2,860 |
| Anglo/American 1883-1977 | | | | |
| □ **BRETT, Harold M.** | ..................... | *paintings* | $350 | $2,750 |
| American 1880-after 1935 | | | | |
| □ **BRETT, John** | ..................... | *paintings* | $187 | $302 |
| English 1830-1902 | | | | |
| □ **BREU, M.** | ..................... | *paintings* | $990 | $1,045 |
| German 19th cent. | | | | |
| □ **BREUER, Henry Joseph** | ..................... | *paintings* | $412 | $1,650 |
| American 1860-1932 | | | | |
| □ **BREUER, Peter** | ..................... | *sculpture* | | $308 |
| German b. 1856 | | | | |
| □ **BREUER, Theodore A.** | ..................... | *paintings* | | $715 |
| American 19th/20th cent. | | | | |
| □ **BREUGELMANS** | ..................... | *paintings* | | $990 |
| □ **BREUKELAAR, Henrick** | ..................... | *paintings* | | $385 |
| Dutch 1809-1839 | | | | |
| □ **BREUL, Franz de** | ..................... | *paintings* | | $1,320 |
| Belgian 19th cent. | | | | |
| □ **BREUL, Harold Guenther** | ..................... | *paintings* | $88 | $242 |
| American b. 1889 | | | | |
| □ **BREUL, Hugo** | ..................... | *paintings* | $110 | $2,860 |
| American 1854-1910 | ..................... | *drawings* | | $143 |
| □ **BREUNINGER, Helmut** | ..................... | *paintings* | | $330 |
| German b. 1921 | | | | |
| □ **BREVOORT, James Renwick** | ..................... | *paintings* | $193 | $3,630 |
| American 1832-1918 | | | | |
| □ **BREWER, Adrian Louis** | ..................... | *paintings* | | $522 |
| American b. 1891 | | | | |
| □ **BREWER, Nicholas Richard** | ..................... | *paintings* | $93 | $3,520 |
| American 1857-1949 | | | | |
| □ **BREWERTON, George Douglas** | ..................... | *drawings* | $275 | $1,540 |
| American 1820-1901 | | | | |
| □ **BREWSTER, Anna Richards** | ..................... | *paintings* | $100 | $2,200 |
| American 1870-1952 | | | | |
| □ **BREWSTER, John (Jr.)** | ..................... | *paintings* | $5,500 | $132,000 |
| American 1766-1854 | | | | |
| □ **BREWTNALL, Edward Frederick** | ..................... | *drawings* | | $522 |
| British 1846-1902 | | | | |
| □ **BREYDEL, Karel** | ..................... | *paintings* | | $5,500 |
| Flemish 1678-1733 | | | | |

| | | Current Price Range | |
|---|---|---|---|
| | | Low | High |
| ☐ **BREYER, Jan Hendrick (Jr.)** ............... *paintings* | | | $286 |
| Dutch b. 1818 | | | |
| ☐ **BREZINI** ........................................ *paintings* | | | $302 |
| ☐ **BRIANCHON, Maurice** ............... *paintings* | | $2,860 | $37,400 |
| French b. 1899 ................................... *drawings* | | | $825 |
| ☐ **BRIAND** .................................... *sculpture* | | $286 | $1,430 |
| ☐ **BRIAND, C.** ..................................... *paintings* | | $660 | $1,000 |
| ☐ **BRIANTE, Ezelino** ........................... *paintings* | | $605 | $715 |
| Italian 1901-1970 | | | |
| ☐ **BRICARD, C.** ................................... *paintings* | | | $715 |
| French 19th/20th cent. | | | |
| ☐ **BRICE, Fanny** .................................. *paintings* | | | $550 |
| ☐ **BRICHARD, Gabrielle Jeanne** ............. *paintings* | | | $2,750 |
| French ac. 1908-1913 | | | |
| ☐ **BRICHER, Alfred Thompson** ............... *paintings* | | $462 | $121,000 |
| American 1837-1908 ............................... *drawings* | | $220 | $52,250 |
| ☐ **BRICKDALE, Eleanor Fortescue** .......... *drawings* | | $1,650 | $2,420 |
| English 1871-1945 | | | |
| ☐ **BRICTEAUX, V.** ................................ *sculpture* | | | $1,078 |
| ☐ **BRIDELL, Frederick Lee** ...................... *paintings* | | | $650 |
| English 1831-1863 | | | |
| ☐ **BRIDGES, Fidelia** ............................. *paintings* | | $1,300 | $3,300 |
| American 1835-1924 ................................ *drawings* | | $302 | $1,000 |
| ☐ **BRIDGES, John** ............................... *paintings* | | | $2,750 |
| British ac. 1818-1854 | | | |
| ☐ **BRIDGMAN, Charles** ........................ *paintings* | | $660 | $715 |
| American | | | |
| ☐ **BRIDGMAN, Frederick Arthur** ............ *paintings* | | $220 | $18,700 |
| American 1847-1928 ................................ *drawings* | | $154 | $1,760 |
| ☐ **BRIDGMAN, George B.** ..................... *paintings* | | | $200 |
| American 1864-1943/44 ............................. *drawings* | | $192 | $192 |
| ☐ **BRIERRE** ...................................... *sculpture* | | | $550 |
| Haitian b. 1938 | | | |
| ☐ **BRIET, Arthur** ................................. *paintings* | | | $2,420 |
| Dutch b. 1867 | | | |
| ☐ **BRIETNER, Georg Hendrik** ................. *paintings* | | | $1,650 |
| ☐ **BRIGANTI, Nicholas P.** ...................... *paintings* | | $330 | $13,750 |
| Italian/American b. 1895 | | | |
| ☐ **BRIGDEN, Frederick H.** ...................... *drawings* | | | $220 |
| Canadian 20th cent. | | | |
| ☐ **BRIGGLE, Artus van** ......................... *paintings* | | $385 | $1,500 |
| American 19th/20th cent. | | | |
| ☐ **BRIGGS, Elizabeth B.** ....................... *paintings* | | | $275 |
| American 19th cent. | | | |
| ☐ **BRIGGS, Ernest** ............................. *paintings* | | $440 | $522 |
| ☐ **BRIGGS, L. A.** ................................. *drawings* | | $660 | $1,540 |
| American late 19th cent. | | | |
| ☐ **BRIGGS, Warren C.** ........................... *paintings* | | $324 | $1,210 |
| American 1867-1903 | | | |

|  | | *Current Price Range* | |
|---|---|---|---|
|  | | *Low* | *High* |
| ☐ **BRIGGS, William Keighley** ................... *paintings* | | | $1,760 |
| English 19th cent. | | | |
| ☐ **BRIGHT, Alfred** ................... *drawings* | | | $3,500 |
| British exhib. 1929 | | | |
| ☐ **BRIGHT, Harry** ............................... *drawings* | | | $220 |
| British ac. 1867-1892 | | | |
| ☐ **BRIGHT, Henry** ............................... *paintings* | | $600 | $5,940 |
| English 1814-1873 ...................................... *drawings* | | $99 | $770 |
| ☐ **BRIGLIA, Giovanni Francesco** .............. *paintings* | | $3,960 | $8,250 |
| Italian 1737-1794 | | | |
| ☐ **BRIL, Paul** ............................................ *paintings* | | | $14,300 |
| Flemish 1554-1626 | | | |
| ☐ **BRILLOUIN, Louis Georges** ............. *paintings* | | $1,430 | $1,760 |
| French 1817-1893 ...................................... *drawings* | | $33 | $176 |
| ☐ **BRIMANT, Jules Ruinart de** ................ *paintings* | | | $2,475 |
| French 1838-1898 | | | |
| ☐ **BRIMMER, H.** ...................................... *paintings* | | $715 | $825 |
| European 19th cent. | | | |
| ☐ **BRINCKMANN, Philipp Hieronymus** .. *paintings* | | | $605 |
| German 1709-1761 | | | |
| ☐ **BRINDESI, Olympio** ............................ *sculpture* | | | $550 |
| ☐ **BRINDLE, E. Melbourne** ..................... *paintings* | | | $3,410 |
| Australian/Amer. b. 1904 | | | |
| ☐ **BRINES, J.F.** ....................................... *sculpture* | | | $1,430 |
| American 19th cent. | | | |
| ☐ **BRINISHOLTZ, A.** .............................. *drawings* | | | $990 |
| ☐ **BRINK, J. Van** ................................... *paintings* | | $302 | $412 |
| ☐ **BRINKMAN, Tracy Beeler** ................. *sculpture* | | | $3,000 |
| American b. 1958 | | | |
| ☐ **BRINLEY, Daniel Putnam** .................... *paintings* | | $200 | $3,300 |
| American 1879-1963 | | | |
| ☐ **BRIOSCHI, Anton** ............................ *paintings* | | | $275 |
| Italian b. 1855 | | | |
| ☐ **BRIOSCHI, Othmar** ............................ *paintings* | | | $750 |
| ☐ **BRISARD, Ferdinand** ........................... *paintings* | | | $522 |
| French b. 1870 | | | |
| ☐ **BRISCO, D.** ........................................ *paintings* | | | $440 |
| American 19th cent. | | | |
| ☐ **BRISCOE, Arthur John Trevor** ............. *paintings* | | $3,190 | $3,740 |
| English b. 1873 | | | |
| ☐ **BRISCOE, Frank D.** ............................ *paintings* | | $88 | $4,840 |
| American 1844-1903 | | | |
| ☐ **BRISPOT, Henri** ................................ *paintings* | | $935 | $6,050 |
| French 1846-1928 | | | |
| ☐ **BRISS, J.S.** ........................................ *paintings* | | | $495 |
| American 19th/20th cent. | | | |
| ☐ **BRISSAUD, Pierre** ............................... *drawings* | | $66 | $242 |
| French b. 1885 | | | |

| | Current Price Range | |
|---|---|---|
| | *Low* | *High* |

| | | Low | High |
|---|---|---|---|
| ☐ **BRISSET, Emile** .................................. *paintings* | | $440 | $1,870 |
| French 19th cent. | | | |
| ☐ **BRISSON, Maurice** ............................. *paintings* | | $137 | $275 |
| French 20th cent. | | | |
| ☐ **BRISSOT DE WARVILLE,** | | | |
| **Felix Saturnin** ...................................... *paintings* | | $242 | $4,125 |
| French 1818-1892 ...................................... *drawings* | | $242 | $990 |
| ☐ **BRISTOL, John Bunyan** ...................... *paintings* | | $82 | $4,620 |
| American 1826-1909 ................................... *drawings* | | $55 | $165 |
| ☐ **BRISTOW, Edmund** ........................... *paintings* | | $990 | $22,000 |
| English 1787-1876 | | | |
| ☐ **BRIT, E. La** ...................................... *paintings* | | | $357 |
| French 19th cent. | | | |
| ☐ **BRITTAN, Charles Edward** ................. *paintings* | | | $770 |
| English b. 1870 ......................................... *drawings* | | $220 | $660 |
| ☐ **BRIULOV, Karl Pavlovich** ................... *drawings* | | | $1,980 |
| Russian 1799-1852 | | | |
| ☐ **BRIZZI, Ary** ...................................... *paintings* | | | $1,430 |
| Argentinian b. 1930 | | | |
| ☐ **BROADHOUSE, John Davies** ............... *drawings* | | $150 | $176 |
| American | | | |
| ☐ **BROCHART, Constant Joseph** ............. *drawings* | | | $990 |
| European | | | |
| ☐ **BROCHET, Francois** ........................... *drawings* | | | $220 |
| French b. 1925 ......................................... *sculpture* | | | $4,180 |
| ☐ **BROCHOCKI, Walery** ........................ *paintings* | | | $825 |
| Polish 1849-1923 | | | |
| ☐ **BROCK, Charles Edmond** .................... *paintings* | | | $522 |
| English b. 1870 | | | |
| ☐ **BROCK, Ernest** ................................. *drawings* | | | $1,760 |
| American or English 19th cent. | | | |
| ☐ **BROCKBANK, A. E.** ........................... *drawings* | | | $264 |
| ☐ **BROCKHURST, Gerald L.** ................... *paintings* | | | $2,200 |
| English b.1890 ......................................... *drawings* | | | $660 |
| ☐ **BROCKMAN, Ann** ............................. *paintings* | | | $275 |
| American b. 1899 | | | |
| ☐ **BROCZIK, Wencelas** ........................... *paintings* | | $198 | $14,300 |
| Hungarian 1851-1901 | | | |
| ☐ **BRODERSON, Morris** ......................... *paintings* | | | $1,650 |
| American b. 1928 ...................................... *drawings* | | $99 | $550 |
| ☐ **BRODIE, Gandy** ................................. *paintings* | | $165 | $2,530 |
| American 1924-1975 ................................... *drawings* | | $137 | $440 |
| ☐ **BRODSKY, Isaac** ............................... *paintings* | | | $2,310 |
| Russian 19th/20th cent. | | | |
| ☐ **BRODT, Stephane** .............................. *paintings* | | | $385 |
| ☐ **BROECK, Clemence van den** ................ *paintings* | | $1,870 | $2,475 |
| Belgian 1843-1922 | | | |
| ☐ **BROECK, Elias van den** ....................... *paintings* | | | $11,000 |
| Dutch 1650-1709 | | | |

|  | | *Current Price Range* | |
|---|---|---|---|
|  | | Low | High |
| ☐ **BROECKER, A.** ................................. *paintings* | | | $550 |
| German 19th cent. | | | |
| ☐ **BROEDILIT, \*\*** ................................. *paintings* | | | $330 |
| Dutch 19th cent. | | | |
| ☐ **BROERS, G.** ..................................... *drawings* | | | $302 |
| European 18th cent. | | | |
| ☐ **BROISAT, A.** ..................................... *paintings* | | | $247 |
| Belgian 19th cent. | | | |
| ☐ **BROMLEY, F.C.** ............................. *paintings* | | | $1,760 |
| American 19th cent. | | | |
| ☐ **BROMLEY, Frank C.** .......................... *paintings* | | | $3,575 |
| American 1860-1890 | | | |
| ☐ **BROMLEY, H. Thomas** ........................ *paintings* | | | $192 |
| British 19th/20th cent. | | | |
| ☐ **BROMLEY, Valentine Walter** .............. *paintings* | | | $1,870 |
| English 1848-1877 | | | |
| ☐ **BROMLEY, William** ............................ *paintings* | $1,100 | $8,250 |
| British ac. 1835-1888 | | | |
| ☐ **BRONNIKOV, Feodor Andreievich** ....... *paintings* | | | $1,650 |
| Russian 1827-1902 | | | |
| ☐ **BRONSCHOHL, L.** .............................. *paintings* | | | $423 |
| ☐ **BRONTE, Charlotte** ............................ *drawings* | | | $550 |
| English 1816-1855 | | | |
| ☐ **BROOK, Alexander** ............................ *paintings* | $110 | $2,860 |
| American 1898-1980 ................................. *drawings* | $132 | $247 |
| ☐ **BROOK, Maria Burnham** ..................... *paintings* | | | $880 |
| British ac. 1872-1885 | | | |
| ☐ **BROOKE, Richard Norris** .................... *paintings* | $140 | $2,310 |
| American 1847-1920 | | | |
| ☐ **BROOKE, S.A.** ................................... *paintings* | $192 | $495 |
| ☐ **BROOKER, Harry** ............................. *paintings* | $6,600 | $9,900 |
| English ac. 1880-1908 | | | |
| ☐ **BROOKES, Samuel Marsdon** ............... *paintings* | $2,860 | $48,400 |
| American 1816-1892 ................................. *drawings* | | $550 |
| ☐ **BROOKS, Alden Finney** ....................... *paintings* | | | $2,200 |
| American b. 1840 | | | |
| ☐ **BROOKS, Carol** ................................. *sculpture* | | | $1,870 |
| American b. 1940 | | | |
| ☐ **BROOKS, Cora Smalley** ...................... *paintings* | $224 | $275 |
| American d. 1930 | | | |
| ☐ **BROOKS, James** ................................. *paintings* | $605 | $23,100 |
| American b. 1906 | | | |
| ☐ **BROOKS, Maria** ............................... *paintings* | | | $1,100 |
| British ac. c. 1869-1890 | | | |
| ☐ **BROOKS, Nicholas Alden** .................... *paintings* | $121 | $26,400 |
| American ac. 1880-1904 | | | |
| ☐ **BROOKS, Thomas** ............................. *paintings* | $220 | $2,090 |
| English 1818-1891 | | | |
| ☐ **BROOKS, W.K.** .................................. *paintings* | | | $550 |

| | Current Price Range | |
|---|---|---|
| | Low | High |
| ☐ **BROOME, G.J.** .................................... *paintings* | | $495 |
| ☐ **BROOS, Jean Jacques Zuidema** ........... *paintings* | | $3,300 |
| Belgian ac. 1891-1900 | | |
| ☐ **BROSSARD, G.** .................................... *paintings* | | $1,540 |
| ☐ **BROSSMAN, F.** .................................... *paintings* | | $300 |
| ☐ **BROTAT, Joan Vilanova** ..................... *paintings* | | $308 |
| Spanish 20th cent. | | |
| ☐ **BROUGIER, Adolf** .............................. *paintings* | | $1,320 |
| German/English 1870-1926 | | |
| ☐ **BROUILLARD, Eugene** ....................... *paintings* | | $385 |
| French b. 1870 | | |
| ☐ **BROUILLET, Pierre Andre Aristide** ..... *paintings* | | $1,100 |
| French 1857-1914 | | |
| ☐ **BROUN, F.** ......................................... *paintings* | | $1,650 |
| ☐ **BROUWER, Adriaen** ........................... *paintings* | | $23,100 |
| Flemish 1605/06-1638 | | |
| ☐ **BROUWER, Barend** ............................ *paintings* | | $550 |
| Dutch 1872-1936 | | |
| ☐ **BROUX, S.** ......................................... *paintings* | $165 | $220 |
| French 19th cent. | | |
| ☐ **BROW, F.** ......................................... *sculpture* | | $330 |
| ☐ **BROWER, Peter** ................................. *paintings* | $110 | $250 |
| Dutch 20th cent. | | |
| ☐ **BROWER, S.** ...................................... *paintings* | | $330 |
| Dutch 19th cent. | | |
| ☐ **BROWERE, Albertis del Orient** ........... *paintings* | $1,760 | $12,100 |
| American 1814-1887 | | |
| ☐ **BROWN, A.E.D.G. Stirling** ................. *paintings* | | $6,600 |
| British 19th/20th cent. | | |
| ☐ **BROWN, Agnes Augusta** ..................... *paintings* | | $302 |
| American 1847-1932 | | |
| ☐ **BROWN, Arthur William** ..................... *drawings* | $110 | $907 |
| Canadian/American 1881-1966 | | |
| ☐ **BROWN, Benjamin Chambers** .............. *paintings* | $375 | $2,090 |
| American 1865-1942 | | |
| ☐ **BROWN, Bolton** ................................. *paintings* | $137 | $1,540 |
| American 1865-1936 | | |
| ☐ **BROWN, Carlyle** ................................. *paintings* | | $1,430 |
| American 1919-1964 ................................. *drawings* | | $55 |
| ☐ **BROWN, Charlotte Harding** ................. *drawings* | | $1,760 |
| American b. 1873 | | |
| ☐ **BROWN, Douglas** ............................... *drawings* | $330 | $357 |
| ☐ **BROWN, Elmore J.** ............................ *paintings* | | $137 |
| b. 1899 ................................................. *drawings* | $110 | $412 |
| ☐ **BROWN, Ernest O.** ........................... *paintings* | | $275 |
| American 20th cent. | | |
| ☐ **BROWN, Ethelbert W.** ........................ *paintings* | $110 | $275 |
| American b. 1870 | | |

| | | Current Price Range | |
|---|---|---|---|
| | | Low | High |
| ☐ **BROWN, F. Griswald** ............... *paintings* | | $137 | $220 |
| American 20th cent. | | | |
| ☐ **BROWN, Ford Madox** ............ *drawings* | | | $990 |
| English 1821-1893 | | | |
| ☐ **BROWN, Francis F.** ............... *paintings* | | $220 | $880 |
| American b. 1891 ........................ *drawings* | | | $33 |
| ☐ **BROWN, Frank A.** ............... *paintings* | | $165 | $3,025 |
| American b. 1876 | | | |
| ☐ **BROWN, George Elmer** ......... *paintings* | | | $220 |
| Canadian .................................... *drawings* | | | $220 |
| ☐ **BROWN, George Henry Alan** ...... *drawings* | | $350 | $880 |
| English b. 1862 | | | |
| ☐ **BROWN, George Loring** ........ *paintings* | | $742 | $10,000 |
| American 1814-1889 ..................... *drawings* | | $110 | $715 |
| ☐ **BROWN, Harley** ................... *paintings* | | $1,265 | $7,500 |
| Canadian b. 1939 ........................ *drawings* | | | $770 |
| ........................................ *sculpture* | | | $800 |
| ☐ **BROWN, Harrison B.** ............. *paintings* | | $220 | $6,600 |
| American 1831-1915 ..................... *drawings* | | $100 | $137 |
| ☐ **BROWN, Henry Kirke** ............ *sculpture* | | | $6,050 |
| American 1814-1886 | | | |
| ☐ **BROWN, J. Randolph** ............. *paintings* | | | $825 |
| American b. 1861 | | | |
| ☐ **BROWN, Joan** ..................... *paintings* | | $1,320 | $7,150 |
| American b. 1938 | | | |
| ☐ **BROWN, John Appleton** ......... *paintings* | | $300 | $28,600 |
| American 1844-1902 ..................... *drawings* | | $385 | $1,320 |
| ☐ **BROWN, John Bunyan** ........... *paintings* | | | $715 |
| American 1826-1909 | | | |
| ☐ **BROWN, John George** ............ *paintings* | | $495 | $99,000 |
| Anglo/American 1831-1913 ............ *drawings* | | $660 | $6,875 |
| ☐ **BROWN, John Lewis** ............. *paintings* | | $660 | $8,800 |
| French 1829-1890 ........................ *drawings* | | | $660 |
| ☐ **BROWN, Joseph Randolph** ....... *paintings* | | $66 | $220 |
| American b. 1861 | | | |
| ☐ **BROWN, Judith** .................... *drawings* | | | $150 |
| American b. 1931 ........................ *sculpture* | | $44 | $302 |
| ☐ **BROWN, M.E.** ..................... *paintings* | | | $198 |
| American 19th cent. | | | |
| ☐ **BROWN, Manneville Elihu Dearing** ....... *paintings* | | $330 | $8,800 |
| American 1810-1896 | | | |
| ☐ **BROWN, Mather** ................... *paintings* | | $495 | $3,500 |
| American,b. London 1761/62-1831 | | | |
| ☐ **BROWN, N.** ........................ *paintings* | | | $275 |
| American 19th cent. | | | |
| ☐ **BROWN, P.** ........................ *paintings* | | | $275 |
| American 19th/20th cent. | | | |
| ☐ **BROWN, Paul** ..................... *paintings* | | $247 | $660 |
| American 1893-1958 ..................... *drawings* | | $165 | $7,150 |

## Recurring Themes

Some artists gain a reputation for painting the same subject over and over again. John George Brown is known for his renderings of newsboys and bootblacks, made picturesque to satisfy the Victorian penchant for laundering reality into sweet sentimentality.

Born in England, Brown moved to the United States when he was twenty-two, worked for three years as a glassblower, and then married the boss's daughter. He spent the rest of his career as a painter of juvenile subjects and portraits.

Popular during his lifetime, Brown's work still finds much public approval. Should you be outbid on a Brown picture at auction, bide your time and read your sales catalogs. In all likelihood, a similar work will come onto the market in a short time. (John George Brown, "Shoe Shine Boy," oil on canvas, 24 x 17 in., Hindman, September 23, 1984, $17,600.)

| | | *Current Price Range* | |
|---|---|---|---|
| | | *Low* | *High* |
| ☐ **BROWN, R.G.** ..................................... *paintings* | | | **$825** |
| American 19th cent. | | | |
| ☐ **BROWN, Robert Woodley** .................... *paintings* | | | **$550** |
| English 19th cent. | | | |
| ☐ **BROWN, Roger** ................................... *paintings* | | **$14,300** | **$19,800** |
| American b. 1941 ...................................... *sculpture* | | | **$17,600** |
| ☐ **BROWN, Roy** ..................................... *paintings* | | **$66** | **$2,200** |
| American 1879-1956 | | | |
| ☐ **BROWN, S. Appleton** .......................... *paintings* | | | **$357** |
| American 19th/20th cent. | | | |
| ☐ **BROWN, Sam** .................................... *paintings* | | | **$1,210** |
| American b. 1907 | | | |
| ☐ **BROWN, Thomas Austen** .................... *paintings* | | | **$660** |
| Scottish 1859-1917 | | | |
| ☐ **BROWN, W. Warren** ........................... *paintings* | | **$82** | **$350** |
| Canadian b. 1881 | | | |

| | | Current Price Range | |
|---|---|---|---|
| | | *Low* | *High* |
| ☐ **BROWN, W.H.** ...................... *paintings* | | **$264** | **$575** |
| American ac. 1875-1890 | | | |
| ☐ **BROWN, Walter Francis** ..................... *paintings* | | **$200** | **$825** |
| American 1853-1929 | | | |
| ☐ **BROWN, William Alden** ..................... *paintings* | | **$176** | **$330** |
| American b. 1877 | | | |
| ☐ **BROWN, William Beattie** ..................... *paintings* | | **$77** | **$1,760** |
| English 1831-1909 | | | |
| ☐ **BROWN, William G.** .......................... *paintings* | | | **$356** |
| American ac. 1844 | | | |
| ☐ **BROWN, William Marshall** ................. *paintings* | | **$1,210** | **$1,540** |
| British 1863-1936 | | | |
| ☐ **BROWN, William Mason** ..................... *paintings* | | **$742** | **$22,000** |
| American 1828-1898 ................................... *drawings* | | | **$170** |
| ☐ **BROWN, William Theo** ..................... *paintings* | | **$440** | **$3,080** |
| American b. 1919 | | | |
| ☐ **BROWNE, Alfred J. Warne** ................. *paintings* | | | **$522** |
| British d. 1915 ........................................ *drawings* | | | **$110** |
| ☐ **BROWNE, B.** ..................................... *paintings* | | | **$301** |
| British 18th/19th cent. | | | |
| ☐ **BROWNE, Belmore** ............................ *paintings* | | | **$412** |
| American 19th/20th cent. | | | |
| ☐ **BROWNE, Byron** ............................ *paintings* | | **$424** | **$9,900** |
| American 1907-1961 ................................. *drawings* | | **$220** | **$1,540** |
| ☐ **BROWNE, Charles F.** .......................... *paintings* | | **$33** | **$2,310** |
| American 1859-1921 | | | |
| ☐ **BROWNE, George Elmer** ..................... *paintings* | | **$143** | **$6,380** |
| American 1871-1946 ................................. *drawings* | | **$302** | **$475** |
| ☐ **BROWNE, Halbot K. (PHIZ)** ................. *drawings* | | | **$1,540** |
| English 1815-1892 | | | |
| ☐ **BROWNE, Harold Putnam** ................. *paintings* | | **$330** | **$550** |
| American 1894-1931 ................................. *drawings* | | **$143** | **$220** |
| ☐ **BROWNE, Henriette** ............................ *paintings* | | **$2,750** | **$7,700** |
| French 1829-1901 | | | |
| ☐ **BROWNE, Margaret Fitzhugh** .............. *paintings* | | **$110** | **$2,640** |
| American 1884-1972 | | | |
| ☐ **BROWNE, Matilda** | | | |
| **(Mrs. Frederick van WYCK)** .................. *paintings* | | **$121** | **$1,430** |
| American 1869-1953 ................................. *drawings* | | | **$154** |
| ☐ **BROWNE, Robert** ............................... *paintings* | | | **$825** |
| Dutch or English 19th cent. | | | |
| ☐ **BROWNE, William Garf.** ..................... *paintings* | | | **$825** |
| ☐ **BROWNELL, Charles de Wolf** .............. *paintings* | | **$7,150** | **$13,200** |
| American 1822-1909 | | | |
| ☐ **BROWNELL, Matilda Auchincloss** ........ *paintings* | | **$246** | **$4,180** |
| American b. 1869 | | | |
| ☐ **BROWNING, Charles A.** ....................... *paintings* | | | **$440** |
| ☐ **BROWNING, George Wesley** ............... *paintings* | | | **$275** |
| American 1868-1951 | | | |

| | | Current Price Range | |
|---|---|---|---|
| | | Low | High |
| ☐ **BROWNSCOMBE, Jennie Augusta** ....... *paintings* | | $440 | $20,900 |
| American 1850-1936 ................................. *drawings* | | $330 | $1,760 |
| ☐ **BROZIK, Wenzel von Vacslaw** ............. *paintings* | | $247 | $14,300 |
| Bohemian 1851-1900/01 ............................ *drawings* | | $165 | $302 |
| ☐ **BRUBIER, W.** .................................... *paintings* | | | $3,500 |
| English or Amer. 19th cent. | | | |
| ☐ **BRUCE, Edward** .............................. *paintings* | | $275 | $1,980 |
| American 1879-1943 | | | |
| ☐ **BRUCE, Granville** ............................. *drawings* | | | $521 |
| American 20th cent. | | | |
| ☐ **BRUCE, James Christie** ..................... *paintings* | | | $385 |
| American School 19th cent. | | | |
| ☐ **BRUCE, William Blair** ....................... *paintings* | | $330 | $1,320 |
| Canadian 1857/59-1906 | | | |
| ☐ **BRUCK, Lajos** .................................. *paintings* | | $605 | $4,620 |
| Hungarian 1846-1910 | | | |
| ☐ **BRUCKE, Wilhelm** ............................. *paintings* | | | $935 |
| German active 1820-70 | | | |
| ☐ **BRUCKER, Ernst** .............................. *paintings* | | | $220 |
| German 20th cent. | | | |
| ☐ **BRUCKMAN, Willem Leendert** ............. *drawings* | | | $440 |
| ☐ **BRUCKMANN, Lodewijk** ..................... *paintings* | | $275 | $2,090 |
| Dutch/American b. 1903 | | | |
| ☐ **BRUCKNER, H.** ................................. *paintings* | | | $2,750 |
| American 19th cent. | | | |
| ☐ **BRUCKNER, K.** ................................ *paintings* | | | $550 |
| German 20th cent. | | | |
| ☐ **BRUCKNER, Theodor** ......................... *paintings* | | | $825 |
| Austrian 1870-1921 | | | |
| ☐ **BRUEGHEL, Ambrosius** ..................... *paintings* | | $33,000 | $41,800 |
| Flemish 1617-1675 | | | |
| ☐ **BRUEGHEL, Jan (the elder)** ................. *paintings* | | $77,000 | $319,000 |
| Flemish 1568-1625 | | | |
| ☐ **BRUEGHEL, Jan (the younger)** ............. *paintings* | | $17,600 | $99,000 |
| Flemish 1601-1678 | | | |
| ☐ **BRUEGHEL, Pieter (the younger)** .......... *paintings* | | $41,800 | $385,000 |
| ☐ **BRUESTLE, Bertram G.** ...................... *paintings* | | $110 | $550 |
| American 20th cent. | | | |
| ☐ **BRUESTLE, George** ........................... *paintings* | | $132 | $3,850 |
| American 1872-1939 | | | |
| ☐ **BRUGAIROLLES, Victor** ..................... *paintings* | | $495 | $990 |
| French b. 1869 | | | |
| ☐ **BRUGES, Pauline Alice Leonide** ........... *paintings* | | | $385 |
| French 1833-1910 | | | |
| ☐ **BRUGNER, Colestin** .......................... *paintings* | | $192 | $660 |
| German 19th cent. | | | |
| ☐ **BRUGNOLI, Emmanuele** ...................... *drawings* | | $297 | $1,210 |
| Italian 19th cent. | | | |

| | Current Price Range | |
|---|---|---|
| | Low | High |
| ☐ **BRULLOFF, Alexandre** ........................ *drawings* | $385 | $1,100 |
| Russian 1798-1877 | | |
| ☐ **BRUMIDI, Constantino** ...................... *paintings* | $6,500 | $29,700 |
| American 1805-1880 ................................. *drawings* | | $220 |
| ☐ **BRUN, C.** ............................................. *paintings* | | $1,540 |
| ☐ **BRUN, Edme Gustave Frederic** ............. *paintings* | | $2,750 |
| French 1817-1881 | | |
| ☐ **BRUN, Renee Eugenie Camille** ............. *paintings* | | $6,050 |
| French 20th cent. | | |
| ☐ **BRUNDAGE, William Tyson** ................. *paintings* | | $275 |
| American 1849-1923 | | |
| ☐ **BRUNEL DE NEUVILLE,** | | |
| **Alfred Arthur** ..................................... *paintings* | $550 | $4,180 |
| French 19th cent. | | |
| ☐ **BRUNELLESCHI, Umberto** ................. *drawings* | $121 | $1,430 |
| Italian b. 1879; ac. 1907-1930 | | |
| ☐ **BRUNERY, Francois** ........................... *paintings* | $660 | $29,700 |
| Italian b. 1845, ac. 1898-1909 | | |
| ☐ **BRUNET-DESBAINES, Alfred Louis** ..... *paintings* | | $2,090 |
| French b. 1845 | | |
| ☐ **BRUNIAS, Augustin** ........................... *paintings* | $1,500 | $1,600 |
| English c. 1735-1810 | | |
| ☐ **BRUNIN, Leon** ................................... *paintings* | | $9,350 |
| Belgian 1861-1949 | | |
| ☐ **BRUNKAL, Erich** ............................... *paintings* | | $1,045 |
| German b. 1859 | | |
| ☐ **BRUNNER, F. Sands** ........................... *paintings* | $411 | $1,650 |
| 20th cent. | | |
| ☐ **BRUNNER, Ferdinand** ........................ *paintings* | | $2,310 |
| Austrian 1870-1945 | | |
| ☐ **BRUNNER, Hans** ............................... *paintings* | | $770 |
| European | | |
| ☐ **BRUNNER, Josef** ............................... *paintings* | | $330 |
| German 1826-1893 | | |
| ☐ **BRUNOT-HOWARD, \*\*\*** ...................... *paintings* | | $4,950 |
| French 19th cent. | | |
| ☐ **BRUNT, R. van** ................................... *paintings* | | $600 |
| American ac. 1857-1876 | | |
| ☐ **BRUSH, George de Forest** ................... *paintings* | $357 | $27,500 |
| American 1855-1941 ................................. *drawings* | $385 | $4,180 |
| ☐ **BRUSSEL, Paul Theodor van** ............... *paintings* | | $11,000 |
| Dutch 1754-1795 | | |
| ☐ **BRUTON, Margaret** ........................... *paintings* | | $302 |
| American d. 1983 | | |
| ☐ **BRUYCKER, Francois-Antoine de** ......... *paintings* | $8,250 | $34,100 |
| Belgian 1816-1882 | | |
| ☐ **BRUYERE, Elise** ................................. *paintings* | | $6,050 |
| French 1776-1842 | | |
| ☐ **BRUYN, Bartholomaeus (the younger)** .... *paintings* | | $4,000 |

| | | | Current Price Range | |
|---|---|---|---|---|
| | | | Low | High |
| ☐ **BRUYN, Chris de** .............. *paintings* | | | | $247 |
| Dutch 20th cent. | | | | |
| ☐ **BRUYN, Jan Cornelis de** ......... *paintings* | | | | $7,700 |
| Dutch | | | | |
| ☐ **BRYAN, Edward C.** ............. *paintings* | | | $55 | $247 |
| American b. 1876 | | | | |
| ☐ **BRYANS, Alice Maude** ......... *paintings* | | | $1,100 | $1,100 |
| British 19th cent. | | | | |
| ☐ **BRYANT, Ann** ................. *paintings* | | | $11 | $192 |
| English 20th cent. | | | | |
| ☐ **BRYANT, Everett Lloyd** ....... *paintings* | | | $77 | $1,100 |
| American 1864-1945 .................. *drawings* | | | $44 | $93 |
| ☐ **BRYANT, Harold E.** ........... *paintings* | | | | $4,180 |
| American 1894-1950 | | | | |
| ☐ **BRYANT, Henry C.** ............ *paintings* | | | | $2,530 |
| American 1812-c. 1881 | | | | |
| ☐ **BRYANT, Miriam** .............. *paintings* | | | | $1,045 |
| American 20th cent. | | | | |
| ☐ **BRYANT, Wallace** ............. *paintings* | | | $187 | $275 |
| American 19th/20th cent. | | | | |
| ☐ **BRYCE, A.J.C.** ................ *paintings* | | | | $190 |
| English 1868-1940 | | | | |
| ☐ **BRYERS, Duane** .............. *paintings* | | | $5,500 | $41,000 |
| American b. 1911 | | | | |
| ☐ **BRYUM, Ruthven H.** .......... *paintings* | | | | $198 |
| American 20th cent. | | | | |
| ☐ **BRZOZOWSKI, Tadeusz** ....... *paintings* | | | | $330 |
| Polish b. 1918 | | | | |
| ☐ **BUBERL, Caspar** .............. *sculpture* | | | | $1,100 |
| American 1834-1899 | | | | |
| ☐ **BUCCI, Lorenzo** .............. *paintings* | | | | $605 |
| Italian 18th/19th cent. | | | | |
| ☐ **BUCCIARELLI, Daniele** ....... *drawings* | | | | $330 |
| Italian 19th cent. | | | | |
| ☐ **BUCHANAN, E.** ............... *paintings* | | | | $192 |
| American late 19th cent. | | | | |
| ☐ **BUCHANAN, Georges F.** ...... *paintings* | | | $466 | $1,320 |
| Scottish ac. 1848-1864 | | | | |
| ☐ **BUCHANAN, J.** ............... *drawings* | | | | $770 |
| British School 19th cent. | | | | |
| ☐ **BUCHANAN, Peter** ............ *paintings* | | | | $440 |
| British 19th cent. | | | | |
| ☐ **BUCHBINDER, Simeon** ....... *paintings* | | | | $550 |
| Polish b. 1853 | | | | |
| ☐ **BUCHE, Josef** ............... *paintings* | | | | $550 |
| Austrian 1848-1917 | | | | |
| ☐ **BUCHER, Karl** ............... *paintings* | | | | $247 |
| Swiss 1819-1891 | | | | |

|  | | Current Price Range | |
|---|---|---|---|
|  | | Low | High |
| ☐ **BUCHHEISTER, Carl (Karl)** ............... *drawings* | | | $412 |
| German 1890-1964 | | | |
| ☐ **BUCHHOLZ, L.** ................................. *paintings* | | | $440 |
| b. 1937 | | | |
| ☐ **BUCHLINDER, S.** ............................. *paintings* | | | $418 |
| European | | | |
| ☐ **BUCHNER, Georg** ........................... *paintings* | | $660 | $1,100 |
| German 1858-1914 | | | |
| ☐ **BUCHNER, Rudolf Josef Johan** ............ *paintings* | | | $330 |
| Austrian 1894-1962 | | | |
| ☐ **BUCHTERKIRCH, Armin** ................... *drawings* | | $55 | $301 |
| American b. 1859 | | | |
| ☐ **BUCK, Adam** ...................................... *drawings* | | $770 | $990 |
| Irish 1759-1883 | | | |
| ☐ **BUCK, Claude** ................................... *paintings* | | $110 | $2,310 |
| American b. 1890 | | | |
| ☐ **BUCK, William H.** ............................. *paintings* | | $2,090 | $25,300 |
| American 1840-1888 | | | |
| ☐ **BUCKLER, Charles E.** ........................ *paintings* | | $60 | $825 |
| American b. 1869 | | | |
| ☐ **BUCKLER, John** ............................... *paintings* | | | $935 |
| British 1770-1851 ...................................... *drawings* | | | $385 |
| ☐ **BUCKLER, William** ........................... *drawings* | | $165 | $220 |
| British 1836-1856/58 | | | |
| ☐ **BUCKLEY, C.F.** ................................. *paintings* | | $308 | $550 |
| English ac. 1841-1869 | | | |
| ☐ **BUCKLEY, Stephen** ........................... *paintings* | | | $2,475 |
| British b. 1944 | | | |
| ☐ **BUCKLIN, Bradley A.** ........................ *paintings* | | $110 | $192 |
| American 1824-1915 | | | |
| ☐ **BUCKLIN, W.S.** ................................. *drawings* | | | $274 |
| American 1851-1928 | | | |
| ☐ **BUCKNALL, Ernest Pile** ...................... *paintings* | | | $825 |
| English 19th/20th cent. | | | |
| ☐ **BUCKNER, Richard** ........................... *paintings* | | | $550 |
| English 19th cent. | | | |
| ☐ **BUDD, F.C.** ...................................... *drawings* | | | $1,870 |
| 19th cent. | | | |
| ☐ **BUDELOT, Philippe** ........................... *paintings* | | $660 | $5,500 |
| French ac. 1793-1841 | | | |
| ☐ **BUDGEN, Frank Spencer Curtis** ........... *paintings* | | $275 | $350 |
| English 20th cent. | | | |
| ☐ **BUDGEON, T.** ................................... *paintings* | | | $1,760 |
| 19th cent. | | | |
| ☐ **BUDNER, T.** ..................................... *paintings* | | | $192 |
| American 20th cent. | | | |
| ☐ **BUDZCINSKI, \*\*\*** ............................. *paintings* | | | $1,540 |
| Polish 19th cent. | | | |

| | | *Current Price Range* | |
|---|---|---|---|
| | | *Low* | *High* |
| ☐ **BUEB, Franz** ..................................... *drawings* | | **$49** | **$352** |
| American 20th cent. | | | |
| ☐ **BUECKELAER, Joachim** ..................... *paintings* | | | **$17,050** |
| Flemish 1530-1573 | | | |
| ☐ **BUEHR, Karl Albert** ........................... *paintings* | | **$357** | **$20,900** |
| German/American b. 1866 | | | |
| ☐ **BUEHR, Mary K.** ................................ *paintings* | | | **$412** |
| American early 20th cent. | | | |
| ☐ **BUEL, Franz de** ................................. *paintings* | | | **$1,760** |
| Belgian 19th cent. | | | |
| ☐ **BUEL, Henri de** ................................ *paintings* | | | **$1,980** |
| Belgian 19th cent. | | | |
| ☐ **BUEL, L. de** ...................................... *paintings* | | | **$715** |
| Belgian 19th cent. | | | |
| ☐ **BUENO, Antonio** ............................... *paintings* | | | **$220** |
| Italian b. 1918 | | | |
| ☐ **BUENO, Xavier** .................................. *paintings* | | **$1,320** | **$5,720** |
| Spanish/Italian b. 1915 | | | |
| ☐ **BUFANO, Beniamino** ......................... *drawings* | | | **$1,320** |
| American 1888-1970 ................................. *sculpture* | | **$770** | **$2,750** |
| ☐ **BUFF, Conrad** .................................. *paintings* | | **$660** | **$3,025** |
| American b. 1886 | | | |
| ☐ **BUFFET, Bernard** ............................. *paintings* | | **$880** | **$46,200** |
| French b. 1928 ....................................... *drawings* | | **$330** | **$10,450** |
| ☐ **BUFFET, L'Abbe Paul** ........................ *paintings* | | | **$385** |
| French b. 1864 ........................................ *drawings* | | | **$308** |
| ☐ **BUFFIN, Carlos** ................................ *paintings* | | | **$18,700** |
| French 19th cent. | | | |
| ☐ **BUGATTI, Rembrandt** ........................ *sculpture* | | **$6,600** | **$20,900** |
| Italian 1883/85-1916 | | | |
| ☐ **BUGGION, M.** ................................... *paintings* | | | **$412** |
| French 20th cent. | | | |
| ☐ **BUGZESTER, Max** ............................. *paintings* | | **$220** | **$302** |
| ☐ **BUHLER, A.W.** .................................. *drawings* | | | **$230** |
| Dutch (?) 19th cent. | | | |
| ☐ **BUHLER, Robert** ............................... *paintings* | | | **$220** |
| English b. 1916 | | | |
| ☐ **BUHLMAN, R.** ................................... *paintings* | | | **$605** |
| Swiss 19th cent. | | | |
| ☐ **BUHLMANN, Johann Rudolf** ............... *paintings* | | | **$825** |
| Swiss 1802-1890 | | | |
| ☐ **BUHLMAYER, Conrad** ........................ *paintings* | | **$4,070** | **$4,400** |
| Austrian 1835-1883 | | | |
| ☐ **BUHOT, Felix Hilaire** ......................... *drawings* | | **$605** | **$5,225** |
| French 1847-1898 | | | |
| ☐ **BUKEN, Jan van** ............................... *paintings* | | | **$3,300** |
| ☐ **BUKLAND, Elsa** ................................ *paintings* | | | **$660** |
| European 19th cent. | | | |

| | | Current Price Range | |
| --- | --- | --- | --- |
| | | Low | High |
| ☐ **BUKOVAC, Vlacho** .............................. *paintings* | | | $5,775 |
| Yugoslavian 1855-1923 | | | |
| ☐ **BULFIELD, J.** ..................................... *paintings* | | | $1,760 |
| English 19th cent. | | | |
| ☐ **BULIO, Jean** ........................................ *sculpture* | | $1,650 | $2,475 |
| French 1827-1911 | | | |
| ☐ **BULL, Charles Livingston** ...................... *paintings* | | $330 | $660 |
| American 1874-1932 ................................... *drawings* | | $143 | $715 |
| ☐ **BULL, J.C.** ......................................... *paintings* | | | $500 |
| ☐ **BULLARD, George Lawrence** ............... *paintings* | | | $330 |
| ☐ **BULLENE, Les** .................................... *paintings* | | | $301 |
| contemporary | | | |
| ☐ **BULLER, Audrey** ................................ *paintings* | | | $880 |
| ☐ **BULLERKOLLER, L.** ........................... *paintings* | | | $2,310 |
| Belgian 19th cent. | | | |
| ☐ **BULLES** .............................................. *paintings* | | | $440 |
| ☐ **BULMAN, Orville** ............................... *paintings* | | $27 | $300 |
| Latin American 20th cent. | | | |
| ☐ **BULTMAN, Fritz** ................................. *drawings* | | $132 | $302 |
| American b. 1919 | | | |
| ☐ **BUNCE, Kate E.** ................................... *paintings* | | | $1,100 |
| English 1858-1927 | | | |
| ☐ **BUNCE, Louis** ...................................... *paintings* | | | $1,100 |
| ☐ **BUNCE, William Gedney** ....................... *paintings* | | $220 | $1,320 |
| American 1840-1916 ................................... *drawings* | | | $550 |
| ☐ **BUNDEL, Willem van den** .................... *paintings* | | | $12,100 |
| Dutch 1577-1655 | | | |
| ☐ **BUNDY, Edgar** ..................................... *paintings* | | $605 | $4,400 |
| English 1862-1922 | | | |
| ☐ **BUNDY, Horace** ................................... *paintings* | | | $1,320 |
| American 1814-1883 | | | |
| ☐ **BUNDY, John Elwood** .......................... *paintings* | | | $467 |
| American 1853-1933 ................................... *drawings* | | | $50 |
| ☐ **BUNING, B.** ......................................... *paintings* | | | $550 |
| Dutch 19th cent. | | | |
| ☐ **BUNKER, Dennis Miller** ....................... *paintings* | | $11,000 | $44,000 |
| American 1861-1890 | | | |
| ☐ **BUNN, George** ..................................... *paintings* | | $330 | $1,705 |
| American 19th/20th cent. | | | |
| ☐ **BUNN, Kenneth Rodney** ....................... *sculpture* | | | $2,000 |
| American b. 1938 | | | |
| ☐ **BUNNER, Andrew Fisher** ...................... *paintings* | | $440 | $6,600 |
| American 1841-1897 ................................... *drawings* | | $40 | $660 |
| ☐ **BUNNER, Rudolph F.** .......................... *drawings* | | $143 | $192 |
| American 19th/20th cent. | | | |
| ☐ **BUNNEY, John Wharlton** ...................... *drawings* | | | $352 |
| English 1828-1882 | | | |

| | | Current Price Range | |
|---|---|---|---|
| | | Low | High |

☐ **BUONACCORSI, Pietro**
  **(called Pierino del Vaga)** ........................ *drawings* | | | $1,650
  Italian 1500-1547

☐ **BUONGIORNO** ................................. *paintings* | | | $192
  Italian 19th cent.

☐ **BUONTALENTI, Bernardo**
  **(called Dalle Girandole)** ........................ *drawings* | | | $990
  Italian 1536-1608

☐ **BURBANK, Elbridge Ayer** ................... *paintings* | $11 | $5,500
  American 1858-1949 ................................... *drawings* | $77 | $330

☐ **BURBURE, Louis de** ........................... *paintings* | | | $4,400
  Belgian b. 1837

☐ **BURCHARTZ, A.** ............................... *paintings* | | | $467
  German 19th cent.

☐ **BURCHFIELD, Charles** ........................ *paintings* | $7,700 | $18,150
  American 1893-1967 ................................... *drawings* | $192 | $148,500

☐ **BURCKHORST, August** ....................... *paintings* | | | $715

☐ **BURDETTE, Hattie E.** ........................ *drawings* | | | $357
  American late 19th/early 20th cent

☐ **BURDICK, Charles** ............................ *paintings* | $165 | $302
  American 19th cent.

☐ **BURDICK, Horace R.** ......................... *paintings* | $99 | $880
  American 1844-1942 ................................... *drawings* | $100 | $550

☐ **BUREAU, Leon** ................................. *sculpture* | | | $1,540
  French 1866-1906

☐ **BURELL, Vander** ............................... *paintings* | | | $440

☐ **BUREN, Richard van** ......................... *drawings* | | | $302
  American b. 1891

☐ **BURFIELD, James M.** ......................... *paintings* | | | $950
  English ac. 1865-1883

☐ **BURFORD, Thomas** ............................ *paintings* | | | $18,700
  English 1710-1774

☐ **BURGADE, Louis** ............................... *paintings* | | | $7,150
  French b. 1803

☐ **BURGARITSKI** .................................. *paintings* | | | $330

☐ **BURGDORFF, Ferdinand** ..................... *paintings* | $99 | $770
  American 1881/83-after 1934 ......................... *drawings* | $137 | $990

☐ **BURGER, Anton** ............................... *paintings* | $8,800 | $11,000
  German 1824-1905 ..................................... *drawings* | | | $2,250

☐ **BURGER, Leopold** ............................. *drawings* | | | $522
  Austrian 1861-1903

☐ **BURGER, Willy Friedrich** .................. *paintings* | | | $247
  German 1882-1964

☐ **BURGERS, Hendricus Jacobus** ............. *paintings* | $440 | $2,600
  Dutch 1834-1899

☐ **BURGESS, George H.** ......................... *paintings* | $1,980 | $2,200
  American 1831-1905

☐ **BURGESS, Henry William** ................... *drawings* | $275 | $495
  English ac. 1809-1844

| | | *Current Price Range* | |
|---|---|---|---|
| | | Low | High |
| ☐ **BURGESS, John Bagnold** ....................... *paintings* | | $242 | $8,800 |
| English 1830-1897 | | | |
| ☐ **BURGESS, Ruth Payne** ........................ *paintings* | | $110 | $300 |
| American d. 1934 | | | |
| ☐ **BURGESS, T.H.** ................................ *paintings* | | | $357 |
| American (?) 19th cent. | | | |
| ☐ **BURGI, Jacob** ..................................... *drawings* | | $1,320 | $1,870 |
| ☐ **BURGULLA** ....................................... *paintings* | | | $495 |
| Continental 19th cent. | | | |
| ☐ **BURGY, F.S.** ..................................... *drawings* | | | $385 |
| American 20th cent. | | | |
| ☐ **BURHENNE, Minnie** ........................ *paintings* | | | $385 |
| ☐ **BURKE, Edgar** ................................ *drawings* | | | $418 |
| American 20th cent. | | | |
| ☐ **BURKE, Lucille K.** .............................. *paintings* | | | $275 |
| 20th cent. | | | |
| ☐ **BURKEL, Heinrich** ........................... *paintings* | | $14,300 | $60,500 |
| German 1802-1869 ...................................... *drawings* | | | $770 |
| ☐ **BURKHARD, Henri** ............................ *paintings* | | $770 | $770 |
| American b. 1892 | | | |
| ☐ **BURKHARDT, Hans Gustav** ................ *paintings* | | $165 | $2,310 |
| Swiss/American b. 1904 ............................. *drawings* | | $521 | $605 |
| ☐ **BURKHARDT, K.** ................................ *paintings* | | | $412 |
| Swiss 19th cent. | | | |
| ☐ **BURKHIMER, M.** ............................... *paintings* | | | $467 |
| ☐ **BURLE-MARX, Roberto** ...................... *drawings* | | | $550 |
| Brazilian b. 1909 | | | |
| ☐ **BURLEIGH, C.C. (Jr.)** ........................ *drawings* | | | $385 |
| ☐ **BURLEIGH, Sydney Richmond** ............ *paintings* | | | $3,850 |
| American 1853-1931 ................................... *drawings* | | $121 | $6,325 |
| ☐ **BURLER, De** ..................................... *paintings* | | | $935 |
| Austrian 19th cent. | | | |
| ☐ **BURLIN, Paul** ................................... *paintings* | | $159 | $1,980 |
| American 1886-1969 .................................. *drawings* | | $55 | $660 |
| ☐ **BURLING, V.** ..................................... *paintings* | | | $302 |
| European 19th cent. | | | |
| ☐ **BURLINGAME, Charles Albert** ............ *paintings* | | $121 | $605 |
| American 1860-1930 | | | |
| ☐ **BURLIUK, David** ................................ *paintings* | | $110 | $8,250 |
| Russian/American 1882-1967 ......................... *drawings* | | $33 | $770 |
| ☐ **BURMUDEZ, Cundo** .......................... *paintings* | | | $3,850 |
| b. Cuba 1914 | | | |
| ☐ **BURN, E.** ....................................... *paintings* | | | $385 |
| British 19th cent. | | | |
| ☐ **BURNE-JONES, Sir Edward Coley** ....... *paintings* | | $7,700 | $110,000 |
| English 1833-1898 ..................................... *drawings* | | $165 | $16,500 |
| ☐ **BURNE-JONES, Sir Philip** ................... *paintings* | | $110 | $3,850 |
| English 1861-1926 | | | |

| | | Current Price Range | |
| --- | --- | --- | --- |
| | | Low | High |
| ☐ **BURNETT, John** .................................. *paintings* | | | $220 |
| Scottish 1784-1868 | | | |
| ☐ **BURNETT, Martha Moore** ................... *paintings* | | | $242 |
| American | | | |
| ☐ **BURNEY, Edward Francis** .................... *drawings* | | | $440 |
| English 1760-1848 | | | |
| ☐ **BURNIER, Richard** ............................ *paintings* | | $90 | $1,210 |
| Dutch 1826-1884 | | | |
| ☐ **BURNS, Charles H.** ........................... *paintings* | | | $880 |
| American b. 1932 | | | |
| ☐ **BURNS, M.J.** ..................................... *drawings* | | | $250 |
| British 19th/20th cent. | | | |
| ☐ **BURNS, Paul C.** ................................ *drawings* | | $165 | $220 |
| American b. 1910 | | | |
| ☐ **BURNS, Robert** ................................. *paintings* | | $209 | $880 |
| British 1869-1941 | | | |
| ☐ **BURNSIDE, Cameron** .......................... *paintings* | | | $275 |
| American 1887-1952 ................................. *drawings* | | | $412 |
| ☐ **BURON, Henri Lucien Joseph** .............. *paintings* | | | $990 |
| French 1880-1969 | | | |
| ☐ **BURPEE, William Partridge** ................ *paintings* | | | $8,250 |
| American b. 1846 | | | |
| ☐ **BURPEE, William R.** ........................... *drawings* | | | $264 |
| American | | | |
| ☐ **BURR, Alexander Hohenlohe** ............... *paintings* | | $330 | $5,225 |
| Scottish 1835-1899 | | | |
| ☐ **BURR, George Brainerd** ....................... *paintings* | | $385 | $1,760 |
| American 1876-1950 | | | |
| ☐ **BURR, George Elbert** .......................... *drawings* | | $110 | $825 |
| American 1859-1939 | | | |
| ☐ **BURR, John** ...................................... *paintings* | | $1,045 | $2,200 |
| Scottish/English 1831/36-1893/94 | | | |
| ☐ **BURR, L. H.** ...................................... *paintings* | | | $880 |
| American 19th cent. | | | |
| ☐ **BURRA, Edward** ................................ *drawings* | | | $2,970 |
| English 1905-1976 | | | |
| ☐ **BURRAS, J.** ....................................... *paintings* | | | $330 |
| ☐ **BURRAS, Thomas (of Leeds)** ................ *paintings* | | | $3,500 |
| English 19th cent. | | | |
| ☐ **BURRELL, James** ............................... *paintings* | | | $2,860 |
| British 19th cent. | | | |
| ☐ **BURRI, Alberto** ................................. *drawings* | | $37,400 | $85,250 |
| Italian b. 1915 ...................................... *sculpture* | | $20,900 | $77,000 |
| ☐ **BURRIDGE, Walter Wilcox** ................. *drawings* | | | $385 |
| American b. 1857 | | | |
| ☐ **BURRILL, Edward E.** .......................... *paintings* | | $137 | $825 |
| American 1835-1913 | | | |
| ☐ **BURRINGTON, Arthur** ......................... *paintings* | | | $3,080 |

|                                                        | *Current Price Range* | |
|                                                        | *Low* | *High* |
|--------------------------------------------------------|-------|--------|
| ☐ **BURRIS, A.** ......................................... *paintings*<br>American 19th cent. | $220 | $440 |
| ☐ **BURROUGHS, Bryson** ........................ *paintings*<br>American 1868-1934 | | $1,100 |
| ☐ **BURROUGHS, Leicester** ...................... *paintings*<br>English ac. 1881 | | $770 |
| ☐ **BURROWS, Robert** ............................. *paintings*<br>British 1851-1855 | | $1,980 |
| ☐ **BURSIEL, R.A.** ................................... *paintings* | | $352 |
| ☐ **BURT, Charles Thomas** ........................ *paintings*<br>English 1823-1902 | $467 | $1,320 |
| ☐ **BURTHE, Leopold** ............................. *paintings*<br>French 19th cent. | | $2,860 |
| ☐ **BURTON, Arthur Gibbs** ........................ *paintings*<br>American b. 1883 | | $220 |
| ☐ **BURTON, C.** ...................................... *drawings*<br>American | | $302 |
| ☐ **BURTON, Hal** ..................................... *paintings* | | $286 |
| ☐ **BURTON, M.** ...................................... *paintings* | | $1,300 |
| ☐ **BURTON, Scott** .................................. *sculpture*<br>American b. 1939 | $247 | $6,600 |
| ☐ **BURTON, William Shakespeare** ............ *drawings*<br>English b. 1830 | | $3,300 |
| ☐ **BURY, L.** .......................................... *paintings* | | $950 |
| ☐ **BURY, Pol** ....................................... *sculpture*<br>Belgian b. 1922 | $935 | $7,150 |
| ☐ **BUSA, Peter** ..................................... *paintings*<br>American b. 1914 | $110 | $220 |
| ☐ **BUSBY, C.A.** ..................................... *drawings*<br>American ac. 1830-1830 | | $2,750 |
| ☐ **BUSCH, Clarence Francis** ..................... *paintings*<br>American b. 1887 | | $990 |
| ☐ **BUSCH, H.** ....................................... *paintings*<br>German 19th cent. | | $825 |
| ☐ **BUSCH, Peter** ................................... *paintings*<br>Danish ac. 1878-1885 | | $385 |
| ☐ **BUSCH, Wilhelm** ............................... *paintings*<br>German 1832-1908 | | $19,800 |
| ☐ **BUSCHELBERGER, A.** ........................ *sculpture*<br>European 20th cent. | | $330 |
| ☐ **BUSCIOLANO** ................................... *paintings*<br>Italian ac. 1890-1915 | | $330 |
| ☐ **BUSH, Jack** ..................................... *paintings*<br>Canadian 1903/09-1977 ........................... *drawings* | $6,600<br>$4,400 | $52,800<br>$4,950 |
| ☐ **BUSH, Norton** ................................. *paintings*<br>American 1834-1894 ................................ *drawings* | $385 | $11,000<br>$330 |
| ☐ **BUSIRI, Giovanni Battista** ................... *drawings*<br>Italian c. 1698-1757 | | $2,530 |

| | *Current Price Range* | |
|---|---|---|
| | Low | High |

☐ **BUSON, Peter Nikolaus** ...................... *paintings* — | | **$1,430**
German 1783-after 1830

☐ **BUSQUETS, Jean** ................... *paintings* | | **$825**
French 20th cent.

☐ **BUSSEY, Reuben** .................... *paintings* | **$1,100** | **$1,430**
British 1818-1893

☐ **BUSSIERE, Gaston** .................... *paintings* | **$2,200** | **$3,850**
French 1862-1929

☐ **BUSSMANN, Fred** ..................... *paintings* | **$247** | **$440**
American 19th cent.

☐ **BUSSON, Charles** .................... *paintings* | **$550** | **$1,650**
French 1822-1908

☐ **BUSSON DU MAURIER,**
**Georges Louis Palmella** ....................... *drawings* | **$220** | **$275**
French 1831/34-1896

☐ **BUSTOS, Hermenegildo** ................... *paintings* | | **$2,860**
b. Mexico 1832-1907

☐ **BUSY** .................................. *paintings* | **$880** | **$1,210**

☐ **BUTHAUD, Rene** ................................ *paintings* | **$2,860** | **$3,520**
French b. 1886

☐ **BUTI, Camillo** ................................. *drawings* | | **$990**

☐ **BUTKEVICH** ............................ *paintings* | | **$2,310**
Russian school

☐ **BUTLER, Charles E.** .................... *paintings* | | **$1,500**
American 19th cent.

☐ **BUTLER, George B.** ...................... *paintings* | | **$4,070**
American 1838-1907

☐ **BUTLER, H.C.** ................................ *paintings* | | **$1,870**
British 19th cent.

☐ **BUTLER, Howard Russell** ................... *paintings* | **$110** | **$3,850**
American 1856-1934 ................................. *drawings* | | **$605**

☐ **BUTLER, James** ................................ *paintings* | **$330** | **$418**

☐ **BUTLER, Mary** ................................ *paintings* | **$49** | **$770**
American 1865-1946

☐ **BUTLER, Philip A.** ..................... *paintings* | **$165** | **$440**
American 19th/20th cent.

☐ **BUTLER, Reg** ................................ *paintings* | | **$440**
English b. 1913 ......................................... *drawings* | **$880** | **$1,045**
........................................................... *sculpture* | **$521** | **$12,100**

☐ **BUTLER, Theodore Earl** ...................... *paintings* | **$935** | **$35,200**
American 1876-c. 1936/37

☐ **BUTLER, Thomas** ............................. *paintings* | **$14,300** | **$63,800**
British ac. 1750-1759

☐ **BUTLER, W.R.C.** ............................. *paintings* | | **$302**

☐ **BUTTERFIELD, Norma D.** ................... *paintings* | | **$247**
American 20th cent.

☐ **BUTTERSACK, Bernhard** ................... *paintings* | | **$550**

☐ **BUTTERSWORTH, James E.** ................ *paintings* | **$715** | **$46,750**
American 1817-1894 ................................. *drawings* | | **$990**

| | Current Price Range | |
|---|---|---|
| | *Low* | *High* |
| ☐ **BUTTERSWORTH, Thomas** ............... *paintings* | $3,410 | $13,200 |
| English ac. 1797-1830 | | |
| ☐ **BUTTERY, W.** ..................................... *paintings* | | $880 |
| ☐ **BUTTGER, Carl** ............................... *paintings* | | $1,320 |
| ☐ **BUTTLER, H.** .................................... *paintings* | $715 | $825 |
| British 19th cent. | | |
| ☐ **BUTTLER, Joseph** ............................ *paintings* | | $3,300 |
| ☐ **BUTTNER, Hans** .............................. *paintings* | $16,500 | $18,700 |
| German b. c. 1850 | | |
| ☐ **BUTTON, Albert Prentice** .................... *paintings* | | $550 |
| American b. 1872 ..................................... *drawings* | | $495 |
| ☐ **BUTTON, John** ................................. *paintings* | $440 | $8,800 |
| American b. 1929 | | |
| ☐ **BUTTS, Amy** .................................... *paintings* | | $330 |
| European ............................................... *drawings* | | $275 |
| ☐ **BUTZEK, B.** ..................................... *sculpture* | | $2,420 |
| ☐ **BUXTON, Robert Hugh** ....................... *drawings* | | $880 |
| English b. 1871 | | |
| ☐ **BUYCK, Edward** ............................... *paintings* | | $275 |
| ☐ **BUYKO, Boleslas** ............................. *paintings* | | $1,760 |
| Polish 19th cent. | | |
| ☐ **BUZZELL, Taylor** ............................. *paintings* | | $990 |
| American | | |
| ☐ **BUZZI, A.** ....................................... *paintings* | | $2,310 |
| ............................................................. *drawings* | $137 | $3,520 |
| ☐ **BYCHKOV, V.** .................................. *paintings* | | $330 |
| ☐ **BYE, Ranulph** ................................. *paintings* | | $200 |
| American b. 1916 ..................................... *drawings* | $75 | $198 |
| ☐ **BYERS, J.** ....................................... *paintings* | | $300 |
| ☐ **BYERS, M.A.** ................................... *paintings* | | $302 |
| American 19th cent. | | |
| ☐ **BYGIL, Antonio** ............................... *paintings* | | $825 |
| ☐ **BYLAND, C.** .................................... *paintings* | | $550 |
| ☐ **BYLANT, A. de** ................................ *paintings* | $242 | $2,200 |
| British ac. 1853-1874 | | |
| ☐ **BYLERT, Jan van** .............................. *paintings* | | $2,750 |
| Dutch 1603-1671 | | |
| ☐ **BYLES, William Hounson** ................... *paintings* | | $1,210 |
| English b. 1872 | | |
| ☐ **BYNG, Robert** ................................. *paintings* | | $1,100 |
| English d. 1850 | | |
| ☐ **BYRON, Bourmond** ........................... *paintings* | $385 | $1,870 |
| Haitian b. 1923 | | |
| ☐ **BYSS, Johann Rudolph** ....................... *paintings* | $715 | $6,000 |
| Swiss 1660-1738 | | |
| ☐ **CABAILLOT, Camille Leopold** | | |
| (called **LASALLE**) ................................ *paintings* | $2,860 | $3,025 |
| French b. 1839 | | |

| | | Current Price Range | |
|---|---|---|---|
| | | *Low* | *High* |

| | | | Low | High |
|---|---|---|---|---|
| ☐ **CABAILLOT, Louis-Simon** | | | | |
| **(called LASSALLE)** | *paintings* | | $550 | $2,860 |
| French b. 1810 | | | | |
| ☐ **CABALLERO, Luis** | *paintings* | | $1,540 | $4,400 |
| Colombian b. 1943 | *drawings* | | | $1,430 |
| ☐ **CABANE, Edouard** | *paintings* | | | $13,200 |
| French b. 1857 | | | | |
| ☐ **CABANEL, Alexandre** | *paintings* | | $330 | $30,800 |
| French 1823-1889 | *drawings* | | $385 | $638 |
| ☐ **CABAT, Nicholas Louis** | *paintings* | | | $1,870 |
| French 1812-93 | | | | |
| ☐ **CABATTIER, L.** | *paintings* | | | $385 |
| ☐ **CABBAEY, \*M\*\*\*** | *drawings* | | | $660 |
| ☐ **CABEL, Adrian van der** | *paintings* | | $1,650 | $2,420 |
| Dutch 1631-1705 | | | | |
| ☐ **CABOT, Edward Clarke** | *drawings* | | | $440 |
| American 1818-1901 | | | | |
| ☐ **CABRERA, Miguel** | *paintings* | | $6,050 | $25,300 |
| Mexican 1695-1768 | | | | |
| ☐ **CABUZEL, Auguste** | *drawings* | | | $605 |
| ☐ **CACCIA, Guglielmo** | | | | |
| **(called IL MONCALVO)** | *drawings* | | | $2,200 |
| Italian 1568-1625 | | | | |
| ☐ **CACCIARELLI, U.** | *paintings* | | | $1,760 |
| Italian 19th cent. | *drawings* | | $1,045 | $5,500 |
| ☐ **CACCIARELLI, Victor** | *paintings* | | $385 | $5,225 |
| Italian 19th cent. | | | | |
| ☐ **CACHARD, Bouvier de** | *paintings* | | | $770 |
| ☐ **CACHET, Carel Lion** | *drawings* | | | $550 |
| Dutch 1864-1945 | | | | |
| ☐ **CACHOUD, Francois Charles** | *paintings* | | $330 | $2,750 |
| French 1866-1943 | *drawings* | | | $715 |
| ☐ **CADEL, Eugene** | *paintings* | | | $1,540 |
| French ac. 1899-1929 | | | | |
| ☐ **CADENASSO, Giuseppe** | *paintings* | | $247 | $825 |
| Italian/American 1858-1918 | *drawings* | | $110 | $302 |
| ☐ **CADES, Giuseppe** | *drawings* | | $550 | $9,075 |
| Italian 1750-1799 | | | | |
| ☐ **CADMUS, Paul** | *drawings* | | $308 | $6,050 |
| American b. 1904 | | | | |
| ☐ **CADY, Gertrude Parmalee** | *drawings* | | | $440 |
| American 20th cent. | | | | |
| ☑ **CADY, Harrison** | *paintings* | | $143 | $1,210 |
| American 1877-1970 | | | | |
| ☐ **CADY, Henry N.** | *paintings* | | $88 | $3,080 |
| American b. 1849 | *drawings* | | $150 | $550 |
| ☑ **CAESAR, Doris** | *sculpture* | | $330 | $2,800 |
| American b. 1892 | | | | |
| ☐ **CAFARELLI, Michele A.** | *paintings* | | | $357 |

|  | | Current Price Range | |
|---|---|---|---|
|  | | Low | High |
| □ **CAFE, Thomas Watt** ............................ *paintings* | | $770 | $2,090 |
| English 1856-1925 | | | |
| □ **CAFFE, Nino** ..................................... *paintings* | | $1,100 | $6,875 |
| Italian b. 1909 | | | |
| □ **CAFFERTY, James H.** ........................ *paintings* | | | $495 |
| American 1819-1869 ................................ *drawings* | | $247 | $1,430 |
| □ **CAFFI, Margherita** ............................ *paintings* | | | $5,500 |
| Italian ac. 1660-1700 | | | |
| □ **CAFFIERI, Francois-Charles** ............... *drawings* | | | $880 |
| French 1667-1729 | | | |
| □ **CAFFYN, William** ............................... *paintings* | | $440 | $3,520 |
| English 19th cent. | | | |
| □ **CAGGIANO** ...................................... *paintings* | | | $247 |
| Italian 20th cent. | | | |
| □ **CAGLI, Corrado** ................................. *paintings* | | $4,125 | $4,400 |
| Italian b. 1910 | | | |
| □ **CAGNIART, Emile** ............................... *paintings* | | $301 | $1,045 |
| French 1851-1911 | | | |
| □ **CAHOON, Charles D.** .......................... *paintings* | | $325 | $3,800 |
| American 1861-1951 | | | |
| □ **CAHOON, Martha** .............................. *paintings* | | $300 | $1,600 |
| American contemporary | | | |
| □ **CAHOON, Ralph** ................................. *paintings* | | $660 | $32,000 |
| American d. 1982 | | | |
| □ **CAILLE, Leon Emile** ......................... *paintings* | | $1,760 | $4,675 |
| French 1836-1907 ...................................... *drawings* | | | $154 |
| □ **CAILLEBOTTE, Gustave** ..................... *paintings* | | $13,200 | $605,000 |
| French 1848-1894 | | | |
| □ **CAIN, Auguste Nicolas** ......................... *sculpture* | | $330 | $990 |
| French 1822-1894 | | | |
| □ **CAIN, Georges Jules Auguste** ............... *paintings* | | $800 | $2,090 |
| French 1856-1919 | | | |
| □ **CAIR, G.I.** ......................................... *drawings* | | | $176 |
| 19th cent. | | | |
| □ **CAIRNES, J.** ...................................... *paintings* | | | $385 |
| □ **CAIRO, Francesco del** | | | |
| (called IL CAVALIERE DEL CAIRO) .... *paintings* | | $1,320 | $6,050 |
| Italian 1598-1674 | | | |
| □ **CAKE, M.** .......................................... *paintings* | | | $247 |
| British 20th cent. | | | |
| □ **CALAGERO, Jean** .............................. *paintings* | | | $440 |
| French contemporary | | | |
| □ **CALAME, Alexandre** .......................... *paintings* | | $550 | $27,500 |
| Swiss 1810-1864 | | | |
| □ **CALANO, T.** ...................................... *drawings* | | | $450 |
| Italian 19th cent. | | | |
| □ **CALBET, Antoine** ............................... *paintings* | | | $1,980 |
| French 1860-1944 | | | |

## 20th-Century American Primitive

The work of certain untrained, self-taught artists whose canvases are, nonetheless, sensitively and beautifully painted is often called primitive or naive art. Due to their lack of formal training, the work of naive painters can be distinguished by a lack of perspective, yet such work retains a vigor and freshness, as well as a powerful sense of creativity, which combine to make it so appealing.

Ralph Cahoon, a 20th-century American naive painter, first painted furniture, then turned to easel paintings. His oil paintings of sailors, balloons, and mermaids, typically painted on masonite, have soared in value since his death in 1982. (Ralph Cahoon, "Nantucket Incident," oil on masonite, 29 x 42 in., Eldred's, November 2, 1985, $32,000.)

|  |  | *Current Price Range* | |
|---|---|---|---|
|  |  | *Low* | *High* |
| ☐ **CALCAGNO, Lawrence** | paintings | | **$1,210** |
| American b. 1916 | drawings | **$44** | **$165** |
| ☐ **CALCOTT, A.W.** | paintings | | **$250** |
| English 1799-1844 | | | |
| ☐ **CALDECOTT, Randolph** | drawings | | **$605** |
| ☐ **CALDER, Alexander** | paintings | **$8,800** | **$22,000** |
| American 1898-1976 | drawings | **$325** | **$9,350** |
| | sculpture | **$1,320** | **$852,500** |
| ☐ **CALDER, Alexander Milne** | sculpture | | **$5,500** |
| American 1846-1923 | | | |
| ☐ **CALDER, Alexander Stirling** | drawings | | **$700** |
| American 1870-1945 | sculpture | | **$6,600** |
| ☐ **CALDER, Norman** | paintings | | **$330** |
| American 19th/20th cent. | | | |

## Affordable Work by a 20th-Century Master

*Alexander Calder is best known for his 1931 invention of the mobile, a form of abstract sculpture which hangs by fine wires and is set in motion by currents of air. Calder, whose work shows a delight in the comic and fantastic, first achieved fame in 1926 when he exhibited his miniature circus of acrobats and animals in Paris (now in the collection of the Whitney Museum in New York). His monumental stabiles, rigid and stationary sculptures, have been installed in sites around the world.*

*From 1952 to his death in 1976, Calder painted many gouaches (heavy, opaque watercolors). Calder's mobiles sell for thousands of dollars, but this 1961 work demonstrates that it is possible to purchase the minor work of important artists at affordable prices. (Alexander Calder, "Cornfield," gouache and ink on paper, 29 x 41 in., Sotheby's, February 27, 1985, $2,475.)*

| | | *Current Price Range* | |
| --- | --- | --- | --- |
| | | *Low* | *High* |
| ☐ **CALDERON, Alvarez** ............ *paintings* | | | **$16,500** |
| 19th cent. | | | |
| ☐ **CALDERON, Charles Clement** ......... *paintings* | | **$1,210** | **$2,750** |
| French 19th/20th cent. | | | |
| ☐ **CALDERON, Philip Hermogenes** ......... *drawings* | | | **$715** |
| French/English 1833-1898 | | | |
| ☐ **CALDWELL, Edmund** ............ *paintings* | | | **$825** |
| British b. 1852 | | | |
| ☐ **CALEGARI, Vittorio** ............ *drawings* | | | **$220** |
| Italian b. 1861 | | | |
| ☐ **CALENDI** ............ *sculpture* | | | **$990** |
| Italian | | | |
| ☐ **CALIARI, Carletto** ............ *paintings* | | | **$2,090** |
| Italian 1570-1596 | | | |
| ☐ **CALIFANO, John (or Giovanni)** ......... *paintings* | | **$110** | **$2,200** |
| Italian 1864-1924 | | | |
| ☐ **CALIFANO, Mundo** ............ *paintings* | | | **$192** |
| Italian 1875-1930 | | | |
| ☐ **CALIGA, Isaac Henry** ............ *paintings* | | **$660** | **$4,290** |
| American b. 1857 | | | |
| ☐ **CALIN, L.** ............ *paintings* | | | **$375** |
| ☐ **CALLADINE, William** ............ *paintings* | | | **$660** |
| Dutch 20th cent. | | | |

| | | | Current Price Range | |
|---|---|---|---|---|
| | | | Low | High |
| ☐ CALLAERT, Jacques | ............... | *paintings* | $82 | $396 |
| | ............... | *drawings* | | $55 |
| ☑ CALLAHAN, Kenneth | ............... | *drawings* | | $250 |
| ☐ CALLCOTT, Sir Augustus Wall | ............... | *paintings* | $330 | $1,870 |
| English 1779-1844 | | | | |
| ☐ CALLE, Paul | ............... | *paintings* | $61,000 | $89,000 |
| American b. 1928 | | | | |
| ☐ CALLENDER | ............... | *sculpture* | | $1,980 |
| English ac. 1780-1800 | | | | |
| ☐ CALLENDER, Julia A. | ............... | *paintings* | | $165 |
| | ............... | *drawings* | | $660 |
| ☐ CALLERY, Mary | ............... | *sculpture* | | $495 |
| ☐ CALLIAS, Horace de | ............... | *paintings* | | $1,100 |
| French d. 1921 | | | | |
| ☐ CALLION, Jean Gaspard | ............... | *sculpture* | | $4,125 |
| French 1713-1810 | | | | |
| ☐ CALLOW, George D. | ............... | *paintings* | $330 | $440 |
| English exhib. 1858-1873 | | | | |
| ☐ CALLOW, John | ............... | *paintings* | $605 | $4,400 |
| English 1822-1878 | ............... | *drawings* | $165 | $5,280 |
| ☐ CALLOW, William | ............... | *paintings* | $605 | $1,650 |
| English 1812-1908 | ............... | *drawings* | $1,650 | $6,875 |
| ☐ CALLOWHILL, James | ............... | *paintings* | $100 | $770 |
| American 19th/20th cent. | | | | |
| ☐ CALLOWHILL, Scott | ............... | *paintings* | | $332 |
| ☐ CALOGERO, Jean | ............... | *paintings* | $60 | $1,210 |
| Italian b. 1922 | | | | |
| ☐ CALOSCI, Arturo | ............... | *paintings* | $1,100 | $1,650 |
| Italian 1854/55-1926 | | | | |
| ☐ CALOT, H. | ............... | *sculpture* | | $495 |
| ☐ CALRAET, Abraham | ............... | *paintings* | $7,150 | $35,200 |
| Dutch 1642/43-1721/22 | | | | |
| ☐ CALS, Adolphe Felix | ............... | *paintings* | | $577 |
| French 1810-1880 | ............... | *drawings* | | $440 |
| ☐ CALVERT, Cecil | ............... | *drawings* | | $176 |
| American (Hopi) | | | | |
| ☐ CALVERT, Edwin Sherwood | ............... | *paintings* | | $330 |
| British b. 1844 | ............... | *drawings* | | $192 |
| ☐ CALVERT, Frederick | ............... | *paintings* | | $192 |
| Irish/English ac. 1815, d. 1845? | | | | |
| ☐ CALVERT, Henry | ............... | *paintings* | $1,870 | $4,180 |
| English ac. 1826-1854 | | | | |
| ☐ CALVERT, Samuel | ............... | *paintings* | | $625 |
| English ac. 1882-1885 | | | | |
| ☐ CALVERT, W. | ............... | *paintings* | | $192 |
| English (?) 19th cent. | | | | |
| ☐ CALVES, Leon Georges | ............... | *paintings* | $440 | $1,540 |
| French b. 1848 | | | | |

|  | | *Current Price Range* | |
| --- | --- | --- | --- |
|  | | *Low* | *High* |
| ☐ **CALVI, Ercole**  ....................... *paintings* | | | **$1,100** |
| Italian 1824-1900 | | | |
| ☐ **CALYO, Nicoling**  ................... *paintings* | | | **$4,300** |
| American 1799-1884 | | | |
| ☐ **CALZADA, Humberto**  .......................... *paintings* | | | **$3,850** |
| Cuban b. 1944 | | | |
| ☐ **CAMACHO, Jorge**  ............................ *paintings* | | | **$2,090** |
| Cuban b. 1934 ........................................... *drawings* | | **$660** | **$660** |
| ☐ **CAMACHO, Paul**  ................................. *drawings* | | **$55** | **$495** |
| American b. 1929 | | | |
| ☐ **CAMARENA, Jorge Gonzalez**  .............. *paintings* | | | **$3,960** |
| Mexican b. 1908 | | | |
| ☐ **CAMARGO, Sergio de**  ........................ *paintings* | | | **$4,400** |
| Brazilian b. 1930 | | | |
| ☐ **CAMASSEI, Andrea**  ........................ *drawings* | | | **$1,210** |
| Italian 1601-1648 | | | |
| ☐ **CAMBI, A.**  ...................................... *sculpture* | | | **$1,100** |
| 19th cent. | | | |
| ☐ **CAMBIASO, Luca**  ............................. *paintings* | | | **$20,900** |
| Italian 1527-1585 ...................................... *drawings* | | **$1,100** | **$9,900** |
| ☐ **CAMBOS, Jean Jules**  ........................ *sculpture* | | **$550** | **$2,750** |
| French 1828-1917 | | | |
| ☐ **CAMERON, Angus**  ............................. *paintings* | | | **$935** |
| British 19th/20th cent. | | | |
| ☐ **CAMERON, Douglas**  .......................... *paintings* | | | **$467** |
| ☐ **CAMERON, Duncan**  ........................... *paintings* | | **$220** | **$1,760** |
| Scottish ac. 1871-1900 | | | |
| ☐ **CAMERON, J.**  ................................... *paintings* | | | **$12,100** |
| 19th cent. | | | |
| ☐ **CAMERON, Marie Gelon**  ..................... *paintings* | | | **$418** |
| French 19th cent. | | | |
| ☐ **CAMERON, R.A.**  ............................... *drawings* | | | **$247** |
| American early 20th cent. | | | |
| ☐ **CAMERON, Sir David Young**  .............. *paintings* | | **$110** | **$1,870** |
| British 1865-1945 ..................................... *drawings* | | **$135** | **$1,210** |
| ☐ **CAMMARANO, Michele**  ...................... *paintings* | | **$3,850** | **$6,600** |
| Italian School 1835-1920 | | | |
| ☐ **CAMOIN, Charles**  ............................. *paintings* | | **$1,210** | **$20,900** |
| French 1879-1965 ...................................... *drawings* | | | **$650** |
| ☐ **CAMPAGNE**  ...................................... *sculpture* | | | **$1,540** |
| French | | | |
| ☐ **CAMPAGNOLA, Domenico**  ................. *drawings* | | | **$6,600** |
| ☐ **CAMPANA, Pedro** | | | |
| **(called KEMPENER)**  ............................ *paintings* | | | **$1,870** |
| Spanish 1503-1580 | | | |
| ☐ **CAMPANELLA, Vincent**  ...................... *paintings* | | | **$198** |
| American b. 1915 | | | |
| ☐ **CAMPANOLA, T.**  ............................... *sculpture* | | | **$715** |
| Italian 19th cent. | | | |

| | Current Price Range | |
|---|---|---|
| | Low | High |

| | | Low | High |
|---|---|---|---|
| ☐ **CAMPBELL, Blendon Reed** ............... *paintings* | | **$165** | **$880** |
| American b. 1872 ..................................... *drawings* | | | **$11** |
| ☐ **CAMPBELL, C.M.** ........................... *drawings* | | | **$1,540** |
| American c. 1900 | | | |
| ☐ **CAMPBELL, Ethel M.** ...................... *drawings* | | | **$220** |
| 19th/20th cent. | | | |
| ☐ **CAMPBELL, George F.** ..................... *paintings* | | | **$1,100** |
| American | | | |
| ☐ **CAMPBELL, Hay** ............................. *paintings* | | **$55** | **$275** |
| English ac. 1892 | | | |
| ☐ **CAMPBELL, John Henry** .................... *drawings* | | | **$242** |
| English 1757-1828 | | | |
| ☐ **CAMPBELL, Kay** ............................ *paintings* | | | **$302** |
| ☐ **CAMPBELL, Kenneth** ....................... *sculpture* | | | **$220** |
| American b. 1913 | | | |
| ☐ **CAMPENDONK, Heinrich** .................. *paintings* | | | **$24,200** |
| German 1889-1957 ................................... *drawings* | | | **$3,300** |
| ☐ **CAMPESINO Y MINGO, Vicente** ......... *paintings* | | | **$1,100** |
| ☐ **CAMPHAUSEN, Wilhelm** ................... *paintings* | | | **$20,900** |
| German 1818-1885 | | | |
| ☐ **CAMPHUYSEN, Govaert** .................... *paintings* | | | **$4,950** |
| Dutch 1623/24-1672 | | | |
| ☐ **CAMPI, A.** ..................................... *paintings* | | | **$440** |
| Italian 19th/20th cent. | | | |
| ☐ **CAMPI, Bernardino** ......................... *drawings* | | | **$1,430** |
| ☐ **CAMPI, Giacomo** ............................ *paintings* | | | **$1,650** |
| Italian 1846-1921 .................................... *drawings* | | | **$660** |
| ☐ **CAMPIGLI, Massimo** ........................ *drawings* | | **$1,870** | **$27,500** |
| Italian 1895-1971 | | | |
| ☐ **CAMPION, George B.** ....................... *drawings* | | | **$1,265** |
| English 1796-1870 | | | |
| ☐ **CAMPO, Federico del** ....................... *paintings* | | **$2,860** | **$34,000** |
| Peruvian 19th cent. ................................. *drawings* | | **$59** | **$1,210** |
| ☐ **CAMPOLINIS, S.** ............................. *paintings* | | | **$550** |
| ☐ **CAMPOREALE, Sergio** ...................... *paintings* | | | **$3,740** |
| Argentinian b. 1937 ................................. *drawings* | | | **$440** |
| ☐ **CAMPOTOSTO, Henry** ...................... *paintings* | | **$990** | **$4,840** |
| Belgian d. 1910 ..................................... *drawings* | | | **$176** |
| ☐ **CAMPRIANI, Alceste** ....................... *paintings* | | **$1,650** | **$8,250** |
| Italian 1848-1933 | | | |
| ☐ **CAMPROBIN, Pedro de** ..................... *paintings* | | | **$19,800** |
| ☐ **CAMUS, George** .............................. *paintings* | | | **$275** |
| French 19th cent. | | | |
| ☐ **CAMUS, Jean Marie** ......................... *sculpture* | | | **$935** |
| French 1877-1955 | | | |
| ☐ **CANA, E.** ...................................... *sculpture* | | | **$1,540** |
| ☐ **CANAL, Gilbert von** ......................... *paintings* | | **$462** | **$3,575** |
| Austrian b. 1849 | | | |

## Souvenir Paintings

*Almost invariably, travelers collect souvenirs of their trips, including paintings. Popular motifs at the turn of the century were the White Mountains of New Hampshire, Niagara Falls, and scenes of Egypt or Italy. Souvenir paintings range from postcard to easel size.*

    *Federico del Campo was born in Peru in the 19th century. He was a prizewinning artist in his day and well known for his paintings of Venice. A "lost" painting, found in a furnace room, was brought to an appraisal day at Bourne's on Cape Cod. Cleaned, restored, and featured on the cover, Federico del Campo's "St. Mark's Cathedral and Square, Venice" sold for $34,000. (Federico del Campo, "St. Mark's Cathedral and Square, Venice," oil on canvas, 18½ x 29¼ in., Bourne, May 13, 1985, $34,000.)*

|  |  | *Current Price Range* | |
|---|---|---|---|
|  |  | *Low* | *High* |
| ☐ **CANAL, Giovanni Antonio** | | | |
| **(called CANALETTO)** ........................... *paintings* | | **$35,200** | **$682,000** |
| Italian 1697-1768 ........................ *drawings* | | | **$3,850** |
| ☐ **CANAS, Benjamin** ............................ *paintings* | | | **$4,400** |
| Brazilian b. 1933 ........................ *drawings* | | **$770** | **$1,430** |
| ☐ **CANCHOIS, Henri** ............................ *paintings* | | | **$2,530** |
| French 19th cent. | | | |
| ☑ **CANDELL, Victor** ............................... *paintings* | | **$38** | **$264** |
| ☐ **CANDLELIGHT MASTER,** | | | |
| **(Trophime Bigot?)** .................................... *paintings* | | | **$24,200** |
| ☐ **CANEDO, Alexander** ........................... *paintings* | | **$275** | **$275** |
| ☐ **CANELLA, A.** ..................................... *drawings* | | | **$1,100** |

| | | Current Price Range | |
|---|---|---|---|
| | | Low | High |
| ☐ **CANELLA, Antonio** ..................... *drawings* | | $220 | $1,045 |
| Italian 19th cent. | | | |
| ☐ **CANELLA, Carlo** .............................. *paintings* | | | $6,050 |
| Italian 19th cent. | | | |
| ☐ **CANELLA, Georgio** ......................... *drawings* | | | $577 |
| Italian 19th cent. | | | |
| ☐ **CANELLA, Giuseppe** ....................... *drawings* | | | $330 |
| Italian 1788-1847 | | | |
| ☐ **CANEREDI** ....................................... *sculpture* | | | $1,210 |
| Italian 19th cent. | | | |
| ☐ **CANEVARI, Carlo** ........................... *paintings* | | $22 | $2,475 |
| Italian b. 1922 | | | |
| ☐ **CANEVARI, V.** ................................. *paintings* | | $99 | $220 |
| Italian 20th cent. | | | |
| ☐ **CANIARO (?), Guido** ...................... *paintings* | | | $715 |
| ☐ **CANIFF, Milton** .............................. *drawings* | | $220 | $522 |
| American b. 1907 | | | |
| ☐ **CANJURA, Noe** ............................... *paintings* | | | $324 |
| ☐ **CANNON, Jack** ............................... *paintings* | | | $176 |
| American 20th cent. | | | |
| ☐ **CANO, Mario** ................................... *paintings* | | $275 | $770 |
| ☐ **CANOGAR, Rafael** ........................... *paintings* | | | $495 |
| Spanish b. 1934/35 | | | |
| ☐ **CANON, Hans von Straschiripka** ........... *paintings* | | | $605 |
| Austrian 1829-1885 | | | |
| ☐ **CANONICA, Pietro** ........................... *sculpture* | | | $6,875 |
| ☐ **CANOON, R.** .................................... *paintings* | | $308 | $440 |
| ☐ **CANOVA** .......................................... *sculpture* | | | $521 |
| ☐ **CANTA, Johannes Antonius** ............... *paintings* | | $3,025 | $3,960 |
| Dutch 1816-1888 | | | |
| ☐ **CANTAGALLINA, Remigio** ................. *drawings* | | $715 | $2,475 |
| Italian 1582-1630 | | | |
| ☐ **CANTARINI, Simone** ......................... *drawings* | | $192 | $660 |
| Italian 1612-1648 | | | |
| ☐ **CANTER, Albert M.** ........................... *paintings* | | | $275 |
| American b. 1892 | | | |
| ☐ **CANTEY, Maurine** ............................. *paintings* | | | $880 |
| American b. 1901 | | | |
| ☐ **CANTIS, Federico** ............................. *drawings* | | | $357 |
| Spanish 20th cent. | | | |
| ☐ **CANTRALL, Harriet M.** ..................... *paintings* | | | $220 |
| American 20th cent. | | | |
| ☐ **CANTU, Frederico** ............................. *drawings* | | $154 | $1,540 |
| Mexican b. 1908 | | | |
| ☐ **CANU, Yvonne** ................................. *paintings* | | $660 | $3,520 |
| French b. 1921 | | | |
| ☐ **CANUTI, Domenico Maria** ................. *drawings* | | | $467 |
| ☐ **CANZIANI, Estella** ............................. *drawings* | | | $330 |
| British 1887-1964 | | | |

| | | Current Price Range | |
|---|---|---|---|
| | | *Low* | *High* |
| ☐ **CAP, Constant Aime Marie** ............... *paintings* | | $1,300 | $8,800 |
| Belgian b. 1842 | | | |
| ☐ **CAPEINICK, Jean** ............................ *paintings* | | | $9,900 |
| Belgian 1838-1890 | | | |
| ☐ **CAPELLE, Alfred Eugene** .................. *paintings* | | | $1,540 |
| French 1834-1887 | | | |
| ☐ **CAPLES, Robert Cole** ...................... *drawings* | | $467 | $550 |
| American 20th cent. | | | |
| ☐ **CAPOBIANCHI, V.** ........................... *paintings* | | $330 | $14,300 |
| Italian ac. 1870-1880 | | | |
| ☐ **CAPOGROSSI, Giuseppe** .................... *paintings* | | $2,475 | $29,700 |
| Italian b. 1900 .................................... *drawings* | | | $2,090 |
| ☐ **CAPONE, Gaetano** .......................... *paintings* | | $137 | $1,980 |
| Italian 1845-1920/24 ........................... *drawings* | | $192 | $495 |
| ☐ **CAPORILE, J.** .................................. *paintings* | | | $8,800 |
| Italian 20th cent. | | | |
| ☐ **CAPP, Al (Alfred Gerald CAPLIN)** ........ *paintings* | | $4,180 | $4,675 |
| American 1909-1979 ............................. *drawings* | | | $132 |
| ☐ **CAPPELLE, Jan van de** ..................... *paintings* | | | $1,650,000 |
| Dutch 1624-1679 | | | |
| ☐ **CAPPONI, Raffaelo** | | | |
| **(called Raffaelo del Garbo)** ............... *paintings* | | | $20,900 |
| Italian 1466/76-1524 | | | |
| ☐ **CAPRIANO, F.** ................................. *paintings* | | | $715 |
| ☐ **CAPRILE, Vincenzo** ......................... *paintings* | | $1,320 | $33,000 |
| Italian 1856-1936 | | | |
| ☐ **CAPRON, Jean Pierre** ....................... *paintings* | | | $550 |
| French b. 1921 | | | |
| ☐ **CAPSER, Mike** ................................ *drawings* | | | $600 |
| American | | | |
| ☐ **CAPUANO, F.** .................................. *paintings* | | | $660 |
| Italian 19th cent. | | | |
| ☐ **CAPULETTI, Jose Manuel** ................. *paintings* | | | $770 |
| Spanish b. 1925 ................................... *drawings* | | $66 | $192 |
| ☐ **CAPUONE, F.** .................................. *paintings* | | | $1,100 |
| ☐ **CAPUTO, Ulisse** ............................. *paintings* | | $2,090 | $6,050 |
| Italian 1872-1948 | | | |
| ☐ **CARABAIN, Jacques Francois** ............ *paintings* | | $825 | $22,000 |
| Belgian 1834-1892 | | | |
| ☐ **CARABAIN, Victor** ........................... *paintings* | | | $1,045 |
| Belgian 19th cent. | | | |
| ☐ **CARABIN, Francois Rupert** ................ *sculpture* | | | $1,650 |
| French early 20th cent. | | | |
| ☐ **CARAUD, A.** ................................... *paintings* | | | $605 |
| French 19th cent. | | | |
| ☐ **CARAUD, Joseph** ............................ *paintings* | | $2,200 | $2,750 |
| French 1821-1905 | | | |
| ☐ **CARAVAGLIA, Angelo** ...................... *sculpture* | | | $356 |

| | | Current Price Range | |
|---|---|---|---|
| | | Low | High |
| ☐ **CARBEE, Scott Clifton** ......................... *paintings* | | | $450 |
| American b. 1860 | | | |
| ☐ **CARBONELL, Manuel** ....................... *sculpture* | | | $440 |
| ☐ **CARBONERO, Jose Moreno** ................ *paintings* | | | $1,100 |
| Spanish b. 1860 | | | |
| ☐ **CARBONI, G.G.** ................................. *paintings* | | | $224 |
| Italian 19th cent. | | | |
| ☐ **CARBONNE, A.** ................................. *sculpture* | | | $605 |
| ☐ **CARBONNEAUX, Charles** ................ *paintings* | | | $412 |
| ☐ **CARCANO, Filippo** .......................... *paintings* | $2,090 | | $4,290 |
| Italian 1840-1910 | | | |
| ☐ **CARDEAUX, De** ................................ *paintings* | $7,700 | | $8,800 |
| ☐ **CARDELL, Mrs. Frank Hale** ................ *paintings* | | | $550 |
| American b. 1905 | | | |
| ☐ **CARDENASSO, Giuseppe** ................... *paintings* | | | $522 |
| American 1858-1918 | | | |
| ☐ **CARDI, Ludovico (called IL CIGOLI)** .... *drawings* | | | $2,200 |
| Italian 1559-1613 | | | |
| ☐ **CARDINAL, A.** ................................... *drawings* | | | $302 |
| ☐ **CARDON, Claude** .............................. *paintings* | | | $500 |
| British 19th cent. | | | |
| ☐ **CARDON, H.** ...................................... *paintings* | | | $302 |
| ☐ **CARDONA, Jose** ................................ *sculpture* | | | $275 |
| ☐ **CARDONA, P.** .................................... *sculpture* | | | $308 |
| ☐ **CARDUCHO, Vincente** ........................ *paintings* | | | $12,100 |
| Italian 1576/78-1638 | | | |
| ☐ **CARELLI, Consalave** .......................... *paintings* | | | $3,520 |
| Italian 1818-1900 ...................................... *drawings* | $260 | | $715 |
| ☐ **CARELLI, G.** ...................................... *drawings* | | | $825 |
| English 19th cent. | | | |
| ☐ **CARELLI, Gabriel** .............................. *drawings* | $1,980 | | $2,310 |
| Italian 1820-1880 | | | |
| ☐ **CARELLI, Giuseppe** ........................... *paintings* | $330 | | $4,125 |
| Italian 1858-1921 | | | |
| ☐ **CARELLI, Gonsalvo** ........................... *paintings* | | | $660 |
| Italian 1818-1900 | | | |
| ☐ **CARESME, Jacques Philippe** ................ *paintings* | | | $8,800 |
| French 1734-1796 ...................................... *drawings* | | | $3,300 |
| ☐ **CAREY, Henry** ................................... *paintings* | | | $440 |
| British 19th cent. | | | |
| ☐ **CAREY, M.** ........................................ *paintings* | | | $990 |
| American 19th cent. | | | |
| ☐ **CARGNEL, Vittore Antonio** ................. *paintings* | | | $467 |
| Italian 1872-1931 | | | |
| ☐ **CARIANI, Varaldo J.** .......................... *paintings* | | | $220 |
| American b. 1897 | | | |
| ☐ **CARIGNANI, Guido** ........................... *paintings* | $2,750 | | $4,620 |
| ☐ **CARILLO, Lilia** ................................. *paintings* | | | $8,800 |
| ☐ **CARINA, F.** ....................................... *paintings* | | | $715 |

| | Current Price Range | |
| | Low | High |
| :--- | :---: | :---: |
| □ **CARINA, F.** ........................... *paintings* | | $1,045 |
| Italian (?) 19th cent. | | |
| □ **CARISS, Henry T.** ............... *paintings* | | $6,325 |
| American 1840-1903 | | |
| □ **CARLANDI, Onorato** ........... *drawings* | $330 | $550 |
| Italian 1848-1939 | | |
| □ **CARLAW, William** ............. *drawings* | | $880 |
| British 1847-1889 | | |
| □ **CARLES, Arthur B.** ............. *paintings* | $330 | $71,500 |
| American 1880/82-1952 ............... *drawings* | $110 | $1,320 |
| □ **CARLETON, Anne** ............... *paintings* | $220 | $1,320 |
| American 1878-1968 | | |
| □ **CARLETON, Clifford** ........... *drawings* | | $247 |
| American 1867-1946 | | |
| □ **CARLETTI, Alicia** ............... *paintings* | | $2,200 |
| Argentinian b. 1946 | | |
| □ **CARLEVARIJS, Luca** ........... *paintings* | | $4,400 |
| □ **CARLIER, Marc Georges** ...... *sculpture* | | $495 |
| French early 20th cent. | | |
| □ **CARLIER, Modeste** ............. *paintings* | | $13,200 |
| Belgian 1820-1878 | | |
| □ **CARLIN, Andrew B.** ........... *paintings* | $2,420 | $9,075 |
| American b.c. 1816 | | |
| □ **CARLIN, John** .................... *paintings* | $935 | $3,575 |
| American 1813-1891 | | |
| □ **CARLINI, Giulio** ................ *paintings* | $440 | $2,530 |
| Italian 1826/30-1887 | | |
| □ **CARLISLE, Mary Helen** ....... *paintings* | $198 | $275 |
| British/American d. 1925 | | |
| □ **CARLO, Chiostri** ................ *paintings* | $1,210 | $1,540 |
| Italian 19th cent. | | |
| □ **CARLONE, Carlo Innocenzo** ...... *paintings* | | $16,500 |
| Italian 1686-1775/76 | | |
| □ **CARLONI, P.** ..................... *paintings* | | $495 |
| Italian 19th cent. | | |
| □ **CARLSEN, Carl** ................. *paintings* | | $9,900 |
| Danish 1853-1917 | | |
| □ **CARLSEN, Dines** ............... *paintings* | $412 | $8,250 |
| American 1901-1966 | | |
| □ **CARLSEN, Soren Emil** ........ *paintings* | $495 | $93,500 |
| Danish/American 1853-1932 ......... *drawings* | | $900 |
| □ **CARLSON, George** ............. *sculpture* | $3,190 | $16,000 |
| American b. 1940 | | |
| □ **CARLSON, John Fabian** ...... *paintings* | $224 | $34,000 |
| Swedish/American 1875-1945 ......... *drawings* | $350 | $660 |
| □ **CARLSON, Paul H.** ............ *paintings* | | $1,760 |
| Swedish b. 1860 | | |
| □ **CARLTON, Anne** ............... *paintings* | | $605 |
| American | | |

| | | | Current Price Range | |
|---|---|---|---|---|
| | | | Low | High |
| ☐ **CARLTON, Frederick** British 19th/20th cent. | ......................... *paintings* | | $77 | $770 |
| ☐ **CARLTON, H.** English 19th cent. | ..................... *drawings* | | $137 | $495 |
| ☐ **CARLTON, Henry** English 19th cent. | ............................ *drawings* | | | $467 |
| ☐ **CARLTON, William Tolman** American 1816-1888 | ................ *paintings* | | | $1,650 |
| ☐ **CARLYLE, May** British 19th/20th cent. | ............................ *paintings* | | | $1,650 |
| ☐ **CARMER, H. Nimmo** | ......................... *paintings* | | | $352 |
| ☐ **CARMICHAEL, Herbert** English b. 1856 | ...................... *paintings* | | | $550 |
| ☐ **CARMICHAEL, James Wilson (John)** English c. 1800-1868 | .... *paintings* | | $440 | $17,600 |
| ☐ **CARMICHAEL, Stewart** Scottish b. 1867 | ...................... *drawings* | | | $230 |
| ☐ **CARMIENCKE, Johann Hermann** German/American 1810-1867 | ........ *paintings* | | $176 | $8,250 |
| ☐ **CARMIGNANI, Guido** Italian 1838-1909 | ......................... *paintings* | | | $550 |
| ☐ **CARNEO, Antonio** Italian ac. 1660 | ............................ *paintings* | | | $8,250 |
| ☐ **CARNERO, G.** Italian 19th cent. | ..................................... *paintings* | | | $1,540 |
| ☐ **CARNEVALI, Carlo** | ............................ *paintings* | | $165 | $330 |
| ☐ **CARNIER, H.** French 19th cent. | .................................... *paintings* | | | $1,760 |
| ☐ **CARO, Anthony** English b. 1924 | ..................................... *drawings* ..................................... *sculpture* | | $5,500 | $825 $26,400 |
| ☐ **CARO, Baldassare de** Italian 18th cent. | ........................... *paintings* | | | $4,400 |
| ☐ **CARO, Bill** Peruvian b. 1949 | ......................................... *paintings* | | $715 | $3,080 |
| ☐ **CAROLIS, Nino** Italian 20th cent. | ................................... *paintings* | | $275 | $412 |
| ☐ **CAROLUS, Jean** Belgian ac.1867-1880 | ............................... *paintings* | | $6,600 | $9,900 |
| ☐ **CAROLUS-DURAN, Emile Auguste** French 1838-1917 | ...... *paintings* ..................................... *drawings* | | $550 | $15,400 $935 |
| ☐ **CARONE, Nicolas** American b. 1917 | ............................... *paintings* ..................................... *drawings* | | $275 $33 | $1,870 $110 |
| ☐ **CARPEAUX, Jean Baptiste** French 1827-1875 | ................... *drawings* ..................................... *sculpture* | | $550 | $605 $16,500 |
| ☐ **CARPENTER, Dudley** American 20th cent. | ........................... *paintings* | | $191 | $356 |
| ☐ **CARPENTER, Ellen Maria** American c. 1831-1909 | ................... *paintings* | | $385 | $1,100 |

| | | Current Price Range | |
|---|---|---|---|
| | | Low | High |
| ☐ **CARPENTER, Francis Bicknell** ............ *paintings* | | $275 | $350 |
| American 1830-1900 | | | |
| ☐ **CARPENTER, Fred Green** ................... *paintings* | | $770 | $6,000 |
| American b. 1882 | | | |
| ☐ **CARPENTER, Kate Holston** ................. *paintings* | | $110 | $220 |
| English b. 1866 | | | |
| ☐ **CARPENTER, Margaret Sarah** ............ *paintings* | | $605 | $4,950 |
| English 1793-1872 ..................................... *drawings* | | $165 | $1,430 |
| ☐ **CARPENTERO,** | | | |
| **Henri Joseph Gommarus** ...................... *paintings* | | $2,200 | $5,500 |
| Belgian 1820-1874 | | | |
| ☐ **CARPENTERO, Henry** ......................... *paintings* | | | $880 |
| ☐ **CARPENTERO, Jean Charles** .............. *paintings* | | | $3,025 |
| Belgian 1774-1823 | | | |
| ☐ **CARPENTIER, Madeleine** ................... *paintings* | | | $1,100 |
| French b. 1865 | | | |
| ☐ **CARPENTIER, Marguerite Jeanne** ....... *paintings* | | | $2,090 |
| American ac. 1904-1929 | | | |
| ☐ **CARPIONI, Giulio** .............................. *drawings* | | $1,320 | $1,980 |
| Italian 1613-1679 | | | |
| ☑ **CARR, John** ....................................... *paintings* | | | $1,650 |
| American d. 1837 | | | |
| ☑ **CARR, Lyell** ...................................... *paintings* | | | $7,150 |
| American 1857-1912 .................................. *drawings* | | | $137 |
| ☑ **CARR, Samuel S.** ............................... *paintings* | | $880 | $55,000 |
| American 1837-1908 .................................. *drawings* | | | $825 |
| ☐ **CARRA, Carlo** ................................... *paintings* | | $19,800 | $20,900 |
| Italian 1881-1966 | | | |
| ☐ **CARRACCI, Agostino** .......................... *drawings* | | | $6,050 |
| Italian 1557-1602 | | | |
| ☐ **CARRE, Johannes** ............................... *paintings* | | | $4,125 |
| Dutch 1698-1772 | | | |
| ☐ **CARRE, Leon Georges Jean Baptiste** ..... *paintings* | | | $275 |
| French 19th cent. | | | |
| ☐ **CARREE, Michiel** ............................... *paintings* | | $1,430 | $2,530 |
| Dutch 1657-1747 | | | |
| ☐ **CARRENO, Mario** .............................. *paintings* | | $1,540 | $30,800 |
| Cuban b. 1913 ......................................... *drawings* | | $550 | $3,575 |
| ☐ **CARRENTON, Victor** .......................... *paintings* | | | $1,650 |
| French 1864-1937 | | | |
| ☐ **CARRIARELLI, U.** ............................. *drawings* | | | $18,700 |
| ☐ **CARRICK, John Mulcaster** ................. *paintings* | | $935 | $1,320 |
| English ac. 1854-1878 | | | |
| ☐ **CARRICK, M.** ..................................... *paintings* | | | $330 |
| ☐ **CARRICK, William A.** ........................ *paintings* | | | $550 |
| ☐ **CARRIER, A.** ..................................... *sculpture* | | | $660 |
| ☐ **CARRIER, A.E.** .................................. *sculpture* | | | $2,090 |
| ☐ **CARRIER, Eugene** .............................. *paintings* | | | $1,540 |
| French 1849-1906 | | | |

| | | | Current Price Range | |
|---|---|---|---|---|
| | | | Low | High |
| ☐ **CARRIER-BELLEUSE, Albert Ernest** | ... *sculpture* | | $193 | $8,525 |
| French 1824-1887 | | | | |
| ☐ **CARRIER-BELLEUSE, Louis Robert** | ... *paintings* | | $2,750 | $3,850 |
| French 1848-1913 | *sculpture* | | $330 | $2,420 |
| ☐ **CARRIER-BELLEUSE, Pierre** | *paintings* | | | $5,280 |
| | *drawings* | | | $418 |
| ☐ **CARRIERA, Rosalba** | *drawings* | | $5,775 | $18,700 |
| Italian 1675-1757 | | | | |
| ☐ **CARRIERE, Eugene** | *paintings* | | $220 | $16,500 |
| French 1849-1906 | *drawings* | | $187 | $605 |
| ☐ **CARRILLO, Lilia** | *paintings* | | | $5,500 |
| b. Mexico 1929 | | | | |
| ☐ **CARRINGTON, Leonora** | *paintings* | | $4,125 | $31,900 |
| English b. 1917 | *drawings* | | $825 | $19,800 |
| ☐ **CARROGIS, Louis** | | | | |
| **(called CARMONTELLE)** | *drawings* | | $4,290 | $11,000 |
| French 1717-1806 | | | | |
| ☐ **CARROLL, J.A.** | *paintings* | | | $467 |
| ☐ **CARROLL, John** | *paintings* | | $220 | $800 |
| American 1892-1959 | *drawings* | | $55 | $242 |
| ☐ **CARROLL, Leon** | *drawings* | | | $440 |
| American | | | | |
| ☐ **CARROLL, W.J.** | *paintings* | | | $990 |
| American 19th cent. | | | | |
| ☐ **CARROLL, William Joseph** | *paintings* | | | $357 |
| ☐ **CARSE, J.H.** | *paintings* | | | $2,750 |
| British ac. 1860-1862 | | | | |
| ☐ **CARSMAN, Jon** | *paintings* | | $220 | $6,875 |
| American contemporary | *drawings* | | | $1,540 |
| ☐ **CARSON, Taylor** | *paintings* | | | $275 |
| Irish 19th/20th cent. | | | | |
| ☐ **CARSTAIRS, C.** | *paintings* | | | $308 |
| ☐ **CARSTENS, Paul** | *paintings* | | | $770 |
| ☐ **CARTE, Anto** | *paintings* | | | $8,250 |
| ☐ **CARTER, Clarence Henry** | *drawings* | | $935 | $2,090 |
| American | | | | |
| ☑ **CARTER, Clarence Holbrook** | *paintings* | | | $4,400 |
| American b. 1904 | | | | |
| ☐ **CARTER, Dennis Malone** | *paintings* | | $1,430 | $7,150 |
| American 1827-1881 | | | | |
| ☐ **CARTER, Frank T.** | *paintings* | | | $231 |
| English 19th/20th cent. | | | | |
| ☐ **CARTER, Gary** | *paintings* | | $2,000 | $10,000 |
| American b.1939 | | | | |
| ☐ **CARTER, Henry Barlow** | *drawings* | | | $192 |
| British 1803-1867 | | | | |
| ☐ **CARTER, J.N.** | *drawings* | | | $357 |
| ☐ **CARTER, M. M.** | *drawings* | | | $302 |
| American 20th cent. | | | | |

|  | | Current Price Range | |
|---|---|---|---|
|  | | Low | High |
| ☐ **CARTER, Pruett A.** ............................ *paintings* | | **$192** | **$3,575** |
| American 1891-1955 | | | |
| ☐ **CARTER, R.A.** ................................. *paintings* | | | **$330** |
| ☐ **CARTER, Sydney** ............................... *paintings* | | **$165** | **$825** |
| British ac. 1894-1936 | | | |
| ☐ **CARTER, William** ............................ *paintings* | | **$440** | **$880** |
| ☐ **CARTER (?), T.A.** ............................ *drawings* | | | **$660** |
| English 19th cent. | | | |
| ☐ **CARTIER** ....................................... *paintings* | | | **$330** |
| ☐ **CARTIER, Thomas Francois** ................ *sculpture* | | **$242** | **$660** |
| French b. 1879 | | | |
| ☐ **CARTIER, Victor-Emile** ...................... *paintings* | | | **$715** |
| French School 1811-1866 | | | |
| ☐ **CARTWRIGHT, Frederick William** ...... *drawings* | | | **$715** |
| ☐ **CARTWRIGHT, Isabel Branson** ........... *paintings* | | **$55** | **$418** |
| American b. 1885 | | | |
| ☐ **CARUCCI, Jacopo** | | | |
| **(called PONTORMO)** ....................... *drawings* | | | **$143,000** |
| ☐ **CARULLA, Ramon** ............................ *drawings* | | | **$385** |
| ☐ **CARUSO, Bruno** ............................... *paintings* | | **$154** | **$522** |
| Italian b. 1927 | | | |
| ☐ **CARUSO, Enrico** .............................. *drawings* | | **$247** | **$2,860** |
| Italian 1873-1921 ................................. *sculpture* | | **$550** | **$1,650** |
| ☐ **CARVALHO, David Nunes** ................... *paintings* | | | **$1,540** |
| American b. 1815 | | | |
| ☐ **CARVALHO, Solomon Nunes** .............. *drawings* | | | **$2,860** |
| American 1815-1894/97 | | | |
| ☐ **CARVALLO, Maria Teresa** ................. *paintings* | | | **$1,430** |
| Peruvian b. 1903 | | | |
| ☐ **CARVOLI, Carlo** .............................. *drawings* | | | **$880** |
| ☐ **CARY, Jack L.** ................................. *paintings* | | | **$1,210** |
| ☐ **CARY, William de la Montagne** ........... *paintings* | | **$770** | **$61,600** |
| American 1840-1922 ............................... *drawings* | | | **$440** |
| ☐ **CARYBE, Hector Julio Bernabo** ........... *paintings* | | | **$5,500** |
| Latin American b. 1911 | | | |
| ☐ **CARZOU, Jean** ............................... *paintings* | | | **$1,320** |
| French b. 1907 | | | |
| ☐ **CASALI, Andrea** .............................. *paintings* | | | **$3,080** |
| ☐ **CASANOVA, A.** ............................... *paintings* | | | **$935** |
| Spanish 19th cent. | | | |
| ☐ **CASANOVA, B.** ............................... *paintings* | | | **$260** |
| ☐ **CASANOVA, Francesco Giuseppe** ......... *paintings* | | | **$5,720** |
| ☐ **CASANOVA Y ESTORACH, Antonio** ... *paintings* | | **$1,650** | **$11,000** |
| Spanish d. 1896 ................................... *drawings* | | | **$110** |
| ☐ **CASCELLA, Michele** ........................... *paintings* | | **$165** | **$5,500** |
| Italian b. 1892 ................................... *drawings* | | **$605** | **$2,090** |
| ☐ **CASCELLA, Pietro** ........................... *sculpture* | | **$440** | **$880** |
| Italian b.1921 | | | |
| ☐ **CASCIARO, Giuseppe** ......................... *drawings* | | **$176** | **$192** |
| Italian 1863-1945 | | | |

| | | Current Price Range | |
|---|---|---|---|
| | | Low | High |
| □ **CASE, Edmund Elisha** .......................... *paintings* | | $495 | $1,650 |
| American 1844-1919 | | | |
| □ **CASENELLI, V.** ............................... *drawings* | | | $440 |
| American 19th cent. | | | |
| □ **CASENELLI, Victor** ............................ *drawings* | | | $3,500 |
| American 1867-1961 | | | |
| □ **CASENTINO, Jacopo del** ....................... *paintings* | | $22,000 | $27,500 |
| Italian 1297-1358 | | | |
| □ **CASER, Ettore** ................................ *paintings* | | $82 | $5,830 |
| Italian/American 1880-1944 | | | |
| □ **CASH, Herbert** ............................... *paintings* | | $20 | $770 |
| American 19th/20th cent. | | | |
| □ **CASILEAR, John William** .................... *paintings* | | $495 | $17,600 |
| American 1811-1893 ............................... *drawings* | | $187 | $330 |
| □ **CASIMIR, Laurent** ............................ *paintings* | | $275 | $715 |
| □ **CASNELLI, Victor** ............................ *paintings* | | $1,375 | $2,200 |
| American 19th/20th cent. ............................. *drawings* | | $1,045 | $2,750 |
| □ **CASO, L.G.** ..................................... *paintings* | | | $1,540 |
| Italian 19th/20th cent. | | | |
| □ **CASOLANI, Alessandro** ...................... *drawings* | | | $605 |
| □ **CASPAR, Carl** ............................... *paintings* | | | $550 |
| □ **CASPER, A.** .................................... *paintings* | | | $495 |
| □ **CASPER, Mike** ............................... *sculpture* | | | $1,550 |
| □ **CASS, George Nelson** ........................ *paintings* | | $302 | $1,320 |
| American 1831-1882 | | | |
| □ **CASS, Kae Dorn** ............................. *paintings* | | | $110 |
| American 1901-1971 ............................... *drawings* | | $75 | $200 |
| □ **CASSANA, Abate Giovanni Agostino** ..... *paintings* | | | $12,100 |
| Italian c. 1658-1720 | | | |
| □ **CASSANI, A. Phillip** ......................... *paintings* | | | $715 |
| Italian 19th cent. | | | |
| □ **CASSARD, Pierre Leon** ....................... *paintings* | | | $385 |
| French 19th/20th cent. | | | |
| □ **CASSATT, Mary** ............................... *paintings* | | $13,750 | $1,100,000 |
| American 1844-1926 ............................... *drawings* | | $412 | $450,000 |
| □ **CASSELL, Frank** ............................... *paintings* | | $605 | $1,980 |
| English 19th cent. | | | |
| □ **CASSELLARI, Vincenzo** ...................... *paintings* | | | $1,210 |
| Italian b. 1841 | | | |
| □ **CASSELLI, Henry** ............................. *drawings* | | | $10,000 |
| American contemporary | | | |
| □ **CASSIA, Charles** ............................. *sculpture* | | | $3,740 |
| Italian late 19th cent. | | | |
| □ **CASSIDY, Ira D. Gerald** ...................... *paintings* | | $1,100 | $20,900 |
| American 1879-1934 ............................... *drawings* | | $1,100 | $3,300 |
| □ **CASSIE, James** ............................... *paintings* | | | $715 |
| English 1819-1879 | | | |
| □ **CASSIERS, Henry** ............................. *paintings* | | $440 | $495 |
| Belgian 1858-1944 ............................... *drawings* | | $192 | $550 |

| | | Current Price Range | |
| --- | --- | --- | --- |
| | | Low | High |
| ☐ CASSIOLI, Amos ..................... paintings | | $1,100 | $1,870 |
| ☐ CASTAGNOLA, Gabriele ..................... paintings | | $605 | $1,870 |
| Italian 1828-1883 | | | |
| ☐ CASTAIGNE, Carlos ..................... paintings | | $302 | $385 |
| Argentinian 19th/20th cent. | | | |
| ☐ CASTAIGNE, J. Andre ..................... paintings | | $110 | $2,420 |
| French 19th/20th cent. | | | |
| ☐ CASTAIGNET ..................... paintings | | $137 | $440 |
| French 20th cent. | | | |
| ☐ CASTALDO, F. Coppola ..................... drawings | | | $374 |
| ☐ CASTAN, Pierre Jean Edmond ............. paintings | | $1,430 | $22,000 |
| French 1817-1892 | | | |
| ☐ CASTANEDA, Alfredo ..................... paintings | | $2,750 | $15,400 |
| b. Mexico 1938 ..................... drawings | | $825 | $1,760 |
| ☐ CASTANEDA, Felipe ..................... sculpture | | $2,420 | $13,200 |
| Mexican b. 1932 | | | |
| ☐ CASTEELS, Paulwel ..................... paintings | | | $7,150 |
| ☐ CASTEELS, Peter ..................... paintings | | $6,600 | $20,900 |
| Flemish 1684-1749 ..................... drawings | | | $198 |
| ☐ CASTEL, Moshe ..................... drawings | | | $4,400 |
| Israeli b.1909 | | | |
| ☐ CASTELLANI, Enrico ..................... paintings | | $1,760 | $6,500 |
| ☐ CASTELLANO, Filippo ..................... paintings | | $1,045 | $1,760 |
| Italian 18th cent. | | | |
| ☐ CASTELLANOS, Julio ..................... paintings | | | $50,600 |
| ..................... drawings | | $330 | $4,400 |
| ☐ CASTELLO, Bernardo ..................... drawings | | $880 | $1,430 |
| Italian 1557-1629 | | | |
| ☐ CASTELLO, Giacomo di ..................... paintings | | | $17,600 |
| ☐ CASTELLO, Giovanni Battista | | | |
| (IL GENOVESE) ..................... paintings | | | $37,400 |
| ☐ CASTELLON, Federico ..................... drawings | | $121 | $605 |
| Spanish/American 1914-1971 | | | |
| ☐ CASTELUCHO, Claudio ..................... paintings | | $250 | $2,970 |
| Spanish 1870-1927 | | | |
| ☐ CASTENADA, Baltazar Martinez .......... sculpture | | | $1,210 |
| Mexican b. 1938 | | | |
| ☐ CASTENEDA, Alfredo ..................... paintings | | $2,640 | $8,250 |
| Mexican b. 1938 ..................... drawings | | $1,100 | $1,650 |
| ☐ CASTIGLIONE, Guiseppe ..................... paintings | | $1,320 | $2,000 |
| Italian 1829-1908 | | | |
| ☐ CASTILLO, Antonio del ..................... drawings | | | $220 |
| Spanish 17th cent. | | | |
| ☐ CASTILLO, Marcos ..................... paintings | | | $15,400 |
| Venezuelan b. 1899 | | | |
| ☐ CASTLE-KEITH, William ..................... paintings | | $330 | $1,430 |
| American 19th/20th cent. | | | |
| ☐ CASTLEDON, F.G. ..................... paintings | | | $301 |
| 20th cent. | | | |

| | | Current Price Range | |
|---|---|---|---|
| | | *Low* | *High* |
| ☐ **CASTOLDI, Gugliemo** .......... *paintings* | | | $4,125 |
| Italian b. 1852 | | | |
| ☐ **CASTRES, Edouard** ............ *paintings* | | $2,420 | $30,800 |
| Swiss 1838-1902 | | | |
| ☐ **CASTRO PACHECO, Fernando** .......... *paintings* | | | $2,200 |
| .......................................... *drawings* | | | $385 |
| ☐ **CASTRO Y VELASCO,** | | | |
| **Antonio Palomino Acisclo de** ............ *drawings* | | | $550 |
| ☐ **CASTRO-CID, Enrique** .......... *paintings* | | | $550 |
| Latin American | | | |
| ☐ **CATALAN, Ramos** ............ *paintings* | | $175 | $1,980 |
| b. Chile 20th cent. | | | |
| ☐ **CATALANO, Luis Alvarez** ............ *paintings* | | | $9,900 |
| ☐ **CATANO, F.** ............ *drawings* | | | $357 |
| Continental 19th cent. | | | |
| ☐ **CATHCART, John** ............ *paintings* | | | $385 |
| American 19th cent. | | | |
| ☐ **CATHELIN, Bernard** ............ *paintings* | | $247 | $935 |
| French b. 1919 | | | |
| ☐ **CATHROW, Ann** ............ *paintings* | | | $462 |
| ☐ **CATLIN, George** ............ *paintings* | | $17,600 | $308,000 |
| American 1796-1872 ............ *drawings* | | $15,000 | $27,500 |
| ☐ **CATS, Jacob** ............ *drawings* | | | $1,760 |
| ☐ **CATTANEO, Achille** ............ *paintings* | | $1,100 | $1,870 |
| Italian 1872-1931 | | | |
| ☐ **CATTERMOLE, Charles** ............ *drawings* | | $176 | $2,475 |
| English 1832-1900 | | | |
| ☐ **CATTERMOLE, George** ............ *drawings* | | $88 | $440 |
| English 1800-1868 | | | |
| ☐ **CAUCHOIS, Eugene Henri** ............ *paintings* | | $1,320 | $6,875 |
| French 1850-1911 | | | |
| ☐ **CAUER, Emil** ............ *sculpture* | | | $330 |
| German | | | |
| ☐ **CAULAERT, Jean Dominique van** ........ *paintings* | | $132 | $1,650 |
| French 20th cent. ............ *drawings* | | $38 | $605 |
| ☐ **CAULDWELL, Leslie Giffen** ............ *paintings* | | $176 | $2,970 |
| American 1861-1941 ............ *drawings* | | | $55 |
| ☐ **CAULFIELD, Patrick** ............ *paintings* | | | $14,300 |
| English b. 1936 | | | |
| ☐ **CAULLERY, Louis de** ............ *paintings* | | $3,080 | $13,000 |
| Flemish ac. 1594-1620 | | | |
| ☐ **CAUSSE, Julien** ............ *sculpture* | | | $4,400 |
| French 19th cent. | | | |
| ☐ **CAUWER, Emile Pierre Joseph de** ........ *paintings* | | $1,980 | $8,250 |
| Belgian 1828-1873 | | | |
| ☐ **CAUWER, Leopold de** ............ *paintings* | | $1,320 | $3,025 |
| German 19th cent. | | | |
| ☐ **CAVACOS, Emmanuel Andre** ............ *sculpture* | | | $220 |
| Greek b. 1885 | | | |

| | | Current Price Range | |
|---|---|---|---|
| | | Low | High |
| ☐ **CAVADA, T.F.** ................................ *paintings* | | | $275 |
| 19th cent. | | | |
| ☐ **CAVAILLES, Jean Jules Louis** ............. *paintings* | | $165 | $5,225 |
| French 1901-1977 | | | |
| ☐ **CAVALCANTE, Jayme** ...................... *paintings* | | $88 | $302 |
| Brazilian 20th cent. | | | |
| ☐ **CAVALIERI, L.** ................................ *paintings* | | | $1,705 |
| Italian 1867-1942 | | | |
| ☐ **CAVALLERI, Fernando** ...................... *paintings* | | | $3,300 |
| Italian 1794-1865 | | | |
| ☐ **CAVALLINO, Bernardo** ...................... *paintings* | | | $11,000 |
| Italian 1616-1656/58 | | | |
| ☐ **CAVALLON, Giorgio** ......................... *paintings* | | $4,620 | $30,800 |
| American b. 1904 ...................................... *drawings* | | $286 | $1,210 |
| ☐ **CAVARO** .............................................. *sculpture* | | | $495 |
| Italian 19th/20th cent. | | | |
| ☐ **CAVAROZZI, Bartolomeo** ................... *paintings* | | $2,750 | $55,000 |
| ☐ **CAVAZZA, Azzo** ............................... *paintings* | | | $385 |
| Italian 19th cent. | | | |
| ☐ **CAVE, Jules Cyrille** ........................... *paintings* | | $800 | $2,750 |
| French b. 1859 | | | |
| ☐ **CAVEDONE, Giacomo** ......................... *drawings* | | $192 | $4,620 |
| Italian 1577-1660 | | | |
| ☐ **CAWSE, John** ................................... *paintings* | | | $2,200 |
| British c. 1779-1862 | | | |
| ☐ **CAWTHORNE, C.** ............................. *paintings* | | | $467 |
| ☐ **CAYRON, Jules** .................................. *paintings* | | | $14,300 |
| French | | | |
| ☐ **CAZAUBON, P.** .................................. *sculpture* | | | $385 |
| ☐ **CAZIN, Jean Charles** ......................... *paintings* | | $715 | $11,000 |
| French 1841-1901 ...................................... *drawings* | | $88 | $165 |
| ☐ **CECCHI, Adriano** .............................. *paintings* | | $385 | $6,050 |
| Italian b. 1850 | | | |
| ☐ **CECCHI, Francesco** ............................ *paintings* | | | $1,100 |
| ☐ **CECCHI, G.** ...................................... *paintings* | | | $495 |
| Italian 19th cent. | | | |
| ☐ **CECCHINI, Guilio** .............................. *paintings* | | $2,750 | $3,190 |
| Italian b. 1832 | | | |
| ☐ **CECCHINI-PRICHARD, Eugenio** ......... *paintings* | | | $2,310 |
| Italian b. 1831 | | | |
| ☐ **CEDERQUIST, Arthur E.** ................... *paintings* | | $440 | $550 |
| American 1884-1955 | | | |
| ☐ **CEDERSTROM, Thure Nikolaus von** .... *paintings* | | | $18,700 |
| Swedish 1843-1924 | | | |
| ☐ **CEDOR, Dieudonne** ............................ *paintings* | | $880 | $1,540 |
| Haitian b. 1925 | | | |
| ☐ **CEI, Cipriano** ................................... *paintings* | | $385 | $4,510 |
| Italian 1864/67-1922 | | | |
| ☐ **CELEBRANO, Francesco** ...................... *paintings* | | | $1,870 |

|  | | Current Price Range | |
|---|---|---|---|
|  | | Low | High |
| □ **CELOMMI, Pasquale** ............................ *paintings* | | $2,640 | $3,520 |
| Italian 1851/60-1928 | | | |
| □ **CELOMMI, Raffaello** ............................ *paintings* | | | $2,750 |
| Italian b.1883 | | | |
| □ **CELS, Albert F.** ..................................... *paintings* | | | $440 |
| Dutch b. 1883 | | | |
| □ **CELS, Emanuel Antoine Joseph** ............ *paintings* | | | $2,640 |
| Belgian 1821-1894 | | | |
| □ **CENNINO DI DREA CENNINI** ............. *paintings* | | | $22,000 |
| Italian c. 1350/70-c. 1398 | | | |
| □ **CENOIR** ................................................. *paintings* | | | $495 |
| □ **CERAMANO, Charles Ferdinand** .......... *paintings* | | $209 | $2,750 |
| Belgian 1829-1909 | | | |
| □ **CERESA, Carlo** ..................................... *paintings* | | $3,300 | $4,400 |
| Italian 1609-1679 ......................................... *drawings* | | | $1,320 |
| □ **CERIA, Edmond** ................................... *paintings* | | $154 | $1,540 |
| French 1884-1955 | | | |
| □ **CERIBELLI, Cesar** ............................... *sculpture* | | $466 | $1,540 |
| French b. 1841 | | | |
| □ **CERNIGLIARO, Salvatore** .................... *sculpture* | | | $10,175 |
| □ **CERNY, Venceslav** ............................... *paintings* | | | $990 |
| □ **CERQUOZZI, Michelangelo** ................. *paintings* | | | $12,100 |
| Italian 1602-1660 | | | |
| □ **CERRA, Mirta** ..................................... *paintings* | | | $2,420 |
| Latin American | | | |
| □ **CERRINI, Giandomenico** ....................... *paintings* | | | $1,210 |
| □ **CERUTI, Giacomo** | | | |
| **(called IL PITOCCHETTO)** .................... *paintings* | | | $71,500 |
| Italian ac. 1724-1738 | | | |
| □ **CESAR, (Cesar BALDACCINI)** ............ *sculpture* | | $352 | $68,750 |
| French b. 1921 | | | |
| □ **CESAR, Gaston Gonzalez** ....................... *sculpture* | | $11,000 | $13,200 |
| Mexican b. 1940 | | | |
| □ **CESARINI, Pier Luigi** ........................... *paintings* | | | $550 |
| □ **CESARONI, P.** ...................................... *paintings* | | | $935 |
| □ **CESTARO, Jacopo** ................................. *paintings* | | | $6,600 |
| □ **CEULEN, Cornelis Janssens van** .......... *paintings* | | $1,100 | $6,050 |
| □ **CEULEN, Cornelis Jonson van** ............. *paintings* | | $5,000 | $13,200 |
| Dutch 1593-c. 1664 | | | |
| □ **CEZANNE, Paul** ................................... *paintings* | | $19,800 | $3,960,000 |
| French 1839-1906 ......................................... *drawings* | | $1,320 | $121,000 |
| □ **CHAB, Victor** ...................................... *paintings* | | | $495 |
| Argentinian b. 1930 ..................................... *drawings* | | | $220 |
| □ **CHABANIAN, Arsene** ........................... *paintings* | | | $550 |
| French 1864-1949 ......................................... *drawings* | | | $165 |
| □ **CHABAS, Maurice** ............................... *paintings* | | | $1,650 |
| French 1862-1947 | | | |
| □ **CHABAS, Paul Emile** ........................... *paintings* | | $1,430 | $40,180 |
| French 1869-1934/37 | | | |

| | Current Price Range | |
|---|---|---|
| | Low | High |

| | | | Low | High |
|---|---|---|---|---|
| ☐ **CHABLIS, E.M.** ................... *paintings* | | | | $2,750 |
| French 19th cent. | | | | |
| ☐ **CHABOR, Moura** ................... *paintings* | | | $110 | $286 |
| ................... *drawings* | | | | $80 |
| ☐ **CHABOT, E.** ................... *paintings* | | | | $1,210 |
| French 19th cent. | | | | |
| ☐ **CHABRIER, G.** ................... *paintings* | | | | $2,000 |
| French 19/20th cent. | | | | |
| ☐ **CHACE, Helen B.** ................... *paintings* | | | | $176 |
| American | | | | |
| ☐ **CHADWICK, Ellen N.** ................... *paintings* | | | | $274 |
| ☐ **CHADWICK, Lynn** ................... *drawings* | | | $300 | $748 |
| English b. 1914 ................... *sculpture* | | | $1,485 | $6,600 |
| ☐ **CHADWICK, William** ................... *paintings* | | | $774 | $6,050 |
| American 1879-1962 | | | | |
| ☐ **CHAESE, Nora** ................... *paintings* | | | $495 | $880 |
| American ac. 1880 | | | | |
| ☐ **CHAESE (?), Emily** ................... *paintings* | | | | $2,420 |
| American 19th cent. | | | | |
| ☐ **CHAFFEE, Oliver Newberry** ................... *paintings* | | | | $660 |
| American 1881-1944 ................... *drawings* | | | | $132 |
| ☐ **CHAFFEE, Samuel R.** ................... *drawings* | | | $33 | $880 |
| American 19th/20th cent. | | | | |
| ☐ **CHAGALL, Marc** ................... *paintings* | | | $93,500 | $660,000 |
| Russian/French 1887-1985 ................... *drawings* | | | $1,210 | $154,000 |
| ☐ **CHAGNOUX, Christine** ................... *drawings* | | | | $192 |
| French 20th cent. | | | | |
| ☐ **CHAHINE, Edgar** ................... *drawings* | | | $209 | $440 |
| French 1874-1947 | | | | |
| ☐ **CHAIGNEAU, Jean Ferdinand** ................... *paintings* | | | $1,760 | $4,180 |
| French 1830-1906 | | | | |
| ☐ **CHAILLAUX** ................... *paintings* | | | | $715 |
| French 20th cent. | | | | |
| ☐ **CHAILLOUX, Robert** ................... *paintings* | | | $220 | $1,100 |
| French b. 1913 | | | | |
| ☐ **CHAIRBAUN, Charles** ................... *paintings* | | | | $275 |
| ☐ **CHALE, Gertrudis** ................... *paintings* | | | | $19,800 |
| ☐ **CHALEM, Celine** ................... *sculpture* | | | $440 | $715 |
| ☐ **CHALFANT, Jefferson David** ................... *paintings* | | | | $22,000 |
| American 1856-1931 | | | | |
| ☐ **CHALGALO** ................... *paintings* | | | | $308 |
| ☐ **CHALGRIN, Jean Francois** ................... *drawings* | | | | $1,430 |
| ☐ **CHALIAPIN, Boris** ................... *paintings* | | | | $192 |
| Russian/American 1904/7-1979 ................... *drawings* | | | | $600 |
| ☐ **CHALLACOMBE, Fred W.** ................... *paintings* | | | | $385 |
| ☐ **CHALLANT, J.D.** ................... *paintings* | | | | $7,150 |
| ☐ **CHALLE, Charles Michel Ange** ................... *drawings* | | | $385 | $2,420 |
| French 1718-1778 | | | | |
| ☐ **CHALLION** ................... *drawings* | | | | $440 |

| | | Current Price Range | |
| | | Low | High |
| --- | --- | --- | --- |
| ☐ CHALLIOT, L. ..................... *drawings* | | | $440 |
| ☐ CHALMERS, George Paul ................... *paintings* | | | $330 |
| ☐ CHALMERS, R. ..................... *paintings* | | | $700 |
| ☐ CHALON, Alfred Edward ................... *drawings* | | $748 | $1,320 |
| Swiss 1780-1860 | | | |
| ☐ CHALON, Henry Bernard ................... *paintings* | | $1,760 | $126,500 |
| English 1770-1849 | | | |
| ☐ CHALON, Kingsley S. ..................... *paintings* | | | $742 |
| English 19th cent. | | | |
| ☐ CHALON, Louis ..................... *paintings* | | | $2,970 |
| French b.1866 | | | |
| ☐ CHALON, Louis ..................... *sculpture* | | | $4,950 |
| French early 20th cent. | | | |
| ☐ CHALON, Maria A. ..................... *paintings* | | $176 | $770 |
| ☐ CHAMAILLARD, Ernest de ................... *paintings* | | | $4,400 |
| ☐ CHAMBERLAIN, John Angus ............. *sculpture* | | $99 | $16,500 |
| American b. 1927 | | | |
| ☐ CHAMBERLAIN, Wynn ................... *paintings* | | $352 | $1,210 |
| American b. 1929 | | | |
| ☐ CHAMBERLIN, Francis X. ................. *drawings* | | | $495 |
| ☐ CHAMBERLIN, Mason (the elder) ......... *paintings* | | $990 | $1,430 |
| English b. 1787 | | | |
| ☐ CHAMBERS, C. Bosseron ................... *paintings* | | $192 | $528 |
| American b. 1883 | | | |
| ☐ CHAMBERS, Charles Edward ............. *paintings* | | $385 | $1,320 |
| American 1883-1941 | | | |
| ☐ CHAMBERS, G.W. ..................... *paintings* | | | $192 |
| American | | | |
| ☐ CHAMBERS, George (Sr.) ................... *paintings* | | $495 | $7,150 |
| English 1803-1840 ..................... *drawings* | | | $150 |
| ☐ CHAMBERS, George W. (Jr.) ............. *paintings* | | $330 | $1,980 |
| English 19th cent. | | | |
| ☐ CHAMBERS, L.E. ..................... *paintings* | | | $1,650 |
| American 1892-1942 | | | |
| ☐ CHAMBERS, Thomas ..................... *paintings* | | | $1,980 |
| American | | | |
| ☐ CHAMBERS, Thomas ..................... *paintings* | | $3,300 | $22,000 |
| American b. c. 1808-1866 | | | |
| ☐ CHAMBON, Marius ..................... *paintings* | | | $192 |
| French 1876-1962 | | | |
| ☐ CHAMPAIGNE, Jean Baptiste de .......... *paintings* | | | $3,300 |
| Flemish 1631-1681 | | | |
| ☐ CHAMPAIGNE, Phillippe de ............... *paintings* | | $24,200 | $159,500 |
| French 1602-1674 | | | |
| ☐ CHAMPION, Edme Theodore ............. *paintings* | | | $3,630 |
| French ac. 1869-1882 | | | |
| ☐ CHAMPNEY, Benjamin ..................... *paintings* | | $160 | $4,125 |
| American 1817-1907 ..................... *drawings* | | $121 | $440 |

|                                                      | Current Price Range | |
|                                                      | Low      | High     |
| --- | --- | --- |
| ☐ **CHAMPNEY, James Wells** ........... *paintings*   | $935     | $44,000  |
| American 1843-1903 ........................ *drawings* | $99      | $1,870   |
| ☐ **CHAN, Eddie** .......................... *paintings* |          | $247     |
| American .................................... *drawings* |          | $176     |
| ☐ **CHANDLER, Henry Daland** ......... *drawings*    | $330     | $1,650   |
| ☐ **CHANDLER, J.W.** ..................... *paintings* |          | $275     |
| ☐ **CHANDLER, Jean** ..................... *paintings* |          | $330     |
| ☐ **CHANDLER, Joseph Goodhue** ...... *paintings*   | $400     | $935     |
| American 1813-1880/84                                 |          |          |
| ☐ **CHANDLER, Rose M.** ................. *paintings* |          | $850     |
| English 19th cent.                                    |          |          |
| ☐ **CHANDLER, Winthrop** ............... *paintings* |          | $55,000  |
| 1747-1790                                             |          |          |
| ☐ **CHANDLES, J.G.** ..................... *paintings* | $302     | $302     |
| American ac. 1850's                                   |          |          |
| ☐ **CHANET, Henri** ...................... *paintings* |          | $715     |
| French 19th cent.                                     |          |          |
| ☐ **CHANEY, Lester Joseph** ............ *paintings* | $275     | $357     |
| American b. Hungary 1907 ................. *drawings* | $165     | $176     |
| ☐ **CHANIN, A.** ........................... *paintings* |          | $247     |
| American 19th/20th cent.                              |          |          |
| ☐ **CHANISLINSKA, H. C.** ............... *paintings* |          | $605     |
| Polish 19th cent.                                     |          |          |
| ☐ **CHANLER, Robert Winthrop** ........ *drawings*  |          | $1,210   |
| American 1872-1930                                    |          |          |
| ☐ **CHANTRELLE, Lucien** ............... *paintings* |          | $286     |
| French b. 1890                                        |          |          |
| ☐ **CHANTRON, Alexandre Jacques** ..... *paintings* | $1,980   | $1,980   |
| French 1842-1918                                      |          |          |
| ☐ **CHAPAMAN, Ch.** ..................... *paintings* |          | $522     |
| 19th cent.                                            |          |          |
| ☐ **CHAPEL, Guy M.** ..................... *paintings* | $275     | $357     |
| American b. 1871                                      |          |          |
| ☐ **CHAPELAIN-MIDY, Roger** ......... *paintings*   | $2,090   | $4,400   |
| French b. 1904 ............................ *drawings* |          | $467     |
| ☐ **CHAPELLE, Bill** ..................... *paintings* |          | $385     |
| ☐ **CHAPERON, Eugene** ................. *paintings* | $5,500   | $66,000  |
| French b. 1857                                        |          |          |
| ☐ **CHAPIN, Bryant** ..................... *paintings* | $100     | $3,025   |
| American 1859-1927 ....................... *drawings* | $88      | $150     |
| ☐ **CHAPIN, C.H.** ........................ *paintings* | $600     | $2,200   |
| American c. 1830-after 1874 .............. *drawings* |          | $660     |
| ☐ **CHAPIN, Francis** ..................... *paintings* | $55      | $300     |
| American 1899-1965 ....................... *drawings* |          | $220     |
| ☐ **CHAPIN, James Ormsbee** ........... *paintings* | $286     | $6,600   |
| American 1887-1975                                    |          |          |
| ☐ **CHAPIN, John R.** ..................... *drawings* | $357     | $660     |
| American b. 1823                                      |          |          |

| | | Current Price Range | |
|---|---|---|---|
| | | Low | High |
| ☐ CHAPLIN, Arthur ............................ *paintings* | | $990 | $6,600 |
| .................................................. *drawings* | | | $825 |
| ☐ CHAPLIN, Charles ........................ *paintings* | | $275 | $23,100 |
| French 1825-1891 ..................................... *drawings* | | | $220 |
| ☐ CHAPLIN, Henry ........................... *paintings* | | | $1,210 |
| ☐ CHAPLIN, Sarah ........................... *drawings* | | | $411 |
| American | | | |
| ☐ CHAPMAN, Carlton Theodore ............. *paintings* | | $137 | $5,500 |
| American 1860-1925/26 .............................. *drawings* | | $33 | $357 |
| ☐ CHAPMAN, Charles S. ...................... *paintings* | | $165 | $3,080 |
| American b. 1879 ...................................... *drawings* | | $198 | $715 |
| ☐ CHAPMAN, Conrad Wise .................. *paintings* | | $990 | $13,200 |
| Italian/American 1842-1910 | | | |
| ☐ CHAPMAN, Cyrus Durand ................. *paintings* | | | $1,760 |
| American | | | |
| ☐ CHAPMAN, Frederick A. ................... *paintings* | | $192 | $220 |
| American | | | |
| ☐ CHAPMAN, J. ................................. *drawings* | | | $357 |
| ☐ CHAPMAN, John Gadsby .................... *paintings* | | $192 | $13,200 |
| American 1808-1889/90 .............................. *drawings* | | | $275 |
| ☐ CHAPMAN, John Linton .................... *paintings* | | $1,210 | $14,300 |
| American 1839-1905 | | | |
| ☐ CHAPMAN, John Watkins .................. *paintings* | | $600 | $1,430 |
| English ac. 1853-1903 | | | |
| ☐ CHAPMAN, Minerva Josephine ............ *paintings* | | $275 | $715 |
| American b. 1858 | | | |
| ☐ CHAPMAN, S.W. ............................ *paintings* | | | $412 |
| ☐ CHAPMAN, W. ............................... *paintings* | | | $225 |
| English 19th cent. | | | |
| ☐ CHAPOTON, Gregoire ....................... *paintings* | | | $1,540 |
| French b. 1845 | | | |
| ☐ CHAPPEL, Alonzo ........................... *paintings* | | $1,265 | $1,320 |
| American 1828-1887 .................................. *drawings* | | $418 | $715 |
| ☐ CHAPPEL, L. ................................. *paintings* | | | $825 |
| French 19th cent. | | | |
| ☐ CHAPPELL, Reuben ......................... *paintings* | | | $2,200 |
| British 1870-1940 | | | |
| ☐ CHAPPELL, William ......................... *paintings* | | $440 | $605 |
| English 19th cent. | | | |
| ☐ CHAPU, Henri Michel Antoine ............. *sculpture* | | | $550 |
| French 1833-1891 | | | |
| ☐ CHARCHOUNE, Serge ....................... *paintings* | | $1,100 | $1,210 |
| Russian 1888-1975 | | | |
| ☐ CHARDIGNY, Jules .......................... *paintings* | | $154 | $522 |
| French d. 1892 | | | |
| ☐ CHARDIN, Jean Baptiste Simeon .......... *paintings* | | | $110,000 |
| French 1699-1779 | | | |
| ☐ CHARETTE-DUVAL, Francois ............. *paintings* | | | $3,080 |
| Belgian ac. 1836-1878 | | | |

| | | | *Current Price Range* | |
| --- | --- | --- | --- | --- |
| | | | *Low* | *High* |
| ☐ **CHARLAMOFF, Alexei Alexeiewitsch** | ... | *paintings* | $165 | $33,000 |
| Russian b. 1849 | | *drawings* | $605 | $1,210 |
| ☐ **CHARLEMAGNE,** | | | | |
| **Adolph Jossifowitsch (Sr.)** | | *drawings* | $357 | $385 |
| ☐ **CHARLEMAGNE, Johnny** | | *paintings* | | $935 |
| ☐ **CHARLEMONT, Eduard** | | *paintings* | $330 | $5,500 |
| Austrian 1848-1906 | | | | |
| ☐ **CHARLEMONT, Hugo** | | *paintings* | $770 | $26,400 |
| Austrian b. 1850 | | | | |
| ☐ **CHARLESON** | | *paintings* | | $660 |
| ☐ **CHARLET, Frantz** | | *paintings* | $2,310 | $3,190 |
| Belgian 1862-1928 | | | | |
| ☐ **CHARLIER, Emile** | | *paintings* | $935 | $990 |
| Belgian 19th cent. | | | | |
| ☐ **CHARLOT, Jean** | | *paintings* | $110 | $7,700 |
| French 1898-1979 | | *drawings* | $110 | $1,320 |
| ☐ **CHARLOT, Louis** | | *paintings* | | $1,265 |
| ☐ **CHARLTON, John** | | *paintings* | $4,400 | $12,100 |
| English 1849-1910 | | | | |
| ☐ **CHARPENTIER** | | *sculpture* | | $1,760 |
| ☐ **CHARPENTIER, Jean Baptiste** | | *paintings* | | $30,800 |
| French 1728-1806 | | | | |
| ☐ **CHARPIN** | | *paintings* | | $412 |
| American 19th/20th cent. | | | | |
| ☐ **CHARPIN, Albert** | | *paintings* | $308 | $935 |
| French 1842-1924 | | | | |
| ☐ **CHARRETON, Victor** | | *paintings* | $1,320 | $8,800 |
| French 1864-1936 | | | | |
| ☐ **CHARTIER, Henri Georges Jacques** | ..... | *paintings* | $1,320 | $2,475 |
| French 1859-1924 | | *drawings* | | $330 |
| ☐ **CHARTON, Ernest** | | *paintings* | | $15,400 |
| French 1815-1877 | | | | |
| ☐ **CHARTRAN, Theobald** | | *paintings* | $3,520 | $9,900 |
| French 1849-1907 | | | | |
| ☐ **CHARTRAND, Esteban** | | *paintings* | $2,750 | $5,280 |
| Spanish 1825-1889 | | | | |
| ☐ **CHARTRAND, P.** | | *paintings* | | $350 |
| ☑ **CHASE, Adelaide Cole** | | *paintings* | $225 | $302 |
| American 1868-1944 | | | | |
| ☑ **CHASE, C.H.** | | *paintings* | | $2,420 |
| American 19th cent. | | | | |
| ☑ **CHASE, E.** | | *paintings* | | $225 |
| American 19th cent. | | | | |
| ☑ **CHASE, Frank Swift** | | *paintings* | $330 | $1,650 |
| American 1886-1958 | | | | |
| ☑ **CHASE, Henry (called Harry)** | | *paintings* | $82 | $4,620 |
| American 1853-1889 | | *drawings* | | $165 |
| ☑ **CHASE, Lila Elizabeth** | | *paintings* | | $990 |
| American | | | | |

| | | | Current Price Range | |
|---|---|---|---|---|
| | | | Low | High |
| ☑ **CHASE, Louisa** | *drawings* | | | $1,540 |
| contemporary | | | | |
| ☑ **CHASE, William Merritt** | *paintings* | | $3,850 | $473,000 |
| American 1849-1916 | *drawings* | | $660 | $28,600 |
| ☐ **CHASSELAT, Pierre** | *drawings* | | $550 | $660 |
| ☐ **CHASSERIAU, Theodore** | *paintings* | | $11,000 | $99,000 |
| French 1819-1856 | *drawings* | | | $990 |
| ☐ **CHASSIN-TRUBERT, Desire** ` | *paintings* | | | $2,200 |
| ☐ **CHATEIGNON, Ernest** | *paintings* | | $192 | $3,520 |
| French ac. 19th cent. | | | | |
| ☐ **CHATELET, Claude Louis** | *drawings* | | $990 | $5,225 |
| French c. 1750-1795 | | | | |
| ☐ **CHATILLON, Charles de** | *paintings* | | | $7,150 |
| ☐ **CHATTERTON, Clarence K.** | *paintings* | | $110 | $6,600 |
| American 1880-1973 | *drawings* | | | $247 |
| ☐ **CHAVES, Glauco** | *paintings* | | | $198 |
| Brazilian 20th cent. | | | | |
| ☐ **CHAVET, Victor Joseph** | *paintings* | | $1,045 | $3,850 |
| French 1822-1906 | | | | |
| ☐ **CHAVEZ, Angel** | *paintings* | | | $385 |
| ☐ **CHAVEZ MORADO, Jose** | *paintings* | | | $4,400 |
| ☐ **CHAVIGNAUD, Georges** | *drawings* | | | $275 |
| ☐ **CHAYLLERY, Eugene Louis** | *paintings* | | | $1,210 |
| French ac. 1894-1906 | | | | |
| ☐ **CHECA Y SANZ, Ulpiano** | *paintings* | | $1,320 | $95,700 |
| Spanish 1860-1916 | *drawings* | | | $462 |
| | *sculpture* | | | $1,870 |
| ☐ **CHECK, R.S.** | *paintings* | | | $400 |
| American 19th cent. | | | | |
| ☐ **CHEE, Robert** | *drawings* | | $825 | $3,850 |
| American (Navajo) b. 1938 | | | | |
| ☐ **CHEEK, C.R.** | *paintings* | | | $2,000 |
| American | | | | |
| ☐ **CHELMINSKI, Jan van** | *paintings* | | $1,320 | $5,830 |
| Polish 1851-1925 | | | | |
| ☐ **CHEMIELINSKI, W.T.** | *paintings* | | | $1,100 |
| Eastern European early 20th cent. | | | | |
| ☐ **CHEMIN, Victor** | *sculpture* | | | $352 |
| French 20th cent. | | | | |
| ☐ **CHEN, Hilo** | *paintings* | | $880 | $2,750 |
| ☐ **CHEN CHI,** | *drawings* | | $880 | $20,000 |
| Chinese/American b. 1912 | | | | |
| ☐ **CHENARD-HUCHE, George** | *paintings* | | | $550 |
| French 1864-1937 | | | | |
| ☐ **CHENART** | *drawings* | | | $385 |
| French 18th/19th cent. | | | | |
| ☐ **CHENEY, Russell** | *paintings* | | $55 | $2,310 |
| American b. 1881 | | | | |
| ☐ **CHENU, F.** | *paintings* | | | $770 |

| | | Current Price Range | |
|---|---|---|---|
| | | *Low* | *High* |
| ☐ **CHEREAU, T.** ................ *drawings* | | | $220 |
| French 19th cent. | | | |
| ☐ **CHEREPEV, J.** ................ *paintings* | | | $385 |
| ☐ **CHERET, Gustave Joseph** ........... *sculpture* | | | $7,150 |
| French 1838-1894 | | | |
| ☐ **CHERET, Jules** ................ *paintings* | | $3,300 | $4,070 |
| French 1836-1932 ................ *drawings* | | $385 | $6,050 |
| ☐ **CHERKAS, Constantine** ........... *paintings* | | $275 | $357 |
| Russian/American 20th cent. | | | |
| ☐ **CHERNEY, Marvin** ........... *paintings* | | $110 | $935 |
| ☐ **CHERNOW, Ann** ........... *paintings* | | | $715 |
| American b. 1936 ................ *drawings* | | $495 | $1,100 |
| ☐ **CHEROVEL, Paul** ........... *paintings* | | | $357 |
| French 20th cent. | | | |
| ☐ **CHERRY, Emma Richardson** ........... *paintings* | | | $275 |
| American b. 1859 ................ *drawings* | | | $110 |
| ☐ **CHERRY, Herman** ........... *paintings* | | | $330 |
| contemporary | | | |
| ☐ **CHERRY, Kathryn** ........... *paintings* | | | $3,410 |
| American b. 1880 | | | |
| ☐ **CHERUBINI, Andrea** ........... *paintings* | | $907 | $3,850 |
| Italian 19th cent. | | | |
| ☐ **CHERY, Jean Rene** ........... *paintings* | | $33 | $1,760 |
| b. Haiti 1929 | | | |
| ☐ **CHESTER, A.** ................ *drawings* | | $170 | $246 |
| English ? 19th cent. | | | |
| ☐ **CHESTER, E.** ................ *paintings* | | | $275 |
| ☐ **CHESTER, George** ........... *paintings* | | | $1,760 |
| British 19th cent. | | | |
| ☐ **CHETTY** ................ *paintings* | | | $180 |
| American 20th cent. | | | |
| ☐ **CHEUILLARD, V.** ................ *paintings* | | | $715 |
| ☐ **CHEUNG LEE, Chee Chin S.** ........... *drawings* | | | $192 |
| Chinese/American 20th cent. | | | |
| ☐ **CHEUREAUSE, Jacquesson de la** ........... *paintings* | | | $462 |
| ☐ **CHEVALA, A.** ................ *paintings* | | | $935 |
| Austrian 19th cent. | | | |
| ☐ **CHEVALIER, G.** ................ *paintings* | | | $198 |
| French 19th cent. | | | |
| ☐ **CHEVALIER, Louis Pierre** ........... *drawings* | | | $440 |
| ☐ **CHEVALIER, R.M.** ........... *paintings* | | | $4,400 |
| French 19th cent. | | | |
| ☐ **CHEVILLIARD,** | | | |
| **Vincent Jean Baptiste** ........... *paintings* | | $110 | $6,325 |
| French 1841-1904 ................ *drawings* | | $605 | $1,100 |
| ☐ **CHEVIOT, Lilian** ........... *paintings* | | | $880 |
| English exhib. 1894-1911 | | | |

| | | Current Price Range | |
|---|---|---|---|
| | | Low | High |
| ☐ CHIA, Sandro ............................ *paintings* | | $9,900 | $46,200 |
| b. 1946 .................................. *drawings* | | $1,760 | $2,420 |
| .................................. *sculpture* | | | $46,750 |
| ☐ CHIALIVA, Luigi ........................ *paintings* | | $3,900 | $8,800 |
| Swiss/Italian 1842-1914 ............... *drawings* | | $1,925 | $2,750 |
| ☐ CHIARI, Giuseppe ...................... *paintings* | | $8,000 | $8,250 |
| .................................. *drawings* | | | $660 |
| ☐ CHIBAUH, Aimee ....................... *drawings* | | | $357 |
| French 19th cent. | | | |
| ☐ CHICA, Olga de ........................ *paintings* | | | $302 |
| ☐ CHICAGO, Judy | | | |
| (Judith GEROWITZ) ................... *paintings* | | | $385 |
| American b. 1939 | | | |
| ☐ CHICHESTER, Cecil .................... *paintings* | | $220 | $2,530 |
| American b. 1891 | | | |
| ☐ CHICK, N.M. ........................... *paintings* | | | $715 |
| ☐ CHICKERING, Charles H. ............. *paintings* | | | $550 |
| American | | | |
| ☐ CHICLANERO, R. ....................... *drawings* | | | $2,090 |
| Spanish 19th cent. | | | |
| ☐ CHIERICI, Alfonso ..................... *paintings* | | $330 | $1,100 |
| Italian 1816-1873 | | | |
| ☐ CHIERICI, Gaetano .................... *paintings* | | $1,650 | $36,300 |
| Italian 1838-1920 | | | |
| ☐ CHIGOT, Eugene Henri Alexandre ....... *paintings* | | $385 | $1,870 |
| French 1860-1923 | | | |
| ☐ CHIKUMBIRIKE, Canaan ............... *sculpture* | | | $330 |
| African | | | |
| ☐ CHIKUMBIRIKE, I.F.R. ............... *sculpture* | | | $495 |
| ☐ CHIKUMBIRIKE, Peter ................ *sculpture* | | $275 | $385 |
| ☐ CHILD, Edwin Burrage ............... *paintings* | | $33 | $1,540 |
| American 1868-1937 | | | |
| ☐ CHILDE, E. ............................. *paintings* | | | $1,155 |
| English 19th cent. | | | |
| ☐ CHILDE, James Warren ............... *drawings* | | | $192 |
| English 1778-1862 | | | |
| ☐ CHILLIDA, Eduardo ................... *sculpture* | | | $55,000 |
| ☐ CHILLMAN (?), P.E. ................... *drawings* | | | $301 |
| American 19th/20th cent. | | | |
| ☐ CHIN, Ten ............................. *paintings* | | | $462 |
| ☐ CHINA TRADE PAINTING .............. *paintings* | | $1,320 | $14,300 |
| ☐ CHINARD, Joseph ...................... *sculpture* | | | $7,700 |
| French 1756-1813 | | | |
| ☐ CHINNERY, George .................... *paintings* | | $24,200 | $33,000 |
| British 1748-1847 ...................... *drawings* | | $247 | $440 |
| ☐ CHINNI, Peter Anthony .............. *sculpture* | | $440 | $5,225 |
| American b. 1928 | | | |
| ☐ CHINTREUIL, Antoine ................. *paintings* | | | $4,400 |
| French 1814/16-1873 | | | |

## China Trade

This portrait of an Oriental woman
evokes the period during the 18th
and 19th centuries when clipper
ships crossed the Pacific to the
Orient, returning with cargoes of
porcelain and silk. The crew, who
often spent months in port while
return cargo was assembled, spent
at least some of their time buying
souvenirs, including some artwork.
The paintings they brought back —
landscapes, portraits, and genre
scenes — are now called "China
Trade paintings." These works,
done by Chinese artists in a
western style that they learned by
studying European prints, manage
to convey the Chinese landscape,
culture, and people, and at the
same time document an era in
American maritime history. This
informal portrait is typical of those
done for export during this period.
("China Trade," oil on canvas, Fine
Arts Co., October 15, 1983, $550.)

|  |  | Current Price Range | |
|---|---|---|---|
|  |  | *Low* | *High* |
| ☐ **CHIPARIUS, Demetre** .......................... *sculpture* | | **$198** | **$55,000** |
| Rumanian ac. 1914-1933 | | | |
| ☐ **CHIRIACKA, Ernest** ............................. *paintings* | | **$715** | **$8,250** |
| American b. 1920 | | | |
| ☐ **CHIRICO, Giorgio de** ........................... *paintings* | | **$14,300** | **$1,045,000** |
| Italian 1888-1978 ....................................... *drawings* | | **$1,320** | **$39,600** |
| ............................................................ *sculpture* | | **$6,050** | **$19,800** |
| ☐ **CHITTENDEN, Alice Brown** ................. *paintings* | | **$137** | **$935** |
| American 1860-1934 | | | |
| ☐ **CHIVERTON, F.** ................................. *drawings* | | | **$418** |
| ☐ **CHLEBOWSKI, S.** .............................. *paintings* | | | **$17,050** |
| ☐ **CHLEBOWSKI, Stanislas von** ............... *paintings* | | **$6,600** | **$30,800** |
| Polish 1835-1884 | | | |
| ☐ **CHMIELINSKI, W.T.** ........................... *paintings* | | | **$1,127** |
| Polish 19th/20th cent. | | | |
| ☐ **CHO LEE, Ming** .................................. *drawings* | | | **$440** |
| ☐ **CHOATE, Nathaniel** ............................. *sculpture* | | | **$1,500** |
| American 1899-1965 | | | |

## Architectural Drawings

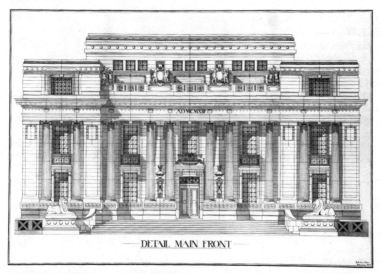

DETAIL MAIN FRONT

*Architectural drawings are created to serve a utilitarian and not an artistic purpose. The Museum of Modern Art's 1975 show of drawings from the Ecole des Beaux Arts provided impetus to the growing interest in collecting architectural drawings, an interest which has accelerated in the last ten years. Architectural drawings are usually included in sales of American drawings and modern decorative arts at the New York houses. The esthetic qualities of a drawing are usually more important in determining its value in the marketplace than its scholarly importance or place in a body of work. Among the 20th-century architects now considered particularly collectible are Eliel Saarinen, Erik Gunnar Asplund, Frank Lloyd Wright, and Le Corbusier. A Wright drawing of the Imperial Hotel in Tokyo has reportedly been sold privately for $200,000. (F. Chiverton, "Elevation of the Facade of a Municipal Building," pen and black ink with gray wash, 24 x 33½ in., Christie's East, May 22, 1985, $418.)*

|  | | Current Price Range | |
|---|---|---|---|
|  | | *Low* | *High* |
| ☐ **CHOCARNE-MOREAU, Paul Charles**   .. *paintings* <br> French 1855-1931 | | **$2,200** | **$3,520** |
| ☐ **CHOCHON, Andre Eugene Louis**   .......... *paintings* <br> French 20th cent. | | **$137** | **$357** |
| ☐ **CHODOWIECKI, Daniel Nicolaus**   ........ *drawings* | | | **$990** |
| ☐ **CHOFFARD, Pierre Phillippe**   .............. *drawings* | | | **$440** |
| ☐ **CHOM, Nessa**   .................................... *sculpture* <br> American 20th cent. | | | **$550** |
| ☐ **CHOULTSE, Ivan F.**   ........................... *paintings* <br> Russian 1877-after 1932 | | **$1,100** | **$12,100** |

| | | Current Price Range | |
| --- | --- | --- | --- |
| | | *Low* | *High* |
| ☐ **CHRETIEN, E.** ........ *sculpture* | | | $1,210 |
| ☐ **CHRETIEN, Rene** ........ *paintings* | | | $770 |
| ☐ **CHRISPEN, June** ........ *sculpture* | | | $440 |
| Zimbabwe contemporary | | | |
| ☐ **CHRISTENSEN, Dan** ........ *paintings* | | $1,000 | $5,500 |
| American b. 1942 | | | |
| ☐ **CHRISTIANSEN, Nils Hans** ........ *paintings* | | $220 | $440 |
| Danish 1873-1960 | | | |
| ☐ **CHRISTIE, James Elder** ........ *paintings* | | $137 | $3,575 |
| British 1847-1914 | | | |
| ☐ **CHRISTO, (Christo JAVACHEFF)** ........ *paintings* | | | $20,900 |
| Bulgarian/American b. 1935 ........ *drawings* | | $1,980 | $38,500 |
| ........ *sculpture* | | | $1,760 |
| ☐ **CHRISTY, Earl** ........ *drawings* | | $264 | $935 |
| b. 1883 | | | |
| ☐ **CHRISTY, Howard Chandler** ........ *paintings* | | $165 | $20,900 |
| American 1873-1952 ........ *drawings* | | $66 | $3,850 |
| ☐ **CHRITON, J.** ........ *paintings* | | | $495 |
| ☐ **CHRYSSA** ........ *paintings* | | | $700 |
| Greek/American b. 1933 ........ *drawings* | | $330 | $1,540 |
| ........ *sculpture* | | $825 | $4,620 |
| ☐ **CHUBLEY, Henry Hadfield** ........ *paintings* | | | $357 |
| British 19th/20th cent. | | | |
| ☐ **CHURCH, Francis** ........ *drawings* | | | $715 |
| Belgian 19th cent. | | | |
| ☐ **CHURCH, Frederick Edwin** ........ *paintings* | | $1,210 | $330,000 |
| American 1826-1900 | | | |
| ☐ **CHURCH, Frederick Stuart** ........ *paintings* | | $192 | $3,575 |
| American 1842-1924 ........ *drawings* | | $110 | $1,870 |
| ☐ **CHURCHILL, Sir Winston** ........ *paintings* | | $6,600 | $26,400 |
| English 1874-1965 | | | |
| ☐ **CHURCHILL, William W.** ........ *paintings* | | $1,045 | $4,950 |
| American 1858-1926 | | | |
| ☐ **CHURCHYARD, Thomas** ........ *paintings* | | $165 | $1,320 |
| English 1798-1865 | | | |
| ☐ **CHUTEAU, J.** ........ *paintings* | | | $330 |
| French 20th cent. | | | |
| ☐ **CHWALA, Adolf** ........ *paintings* | | $1,760 | $2,475 |
| Czechoslovakian 1836-1900 | | | |
| ☐ **CHWALA, Fritz** ........ *paintings* | | $330 | $550 |
| ☐ **CHWAWA, Edward** ........ *sculpture* | | $99 | $357 |
| ☐ **CIAFRONE** ........ *paintings* | | $440 | $700 |
| ☐ **CIAMPAGLIA, Carlo** ........ *paintings* | | | $467 |
| American b. 1891 | | | |
| ☐ **CIAMPELLI, Agostino** ........ *drawings* | | | $1,760 |
| Italian 1578-1640 | | | |
| ☐ **CIANI, Cesare** ........ *paintings* | | | $1,430 |
| Italian 1854-1925 | | | |

| | | | Current Price Range | |
|---|---|---|---|---|
| | | | *Low* | *High* |
| ☐ **CIAPPA, F.A.** | *paintings* | | $121 | $495 |
| Italian early 20th cent. | | | | |
| ☐ **CIARDI, Beppe** | *paintings* | | | $8,800 |
| Italian 1875-1932 | | | | |
| ☐ **CIARDI, Emma** | *paintings* | | $1,430 | $6,050 |
| Italian 1879-1933 | | | | |
| ☐ **CIARDI, Guglielmo** | *paintings* | | | $2,200 |
| Italian 1842/43-1917 | | | | |
| ☐ **CIBOT, Marie** | *drawings* | | | $275 |
| French 19th cent. | | | | |
| ☐ **CIBOURE, Vallgren** | *sculpture* | | | $264 |
| ☐ **CICERI, Enrique** | *paintings* | | | $1,650 |
| ☐ **CICERI, Ernest** | *drawings* | | $165 | $660 |
| American 1817-1866 | | | | |
| ☐ **CICERI, Eugene** | *paintings* | | $1,320 | $6,325 |
| French 1813-1890 | *drawings* | | $264 | $5,500 |
| ☐ **CICOGNA, Giammaria** | *paintings* | | | $825 |
| Italian 1813-1849 | | | | |
| ☐ **CID, Enrique Castro** | *drawings* | | $440 | $1,650 |
| ☐ **CIECI (?), L.** | *paintings* | | | $1,045 |
| Italian 19th cent. | | | | |
| ☐ **CIESZKOWSKI, Henryk** | *paintings* | | $550 | $2,530 |
| Polish 1835-1895 | | | | |
| ☐ **CIGNANI, Carlo** | *paintings* | | | $10,450 |
| Italian 1628-1719 | | | | |
| ☐ **CIKOVSKY, Nicolai** | *paintings* | | $137 | $715 |
| Russian/American 1894-after 1934 | *drawings* | | $55 | $467 |
| ☐ **CILFONE, Gianni L.** | *paintings* | | | $302 |
| 20th cent. | | | | |
| ☐ **CIMAGLIA, Giuseppe** | *paintings* | | $330 | $1,650 |
| Italian 1849-1905 | | | | |
| ☐ **CIMINO** | *paintings* | | | $577 |
| Italian 18th/19th cent. | | | | |
| ☐ **CIMIOTTI, Gustave** | *paintings* | | $88 | $3,575 |
| American 1875-after 1929 | *drawings* | | | $165 |
| ☐ **CINCINNATI, Cyrus** | *paintings* | | | $247 |
| American 1878-1916 | | | | |
| ☐ **CINE, Theo van** | *paintings* | | | $352 |
| ☐ **CINELLA** | *paintings* | | | $900 |
| ☐ **CINFUEGOS, Gonzalo** | *paintings* | | $1,100 | $4,125 |
| Latin American | | | | |
| ☐ **CINGLOUVSKI, T.** | *drawings* | | | $522 |
| ☐ **CIONE, Jacopo di** | *paintings* | | $26,400 | $110,000 |
| Italian 1308-1394 | | | | |
| ☐ **CIOTTA, F.** | *paintings* | | | $825 |
| ☐ **CIPHARD, Annie** | *paintings* | | | $880 |
| American 19th cent. | | | | |
| ☐ **CIPOLLA, Fabio** | *paintings* | | $660 | $3,850 |
| Italian b. 1854 | | | | |

| | Current Price Range | |
|---|---|---|
| | *Low* | *High* |

☐ **CIPPER, Giacomo Francesco**
**(called IL TODESCHINI)** ........................ *paintings* | $2,200 | $15,950
Italian c. 1670-1738

☐ **CIPRIANI, A.** ..................................... *sculpture* | $660 | $880
Italian 19th/20th cent.

☐ **CIPRIANI, C.** ..................................... *sculpture* | $484 | $495
Italian 19th/20th cent.

☐ **CIPRIANI, Giovanni Battista** .............. *paintings* | | $1,100
Italian 1727-1785/1790 ............................... *drawings* | $385 | $1,100

☐ **CIPRIANI, Giovanni Pinotti** ................. *sculpture* | | $715

☐ **CIPRIANI, Nazzarreno** ....................... *drawings* | $385 | $1,320
Italian 1843-1925

☐ **CIPRICO, Marguerite** ......................... *paintings* | | $192
American 20th cent.

☐ **CIRATELLI** ....................................... *drawings* | | $1,540

☐ **CIRCIGNANO, Niccolo**
**(called Do Pomarance)** ........................... *paintings* | | $2,420
Italian 1517-c. 1596

☐ **CIRINO, Antonio** ............................... *paintings* | $192 | $2,090
Italian/American b. 1889

☐ **CIRY, Michel** .................................... *paintings* | $330 | $2,200
French b. 1919 ...................................... *drawings* | | $176

☐ **CISTELLO,**
**Vicomtesse Julie de la Bourdonnay**
**(b. G. ROQUE)** .................................... *paintings* | | $1,320
Brazilian 19th/20th cent.

☐ **CITTADINI, Pier Francesco** ................. *paintings* | | $2,420
Italian 1616-1681

☐ **CIUSA-ROMAGNA, Giovanni** .............. *paintings* | | $275
Italian 20th cent.

☐ **CKRIEGHOFF** ................................... *paintings* | | $522
Canadian 19th cent.

☐ **CLAES, Constant Guillaume** ................ *paintings* | | $1,045
Belgian 1826-1905

☐ **CLAES, Trous** ................................... *paintings* | $70 | $300

☐ **CLAESSENS, Anthonie** ....................... *paintings* | | $7,700
Flemish 15th cent.

☐ **CLAESZ, Anthony (I)** ......................... *paintings* | | $71,500
Dutch 1592-1635/36

☐ **CLAESZ, Pieter** ................................. *paintings* | $44,000 | $71,500
Dutch c. 1597-1661

☐ **CLAEUW, Jacques de** ......................... *paintings* | | $7,000
Dutch d. 1676

☐ **CLAGG, T.** ....................................... *paintings* | | $374
English early 20th cent.

☐ **CLAGHORN, Joseph C.** ...................... *paintings* | $165 | $7,150
American 1869-after 1934 ........................... *drawings* | $220 | $990

☐ **CLAGUE, Richard** .............................. *paintings* | | $1,485
American 1816-1878

| | | Current Price Range | |
|---|---|---|---|
| | | Low | High |
| ☐ **CLAIR, Charles** ................................. *paintings* <br> French 19th/20th cent. | | $440 | $2,860 |
| ☐ **CLAIR, R.A.** ................................. *paintings* <br> American 19th cent. | | $495 | $1,650 |
| ☐ **CLAIRE, R. le** ................................. *paintings* | | | $330 |
| ☐ **CLAIRIN, Georges Jules Victor** ............ *paintings* <br> French 1843-1919 .................................... *drawings* | | $3,520 <br> $165 | $22,000 <br> $1,430 |
| ☐ **CLAIRIN, Pierre Eugene** ..................... *paintings* <br> French 1897-1980 | | $55 | $220 |
| ☐ **CLAIRMONT, J.G.** ........................... *paintings* | | | $495 |
| ☐ **CLAISSE, Genevieve** ......................... *paintings* | | | $550 |
| ☐ **CLAITON, J.** ................................. *paintings* <br> 19th/20th cent. | | $231 | $495 |
| ☐ **CLAPP, William Henry** ..................... *paintings* <br> American 1879-1954 | | $44 | $5,500 |
| ☐ **CLARA, Juan (or Jose)** .................... *sculpture* <br> Spanish 1875/78-1958 | | $360 | $1,045 |
| ☐ **CLARE, George** ............................. *paintings* <br> English ac. c. 1860-1900 ......................... *drawings* | | $412 | $4,950 <br> $440 |
| ☐ **CLARE, J.** ................................. *paintings* | | | $935 |
| ☐ **CLARE, Oliver** ............................. *paintings* <br> British c. 1853-1927 ............................. *drawings* | | $330 | $5,170 <br> $412 |
| ☐ **CLARE, Vincent** ........................... *paintings* <br> British c. 1855-1925/30 .......................... *drawings* | | $660 | $4,125 <br> $605 |
| ☐ **CLARENBACH, Max** ........................ *paintings* <br> German 1880-1952 | | | $2,090 |
| ☐ **CLARK, Allan** ............................. *sculpture* <br> American 1896/98-1950 | | $550 | $12,100 |
| ☐ **CLARK, Alson Skinner** ..................... *paintings* <br> American 1876-1949 | | $1,045 | $17,000 |
| ☐ **CLARK, Benton** ............................. *paintings* <br> American 1895/1900-1964 | | $143 | $1,980 |
| ☐ **CLARK, Dixon** ............................. *paintings* <br> English | | | $550 |
| ☐ **CLARK, Edgar** ............................. *paintings* | | | $770 |
| ☐ **CLARK, Eliot Candee** ...................... *paintings* <br> American 1883-1980 | | $165 | $4,620 |
| ☐ **CLARK, Francis Herbert** ................... *paintings* <br> American b. 1876 | | | $192 |
| ☐ **CLARK, Frank Scott** ....................... *paintings* <br> American | | | $275 |
| ☐ **CLARK, Freeman** ........................... *paintings* <br> American 20th cent. | | $550 | $660 |
| ☐ **CLARK, George Merritt** .................... *paintings* <br> American d. 1904 .............................. *drawings* | | $192 <br> $55 | $1,000 <br> $385 |
| ☐ **CLARK, James** ............................. *paintings* <br> British | | $742 | $3,850 |
| ☐ **CLARK, James Lippitt** ..................... *sculpture* <br> American 1883-1957 | | $880 | $4,400 |

**Which Clark Painted This Cow?**

*Three British artists, all named James Clark, painted animals in the late 19th century. This painting is most likely the work of Albert James Clark who, according to reference sources, painted horses and an occasional prize heifer. It is signed "James Clark," and the name of the subject, "Pineapple," is inscribed on the back.*

*Many landowners and farmers favored paintings of livestock, partly as a record of their holdings and partly for the publicity the pictures brought. Paintings of prize cattle were reproduced as prints and sometimes sold in the thousands. Portraits of sheep and pigs, the heftier the better, were also popular. (James Clark, "Pineapple," oil on canvas, 20 x 24 in., Christie's East, May 22, 1985, $1,210.)*

|  | | *Current Price Range* | |
| --- | --- | --- | --- |
|  | | *Low* | *High* |
| ☐ **CLARK, Jean van der** .......................... *paintings* | | | **$715** |
| ☐ **CLARK, Joseph** ................................ *paintings* | | **$775** | **$2,200** |
| English 1834-1919 | | | |
| ☐ **CLARK, Joseph Benwell** ...................... *paintings* | | | **$3,080** |
| English b. 1857 | | | |
| ☐ **CLARK, L.G.** ..................................... *paintings* | | | **$2,200** |
| British 19th cent. | | | |
| ☐ **CLARK, Lillian B.** ............................. *paintings* | | | **$350** |
| American 19th cent. | | | |
| ☐ **CLARK, Michael** ................................ *paintings* | | | **$467** |
| American contemporary | | | |
| ☐ **CLARK, Myron** ................................. *paintings* | | | **$385** |

|  | | Current Price Range | |
|---|---|---|---|
|  | | Low | High |
| ☐ **CLARK, Octavius T.** ............................ *paintings* | | $467 | $1,100 |
| English 1850-1921 | | | |
| ☐ **CLARK, Oliver** ................................... *paintings* | | | $302 |
| ☐ **CLARK, Pierre** .................................... *paintings* | | | $275 |
| ☐ **CLARK, Roland** ................................... *drawings* | | | $715 |
| American 1874-1957 | | | |
| ☐ **CLARK, Roy C.** ................................... *paintings* | | | $247 |
| American b. 1889 | | | |
| ☐ **CLARK, S. Joseph** ............................... *paintings* | | | $6,600 |
| English | | | |
| ☐ **CLARK, Thomas** ................................. *paintings* | | | $9,900 |
| Irish 18th cent. | | | |
| ☐ **CLARK, Virginia Keep** ........................ *paintings* | | | $192 |
| American b. 1878 ..................................... *drawings* | | | $385 |
| ☐ **CLARK, Walter A.** ............................... *paintings* | | $467 | $2,310 |
| American 1848-1917 | | | |
| ☐ **CLARK, Walter Appleton** ..................... *paintings* | | | $1,430 |
| American 1876-1906 | | | |
| ☐ **CLARK, Walter Leighton** ..................... *paintings* | | | $550 |
| American 1859-1935 | | | |
| ☐ **CLARKE, Frederick Benjamin** .............. *sculpture* | | | $2,500 |
| American 1874-1943 | | | |
| ☐ **CLARKE, John Clem** .......................... *paintings* | | $605 | $6,600 |
| American b. 1937 ..................................... *drawings* | | | $1,540 |
| ☐ **CLARKE, Joseph Clayton (KYD)** ........... *drawings* | | | $275 |
| ☐ **CLARKE, Maud U.** ............................. *paintings* | | | $3,000 |
| ☐ **CLARKE, Remington** .......................... *sculpture* | | $1,760 | $2,090 |
| ☐ **CLARKE, Samuel Barling** .................... *paintings* | | $2,420 | $3,410 |
| English ac. 1852-1878 | | | |
| ☐ **CLARKE, William Hanna** .................... *paintings* | | | $1,100 |
| English | | | |
| ☐ **CLARKSON, Edward** .......................... *paintings* | | $1,100 | $2,530 |
| ac. 1855-1860 | | | |
| ☐ **CLAS, Klara** ...................................... *sculpture* | | | $198 |
| Austrian | | | |
| ☐ **CLASSEN, Otto** ................................. *paintings* | | | $247 |
| American 20th cent. | | | |
| ☐ **CLASSENS, J.J.** ................................. *paintings* | | | $418 |
| ☐ **CLAUDE, Jean Maxime** ....................... *paintings* | | | $7,700 |
| French 1823-1904 | | | |
| ☐ **CLAUDET, Max** ................................. *sculpture* | | | $550 |
| French 1840-1893 | | | |
| ☐ **CLAUDIUS, A.** .................................. *paintings* | | | $412 |
| contemporary | | | |
| ☐ **CLAUDOT, Jean Baptiste Charles** ......... *paintings* | | | $3,575 |
| French 1733-1805 | | | |
| ☐ **CLAUS, Emile** ................................... *paintings* | | | $8,525 |
| Belgian 1849-1924 | | | |

| | Current Price Range | |
|---|---|---|
| | *Low* | *High* |
| ☐ **CLAUSADE, Pierre de** .................... *paintings* <br> French b. 1910 | **$1,100** | **$1,320** |
| ☐ **CLAUSELL, Joaquin** ............. *paintings* <br> Mexican 1866-1935 | **$1,980** | **$99,000** |
| ☐ **CLAUSEN, Peter** ................... *paintings* <br> American 1830-1924 | | **$605** |
| ☐ **CLAUSEN, Sir George** .............. *paintings* <br> English 1852-1944 | **$2,200** | **$7,700** |
| ☐ **CLAVE, Antoni** ................... *paintings* <br> French, b. Spain 1913 .................... *drawings* <br> .................... *sculpture* | **$1,650** <br> **$418** | **$4,950** <br> **$4,125** <br> **$3,300** |
| ☐ **CLAVERIE, Jules Justin** .............. *paintings* <br> French 1859-1932 | **$2,860** | **$4,400** |
| ☐ **CLAVIERE, Bernard de** .............. *paintings* <br> French 20th cent. | | **$352** |
| ☐ **CLAVY, F.** .................... *paintings* | | **$466** |
| ☐ **CLAWSON, Rex** .................. *paintings* <br> American b. 1930 .................... *drawings* | | **$242** <br> **$176** |
| ☐ **CLAXTON, M.** ................... *paintings* | | **$2,530** |
| ☐ **CLAY, Mary F.R.** .................. *paintings* <br> American d. 1939 | **$357** | **$900** |
| ☐ **CLAYDEN, L.** ................. *paintings* | | **$605** |
| ☐ **CLAYES, Berthe des** .............. *drawings* <br> Canadian 20th cent. | **$350** | **$600** |
| ☐ **CLAYS, Paul Jean** ................ *paintings* <br> Belgian 1819-1900 .................... *drawings* | **$522** | **$7,150** <br> **$1,320** |
| ☐ **CLAYTON, Charles** ............. *sculpture* | | **$385** |
| ☐ **CLAYTON, J. Hughes** ............ *paintings* <br> English 19th cent. .................... *drawings* | | **$20** <br> **$330** |
| ☐ **CLEAR, G.** .................... *paintings* | **$220** | **$352** |
| ☐ **CLEAVES, W.R.** ................ *paintings* <br> American late 19th cent. | | **$231** |
| ☐ **CLEE, Henry** .................... *paintings* <br> American 20th cent. | | **$385** |
| ☐ **CLEEMPUT, J. van** .............. *paintings* <br> Belgian 20th cent. | | **$330** |
| ☐ **CLEENEWERCK, Henry** ............ *paintings* <br> Belgian 19th cent. | **$1,650** | **$19,800** |
| ☐ **CLEMENCIN, Francois Andre** ......... *sculpture* <br> French b. 1878 | | **$880** |
| ☐ **CLEMENS, Paul** ................ *paintings* | | **$770** |
| ☐ **CLEMENT, Charles** ............ *paintings* <br> Swiss b. 1889 | | **$825** |
| ☐ **CLEMENT, Felix Auguste** ............ *paintings* <br> French 1826-1888 | | **$5,775** |
| ☐ **CLEMENT, Marcel** ............. *paintings* | | **$528** |
| ☐ **CLEMENT, Maxime** ............ *drawings* <br> French 19th/20th cent. | | **$522** |

| | | Current Price Range | |
|---|---|---|---|
| | | *Low* | *High* |
| ☐ **CLEMENT, S.** .................... *paintings* | | | $2,640 |
| Spanish 19th cent. | | | |
| ☐ **CLEMENTE, Francesco** .......... *paintings* | | | $8,800 |
| contemporary ........................ *drawings* | | $2,640 | $8,800 |
| ☐ **CLEMENTI** ...................... *sculpture* | | | $325 |
| East African 20th cent. | | | |
| ☐ **CLEMENTS, A.H.** .............. *paintings* | | | $880 |
| English 19th cent. | | | |
| ☐ **CLEMENTS, Gabrielle de Veaux** ......... *paintings* | | | $247 |
| American b. 1858 | | | |
| ☐ **CLEMENTS, George H.** ........ *paintings* | | | $220 |
| American 1854-1935 | | | |
| ☐ **CLEMENTZ, Hermann** .......... *paintings* | | $2,475 | $3,575 |
| German b. 1852 | | | |
| ☐ **CLEMINSON, Robert** .......... *paintings* | | $605 | $715 |
| English ac. 1865-1868 | | | |
| ☐ **CLERC, A. le** ................... *drawings* | | $220 | |
| French late 19th cent. | | | |
| ☐ **CLERCQ, Alfons de** ............ *paintings* | | | $1,320 |
| Belgian b. 1868 | | | |
| ☐ **CLERISSEAU, Charles Louis** ...... *paintings* | | | $6,600 |
| French 1721-1820 ..................... *drawings* | | $550 | $2,420 |
| ☐ **CLESINGER, J.** ................. *sculpture* | | $1,650 | $3,850 |
| French 1814-1883 | | | |
| ☐ **CLESINGER, Jean-Baptiste** ....... *paintings* | | | $3,080 |
| French 19th cent. | | | |
| ☐ **CLESSINGER, Georges Philippe** .......... *sculpture* | | | $4,675 |
| French b. 1788 | | | |
| ☐ **CLEVE, Cornelis van** .......... *paintings* | | $2,860 | $9,900 |
| French 1520-c. 1567 | | | |
| ☐ **CLEVE, Joos van** .............. *paintings* | | | $40,000 |
| Flemish | | | |
| ☐ **CLEVELEY, John** ............... *drawings* | | $495 | $1,980 |
| British 18th/19th cent. | | | |
| ☐ **CLEVELEY, Robert** ........... *paintings* | | | $6,600 |
| English 1747-1809 | | | |
| ☐ **CLIBBORN, W.** ................ *drawings* | | $770 | $990 |
| 19th/20th cent. | | | |
| ☐ **CLIFFORD, Edward** ........... *drawings* | | $110 | $7,700 |
| English 1844-1907 | | | |
| ☐ **CLIME, Winfield Scott** ........ *paintings* | | $137 | $440 |
| American b. 1881 | | | |
| ☐ **CLIMENT** ..................... *drawings* | | | $300 |
| 20th cent. | | | |
| ☐ **CLINEDINST, Benjamin West** ......... *paintings* | | $165 | $4,290 |
| American 1859-1931 .................. *drawings* | | $220 | $302 |
| ☐ **CLINT, Alfred** ................. *paintings* | | | $1,320 |
| English 1807-1883 | | | |
| ☐ **CLINTON, F.C.** ................ *paintings* | | $330 | $1,650 |

| | | Current Price Range | |
|---|---|---|---|
| | | Low | High |
| ☐ **CLIVIA** ............................................ *sculpture* | | $220 | $286 |
| American | | | |
| ☐ **CLODION, Claude Michel** ..................... *sculpture* | | $280 | $4,400 |
| French 1738-1814 | | | |
| ☐ **CLONESSY, W.** ................................. *paintings* | | | $440 |
| American 19th cent. | | | |
| ☐ **CLONNEY, James Goodwyn** ................ *paintings* | | $82,500 | $198,000 |
| American 1812-1867 ................................. *drawings* | | | $9,900 |
| ☐ **CLOSE, Chuck** ................................... *drawings* | | $6,600 | $17,600 |
| American b. 1940 | | | |
| ☐ **CLOSSON, William Baxter Palmer** ....... *paintings* | | $110 | $1,155 |
| American 1848-1926 | | | |
| ☐ **CLOSTERMAN, Johann** ....................... *paintings* | | $1,320 | $1,650 |
| German 1660-1713 | | | |
| ☐ **CLOTTU, Jean** ................................... *paintings* | | | $1,210 |
| ☐ **CLOUGH, D.A.** ................................... *paintings* | | | $700 |
| ☐ **CLOUGH, George L.** .......................... *paintings* | | $550 | $4,400 |
| American 1824-1901 | | | |
| ☐ **CLOUGH, Stanley Thomas** ................... *paintings* | | $137 | $350 |
| American b. 1905 | | | |
| ☐ **CLOWES, Daniel** ............................... *paintings* | | | $4,180 |
| English ac. 1790-1835 | | | |
| ☐ **CLUZEL, F.** ..................................... *sculpture* | | | $330 |
| ☐ **CLYMER, John F.** ............................. *paintings* | | $1,320 | $130,000 |
| American b. 1907 ..................................... *drawings* | | $5,750 | $8,800 |
| ☐ **CLYNE, A.J.** .................................... *paintings* | | | $192 |
| American 20th cent. | | | |
| ☐ **COALE, Griffith Bailay** ....................... *paintings* | | | $1,320 |
| American b. 1890 | | | |
| ☐ **COAST, Oscar Regan** .......................... *paintings* | | $110 | $450 |
| American 1851-1931 | | | |
| ☐ **COATES, Edmund C.** .......................... *paintings* | | $440 | $4,950 |
| American 1816-1871 | | | |
| ☐ **COATS, R.L.** ..................................... *paintings* | | | $209 |
| American 20th cent. | | | |
| ☐ **COATS, Randolph** ............................. *paintings* | | | $665 |
| American b. 1891 | | | |
| ☐ **COBB, C.G.** ..................................... *paintings* | | | $385 |
| ☐ **COBB, Darius** ................................... *paintings* | | $100 | $1,320 |
| American 1834-1919 | | | |
| ☐ **COBB, Henry Ives** .............................. *paintings* | | | $220 |
| American 1859-1931 ................................. *drawings* | | | $198 |
| ☐ **COBBETT, Edward John** ...................... *paintings* | | $1,100 | $4,400 |
| English 1815-1899 | | | |
| ☐ **COBLITZ, L.** ..................................... *paintings* | | | $550 |
| French 19th cent. | | | |
| ☐ **COBURG, Frank** ............................... *paintings* | | | $440 |
| ☐ **COBURN, Frederick Simpson** .............. *paintings* | | $1,870 | $15,400 |
| American 1871-1960 | | | |

| | | Current Price Range | |
|---|---|---|---|
| | | Low | High |
| ☐ **COCCETTI, V.** ...................... *paintings* | | | $770 |
| ☐ **COCCORANTE, Leonardo** ............... *paintings* | | $2,530 | $4,620 |
| Italian 1700-1750 | | | |
| ☐ **COCHERET, L.** ........................ *sculpture* | | | $220 |
| French | | | |
| ☐ **COCHIN, Charles Nicolas** | | | |
| **(the younger)** ...................... *paintings* | | | $1,100 |
| French 1715-1790 | | | |
| ☐ **COCHON, Andre** ..................... *paintings* | | $220 | $275 |
| ☐ **COCHRAN, Allen D.** ................. *paintings* | | $275 | $440 |
| American 1888-1935 | | | |
| ☐ **COCHRAN, Bruce L.** ............... *drawings* | | | $418 |
| ☐ **COCHRANE, Constance** ............ *paintings* | | $121 | $407 |
| American ac. 1915-1947 | | | |
| ☐ **COCHRANE, Helen L.** ............ *drawings* | | | $302 |
| English 20th cent. | | | |
| ☐ **COCK, Cesar de** ..................... *paintings* | | $770 | $3,575 |
| Flemish 1823-1904 | | | |
| ☐ **COCK, Jan de (the Putative)** ........... *paintings* | | | $36,300 |
| ☐ **COCK, Xavier de** ..................... *paintings* | | | $440 |
| Belgian 1818-1896 | | | |
| ☐ **COCKCROFT** ........................ *paintings* | | | $880 |
| ☐ **COCTEAU, Jean** ..................... *paintings* | | $110 | $37,400 |
| French 1889-1963 ...................... *sculpture* | | | $2,750 |
| ☐ **CODAZZI, Niccolo Viriani** ............ *paintings* | | | $6,875 |
| Italian c. 1648-1693 | | | |
| ☐ **CODAZZI, Viviano** ................. *paintings* | | | $3,300 |
| Italian 1603-1672 | | | |
| ☐ **CODDE, Carel** ..................... *paintings* | | | $2,200 |
| ☐ **CODDE, Pieter Jacobs** ............ *paintings* | | $1,540 | $18,700 |
| Dutch 1599-1678 | | | |
| ☐ **CODMAN, Charles** ............... *paintings* | | $1,100 | $6,050 |
| American 1800-1842 | | | |
| ☐ **CODMAN, Edwin E.** ............ *paintings* | | | $200 |
| American 19th cent. | | | |
| ☐ **CODMAN, G.** ..................... *sculpture* | | | $330 |
| American | | | |
| ☐ **CODMAN, John Amory** ............ *paintings* | | $500 | $1,650 |
| American 1824-1886 | | | |
| ☐ **CODY, James** ..................... *drawings* | | | $550 |
| American | | | |
| ☐ **COE, Theodore** ..................... *paintings* | | | $357 |
| American b. 1866 | | | |
| ☐ **COECKE VAN AELST, Pieter** ............ *paintings* | | | $88,000 |
| Flemish | | | |
| ☐ **COEFFIER, Marie Pauline Adrienne** ..... *paintings* | | | $550 |
| French 1814-1900 | | | |
| ☐ **COENE, Constantinus Fidelio** ............ *paintings* | | | $1,870 |
| Flemish 1780-1840 | | | |

| | | Current Price Range | |
|---|---|---|---|
| | | Low | High |
| ☐ **COENE, Jean-Henri de** ........................ *paintings* | | $5,500 | $11,000 |
| Belgian 1798-1866 | | | |
| ☐ **COES, Kent Day** ............................... *drawings* | | | $330 |
| 20th cent. | | | |
| ☐ **COESSIN DE LA FOSSE,** | | | |
| **Charles Alexandre** ............................. *paintings* | | $1,650 | $5,775 |
| French b. 1829 ......................................... *drawings* | | | $1,650 |
| ☐ **COEYLAS, Henri** ............................... *paintings* | | | $3,850 |
| French 19th/20th cent. | | | |
| ☐ **COFFERMANS, Marcellus** | | | |
| **(or COFFEEMAKER)** ........................... *paintings* | | | $9,350 |
| Flemish d. after 1575 | | | |
| ☐ **COFFIN, Elizabeth R.** ........................ *paintings* | | $1,650 | $1,760 |
| American 1851-1930 | | | |
| ☐ **COFFIN, George Albert** ................... *paintings* | | | $220 |
| American ac. 1856-1922 | | | |
| ☐ **COFFIN, Raphael** ............................. *drawings* | | | $1,045 |
| ☐ **COFFIN, William Anderson** ................ *paintings* | | $165 | $3,025 |
| American 1855-1925/26 ............................... *drawings* | | | $825 |
| ☐ **COFFIN, William Haskell** .................... *paintings* | | $88 | $1,210 |
| American d. 1941 ..................................... *drawings* | | $770 | $1,540 |
| ☐ **COGGESHALL, Calvert** ...................... *paintings* | | | $192 |
| American b. 1907 | | | |
| ☐ **COGGESHALL, John I.** ....................... *paintings* | | | $660 |
| American 1856-1927 | | | |
| ☐ **COGGINS, Leola** ............................... *drawings* | | | $302 |
| American 19th cent. | | | |
| ☐ **COGSWELL, William** ........................ *paintings* | | | $2,200 |
| American 1819-1903 | | | |
| ☐ **COHEN, Eduard** ............................... *paintings* | | $4,400 | $6,050 |
| German 1838-1910 | | | |
| ☐ **COHEN, Frederick E.** ........................ *paintings* | | | $2,860 |
| American ac.1837-1855 | | | |
| ☐ **COHEN, George W.** ........................... *paintings* | | | $770 |
| American | | | |
| ☐ **COHEN, Lewis** ................................. *paintings* | | $330 | $2,530 |
| American 1857-1915 | | | |
| ☐ **COHET** ........................................ *paintings* | | | $257 |
| American 19th/20th cent. | | | |
| ☐ **COIGNARD, James** ........................... *paintings* | | $220 | $1,100 |
| French b. 1925 ......................................... *drawings* | | | $605 |
| ☐ **COIGNARD, Louis** ............................. *paintings* | | | $495 |
| French 1810-1883 | | | |
| ☐ **COIGNET, Jules** ............................... *drawings* | | $110 | $797 |
| French 1798-1860 | | | |
| ☐ **COINCHON,** | | | |
| **Jacques Antoine Theodore** ...................... *sculpture* | | | $880 |
| French 1814-1881 | | | |

| | | | *Current Price Range* | |
|---|---|---|---|---|
| | | | *Low* | *High* |
| ☐ **COIT, Caroline** | ................................ | *drawings* | | **$198** |
| American d. 1934 | | | | |
| ☐ **COL, Jan David** | ................................ | *paintings* | **$7,150** | **$25,300** |
| Belgian 1822-1900 | ................................ | *drawings* | **$110** | **$522** |
| ☐ **COLACICCO, Salvatore** | ................................ | *paintings* | | **$1,800** |
| ☐ **COLANDRELLI** | ................................ | *sculpture* | | **$363** |
| ☐ **COLAS, Pierre le** | ................................ | *paintings* | | **$308** |
| ☐ **COLBERT, J.** | ................................ | *paintings* | | **$605** |
| French 19th cent. | | | | |
| ☐ **COLBERT, R.** | ................................ | *paintings* | | **$330** |
| ☐ **COLBY, George E.** | ................................ | *paintings* | **$90** | **$550** |
| American b. 1859 | ................................ | *drawings* | **$82** | **$137** |
| ☐ **COLBY, Josephine Wood** | ................................ | *paintings* | **$120** | **$660** |
| American 1862/64-1930 | | | | |
| ☐ **COLCHIDAS, Gus** | ................................ | *paintings* | | **$852** |
| American 20th cent. | | | | |
| ☐ **COLDER, Frank** | ................................ | *paintings* | | **$325** |
| Scottish 19th/20th cent. | | | | |
| ☐ **COLE, A.** | ................................ | *paintings* | | **$1,650** |
| English 19th cent. | | | | |
| ☐ **COLE, Alphaeus Philemon** | ................................ | *paintings* | **$88** | **$330** |
| American b. 1876 | | | | |
| ☐ **COLE, Charles Octavius** | ................................ | *paintings* | | **$880** |
| American b. 1814 | | | | |
| ☐ **COLE, Chislom** | ................................ | *paintings* | | **$495** |
| English ac. 1837-1868 | | | | |
| ☐ **COLE, Ernest** | ................................ | *paintings* | **$40** | **$356** |
| ☐ **COLE, F. (Jr.)** | ................................ | *paintings* | | **$550** |
| English 19th cent. | | | | |
| ☐ **COLE, George** | ................................ | *paintings* | **$440** | **$9,900** |
| English 1810-1883 | | | | |
| ☐ **COLE, George Vicat** | ................................ | *paintings* | **$302** | **$16,500** |
| English 1833-1893 | ................................ | *drawings* | | **$308** |
| ☐ **COLE, H.** | ................................ | *paintings* | | **$308** |
| ☐ **COLE, J. Everett** | ................................ | *paintings* | | **$412** |
| ☐ **COLE, Joseph Foxcroft** | ................................ | *paintings* | **$247** | **$2,860** |
| Anglo/American 1837-1892 | ................................ | *drawings* | | **$22** |
| ☐ **COLE, Joseph Greenleaf** | ................................ | *paintings* | | **$825** |
| American 1803-1858 | | | | |
| ☐ **COLE, Lyman Emerson** | ................................ | *paintings* | | **$3,190** |
| American 1812-c. 1878 | | | | |
| ☐ **COLE, Rex Vicat** | ................................ | *paintings* | **$495** | **$2,760** |
| British 1870-1940 | | | | |
| ☐ **COLE, Thomas** | ................................ | *paintings* | **$4,950** | **$900,000** |
| American 1801-1848 | | | | |
| ☐ **COLE, Thomas Casilear** | ................................ | *paintings* | **$110** | **$6,600** |
| American b. 1888 | | | | |
| ☐ **COLEGROVE, M.B.** | ................................ | *paintings* | **$110** | **$522** |
| American School 19th cent. | | | | |

|  | | | *Current Price Range* | |
|--|--|--|--|--|
|  | | | Low | High |

| | | | Low | High |
|---|---|---|---|---|
| ☐ **COLEMAN, Charles** ............................ *paintings* | | | | $2,860 |
| English d. 1874 | | | | |
| ☐ **COLEMAN, Charles Caryl** ................... *paintings* | | | $324 | $170,500 |
| American 1840-1928 .................................. *drawings* | | | $210 | $1,760 |
| ☐ **COLEMAN, Enrico** ............................. *drawings* | | | $576 | $5,500 |
| Italian 1846-1911 | | | | |
| ☐ **COLEMAN, Francesco** ......................... *drawings* | | | | $23,100 |
| Italian b. 1851 | | | | |
| ☐ **COLEMAN, Glenn O.** .......................... *paintings* | | | $16,500 | $18,700 |
| American 1884/87-1932 ............................... *drawings* | | | | $1,210 |
| ☐ **COLEMAN, H.** .................................. *drawings* | | | | $715 |
| ☐ **COLEMAN, M.J.** ............................... *paintings* | | | | $880 |
| American | | | | |
| ☐ **COLEMAN, Michael** ........................... *paintings* | | | $935 | $13,200 |
| American b. 1946 .................................... *drawings* | | | $4,675 | $12,650 |
| ☐ **COLEMAN, Michael L.** ........................ *drawings* | | | $6,000 | $7,500 |
| American b. 1941 | | | | |
| ☐ **COLEMAN, R. Clarkson** ...................... *paintings* | | | | $650 |
| American b. 1884 | | | | |
| ☐ **COLEMAN, Ralph Pallen** ..................... *paintings* | | | | $495 |
| American b. 1892 | | | | |
| ☐ **COLEMAN, Samuel** ............................ *paintings* | | | | $700 |
| American 1832-1920 | | | | |
| ☐ **COLEMAN, William Stephen** ............... *paintings* | | | $1,760 | $3,575 |
| English 1829/30-1904 | | | | |
| ☐ **COLES, Harry** ................................. *paintings* | | | | $412 |
| ☐ **COLGROVE, R.** ................................ *paintings* | | | | $247 |
| American contemporary | | | | |
| ☐ **COLIN, Alexandre Marie** ..................... *paintings* | | | | $825 |
| French 19th cent. | | | | |
| ☐ **COLIN, Georges** ............................... *sculpture* | | | | $1,210 |
| French b. 1876 | | | | |
| ☐ **COLIN, Gustave Henri** ........................ *paintings* | | | $385 | $440 |
| French 1828-1910/11 | | | | |
| ☐ **COLIN, Paul** .................................... *drawings* | | | $220 | $3,300 |
| French 20th cent. | | | | |
| ☐ **COLINET, Claire Jeanne Roberte** ......... *sculpture* | | | $550 | $24,200 |
| French ac. 1929 | | | | |
| ☐ **COLIS, P.** ....................................... *paintings* | | | | $418 |
| ☐ **COLKETT, Samuel David** ................... *paintings* | | | $330 | $2,640 |
| British 1800/6-1863 | | | | |
| ☐ **COLKETT, Victoria** ........................... *paintings* | | | | $2,860 |
| English 1859-1893 | | | | |
| ☐ **COLL, Joseph Clement** ........................ *drawings* | | | $220 | $770 |
| American 1881-1921 | | | | |
| ☐ **COLLAR, J.** ..................................... *paintings* | | | $55 | $357 |
| Spanish b. 1941 | | | | |
| ☐ **COLLART, Marie** ............................... *paintings* | | | | $1,540 |
| Dutch 1842-1911 | | | | |

| | Current Price Range | |
|---|---|---|
| | Low | High |

| | | Low | High |
|---|---|---|---|
| ☐ **COLLET, N.** ........................ *drawings* | | | $550 |
| French late 18th cent. | | | |
| ☐ **COLLI (?), Leone** ..................... *paintings* | | | $715 |
| Italian 19th cent. | | | |
| ☐ **COLLIER, Evert** ..................... *paintings* | | $1,100 | $28,600 |
| Dutch ac. 1662, d. 1702/03 | | | |
| ☐ **COLLIER, S.** ......................... *paintings* | | | $550 |
| English? 19th/20th cent. | | | |
| ☐ **COLLIER, Thomas Frederick** .............. *paintings* | | | $2,750 |
| English ac. 1855-1874 ..................... *drawings* | | $550 | $1,210 |
| ☐ **COLLIER, William R.** ......................... *paintings* | | | $1,100 |
| ☐ **COLLIN, A.** ..................... *paintings* | | | $440 |
| English 19th cent. | | | |
| ☐ **COLLIN, Louis Joseph Raphael** ............ *paintings* | | $3,190 | $19,800 |
| French 1850-1916 | | | |
| ☐ **COLLIN DE VERMONT, Hyacinthe** ..... *drawings* | | | $880 |
| French 1693-1761 | | | |
| ☐ **COLLINDO** ........................ *paintings* | | | $440 |
| ☐ **COLLINS, Cecil** ..................... *paintings* | | $2,200 | $8,800 |
| English b. 1908 | | | |
| ☐ **COLLINS, Charles** ..................... *paintings* | | $1,320 | $2,090 |
| British 1851-1921 ..................... *drawings* | | | $220 |
| ☐ **COLLINS, Earl** ..................... *paintings* | | $990 | $1,210 |
| American b. 1925 | | | |
| ☐ **COLLINS, Frank H.** ..................... *paintings* | | | $467 |
| American d. 1935 | | | |
| ☐ **COLLINS, Hugh** ..................... *paintings* | | | $2,200 |
| English 19th cent. | | | |
| ☐ **COLLINS, James** ..................... *paintings* | | | $935 |
| ☐ **COLLINS, Reginald** ..................... *paintings* | | | $198 |
| British 19th/20th cent. | | | |
| ☐ **COLLINS, William** ..................... *paintings* | | $770 | $20,900 |
| English 1788-1847 | | | |
| ☐ **COLLINS, William P.** ..................... *drawings* | | $385 | $880 |
| American 1826-1850 | | | |
| ☐ **COLLIVER, George** ..................... *paintings* | | | $374 |
| English School 19th cent. | | | |
| ☐ **COLLMAN, L.** ..................... *drawings* | | | $660 |
| ☐ **COLLS, Ebenezer** ..................... *paintings* | | $300 | $1,320 |
| British ac. 1852-54 | | | |
| ☐ **COLLUM, W.F.** ..................... *paintings* | | $80 | $475 |
| ☐ **COLMAN, Roi Clarkson** ..................... *paintings* | | $220 | $935 |
| American b. 1884 | | | |
| ☐ **COLMAN, Samuel** ..................... *paintings* | | $616 | $11,500 |
| American 1832-1920 ..................... *drawings* | | $200 | $3,300 |
| ☐ **COLMO(?), G.** ..................... *paintings* | | $247 | $275 |
| ☐ **COLOMBEL, Nicolas** ..................... *paintings* | | $8,580 | $20,900 |
| French 1644-1717 | | | |
| ☐ **COLOMBIER, Amelia** ..................... *sculpture* | | | $770 |

| | | *Current Price Range* | |
|---|---|---|---|
| | | *Low* | *High* |
| ☐ **COLOMBO, D.** ................................. *drawings* | | | $357 |
| Italian 19th cent. | | | |
| ☐ **COLOMBO, Virgilio** ........................... *drawings* | | $60 | $1,100 |
| Italian 19th cent. | | | |
| ☐ **COLSON** ..................................... *paintings* | | | $1,100 |
| ☐ **COLSON, Jean Francois Gille** .............. *drawings* | | | $1,100 |
| French 1733-1803 | | | |
| ☐ **COLSON, P.** ................................. *paintings* | | | $357 |
| British 19th cent. | | | |
| ☐ **COLSONTE, G.** ............................., *paintings* | | | $480 |
| ☐ **COLTMAN, Ora** ................................ *paintings* | | $209 | $990 |
| American b. 1860 ................................ *drawings* | | $66 | $165 |
| ☐ **COLUNGA, Alejandro** ........................ *drawings* | | | $2,750 |
| ..................................... *sculpture* | | | $880 |
| ☐ **COLVIN, J. Mc.** .............................. *paintings* | | | $357 |
| late 19th/early 20th cent | | | |
| ☐ **COLVON, S.M.** ................................ *paintings* | | | $187 |
| American late 19th cent | | | |
| ☐ **COLYAR, D.M.** ................................ *drawings* | | | $270 |
| American 19th/20th cent. | | | |
| ☐ **COLYER, Vincent** ............................ *drawings* | | $220 | $880 |
| American 1825-1888 | | | |
| ☐ **COLYNS, David** ................................ *paintings* | | | $660 |
| Dutch 1582-1668 | | | |
| ☐ **COMAN, Charlotte Buell** ..................... *paintings* | | $121 | $605 |
| American 1833-1924 | | | |
| ☐ **COMEGYS, G.M.** .............................. *paintings* | | $247 | $605 |
| American 19th cent. | | | |
| ☐ **COMERRE, Leon Francois** .................. *paintings* | | $3,190 | $16,500 |
| French 1850-1916 | | | |
| ☐ **COMINCINI, Lucio** ........................... *paintings* | | | $1,210 |
| ☐ **COMINICIS, Achille de** ....................... *drawings* | | | $550 |
| Italian 19th cent. | | | |
| ☐ **COMMERE, Jean** .............................. *paintings* | | | $1,320 |
| French b. 1920 | | | |
| ☐ **COMMERE, Y.** ................................. *paintings* | | | $231 |
| French 20th cent. | | | |
| ☐ **COMOSENTIS** .................................. *paintings* | | | $275 |
| contemporary | | | |
| ☐ **COMPARA, Alexander** ........................ *paintings* | | | $247 |
| American | | | |
| ☐ **COMPTE, A.** ..................................... *drawings* | | | $825 |
| French 19th cent. | | | |
| ☐ **COMPTE-CALIX, Francois Claudius** .... *paintings* | | | $4,950 |
| French 1813-1880 | | | |
| ☐ **COMPTON, Edward Harrison** .............. *paintings* | | $3,300 | $3,740 |
| British b. 1881 | | | |
| ☐ **COMPTON, Edward Theodore** ............. *drawings* | | | $330 |

| | | Current Price Range | |
|---|---|---|---|
| | | Low | High |
| ☐ **CONANT, Lucy S.** ............................. *paintings* | | $550 | $1,100 |
| American 1867-1921 .................................. *drawings* | | $50 | $247 |
| ☐ **CONARROE, George W.** ..................... *paintings* | | $275 | $770 |
| American 1803-1882 | | | |
| ☐ **CONAWAY, J.** ................................... *paintings* | | | $660 |
| ☐ **CONCA, Sebastiano** ........................... *paintings* | | | $495 |
| Italian 1676/80-1764 | | | |
| ☐ **CONDAMY, Charles Fernand de** .......... *drawings* | | $77 | $1,980 |
| French ac. 1878-1882 | | | |
| ☐ **CONDER, Charles** .............................. *drawings* | | $165 | $1,430 |
| English 1868-1909 | | | |
| ☐ **CONDON, Andre** ................................ *paintings* | | $220 | $1,045 |
| French b. 1943 | | | |
| ☐ **CONDY, Nicholas Matthew** ................... *paintings* | | | $2,420 |
| English 1816-1851 | | | |
| ☐ **CONELY, William B.** ........................... *paintings* | | | $2,420 |
| American 1830-1911 | | | |
| ☐ **CONGDON, Adairene Vose** ................... *paintings* | | | $1,320 |
| American 19th cent. | | | |
| ☐ **CONGDON, Thomas Raphael** ............... *paintings* | | $825 | $3,575 |
| American 1859/62-1917 ............................... *drawings* | | $192 | $220 |
| ☐ **CONGDON, William** ........................... *paintings* | | $220 | $400 |
| American b. 1912 | | | |
| ☐ **CONGER, William** .............................. *drawings* | | | $302 |
| ☐ **CONGERS, C.** .................................... *paintings* | | | $275 |
| European late 19th cent. | | | |
| ☐ **CONINCK, David de** | | | |
| **(or KONINCK) (called ROMELAER)** ..... *paintings* | | | $6,050 |
| Flemish c. 1636-1699 | | | |
| ☐ **CONINCK, Pierre Joseph Louis de** ........ *paintings* | | $605 | $1,540 |
| French 1828-1910 | | | |
| ☐ **CONINCK, R. de** ................................ *paintings* | | | $330 |
| ☐ **CONKLING, Mabel** ............................. *sculpture* | | $385 | $6,600 |
| American b. 1871 | | | |
| ☐ **CONKWRIGHT** .................................. *paintings* | | | $400 |
| ☐ **CONLEY, W.B.** ................................... *paintings* | | | $250 |
| ☐ **CONN, Budwin** .................................. *paintings* | | | $550 |
| American 20th cent. | | | |
| ☐ **CONNAWAY, Jay Hall** ........................ *paintings* | | $125 | $5,500 |
| American 1893-1970 | | | |
| ☐ **CONNEAU, E.** .................................... *paintings* | | | $1,430 |
| French 19th cent. | | | |
| ☐ **CONNELLY, A.** ................................... *drawings* | | | $275 |
| British 19th cent. | | | |
| ☐ **CONNER, Bruce** ................................. *drawings* | | $88 | $1,650 |
| American b. 1933 | | | |
| ☐ **CONNER, Charles** .............................. *paintings* | | | $330 |
| American 1857-1905 | | | |

| | | *Current Price Range* | |
|---|---|---|---|
| | | *Low* | *High* |
| ☐ **CONNER, John Anthony** .................... *paintings* | | $192 | $440 |
| American 20th cent. | | | |
| ☐ **CONNER, John Ramsey** ...................... *paintings* | | $110 | $1,045 |
| American 1869-1952 | | | |
| ☐ **CONNORS, R.** .................................... *paintings* | | | $1,210 |
| ☐ **CONNOYER, Paul** ........................... *paintings* | | $300 | $1,210 |
| American 1864-1925 | | | |
| ☐ **CONRAD, F.O.** ................................... *paintings* | | | $412 |
| ☐ **CONRAD, G.** ...................................... *drawings* | | | $275 |
| ☐ **CONRADE, Alfred Charles** ................... *drawings* | | $605 | $990 |
| British 1863-1955 | | | |
| ☐ **CONROW, Wilford S.** ......................... *paintings* | | $110 | $297 |
| American 20th cent. | | | |
| ☐ **CONROY, George** ............................... *paintings* | | $88 | $330 |
| American 19th cent. | | | |
| ☐ **CONSAGRA, Pietro** ........................... *sculpture* | | $1,320 | $4,950 |
| Italian b. 1920 | | | |
| ☐ **CONSTABLE, G.** ................................ *paintings* | | | $522 |
| English 19th cent. | | | |
| ☐ **CONSTABLE, J.** ................................. *paintings* | | | $525 |
| ☐ **CONSTABLE, John** ............................ *drawings* | | $1,210 | $17,050 |
| English 1776-1837 | | | |
| ☐ **CONSTABLE, William** ......................... *drawings* | | $1,320 | $1,980 |
| English 19th cent. | | | |
| ☐ **CONSTANS, Louis Aristide Leon** .......... *paintings* | | | $2,090 |
| French 19th cent. | | | |
| ☐ **CONSTANT, George Z.** ....................... *drawings* | | $27 | $247 |
| American 1892-1978 | | | |
| ☐ **CONSTANT, Jean Joseph Benjamin** ...... *paintings* | | $385 | $46,200 |
| French 1845-1902 ...................................... *drawings* | | | $880 |
| ☐ **CONSTANT, Maurice** .......................... *sculpture* | | $220 | $500 |
| French 19th cent. | | | |
| ☐ **CONSTANTIN, Marie** .......................... *paintings* | | | $357 |
| French 1895-1903 | | | |
| ☐ **CONSTANTIN, S.** ............................... *paintings* | | | $1,650 |
| Italian 19th cent. | | | |
| ☐ **CONSTANTIN, S.** ............................... *paintings* | | | $330 |
| ☐ **CONSTANTINI, Giovanni** ................... *paintings* | | | $1,650 |
| Italian 19th cent. | | | |
| ☐ **CONSTANTINI, Giuseppe** ................... *paintings* | | | $4,400 |
| Italian 19th cent. | | | |
| ☐ **CONSUEGRA, Hugo** ........................... *paintings* | | $660 | $1,100 |
| Cuban b. 1929 | | | |
| ☐ **CONTAIT, Louis** ................................ *paintings* | | | $440 |
| ☐ **CONTE, Jacopino del** ........................ *paintings* | | | $11,550 |
| Italian 1510-1598 | | | |
| ☐ **CONTENT, Dan** ................................. *paintings* | | $660 | $1,100 |
| American b. 1902 | | | |
| ☐ **CONTI, Metrodoro** ............................. *drawings* | | $385 | $605 |

| | | Current Price Range | |
|---|---|---|---|
| | | *Low* | *High* |
| ☐ **CONTI, Tito** ....................... *paintings* | | | $1,430 |
| .................................................. *drawings* | | | $660 |
| ☐ **CONTICH, Karel van** .......... *paintings* | | | $330 |
| Dutch 19th cent. | | | |
| ☐ **CONTORT, Louis** ............... *paintings* | | $715 | $935 |
| ☐ **CONTRI, C.** ....................... *sculpture* | | | $279 |
| ☐ **CONTUIL (?), Louis** ........... *paintings* | | | $375 |
| American (?) 19th cent. | | | |
| ☐ **CONVERS, Louis** ............... *sculpture* | | | $797 |
| French c. 1898 | | | |
| ☐ **CONWAY, Fred** .................. *paintings* | | | $187 |
| American 1900-1972 ................. *drawings* | | $121 | $770 |
| ☐ **CONZ, Walter** ................... *paintings* | | | $1,650 |
| ☐ **COOGHEN, Leendert van der** ......... *drawings* | | | $2,420 |
| Dutch 1610-1681 | | | |
| ☐ **COOK, C.H.** ...................... *paintings* | | | $385 |
| English 19th cent. | | | |
| ☐ **COOK, Ebenezer Wake** ........ *drawings* | | $82 | $4,125 |
| British 1843-1926 | | | |
| ☑ **COOK, Howard** .................. *drawings* | | | $2,090 |
| American | | | |
| ☐ **COOK, Isaac** ..................... *drawings* | | | $825 |
| ☐ **COOK, John A.** .................. *drawings* | | $99 | $220 |
| American 1870-1936 | | | |
| ☐ **COOK, Marion** ................... *paintings* | | | $750 |
| American | | | |
| ☐ **COOK, Nelson** .................. *paintings* | | | $1,210 |
| American 1817-1892 | | | |
| ☐ **COOK, Otis** ...................... *paintings* | | $192 | $286 |
| ☐ **COOKE, C.H.** .................... *paintings* | | | $220 |
| British ac. 1885 | | | |
| ☐ **COOKE, Edward William** ........ *paintings* | | $2,750 | $16,500 |
| English 1811-1880 | | | |
| ☐ **COOKE, George** ................. *paintings* | | $825 | $3,190 |
| American 1793-1849 | | | |
| ☐ **COOKESLEY, M. Murray** ....... *paintings* | | | $850 |
| British 19th cent. | | | |
| ☐ **COOKMAN, Charles Edwin** .......... *paintings* | | $290 | $1,100 |
| American 1856-1913 | | | |
| ☐ **COOLEY, B.** ...................... *paintings* | | | $3,300 |
| 19th cent. | | | |
| ☐ **COOLIDGE, Jack** ................ *paintings* | | | $935 |
| American 1918-1984 | | | |
| ☐ **COOLIDGE, Rosamond** ........ *paintings* | | | $247 |
| American b. 1884 | | | |
| ☐ **COOLLINS, H.S.** ................. *drawings* | | | $308 |
| ☐ **COOLWIJK, J. Schreuder van de** ......... *paintings* | | $220 | $440 |
| Dutch 20th cent. | | | |

| | | *Current Price Range* | |
|---|---|---|---|
| | | *Low* | *High* |
| ☐ **COOMANS, Auguste** ............................ *paintings* | | $715 | $1,760 |
| Belgian ac. c. 1850 | | | |
| ☐ **COOMANS, Diana** ............................. *paintings* | | $660 | $9,075 |
| Belgian 19th cent. | | | |
| ☐ **COOMANS, Heva** ............................. *paintings* | | $1,320 | $3,850 |
| Belgian 19th cent. ....................................... *drawings* | | | $308 |
| ☐ **COOMANS, Pierre Olivier Joseph** ......... *paintings* | | $925 | $15,400 |
| Belgian 1816-1889 | | | |
| ☐ **COOMBS, Delbert Dana** ....................... *paintings* | | $132 | $2,000 |
| American 1850-1938 ................................... *drawings* | | | $275 |
| ☐ **COOPER, Abraham** ............................. *paintings* | | $1,350 | $2,310* |
| English 1787-1868 | | | |
| ☐ **COOPER, Alexander Davis** .................... *paintings* | | | $2,420 |
| British 19th cent. | | | |
| ☐ **COOPER, Astley David Montague** ......... *paintings* | | $192 | $8,250 |
| American 1856-1924 | | | |
| ☐ **COOPER, Colin Campbell** .................... *paintings* | | $27 | $33,000 |
| American 1856-1937 ................................... *drawings* | | $143 | $4,675 |
| ☐ **COOPER, E.N.** ................................... *paintings* | | | $1,760 |
| ☐ **COOPER, Edwin** ................................ *paintings* | | $2,500 | $18,700 |
| English fl. 1803-1831 | | | |
| ☐ **COOPER, Emma Lampert** .................... *drawings* | | $110 | $660 |
| American d. 1920 | | | |
| ☐ **COOPER, F.C.** ................................... *paintings* | | | $715 |
| ☐ **COOPER, Helen A.** ............................ *paintings* | | $302 | $412 |
| 19th cent. | | | |
| ☐ **COOPER, Henry** ................................ *paintings* | | $330 | $440 |
| American b. 1905 | | | |
| ☐ **COOPER, Henry** ................................ *paintings* | | $100 | $440 |
| English 19th/20th cent. | | | |
| ☐ **COOPER, J. Savage** ............................ *paintings* | | $1,210 | $2,750 |
| British 19th cent. | | | |
| ☐ **COOPER, Mario** ................................ *drawings* | | | $522 |
| b. 1905 | | | |
| ☐ **COOPER, R.** ..................................... *drawings* | | | $330 |
| British 19th cent. | | | |
| ☐ **COOPER, Robert** ............................... *drawings* | | | $770 |
| American | | | |
| ☐ **COOPER, T. George** ............................ *paintings* | | | $1,650 |
| English 19th cent. | | | |
| ☐ **COOPER, Thomas Sidney** ...................... *paintings* | | $302 | $33,000 |
| English 1803-1902 ...................................... *drawings* | | $605 | $1,980 |
| ☐ **COOPER, W. Sidney** ............................ *paintings* | | | $187 |
| English ac. 1871-1908 | | | |
| ☐ **COOPER, William Heaton** .................... *paintings* | | | $440 |
| English b. 1903 | | | |
| ☐ **COOSEMANS, Alexander** ...................... *paintings* | | | $49,500 |
| Flemish bap. 1627-d. 1689 | | | |

| | | Current Price Range | |
|---|---|---|---|
| | | Low | High |
| ☐ **COOTER, Ramma J.** .......................... *paintings* | | | $495 |
| English 19th cent. | | | |
| ☐ **COOTES, F. Graham** .......................... *drawings* | | | $275 |
| 1879-1960 | | | |
| ☐ **COPE, Charles West (Jr.)** ..................... *paintings* | | $1,650 | $6,600 |
| English 1811-1890 | | | |
| ☐ **COPE, George** ..................................... *paintings* | | $385 | $33,000 |
| American 1855-1929 | | | |
| ☐ **COPE, Gordon** ..................................... *paintings* | | | $330 |
| American b. 1906 | | | |
| ☐ **COPELAND, Alfred Bryant** ................. *paintings* | | $275 | $8,250 |
| American 1840-1909 | | | |
| ☐ **COPELAND, Charles G.** ...................... *paintings* | | $385 | $770 |
| American 1858-1945 .................................... *drawings* | | $82 | $605 |
| ☐ **COPELAND, Emma F.** ......................... *paintings* | | | $577 |
| American 19th cent. | | | |
| ☐ **COPELAND, I.F.** ................................. *paintings* | | | $1,045 |
| American | | | |
| ☐ **COPETTI, A.** ....................................... *paintings* | | | $275 |
| Italian 19th/20th cent. | | | |
| ☐ **COPLESFORD, Edwin** .......................... *paintings* | | | $250 |
| American 19th cent. | | | |
| ☐ **COPLEY, John Singleton** ..................... *paintings* | | $132,000 | $385,000 |
| American 1737-1815 | | | |
| ☐ **COPLEY, William** .............................. *paintings* | | $550 | $14,300 |
| American b. 1919 .................................... *drawings* | | $77 | $2,310 |
| ☐ **COPNALL, Frank T.** ........................... *paintings* | | | $495 |
| English b. 1870 | | | |
| ☐ **COPPEDGE, Fern I.** ........................... *paintings* | | $165 | $1,300 |
| American 1888-1951 | | | |
| ☐ **COPPIN, G.W.** .................................... *drawings* | | | $467 |
| ☐ **COQUES, Gonzales** | | | |
| (called Le Petit Van Dyck) ...................... *paintings* | | | $3,850 |
| Flemish 1614-1684 | | | |
| ☐ **CORBELLI, L.** ..................................... *paintings* | | | $1,045 |
| ☐ **CORBELLINI, Luigi** ........................... *paintings* | | $165 | $1,760 |
| Italian 1901-1968 | | | |
| ☐ **CORBELLINI, Nicole** .......................... *paintings* | | $418 | $550 |
| ☐ **CORBET, Philip** ................................. *paintings* | | | $302 |
| English 19th cent. | | | |
| ☐ **CORBETT, Edward** ............................. *paintings* | | | $198 |
| American 1919-1971 | | | |
| ☐ **CORBINO, Jon** ................................... *paintings* | | $110 | $4,180 |
| Italian/American 1905-1964 ......................... *drawings* | | $132 | $297 |
| ☐ **CORBOULD, A.** ................................... *paintings* | | | $352 |
| ☐ **CORBOULD, Alfred H.** ....................... *paintings* | | | $5,500 |
| British ac. 1844-1864 | | | |
| ☐ **CORBOULD, Edward Henry** ................ *paintings* | | $130 | $500 |
| English 1815-1905 .................................... *drawings* | | $825 | $2,200 |

|  | | Current Price Range | |
|---|---|---|---|
|  | | Low | High |
| ☐ **CORCHON Y DIAQUE, Federico** ......... *paintings* | | | $1,320 |
| Spanish 19th cent. | | | |
| ✓☐ **CORCOS, Vittorio Matteo** ................... *paintings* | | $3,850 | $15,400 |
| Italian 1859-1933 | | | |
| ☐ **CORDERO, Riccardo** ......................... *paintings* | | | $330 |
| ☐ **CORDIER, Charles Henri Joseph** .......... *sculpture* | | $2,420 | $6,600 |
| French 19th cent. | | | |
| ☐ **CORDREY, Earl Somers** ..................... *drawings* | | $209 | $385 |
| American b. 1902 | | | |
| ☐ **CORDREY, John** ............................... *paintings* | | $3,850 | $6,600 |
| ☐ **CORELLI, Augusto** ............................ *paintings* | | | $1,870 |
| Italian b. 1853 ....................................... *drawings* | | $99 | $192 |
| ☐ **CORENZIO, Belissario** ........................ *drawings* | | | $880 |
| Greek 1558-1640 | | | |
| ☐ **CORETTI, G.** .................................... *drawings* | | | $1,540 |
| Italian 19th cent. | | | |
| ☐ **COREY, Bernard** ............................... *paintings* | | $220 | $412 |
| American 20th cent. | | | |
| ☐ **CORINTH, Lovis** ............................... *paintings* | | $6,325 | $19,250 |
| German 1858-1925 .................................. *drawings* | | $242 | $1,760 |
| ☐ **CORMERY, Louis** .............................. *paintings* | | | $220 |
| English 19th cent. | | | |
| ☐ **CORMIER, Joseph J. Emmanuel** | | | |
| (Joseph J. Emmanuel DESCOMPS) ........ *sculpture* | | $264 | $2,200 |
| French 1869-1952 | | | |
| ☐ **CORMON, Fernand Anne Piestre** .......... *paintings* | | | $5,500 |
| French 1854-1924 | | | |
| ☐ **CORNE, Michele Felice** ....................... *drawings* | | | $8,800 |
| Italian/American 1752-1845 | | | |
| ☐ **CORNEILLE,** | | | |
| (Cornelius Guillaume BEVERLOO) ........ *paintings* | | $2,420 | $12,650 |
| Dutch b. 1922 ....................................... *drawings* | | $770 | $1,320 |
| ☐ **CORNEILLE, Jean Baptiste** ................. *drawings* | | | $247 |
| French 1649-1695 | | | |
| ☐ **CORNEILLE, Michel** ........................... *drawings* | | | $715 |
| French 1602-1664 | | | |
| ☐ **CORNEILLE, Michel (the younger)** ........ *drawings* | | | $2,750 |
| French 1641-1708 | | | |
| ☐ **CORNEILLE, Pierre** ........................... *drawings* | | | $2,530 |
| Italian 1580-1616 | | | |
| ☐ **CORNEILLE DE LYON, Claude** .......... *paintings* | | | $18,150 |
| Flemish 1500/05-1574 | | | |
| ☐ **CORNELISZ, Jacob van Oostsanen** | | | |
| (called Jacob d'Amsterdam) ................... *paintings* | | | $72,600 |
| Dutch c. 1477-c. 1533 | | | |
| ☐ **CORNELISZ VAN HAARLEM,** | | | |
| Cornelis ............................................. *paintings* | | $330 | $27,500 |
| Dutch 1562-1638 .................................... *drawings* | | | $8,250 |

| | | | *Current Price Range* | |
|---|---|---|---|---|
| | | | Low | High |
| ☐ **CORNELL, John V.** | ............ | *paintings* | $330 | $10,450 |
| American ac. 1838-1849 | | | | |
| ☐ **CORNELL, Joseph** | ............ | *drawings* | $1,650 | $17,600 |
| American 1903-1972 | ............ | *sculpture* | $4,400 | $70,400 |
| ☐ **CORNOYER, Paul** | ............ | *paintings* | $110 | $28,600 |
| American 1864-1923 | ............ | *drawings* | | $352 |
| ☐ **CORNU, Pierre** | ............ | *paintings* | | $550 |
| French b. 1895 | | | | |
| ☐ **CORNU, Vital** | ............ | *sculpture* | $440 | $1,100 |
| French late 19th cent. | | | | |
| ☐ **CORNUT, Louis** | ............ | *paintings* | | $385 |
| French 20th cent. | | | | |
| ☐ **CORNWALL, Martha Jackson** | ............ | *sculpture* | | $650 |
| American b. 1869 | | | | |
| ☐ **CORNWALLIS, Brownell** | ............ | *paintings* | $165 | $220 |
| British 19th/20th cent. | | | | |
| ☐ **CORNWELL, Dean** | ............ | *paintings* | $137 | $33,000 |
| American 1892-1960 | ............ | *drawings* | $275 | $3,850 |
| ☐ **CORONEL, Pedro** | ............ | *paintings* | $4,950 | $22,000 |
| Mexican b. 1923 | | | | |
| ☐ **CORONEL, Rafael** | ............ | *paintings* | $1,540 | $17,600 |
| Mexican b. 1932 | ............ | *drawings* | $990 | $1,430 |
| ☐ **COROT, Jean Baptiste Camille** | ............ | *paintings* | $2,200 | $3,850,000 |
| French 1796-1875 | ............ | *drawings* | $350 | $2,200 |
| ☐ **CORPER, M.** | ............ | *paintings* | $137 | $495 |
| British 19th cent. | | | | |
| ☐ **CORPORA, Antonio** | ............ | *paintings* | $198 | $600 |
| Italian b. 1909 | | | | |
| ☐ **CORPUZ, F.** | ............ | *paintings* | | $467 |
| ☐ **CORRADETTI, Romano** | ............ | *paintings* | | $577 |
| Italian 20th cent. | | | | |
| ☐ **CORRADI, Konrad** | ............ | *drawings* | | $3,300 |
| Swiss 1813-1878 | | | | |
| ☐ **CORREGGIO, Joseph** | ............ | *paintings* | $2,310 | $3,300 |
| German 1810-1891 | | | | |
| ☐ **CORREGGIO, Ludwig** | ............ | *paintings* | | $715 |
| German b. 1846 | | | | |
| ☐ **CORRENS, Erich** | ............ | *paintings* | | $660 |
| German 1821-1877 | | | | |
| ☐ **CORRI, F.J.** | ............ | *drawings* | | $770 |
| English 19th cent. | | | | |
| ☐ **CORRIGLIA, G.B.** | ............ | *paintings* | | $13,200 |
| Italian 19th cent. | | | | |
| ☐ **CORRODI, Arnold** | ............ | *paintings* | | $11,000 |
| Italian 1846-1874 | | | | |
| ☐ **CORRODI, Hermann David Salomon** | .... | *paintings* | $330 | $17,600 |
| Italian 1844-1905 | ............ | *drawings* | $440 | $2,475 |
| ☐ **CORRODI, Salomon** | ............ | *drawings* | $660 | $4,950 |
| Italian 1810-1892 | | | | |

|  | | *Current Price Range* | |
|---|---|---|---|
|  | | *Low* | *High* |
| ☐ **CORSI, Nicolas de** .............................. *paintings* | | $302 | $715 |
| Italian b. 1882 | | | |
| ☐ **CORSINI, Douglas** .............................. *sculpture* | | $3,300 | $5,500 |
| ☐ **CORSINI, Raffael** .............................. *drawings* | | | $6,250 |
| Italian mid 19th cent. | | | |
| ☐ **CORSON, Charles Schell** ...................... *paintings* | | $550 | $4,400 |
| American d. 1921 | | | |
| ☐ **CORT, Hendrik Frans de** ...................... *paintings* | | | $24,200 |
| Dutch 1742-1810 | | | |
| ☐ **CORTA, F. del** ................................... *paintings* | | | $880 |
| ☐ **CORTAN, G.** ...................................... *paintings* | | | $1,100 |
| ☐ **CORTAZZI, Michele** ........................... *paintings* | | | $385 |
| ☐ **CORTAZZO, Oreste** ........................... *paintings* | | $110 | $5,500 |
| Italian b. 1830 ....................................... *drawings* | | $192 | $550 |
| ☐ **CORTELLINI Y HERNANDEZ,** | | | |
| **Angel-Maria** ...................................... *paintings* | | | $2,420 |
| Spanish b. 1820 | | | |
| ☐ **CORTER, P.R.** ................................... *paintings* | | | $1,980 |
| Dutch 19th cent. | | | |
| ☐ **CORTES, A.** ....................................... *paintings* | | | $440 |
| French 19th cent. | | | |
| ☐ **CORTES, Antonio** .............................. *paintings* | | $2,200 | $3,025 |
| Spanish 19th cent. | | | |
| ☐ **CORTES, Edouard Leon** ...................... *paintings* | | $330 | $12,650 |
| French b. 1882 | | | |
| ☐ **CORTEZ, Andre** ................................. *paintings* | | | $330 |
| Spanish 19th cent. | | | |
| ☐ **CORTOT, Jean Pierre** ......................... *sculpture* | | | $1,320 |
| French 19th cent. | | | |
| ☐ **CORWIN, Charles Abel** ....................... *paintings* | | $632 | $2,310 |
| American 1857-1938 | | | |
| ☐ **CORZAS, Francisco** ........................... *paintings* | | | $19,800 |
| Mexican b. 1936 ..................................... *drawings* | | $880 | $5,390 |
| ☐ **COS, A.M.** ........................................ *paintings* | | | $385 |
| American | | | |
| ☐ **COSSAAR, Jacobus Cornelius Wyand** ... *paintings* | | | $357 |
| Dutch 1874-1966 ..................................... *drawings* | | $27 | $55 |
| ☐ **COSSIERS, Jan** .................................. *paintings* | | $4,180 | $8,250 |
| Flemish 1600-1671 | | | |
| ☐ **COSSIO, Francisco** ............................. *paintings* | | | $3,850 |
| Spanish b. 1894 | | | |
| ☐ **COSSMANN, Maurice** .......................... *paintings* | | | $1,430 |
| French | | | |
| ☐ **COSSON, Jean Louis Marcel** ................ *paintings* | | $308 | $2,640 |
| French 1878-1956 | | | |
| ☐ **COSTA, A.** ........................................ *paintings* | | | $2,090 |
| ☐ **COSTA, C.** ........................................ *paintings* | | | $302 |
| Italian 19th cent. | | | |

| | | *Current Price Range* | |
|---|---|---|---|
| | | Low | High |
| ☐ **COSTA, Emanuele** .............................. *paintings* | | $1,980 | $3,300 |
| Italian b. 1875 | | | |
| ☐ **COSTA, Giovanni** .............................. *paintings* | | $550 | $10,450 |
| Italian 1826/1833-1903 .............................. *drawings* | | | $4,180 |
| ☐ **COSTA, Guiseppe** .............................. *paintings* | | | $1,760 |
| Italian b. 1852 | | | |
| ☐ **COSTA, Joachim** .............................. *sculpture* | | | $770 |
| French early 20th cent. | | | |
| ☐ **COSTA, Olga** ..................................... *paintings* | | | $2,200 |
| Mexican b. 1913 | | | |
| ☐ **COSTA, Oreste** .................................. *paintings* | | $440 | $17,600 |
| Italian b. 1851 | | | |
| ☐ **COSTAIGNE, J. Andrea** ...................... *drawings* | | | $275 |
| German 1860-1930 | | | |
| ☐ **COSTANTINI, Giovanni** ........................ *paintings* | | | $770 |
| Italian b. 1872 | | | |
| ☐ **COSTANTINI, Giuseppe** ....................... *paintings* | | $660 | $1,210 |
| Italian 1844-1894 | | | |
| ☐ **COSTANZI, Placido** ........................... *paintings* | | | $4,620 |
| Italian c. 1690-1759 | | | |
| ☐ **COSTER, Adam de** ............................. *paintings* | | | $880 |
| Flemish 1586-1643 | | | |
| ☐ **COSTER, C. de** .................................. *paintings* | | | $632 |
| French 19th cent. | | | |
| ☐ **COSTIGAN, John Edward** .................... *paintings* | | $357 | $14,025 |
| American 1888-1972 ................................. *drawings* | | $99 | $1,100 |
| ☐ **COSWAY, Richard** ............................. *paintings* | | $440 | $8,800 |
| British 1742-1821 ..................................... *drawings* | | | $495 |
| ☐ **COSYN, Aert** ..................................... *drawings* | | | $770 |
| Dutch ac. 1662 | | | |
| ☐ **COTE, Alan** ...................................... *paintings* | | $2,530 | $2,800 |
| American b. 1937 | | | |
| ☐ **COTES, Francis** ................................. *paintings* | | $1,760 | $82,500 |
| English 1725/26-1770 | | | |
| ☐ **COTTET, Charles** ............................... *paintings* | | $1,650 | $7,700 |
| French 1863-1925 | | | |
| ☐ **COTTIN, Emile** .................................. *paintings* | | | $660 |
| ..................................................................... *drawings* | | | $880 |
| ☐ **COTTINGHAM, Robert** ....................... *paintings* | | $13,200 | $18,700 |
| American b. 1935 ..................................... *drawings* | | $935 | $3,300 |
| ☐ **COTTON, John** .................................. *paintings* | | | $275 |
| British 1844-1934 | | | |
| ☐ **COTTON, William H.** .......................... *paintings* | | $44 | $6,325 |
| American 1880-1958 ................................. *drawings* | | $132 | $550 |
| ☐ **COUBINE, Othon** ............................... *paintings* | | $357 | $990 |
| Czechoslovakian 1883-1969 | | | |
| ☐ **COUDER, Jean Alexandre Remy** .......... *paintings* | | $250 | $2,970 |
| French 1808-1879 | | | |

| | | Current Price Range | |
|---|---|---|---|
| | | Low | High |
| ☐ **COUDER, Louis August** ......................... *paintings* | | | **$1,650** |
| French 1790-1873 | | | |
| ☐ **COUDOUR, Henri** .............................. *paintings* | | **$275** | **$577** |
| French 19th/20th cent. | | | |
| ☐ **COUDRAY, George Charles** ................. *sculpture* | | | **$1,100** |
| French c. 1883-1903 | | | |
| ☐ **COUDRAY, Marie Alexandre Lucien** .... *sculpture* | | | **$2,090** |
| French | | | |
| ☐ **COULANGE-LAUTREC, Emmanuel** .... *paintings* | | | **$2,750** |
| French ac. 1869 | | | |
| ☐ **COULAUD, Martin** ............................ *paintings* | | **$550** | **$1,870** |
| French d. 1906 | | | |
| ☐ **COULDERY, Horatio H.** ....................... *paintings* | | **$770** | **$3,300** |
| British b. 1832 | | | |
| ☐ **COULES** ........................................ *paintings* | | | **$1,045** |
| ☐ **COULET, Pierre Guillaume** ................. *paintings* | | | **$550** |
| French 18th cent. | | | |
| ☐ **COULON, George David** ....................... *paintings* | | **$687** | **$1,650** |
| American 1822-1904 | | | |
| ☐ **COULON, Renee** ............................... *paintings* | | | **$770** |
| French | | | |
| ☐ **COULSON, Gerald D.** .......................... *paintings* | | | **$2,750** |
| English early 20th cent. | | | |
| ☐ **COULSON, J.** ................................... *paintings* | | | **$250** |
| ☐ **COULTER, William Alexander** ............. *paintings* | | **$715** | **$16,500** |
| American 1849-1936 ................................ *drawings* | | | **$1,320** |
| ☐ **COUNIS, Salomon Guillaume** .............. *drawings* | | | **$3,850** |
| Swiss 1785-1859 | | | |
| ☐ **COURBET, Gustave** ........................... *paintings* | | **$13,750** | **$1,210,000** |
| French 1819-1877 .................................... *drawings* | | | **$4,180** |
| ☐ **COURBIER, Marcel Louis Maurice** ....... *sculpture* | | | **$880** |
| French early 20th cent. | | | |
| ☐ **COURNAULT, Etienne** ....................... *paintings* | | **$4,400** | **$5,500** |
| French 1891-1948 | | | |
| ☐ **COURTAT, Louis** .............................. *paintings* | | | **$4,950** |
| French d. 1909 | | | |
| ☐ **COURTEILLE, Eugene** ....................... *paintings* | | **$2,090** | **$2,860** |
| French ac. 1790-1820 | | | |
| ☐ **COURTEN, Angelode** .......................... *paintings* | | | **$2,530** |
| Italian b. 1848 | | | |
| ☐ **COURTEN, Lodovico de** ....................... *drawings* | | **$88** | **$440** |
| Italian 19th cent. | | | |
| ☐ **COURTENS, Franz** ............................ *paintings* | | | **$742** |
| Belgian 1854-1943 | | | |
| ☐ **COURTENS, Herman** .......................... *paintings* | | | **$1,430** |
| Belgium 1884-1956 | | | |
| ☐ **COURTER, F.C.** ................................ *paintings* | | **$330** | **$412** |
| American 19th cent. | | | |
| ☐ **COURTIER, J.C. le** ............................ *sculpture* | | | **$1,815** |

| | | Current Price Range | |
|---|---|---|---|
| | | Low | High |
| ☐ **COURTIN, Caroline** ............................ *paintings* | | | $660 |
| French c. 1875 | | | |
| ☐ **COURTOIS, Gustave Claude Etienne** .... *paintings* | | $2,640 | $19,800 |
| French 1853-1923 | | | |
| ☐ **COUSE, Eanger Irving** ........................ *paintings* | | $700 | $77,000 |
| American 1866-1936 ................................ *drawings* | | $495 | $20,000 |
| ☐ **COUSIN, Charles Louis Auguste** .......... *paintings* | | | $4,510 |
| French 1807-1887 | | | |
| ☐ **COUSIN, Jean** ................................ *paintings* | | | $1,650 |
| ☐ **COUSSAINT, Pierre Joseph** ................ *paintings* | | | $4,400 |
| Belgian 1822-1888 | | | |
| ☐ **COUSTOU** ........................................ *sculpture* | | $220 | $825 |
| late 19th cent. | | | |
| ☐ **COUSTURIER, Lucie** ........................ *paintings* | | | $880 |
| French 1870-1925 | | | |
| ☐ **COUTAN, Amable Paul** ........................ *drawings* | | | $330 |
| French 1792-1837 | | | |
| ☐ **COUTAN, Jules** ................................ *sculpture* | | | $7,150 |
| French 1848-1939 | | | |
| ☐ **COUTTS, Alice** ................................ *paintings* | | $467 | $4,400 |
| American 1865-1937 | | | |
| ☐ **COUTTS, Gordon** ............................ *paintings* | | $250 | $3,630 |
| American 1868/80-1937 | | | |
| ☐ **COUTURE, Thomas** .......................... *paintings* | | $1,320 | $8,250 |
| French 1815-1879 ................................ *drawings* | | $715 | $3,960 |
| ☐ **COUTURIER, Philibert Leon** ................ *paintings* | | $935 | $3,520 |
| French 1823-1901 | | | |
| ☐ **COVARRUBIAS, Miguel** ...................... *paintings* | | $385 | $8,800 |
| Mexican 1904-1957 ................................ *drawings* | | $220 | $6,050 |
| ☐ **COVENTRY, C.C.** ............................ *paintings* | | | $5,830 |
| British ac. 1802-1812 | | | |
| ☐ **COVEY, Arthur S.** ............................ *paintings* | | | $3,000 |
| American b. 1877 | | | |
| ☐ **COVEYN, Reynier** ............................ *paintings* | | $1,100 | $10,450 |
| b. 1636 | | | |
| ☐ **COW, J.** ........................................ *paintings* | | | $770 |
| American 19th cent. | | | |
| ☐ **COWAN, Guy R.** ............................ *sculpture* | | | $2,475 |
| American b. 1884 | | | |
| ☐ **COWAN, Sarah Eakin** ........................ *paintings* | | | $220 |
| American 19th/20th cent. | | | |
| ☐ **COWARD, Noel** ................................ *paintings* | | | $220 |
| British 1899-1973 | | | |
| ☐ **COWEN, Lionel J.** ............................ *paintings* | | | $275 |
| British 19th cent. | | | |
| ☐ **COWLES, Fleur** ................................ *paintings* | | | $286 |
| ☐ **COWLES, Jules** ................................ *paintings* | | | $440 |
| ☐ **COWLES, Russell** ............................ *paintings* | | $55 | $660 |
| American b. 1887 | | | |

| | | | Current Price Range | |
| --- | --- | --- | --- | --- |
| | | | Low | High |
| ☐ **COX, Albert Scott** | ............................... | *paintings* | $495 | $2,250 |
| American 1863-1920 | ................................. | *drawings* | | $330 |
| ☐ **COX, Allyn** | ..................................... | *paintings* | $11 | $495 |
| American 1896-1982 | ................................. | *drawings* | $22 | $286 |
| ☐ **COX, C.S.** | ......................................... | *paintings* | | $302 |
| American 19th/20th cent. | | | | |
| ☐ **COX, Charles Brinton** | .......................... | *paintings* | $440 | $1,430 |
| American 1864-1905 | | | | |
| ☐ **COX, David** | ......................................... | *drawings* | $220 | $1,540 |
| English 1809-1885 | | | | |
| ☐ **COX, David (the elder)** | .......................... | *drawings* | $385 | $4,125 |
| English 1783-1859 | | | | |
| ☐ **COX, F.** | ............................................ | *paintings* | | $715 |
| ☐ **COX, Jimmy** | ....................................... | *sculpture* | | $2,500 |
| American contemporary | | | | |
| ☐ **COX, Kenyon** | ..................................... | *paintings* | $200 | $4,400 |
| American 1856-1917/19 | ............................... | *drawings* | $66 | $324 |
| ☐ **COX, Louise Howland King** | ................. | *paintings* | | $165 |
| American 1865-1945 | ................................. | *drawings* | $88 | $247 |
| ☐ **COX, Palmer** | ...................................... | *drawings* | | $550 |
| Canadian/American 1840-1924 | | | | |
| ☐ **COX, Tim** | ........................................... | *paintings* | $5,000 | $9,000 |
| American contemporary | | | | |
| ☐ **COX, Walter I.** | .................................... | *paintings* | | $187 |
| American 1866-1930 | | | | |
| ☐ **COXE, Reginald Cleveland** | ................... | *paintings* | $110 | $770 |
| American b. 1855 | | | | |
| ☐ **COXON, Raymond James** | ..................... | *paintings* | | $192 |
| British b. 1897 | | | | |
| ☐ **COYLIERIS** | ....................................... | *paintings* | | $220 |
| Italian 20th cent. | | | | |
| ☐ **COYPEL, Antoine** | .............................. | *drawings* | $330 | $1,760 |
| French 1661-1722 | | | | |
| ☐ **COYPEL, Charles Antoine** | ................... | *paintings* | | $7,500 |
| French 1694-1752 | ................................. | *drawings* | $522 | $1,870 |
| ☐ **COYPEL, Noel Nicolas** | ......................... | *paintings* | $2,750 | $19,800 |
| French 1690-1734 | ................................. | *drawings* | | $605 |
| ☐ **COZENS, Alexander** | ........................... | *drawings* | | $1,540 |
| England d. 1786 | | | | |
| ☐ **COZZENS, Frederick Schiller** | ............... | *paintings* | $192 | $6,600 |
| American 1856-1928 | | | | |
| ☐ **COZZI, Fiora** | ...................................... | *paintings* | $137 | $224 |
| American contemporary | | | | |
| ☐ **COZZI, M.** | ......................................... | *paintings* | $302 | $412 |
| Italian 19th cent. | | | | |
| ☐ **COZZOLINO, Ciro** | ............................. | *paintings* | | $495 |
| Italian 19th cent. | | | | |
| ☐ **CRABB, Gordon** | ................................. | *paintings* | | $7,500 |
| American | | | | |

| | | Current Price Range | |
|---|---|---|---|
| | | Low | High |
| ☐ **CRABBELS, Florent Nicolas** .............. *paintings* | | | $4,125 |
| Belgian 1829-1896 | | | |
| ☐ **CRADDOCK, Marmaduke** ............... *paintings* | | $1,760 | $4,620 |
| English c. 1660-1717 | | | |
| ☐ **CRAESBEECK, Joos van** .............. *paintings* | | | $4,675 |
| Flemish c. 1606-1654/61 | | | |
| ☐ **CRAIG, Charles** ........................ *paintings* | | $1,980 | $6,050 |
| American 1846-1931 ....................... *drawings* | | | $385 |
| ☐ **CRAIG, Emmett Junius** ............... *paintings* | | | $302 |
| American b. 1878 | | | |
| ☐ **CRAIG, Isaac Eugene** ................ *paintings* | | | $1,210 |
| American 19th cent. | | | |
| ☐ **CRAIG, J. Humbert** ................... *paintings* | | | $1,210 |
| British d. 1944 | | | |
| ☐ **CRAIG, Martin** ....................... *sculpture* | | | $330 |
| American b. 1906 | | | |
| ☐ **CRAIG, R.H.** .......................... *paintings* | | | $330 |
| ☐ **CRAIG, Thomas Bigelow** .............. *paintings* | | $165 | $3,575 |
| American 1849-1924 ....................... *drawings* | | $82 | $605 |
| ☐ **CRAIG, William** ....................... *paintings* | | | $125 |
| American 1829-1875 ....................... *drawings* | | | $286 |
| ☐ **CRAIG, Z.S.** .......................... *paintings* | | | $352 |
| ☐ **CRAM, Allen Gilbert** ................. *paintings* | | | $187 |
| American b. 1886 | | | |
| ☐ **CRAMER, Carl Cesar Adelbert** .......... *paintings* | | | $1,430 |
| Danish 1822-1889 | | | |
| ☐ **CRAMER, Konrad** ..................... *paintings* | | | $3,300 |
| German/American 1888-1965 ............... *drawings* | | | $440 |
| ☐ **CRAMPEL, Paul** ....................... *drawings* | | $99 | $467 |
| French ac. 1896-1903 | | | |
| ☐ **CRANACH, Lucas (the elder)** .............. *paintings* | | $38,500 | $88,000 |
| German 1472-1553 | | | |
| ☐ **CRANCH, Christopher Pearse** ............. *paintings* | | $220 | $1,540 |
| American 1813-1892 | | | |
| ☐ **CRANDELL, Bradshaw** .................. *drawings* | | $110 | $2,970 |
| American 1896-1966 | | | |
| ☐ **CRANE, Ann** ........................... *paintings* | | | $412 |
| American d. 1948 | | | |
| ☐ **CRANE, Robert Bruce (or Bruce)** .......... *paintings* | | $385 | $15,400 |
| American 1857-1937 ....................... *drawings* | | $418 | $1,760 |
| ☐ **CRANE, Stanley William** ................ *paintings* | | $660 | $1,100 |
| American b. 1905 | | | |
| ☐ **CRANE, Walter** ....................... *drawings* | | $800 | $7,700 |
| English 1845-1915 | | | |
| ☐ **CRANE, Wilbur** ....................... *paintings* | | | $302 |
| American b. 1875 | | | |
| ☐ **CRANKSHAW, C.E.** .................... *paintings* | | $357 | $412 |
| ☐ **CRANS, Johannes Marinus Schmidt** ...... *paintings* | | | $950 |
| Dutch 1830-1908 | | | |

| | | *Current Price Range* | |
|---|---|---|---|
| | | *Low* | *High* |
| ☐ **CRAPELET, Louis Amable** .................. *paintings* | | | $13,200 |
| French 1822/23-1867 | | | |
| ☐ **CRARAR, A. Piazza** ............................ *sculpture* | | | $418 |
| Italian 19th cent. | | | |
| ☐ **CRAVEN, E.** ...................................... *paintings* | | $154 | $1,430 |
| ..................................................... *drawings* | | | $154 |
| ☐ **CRAWFORD, Earl Stetson** .................. *paintings* | | $2,090 | $3,080 |
| American b. 1877 | | | |
| ☐ **CRAWFORD, Edmund Thornton** .......... *paintings* | | $770 | $1,650 |
| Scottish 1806-1885 | | | |
| ☐ **CRAWFORD, James W.** ...................... *paintings* | | $124 | $660 |
| American b. 1832 ..................................... *drawings* | | $50 | $632 |
| ☐ **CRAWFORD, Mel T.** ......................... *paintings* | | | $330 |
| American 20th cent. | | | |
| ☐ **CRAWFORD, Ralston** ......................... *paintings* | | $14,300 | $187,000 |
| American 1906-1977 | | | |
| ☐ **CRAWFORD, Will** .............................. *drawings* | | $110 | $330 |
| American 1869-1944 | | | |
| ☐ **CRAWFORD, William** ......................... *paintings* | | | $1,870 |
| British 1825-1869 | | | |
| ☐ **CRAYER, Gaspar de** ........................... *paintings* | | | $1,045 |
| Flemish 1584-1669 | | | |
| ☐ **CREDISTZ** ....................................... *paintings* | | | $522 |
| ☐ **CREEFT, Jose de** .............................. *drawings* | | $33 | $750 |
| Spanish b. 1884 ..................................... *sculpture* | | $935 | $5,170 |
| ☐ **CREIFELDS, Richard** .......................... *paintings* | | $33 | $1,320 |
| American 1853-1939 | | | |
| ☐ **CREIXAMS, Pierre** ............................. *paintings* | | | $440 |
| Spanish 1893-1965 | | | |
| ☐ **CREMIEUX, Edouard** .......................... *paintings* | | | $2,035 |
| French b. 1856 | | | |
| ☐ **CREMONINI, Leonardo** ....................... *paintings* | | | $935 |
| ..................................................... *drawings* | | | $143 |
| ☐ **CREO, Leonard** ................................. *paintings* | | $77 | $770 |
| ☐ **CREPIN, Louis Philippe** ...................... *paintings* | | $605 | $1,760 |
| French 1772-1851 | | | |
| ☐ **CRESPI, Giuseppe Maria** ..................... *paintings* | | | $935 |
| Italian 1665-1747 ..................................... *drawings* | | | $770 |
| ☐ **CRESPI, Luigi** ................................. *paintings* | | | $7,700 |
| Italian c. 1709/10-1779 | | | |
| ☐ **CRESSWELL, Albert** .......................... *paintings* | | | $352 |
| ☐ **CRESWICK, Thomas** .......................... *paintings* | | $220 | $2,860 |
| English 1811-1869 | | | |
| ☐ **CRETEN-GEORGES** ........................... *paintings* | | | $440 |
| ☐ **CRETI, Donato** ................................. *drawings* | | $440 | $1,210 |
| ☐ **CRETI, Giuseppe** .............................. *paintings* | | | $550 |
| Italian 1840-1914 | | | |
| ☐ **CRINILER** ....................................... *paintings* | | | $800 |

|  | Current Price Range | |
|---|---|---|
|  | Low | High |
| ☐ **CRIPPA, Roberto** ................................ *paintings* |  | **$660** |
| Italian 1912-1972 ........................................ *drawings* |  | **$1,980** |
| ☐ **CRIPPENDORF, William** .................... *paintings* |  | **$1,650** |
| Austrian 19th cent. |  |  |
| ☐ **CRIPS, G.A.** ........................................ *paintings* |  | **$330** |
| American 19th/20th cent. |  |  |
| ☐ **CRISS, Francis H.** ............................. *paintings* | **$1,650** | **$2,420** |
| American 1901-1973 |  |  |
| ☐ **CRITCHER, Catherine Carter** .............. *paintings* |  | **$30,800** |
| American |  |  |
| ☐ **CRIVELLI, Angelo Maria** |  |  |
| **(called LE CRIVELLONE)** .................... *paintings* |  | **$880** |
| Italian d. c. 1730 or 1760 |  |  |
| ☐ **CRNCIC, Menzi C.** ............................. *paintings* |  | **$275** |
| ☐ **CROCE, Francesco da Santa** ............... *paintings* |  | **$440** |
| ☐ **CROCHEPIERRE, Andre Antoine** ........ *paintings* | **$1,760** | **$4,675** |
| French b. 1860 |  |  |
| ☐ **CROCKER, Charles M.** ....................... *paintings* | **$165** | **$605** |
| American 20th cent. |  |  |
| ☐ **CROCKER, J.D.** ................................. *paintings* |  | **$1,500** |
| American b. 1823 |  |  |
| ☐ **CROCKER, Martha** ........................... *paintings* |  | **$357** |
| American 20th cent. |  |  |
| ☐ **CROCKWELL, Douglass S.** ................. *paintings* |  | **$660** |
| American 1904-1968 |  |  |
| ☐ **CROEGAERT, Georges** ...................... *paintings* | **$660** | **$13,200** |
| Dutch b. 1848 |  |  |
| ☐ **CROFT, Arthur** ................................. *drawings* |  | **$522** |
| British 19th cent. |  |  |
| ☐ **CROFT, C.W.** ................................... *paintings* | **$165** | **$275** |
| British 19th/20th cent. |  |  |
| ☐ **CROFTS, Ernest** ............................... *paintings* | **$660** | **$3,630** |
| British 1847-1911 |  |  |
| ☐ **CROFTS, W.** ..................................... *paintings* |  | **$253** |
| ☐ **CROISSANT, August** .......................... *paintings* |  | **$770** |
| German b. 1870 |  |  |
| ☐ **CROISY, Aristide-Onesime** ................. *sculpture* | **$495** | **$660** |
| French 1840-1899 |  |  |
| ☐ **CROIXY** ......................................... *sculpture* |  | **$2,420** |
| ☐ **CROME, John** ................................... *paintings* | **$1,650** | **$2,200** |
| British 19th cent. |  |  |
| ☐ **CROME, John** ................................... *paintings* |  | **$1,870** |
| English 1769-1821 |  |  |
| ☐ **CROME, John Berney** ......................... *paintings* | **$440** | **$880** |
| English 1793/94-1842 |  |  |
| ☐ **CROMEK, Thomas Hartley** ................. *paintings* |  | **$3,850** |
| English 1809-1873 |  |  |
| ☐ **CROMPTON, James Shaw** ................... *paintings* |  | **$125** |
| English 1853-1916 ................................... *drawings* |  | **$990** |

|  | | | Current Price Range | |
|---|---|---|---|---|
|  | | | Low | High |
| ☐ **CRONBACH, Robert M.** | ................... | *sculpture* | | $420 |
| American b. 1908 | | | | |
| ☐ **CROOK, Don** | ................... | *paintings* | | $3,400 |
| American | | | | |
| ☐ **CROOKE, Stephen** | ................... | *paintings* | | $1,980 |
| English 20th cent. | | | | |
| ☐ **CROOKES, J.E.W.** | ................... | *paintings* | | $192 |
| English (?) 19th cent. | | | | |
| ☐ **CROOS, Anthony Jansz van der** | ........... | *paintings* | $6,500 | $23,100 |
| Dutch c.1601- after 1662 | | | | |
| ☐ **CROOS, Jacob van der** | ................... | *paintings* | $2,860 | $3,850 |
| Dutch ac. 1690-d. before 1700 | | | | |
| ☐ **CROOS, Pieter van der** | ................... | *paintings* | $1,320 | $4,400 |
| Dutch b. c. 1601-d. after 1662 | | | | |
| ☐ **CROPSEY, C.** | ................... | *paintings* | | $800 |
| ☐ **CROPSEY, Jasper Francis** | ................... | *paintings* | $1,500 | $666,000 |
| American 1823-1900 | ................... | *drawings* | $330 | $10,450 |
| ☐ **CROSBY, Raymond Moreau** | ................... | *paintings* | | $77 |
| American 1877-1945 | ................... | *drawings* | $27 | $286 |
| ☐ **CROSIO, Luigi** | ................... | *paintings* | | $7,700 |
| Italian 1835-1915 | | | | |
| ☐ **CROSNIER, Jules** | ................... | *drawings* | | $330 |
| Swiss b. 1843 | | | | |
| ☐ **CROSS, A.K.** | ................... | *paintings* | | $308 |
| ☐ **CROSS, B.N.** | ................... | *paintings* | | $275 |
| ☐ **CROSS, Henri Edmond** | | | | |
| (Henri Edmond DELACROIX) | ................... | *paintings* | $23,100 | $74,800 |
| French 1856-1910 | ................... | *drawings* | $522 | $14,850 |
| ☐ **CROSS, Henry H.** | ................... | *paintings* | $110 | $4,750 |
| American 1837-1918 | | | | |
| ☐ **CROSS, Penni Anne** | ................... | *drawings* | $5,500 | $5,500 |
| American b. 1939 | | | | |
| ☐ **CROSSMEN, William H.** | ................... | *paintings* | | $550 |
| ☐ **CROTIN, H.** | ................... | *paintings* | $275 | $330 |
| French 20th cent. | | | | |
| ☐ **CROTTI, Jean** | ................... | *paintings* | | $467 |
| French 1878-1958 | | | | |
| ☐ **CROUCH, William** | ................... | *drawings* | | $550 |
| English ac. 1817-1840 | | | | |
| ☐ **CROUSE, M.** | ................... | *paintings* | | $247 |
| Dutch 19th cent. | | | | |
| ☐ **CROVELLO, William** | ................... | *sculpture* | | $357 |
| American b. 1929 | | | | |
| ☐ **CROW, B.** | ................... | *paintings* | | $440 |
| British 19th cent. | | | | |
| ☐ **CROWE, Eyre** | ................... | *paintings* | $800 | $4,950 |
| English 1824-1910 | | | | |
| ☐ **CROWE, Phillip** | ................... | *paintings* | $64,000 | $65,000 |
| American contemporary | | | | |

## Hudson River School

Nineteenth-century American artists who chose to paint American landscapes sought to convey the vast panorama of the untamed wilderness. Their work differed sharply from the European paintings of that genre, which often featured classical ruins. American painters depicted natural settings: rivers, forests, mountains, and oceans.

Such paintings are usually called "Hudson River School Paintings," even though they encompass virtually the entire country, including the Rocky Mountains and the Far West. Among the best known members of the Hudson River School are Albert Bierstadt, Frederic Church, Thomas Cole, Jasper Francis Cropsey, John Frederick Kensett, and T. Worthington Whittredge.

Cropsey (1823 - 1900) began his career as an architect, but while recuperating in the country from an illness he began to paint the surrounding landscape. Most of his work depicts locales in New York State, and he is best known for his autumnal landscapes. "Greenwood Lake," completed around 1870, was donated to the Seneca Falls, New York, school system in 1903. In 1959, a building superintendent was directed to destroy the work. Instead, he covered it, put it on pads to keep it off the floor, and stored it in the basement of the town's Historical Society. It remained there until 1983 when an appraiser, called in to examine another work, saw the records of Cropsey's original donation and asked where the painting was. The work was subsequently consigned to Sotheby's, where it sold for $286,000. (Jasper Francis Cropsey, "Greenwood Lake," oil on canvas-backed panel, 38¼ x 68¼ in., Sotheby's, June 2, 1983, $286,000.)

|  | *Current Price Range* | |
|---|---|---|
|  | *Low* | *High* |
| ☐ **CROWLEY, Don**  ................................. *drawings* |  | **$1,900** |
| American contemporary |  |  |
| ☐ **CROWLEY, J.M.**  ............................... *drawings* |  | **$1,045** |
| American early 19th cent. |  |  |

|  | | *Current Price Range* | |
|---|---|---|---|
|  | | Low | High |
| ☐ **CROWNINSHIELD, Frederic** ............... *paintings* | | | $3,300 |
| American 1845-1918 | | | |
| ☐ **CRUICKSHANK, William** .................... *paintings* | | | $770 |
| English 1844/49-1922 .................................. *drawings* | | $71 | $1,980 |
| ☐ **CRUIKSHANK, George** ......................... *paintings* | | | $330 |
| English 1792-1878 ...................................... *drawings* | | $181 | $3,575 |
| ☐ **CRUIKSHANK, Robert Isaac** ............... *drawings* | | $110 | $440 |
| English 1789-1856 | | | |
| ☐ **CRUMENBER** ...................................... *paintings* | | | $385 |
| ☐ **CRUTCHFIELD, William** ...................... *drawings* | | | $550 |
| ☐ **CRUZ-DIEZ, Carlos** ........................... *paintings* | | $2,640 | $5,500 |
| Venezuelan b. 1923 ................................... *drawings* | | $1,210 | $4,400 |
| ☐ **CRUZ-HERRERA, Jose Herreilla** ......... *paintings* | | $1,650 | $3,300 |
| Spanish b. 1890 | | | |
| ☐ **CSAKY, Joseph** ................................... *sculpture* | | $770 | $11,000 |
| Hungarian/French 1888-1971 | | | |
| ☐ **CSAPO, G.** ......................................... *paintings* | | | $220 |
| Hungarian 20th cent. | | | |
| ☐ **CSOK, Istvan** ..................................... *paintings* | | | $1,100 |
| Hungarian b. 1865 | | | |
| ☐ **CSOKA, Stephen** ................................. *paintings* | | $220 | $440 |
| American b. 1897 | | | |
| ☐ **CUARTAS VELASQUEZ, Gregorio** ...... *paintings* | | $2,750 | $7,150 |
| Colombian b. 1938 .................................... *drawings* | | $880 | $1,980 |
| ☐ **CUBLEY, H. Hadfield** ......................... *paintings* | | $165 | $605 |
| English ac. 1884-1887 | | | |
| ☐ **CUCARO, Pascal** ................................ *paintings* | | $11 | $302 |
| American 20th cent. | | | |
| ☐ **CUCCHI, A.** ....................................... *paintings* | | | $660 |
| ☐ **CUCUEL, Edward** ............................... *paintings* | | $220 | $34,100 |
| American b. 1879 | | | |
| ☐ **CUEVAS, Jose Luis** ............................ *paintings* | | | $3,575 |
| Mexican b. 1933/34 ................................... *drawings* | | $297 | $11,000 |
| ☐ **CUGAT, Delia** ................................... *paintings* | | | $5,500 |
| Argentinian ............................................... *drawings* | | | $440 |
| ☐ **CUGAT, Xavier** ................................. *paintings* | | $192 | $600 |
| Cuban 20th cent. | | | |
| ☐ **CUGNIART, Emile** .............................. *paintings* | | | $330 |
| French b. 1851 | | | |
| ☐ **CUGNOTET, Edouard** ......................... *paintings* | | | $264 |
| ☐ **CUITT, George** .................................. *paintings* | | | $13,200 |
| English | | | |
| ☐ **CUIXART, Modest** .............................. *paintings* | | | $1,210 |
| ☐ **CULL, James Allenson** ......................... *paintings* | | | $2,200 |
| English 19th cent. | | | |
| ☐ **CULLEN, Maurice Galbraith** ............... *paintings* | | | $14,300 |
| Canadian 1866-1934 | | | |
| ☐ **CULVER, Charles** .............................. *drawings* | | $94 | $495 |
| American b. 1908 | | | |

|  | | *Current Price Range* | |
|---|---|---|---|
|  | | *Low* | *High* |
| ☐ **CULVERHOUSE, Johann Mongels** ....... *paintings* | | $165 | $13,200 |
| Dutch b. 1820, ac. 1859-91 | | | |
| ☐ **CUMING, Beatrice Lavis** ..................... *drawings* | | | $192 |
| American b. 1903 | | | |
| ☐ **CUMMING, E. Gordon** ....................... *paintings* | | | $301 |
| ☐ **CUMMINGS, E.E.** ............................. *drawings* | | | $474 |
| ☐ **CUMMINGS, Melvin Earl** ................... *sculpture* | | | $1,320 |
| American b. 1876 | | | |
| ☐ **CUNDALL, Charles** ........................... *paintings* | | | $400 |
| English 1890-1971 | | | |
| ☐ **CUNDELL, Nora L. M.** ....................... *paintings* | | $1,155 | $1,700 |
| English 1889-1948 | | | |
| ☐ **CUNEO, Cyrus Cincinnati** ................... *paintings* | | $137 | $247 |
| American 1878-1916 | | | |
| ☐ **CUNEO, Jose** ................................. *paintings* | | $1,650 | $2,420 |
| b. Uruguay 1889 ................................... *drawings* | | | $880 |
| ☐ **CUNEO, Richard (or Rinaldo)** ............. *paintings* | | $247 | $1,100 |
| American 1877-1939 | | | |
| ☐ **CUNIO** ....................................... *paintings* | | | $1,980 |
| ☐ **CUNLIFFE, David** ............................ *paintings* | | | $4,620 |
| English 19th cent. | | | |
| ☐ **CUNNINGHAM, Ben** ......................... *paintings* | | $165 | $385 |
| American 20th cent. | | | |
| ☐ **CUNNINGHAM, Patricia Stanley** .......... *paintings* | | | $880 |
| American b. 1919 | | | |
| ☐ **CUNNINGTON, A.** ............................ *paintings* | | | $302 |
| British 19th cent. | | | |
| ☐ **CUPRIEN, Frank W.** ......................... *paintings* | | $356 | $1,320 |
| American 1871-1948 | | | |
| ☐ **CURADZE, H.** ................................. *sculpture* | | | $605 |
| Continental 19th cent. | | | |
| ☐ **CUREL-SYLVESTRE, Roger** ................ *paintings* | | $82 | $385 |
| French b. 1884 | | | |
| ☐ **CURIA, E. Ubando** ........................... *sculpture* | | | $1,210 |
| Mexican 20th cent. | | | |
| ☐ **CURIA, Francesco** ............................ *paintings* | | | $990 |
| Italian 1538-1610 | | | |
| ☐ **CURRAN, C.E.L.** ............................. *paintings* | | | $6,050 |
| 19th/20th cent. | | | |
| ☐ **CURRAN, Charles Courtney** ................ *paintings* | | $935 | $80,000 |
| American 1861-1942 ................................. *drawings* | | | $1,430 |
| ☐ **CURRAN, J.** ................................... *paintings* | | | $1,100 |
| American 19th/20th cent. | | | |
| ☐ **CURRIA, Bruce** ............................... *paintings* | | | $192 |
| American 20th cent. | | | |
| ☐ **CURRIE, William** ............................. *paintings* | | | $660 |
| British 19th cent. | | | |
| ☐ **CURRIER, C.B.** ............................... *paintings* | | | $220 |
| American 20th cent. | | | |

|  | | Current Price Range | |
|---|---|---|---|
|  | | Low | High |
| □ **CURRIER, Edward Wilson** ................... *paintings* | | $66 | $660 |
| American 1857-1918 | | | |
| □ **CURRIER, J. Frank** ........................... *paintings* | | | $550 |
| American 1843-1909 ................................. *drawings* | | | $77 |
| □ **CURRIER, R. W.** ............................... *paintings* | | | $550 |
| British ac. 1835-40 | | | |
| □ **CURRIER, Walter Barron** ................... *paintings* | | | $192 |
| American 1879-1934 | | | |
| □ **CURRUCHICHE, R. Santiago** ............. *paintings* | | | $605 |
| □ **CURRY, John Steuart** .......................... *paintings* | | $1,540 | $20,900 |
| American 1897-1946 ................................... *drawings* | | $550 | $2,750 |
| □ **CURRY, Robert F.** .............................. *paintings* | | $310 | $1,870 |
| American b. 1872 | | | |
| □ **CURTIN, Thomas R.** ........................... *paintings* | | | $440 |
| American School 20th cent. | | | |
| □ **CURTIS, C.** ...................................... *paintings* | | | $286 |
| □ **CURTIS, Calvin** ............................... *paintings* | | $247 | $700 |
| American 1822-1893 | | | |
| □ **CURTIS, Elizabeth** ........................... *paintings* | | $137 | $440 |
| American b. 1873 | | | |
| □ **CURTIS, Emile** ................................ *paintings* | | | $385 |
| American 20th cent. | | | |
| □ **CURTIS, George** ............................... *paintings* | | $500 | $1,430 |
| American 1826-1881 | | | |
| □ **CURTIS, George Washington** ............... *paintings* | | | $525 |
| American 1869-1927 | | | |
| □ **CURTIS, Leland** ............................... *paintings* | | $137 | $1,760 |
| American b. 1897 ..................................... *drawings* | | $467 | $467 |
| □ **CURTIS, Ralph Wormsley** ................... *drawings* | | $115 | $302 |
| Anglo/American 1854-1922 | | | |
| □ **CURTIS, S.W.** .................................. *paintings* | | | $357 |
| American 19th cent. | | | |
| □ **CURTIS, William Fuller** ..................... *paintings* | | | $2,310 |
| American b. 1873 | | | |
| □ **CURTS, T.** ...................................... *sculpture* | | $660 | $990 |
| □ **CUSACHS Y CUSACHS, Jose** ............. *paintings* | | | $1,870 |
| Spanish 1851-1908 | | | |
| □ **CUSHING, Howard Gardiner** ............... *paintings* | | | $770 |
| American 1869-1915 ................................. *drawings* | | | $275 |
| □ **CUSHING, J.G.** ................................ *paintings* | | | $247 |
| American | | | |
| □ **CUSTER, Edward L.** ........................... *paintings* | | | $495 |
| 1837-1881 | | | |
| □ **CUSTODIS, H.** .................................. *paintings* | | | $2,090 |
| □ **CUTHBERT, Y.** ................................ *paintings* | | | $385 |
| American 19th/20th cent. | | | |
| □ **CUTHER, C.** ..................................... *paintings* | | | $550 |
| American 19th cent. | | | |
| □ **CUTTS, J.** ....................................... *drawings* | | | $302 |

| | | Current Price Range | |
|---|---|---|---|
| | | *Low* | *High* |
| ☐ **CUVILLON, Louis Robert de** ............... *drawings* <br> French b. 1848 | | $302 | $660 |
| ☐ **CUYLENBORCH, Abraham van** ........... *paintings* <br> Dutch c. 1620-1658 | | $1,100 | $4,400 |
| ☐ **CUYP, Albert** ...................................... *paintings* <br> Dutch 1620-1691 | | $17,600 | $286,000 |
| ☐ **CUYP, Benjamin Gerritsz** ..................... *paintings* <br> Dutch 1612-1652 | | $1,650 | $8,800 |
| ☐ **CUYP, Jacob Gerritz** ............................ *paintings* <br> Dutch 1594-1651 | | $5,500 | $6,600 |
| ☐ **CUZ, Nan** ......................................... *paintings* | | | $660 |
| ☐ **CYRSKY, Frank** ................................ *paintings* | | | $880 |
| ☐ **CZABO, Balazs** ................................. *paintings* | | $165 | $440 |
| ☐ **CZACHORSKI, Wladyslaw** .................. *paintings* <br> Polish 1850-1911 | | $3,740 | $19,800 |
| ☐ **CZAKY, Josef** ...................................... *sculpture* <br> Hungarian/French 1888-1971 | | | $4,950 |
| ☐ **CZEDEKOWSKI, Boleslas Jan** ............. *paintings* <br> Polish b. 1885 | | $467 | $660 |
| ☐ **CZERNICKI, M.** ................................. *paintings* <br> Polish 19th cent. | | | $275 |
| ☐ **CZERNOTZKY, Ernst** ........................ *paintings* <br> Austrian b. 1869 | | $770 | $1,320 |
| ☐ **CZERNY, Ludwig** .............................. *drawings* | | | $462 |
| ☐ **CZOBEL, Bela** ................................... *paintings* | | | $440 |
| ☐ **D'ARISTA, Robert** ............................. *paintings* <br> American b. 1929 | | | $192 |
| ☐ **D'ASCENZO, Nicola** ........................... *paintings* <br> Italian/American b. 1869/71 ........................... *drawings* | | $330 <br> $77 | $825 <br> $742 |
| ☐ **D'EGVILLE, James T. Herve** .............. *drawings* <br> British d. 1880 | | | $302 |
| ☐ **DA COSTA, Julio** ................................. *paintings* <br> Portugese b. 1855 | | | $880 |
| ☐ **DABELSTEIN, H.F.** ............................ *paintings* <br> 19th/20th cent. | | | $880 |
| ☐ **DABELSTEIN, W.M.** .......................... *paintings* | | | $356 |
| ☐ **DABO, Leon** ...................................... *paintings* <br> American 1868-1960 | | $121 | $7,000 |
| ☐ **DABO, Theodore Scott** ........................ *paintings* <br> American b. 1877 | | | $302 |
| ☐ **DADD, Frank** ...................................... *drawings* <br> British 1851-1929 | | | $1,200 |
| ☐ **DADD, Richard** ................................... *drawings* <br> 19th cent. | | | $275 |
| ☐ **DAEL, Jan Frans van** .......................... *paintings* <br> Flemish 1764-1840 | | $2,090 | $6,050 |
| ☐ **DAELE, Charles van den** ...................... *paintings* <br> Belgian 1818-1880 | | $54 | $3,300 |

|                                                    | *Current Price Range* | |
|----------------------------------------------------|-----------|-----------|
|                                                    | *Low*     | *High*    |
| ☐ **DAELE, F. van den** ............................. *paintings* |           | $715      |
| American 20th cent.                                |           |           |
| ☐ **DAELEN, Edward** ............................. *paintings* |           | $440      |
| German b. 1848                                     |           |           |
| ☐ **DAGGY, Richard S.** ........................... *drawings* | $550      | $605      |
| American b. 1892                                   |           |           |
| ☐ **DAGNAC-RIVIERE, Charles** ............... *paintings* |           | $550      |
| French 1864-1945                                   |           |           |
| ☐ **DAGNAN-BOUVERET,**                             |           |           |
| **Pascal Adolphe Jean** ........................... *paintings* | $4,400    | $26,400   |
| French 1852-1929 ...................................... *drawings* |           | $330      |
| ☐ **DAHL, Hans** ..................................... *paintings* | $411      | $12,650   |
| Norwegian 1849-1937                                |           |           |
| ☐ **DAHL, Hans Andreas** ........................... *paintings* | $880      | $4,950    |
| ☐ **DAHL, Michael** ................................... *paintings* | $550      | $1,760    |
| Swedish                                            |           |           |
| ☐ **DAHLAGER, Jules** .............................. *paintings* |           | $1,045    |
| American 20th cent.                                |           |           |
| ☐ **DAHLGREEN, Charles W.** .................. *paintings* | $495      | $1,540    |
| American 1864-1955                                 |           |           |
| ☐ **DAHLGREN, Carl Christian** ................ *paintings* | $165      | $1,650    |
| Danish/American 1841-1920?                         |           |           |
| ☐ **DAHLGREN, Marius** ........................... *paintings* | $522      | $880      |
| American 1844-1920                                 |           |           |
| ☐ **DAILLIN, Horace** ............................. *sculpture* |           | $1,650    |
| French 1854-1938                                   |           |           |
| ☐ **DAIMEE** ........................................... *paintings* |           | $1,100    |
| French 19th cent.                                  |           |           |
| ☐ **DAINGERFIELD, Elliott** ...................... *paintings* | $330      | $5,000    |
| American 1859-1932 ................................. *drawings* |           | $302      |
| ☐ **DAINI, Augusto** ................................. *drawings* | $605      | $1,540    |
| ☐ **DAIO, David** ..................................... *paintings* |           | $825      |
| ☐ **DAIWAILLE, Alexander Joseph** ........... *paintings* |           | $6,325    |
| Dutch 1818-1888                                    |           |           |
| ☐ **DAKET, Carl** ..................................... *paintings* |           | $302      |
| ☐ **DAKIN, Sydney Tilden** ........................ *paintings* | $110      | $550      |
| American 1876-1935                                 |           |           |
| ☐ **DALBIAC, F.** ..................................... *paintings* |           | $275      |
| American 20th cent.                                |           |           |
| ☐ **DALBY, David (called Dalby of York)** .... *paintings* | $3,300    | $16,000   |
| English b. 1790                                    |           |           |
| ☐ **DALBY, John** ..................................... *paintings* | $4,400    | $27,500*  |
| British 1826-1853                                  |           |           |
| ☐ **DALERY, G.** ..................................... *paintings* |           | $715      |
| ☐ **DALI, Louis** ..................................... *paintings* | $60       | $1,100    |
| French 20th cent.                                  |           |           |

## Surrealism

*Salvador Dali's name is
synonymous with the Surrealist
movement in art, which included
such other well-known painters as
Giorgio de Chirico, Max Ernst, and
Rene Magritte.*

*This self-portrait by Dali depicts
him as an umbrella, a skull perched
on top of the handle, and the point
of the umbrella as the tip of his
phallus.*

*The development of Surrealist art
coincided with the growing interest
and curiosity about the unconscious
that was very much a part of the
intellectual life of the post–World
War I period. Surrealist art is
nontraditional — its inspiration is the
unconscious. Its hallmarks are the
juxtaposition of nonharmonious
objects in a dreamlike atmosphere.
The same painting may contain
both dark and amusing themes.
(Salvador Dali, "Portrait de l'Artiste,"
circa 1942, oil en grisaille on paper,
12½ x 9 in., Weschler's, March 1,
1985, $8,250.)*

|  |  | Current Price Range | |
|---|---|---|---|
|  |  | *Low* | *High* |
| ☐ **DALI, Salvador** | *paintings* | **$1,540** | **$517,000** |
| Spanish b. 1904 | *drawings* | **$577** | **$121,000** |
|  | *sculpture* | **$605** | **$5,500** |
| ☐ **DALIN, Louis** | *paintings* |  | **$275** |
| French 20th cent. |  |  |  |
| ☐ **DALLEMAGNE, Adolphe** | *paintings* |  | **$1,980** |
| French b. 1811 |  |  |  |
| ☐ **DALLEMAGNE, Leon** | *paintings* | **$242** | **$880** |
| French 19th cent. |  |  |  |
| ☐ **DALLIN, Cyrus Edwin** | *paintings* |  | **$1,540** |
| American 1861-1944 | *sculpture* | **$900** | **$30,800** |
| ☐ **DALOU, Aime Jules** | *paintings* | **$264** | **$5,280** |
| French 1838-1902 |  |  |  |
| ☐ **DALRINCON Y TRIVES, Martinez** | *paintings* |  | **$440** |
| Spanish 1840-1892 |  |  |  |
| ☐ **DALTON, H.** | *paintings* |  | **$550** |
| ☐ **DALTON, Peter** | *paintings* |  | **$770** |
| American |  |  |  |

| | | Current Price Range | |
|---|---|---|---|
| | | *Low* | *High* |
| ☐ **DALTON, S.** .......................................... *paintings* | | | $440 |
| American 19th cent. | | | |
| ☐ **DALVI-ROUSMAN (?)** ......................... *paintings* | | | $550 |
| German 19th cent. | | | |
| ☐ **DALZIEL, James** ............................... *paintings* | | | $1,650 |
| ☐ **DAMAS, Eugene** ................................ *paintings* | | | $2,200 |
| French b. 1848 | | | |
| ☐ **DAME, E.** ........................................... *sculpture* | | | $467 |
| ☐ **DAMERON, Emile Charles** ................... *paintings* | | $1,000 | $1,430 |
| French 1848-1908 | | | |
| ☐ **DAMME, Frans van** ............................ *paintings* | | | $1,000 |
| Flemish b. 1860 | | | |
| ☐ **DAMME-SYLA, Emile van** ................. *paintings* | | $330 | $1,045 |
| Belgian 1853-1935 | | | |
| ☐ **DAMOYE, Pierre Emmanuel** ................ *paintings* | | $550 | $9,350 |
| French 1847-1916 | | | |
| ☐ **DAMROW, Charles** ............................ *paintings* | | $77 | $3,025 |
| American b. 1916 | | | |
| ☐ **DAMSCHROEDER, Jan Jac Matthys** .... *paintings* | | $1,430 | $6,600 |
| German ac. 1850-1909 | | | |
| ☐ **DANA, Charles E.** ............................... *drawings* | | | $209 |
| American 1843-1924 | | | |
| ☐ **DANA, William Parsons Winchester** ...... *paintings* | | | $1,100 |
| American 1833-1927 | | | |
| ☐ **DANAT, M.** ........................................ *paintings* | | | $480 |
| ☐ **DANBY, Francis** ................................ *paintings* | | | $750 |
| British 1793-1861 ................................. *drawings* | | | $1,265 |
| ☐ **DANBY, G.** ....................................... *paintings* | | | $550 |
| English 19th cent. | | | |
| ☐ **DANBY, James Francis** ........................ *paintings* | | $1,100 | $2,090 |
| British 1816-1875 | | | |
| ☐ **DANBY, M.** ...................................... *paintings* | | | $357 |
| French 19th cent. | | | |
| ☐ **DANBY, Thomas** ............................... *paintings* | | $1,210 | $1,870 |
| British 1818-1886 | | | |
| ☐ **DANCE, Sir Nathaniel** | | | |
| (**DANCE-HOLLAND**) ........................... *paintings* | | $1,870 | $12,000 |
| English 1734-1811 | | | |
| ☐ **DANCKERTS, Johan** ......................... *paintings* | | | $5,500 |
| Dutch c. 1615-1681/87 | | | |
| ☐ **DANDINI, Cesare** .............................. *paintings* | | | $6,600 |
| Italian 1646-1712 | | | |
| ☐ **DANDINI, Pietro** .............................. *paintings* | | $3,960 | $4,180 |
| Italian 1646-1712 | | | |
| ☐ **DANDRIDGE, Bartholomew** ................. *paintings* | | | $4,675 |
| English 1691-1751 | | | |
| ☐ **DANESI** ........................................... *paintings* | | | $495 |
| ☐ **DANFORTH, Charles** ......................... *paintings* | | | $1,045 |
| British 19th cent. | | | |

| | | | Current Price Range | |
|---|---|---|---|---|
| | | | *Low* | *High* |
| ☐ **DANGER, Henri Camille** ...................... *paintings* | | | | $1,760 |
| French 1857-after 1937 | | | | |
| ☐ **DANHAUSER, Josef** ............................ *paintings* | | | | $3,300 |
| Austrian 1805-1845 | | | | |
| ☐ **DANIEL, Gerome** ............................... *drawings* | | | | $357 |
| French 17th cent. | | | | |
| ☐ **DANIELL, William Swift** ...................... *paintings* | | | | $220 |
| American b. 1865 | | | | |
| ☐ **DANIELS, Andries** .............................. *paintings* | | | | $1,650 |
| Flemish b. 1580 | | | | |
| ☐ **DANIELS, George Fisher** ...................... *paintings* | | | | $550 |
| American b. 1821 | | | | |
| ☐ **DANILOWATZ, Joseph** ......................... *paintings* | | | | $825 |
| Austrian b. 1877 | | | | |
| ☐ **DANKMEYER, Charles B.** ..................... *paintings* | | $440 | | $605 |
| Dutch b. 1861 | | | | |
| ☐ **DANKWORTH, August** ........................ *paintings* | | | | $3,300 |
| German 1813-1854 | | | | |
| ☐ **DANLON, F. (Jr.)** ............................... *paintings* | | | | $1,100 |
| American 19th/20th cent. | | | | |
| ☐ **DANLOUX, Henri Pierre** ..................... *paintings* | | $1,540 | | $26,400 |
| French 1753-1809 .................................... *drawings* | | | | $2,200 |
| ☐ **DANNAT, William Turner** .................... *paintings* | | $605 | | $1,760 |
| American 1853-1929 | | | | |
| ☐ **DANNER, Sara Kalb** ........................... *paintings* | | | | $495 |
| American 20th cent. | | | | |
| ☐ **DANNHAUSEN, Eldon** ......................... *sculpture* | | | | $330 |
| ☐ **DANSAERT, Leon Marie Constant** ........ *paintings* | | $660 | | $2,420 |
| Belgian 1830-1909 | | | | |
| ☐ **DANTAN, Antoine Laurent** ................... *sculpture* | | | | $192 |
| French 1798-1878 | | | | |
| ☐ **DANTON, A.F.** .................................. *paintings* | | | | $4,125 |
| British 20th cent. | | | | |
| ☐ **DANTON, F.** ..................................... *paintings* | | | | $1,045 |
| ☐ **DANTZE, Johannes Bertholomaus** ......... *paintings* | | | | $1,320 |
| 1823-1895 | | | | |
| ☐ **DANTZIG, M.** .................................... *paintings* | | $121 | | $330 |
| American 19th cent. | | | | |
| ☐ **DANY** ............................................. *drawings* | | | | $330 |
| ☐ **DANZ, Robert** .................................. *paintings* | | | | $356 |
| German b. 1841 ..................................... *drawings* | | | | $77 |
| ☐ **DAPHNIS, Nassos** ............................. *paintings* | | $330 | | $495 |
| American b. 1914 | | | | |
| ☐ **DAQIAN, Zhang** ................................ *drawings* | | | | $3,500 |
| ☐ **DARAGNES, Jean Gabriel** ................... *paintings* | | $715 | | $1,430 |
| French 1886-1950 | | | | |
| ☐ **DARBY, Elizabeth Clorinda** ................. *paintings* | | | | $1,100 |
| American (?) d. 1906 | | | | |

|  | | Current Price Range | |
| --- | --- | --- | --- |
|  | | Low | High |
| ☐ **DARBY, Felix O.C.** ............................. *drawings* | | | $275 |
| American 20th cent. | | | |
| ☐ **DARCHE, T.** ...................................... *drawings* | | | $357 |
| ☐ **DARGE, Fred** ................................... *paintings* | | $136 | $412 |
| American b. 1900 | | | |
| ☐ **DARGELAS, Andre Henri** ................... *paintings* | | $3,850 | $221,000 |
| French 1828-1906 | | | |
| ☐ **DARIEL-RENARD, J.C.** ...................... *paintings* | | | $715 |
| ☐ **DARLEY, Felix Octavius Carr** .............. *drawings* | | $385 | $1,210 |
| American 1822-1888 | | | |
| ☐ **DARLING, William** ............................ *paintings* | | | $302 |
| ☐ **DARNAUT, Hugo** ............................... *paintings* | | $1,600 | $2,420 |
| Austrian 1851-1937 | | | |
| ☐ **DARNELL, H.** ................................... *paintings* | | | $302 |
| 19th cent. | | | |
| ☐ **DARRAH, Ann Sophia Towne** .............. *paintings* | | $121 | $6,600 |
| American 1819-1881 | | | |
| ☐ **DARRO, Tom** ................................... *paintings* | | | $1,100 |
| American 20th cent. | | | |
| ☐ **DARSOW, H.** ................................... *sculpture* | | | $350 |
| ☐ **DASBURG, Andrew Michael** ................. *paintings* | | $10,450 | $55,000 |
| American 1887-1979 ................................. *drawings* | | $550 | $2,310 |
| ☐ **DASH, Robert** ................................... *paintings* | | $55 | $1,980 |
| American b. 1934 | | | |
| ☐ **DASTON (?), Ferdinand** ....................... *paintings* | | | $358 |
| French 19th cent. | | | |
| ☐ **DASTUGUE, Maxime** .......................... *paintings* | | | $935 |
| French 19th cent. | | | |
| ☐ **DATZ, A. Mark** ................................. *paintings* | | $22 | $192 |
| American 1883/96-1968 | | | |
| ☐ **DAUBIGNY, Charles** ........................... *paintings* | | | $3,300 |
| French 1740-1830 | | | |
| ☐ **DAUBIGNY, Charles Francois** ............. *paintings* | | $2,310 | $44,000 |
| French 1817-1878 ................................. *drawings* | | $400 | $1,760 |
| ☐ **DAUBIGNY, J.** .................................. *drawings* | | | $1,760 |
| ☐ **DAUBIGNY, Karl Pierre** ...................... *paintings* | | $357 | $6,050 |
| French 1846-1886 | | | |
| ☐ **DAUCHOT, Gabriel** ............................ *paintings* | | $440 | $1,210 |
| French b. 1927 | | | |
| ☐ **DAUGHERTY, James Henry** ................ *paintings* | | $1,980 | $22,000 |
| American 1886/89-1974 ............................. *drawings* | | $330 | $880 |
| ☐ **DAUGHERTY, Paul** ............................ *paintings* | | $198 | $2,200 |
| American 1877-1947 ................................. *drawings* | | $275 | $330 |
| ☐ **DAUMIER, Honore** ............................ *paintings* | | $36,750 | $462,000 |
| French 1808-1879 ...................................... *drawings* | | $2,310 | $9,900 |
| ................................................ *sculpture* | | $1,320 | $49,500 |
| ☐ **DAUMIER, Jean** ................................. *paintings* | | $247 | $301 |
| French contemporary | | | |

| | | | Current Price Range | |
| --- | --- | --- | --- | --- |
| | | | *Low* | *High* |
| ☐ **DAUX, Charles Edmond** | *paintings* | | $14,850 | $16,000 |
| French 1817-1888 | | | | |
| ☐ **DAUZATS, Adrien** | *drawings* | | | $440 |
| French 1804-1868 | | | | |
| ☐ **DAVENPORT, Edmund** | *paintings* | | | $330 |
| American 20th cent. | | | | |
| ☐ **DAVENPORT, Henry** | *drawings* | | | $550 |
| American b. 1882 | | | | |
| ☐ **DAVENPORT, W.S.** | *paintings* | | | $770 |
| American | | | | |
| ☐ **DAVEY, Randall** | *paintings* | | $770 | $52,800 |
| American 1887-1964 | *drawings* | | $385 | $26,400 |
| ☐ **DAVID, Giovanni** | *drawings* | | | $1,210 |
| Italian 1743-1790 | | | | |
| ☐ **DAVID, Gustave** | *drawings* | | $605 | $1,430 |
| French 1824-1891 | | | | |
| ☐ **DAVID, Hermine** | *paintings* | | $55 | $467 |
| French 1886-1971 | *drawings* | | | $330 |
| ☐ **DAVID, Jacques Louis** | *paintings* | | | $858,000 |
| French 1748-1825 | *drawings* | | $2,750 | $3,575 |
| ☐ **DAVID, Jules** | *drawings* | | | $275 |
| ☐ **DAVID, Pierre Jean** | | | | |
| **(called David D'ANGERS)** | *sculpture* | | $385 | $660 |
| French 1788-1856 | | | | |
| ☐ **DAVID-NILLET, Germain** | *paintings* | | $715 | $935 |
| French 1861-1932 | | | | |
| ☐ **DAVIDSON, Allan D.** | *paintings* | | $220 | $1,045 |
| British 1873-1932 | | | | |
| ☐ **DAVIDSON, Charles Grant** | *paintings* | | $220 | $440 |
| English 1820-1902 | *drawings* | | | $357 |
| ☐ **DAVIDSON, George** | *paintings* | | | $330 |
| American 1889-1965 | | | | |
| ☐ **DAVIDSON, J.A.** | *paintings* | | | $990 |
| English 19th cent. | | | | |
| ☐ **DAVIDSON, Jeremiah** | *paintings* | | | $4,620 |
| English c. 1695-1745 | | | | |
| ☐ **DAVIDSON, Jo** | *drawings* | | $22 | $192 |
| American 1883-1952 | *sculpture* | | $385 | $6,600 |
| ☐ **DAVIDSON, Morris** | *paintings* | | | $44 |
| American 1898-1979 | *drawings* | | | $275 |
| ☐ **DAVIDSON, Thomas** | *paintings* | | $2,200 | $4,400 |
| British ac. 1863-1903 | | | | |
| ☐ **DAVIE, Alan** | *paintings* | | $467 | $11,000 |
| English b. 1920 | *drawings* | | $990 | $1,320 |
| ☐ **DAVIES, Albert W.** | *paintings* | | $495 | $715 |
| American 20th cent. | | | | |
| ☐ **DAVIES, Arthur B.** | *paintings* | | $140 | $14,300 |
| American 1862-1928 | *drawings* | | $75 | $2,750 |

**Mailing Lists**

*While Sotheby's and Christie's sell 90 percent of all cataloged auction lots throughout the United States, thousands of other lots are sold at other houses. If you are collecting, particularly in a highly specialized area, it is important that you be on the mailing lists of all the auction houses. Sometimes catalogs contain lots in specialty areas that rarely come to auction.*

*Major drawings by Old Masters do not often appear at auction. A notable exception was the 1985 sale of a private art collection, including two small Old Master drawings, to benefit the Saginaw Art Museum in Michigan. Francisco Goya's "Transport d'un Blesse" and Jacques Louis David's "Cupid and Psyche" (the latter being the final study for David's major painting of the same name) were both sold. The Goya (8 x 5⅝), numbered and with the collector's stamp, sold for $242,000. (Jacques Louis David, "Cupid and Psyche," watercolor and wash drawing, 6½ x 8¾ in., Frank H. Boos Gallery, July 27, 1985, $82,250.)*

|  | | *Current Price Range* | |
|---|---|---|---|
|  | | *Low* | *High* |
| ☐ **DAVIES, Harold Christopher** ............... *paintings* | | | **$2,640** |
| 1891-1976 .................................................. *drawings* | | **$385** | **$385** |
| ☐ **DAVIES, Norman Prescott** .................... *paintings* | | **$440** | **$1,595** |
| English 1862-1915 | | | |
| ☐ **DAVIES, William** .............................. *paintings* | | | **$825** |
| British 1826-1901 | | | |
| ☐ **DAVIS, A.F.** ........................................ *paintings* | | | **$550** |
| American | | | |

| | | Current Price Range | |
|---|---|---|---|
| | | Low | High |
| ☐ **DAVIS, A.P.** ........................................ *paintings* | | | $400 |
| American 19th cent. | | | |
| ☐ **DAVIS, Alexander Jackson** ................. *drawings* | | | $17,050 |
| American 1803-1892 | | | |
| ☐ **DAVIS, Arthur** ...................................... *paintings* | | | $1,430 |
| ☐ **DAVIS, Arthur H.** ............................... *paintings* | | $110 | $2,530 |
| English ac. 1871-1894 | | | |
| ☐ **DAVIS, Brad** ........................................ *paintings* | | $4,400 | $8,250 |
| American b. 1942 | | | |
| ☐ **DAVIS, Charles** ................................... *paintings* | | | $550 |
| English 19th/20th cent. | | | |
| ☐ **DAVIS, Charles Harold** ...................... *paintings* | | $550 | $12,650 |
| American 1856-1933 ............................... *drawings* | | | $1,870 |
| ☐ **DAVIS, Charles Henry** ........................ *paintings* | | | $550 |
| American 1845-1921 | | | |
| ☐ **DAVIS, E. Cassary** .............................. *paintings* | | | $440 |
| ☐ **DAVIS, F. Coulson** .............................. *drawings* | | | $275 |
| ☐ **DAVIS, F. Watson** ............................... *drawings* | | | $440 |
| American 19th/20th cent. | | | |
| ☐ **DAVIS, Floyd MacMillan** ..................... *drawings* | | | $412 |
| English 1896-1966 | | | |
| ☐ **DAVIS, Fred W.** ................................... *paintings* | | | $825 |
| English 19th cent. | | | |
| ☐ **DAVIS, G.A.** ........................................ *drawings* | | | $300 |
| ☐ **DAVIS, G.R.** ........................................ *paintings* | | $330 | $418 |
| ☐ **DAVIS, Gene** ........................................ *paintings* | | $605 | $16,500 |
| American b. 1920 | | | |
| ☐ **DAVIS, Geoff** ...................................... *paintings* | | | $385 |
| ☐ **DAVIS, Gladys Rockmore** .................... *paintings* | | $154 | $4,400 |
| American 1901-1967 ................................ *drawings* | | $356 | $495 |
| ☐ **DAVIS, Henry William Banks** .............. *paintings* | | $880 | $1,100 |
| British 1833-1914 | | | |
| ☐ **DAVIS, John Steeple** ........................... *paintings* | | $220 | $440 |
| American 1844-1917 | | | |
| ☐ **DAVIS, Joseph** ..................................... *drawings* | | | $6,600 |
| American ac. 1832-1837 | | | |
| ☐ **DAVIS, Leonard Moore** ........................ *paintings* | | $77 | $2,090 |
| American 1864-1938 | | | |
| ☐ **DAVIS, Owen** ...................................... *paintings* | | | $357 |
| American 20th cent. | | | |
| ☐ **DAVIS, Phil** ........................................ *drawings* | | $550 | $715 |
| 1906-1964 | | | |
| ☐ **DAVIS, Richard Barrett** ....................... *paintings* | | $6,000 | $33,000 |
| English 1782-1854 | | | |
| ☐ **DAVIS, Robert B.** ............................... *paintings* | | | $357 |
| American 19th cent. | | | |
| ☐ **DAVIS, Ron** ........................................ *paintings* | | $1,100 | $16,500 |
| American b. 1937 ..................................... *sculpture* | | $6,600 | $17,600 |

| | | Current Price Range | |
|---|---|---|---|
| | | Low | High |
| ☐ **DAVIS, Stuart** ........................... *paintings* | | **$9,350** | **$77,000** |
| American 1894-1964 ........................... *drawings* | | **$825** | **$52,800** |
| ☐ **DAVIS, Val** ............................... *drawings* | | | **$1,210** |
| English b. 1854 | | | |
| ☐ **DAVIS, Vestie E.** ................... *paintings* | | **$1,100** | **$4,620** |
| American 1904-1978 | | | |
| ☐ **DAVIS, W.H.** ........................... *paintings* | | | **$600** |
| American 19th cent. | | | |
| ☐ **DAVIS, Walter** ........................ *drawings* | | | **$1,375** |
| American 19th cent. | | | |
| ☐ **DAVIS, Warren B.** ................... *paintings* | | **$110** | **$2,000** |
| American 1865-1928 ........................ *drawings* | | **$66** | **$357** |
| ☐ **DAVIS, William Henry** ............ *paintings* | | **$3,300** | **$9,900** |
| English ac. 1803-1849 | | | |
| ☐ **DAVIS, William M.** ................. *paintings* | | **$3,800** | **$8,250***  |
| American 1829-1920 ........................ *drawings* | | | **$660** |
| ☐ **DAVISON, Thomas Raffles** ...... *paintings* | | | **$1,870** |
| British 1853-1937 | | | |
| ☐ **DAWAKEMA** ........................ *paintings* | | | **$200** |
| American Indian 20th cent. | | | |
| ☐ **DAWE, George** ...................... *paintings* | | | **$2,420** |
| English 1781-1829 | | | |
| ☐ **DAWES, Edwin M.** ................. *paintings* | | **$174** | **$1,050** |
| American 1872-1934/45 | | | |
| ☐ **DAWLEY, Joseph** ................... *paintings* | | | **$4,000** |
| American b. 1936 | | | |
| ☐ **DAWS, H.M.** ......................... *paintings* | | | **$1,980** |
| ☐ **DAWSON, Alfred** ................... *paintings* | | **$301** | **$2,722** |
| British 1860-1894 | | | |
| ☐ **DAWSON, Henry** ..................... *paintings* | | **$1,870** | **$4,950** |
| English 1811-1878 ........................ *drawings* | | **$220** | **$247** |
| ☐ **DAWSON, John** ...................... *paintings* | | | **$3,000** |
| American | | | |
| ☐ **DAWSON, Mark** ..................... *paintings* | | | **$400** |
| American 19th cent. | | | |
| ☐ **DAWSON, Montague J.** ........... *paintings* | | **$1,210** | **$77,000** |
| English 1895-1973 ........................ *drawings* | | **$1,320** | **$13,200** |
| ☐ **DAWSON, Rex** ...................... *paintings* | | **$44** | **$715** |
| ☐ **DAWSON, S.** ......................... *paintings* | | | **$797** |
| British 19th cent. | | | |
| ☐ **DAWSON-WATSON, Dawson** ...... *paintings* | | **$220** | **$8,800** |
| American b. 1864 | | | |
| ☐ **DAY, Edwin** ........................ *paintings* | | | **$302** |
| British 19th cent. | | | |
| ☐ **DAY, Francis** ....................... *paintings* | | **$220** | **$7,040** |
| American 1863-1942 | | | |
| ☐ **DAY, Herlot** ........................ *paintings* | | | **$330** |
| ☐ **DAY, Nellie M.** ..................... *paintings* | | | **$700** |
| American 19th cent. | | | |

| | | Current Price Range | |
|---|---|---|---|
| | | *Low* | *High* |
| ☐ **DAYEZ, Georges** .................................. *paintings* | | $154 | $357 |
| French b. 1907 | | | |
| ☐ **DAYNE, Edgar Alwin** .......................... *paintings* | | | $1,017 |
| American 1882-1947 | | | |
| ☐ **DE CAMP, Joseph R.** .......................... *paintings* | | $6,600 | $29,700 |
| American 1858-1923 .................................. *drawings* | | | $55 |
| ☐ **DE CAMP, Ralph Earll** ....................... *paintings* | | $605 | $1,980 |
| American 1858-1936 | | | |
| ☐ **DE CARO, Lorenzo** ............................ *paintings* | | | $2,200 |
| Italian 18th cent. | | | |
| ☐ **DE ERDELY, Francis** ........................... *paintings* | | $220 | $2,750 |
| American 1904-1959 .................................. *drawings* | | $77 | $1,100 |
| ☐ **DE FOREST, Lockwood** ....................... *paintings* | | $70 | $715 |
| American 1850-1932 | | | |
| ☐ **DE FOREST, Roy** ............................... *paintings* | | | $2,090 |
| American b. 1930 .................................... *drawings* | | | $3,080 |
| ☐ **DE FRANCA, Manuel Joachim** ............. *paintings* | | $450 | $3,300 |
| Portuguese/American 1808-1865 | | | |
| ☐ **DE GRAZIA, Ted** ................................ *paintings* | | | $1,760 |
| American b. 1909 .................................... *drawings* | | $275 | $550 |
| ☐ **DE HAVEN, Franklin** .......................... *paintings* | | $100 | $7,150 |
| Portuguese/Amererican 1865-1934 *drawings* | | $110 | $220 |
| ☐ **DE JONG, Betty** ................................. *paintings* | | | $935 |
| French/American 1886-1916 | | | |
| ☐ **DE KYLN, Charles F.** .......................... *paintings* | | $247 | $385 |
| American | | | |
| ☐ **DE MARTELLY, John S.** ...................... *paintings* | | | $2,300 |
| American b. 1903 | | | |
| ☐ **DE NIRO, Robert** ............................... *paintings* | | $385 | $1,430 |
| American b. 1922 | | | |
| ☐ **DE RIBCOWSKY, Dey** ......................... *paintings* | | $275 | $852 |
| American b. 1880 | | | |
| ☐ **DE THULSTRUP, Thure** ....................... *paintings* | | $165 | $5,225 |
| Swedish/American 1848-1930 ....................... *drawings* | | $121 | $990 |
| ☐ **DE TREVILLE** ................................... *paintings* | | $77 | $440 |
| American 19th/20th cent. | | | |
| ☐ **DE VIGNE** ....................................... *paintings* | | | $880 |
| Belgian 19th cent. | | | |
| ☐ **DE VOLL, F. Usher** ............................ *paintings* | | $99 | $2,750 |
| American 1873-1941 .................................. *drawings* | | $154 | $440 |
| ☐ **DE YONG, Joe** .................................. *paintings* | | $1,100 | $4.400 |
| American 1894-1975 .................................. *drawings* | | $77 | $825 |
| .................................................. *sculpture* | | $385 | $385 |
| ☐ **DEAKIN, Edwin** ................................ *paintings* | | $302 | $20,900 |
| American 1838-1923 .................................. *drawings* | | | $467 |
| ☐ **DEAN, Edward Clarence** ..................... *drawings* | | | $660 |
| ☐ **DEAN, Peter** .................................... *paintings* | | $247 | $770 |
| American b. 1939 | | | |

| | | | Current Price Range | |
|---|---|---|---|---|
| | | | Low | High |
| ☐ **DEAN, Walter L.** ............................ | *paintings* | | $99 | $825 |
| American 1854-1912 ................................ | *drawings* | | | $247 |
| ☐ **DEANDREA, John** ......................... | *sculpture* | | $18,700 | $30,800 |
| American b. 1941 | | | | |
| ☐ **DEANDREIS** ...................................... | *paintings* | | | $6,050 |
| Belgian 19th cent. | | | | |
| ☐ **DEANE, Dennis Wood** ...................... | *paintings* | | $140 | $1,100 |
| English 19th cent. | | | | |
| ☐ **DEANE, J.** ........................................ | *paintings* | | | $385 |
| ☐ **DEARBORN, Samuel H.** ..................... | *drawings* | | | $1,100 |
| American fl. ca. 1801-1823 | | | | |
| ☐ **DEARTH, Henry** ................................ | *paintings* | | $246 | $5,500 |
| American 1864-1918 | | | | |
| ☐ **DEBAINS, Therese** ........................... | *paintings* | | | $330 |
| French b. 1907 | | | | |
| ☐ **DEBARL(?), Frans** ............................ | *paintings* | | | $715 |
| European late 19th cent. | | | | |
| ☐ **DEBAT-PONSAN, Edouard Bernard** ..... | *paintings* | | $1,650 | $4,620 |
| French 1847-1913 | | | | |
| ☐ **DEBEREINER, G.** ............................... | *paintings* | | | $440 |
| ☐ **DEBEUL, Laurent** .............................. | *paintings* | | | $2,475 |
| Belgian 19th cent. | | | | |
| ☐ **DEBIE, C.** ......................................... | *paintings* | | | $2,090 |
| French School 19th cent. | | | | |
| ☐ **DEBLOIS, F.B.** .................................. | *paintings* | | | $495 |
| Canadian 19th cent. | | | | |
| ☐ **DEBLOIS, Francois B.** ....................... | *paintings* | | | $200 |
| Canadian c. 1829-1913 | | | | |
| ☐ **DEBRE, O.** ........................................ | *paintings* | | | $275 |
| ☐ **DEBRE, Olivier** ................................ | *paintings* | | $192 | $550 |
| French b. 1920 | | | | |
| ☐ **DEBROSSES, Jean** .............................. | *paintings* | | | $660 |
| ☐ **DEBUCOURT, Philibert Louis** .............. | *paintings* | | | $1,760 |
| French 1755-1832 | | | | |
| ☐ **DEBUELL, J.** ..................................... | *paintings* | | | $440 |
| European 19th cent. | | | | |
| ☐ **DEBUT, D.** ........................................ | *sculpture* | | | $600 |
| ☐ **DEBUT, Jean Didier** ........................... | *sculpture* | | $1,210 | $3,025 |
| French 1824-1893 | | | | |
| ☐ **DEBUT, Marcel** ................................. | *sculpture* | | | $660 |
| ☐ **DECAISNE, Henri** .............................. | *paintings* | | | $1,540 |
| Belgian 1799-1852 | | | | |
| ☐ **DECAMPS, Alexandre Gabriel** .............. | *paintings* | | $357 | $20,900 |
| French 1803-1860 ................................. | *drawings* | | $165 | $22,000 |
| ☐ **DECHAR, Peter** ................................. | *paintings* | | $1,100 | $3,850 |
| American b. 1942 | | | | |
| ☐ **DECICCO** .......................................... | *paintings* | | | $907 |
| ☐ **DECKER, Cornelis Gerritsz** .................. | *paintings* | | $6,050 | $14,300 |
| Dutch c. 1600-1678 | | | | |

| | | Current Price Range | |
| --- | --- | --- | --- |
| | | Low | High |
| ☐ **DECKER, Joseph** .................... *paintings* | | $8,250 | $38,000* |
| German/American 1853-1924 | | | |
| ☐ **DECKER, Robert M.** ...................... *paintings* | | $220 | $385 |
| American b. 1847 | | | |
| ☐ **DECOENE, Henri** ............................ *paintings* | | | $4,675 |
| Belgian 1798-1866 | | | |
| ☐ **DECOUX** ......................................... *sculpture* | | | $2,750 |
| ☐ **DECRANO, Felix** ............................ *paintings* | | | $1,045 |
| ☐ **DEDECKER, Thomas** ........................ *paintings* | | $400 | $3,250 |
| American b. 1951 | | | |
| ☐ **DEDREUX, Alfred** ........................... *paintings* | | $1,540 | $99,000 |
| French 1810-1860 ...................................... *drawings* | | $3,960 | $11,000 |
| ☐ **DEEM, George** .................................. *paintings* | | | $357 |
| American | | | |
| ☐ **DEERING, Roger** ............................ *paintings* | | | $632 |
| ☐ **DEFAUX, Alexandre** .......................... *paintings* | | $440 | $7,700 |
| French 1826-1900 | | | |
| ☐ **DEFEO, Charles** ............................... *paintings* | | | $242 |
| 1892-1978 ..................................... *drawings* | | | $275 |
| ☐ **DEFFNER, Ludwig** ........................... *paintings* | | $275 | $4,950 |
| German 19th/20th cent. | | | |
| ☐ **DEFRANCE, Leonard** ........................ *paintings* | | | $1,980 |
| Flemish 1735-1805 | | | |
| ☐ **DEFREES, T.** ..................................... *paintings* | | $495 | $605 |
| English late 19th cent. | | | |
| ☐ **DEFREES, T.** ..................................... *paintings* | | $174 | $224 |
| American late 19th cent. | | | |
| ☐ **DEFREGGER, Franz von** ..................... *paintings* | | $3,575 | $79,750 |
| German 1835-1921 | | | |
| ☐ **DEFSUALAVY, J.** ........................... *paintings* | | | $1,210 |
| European 19th cent. | | | |
| ☐ **DEGAS, Edgar** ................................. *paintings* | | $33,000 | $2,420,000 |
| French 1834-1917 ..................................... *drawings* | | $990 | $3,740,000 |
| ........................................... *sculpture* | | $20,900 | $121,000 |
| ☐ **DEGRANGE, Castex** .......................... *paintings* | | | $6,050 |
| ☐ **DEGRAVE, Jules Alex Patrouillard** ....... *paintings* | | | $1,760 |
| French 19th cent. | | | |
| ☐ **DEGREGORIO, L.** ........................... *paintings* | | | $220 |
| American 19th/20th cent. | | | |
| ☐ **DEHAUSSY, Jules Jean Baptiste** .......... *paintings* | | | $1,320 |
| French 1812-1891 | | | |
| ☐ **DEHN, Adolf Arthur** .......................... *paintings* | | $550 | $3,850 |
| American 1895-1968 ................................. *drawings* | | $110 | $2,750 |
| ☐ **DEHODENCQ, Edme Alexis Alfred** ....... *drawings* | | $110 | $990 |
| French 1822-1882 | | | |
| ☐ **DEIBL, Anton** ................................... *paintings* | | | $3,520 |
| European 19th cent. | | | |
| ☐ **DEIKER, Carl Freidrich** ..................... *paintings* | | $550 | $1,600 |
| German 1836-1892 | | | |

## World of Dance

*French Impressionist artist Edgar Degas was interested in the nature of movement
and scenes of contemporary life. He is noted for his pictures of the ballet, both in
rehearsal and performance. He is also known for his many scenes of the horse races,
of milliners and laundresses and women at their toilet, and for the many portraits of
his family and friends.*

*Many of his early works were oils, but as his eyesight began to fail later in his life,
he started to use pastel, pencil, gouache, and distemper, more fluid media which
permitted him to achieve the effects of line he was striving for.*

*Degas is also known as a sculptor of dancers, horses, and bathing nudes, but it
was not a reputation achieved during his lifetime. All but one of his sculptures were
private experiments executed in clay or plasticene and left to lie crumbling in the
studio. After his death, those which were at all intact were cast in bronze in limited
editions. Never intended for the public eye, they show his mastery of form in
movement. (Edgar Degas, "Groupe de Danseuses," charcoal with traces of blue
pastel on buff paper laid down on board, 15 x 20¾ in., Christie's,
May 16, 1985, $71,500.)*

|  | | *Current Price Range* | |
|---|---|---|---|
|  | | *Low* | *High* |
| ☐ **DEIKER, Johanne-Christian** ............... *paintings* | | | **$1,980** |
| German b. 1822 | | | |
| ☐ **DEIRA, Ernesto** ................................. *paintings* | | | **$1,320** |
| Argentinian b. 1928 | | | |
| ☐ **DEKOVL, R.** ...................................... *paintings* | | | **$440** |
| ☐ **DEL MUE, Maurice** ............................ *paintings* | | | **$660** |
| American b. 1878 | | | |

|  | | Current Price Range | |
|--|--|--------------------|--|
|  | | Low | High |
| ☐ **DELA** ................................................ *paintings* | | | **$660** |
| French 19th cent. | | | |
| ☐ **DELABRIERE, Paul Edouard** ............... *sculpture* | | **$308** | **$3,520** |
| French 1829-1912 | | | |
| ☐ **DELACHAUX, Leon** ........................... *paintings* | | **$400** | **$9,350** |
| Swiss 1850-1919 | | | |
| ☐ **DELACOUR, C.** .................................. *sculpture* | | | **$2,200** |
| ☐ **DELACROIX, Auguste** ......................... *paintings* | | **$1,870** | **$2,200** |
| French 1809-1868 | | | |
| ☐ **DELACROIX, Emilienne** ...................... *paintings* | | | **$275** |
| French b. 1893 | | | |
| ☐ **DELACROIX, Eugene** ........................... *paintings* | | **$880** | **$286,000** |
| French 1798-1863 ....................................... *drawings* | | **$44** | **$35,200** |
| ☐ **DELACROIX, Henri Eugene** ................ *paintings* | | **$4,125** | **$4,620** |
| French 1845-1930 | | | |
| ☐ **DELACROIX, Paul** ............................. *paintings* | | **$302** | **$920** |
| French 19th/20th cent. | | | |
| ☐ **DELAFOSSE, Jean Charles de** ............. *drawings* | | | **$495** |
| French 1734-1789 | | | |
| ☐ **DELAGRANGE, Leon Noel** ................. *sculpture* | | **$715** | **$825** |
| French 1872-1910 | | | |
| ☐ **DELAHOGUE, Alexis Auguste** .............. *paintings* | | **$418** | **$1,430** |
| French b. 1867 | | | |
| ☐ **DELAMAIN, Paul** ............................... *paintings* | | | **$4,180** |
| French 1821-1882 | | | |
| ☐ **DELAN, J.** ......................................... *paintings* | | | **$440** |
| European 19th cent. | | | |
| ☐ **DELANCE, Paul Louis** ......................... *paintings* | | **$330** | **$330** |
| French 1848-1924 | | | |
| ☐ **DELAND, Clyde Osmer** ........................ *paintings* | | **$55** | **$330** |
| American 1872-1947 | | | |
| ☐ **DELANEY, Beauford** ........................... *paintings* | | **$176** | **$715** |
| American 1902/10-1979 | | | |
| ☐ **DELANEY, Joseph** ............................... *paintings* | | **$600** | **$715** |
| American ................................................ *drawings* | | | **$44** |
| ☐ **DELANNOY, Maurice** ......................... *sculpture* | | | **$275** |
| ☐ **DELANO, Gerard Curtis** ...................... *paintings* | | **$15,000** | **$27,500** |
| American 1890-1972 | | | |
| ☐ **DELANOY, Hippolyte Pierre** ................ *paintings* | | **$700** | **$825** |
| French 1849-1899 | | | |
| ☐ **DELAPCHIEZ, Eugene** ......................... *sculpture* | | | **$176** |
| French 19th cent. | | | |
| ☐ **DELAPORTE, Roger** ............................. *paintings* | | | **$660** |
| French 1907-1972 | | | |
| ☐ **DELAROCHE, Paul** | | | |
| **(Hippolyte DELAROCHE)** ...................... *paintings* | | **$385** | **$660** |
| French 1797-1856 ....................................... *drawings* | | | **$6,050** |
| ☐ **DELARUE, Lucien** ............................... *paintings* | | | **$550** |
| French contemporary | | | |

| | | Current Price Range | |
|---|---|---|---|
| | | Low | High |
| ☐ **DELASALLE, Angele** .......................... *paintings* | | | $935 |
| French 19th cent. | | | |
| ☐ **DELATTRE, Henri** ........................... *paintings* | | $7,700 | $88,000 |
| French 1801-1876 | | | |
| ☐ **DELATTRE, M.** ................................ *paintings* | | | $2,310 |
| British 19th cent. | | | |
| ☐ **DELAUNAY, Jules** ........................... *paintings* | | $770 | $1,100 |
| French d. 1906 | | | |
| ☐ **DELAUNAY, Jules Elie** ........................ *drawings* | | | $286 |
| French 1828-1891 | | | |
| ☐ **DELAUNAY, Robert** .......................... *paintings* | | $33,000 | $319,000 |
| French 1885-1941 ..................................... *drawings* | | $13,200 | $38,500 |
| ☐ **DELAUNAY, Sonia** ........................... *paintings* | | $41,800 | $99,000 |
| Russian/French 1885/86-1979 ........................ *drawings* | | $550 | $25,300 |
| ☐ **DELAUNEY, Joseph** .......................... *paintings* | | | $1,430 |
| ☐ **DELAYE, Alice** ................................ *paintings* | | | $577 |
| French 1884-1963 | | | |
| ☐ **DELBEKE, Louis Auguste Corneille** ...... *paintings* | | $1,980 | $12,100 |
| Belgian 1821-1891 | | | |
| ☐ **DELBOS, Julius** ................................ *paintings* | | $100 | $2,090 |
| American b. 1879 ..................................... *drawings* | | $49 | $715 |
| ☐ **DELCOUR, Pierre** ........................... *paintings* | | $495 | $1,430 |
| French 19th cent. | | | |
| ☐ **DELCOURT** ................................... *paintings* | | | $462 |
| ☐ **DELDERENNE, Leon** .......................... *paintings* | | $357 | $495 |
| Belgian 19th/20th cent. | | | |
| ☐ **DELECLUSE, Auguste Joseph** .............. *paintings* | | | $1,375 |
| French 1855-1928 | | | |
| ☐ **DELEHAYE, F.** ................................ *paintings* | | | $715 |
| Flemish b. 1843 | | | |
| ☐ **DELEN, Dirk van** ................................ *paintings* | | | $19,800 |
| Dutch 1605-1671 | | | |
| ☐ **DELERIEVE, Albert** .......................... *paintings* | | | $990 |
| ☐ **DELERIVE, Nicolas Louis Albert** .......... *paintings* | | | $660 |
| French 18th cent. | | | |
| ☐ **DELEROISE, C.** ................................ *paintings* | | | $412 |
| American 19th cent. | | | |
| ☐ **DELESTRE, Adolphe Alexandre** ........... *paintings* | | | $20,900 |
| French 19th cent. | | | |
| ☐ **DELFAU, Andre** ................................ *paintings* | | $88 | $220 |
| French 20th cent. | | | |
| ☐ **DELFGAAUW, G.J.** ........................... *paintings* | | | $660 |
| Dutch 1882-1947 | | | |
| ☐ **DELFIN, Victor** ................................ *sculpture* | | $3,080 | $8,800 |
| Latin American | | | |
| ☐ **DELFOSSE, Auguste** .......................... *paintings* | | $1,210 | $2,420 |
| Belgium ac. 1845 | | | |
| ☐ **DELFT, Cornelis Jacobsz.** .................... *paintings* | | $9,350 | $11,550 |
| Dutch 1571-c. 1643 | | | |

|                                          |            | Current Price Range |           |
|                                          |            | Low       | High    |
|------------------------------------------|------------|-----------|-----------|
| ☐ **DELISSER, R. Lionel** ............... *drawings* |            |           | $297      |
| English 19th/20th cent.                  |            |           |           |
| ☐ **DELIUS, H.** ....................... *drawings* |            |           | $192      |
| American 19th cent.                      |            |           |           |
| ☐ **DELL'ACQUA, Cesare Felix Georges** .... *paintings* |      |           | $5,225    |
| Austrian 1821-1904                       |            |           |           |
| ☐ **DELLA GATTA, Saverio** ............ *drawings* | $192      | $1,100    |
| Italian 18th/19th cent.                  |            |           |           |
| ☐ **DELLA ROCCA, G.** ............... *paintings* |            |           | $353      |
| ☐ **DELLENBAUGH, Frederick Samuel** ..... *paintings* | $770  | $6,600    |
| American 1853-1935                       |            |           |           |
| ☐ **DELLETTER, P.** ................ *paintings* |            |           | $3,300    |
| ☐ **DELMAR, V.** ..................... *paintings* |          |           | $900      |
| ☐ **DELMOTTE, Marcel** ............. *paintings* |            |           | $825      |
| French b. 1901                           |            |           |           |
| ☐ **DELOBBE, Francois Alfred** ........ *paintings* | $660    | $5,225    |
| French 1835-1920                         |            |           |           |
| ☐ **DELORGE** ....................... *drawings* | $132      | $176      |
| American 20th cent.                      |            |           |           |
| ☐ **DELORME, Anthonie** ............. *paintings* |          |           | $2,860    |
| Dutch d. 1673                            |            |           |           |
| ☐ **DELORME, Marguerite Anne Rose** ...... *paintings* |    |           | $1,320    |
| French 1876-1946                         |            |           |           |
| ☐ **DELORME, Raphael** ............. *paintings* |           |           | $6,500    |
| French 20th cent.                        |            |           |           |
| ☐ **DELORT, Charles Edouard** ......... *paintings* | $1,320 | $41,250   |
| French 1841-1895 ....................... *drawings* | $990   | $1,650    |
| ☐ **DELPECH, Jean** ................ *drawings* |            |           | $412      |
| French 20th cent.                        |            |           |           |
| ☐ **DELPECHE, Herman** ............ *paintings* |            |           | $440      |
| ☐ **DELPY, Hippolyte Camille** ......... *paintings* | $467   | $15,400   |
| French 1842-1910                         |            |           |           |
| ☐ **DELPY, Jacques Henry** .......... *paintings* | $231     | $2,860    |
| French 1877-1957                         |            |           |           |
| ☐ **DELUCHAUX, Leon** ............. *paintings* |           |           | $660      |
| ☐ **DELVAILLE, H. Caro** ........... *paintings* |          |           | $385      |
| ☐ **DELVAUX, Paul** ............... *paintings* | $121,000  | $286,000  |
| Belgian b. 1897 ..................... *drawings* | $3,300    | $55,000   |
| ☐ **DELYEN, Jacques Francois** ....... *paintings* |        |           | $3,500    |
| French 1684-1761                         |            |           |           |
| ☐ **DEMACHY, Pierre Antoine** ........ *paintings* |        |           | $4,675    |
| French 1723-1807                         |            |           |           |
| ☐ **DEMAN, Herbert** .............. *paintings* |           |           | $467      |
| American 1855-1903                       |            |           |           |
| ☐ **DEMANET, Victor** ............. *sculpture* |           |           | $440      |
| ☐ **DEMAREST, Guillaume Albert** ......... *paintings* |    |           | $3,850    |
| French 1848-1906                         |            |           |           |
| ☐ **DEMAREST, Margaret** .......... *drawings* |            |           | $275      |
| b. 1810                                  |            |           |           |

| | | | Current Price Range | |
|---|---|---|---|---|
| | | | Low | High |
| ☐ **DEMARET, Victor** | ............................. | *sculpture* | | **$1,320** |
| ☐ **DEMARLE** | ......................................... | *paintings* | **$660** | **$770** |
| French 19th cent. | | | | |
| ☐ **DEMARNE, Jean Louis** | ....................... | *paintings* | **$700** | **$14,000** |
| French 1744 or 1754-1829 | | | | |
| ☐ **DEMARTINO, Louis** | ............................ | *sculpture* | | **$1,100** |
| ☐ **DEMEREST, Suzanne** | ......................... | *paintings* | **$192** | **$247** |
| French contemporary | | | | |
| ☐ **DEMETRIOS, G.** | .................................. | *sculpture* | | **$8,250** |
| American | | | | |
| ☐ **DEMILLE, Leslie B.** | ............................ | *paintings* | | **$1,900** |
| American b. 1927 | | | | |
| ☐ **DEMING, Edwin Willard** | ...................... | *paintings* | **$385** | **$33,000** |
| American 1860-1942 | ................................. | *drawings* | **$165** | **$3,300** |
| ☐ **DEMONCHY, Andre** | ............................ | *paintings* | **$330** | **$440** |
| French b. 1914 | | | | |
| ☐ **DEMONT-BRETON, Virginie** | .............. | *paintings* | **$4,675** | **$8,800** |
| French 1859-1935 | | | | |
| ☐ **DEMUTH, Charles** | ............................. | *paintings* | | **$9,900** |
| American 1883-1935 | ................................. | *drawings* | **$220** | **$110,000** |
| ☐ **DENAVE, Gerard Bor** | ......................... | *paintings* | | **$1,925** |
| Dutch 19th/20th cent. | | | | |
| ☐ **DENEUX, Gabriel Charles** | .................. | *paintings* | | **$8,800** |
| French b. 1856 | ......................................... | *drawings* | | **$137** |
| ☐ **DENIS** | ............................................ | *sculpture* | **$220** | **$357** |
| ☐ **DENIS, Maurice** | ................................ | *paintings* | **$880** | **$28,600** |
| French 1870-1943 | ..................................... | *drawings* | **$880** | **$990** |
| ☐ **DENISE, Ira Condit** | ........................... | *paintings* | | **$357** |
| ☐ **DENISOFF-URALSKY, A.K.** | .............. | *paintings* | | **$495** |
| Russian 19th/20th cent. | | | | |
| ☐ **DENISON, George H.** | .......................... | *paintings* | | **$320** |
| American 1867-1944 | | | | |
| ☐ **DENK, A.** | ......................................... | *paintings* | | **$440** |
| German School 19th cent. | | | | |
| ☐ **DENNER, Balthasar** | ........................... | *paintings* | | **$3,300** |
| German 1685-1749 | | | | |
| ☐ **DENNIS, J. Morgan** | ........................... | *drawings* | **$121** | **$660** |
| American b. 1891 | | | | |
| ☐ **DENNIS, J.H.** | ..................................... | *paintings* | | **$572** |
| American 20th cent. | ................................. | *drawings* | | **$192** |
| ☐ **DENNIS, L.** | ...................................... | *paintings* | **$110** | **$176** |
| American 19th/20th cent. | | | | |
| ☐ **DENNY, A.J.** | ..................................... | *paintings* | | **$715** |
| ☐ **DENNY, Gideon Jacques** | ................... | *paintings* | **$770** | **$1,870** |
| American 1830-1886 | | | | |
| ☐ **DENNY, J.C.** | ..................................... | *paintings* | **$247** | **$1,700** |
| American d. 1900 | | | | |
| ☐ **DENON** | ........................................... | *paintings* | **$550** | **$660** |
| Continental 19th cent. | | | | |

| | | Current Price Range | |
|---|---|---|---|
| | | Low | High |
| ☐ **DENOTER, David** ............................. *drawings* | | | $770 |
| ☐ **DENT, F.** ........................................... *paintings* | | | $352 |
| ☐ **DENTMANN, F.** ............................... *paintings* | | | $467 |
| European 19th cent. | | | |
| ☐ **DEPAUW, Robert** ............................. *paintings* | | | $1,045 |
| European | | | |
| ☐ **DEPELCHIN** ...................................... *paintings* | | | $605 |
| Flemish 18th cent. | | | |
| ☐ **DERAIN, Andre** .................................. *paintings* | $880 | $418,000 |
| French 1880-1954 ...................................... *drawings* | $27 | $72,600 |
| ............................................................ *sculpture* | $550 | $1,870 |
| ☐ **DERAUX, Marchand** ........................... *paintings* | | | $550 |
| French 20th cent. | | | |
| ☐ **DERENNE** ......................................... *sculpture* | $286 | $660 |
| ☐ **DERIJCKE, J.L.** ................................ *paintings* | | | $440 |
| American 20th cent. | | | |
| ☐ **DERMANCY, V.** .................................. *paintings* | | | $715 |
| ☐ **DEROUCH, Maryse** ........................... *paintings* | | | $2,640 |
| ☐ **DERRENNE** ....................................... *sculpture* | | | $770 |
| ☐ **DERREY, Jacques Charles** ................... *drawings* | $55 | $330 |
| French b. 1907 | | | |
| ☐ **DERRICK, William Rowell** ................. *paintings* | $132 | $1,100 |
| American 1858-1941 ................................... *drawings* | $250 | $357 |
| ☐ **DERUJINSKY, Gleb W.** ...................... *sculpture* | | | $1,650 |
| American | | | |
| ☐ **DERY, Koloman** ................................ *paintings* | | | $1,870 |
| Hungarian b. 1859 | | | |
| ☐ **DES CLAYES, Berthe** ......................... *drawings* | $350 | $600 |
| Canadian 20th cent. | | | |
| ☐ **DES FONTAINES, Andre** ..................... *drawings* | | | $330 |
| French b. 1869 | | | |
| ☐ **DES ISNARD, Louis Marquis** ............... *paintings* | | | $1,320 |
| French 1805-1888 | | | |
| ☐ **DESAN, Charles** ................................. *paintings* | $550 | $715 |
| Belgian 19th cent. | | | |
| ☐ **DESANDRE, Jules Marie** ..................... *paintings* | | | $2,970 |
| French 19th cent. | | | |
| ☐ **DESATNICK, Mike** ............................. *paintings* | $10,000 | $13,000 |
| American b. 1943 | | | |
| ☐ **DESCAMPS, Alexandre Gabriel** ............ *paintings* | | | $990 |
| French 1803-1860 | | | |
| ☐ **DESCH, Frank H.** .............................. *paintings* | | | $605 |
| American 20th cent. | | | |
| ☐ **DESCHAMPS, Gabriel** ......................... *paintings* | $330 | $1,320 |
| French b. 1919 | | | |
| ☐ **DESCHAMPS, Louis Henri** ................... *paintings* | | | $3,300 |
| French 1846-1902 | | | |
| ☐ **DESCHAMPS, P.** ................................ *paintings* | | | $192 |
| French 20th cent. | | | |

|  | | | *Current Price Range* | |
|--|--|--|--|--|
|  | | | *Low* | *High* |
| ☐ **DESCOMPS, J.** ..................................... *sculpture* | | | | $1,760 |
| ☐ **DESCOURS, Georges** ........................... *paintings* | | | | $577 |
| French 1890-1956 | | | | |
| ☐ **DESENFANS, Albrecht Constant** .......... *sculpture* | | | | $1,540 |
| Belgian b. 1845 | | | | |
| ☐ **DESGOFFE, Blaise** .............................. *paintings* | | | $1,100 | $9,900 |
| French 1830-1901 | | | | |
| ☐ **DESHAYES, B.** ..................................... *paintings* | | | | $528 |
| ☐ **DESHAYES, Celestin** ........................... *paintings* | | | | $550 |
| French 1817-1884 | | | | |
| ☐ **DESHAYES, Charles Felix Edouard** ...... *paintings* | | | $825 | $935 |
| French b. 1831 | | | | |
| ☐ **DESHAYES, Eugene** ........................... *paintings* | | | $385 | $4,950 |
| French 1828-1890 | | | | |
| ☐ **DESHAYES, Frederic Leon** ................. *paintings* | | | | $275 |
| ☐ **DESHAYES, Jean Baptiste** ................... *drawings* | | | | $2,750 |
| French 1729-1765 | | | | |
| ☐ **DESIMONE, Thomas** ........................... *drawings* | | | | $495 |
| American 19th/20th cent. | | | | |
| ☐ **DESIMONE, Tomaso** ........................... *drawings* | | | $625 | $1,320 |
| American | | | | |
| ☐ **DESIRE, Raymond** ............................. *paintings* | | | $330 | $522 |
| ☐ **DESKEY, Donald** ............................... *paintings* | | | | $440 |
| ☐ **DESMANNLUNG** ................................. *paintings* | | | | $495 |
| ☐ **DESMAREES, Georges** ........................ *paintings* | | | | $1,650 |
| Swedish 1697-1776 | | | | |
| ☐ **DESNOYER, Francois** ........................ *paintings* | | | | $935 |
| French 1894-1972 | | | | |
| ☐ **DESPIAU, Charles** ............................. *drawings* | | | $154 | $935 |
| French 1874-1946 ..................................... *sculpture* | | | $4,290 | $56,100 |
| ☐ **DESPIERRE, Jacques** ........................... *paintings* | | | | $220 |
| French b. 1912 | | | | |
| ☐ **DESPORTES, Alexandre Francois** ......... *paintings* | | | $13,200 | $50,600 |
| French 1661-1743 | | | | |
| ☐ **DESRAIS, Claude Louis** ...................... *drawings* | | | $1,210 | $1,430 |
| French 1746-1816 | | | | |
| ☐ **DESROUSSEAUX, Lamont** ................... *paintings* | | | | $1,650 |
| ☐ **DESSAR, Louis Paul** ........................... *paintings* | | | $440 | $2,100 |
| American 1867-1952 | | | | |
| ☐ **DESTOUCHES, Johanna von** ................ *paintings* | | | | $440 |
| German b. 1869 | | | | |
| ☐ **DESTREE, Johannes Joseph** ................ *paintings* | | | | $770 |
| ☐ **DESUBLEO, Michele** | | | | |
| (called Michele FIAMMINGO) .............. *paintings* | | | | $7,700 |
| ☐ **DESVARREUX, Raymond** ................... *paintings* | | | $1,210 | $2,420 |
| French 1876-1961 | | | | |
| ☐ **DESVARREUX-LARPENTEUR,** | | | | |
| **James** .................................................. *paintings* | | | $200 | $1,540 |
| American b. 1847 | | | | |

| | Current Price Range | |
|---|---|---|
| | *Low* | *High* |

| | | | |
|---|---|---|---|
| ☐ **DESVIGNES, Herbert Clayton** ............. *paintings* | | | $3,300 |
| English 19th cent. | | | |
| ☐ **DETAILLE, Jean Baptiste Edouard** ....... *paintings* | | $660 | $8,800 |
| French 1848-1912 ..................................... *drawings* | | $220 | $6,050 |
| ☐ **DETHLOFF, Peter Hans** ...................... *drawings* | | | $220 |
| American b. 1869 | | | |
| ☐ **DETJENS, H.** ..................................... *paintings* | | | $385 |
| Dutch 19th cent. | | | |
| ☐ **DETMOLD, Charles Maurice** ............... *drawings* | | $440 | $990 |
| English 1883-1908 | | | |
| ☐ **DETMOLD, Henry E.** ......................... *paintings* | | | $440 |
| British b. 1854 | | | |
| ☐ **DETRIER, Pierre Louis** ........................ *sculpture* | | | $1,760 |
| French 1822-1897 | | | |
| ☐ **DETROY, Leon** ................................... *paintings* | | | $980 |
| ☐ **DETTI, Cesare Auguste** ....................... *paintings* | | $1,100 | $35,200 |
| Italian 1847-1914 ..................................... *drawings* | | $440 | $1,980 |
| ☐ **DETTMAN, W.** ................................... *paintings* | | | $330 |
| German 20th cent. | | | |
| ☐ **DETTMANN, Ludwig Julius Christian** .. *drawings* | | | $330 |
| European | | | |
| ☐ **DETTMER, A.** ..................................... *paintings* | | | $880 |
| German 19th cent. | | | |
| ☐ **DETWILLER, Frederick K.** .................. *paintings* | | $176 | $800 |
| American ................................................. *drawings* | | | $143 |
| ☐ **DEULLY, Eugene Auguste Francois** ...... *paintings* | | | $9,350 |
| French b. 1860 | | | |
| ☐ **DEURER, Peter Ferdinand** ................... *paintings* | | | $495 |
| German 1777-1884 | | | |
| ☐ **DEUTMANN, Frans** ............................ *paintings* | | | $825 |
| ................................................................. *drawings* | | | $550 |
| ☐ **DEUTSCH, Boris** ................................ *paintings* | | $275 | $522 |
| Russian/American b. 1895 ........................... *drawings* | | | $165 |
| ☐ **DEUTSCH, Ludwig** ............................ *paintings* | | $1,485 | $220,000 |
| Austrian b. 1855 | | | |
| ☐ **DEUUS, Jesus** .................................... *paintings* | | | $715 |
| Mexican 20th cent. | | | |
| ☐ **DEVAMBEZ, Andre Victor Edouard** ..... *paintings* | | $82 | $1,320 |
| French 1867-1943 | | | |
| ☐ **DEVAULX** ......................................... *sculpture* | | | $2,090 |
| ☐ **DEVAUX, T.** ....................................... *paintings* | | | $385 |
| French School 19th cent. | | | |
| ☐ **DEVEDEUX, Louis** ............................ *paintings* | | $330 | $1,210 |
| French 1820-1874 | | | |
| ☐ **DEVEIQUE, J.** .................................... *paintings* | | | $22,000 |
| British 19th cent. | | | |
| ☐ **DEVELLY** ......................................... *drawings* | | | $1,430 |
| ☐ **DEVENTER, C.** .................................. *paintings* | | $1,100 | $1,100 |
| English School 19th cent. | | | |

| | | Current Price Range | |
|---|---|---|---|
| | | *Low* | *High* |
| ☐ **DEVENTER, Willem Antonie van** ......... *paintings* | | | $880 |
| ☐ **DEVEREAUX, Charles** ......................... *paintings* | | | $1,540 |
| ☐ **DEVERGER, Emmanuel Theophile** ....... *paintings* | | | $3,300 |
| French b. 1821 | | | |
| ☐ **DEVERIA, Achille Jacques Jean Marie** .. *drawings* | | $231 | $1,650 |
| French 1800-1857 | | | |
| ☐ **DEVERIA,** | | | |
| **Eugene Francois Marie Joseph** .............. *drawings* | | $242 | $1,980 |
| French 1805/8-1865 | | | |
| ☐ **DEVERIN, Roger** ................................. *paintings* | | | $300 |
| French b. 1884 | | | |
| ☐ **DEVEUX** ............................................. *paintings* | | | $715 |
| European 19th cent. | | | |
| ☐ **DEVICH, John** .................................... *paintings* | | | $250 |
| American | | | |
| ☐ **DEVIS, Arthur** ................................... *paintings* | | | $5,500 |
| English | | | |
| ☐ **DEVITY, A.** ........................................ *paintings* | | $198 | $522 |
| Italian contemporary | | | |
| ☐ **DEVLAN, Francis Daniel** ...................... *paintings* | | | $715 |
| American 1835-1870 | | | |
| ☐ **DEVORSS, Billy** ................................. *drawings* | | | $275 |
| ☐ **DEVOS, Corneille** ............................... *paintings* | | | $1,760 |
| Flemish 19th cent. | | | |
| ☐ **DEVOS, Vincent** ................................. *paintings* | | | $2,420 |
| Belgian 1829-1875 | | | |
| ☐ **DEVRIEZ** ........................................... *sculpture* | | | $1,100 |
| ☐ **DEWASNE, Jean** ................................. *drawings* | | | $2,640 |
| French b. 1921 | | | |
| ☐ **DEWEY, C.H.** ..................................... *paintings* | | | $3,300 |
| ☐ **DEWEY, Charles Melville** ...................... *paintings* | | $412 | $2,420 |
| American 1849-1937 ................................... *drawings* | | | $192 |
| ☐ **DEWEY, David** .................................... *drawings* | | | $1,430 |
| American b. 1946 | | | |
| ☐ **DEWEY, Edward H.** ............................ *paintings* | | | $2,530 |
| American 1850-1939 | | | |
| ☐ **DEWEY, James** .................................. *paintings* | | $440 | $880 |
| American 19th/20th cent. | | | |
| ☐ **DEWEY, Julia Henshaw** ....................... *paintings* | | | $192 |
| American d. 1928 | | | |
| ☐ **DEWILDE, J.** ...................................... *paintings* | | | $385 |
| Dutch 19th cent. | | | |
| ☐ **DEWING, Maria Richards Oakey** ......... *paintings* | | | $935 |
| American 1845-1927 | | | |
| ☐ **DEWING, R.A.** .................................... *paintings* | | | $375 |
| American 19th/20th cent. | | | |
| ☐ **DEWING, Thomas Wilmer** ................... *paintings* | | $6,600 | $13,200 |
| American 1851-1938 ................................... *drawings* | | $9,020 | $22,000 |

| | | Current Price Range | |
|---|---|---|---|
| | | Low | High |

☐ **DEWIT, Jacob** ...................................... *paintings* | | **$2,750**
Dutch 19th cent.

☐ **DEWITT, Jerome Pennington** ............... *paintings* | | **$220**
American 1895-1940

☐ **DEWOLF, Johannes Petrus** .................. *paintings* | | **$550**
Dutch 19th cent.

☐ **DEZARATE, Manuel Oritz** .................. *drawings* | | **$330**
French 1886-1946

☐ **DHURMER, Lucien Levy** ...................... *drawings* | | **$440**
French 1865-1953

☐ **DI CAVALCANTI, Emiliano** ............... *paintings* | **$2,420** | **$67,100**
Brazilian b. 1897 ...................................... *drawings* | **$550** | **$18,700**

☐ **DI GIORGIO, Joseph** ........................... *drawings* | | **$330**

☐ **DI GIOVANNI, Bartolommeo** ............... *paintings* | | **$33,000**
Italian

☐ **DI PIETRO, Sano** ................................ *paintings* | | **$14,300**

☐ **DI SUVERO, Mark** ............................. *drawings* | **$990** | **$1,430**
American b. 1933 ...................................... *sculpture* | **$1,320** | **$41,800**

☐ **DI VALENTIN, Louis** ......................... *paintings* | | **$330**
American b. 1908

☐ **DI VOLO, Silvio** ................................ *paintings* | | **$1,760**
Italian b. 1907

☐ **DIAGO, Roberto** ................................. *drawings* | | **$935**
b. Cuba 1920-1955

☐ **DIAKOFF, G.** ...................................... *paintings* | | **$3,520**

☐ **DIAMONDSTEIN, Norton** .................... *sculpture* | | **$275**
contemporary

☐ **DIAO, David** ...................................... *paintings* | **$300** | **$850**

☐ **DIART, Jules Edouard** ........................ *paintings* | **$660** | **$4,950**
French 19th cent.

☐ **DIAS, Cecilio** ...................................... *paintings* | | **$1,650**
Brazilian b. 1908

☐ **DIAZ** .................................................. *paintings* | | **$3,850**
French 19th cent.

☐ **DIAZ, Gumersindo** ............................. *paintings* | | **$302**
Spanish 1841-1891

☐ **DIAZ, Luis** ........................................ *paintings* | | **$5,060**
Spanish 19th cent.

☐ **DIAZ, N.** ............................................ *paintings* | **$302** | **$325**

☐ **DIAZ DE LA PENA, Narcisse Virgile** .... *paintings* | **$198** | **$34,100**
French 1807-1876 ...................................... *drawings* | | **$1,540**

☐ **DIBDIN, Thomas Colman** ..................... *drawings* | **$220** | **$2,200**
English 1810-1893

☐ **DICK, H.R.** ........................................ *paintings* | | **$2,750**
American

☐ **DICK, M.G.** ........................................ *paintings* | | **$357**
American 19th/20th cent.

☐ **DICKERMAN, Albert** ........................... *paintings* | | **$2,750**
American 19th/20th cent.

| | | *Current Price Range* | |
|---|---|---|---|
| | | *Low* | *High* |
| ☐ **DICKEY, W. Winthrop** ........................ *paintings* | | | $325 |
| ☐ **DICKINSON, Darol** ............................. *paintings* | | | $3,000 |
| American b. 1942 | | | |
| ☐ **DICKINSON, Edwin W.** ....................... *paintings* | | $4,125 | $10,450 |
| American 1891-1979 | | | |
| ☐ **DICKINSON, Howard Clinton** ............. *paintings* | | $99 | $412 |
| American 20th cent. | | | |
| ☐ **DICKINSON, J.S.** ............................... *paintings* | | | $200 |
| American 19th cent. | | | |
| ☐ **DICKINSON, John R.** ......................... *drawings* | | | $220 |
| English late 19th cent. | | | |
| ☐ **DICKINSON, Preston** ........................... *paintings* | | $440 | $18,700 |
| American 1891-1930 ................................. *drawings* | | $495 | $6,325 |
| ☐ **DICKMAN** ...................................... *paintings* | | | $424 |
| 19th/20th cent. | | | |
| ☐ **DICKSEE, Frank Bernard** .................... *paintings* | | | $5,775 |
| British 1853-1928 | | | |
| ☐ **DICKSON** ........................................ *paintings* | | | $605 |
| American 19th/20th cent. | | | |
| ☐ **DIDAY, Francois** ............................... *paintings* | | | $4,950 |
| Swiss 1802-1877 | | | |
| ☐ **DIDIER, Clovis Francois Auguste** .......... *paintings* | | $7,425 | $8,800 |
| French b. 1858 | | | |
| ☐ **DIDIER, Jules** .................................. *paintings* | | $770 | $2,200 |
| French 1831-1892 | | | |
| ☐ **DIDIER-POUGET, William** ................... *paintings* | | $660 | $3,080 |
| French 1864-1959 | | | |
| ☐ **DIDIONI, Francesco** ........................... *drawings* | | | $192 |
| Italian 1859-1895 | | | |
| ☐ **DIDONATO** ..................................... *sculpture* | | | $275 |
| ☐ **DIEBENKORN, Richard** ....................... *paintings* | | $7,700 | $440,000 |
| American b. 1922 ..................................... *drawings* | | $3,630 | $79,750 |
| ....................................................... *sculpture* | | | $1,430 |
| ☐ **DIEBOLT, George** .............................. *sculpture* | | | $550 |
| French mid 19th cent. | | | |
| ☐ **DIEDERICH, Wilhelm Hunt** ................. *sculpture* | | | $4,070 |
| American b. 1884 | | | |
| ☐ **DIEFFENBACH, Anton** ......................... *paintings* | | $1,650 | $4,290 |
| German 1831-1914 | | | |
| ☐ **DIEFFENBACHER, August Wilhelm** .... *paintings* | | | $301 |
| ☐ **DIEGEM, H. van** ............................... *paintings* | | | $935 |
| ☐ **DIEGHEM, A. van** ............................. *paintings* | | | $1,045 |
| Dutch fl. 1864-1909 | | | |
| ☐ **DIEGHEM, Jacob van** ......................... *paintings* | | $440 | $3,300 |
| Dutch 19th cent. | | | |
| ☐ **DIEGHEM, Joseph van** ........................ *paintings* | | | $13,020 |
| ☐ **DIEHL, Arthur Vidal** .......................... *paintings* | | $90 | $825 |
| American 1870-1929 | | | |

| | | Current Price Range | |
|---|---|---|---|
| | | Low | High |
| ☐ **DIEHL-WALLENDORF, Hans** ............ *paintings* | | | $275 |
| German b. 1877 | | | |
| ☐ **DIELMAN, Frederick** .......................... *drawings* | | $137 | $5,000 |
| German/American 1847/48-1935 | | | |
| ☐ **DIELMAN, Pierre Emmanuel** ............... *paintings* | | $2,860 | $3,025 |
| Belgian 1800-1858 | | | |
| ☐ **DIELMANN, Jacob Furchtegott** ............ *drawings* | | | $3,250 |
| German 1809-1885 | | | |
| ☐ **DIELZE, Carl** ..................................... *paintings* | | | $1,100 |
| ☐ **DIEMER, Michael Zeno** ...................... *paintings* | | $200 | $1,100 |
| German 1867-1929/39 | | | |
| ☐ **DIEPRAEM, Abraham** ......................... *paintings* | | $400 | $8,900 |
| Dutch 1622-1670 | | | |
| ☐ **DIEST, Adriaen van** ........................... *paintings* | | | $2,200 |
| Dutch 1655-1704 | | | |
| ☐ **DIEST, Jeronimus van** ........................ *paintings* | | | $30,800 |
| Dutch 1631?-1673 | | | |
| ☐ **DIEST, Johan van** ............................. *paintings* | | | $1,320 |
| Dutch 17th/18th cent. | | | |
| ☐ **DIETERLE, Marie** ............................. *paintings* | | $1,210 | $3,300 |
| French 1856-1935 | | | |
| ☐ **DIETLER, Johann Friedrich** ............... *paintings* | | | $385 |
| ........................................................... *drawings* | | | $770 |
| ☐ **DIETMAR, Oscar** ............................. *paintings* | | | $550 |
| German 19th cent. | | | |
| ☐ **DIETRICH, Adelheid** ......................... *paintings* | | $27,500 | $63,250 |
| German b. 1827 | | | |
| ☐ **DIETRICH, Adolf** .............................. *paintings* | | | $7,150 |
| Swiss 1877-1957 | | | |
| ☐ **DIETRICH, Christian Wilhelm Ernst** .... *paintings* | | $660 | $12,650 |
| German 1712-1774 ................................... *drawings* | | $220 | $660 |
| ☐ **DIETZ, O.** ........................................ *paintings* | | | $247 |
| late 19th cent. | | | |
| ☐ **DIETZ, W.** ........................................ *paintings* | | | $175 |
| American (?) 19th cent. | | | |
| ☐ **DIETZSCH, Barbara Regina** ............... *drawings* | | | $4,200 |
| German 1706-1783 | | | |
| ☐ **DIETZSCH, Johann Christoph** ............. *drawings* | | $330 | $1,760 |
| ☐ **DIETZSCH, Johann Jakob** ................. *drawings* | | | $2,750 |
| ☐ **DIEY, Yves** ...................................... *paintings* | | $522 | $715 |
| French 20th cent. | | | |
| ☐ **DIGHTON, Richard** ........................... *drawings* | | $165 | $220 |
| British 1785-1880 | | | |
| ☐ **DIJSSEHOF, G. W.** ............................ *paintings* | | | $990 |
| European | | | |
| ☐ **DIKE, Philip Latimer** ......................... *drawings* | | $192 | $330 |
| American b. 1906 | | | |
| ☐ **DILL, Bryan** ...................................... *paintings* | | | $247 |
| English 19th cent. | | | |

## Mysterious Still Life Painter

*Adelheid Dietrich, born in 1827 in Germany, was well known for her paintings of flowers and fruit. The daughter of painter Eduard Dietrich, she travelled to Italy and Germany. Oils and watercolors by A. Dietrich were exhibited at the Brooklyn Art Association from 1866 to 1873 and again in 1875. In 1875, 1880 to 1881, and 1893 her works were shown in the San Francisco area. Did she travel to the United States? Did she live in New York or San Francisco? Were her works perhaps brought to this country by collectors? Her meticulously executed oils sell from $27,000 to $63,000, and yet little is known. (Adelheid Dietrich, "Still Life With Flowers," oil on panel, 10¾ x 7¾ in., Butterfield, June 20, 1985, $35,750.)*

| | | Current Price Range | |
|---|---|---|---|
| | | *Low* | *High* |
| ☐ **DILL, Ludwig** .................................... *paintings* | | **$1,540** | **$5,225** |
| German 1848-1940 .................................... *drawings* | | | **$357** |
| ☐ **DILL, Otto** ........................................ *paintings* | | | **$6,050** |
| German 1884-1957 .................................... *drawings* | | **$880** | **$1,045** |
| ☐ **DILL-MALBURG, J.** ........................ *paintings* | | | **$220** |
| German 19th/20th cent. | | | |
| ☐ **DILLAWAY, Theodore M.** ................... *paintings* | | **$40** | **$412** |
| American b. 1874 | | | |
| ☐ **DILLENS, Adolf** ................................ *paintings* | | **$605** | **$3,850** |
| Belgian 1821-1877 | | | |
| ☐ **DILLER, Burgoyne** ............................ *paintings* | | **$18,700** | **$35,200** |
| American 1906-1965 ................................. *drawings* | | **$4,620** | **$6,380** |
| ☐ **DILLER, H.** ........................................ *sculpture* | | | **$350** |
| ☐ **DILLEY, Ramon** ................................ *paintings* | | **$110** | **$495** |
| ☐ **DILLON, A.** ........................................ *paintings* | | | **$357** |
| ☐ **DILLON, Frank** ................................ *paintings* | | | **$250** |
| British 1823-1909 | | | |

| | | | *Current Price Range* | |
| | | | *Low* | *High* |
| ☐ **DILLON (?), T.C.** .............. *drawings* | | | | $220 |
| English 19th cent. | | | | |
| ☐ **DILLWORTH, C.** .............. *paintings* | | | | $500 |
| American 19th cent. | | | | |
| ☐ **DINE, Jim** ...................... *paintings* | | | $2,530 | $66,000 |
| American b. 1935 ................... *drawings* | | | $660 | $60,500 |
| ............................... *sculpture* | | | | $14,300 |
| ☐ **DINET, E.** ....................... *paintings* | | | | $495 |
| ☐ **DINGER, Otto** ................. *paintings* | | | $110 | $330 |
| German b. 1860 | | | | |
| ☐ **DINGLE, Thomas** ............. *paintings* | | | | $385 |
| ☐ **DINNERSTEIN, Harvey** ...... *drawings* | | | | $187 |
| American b. 1928 | | | | |
| ☐ **DIRANIAN, Serkis** ........... *paintings* | | | $352 | $2,420 |
| Turkish 19th cent. | | | | |
| ☐ **DIRKS, Rudolph** .............. *drawings* | | | $60 | $192 |
| American 1877-1968 | | | | |
| ☐ **DISLER, Martin** .............. *paintings* | | | | $9,900 |
| contemporary ....................... *drawings* | | | $1,045 | $1,540 |
| ☐ **DISNEY,** | | | | |
| **see WALT DISNEY PRODUCTIONS** | | | | |
| ☐ **DISPO, J.L.** .................... *paintings* | | | | $247 |
| Dutch 20th cent. | | | | |
| ☐ **DITSCHEINER, Adolf Gustave** ...... *paintings* | | | | $1,320 |
| German 1846-1904 | | | | |
| ☐ **DITTEN, J.V.** ................... *paintings* | | | | $1,650 |
| Scandinavian School 19th cent. | | | | |
| ☐ **DITTMAN, E.** ................... *paintings* | | | | $660 |
| ☐ **DITTMANN, Johan** ............ *paintings* | | | | $330 |
| Austrian d. 1847 | | | | |
| ☐ **DITZLER, H.** .................... *paintings* | | | | $275 |
| 19th cent. | | | | |
| ☐ **DIULGHEROFF, Nicolay** ...... *paintings* | | | $1,980 | $2,750 |
| Italian b. 1901 ..................... *drawings* | | | $1,650 | $3,080 |
| ☐ **DIVRAS, F.** ..................... *paintings* | | | | $770 |
| ☐ **DIX, Charles** .................. *paintings* | | | $82 | $275 |
| American 1838-1872/73 ........... *drawings* | | | $110 | $181 |
| ☐ **DIX, Otto** ...................... *drawings* | | | $1,430 | $13,200 |
| German 1891-1969 | | | | |
| ☐ **DIXON, Arthur A.** ............ *drawings* | | | | $550 |
| British fl. 1892-1927 | | | | |
| ☐ **DIXON, Charles** ............... *paintings* | | | | $605 |
| British 1872-1934 ................. *drawings* | | | $350 | $1,650 |
| ☐ **DIXON, Emily** ................. *paintings* | | | $825 | $880 |
| British 19th cent. | | | | |
| ☐ **DIXON, Francis Stillwell** ...... *paintings* | | | $33 | $1,210 |
| American 1879-1967 | | | | |
| ☐ **DIXON, Harley** ............... *drawings* | | | | $550 |

| | | | *Current Price Range* | |
|---|---|---|---|---|
| | | | *Low* | *High* |
| ☐ **DIXON, Lafayette Maynard** | ................. | *paintings* | $715 | $44,000 |
| American 1875-1946 | ................................. | *drawings* | $110 | $8,800 |
| ☐ **DIZIANI, Gaspare** | ................. | *paintings* | | $14,000 |
| Italian 1689-1767 | | | | |
| ☐ **DJABIAN, M.** | ...................... | *paintings* | | $374 |
| ☐ **DMITRIEV-ORENBURGSKY,** | | | | |
| **Nikolai Dmitrievich** | ............................ | *paintings* | | $3,300 |
| Russian 1838-1898 | | | | |
| ☐ **DOBBIN, John** | ...................... | *drawings* | | $385 |
| British 1815-1884 | | | | |
| ☐ **DOBKIN, Alexander** | ........................... | *paintings* | | $240 |
| Italian/American 1908-1975 | | | | |
| ☐ **DOBOUJINSKY, Mstislav** | ................. | *paintings* | | $3,300 |
| Russian 1875-1957 | ..................................... | *drawings* | $220 | $2,420 |
| ☐ **DOBSON, Henry John** | ................. | *paintings* | $165 | $522 |
| Scottish 1858-1928 | | | | |
| ☐ **DOBSON, Robert** | ...................... | *drawings* | | $192 |
| British 19th/20th cent. | | | | |
| ☐ **DOBSON, William Charles Thomas** | ....... | *paintings* | $176 | $1,650 |
| German/English 1817-1898 | ........................... | *drawings* | $330 | $528 |
| ☐ **DOCHARTY, Alexander Brownlie** | ......... | *paintings* | | $2,310 |
| British b. 1862 | | | | |
| ☐ **DOCHARTY, James** | ........................... | *paintings* | $275 | $330 |
| Scottish 1829-1878 | | | | |
| ☐ **DOCHLEIN (?), Elsie** | ................. | *paintings* | | $1,980 |
| German 19th cent. | | | | |
| ☐ **DOCKREE, M.I.** | ...................... | *paintings* | | $500 |
| ☐ **DOCKREE, Mark Edwin** | ...................... | *paintings* | | $900 |
| British 19th cent. | | | | |
| ☐ **DODD, Arthur Charles** | ........................ | *paintings* | | $1,100 |
| British ac. 1878-1890 | | | | |
| ☐ **DODD, Lamar** | ..................................... | *paintings* | $1,210 | $1,870 |
| American b. 1909 | | | | |
| ☐ **DODD, Robert** | ..................................... | *paintings* | $9,350 | $26,400 |
| English 1748-1816 | | | | |
| ☐ **DODGE, J.F.** | ..................................... | *drawings* | | $825 |
| English 19th cent. | | | | |
| ☐ **DODGE, John Wood** | ........................... | *paintings* | | $605 |
| American 1807-1893 | | | | |
| ☐ **DODGE, William de Leftwich** | ............... | *paintings* | $495 | $8,250 |
| American 1867-1935 | | | | |
| ☐ **DODGSON, George Haydock** | ............... | *drawings* | | $1,320 |
| British 1811-1880 | | | | |
| ☐ **DODSON, Richard Whatcoat** | ................ | *drawings* | | $577 |
| American 1812-1867 | | | | |
| ☐ **DODSON, Sarah Ball** | ........................... | *paintings* | $1,430 | $2,200 |
| American 1847-1906 | | | | |
| ☐ **DOES, Simon van der** | ........................... | *paintings* | | $2,750 |
| Dutch 1653-1717 | | | | |

| | | Current Price Range | |
|---|---|---|---|
| | | Low | High |
| ☐ **DOFFLEMEYER** ............................... *paintings* | | | **$412** |
| American 19th/20th cent. | | | |
| ☐ **DOHANOS, Stevan** ............................ *paintings* | | **$440** | **$9,350** |
| American b. 1907 ...................................... *drawings* | | **$825** | **$1,540** |
| ☐ **DOLCI, Carlo** ...................................... *paintings* | | **$412** | **$18,700** |
| Italian 1616-1686 | | | |
| ☐ **DOLE, William** ................................... *drawings* | | | **$825** |
| ☐ **DOLGAN, Feliks** ................................ *paintings* | | | **$440** |
| Polish 20th cent. | | | |
| ☐ **DOLICE, Leon** .................................... *paintings* | | **$121** | **$528** |
| American 20th cent. ................................ *drawings* | | **$116** | **$352** |
| ☐ **DOLL, A.** ............................................. *drawings* | | | **$715** |
| ☐ **DOLL, Anton** ...................................... *paintings* | | **$1,760** | **$15,400** |
| German 1826-1887 | | | |
| ☐ **DOLLMAN, John Charles** ............... *paintings* | | | **$3,300** |
| English 1851-1934 ................................... *drawings* | | | **$82** |
| ☐ **DOLPH, John Henry** ........................... *paintings* | | **$253** | **$12,650** |
| American 1835-1903 | | | |
| ☐ **DOMAIGE, Etienne Henry** ................. *sculpture* | | | **$264** |
| French late 19th cent. | | | |
| ☐ **DOMBA, R.** ......................................... *paintings* | | **$440** | **$660** |
| Italian (?) 19th cent. | | | |
| ☐ **DOMBROWSKI, Carl Ritter von** .......... *paintings* | | | **$550** |
| Austrian 19th cent. | | | |
| ☐ **DOMELA, Cesar** ................................. *drawings* | | **$1,210** | **$1,320** |
| Dutch b. 1900 | | | |
| ☐ **DOMENECH** ....................................... *sculpture* | | | **$660** |
| French 19th cent. | | | |
| ☐ **DOMENICHINO,** | | | |
| **(called Domenico ZAMPIERI)** ............... *drawings* | | | **$1,870** |
| Italian 1581-1641 | | | |
| ☐ **DOMENICI, Carlo** ............................... *paintings* | | **$1,100** | **$1,210** |
| Italian b. 1898 | | | |
| ☐ **DOMERGUE, Jean Gabriel** ................. *paintings* | | **$330** | **$3,520** |
| French 1889-1962 | | | |
| ☐ **DOMICENT, Martin** ............................ *paintings* | | **$330** | **$500** |
| Flemish b. 1823 | | | |
| ☐ **DOMINGO, Claudius** ........................... *paintings* | | | **$325** |
| ☐ **DOMINGO Y FALLOLA, Roberto** ........ *drawings* | | **$1,320** | **$2,530** |
| Spanish 1867-1956 | | | |
| ☐ **DOMINGO Y MARQUES, Francisco** .... *paintings* | | **$850** | **$14,300** |
| Spanish 1842-1920 | | | |
| ☐ **DOMINGO Y MUNOZ, Francesco** ........ *paintings* | | | **$12,100** |
| ☐ **DOMINGO Y MUNOZ, Jose** ................. *paintings* | | **$935** | **$3,850** |
| Spanish b. 1843 | | | |
| ☐ **DOMINGUEZ, Jose Becquer** ............... *paintings* | | | **$1,980** |
| ☐ **DOMINGUEZ, Oscar** ........................... *paintings* | | **$1,870** | **$5,500** |
| ............................................................. *drawings* | | **$605** | **$715** |

| | | *Current Price Range* | |
|---|---|---|---|
| | | *Low* | *High* |
| ☐ **DOMINICIS, Achille de** ........................ *paintings* | | | **$2,420** |
| Italian 19th cent. | | | |
| ☐ **DOMINIQUE, A.** ............................... *paintings* | | | **$2,420** |
| European late 19th cent. | | | |
| ☐ **DOMINIQUE, S.** ............................... *paintings* | | | **$550** |
| ☐ **DOMINIUZ, A. de** ............................. *drawings* | | | **$990** |
| Italian 19th cent. | | | |
| ☐ **DOMMERS, William** ........................... *paintings* | | | **$2,200** |
| European 19th cent. | | | |
| ☐ **DOMMERSEN, Pieter Christian** ........... *paintings* | | **$660** | **$7,700** |
| Dutch 1834-1908 | | | |
| ☐ **DOMMERSEN, William R.** ................. *paintings* | | **$440** | **$9,350** |
| Dutch d. 1927 | | | |
| ☐ **DOMMERSHUIZEN,** | | | |
| **Cornelis Christian** ............................... *paintings* | | **$880** | **$13,200** |
| Dutch 1842-1928 | | | |
| ☐ **DOMMERSON, William** ....................... *paintings* | | **$440** | **$9,350** |
| English 19th cent. | | | |
| ☐ **DOMOND, Wilmino** ........................... *paintings* | | **$825** | **$2,750** |
| Haitian b. 1925 | | | |
| ☐ **DOMOTO, Hisao** .............................. *paintings* | | | **$5,775** |
| Japanese b. 1928 | | | |
| ☐ **DONADONI, Stefano** .......................... *paintings* | | | **$2,310** |
| Italian 1844-1911 ...................................... *drawings* | | | **$250** |
| ☐ **DONAGHY, John** .............................. *paintings* | | **$715** | **$3,080** |
| American 1838-1931 | | | |
| ☐ **DONALDSON, Andrew Benjamin** ......... *paintings* | | **$330** | **$550** |
| British 1840-1919 | | | |
| ☐ **DONAT, F.R.** .................................... *paintings* | | **$300** | **$1,430** |
| Belgian (?) 19th cent. | | | |
| ☐ **DONAT, M.** ..................................... *paintings* | | **$302** | **$880** |
| Belgian mid 19th cent. | | | |
| ☐ **DONATI, Enrico** ............................... *paintings* | | **$385** | **$3,850** |
| Italian/American b. 1909 .......................... *drawings* | | | **$11,000** |
| ☐ **DONATI, L.** ..................................... *paintings* | | | **$440** |
| Italian 20th cent. | | | |
| ☐ **DONATI, Lazzaro** ............................. *paintings* | | **$275** | **$1,045** |
| Italian b. 1926 | | | |
| ☐ **DONATINI, B.** ................................... *paintings* | | | **$385** |
| ☐ **DONAVAN, C. V.** ............................. *paintings* | | | **$528** |
| ☐ **DONCK, G\*\*\*** ................................... *paintings* | | **$3,300** | **$14,850** |
| 17th cent. | | | |
| ☐ **DONCK, Gerrit** ............................... *paintings* | | | **$6,600** |
| ☐ **DONCKER, Herman Mignerts** .............. *paintings* | | | **$29,700** |
| Dutch c. 1620-c. 1656 | | | |
| ☐ **DONCRE,** | | | |
| **Guillaume Dominique Jacques** .............. *paintings* | | | **$16,500** |
| French 1743-1820 | | | |

| | | *Current Price Range* | |
|---|---|---|---|
| | | *Low* | *High* |
| ☐ **DONGEN, Hendrick van** ....................... *paintings* | | | $330 |
| Dutch 20th cent. | | | |
| ☐ **DONGEN, Kees van** ...................... *paintings* | | $3,300 | $363,000 |
| Dutch/French 1877-1968 ........................... *drawings* | | $418 | $50,600 |
| ☐ **DONNALLY, Thomas** ...................... *paintings* | | | $176 |
| American | | | |
| ☐ **DONNATUS, B.** ................................ *paintings* | | | $440 |
| ☐ **DONNE, J.M.** ................................... *paintings* | | | $770 |
| British 19th cent. | | | |
| ☐ **DONNELL, Carson** ........................... *paintings* | | $143 | $275 |
| American b. 1886 | | | |
| ☐ **DONNELL, John** ............................... *paintings* | | | $319 |
| American early 20th cent. | | | |
| ☐ **DONNISON, Phil** .............................. *paintings* | | | $325 |
| ☐ **DONOHO, Gaines Ruger** ...................... *paintings* | | $412 | $6,875 |
| American 1857-1916 ................................ *drawings* | | $132 | $137 |
| ☐ **DONOVAN, J.** ................................... *paintings* | | | $632 |
| English 19th cent. | | | |
| ☐ **DONZEL, Charles** ............................ *drawings* | | | $660 |
| French 1824-1889 | | | |
| ☐ **DOOLJEWARD, Jacob** ........................ *paintings* | | $440 | $650 |
| Dutch b. 1876 | | | |
| ☐ **DOORE, C.** ...................................... *paintings* | | | $220 |
| contemporary | | | |
| ☐ **DOORNIK, G. van** ............................. *paintings* | | | $385 |
| ☐ **DOPPELMAYR, Friedrich Wilhelm** ...... *drawings* | | | $825 |
| ☐ **DORAT, M.** ..................................... *paintings* | | | $330 |
| ☐ **DORAZIO, Piero** .............................. *paintings* | | $1,980 | $3,410 |
| Italian b. 1927 | | | |
| ☐ **DORCE, Jacque** ................................ *paintings* | | $220 | $660 |
| ☐ **DORE, Gustave** ................................ *paintings* | | $1,430 | $88,000 |
| French 1832-1883 .................................... *drawings* | | $330 | $11,000 |
| ☐ **DORIAN, C.S.** ................................... *paintings* | | | $990 |
| 19th/20th cent. | | | |
| ☐ **DORIANI, William** ............................ *paintings* | | | $220 |
| Russian/American b. 1893 | | | |
| ☐ **DORIEL, L.** ..................................... *paintings* | | | $385 |
| French 19th cent. | | | |
| ☐ **DORIES, L.** ...................................... *paintings* | | | $825 |
| French 19th cent. | | | |
| ☐ **DORINZ, D.** ..................................... *drawings* | | | $660 |
| ☐ **DORION, C.S.** .................................. *paintings* | | | $715 |
| ☐ **DORLEANS, R.** ................................. *paintings* | | $165 | $770 |
| ☐ **DORN, Alois** ................................... *paintings* | | | $467 |
| Austrian 1840-c. 1890 | | | |
| ☐ **DORN, Ernst** ................................... *paintings* | | $1,540 | $1,980 |
| German b. 1889 | | | |
| ☐ **DORNE, Albert** ................................ *drawings* | | | $467 |
| American 19th cent. | | | |

| | | *Current Price Range* | |
| | | *Low* | *High* |
| --- | --- | --- | --- |
| ☐ **DORNE, Martin van** ............... *paintings* | | | $10,450 |
| Flemish 1736-1808 | | | |
| ☐ **DORNER, Johann Jakob (the younger)** ... *paintings* | | | $8,250 |
| German 1775-1852 | | | |
| ☐ **DORNMERSER, C.** ............... *paintings* | | | $1,045 |
| Dutch 19th cent. | | | |
| ☐ **DORP, Moritz van** ............... *paintings* | | $495 | $990 |
| Dutch 19th cent. | | | |
| ☐ **DOSAMENTES, Francisco** ............... *paintings* | | | $2,970 |
| Mexican b. 1911 | | | |
| ☐ **DOSSIEKIN, Nicolai Wassilievitch** ........ *paintings* | | $3,300 | $3,575 |
| Russian b. 1863 | | | |
| ☐ **DOU, Gerrit (Gerard)** ............... *paintings* | | $27,500 | $27,500 |
| Dutch 1613-1675 | | | |
| ☐ **DOUCET, Henri Lucien** ............... *paintings* | | $715 | $825 |
| French 1856-1895 | | | |
| ☐ **DOUGHERTY, Parke Custis** ............... *paintings* | | $275 | $6,270 |
| American b. 1867 | | | |
| ☐ **DOUGHERTY, Paul** ............... *paintings* | | $110 | $3,850 |
| American 1877-1947 ............... *drawings* | | $110 | $192 |
| ☐ **DOUGHTY, Thomas** ............... *paintings* | | $2,300 | $27,500 |
| American 1793-1856 ............... *drawings* | | | $1,430 |
| ☐ **DOUGLAS, Andrew** ............... *paintings* | | $385 | $412 |
| English 1871-1935 | | | |
| ☐ **DOUGLAS, Edward Algernon Stuart** .... *paintings* | | $4,400 | $6,600 |
| English 19th cent. ............... *drawings* | | $880 | $1,600 |
| ☐ **DOUGLAS, Edwin** ............... *paintings* | | | $2,530 |
| British 1848-1914 | | | |
| ☐ **DOUGLAS, James** ............... *drawings* | | $137 | $412 |
| British 19th cent. | | | |
| ☐ **DOUGLAS, Luther** ............... *paintings* | | | $330 |
| American 20th cent. | | | |
| ☐ **DOUGLAS, Richard** ............... *paintings* | | | $330 |
| ☐ **DOUGLAS, Walter** ............... *paintings* | | $550 | $1,210 |
| American b. 1868 ............... *drawings* | | | $150 |
| ☐ **DOUGLAS-HAMILTON, A. M. R.** ........ *drawings* | | | $357 |
| English 19th cent. | | | |
| ☐ **DOUMET, Zacharie Felix** ............... *drawings* | | | $440 |
| French 1761-1818 | | | |
| ☐ **DOUSSAINT, C.** ............... *drawings* | | | $352 |
| ☐ **DOUST, Jan van** ............... *paintings* | | $467 | $522 |
| Dutch 19th/20th cent. | | | |
| ☐ **DOUTHERS, M.** ............... *paintings* | | | $400 |
| German 19th cent. | | | |
| ☐ **DOUVEN, Jan Frans van** ............... *paintings* | | $2,090 | $3,025 |
| Dutch 1656-1727 | | | |
| ☐ **DOUW, Simon van** ............... *paintings* | | | $4,400 |
| Flemish 1630-c. 1677 | | | |

*Current Price Range*

| | Low | High |
|---|---|---|
| ☐ **DOUWES, Gabriel** ............................. *paintings* | | $605 |
| Dutch 20th cent. | | |
| ☐ **DOUWES, J.** ..................................... *paintings* | | $275 |
| ☐ **DOUZETTE, Louis** ............................ *paintings* | $300 | $3,575 |
| German 1834-1924 | | |
| ☐ **DOVASTON, Marie** .......................... *paintings* | $3,850 | $5,500 |
| British 20th cent. | | |
| ☐ **DOVE, Arthur Garfield** ...................... *paintings* | $35,200 | $176,000 |
| American 1880-1946 ............................... *drawings* | $2,420 | $7,700 |
| ☐ **DOW, Arthur W.** .............................. *paintings* | | $1,100 |
| ☐ **DOW, Nell Pierce** ............................ *paintings* | | $275 |
| American 20th cent. | | |
| ☐ **DOW, Olin** ..................................... *drawings* | | $550 |
| American | | |
| ☐ **DOWD, B.J.** ..................................... *paintings* | | $302 |
| American 19th cent. | | |
| ☐ **DOWLING, Robert** ............................ *paintings* | | $880 |
| Austrian 1827-1886 | | |
| ☐ **DOWNARD, Ebeneezer Newman** .......... *paintings* | | $935 |
| British School 19th cent. | | |
| ☐ **DOWNES, P.S.** ................................. *drawings* | | $1,210 |
| American late 19th cent. | | |
| ☐ **DOWNIE, Patrick** ............................ *paintings* | $220 | $1,100 |
| Scottish 1854-1945 | | |
| ☐ **DOWNING, Charles Palmer** ................. *paintings* | | $770 |
| British 19th cent. | | |
| ☐ **DOWNING, Delapoer** .......................... *paintings* | | $2,200 |
| British ac. 1900 | | |
| ☐ **DOWNING, M.** ................................. *paintings* | | $250 |
| ☐ **DOWNING, Thomas** ........................... *paintings* | $132 | $990 |
| American b. 1928 | | |
| ☐ **DOWNMAN, John** ............................ *paintings* | $550 | $3,300 |
| British 1750-1824 ................................. *drawings* | $990 | $2,860 |
| ☐ **DOXEY, Don** ................................... *paintings* | $2,700 | $5,000 |
| American contemporary | | |
| ☐ **DOYLE, Tom** ................................... *drawings* | | $275 |
| contemporary | | |
| ☐ **DRAHONET, Alexandre Jean Dubois** .... *paintings* | | $990 |
| French 1791-1834 | | |
| ☐ **DRAKE, Charles E.** ........................... *paintings* | $192 | $2,475 |
| American 1865-1918 | | |
| ☐ **DRAKE, William Henry** ....................... *drawings* | $121 | $522 |
| American 1856-1926 | | |
| ☐ **DRAMBURG, A.** ................................ *paintings* | | $2,200 |
| British 19th cent. | | |
| ☐ **DRAPER, W.** ................................... *paintings* | | $2,640 |
| ☐ **DRAPER, William F.** ........................ *drawings* | | $330 |
| American b. 1912 | | |

| | Current Price Range | |
|---|---|---|
| | *Low* | *High* |
| ☐ **DRAVER, Orrin** .................................... *paintings* | $220 | $247 |
| American 20th cent. | | |
| ☐ **DRAYTON, Grace G.** ........................... *drawings* | $660 | $990 |
| American 1877-1936 | | |
| ☐ **DRECHSLER, Alexandre** ..................... *paintings* | | $1,155 |
| German c. 1860-1897 | | |
| ☐ **DRECHSLER, Johann Baptist** .............. *paintings* | $27,500 | $88,000 |
| Austrian 1756-1811 | | |
| ☐ **DREHER, R.** ...................................... *paintings* | | $302 |
| German 19th cent. | | |
| ☐ **DRESSLER, Conrad** ........................... *sculpture* | | $1,650 |
| 1856-1940 | | |
| ☐ **DREUX-DORCY, Pierre Joseph de** ........ *paintings* | | $495 |
| French 1789-1874 | | |
| ☐ **DREW, Clement** .................................... *paintings* | $275 | $4,500 |
| American 1806/08-1889 | | |
| ☐ **DREW, George W.** ............................... *paintings* | $99 | $2,860 |
| American b. 1875 | | |
| ☐ **DREW, John** ....................................... *paintings* | $44 | $396 |
| American 20th cent. | | |
| ☐ **DREW-BEAR, Jessie** ............................ *paintings* | $121 | $451 |
| American 20th cent. | | |
| ☐ **DREWES, Werner** ............................. *paintings* | $700 | $3,025 |
| German/American b. 1899 ............................ *drawings* | $220 | $550 |
| ☐ **DREXEL, Francis Martin** ..................... *paintings* | $2,530 | $2,860 |
| American 1792-1863 | | |
| ☐ **DREYFUS, Bernard** ............................ *paintings* | | $2,860 |
| Nicaraguan b. 1940 ..................................... *drawings* | $385 | $4,675 |
| ☐ **DRIELST, Egbert van** .......................... *drawings* | | $825 |
| Dutch 1746-1818 | | |
| ☐ **DRIGGS, Elsie** .................................... *drawings* | $330 | $1,430 |
| American b. 1898 | | |
| ☐ **DRIVIER, Leon Ernest** ......................... *sculpture* | | $3,025 |
| French b. 1878 | | |
| ☐ **DROFNAH, Marie** ............................. *drawings* | | $990 |
| ☐ **DROLLING, Martin** ............................ *paintings* | | $2,310 |
| French 1786-1851 | | |
| ☐ **DROLLING, Martin** ........................... *paintings* | $1,320 | $16,500 |
| French 1752-1817 | | |
| ☐ **DROOCHSLOOT, Joost Cornelisz** ........ *paintings* | $4,400 | $66,000 |
| Dutch 1586-1666 | | |
| ☐ **DROUAIS, Francois Hubert** .................. *paintings* | | $16,500 |
| French 1727-1775 | | |
| ☐ **DROUEL, P.** ....................................... *paintings* | | $2,090 |
| 19th cent. | | |
| ☐ **DROUET, Jean Gillaume** ...................... *paintings* | | $385 |
| French 1764-1836 | | |
| ☐ **DROUOT, Edouard** ............................ *sculpture* | $418 | $3,750 |
| French 1859-1945 | | |

| | | Current Price Range | |
| --- | --- | --- | --- |
| | | Low | High |
| ☐ **DRULMAN, Marinus Johannes** | | | |
| **(called M. De Jongere)** ........................ *paintings* | | | $660 |
| Dutch b. 1912 | | | |
| ☐ **DRUMLEVITCH, Seymour** ................ *paintings* | | | $275 |
| contemporary | | | |
| ☐ **DRUMMOND, Arthur** ........................ *paintings* | | | $2,250 |
| British 1871-1951 | | | |
| ☐ **DRUMMOND, E.S.** ............................ *drawings* | | | $192 |
| English 19th cent. | | | |
| ☐ **DRUMMOND, H.** .............................. *paintings* | | $797 | $852 |
| English 19th/20th cent. | | | |
| ☐ **DRUMMOND, Hazelet** ....................... *paintings* | | | $715 |
| American b. 1924 | | | |
| ☐ **DRURY, John H.** .............................. *paintings* | | | $330 |
| American b. 1816 | | | |
| ☐ **DRYDEN, Helen** ............................... *drawings* | | $275 | $880 |
| American b. 1887 | | | |
| ☐ **DRYSDALE, Alexander John** ............... *paintings* | | $550 | $4,675 |
| American 1870-1934 ................................ *drawings* | | $165 | $1,540 |
| ☐ **DU BOIS, Guy Pene** ......................... *paintings* | | $1,760 | $66,000 |
| American 1884-1958 ................................ *drawings* | | $462 | $6,160 |
| ☐ **DU BOIS, Raoul Pene** ........................ *drawings* | | | $385 |
| American b. 1912 | | | |
| ☐ **DU CHATTEL,** | | | |
| **Fredericus Jacobus van Rossum** ............ *paintings* | | $1,045 | $1,320 |
| Dutch 1856-1917 | | | |
| ☐ **DU FAUR, Otto von Faber** ................... *drawings* | | | $935 |
| German 1828-1901 | | | |
| ☐ **DU MAURIER, George** ....................... *paintings* | | | $176 |
| English 1834-1896 | | | |
| ☐ **DU TANT, Charles** ............................ *paintings* | | $330 | $1,650 |
| American b. 1908 | | | |
| ☐ **DUBAN, A.** ..................................... *drawings* | | | $1,320 |
| French c. 1800 | | | |
| ☐ **DUBBELS, Hendrik** ........................... *paintings* | | | $16,500 |
| Dutch 1620/21-1676 | | | |
| ☐ **DUBE, Mathie** ................................. *paintings* | | | $1,210 |
| American b. 1861 | | | |
| ☐ **DUBOIS, C.H.** ................................. *paintings* | | | $385 |
| ☐ **DUBOIS, Catherina** ........................... *drawings* | | | $1,650 |
| Dutch d. 1776 | | | |
| ☐ **DUBOIS, Charles** ............................. *paintings* | | | $357 |
| American 1847-1885 ................................ *drawings* | | | $165 |
| ☐ **DUBOIS, D.N.** ................................. *paintings* | | | $550 |
| American 19th cent. | | | |
| ☐ **DUBOIS, F.** ..................................... *paintings* | | | $330 |
| ☐ **DUBOIS, Grace** ................................ *paintings* | | | $500 |
| American 20th cent. | | | |

| | | Current Price Range | |
|---|---|---|---|
| | | Low | High |
| ☐ **DUBOIS, Guillam** ................ *paintings*<br>Dutch 1610-1680 | | $7,700 | $17,600 |
| ☐ **DUBOIS, Henri Pierre Hippolyte** .......... *paintings*<br>French 1837-1909 | | $301 | $23,100 |
| ☐ **DUBOIS, L.** ............................ *paintings*<br>French 19th/20th cent. | | | $440 |
| ☐ **DUBOIS, P.** ............................ *paintings*<br>French 19th cent. | | $880 | $2,750 |
| ☐ **DUBOIS, Paul** ...................... *paintings*<br>French 1829-1905 ...................... *sculpture* | | $185<br>$1,200 | $880<br>$3,740 |
| ☐ **DUBOIS, Willem** ................... *paintings*<br>Dutch d. 1680 | | $8,800 | $46,200 |
| ☐ **DUBOIS-PILLET, Albert** ............... *paintings*<br>French 1845-1890 | | | $23,100 |
| ☐ **DUBOS, Julius** ..................... *paintings* | | | $522 |
| ☐ **DUBOURG, Louis Alexandre** ............... *paintings*<br>French 1825-1891 | | | $2,640 |
| ☐ **DUBOURG, Louis Fabricius** ................ *drawings*<br>Dutch 1693-1775 | | | $715 |
| ☐ **DUBOVSKOI, Nikolai Nikanorovich** ...... *paintings*<br>Russian 1859-1918 | | | $12,650 |
| ☐ **DUBREUIL, Victor** ............................ *paintings*<br>American ac. 1880-1910 | | $5,500 | $14,300 |
| ☐ **DUBUCAND, Alfred** ............................ *sculpture*<br>French b. 1828 | | $198 | $4,620 |
| ☐ **DUBUFE, Edouard** ............................ *paintings*<br>French 1820-1883 | | $1,870 | $5,500 |
| ☐ **DUBUFFE, Guillaume** .......................... *paintings*<br>French 1853-1909 | | | $825 |
| ☐ **DUBUFFET, Jean** ............................ *paintings*<br>French b. 1901 ...................... *drawings*<br>...................................... *sculpture* | | $22,000<br>$1,320 | $209,000<br>$104,500<br>$40,700 |
| ☐ **DUCAIRE-ROQUE, Maryse** ................ *paintings*<br>French 20th cent. | | $110 | $302 |
| ☐ **DUCASSE, G. Emmanuel** ............... *paintings*<br>Haitian b. 1903 | | $165 | $440 |
| ☐ **DUCHAMP, Gov. Alexander** ................ *drawings*<br>French 1887-1968 | | | $374 |
| ☐ **DUCHAMP, Marcel** .......................... *drawings*<br>French/American 1887-1968 ......................... *sculpture* | | $3,520<br>$12,650 | $11,550<br>$25,300 |
| ☐ **DUCHAMP, Suzanna** ........................ *paintings*<br>French 20th cent. | | | $198 |
| ☐ **DUCHAMP-VILLON, Raymond** .......... *sculpture*<br>French 1876-1918 | | | $19,800 |
| ☐ **DUCHESNE, Charles** ......................... *paintings*<br>French d. 1823 | | | $3,080 |
| ☐ **DUCHESNE, Edmund Percy** ................ *paintings* | | | $2,090 |
| ☐ **DUCHMANH** ...................................... *drawings*<br>contemporary | | $77 | $247 |

| | | Current Price Range | |
|---|---|---|---|
| | | Low | High |
| ☐ **DUCHOISELLE** .................... *sculpture* | | | $605 |
| ☐ **DUCK, Jacob** .................... *paintings* | | $19,800 | $55,000 |
| Dutch c. 1600-after 1660 | | | |
| ☐ **DUCKER, E.** .................... *paintings* | | | $825 |
| ☐ **DUCKER, Eugene Gustav** .................... *paintings* | | $605 | $1,870 |
| German b. 1841 | | | |
| ☐ **DUCKER, James** .................... *paintings* | | | $660 |
| British 19th cent. | | | |
| ☐ **DUCKETT, V.F.** .................... *drawings* | | | $220 |
| American 20th cent. | | | |
| ☐ **DUCKORT (?), J.** .................... *paintings* | | | $1,320 |
| Continental 19th cent. | | | |
| ☐ **DUCLAUX, Jean Antoine** .................... *paintings* | | | $22,000 |
| French 1783-1868 .................... *drawings* | | $44 | $440 |
| ☐ **DUCMELIC, Zdravko** .................... *paintings* | | | $1,760 |
| ☐ **DUCORDEAU, Pierre** .................... *paintings* | | | $935 |
| ☐ **DUCROS, Abraham Louis Rudolphe** ..... *paintings* | | | $7,150 |
| Swiss 1748-1810 | | | |
| ☐ **DUDLEY, Frank V.** .................... *paintings* | | $75 | $1,430 |
| American 1868-1957 | | | |
| ☐ **DUDLEY, Katherine** .................... *drawings* | | | $330 |
| American contemporary | | | |
| ☐ **DUDOUET, Marcel Georges** .................... *paintings* | | $99 | $192 |
| French b. 1924 | | | |
| ☐ **DUER, Douglas** .................... *paintings* | | $45 | $385 |
| American 1887-1964 | | | |
| ☐ **DUERBO, R.** .................... *sculpture* | | | $302 |
| ☐ **DUESSEL, H.A.** .................... *paintings* | | $137 | $302 |
| American 19th cent. | | | |
| ☐ **DUEZ, Ernest** .................... *drawings* | | | $330 |
| French 19th cent. | | | |
| ☐ **DUEZ, Ernest Ange** .................... *paintings* | | $2,750 | $9,900 |
| French 1843-1896 | | | |
| ☐ **DUFAUX, Frederic** .................... *paintings* | | | $412 |
| Swiss 1852-1943 | | | |
| ☐ **DUFAY, J. B.** .................... *paintings* | | | $357 |
| ☐ **DUFEU, Edouard Jacques** .................... *paintings* | | | $1,650 |
| French 1840-1900 .................... *drawings* | | | $176 |
| ☐ **DUFFAUD, Jean Baptiste** .................... *paintings* | | | $2,475 |
| French 1853-1927 | | | |
| ☐ **DUFFAUT, Prefete** .................... *paintings* | | $247 | $9,900 |
| Haitian b. 1923 .................... *drawings* | | $605 | $1,045 |
| ☐ **DUFFY, Richard L.** .................... *sculpture* | | | $467 |
| ☐ **DUFNER, Edward** .................... *paintings* | | $1,650 | $14,300 |
| American 1871/72-1957 .................... *drawings* | | $1,650 | $11,000 |
| ☐ **DUFOUR, A.** .................... *paintings* | | | $522 |
| French 19th cent. | | | |
| ☐ **DUFOUR, Camille** .................... *paintings* | | | $1,045 |
| French b. 1841 | | | |

| | | *Current Price Range* | |
|---|---|---|---|
| | | *Low* | *High* |
| ☐ **DUFOUR, R.** .......................... *paintings* | | | **$660** |
| ☐ **DUFRANC, Charles** ........................ *paintings* | | **$143** | **$176** |
| Haitian 20th cent. | | | |
| ☐ **DUFRESNE, Charles Georges** ............ *paintings* | | **$165** | **$2,090** |
| French 1876-1938 ................................ *drawings* | | **$192** | **$1,400** |
| ☐ **DUFY, Jean** .......................... *paintings* | | **$1,320** | **$21,450** |
| French 1888-1964 ................................ *drawings* | | **$220** | **$10,175** |
| ☐ **DUFY, Raoul** .......................... *paintings* | | **$4,400** | **$341,000** |
| French 1877-1953 ................................ *drawings* | | **$191** | **$63,250** |
| ☐ **DUGARDIER, Raoul** ..................... *paintings* | | | **$880** |
| ☐ **DUGEN, A. van** .......................... *paintings* | | | **$715** |
| ☐ **DUGHET, Alphonse** ..................... *paintings* | | | **$300** |
| ☐ **DUGHET, Gaspard** ..................... *paintings* | | **$605** | **$11,000** |
| French 1615-1675 | | | |
| ☐ **DUGMORE, Edward** ..................... *paintings* | | | **$1,760** |
| American b. 1915 | | | |
| ☐ **DUGOURC, Jean Demosthene** ............ *drawings* | | **$330** | **$14,300** |
| French 1749-1825 | | | |
| ☐ **DUGUID, Henry G.** ..................... *paintings* | | | **$1,760** |
| British 19th cent. | | | |
| ☐ **DUJARDIN, Karel** ..................... *paintings* | | **$3,025** | **$63,250** |
| Dutch c. 1622-1678 ................................ *drawings* | | **$275** | **$2,640** |
| ☐ **DUKE, Alfred** .......................... *paintings* | | **$825** | **$1,100** |
| English 19th/20th cent. | | | |
| ☐ **DULAC, Edmund** ..................... *paintings* | | | **$12,100** |
| French 1882-1953 ................................ *drawings* | | **$220** | **$73,700** |
| ☐ **DULL, John J.** .......................... *paintings* | | **$797** | **$1,430** |
| American b. 1862 ................................ *drawings* | | **$74** | **$132** |
| ☐ **DULUARD, Hippolyte Francois Leon** .... *paintings* | | **$357** | **$3,740** |
| French b. 1871 | | | |
| ☐ **DUMAIGE** .......................... *sculpture* | | | **$467** |
| ☐ **DUMAIGE, Etienne Henry** ................. *sculpture* | | | **$242** |
| 19th cent. | | | |
| ☐ **DUMELLE, Leon** ..................... *paintings* | | | **$187** |
| French 19th cent. | | | |
| ☐ **DUMITRESCO, Natalia** .................. *paintings* | | | **$200** |
| French b. 1915 | | | |
| ☐ **DUMLER, M.G.** ..................... *paintings* | | | **$200** |
| American 1868-after 1934 | | | |
| ☐ **DUMOND, Frank Vincent** .................. *paintings* | | **$522** | **$3,300** |
| American 1865-1951 | | | |
| ☐ **DUMONS, T.** .......................... *paintings* | | | **$264** |
| ☐ **DUMONT** .......................... *paintings* | | | **$357** |
| French School 19th cent. | | | |
| ☐ **DUMONT, C.** .......................... *paintings* | | | **$880** |
| ☐ **DUMONT, Cesar Alvarez** .................. *paintings* | | | **$1,650** |
| French 19th cent. | | | |
| ☐ **DUMONT, Francois** ..................... *paintings* | | **$660** | **$880** |
| Belgian 19th cent. | | | |

| | Current Price Range | |
|---|---|---|
| | Low | High |
| ☐ **DUMONT, Jo** ........................ *paintings* | | $550 |
| ☐ **DUMONT, Paul** ........................ *paintings* | | $577 |
| American 20th cent. | | |
| ☐ **DUMONT, Pierre** ........................ *paintings* | | $2,090 |
| ☐ **DUNAND, Jean** ........................ *sculpture* | $2,530 | $73,700 |
| Swiss 1877-1942 | | |
| ☐ **DUNANT** ........................ *paintings* | | $770 |
| French (?) 19th cent. | | |
| ☐ **DUNBAR, Harold** ........................ *paintings* | $25 | $600 |
| American b. 1882 | | |
| ☐ **DUNBAR, Patrick** ........................ *paintings* | $495 | $1,210 |
| 19th/20th cent. | | |
| ☐ **DUNBIER, Augustus W.** ........................ *paintings* | $825 | $1,210 |
| American 1888-1977 | | |
| ☐ **DUNCAN, Edward** ........................ *paintings* | $220 | $6,600 |
| English 1803-1882 | | |
| ☐ **DUNCAN, John** ........................ *drawings* | | $275 |
| British b. 1866 | | |
| ☐ **DUNCAN, Laurence** ........................ *drawings* | | $1,210 |
| English 19th cent. | | |
| ☐ **DUNCAN, Robert** ........................ *paintings* | | $14,000 |
| ☐ **DUNCAN, Scott** ........................ *paintings* | | $425 |
| contemporary | | |
| ☐ **DUNCAN, Thomas** ........................ *paintings* | | $1,320 |
| British 1807-1845 | | |
| ☐ **DUNCANSON, Robert S.** ........................ *paintings* | $6,600 | $18,700 |
| American 1817/22-1872 | | |
| ☐ **DUNING, F.** ........................ *paintings* | | $1,210 |
| ☐ **DUNINGTON, A.** ........................ *paintings* | $192 | $1,430 |
| English exhib. 1885 | | |
| ☐ **DUNKER, Balthasar Anton** ........................ *drawings* | | $1,760 |
| German 1746-1807 | | |
| ☐ **DUNKIN, B.S.** ........................ *paintings* | $357 | $357 |
| ☐ **DUNLAP, Edward** ........................ *paintings* | | $352 |
| ☐ **DUNLAP, Helena** ........................ *paintings* | | $440 |
| American 20th cent. | | |
| ☐ **DUNLAP, M.S.** ........................ *paintings* | | $770 |
| ☐ **DUNLAP, Mary Stewart** ........................ *paintings* | | $198 |
| American 20th cent. | | |
| ☐ **DUNLAP, William** ........................ *paintings* | | $2,750 |
| American 1766-1839 | | |
| ☐ **DUNLOP, Ronald Ossory** ........................ *paintings* | $165 | $275 |
| British 1894-1973 | | |
| ☐ **DUNN, Charles A.** ........................ *drawings* | | $247 |
| American b. 1895 | | |
| ☐ **DUNN, Harvey T.** ........................ *paintings* | $2,090 | $63,800 |
| American 1884-1952 ........................ *drawings* | $440 | $2,970 |
| ☐ **DUNN, Joseph (of Worcester)** ........................ *paintings* | $1,540 | $3,025 |
| British 19th cent. | | |

| | | *Current Price Range* | |
|---|---|---|---|
| | | Low | High |
| ☐ **DUNN, Julia E.** ................................. *drawings* | | | $247 |
| American b. 1850 | | | |
| ☐ **DUNNING, Robert Spear** .................. *paintings* | | $990 | $60,500* |
| American 1829-1905 | | | |
| ☐ **DUNNINGTON, A.** ............................ *paintings* | | | $1,210 |
| ☐ **DUNNINGTON, Albert** ......................... *paintings* | | | $385 |
| British ac. 1886 | | | |
| ☐ **DUNOUY, Alexandre Hyacinthe** ............ *paintings* | | $1,650 | $11,000 |
| French 1757-1841 | | | |
| ☐ **DUNOYER DE SEGONZAC, Andre** ..... *paintings* | | $6,050 | $33,000 |
| French 1884-1974 ....................................... *drawings* | | $176 | $35,200 |
| ☐ **DUNSMORE, John Ward** ...................... *paintings* | | $247 | $1,870 |
| American 1856-1945 ................................. *drawings* | | | $55 |
| ☐ **DUNSTAN, Bernard** ............................ *paintings* | | | $522 |
| ☐ **DUNTON, W. Herbert** ......................... *paintings* | | $192 | $57,750 |
| American 1878-1936 .................................. *drawings* | | $27 | $6,500 |
| ☐ **DUNTZE, Johann Bartholomaus** .......... *paintings* | | $11,000 | $17,600 |
| German 1823-1895 | | | |
| ☐ **DUNZ, A.** ......................................... *paintings* | | | $275 |
| ☐ **DUPAIN, E.** ...................................... *paintings* | | | $330 |
| ☐ **DUPAS, Jean Theodore** ........................ *paintings* | | $3,520 | $30,800 |
| French 1882-1964 ...................................... *drawings* | | $2,200 | $6,600 |
| ☐ **DUPERRE, Gabriel** ............................. *paintings* | | $8,800 | $15,400 |
| French 19th cent. | | | |
| ☐ **DUPERRON, Adolphe** ......................... *drawings* | | | $220 |
| French 19th cent. | | | |
| ☐ **DUPIN, P.** ........................................ *drawings* | | | $308 |
| ☐ **DUPLESSIS, Joseph Siffrein** ................ *paintings* | | | $1,980 |
| French 1725-1802 ...................................... *drawings* | | | $352 |
| ☐ **DUPON, Jozue** ..................................... *sculpture* | | | $330 |
| ☐ **DUPONT, Gainsborough** ...................... *paintings* | | $395 | $6,050 |
| English c. 1754-1797 | | | |
| ☐ **DUPONT, J.B.** ................................... *paintings* | | | $220 |
| French 20th cent. | | | |
| ☐ **DUPONT, Kedma** ............................... *paintings* | | | $220 |
| American 20th cent. | | | |
| ☐ **DUPONT, N.** ..................................... *paintings* | | $3,850 | $4,620 |
| French | | | |
| ☐ **DUPONT, Richard J.M.** ....................... *paintings* | | | $880 |
| ☐ **DUPRAT, Albert-Ferdinand** ................. *paintings* | | $715 | $1,600 |
| Italian b. 1882 | | | |
| ☐ **DUPRAY, H.** ...................................... *paintings* | | | $440 |
| ☐ **DUPRAY, Henry Louis** ........................ *paintings* | | $1,100 | $2,750 |
| French 1841-1909 | | | |
| ☐ **DUPRE, Ferdinand** .............................. *paintings* | | | $660 |
| European | | | |
| ☐ **DUPRE, H.** ........................................ *paintings* | | | $385 |
| French contemporary | | | |

| | | | *Current Price Range* | |
|---|---|---|---|---|
| | | | *Low* | *High* |
| ☐ **DUPRE, Jules** | *paintings* | | $550 | $28,600 |
| French 1811-1889 | | | | |
| ☐ **DUPRE, Julien** | *paintings* | | $522 | $29,700 |
| French 1851-1910 | *drawings* | | $550 | $1,980 |
| ☐ **DUPRE, L.** | *paintings* | | $110 | $192 |
| American 20th cent. | | | | |
| ☐ **DUPRE, Leon Victor** | *paintings* | | $1,000 | $10,450 |
| French 1816-1879 | | | | |
| ☐ **DUPUY, Lawrence** | *sculpture* | | $385 | $495 |
| ☐ **DUPUY, Louis** | *paintings* | | | $660 |
| ☐ **DURA, G.** | *drawings* | | $440 | $825 |
| Italian 19th cent. | | | | |
| ☐ **DURAN, Jules** | *paintings* | | | $440 |
| French 19th cent. | | | | |
| ☐ **DURAND, Asher B.** | *paintings* | | $2,310 | $57,200 |
| American 1796-1886 | *drawings* | | $1,045 | $3,300 |
| ☐ **DURAND, E.L.** | *paintings* | | | $2,200 |
| American 19th cent. | | | | |
| ☐ **DURAND, Elias W.** | *paintings* | | $330 | $330 |
| ☐ **DURAND, Gustave** | *paintings* | | | $3,575 |
| French 19th/20th cent. | | | | |
| ☐ **DURAND, John** | *paintings* | | $1,155 | $2,300 |
| American 19th cent. | | | | |
| ☐ **DURAND-BRAGER,** | | | | |
| **Jean Baptiste Henri** | *paintings* | | $715 | $2,420 |
| French 1814-1879 | | | | |
| ☐ **DURANTI, Fortunato** | *drawings* | | $605 | $770 |
| Italian | | | | |
| ☐ **DURCUIS** | *paintings* | | $44 | $440 |
| French 20th cent. | | | | |
| ☐ **DUREAU, George** | *paintings* | | $770 | $4,840 |
| American b. 1930 | *drawings* | | $220 | $1,210 |
| ☐ **DUREL, Auguste** | *paintings* | | | $385 |
| ☐ **DUREN, Karl** | *paintings* | | | $2,310 |
| American 19th/20th cent. | | | | |
| ☐ **DUREN, Terrence** | *paintings* | | $110 | $275 |
| American b. 1906 | | | | |
| ☐ **DURENNE, Eugene Antoine** | *paintings* | | | $2,640 |
| French 1860-1944 | | | | |
| ☐ **DURET, C.** | *paintings* | | | $495 |
| 19th cent. | | | | |
| ☐ **DURET, Francisque Joseph** | *sculpture* | | | $2,200 |
| ☐ **DUREUIL, Michel** | *paintings* | | $88 | $605 |
| French 20th cent. | | | | |
| ☐ **DURHAM, C.J.** | *paintings* | | $74 | $495 |
| ☐ **DURING, Sebastian** | *paintings* | | | $2,750 |
| Swiss 1671-1723 | | | | |
| ☐ **DURRIE, George Henry** | *paintings* | | $4,730 | $99,000 |
| American 1820-1863 | | | | |

|  | | *Current Price Range* | |
|---|---|---|---|
|  | | *Low* | *High* |
| ☐ **DURUN, F.** ........................................ *paintings* | | | **$742** |
| German 19th cent. | | | |
| ☐ **DUSART, Cornelius** ......................... *paintings* | | | **$52,800** |
| Dutch 1660-1704 ...................................... *drawings* | | **$2,090** | **$11,000** |
| ☐ **DUSSANT, Gustave** ............................ *sculpture* | | | **$275** |
| b. 1875 | | | |
| ☐ **DUTHEIL, E.** ...................................... *paintings* | | **$220** | **$357** |
| American 19th/20th cent. | | | |
| ☐ **DUTHOIT, Paul** ................................ *paintings* | | | **$495** |
| French b. 1858 | | | |
| ☐ **DUTMER, J.H.** .................................... *paintings* | | **$385** | **$385** |
| American 20th cent. | | | |
| ☐ **DUVAL, C.A.** ...................................... *drawings* | | | **$275** |
| English 1808-1872 | | | |
| ☐ **DUVAL, Edward J.** ............................. *drawings* | | | **$605** |
| British 19th cent. | | | |
| ☐ **DUVAL, G.** ......................................... *paintings* | | | **$550** |
| French 20th cent. | | | |
| ☐ **DUVAL, J.** ......................................... *paintings* | | | **$385** |
| ☐ **DUVAL, Pierre** .................................. *paintings* | | **$220** | **$935** |
| French 19th cent. | | | |
| ☐ **DUVAL, Victor** .................................. *paintings* | | **$825** | **$4,125** |
| French 19th cent. | | | |
| ☐ **DUVAL-GOZLAN, Leon** ...................... *paintings* | | | **$1,980** |
| French 1853-1941 | | | |
| ☐ **DUVALL, Etienne** .............................. *paintings* | | | **$1,540** |
| French 1824-1914 | | | |
| ☐ **DUVALL, Thomas George** .................... *paintings* | | | **$1,320** |
| ☐ **DUVENECK, Frank** ........................... *paintings* | | **$660** | **$19,800*** |
| American 1848-1919 .................................. *drawings* | | **$137** | **$660** |
| ☐ **DUVENT, Charles Jules** ....................... *paintings* | | | **$650** |
| French 1867-1940 | | | |
| ☐ **DUVERGER, Paul** ............................. *paintings* | | **$825** | **$1,430** |
| French 19th cent. | | | |
| ☐ **DUVERGER, Theophile Emmanuel** ....... *paintings* | | **$2,200** | **$14,850** |
| French b. 1821 ....................................... *drawings* | | | **$44** |
| ☐ **DUVERGNE, P.** ................................... *paintings* | | **$357** | **$605** |
| ☐ **DUVIEUX, Henri** .............................. *paintings* | | **$275** | **$1,210** |
| French 19th cent. | | | |
| ☐ **DUXA, Carl** ...................................... *paintings* | | **$990** | **$3,025** |
| Austrian 1871-1937 | | | |
| ☐ **DUYK, F.** .......................................... *paintings* | | **$220** | **$440** |
| ☐ **DUYSTER, William Cornelisz.** .............. *paintings* | | | **$18,700** |
| Dutch 1599-1635 | | | |
| ☐ **DUYTS, Gustave den** .......................... *paintings* | | **$1,320** | **$1,760** |
| Belgian 1850-1897 | | | |
| ☐ **DWIGHT, Ed** ..................................... *sculpture* | | | **$1,400** |
| American | | | |

| | | Current Price Range | |
|---|---|---|---|
| | | Low | High |
| ☐ **DWYER** ............................................... *drawings* | | | $275 |
| American 19th cent. | | | |
| ☐ **DWYER, A.** .................................... *paintings* | | | $220 |
| American 19th cent. | | | |
| ☐ **DYCK, Abraham van** .......................... *drawings* | | | $3,960 |
| Dutch 1635-1672 | | | |
| ☐ **DYCK, Sir Anthony van** ...................... *paintings* | | $41,000 | $55,000 |
| Flemish 1599-1641 ..................................... *drawings* | | | $3,960 |
| ☐ **DYE, Charlie** ..................................... *paintings* | | $30,000 | $80,000 |
| American 1906-1972/73 | | | |
| ☐ **DYE, Clarkson** ................................... *paintings* | | $246 | $770 |
| American 1869-1945 | | | |
| ☐ **DYE, Jim C.** ...................................... *sculpture* | | $1,100 | $1,200 |
| ☐ **DYER, Charles Gifford** .......................... *paintings* | | $165 | $1,650 |
| American 1840-1912 | | | |
| ☐ **DYER, Elizabeth Griffin** ...................... *paintings* | | | $275 |
| American 19th cent. | | | |
| ☐ **DYER, H.** ......................................... *drawings* | | | $330 |
| ☐ **DYER, H. Anthony** ............................. *paintings* | | | $500 |
| American 1872-1943 ................................... *drawings* | | $30 | $2860 |
| ☐ **DYER, Lowell** ................................... *paintings* | | $500 | $825 |
| American 19th cent. | | | |
| ☐ **DYER, Uriah N.** ................................. *paintings* | | | $880 |
| American 19th cent. | | | |
| ☐ **DYF, Marcel Dreyfus** ........................... *paintings* | | $400 | $4,675 |
| French b. 1899 | | | |
| ☐ **DYFVERMAN, Viktor** ......................... *paintings* | | | $522 |
| Continental School 20th cent. | | | |
| ☐ **DYK, Philip van** .................................. *paintings* | | $7,150 | $10,000 |
| Dutch 1680-1753 | | | |
| ☐ **DYKE, Samuel P.** ............................... *paintings* | | $495 | $3,575 |
| American 19th cent. | | | |
| ☐ **DYSSELHOF, Gerrit Willem** ............... *paintings* | | | $495 |
| ☐ **DYXHOORN, Pieter Arnout** ................. *paintings* | | | $1,925 |
| Dutch 1810-1839 | | | |
| ☐ **DZIGURSKI, Alex** ............................... *paintings* | | $220 | $1,540 |
| Yugoslav/American b. 1911 | | | |
| ☐ **DZUBAS, Friedel** .............................. *paintings* | | $1,320 | $15,400 |
| German/American b. 1915 | | | |
| ☐ **EAKINS, Susan Hannah MacDowell** ...... *paintings* | | | $715 |
| American d. 1938 | | | |
| ☐ **EAKINS, Thomas** ............................... *paintings* | | $9,900 | $308,000 |
| American 1844-1916 ............................... *drawings* | | $9,350 | $550,000 |
| ☐ **EAMERSON, Samuel** .......................... *paintings* | | | $412 |
| English 19th cent. | | | |
| ☐ **EAMES, Mary S.** ................................ *paintings* | | | $242 |
| American d. 1964 | | | |
| ☐ **EANY, Marum** ................................... *paintings* | | | $275 |

|                                              |          | Current Price Range |           |
|----------------------------------------------|----------|---------------------|-----------|
|                                              |          | Low                 | High      |
| ☐ **EARHART, John Franklin** .................... *paintings* |          |                     | **$500**  |
| American 1853-1938                           |          |                     |           |
| ☐ **EARL, George** ..................................... *paintings* |          | **$770**            | **$3,080** |
| English 19th cent.                           |          |                     |           |
| ☐ **EARL, James** ...................................... *paintings* |          | **$4,840**          | **$5,225** |
| American                                     |          |                     |           |
| ☐ **EARL, Maud** ...................................... *paintings* |          | **$44**             | **$5,500** |
| English ac. 1884-1934; d. 1943               |          |                     |           |
| ☐ **EARL, Ralph** ...................................... *paintings* |          | **$4,070**          | **$20,900** |
| American 1785-1837/38                        |          |                     |           |
| ☐ **EARL, Ralph** ...................................... *paintings* |          |                     | **$550**  |
| American 1751-1801                           |          |                     |           |
| ☐ **EARL, Thomas** .................................. *paintings* |          |                     | **$3,300** |
| ☐ **EARLE, Eyvind** ................................. *paintings* |          | **$935**            | **$2,090** |
| American b. 1916 ................................... *drawings* |          | **$302**            | **$467**  |
| ☐ **EARLE, Lawrence Carmichael** ............. *paintings* |          | **$308**            | **$2,200** |
| American 1845-1921 ............................... *drawings* |          | **$137**            | **$1,540** |
| ☐ **EARLY, Miles J.** ................................ *paintings* |          | **$26**             | **$412**  |
| American 20th cent.                          |          |                     |           |
| ☐ **EARP, H.** .......................................... *paintings* |          |                     | **$600**  |
| British 19th cent. ..................................... *drawings* |          |                     | **$165**  |
| ☐ **EAST, Barbara A.** ............................... *drawings* |          |                     | **$1,850** |
| American b. 1950                             |          |                     |           |
| ☐ **EAST, Harry** ..................................... *paintings* |          |                     | **$495**  |
| ☐ **EAST, Sir Alfred** ................................ *drawings* |          | **$357**            | **$495**  |
| English 1849-1913                           |          |                     |           |
| ☐ **EASTAWAY, J.H.** .............................. *paintings* |          |                     | **$715**  |
| American                                     |          |                     |           |
| ☐ **EASTLAKE, Sidney** ........................... *paintings* |          |                     | **$350**  |
| ☐ **EASTMAN, Col. Seth** ......................... *paintings* |          |                     | **$2,200** |
| American 1808-1875                           |          |                     |           |
| ☐ **EASTMAN, Emily** ............................... *drawings* |          |                     | **$4,950** |
| American ac. London 1820-1830               |          |                     |           |
| ☐ **EASTMAN, William Joseph** ................ *paintings* |          | **$150**            | **$375**  |
| American 1888-1950 ............................... *drawings* |          | **$22**             | **$350**  |
| ☐ **EATON, Charles Harry** ....................... *paintings* |          | **$385**            | **$1,980** |
| American 1850-1901 ................................ *drawings* |          |                     | **$175**  |
| ☐ **EATON, Charles Warren** ..................... *paintings* |          | **$165**            | **$7,150** |
| American 1857-1937 ................................ *drawings* |          | **$121**            | **$1,320** |
| ☐ **EATON, Joseph Oriel** ........................... *paintings* |          | **$500**            | **$774**  |
| American 1829-1875                           |          |                     |           |
| ☐ **EATON, VaLoy** ................................... *paintings* |          | **$1,400**          | **$7,150** |
| American b. 1938 ................................... *drawings* |          |                     | **$1,980** |
| ☐ **EATON, Walter B.** .............................. *paintings* |          |                     | **$552**  |
| American 19th cent.                          |          |                     |           |
| ☐ **EATON, Wyatt** .................................. *paintings* |          |                     | **$440**  |
| Canadian/American 1849-1896 ..................... *drawings* |          |                     | **$990**  |
| ☐ **EBERHARD, Leopold** .......................... *paintings* |          |                     | **$380**  |

|                                                          | *Current Price Range* | |
|---|---|---|
|                                                          | *Low* | *High* |
| ☐ **EBERLE** .............................................. *paintings* |  | **$2,420** |
| Austrian 18th cent. | | |
| ☐ **EBERLE, Abastenia St. Leger** ............... *sculpture* | **$1,320** | |
| American 1878-1942 | | |
| ☐ **EBERLE, Adolf** .................................... *paintings* | **$4,070** | **$35,200** |
| German 1843-1914 | | |
| ☐ **EBERSBERGER, Max** .......................... *paintings* | **$2,750** | **$6,600** |
| German b. 1852 | | |
| ☐ **EBERT, Anton** ...................................... *paintings* | **$385** | **$7,150** |
| Czechoslovakian 1845-1896 | | |
| ☐ **EBERT, Carl** ...................................... *paintings* |  | **$30,800** |
| German 1821-1885 | | |
| ☐ **EBERT, Charles H.** ............................ *paintings* | **$143** | **$4,125** |
| American 1873-1959 ................................. *drawings* |  | **$90** |
| ☐ **EBERT, Leopold** ................................ *paintings* |  | **$357** |
| British 19th cent. | | |
| ☐ **EBERT, Mary Robert** ........................... *drawings* | **$224** | **$687** |
| American 1873-1956 | | |
| ☐ **EBIHARA, Kinosuke** ......................... *paintings* |  | **$3,080** |
| Japanese 1904-1970 | | |
| ☐ **EBY, Kerr** ...................................... *drawings* | **$60** | **$1,210** |
| American 1889-1946 | | |
| ☐ **ECHAVE, Balthasar (the elder)** .............. *paintings* |  | **$15,000** |
| Mexican School 17th cent. | | |
| ☐ **ECHENA, Jose** .................................... *paintings* |  | **$19,800** |
| Spanish 1845-1909? | | |
| ☐ **ECHEVARRIA, Enrique** ....................... *paintings* | **$495** | **$2,090** |
| b. Mexico 1932 | | |
| ☐ **ECHTLER, Adolf** ............................... *paintings* | **$1,045** | **$6,600** |
| German 1843-1914 | | |
| ☐ **ECKENBRECHER, Themistocles von** .... *paintings* | **$1,100** | **$6,050** |
| German 1842-1921 ................................. *drawings* |  | **$1,100** |
| ☐ **ECKENFELDER, Frederich** ................. *paintings* | **$6,050** | **$10,450** |
| German b. 1861 | | |
| ☐ **ECKER, Van** ...................................... *paintings* |  | **$1,100** |
| ☐ **ECKERMANS, Alice** ........................... *paintings* |  | **$1,430** |
| ☐ **ECKERSBERG, Christopher Wilhelm** ... *paintings* |  | **$25,300** |
| Danish 1783-1853 | | |
| ☐ **ECKHARDT, Edris** ............................. *paintings* | **$82** | **$1,650** |
| American b. 1907 | | |
| ☐ **ECKHARDT VON ECKHARDSBURG,** | | |
| **Victor** ............................................... *paintings* |  | **$2,420** |
| German 1864-1946 | | |
| ☐ **EDDIS, Eden Upton** ........................... *paintings* |  | **$5,280** |
| British 1812-1901 | | |
| ☐ **EDDISS, Caroline M.** ........................ *drawings* |  | **$357** |
| ☐ **EDDY, Don** ...................................... *paintings* |  | **$26,400** |
| American b. 1844 | | |

| | | Current Price Range | |
|---|---|---|---|
| | | *Low* | *High* |
| ☐ **EDDY, Henry Stephens** ................ *paintings* | | $275 | $1,155 |
| American b. 1878 | | | |
| ☐ **EDE, Frederic** ...................... *paintings* | | $1,210 | $1,980 |
| ☐ **EDELFELT, Albert Gustaf Aristides** ..... *paintings* | | | $22,000 |
| Finnish 1854-1905 | | | |
| ☐ **EDELMANN, Charles A.** ................. *paintings* | | | $522 |
| ☐ **EDER Y GATTENS, Frederico Maria** ... *paintings* | | | $2,200 |
| Spanish 19th cent. | | | |
| ☐ **EDERER, Carl** ...................... *drawings* | | | $357 |
| Austrian b. 1875 | | | |
| ☐ **EDGAR, Louis** ...................... *paintings* | | | $396 |
| American 20th cent. | | | |
| ☐ **EDLICH, Stephen** ................... *drawings* | | $605 | $9,900 |
| American b. 1944 | | | |
| ☐ **EDMONDS, Francis William** ............. *paintings* | | $1,870 | $49,500 |
| American 1806-1863 ................... *drawings* | | | $660 |
| ☐ **EDMONDSON, William** ................. *sculpture* | | | $4,950 |
| American ac. c. 1934-1939 | | | |
| ☐ **EDMONDSON, William J.** ................. *paintings* | | $750 | $1,430 |
| American 1868-1951/66 | | | |
| ☐ **EDOUARD, Albert Jules** .................. *paintings* | | $330 | $2,860 |
| French b. 1845 | | | |
| ☐ **EDOUART,** | | | |
| **Augustin Amant Constant Fidele** ........... *paintings* | | $242 | $247 |
| French 1789-1861 ...................... *drawings* | | $495 | $715 |
| ☐ **EDUGENE, Pierre** ..................... *paintings* | | | $495 |
| ☐ **EDWARDS, Alice** ..................... *paintings* | | | $242 |
| American 19th cent. | | | |
| ☐ **EDWARDS, Charles** ..................... *paintings* | | $275 | $275 |
| American 1797-1868 | | | |
| ☐ **EDWARDS, George** ................... *drawings* | | | $462 |
| ☐ **EDWARDS, George Wharton** ............. *paintings* | | $275 | $2,310 |
| American 1858-1950 ..................... *drawings* | | $88 | $231 |
| ☐ **EDWARDS, H.C.** ..................... *paintings* | | | $495 |
| American 1868-1922 ..................... *drawings* | | | $176 |
| ☐ **EDWARDS, John** ..................... *paintings* | | | $330 |
| 18th cent. | | | |
| ☐ **EDWARDS, Lionel** ................... *paintings* | | $2,750 | $19,800 |
| English 1877/78-1966 ................... *drawings* | | $330 | $11,000 |
| ☐ **EDWARDS, Roy** ..................... *paintings* | | $275 | $385 |
| ☐ **EDWARDS, Thomas** ................... *paintings* | | | $880 |
| American ac. 1822-1856 | | | |
| ☐ **EDWARDS-HOROWITZ** ................... *paintings* | | | $1,760 |
| French 19th cent. | | | |
| ☐ **EDY-LEGRAND, Edward Leon Louis** ... *paintings* | | | $605 |
| French 1892-1970 ..................... *drawings* | | $302 | $1,100 |
| ☐ **EDZARD, Dietz** ..................... *paintings* | | $165 | $7,150 |
| German 1893-1963 | | | |

| | | *Current Price Range* | |
|---|---|---|---|
| | | Low | High |
| ☐ **EECKHOUT, Gerbrand van den** .......... *drawings* | | | $7,975 |
| Dutch 1621-1674 | | | |
| ☐ **EECKHOUT, Victor** ............................ *paintings* | | | $907 |
| Flemish 1821-1879 | | | |
| ☐ **EEDEN, N. van den** ........................... *paintings* | | | $1,100 |
| ☐ **EERDEN, E. van** ................................ *paintings* | | | $275 |
| Dutch 20th cent. | | | |
| ☐ **EFFIE, William** .................................. *paintings* | | | $2,750 |
| ac. c. 1833-1848 | | | |
| ☐ **EGAS, C.** ............................................. *paintings* | | | $550 |
| ☐ **EGAZ, Camille** .................................. *paintings* | | | $880 |
| Latin American | | | |
| ☐ **EGEA, Z.** ............................................. *paintings* | | | $191 |
| Spanish 19th cent. | | | |
| ☐ **EGERTON, Daniel Thomas** ................. *paintings* | | | $16,500 |
| British ac. 1824, d. 1842 | | | |
| ☐ **EGG, Augustus Leopold** ........................ *paintings* | | | $1,650 |
| English 1816-1863 | | | |
| ☐ **EGGEL, Emma** ................................ *paintings* | | | $440 |
| German 1848-1890 | | | |
| ☐ **EGGELSTON, Benjamin** ...................... *paintings* | | | $522 |
| American 1867-1937 | | | |
| ☐ **EGGENA, Gustav** .............................. *paintings* | $302 | $660 |
| German b. 1850 | | | |
| ☐ **EGGENHOFER, Nick** ......................... *paintings* | $786 | $29,700 |
| American b. 1897 ..................................... *drawings* | $137 | $18,000 |
| ☐ **EGGENMEYER, Mavic Kaufmann** ....... *paintings* | | | $275 |
| ☐ **EGGER-LIENZ, Albin** ........................ *paintings* | $5,720 | $13,200 |
| Swiss 1868-1926 | | | |
| ☐ **EGGERT, Sigmund** ............................ *paintings* | $9,350 | $11,550 |
| German 1839-1896 | | | |
| ☐ **EGGINTON, Frank** ............................ *drawings* | $220 | $302 |
| British b. 1908 | | | |
| ☐ **EGGLESTON, Anna C.** ....................... *paintings* | | | $495 |
| American early 20th cent. | | | |
| ☐ **EGGLESTON, Benjamin Osro** .............. *paintings* | $137 | $5,280 |
| American 1867-1937 ................................ *drawings* | | | $55 |
| ☐ **EGIDI, I.** ........................................... *paintings* | | | $495 |
| ☐ **EGLAU, Max** ..................................... *paintings* | $1,650 | $2,640 |
| German/American b. 1825 | | | |
| ☐ **EGNER, Marie** ................................... *paintings* | $220 | $412 |
| ☐ **EGORNOV, Aleksandr Simionovich** ...... *paintings* | $440 | $550 |
| Russian 1858-1902 | | | |
| ☐ **EGUCHI, Shyu** ................................... *sculpture* | | | $1,100 |
| Japanese b. 1932 | | | |
| ☐ **EGUSQUIZA, Rogelio** ........................ *paintings* | $7,700 | $33,000 |
| Spanish 19th cent. | | | |
| ☐ **EHB** ................................................... *drawings* | | | $400 |

| | | Current Price Range | |
| | | Low | High |
| --- | --- | --- | --- |

☐ **EHCOSTYM, L.** ............................... *paintings* | | $3,575
British 19th cent.

☐ **EHNINGER, John Whetten** .................. *paintings* | $385 | $14,300
American 1827-1889 ................................ *drawings* | | $165

☐ **EHRENBERG, Pual** ........................... *paintings* | | $440
German 1876-1949

☐ **EHRET, Georg Dyonis** ........................ *drawings* | | $5,500
German/British 1710-1770

☐ **EHRIG, William** ............................... *paintings* | $330 | $770

☐ **EIBISCHE, Eugene** ........................... *paintings* | | $440

☐ **EICHHOLTZ, Jacob** ........................... *paintings* | $660 | $3,850*
American 1776-1842

☐ **EICHINGER, Erwin** ........................... *paintings* | $357 | $1,045
German 19th/20th cent.

☐ **EICHINGER, Otto** ............................. *paintings* | $352 | $3,300
Austrian

☐ **EICHLER, Antoine** ........................... *paintings* | | $1,210
German 19th cent.

☐ **EICHLER, Hermann** .......................... *paintings* | | $385

☐ **EICKELBERG, Willem Hendrik** ........... *paintings* | $302 | $2,420
Dutch 1845-1920

☐ **EICKEN, Elizabeth von** ........................ *paintings* | | $412
German 19th cent.

☐ **EICKHAUT, J.J.** ............................... *paintings* | | $418

☐ **EILSHEMIUS, Louis Michel** ................. *paintings* | $165 | $4,400
American 1864-1942 ................................. *drawings* | $55 | $800

☐ **EINSCHLAG, Edouard** ........................ *drawings* | | $715

☐ **EISELE, C.** ..................................... *paintings* | $176 | $770
American 19th/20th cent.

☐ **EISEMANN, Johann Anton** .................. *paintings* | | $2,090

☐ **EISEN, Charles Dominique Joseph** ........ *paintings* | $660 | $2,090
French 1720-1778

☐ **EISEN, Francois** ............................... *paintings* | | $1,430
Flemish c. 1695-after 1778

☐ **EISENDIECK, Suzanne** ........................ *paintings* | $440 | $2,860
German b. 1908 ...................................... *drawings* | | $935

☐ **EISENLOHR, Edward G.** ..................... *paintings* | $495 | $935
American 1872-1961

☐ **EISENLOHR, L.W.** ............................ *paintings* | | $1,045
European late 19th cent.

☐ **EISENMAN, Michael** .......................... *paintings* | | $192
American 20th cent.

☐ **EISENSCHITZ, Willy** ......................... *drawings* | $66 | $200
French 1889-1974

☐ **EISER** ........................................... *paintings* | | $495

☐ **EISERTH, L.** ................................... *paintings* | | $275
early 20th cent.

☐ **EKBLAD, Felix** ................................ *paintings* | $253 | $330
European 19th cent.

| | | Current Price Range | |
|---|---|---|---|
| | | Low | High |
| ☐ **EKENAES, Jahn** ................. *paintings* | | $495 | $14,300 |
| Norwegian b. 1847 ..................... *drawings* | | | $385 |
| ☐ **EKWALL, Knut** ................. *paintings* | | $20,900 | $38,500 |
| Swedish 1843-1912 | | | |
| ☐ **ELDRED, Lemuel D.** .......... *paintings* | | $770 | $4,500 |
| American 1848-1921 ................. *drawings* | | | $385 |
| ☐ **ELDRIDGE, Henry** ........... *drawings* | | | $550 |
| ☐ **ELEN, Philippe-West** ........... *paintings* | | | $450 |
| British 19th cent. | | | |
| ☐ **ELENSER, H.** ..................... *paintings* | | | $550 |
| American contemporary | | | |
| ☐ **ELEON** ................. *paintings* | | | $440 |
| Hungarian b. 1904 | | | |
| ☐ **ELES, U.** ..................... *paintings* | | | $770 |
| Continental School 19th cent. | | | |
| ☐ **ELGOOD, George Samuel** ............ *drawings* | | $440 | $880 |
| English 1851-1943 | | | |
| ☐ **ELHAFEN, Ignaz** .............. *sculpture* | | | $25,300 |
| German late 17th cent. | | | |
| ☐ **ELHOFF, Richard** ............. *paintings* | | | $550 |
| ☐ **ELIASZ, Nicolaes (called PICKENOY)** ... *paintings* | | | $8,800 |
| Dutch 1590/91-1953/56 | | | |
| ☐ **ELIM, F.** ..................... *paintings* | | $2,420 | $3,300 |
| French 20th cent. | | | |
| ☐ **ELIOT, V.** ..................... *paintings* | | | $825 |
| ☐ **ELKINS, Henry Arthur** .......... *paintings* | | $330 | $935 |
| American 1847-1884 | | | |
| ☐ **ELKINS, L.A.** ..................... *paintings* | | $297 | $363 |
| ☐ **ELLIGER, Ottmar** .............. *paintings* | | | $11,000 |
| German | | | |
| ☐ **ELLIOT, James** ................. *paintings* | | $385 | $2,310 |
| English ac. 1848-1873 | | | |
| ☐ **ELLIOT, John** ................. *paintings* | | | $1,430 |
| English 1858-1925 | | | |
| ☐ **ELLIOTT, Charles Loring** .......... *paintings* | | $330 | $3,740 |
| American 1812-1868 | | | |
| ☐ **ELLIS, A.** ..................... *paintings* | | | $275 |
| ☐ **ELLIS, Clyde G.** .............. *paintings* | | $99 | $247 |
| American b. 1879 | | | |
| ☐ **ELLIS, Edmund** .............. *paintings* | | $110 | $302 |
| ☐ **ELLIS, Edwin John** ............. *paintings* | | $412 | $770 |
| English 1841-1895 ................. *drawings* | | | $77 |
| ☐ **ELLIS, Fremont F.** ............. *paintings* | | $1,430 | $15,000 |
| American b. 1897 | | | |
| ☐ **ELLIS, W.E.** ..................... *paintings* | | $165 | $770 |
| British 19th cent. | | | |
| ☐ **ELLSWORTH, Clarence Arthur** .......... *paintings* | | $880 | $9,000 |
| American 1885-1961 ................. *drawings* | | | $450 |
| ☐ **ELLSWORTH, E.** .............. *paintings* | | | $440 |

| | | | Current Price Range | |
| | | | Low | High |
|---|---|---|---|---|
| ☐ **ELLSWORTH, James** ............... *drawings* | | | | $1,650 |
| American c. 1840 | | | | |
| ☐ **ELMBLAD, H.** ............... *paintings* | | | $308 | $880 |
| Norwegian 19th cent. | | | | |
| ☐ **ELMER, Stephen** ............... *paintings* | | | $2,200 | $29,700 |
| English c. 1714-1796 | | | | |
| ☐ **ELMIGER, Franz** ............... *paintings* | | | | $1,430 |
| Swiss 1882-1934 | | | | |
| ☐ **ELMORE, Richard** ............... *paintings* | | | | $880 |
| ☐ **ELOUT, Franchoys** ............... *paintings* | | | | $33,000 |
| Dutch 1597-c. 1641 | | | | |
| ☐ **ELSASSER, Frederick Auguste** ............ *paintings* | | | | $2,090 |
| German 1810-1845 | | | | |
| ☐ **ELSHOLTZ, Ludwig** ............... *paintings* | | | | $3,850 |
| German 1805-1850 | | | | |
| ☐ **ELSLEY, Arthur John** ............... *paintings* | | | $1,100 | $15,400 |
| English b. 1861; ac. 1903 | | | | |
| ☐ **ELSTER, Gottlieb** ............... *sculpture* | | | | $330 |
| German 19th cent. | | | | |
| ☐ **ELTING, N.D.** ............... *paintings* | | | $77 | $302 |
| American 19th cent. | | | | |
| ☐ **ELWELL, D. Jerome** ............... *paintings* | | | $330 | $1,650 |
| American 1847/57-1912 ............... *drawings* | | | $137 | $250 |
| ☐ **ELWELL, Fred** ............... *paintings* | | | $3,250 | $12,100 |
| 20th cent. | | | | |
| ☐ **ELWELL, Frederick W.** ............... *paintings* | | | | $350 |
| British 1870-1958 | | | | |
| ☐ **ELWELL, J.D.** ............... *drawings* | | | $137 | $302 |
| American 1847-1912 | | | | |
| ☐ **ELWELL, R. Farrington** ............... *paintings* | | | $495 | $1,760 |
| American 1874-1962 ............... *drawings* | | | $77 | $330 |
| ☐ **ELWES, Simon** ............... *paintings* | | | | $660 |
| ☐ **EMANUEL, Frank Lewis** ............... *paintings* | | | $187 | $660 |
| English 1865-1948 ............... *drawings* | | | | $247 |
| ☐ **EMANUELOV, Victor** ............... *paintings* | | | $247 | $1,210 |
| Russian 1884-1940 | | | | |
| ☐ **EMBLETON, Ron** ............... *paintings* | | | | $880 |
| ☐ **EMBRO, L.** ............... *paintings* | | | | $522 |
| Italian 19th cent. | | | | |
| ☐ **EMBRY, Norris** ............... *paintings* | | | | $770 |
| American 1921-1981 ............... *drawings* | | | $495 | $1,980 |
| ☐ **EMELE, Wilhelm** ............... *paintings* | | | | $14,300 |
| German 1830-1905 | | | | |
| ☐ **EMELEN, Adolf van** ............... *paintings* | | | | $220 |
| Dutch 19th/20th cent. | | | | |
| ☐ **EMERICH, Harvey** ............... *paintings* | | | | $302 |
| American b. 1884 | | | | |
| ☐ **EMERSON, Arthur Webster** ............... *paintings* | | | | $302 |
| American b. 1885 | | | | |

| | | | Current Price Range | |
|---|---|---|---|---|
| | | | Low | High |
| ☐ EMERSON, Charles Chase | .................... | *paintings* | $192 | $1,210 |
| American d. 1922 | | | | |
| ☐ EMERSON, Edith | ............................. | *paintings* | | $220 |
| American b. 1888 | ...................................... | *drawings* | $66 | $176 |
| ☐ EMERSON, W.C. | ............................. | *paintings* | $247 | $825 |
| Anglo/American 19th/20th cent. | | | | |
| ☐ EMERY, James | .................................... | *paintings* | $1,100 | $2,700 |
| American 19th cent. | | | | |
| ☐ EMMER, F. | ........................................ | *paintings* | | $550 |
| German early 20th cent. | | | | |
| ☐ EMMERIK, Govert van | ..................... | *paintings* | $577 | $1,540 |
| Dutch 1808-1882 | | | | |
| ☐ EMMET, Ellen G. | ............................. | *paintings* | | $1,100 |
| American 1876-1941 | ................................. | *drawings* | $192 | $192 |
| ☐ EMMET, Lydia Field | ......................... | *paintings* | $1,760 | $7,150 |
| American 1866-1952 | | | | |
| ☐ EMMETT, J.S. | ................................... | *paintings* | | $425 |
| ☐ EMMONS, Alexander Hamilton | ............ | *paintings* | | $247 |
| American 1816-1879 | | | | |
| ☐ EMMONS, Dorothy Stanley | ................. | *paintings* | $450 | $650 |
| American b. 1891 | | | | |
| ☐ EMMS, John | ...................................... | *paintings* | $880 | $6,050 |
| English 1843-1912 | | | | |
| ☐ EMPEL, Jan van | ............................... | *paintings* | | $2,090 |
| American 20th cent. | | | | |
| ☐ EMSLIE, Alfred | ............................. | *drawings* | $165 | $440 |
| English 1848-1917 | | | | |
| ☐ ENAULT, Alix Louise | .......................... | *paintings* | $220 | $19,250 |
| French d. 1913 | | | | |
| ☐ ENDE, Hansam | ................................. | *paintings* | | $880 |
| German b. 1864 | | | | |
| ☐ ENDER, Axel Hjalmar | ......................... | *paintings* | $550 | $3,850 |
| Norwegian 1853-1920 | | | | |
| ☐ ENDER, Edouard | ............................. | *paintings* | $7,700 | $15,400 |
| Austrian 1822-1883 | | | | |
| ☐ ENDER, Thomas | ............................. | *paintings* | $2,860 | $3,740 |
| Austrian 1793-1875 | | | | |
| ☐ ENDERS, Frank | ................................. | *paintings* | | $1,210 |
| American 20th cent. | | | | |
| ☐ ENDERS, Oscar | ................................. | *paintings* | | $220 |
| American | | | | |
| ☐ ENDLER, Enry | ................................. | *paintings* | | $770 |
| German 19th cent. | | | | |
| ☐ ENDLICH, H. | ................................... | *paintings* | | $275 |
| Dutch 20th cent. | | | | |
| ☐ ENDOGOUROV, Ivan Ivanovich | ........... | *paintings* | $1,100 | $6,875 |
| Russian 1861-1898 | | | | |
| ☐ ENDRES, Bernard | ............................. | *paintings* | | $467 |
| ☐ ENDSTORFER, A. | ............................. | *sculpture* | | $385 |

|  | | | Current Price Range | |
|---|---|---|---|---|
|  | | | Low | High |
| ☐ **ENGELBRECHTSZ, Cornelis** ............... *paintings* | | | **$4,400** | **$10,450** |
| ☐ **ENGELFELT, F.** .................................... *paintings* | | | **$121** | **$220** |
| German (?) 19th/20th cent. | | | | |
| ☐ **ENGELHARD, Friedrich Wilhelm** ......... *paintings* | | | | **$4,675** |
| German 1813-1902 | | | | |
| ☐ **ENGELHARDT, Edna Palmer** ............... *paintings* | | | **$99** | **$550** |
| American 20th cent. | | | | |
| ☐ **ENGELHARDT, Georg** ....................... *paintings* | | | **$660** | **$5,500** |
| German 1823-1883 | | | | |
| ☐ **ENGELHARDT, Hermann von** ............. *paintings* | | | | **$1,210** |
| German 1858-1914 | | | | |
| ☐ **ENGELHARDT, Leop?** ........................ *paintings* | | | | **$302** |
| American early 20th cent. | | | | |
| ☐ **ENGELHART, Catherine** ..................... *drawings* | | | | **$9,900** |
| Danish b. 1845 | | | | |
| ☐ **ENGELHART, Joseph** .......................... *paintings* | | | **$247** | **$440** |
| American ac. 1890 | | | | |
| ☐ **ENGELS, Robert** ............................... *paintings* | | | | **$2,200** |
| German b. 1866 | | | | |
| ☐ **ENGL, Hugo** ....................................... *paintings* | | | | **$17,050** |
| ☐ **ENGLAND, E.S.** ................................. *paintings* | | | | **$550** |
| English 19th cent. | | | | |
| ☐ **ENGLE, H.L.** ..................................... *paintings* | | | | **$247** |
| American | | | | |
| ☐ **ENGLEHART, John J.** ........................ *paintings* | | | **$99** | **$1,980** |
| American 19th cent. | | | | |
| ☐ **ENGLER, P.** ....................................... *paintings* | | | | **$521** |
| French d. 1879 | | | | |
| ☐ **ENGLISH, Frank F.** ............................ *paintings* | | | **$550** | **$2,530** |
| American 1854-1922 .................................. *drawings* | | | **$88** | **$1,980** |
| ☐ **ENGLISH, Mabel Bacon Plimpton** ........ *paintings* | | | **$176** | **$198** |
| American b. 1861 | | | | |
| ☐ **ENGRAND, Georges** ........................... *sculpture* | | | | **$1,650** |
| French early 20th cent. | | | | |
| ☐ **ENHUBER, Karl von** ........................... *paintings* | | | | **$15,400** |
| German 1811-1867 | | | | |
| ☐ **ENJOLRAS, Delphin** ........................... *paintings* | | | **$2,200** | **$3,575** |
| French b. 1857 ....................................... *drawings* | | | | **$4,950** |
| ☐ **ENNEKING, John Joseph** .................... *paintings* | | | **$385** | **$34,100** |
| American 1841-1916 .................................. *drawings* | | | **$385** | **$880** |
| ☐ **ENNEKING, Joseph Eliot** .................... *paintings* | | | **$220** | **$700** |
| American d. 1946 | | | | |
| ☐ **ENNIS, George Pearce** ........................ *paintings* | | | **$715** | **$1,650** |
| American 20th cent. .................................. *drawings* | | | **$300** | **$385** |
| ☐ **ENRIQUEZ, Antonio** ........................... *paintings* | | | | **$7,150** |
| Mexican ac. 18th cent. | | | | |
| ☐ **ENRIQUEZ, Carlos** ............................. *paintings* | | | **$300** | **$1,650** |
| b. Cuba 1900-1955 .................................. *drawings* | | | **$300** | **$385** |
| ☐ **ENSOL, E.** ......................................... *paintings* | | | **$88** | **$495** |

## Genre Paintings

Genre paintings are paintings of particular scenes, often drawn from everyday life. Domestic interiors, "typical" villages, peasants, and rural scenes all qualify as genre paintings.

This portrait of a man in a Tyrolean hat by German artist Rudolf Epp is a good example of genre portraiture and is of a type frequently found at auction. Epp (1834–1910) was a favorite genre painter and portrait artist of the 19th century. (Rudolf Epp, "Portrait of a Man in a Tyrolean Hat," oil on canvas, 9 x 11½ in., Milwaukee, September 17, 1984, $3,300.)

|  |  | Current Price Range | |
|---|---|---|---|
|  |  | *Low* | *High* |
| ☐ **ENSOR, James** ..................... *paintings* | | **$24,200** | **$385,000** |
| Belgian 1860-1949 ..................... *drawings* | | **$2,420** | **$6,050** |
| ☐ **ENSOR, Mary** ..................... *paintings* | | **$1,089** | **$2,200** |
| British ac. 1871-1874 | | | |
| ☐ **ENTRAYGUES, Charles Bertrand d'** .... *paintings* | | **$715** | **$935** |
| French b. 1851 | | | |
| ☐ **ENWRIGHT, J.J.** ............... *paintings* | | | **$286** |
| American b. 1905 | | | |
| ☐ **EPERRIE, B.** ..................... *paintings* | | | **$220** |
| French 19th/20th cent. | | | |
| ☐ **EPINAY, Marie d'** ............... *paintings* | | | **$1,100** |
| French 19th cent. | | | |
| ☐ **EPKO** ..................... *paintings* | | **$220** | **$440** |
| ☐ **EPOSITO, Benito** ............... *paintings* | | | **$4,675** |
| ☐ **EPP, Rudolf** ..................... *paintings* | | **$2,530** | **$8,525** |
| German 1834-1910 | | | |
| ☐ **EPSTEIN, Henri** ............... *paintings* | | | **$825** |
| ☐ **EPSTEIN, Jehudo** ............... *paintings* | | **$715** | **$2,475** |
| Polish 1870-1946 | | | |
| ☐ **EPSTEIN, Sir Jacob** ............... *drawings* | | **$176** | **$880** |
| English 1880-1959 ..................... *sculpture* | | **$550** | **$5,775** |
| ☐ **ERDMAN, B.** ..................... *paintings* | | | **$275** |

| | | Current Price Range | |
|---|---|---|---|
| | | Low | High |
| ☐ **ERDMANN, Heinrich Eduard Moritz** .... *paintings* | | | $3,960 |
| German 1845-1919 | | | |
| ☐ **ERDMANN, Otto** ................................ *paintings* | | $522 | $6,600 |
| German 1834-1905 | | | |
| ☐ **ERGANIAN, S.** ...................................... *paintings* | | | $550 |
| ☐ **ERGO, Englebert** ............................... *paintings* | | | $14,300 |
| Flemish 17th cent. | | | |
| ☐ **ERHT, H.** ........................................... *sculpture* | | | $330 |
| ☐ **ERICH, H.** ........................................... *sculpture* | | | $286 |
| German late 19th cent. | | | |
| ☐ **ERICKSON, W.** ................................... *paintings* | | | $495 |
| ☐ **ERICSON, David** ............................... *paintings* | | $319 | $1,045 |
| Swedish/American 1870/73-1946 | | | |
| ☐ **ERIKA** ........................................... *paintings* | | | $660 |
| American 20th cent. | | | |
| ☐ **ERIKSEN, N.** ..................................... *paintings* | | | $825 |
| ☐ **ERISTOFF-KASAK, Princess Marie** ...... *paintings* | | | $16,500 |
| Russian b. 19th cent. | | | |
| ☐ **ERKLAND, P.** ..................................... *drawings* | | | $412 |
| ☐ **ERMLEAFER, A.** ................................ *sculpture* | | | $308 |
| ☐ **ERMLER, A.** ...................................... *sculpture* | | | $528 |
| ☐ **ERNESTI, Ethel** ................................ *paintings* | | $247 | $550 |
| American 19th/20th cent. | | | |
| ☐ **ERNI, Hans** ........................................ *paintings* | | $250 | $5,500 |
| Swiss b. 1909 ....................................... *drawings* | | $22 | $1,430 |
| ☐ **ERNST, Jimmy** ................................... *paintings* | | $412 | $2,310 |
| German/American b. 1920 ........................... *drawings* | | $224 | $1,980 |
| ☐ **ERNST, Max** ..................................... *paintings* | | $5,060 | $165,000 |
| French 1891-1976 ..................................... *drawings* | | $1,650 | $44,000 |
| ........................................................ *sculpture* | | $990 | $962,500 |
| ☐ **ERNST, Rudolf** .................................. *paintings* | | $1,650 | $107,250 |
| Austrian b. 1854 ...................................... *drawings* | | $660 | $4,180 |
| ☐ **ERRI, Bartolomeo Degli** ..................... *paintings* | | | $49,500 |
| ☐ **ERRINGTON, J.** ................................. *paintings* | | | $286 |
| British | | | |
| ☐ **ERTE, (Romain de TIRTOFF)** ............. *paintings* | | $330 | $1,980 |
| Russian b. 1892 ...................................... *drawings* | | $200 | $3,740 |
| ☐ **ERTZ, Edward Frederick** .................... *paintings* | | $55 | $412 |
| American b. 1862 | | | |
| ☐ **ES, Jacob van** .................................... *paintings* | | $22,000 | $35,200 |
| Flemish 1596-1666 | | | |
| ☐ **ESCARS, Yves Edgard Muller d'** .......... *paintings* | | | $2,860 |
| French 1876-1958 | | | |
| ☐ **ESCCULA** ........................................ *sculpture* | | | $275 |
| ☐ **ESCH, Mathilde** ............................... *paintings* | | | $1,320 |
| ☐ **ESCHMANN, Ch.** ............................... *paintings* | | | $522 |
| German 19th cent. | | | |
| ☐ **ESCHWEGE, Elmer von** ...................... *paintings* | | | $49,500 |
| German b. 1856 | | | |

| | | Current Price Range | |
|---|---|---|---|
| | | Low | High |
| ☐ **ESCOBEDO, Augusto** ............ *sculpture* | | $335 | $935 |
| Mexican/American b. 1914 | | | |
| ☐ **ESCOSURA, Ignacio Leon y** ........ *paintings* | | $2,750 | $23,100 |
| Spanish 1834-1901 | | | |
| ☐ **ESCRIBE, CH.** ................. *drawings* | | | $550 |
| ☐ **ESKILSSON, Peter** ............ *paintings* | | $462 | $1,650 |
| Swedish 1820-1872 | | | |
| ☐ **ESLEY, Donald W.** ............ *drawings* | | | $247 |
| American 20th cent. | | | |
| ☐ **ESNAULT, Maurice** ............ *paintings* | | | $220 |
| American 20th cent. | | | |
| ☐ **ESPAGNAT, Georges d'** ........ *paintings* | | $1,320 | $44,000 |
| French 1870-1950 | | | |
| ☐ **ESPARTERO, E.** ............ *paintings* | | | $330 |
| ☐ **ESPAY, A.** ................. *paintings* | | $33 | $450 |
| ☐ **ESPINOS, J.** ................. *paintings* | | | $715 |
| ☐ **ESPOSITO, Gaetano** ............ *paintings* | | $385 | $15,400 |
| Italian 1858-1911 ................. *drawings* | | | $935 |
| ☐ **ESPOSITO, V. d'** ............ *drawings* | | | $220 |
| Italian 19th cent. | | | |
| ☐ **ESPOY, Angel DeService** ........ *paintings* | | $165 | $1,320 |
| American 1869-1964 | | | |
| ☐ **ESPOY, L.** ................. *paintings* | | | $605 |
| 20th cent. | | | |
| ☐ **ESSELENS, Jacob** ............ *paintings* | | | $6,050 |
| Dutch 1626-1687 | | | |
| ☐ **ESSEN, Johannes Cornelis (Jan) van** ..... *paintings* | | | $715 |
| Dutch 1854-1936 ................. *drawings* | | | $330 |
| ☐ **ESSEY, Jan van** ............ *drawings* | | | $467 |
| American 19th cent. | | | |
| ☐ **ESSIG, George E.** ............ *paintings* | | $770 | $3,300 |
| American b. 1838 ................. *drawings* | | $22 | $660 |
| ☐ **ESTABEN Y LIZCANO** ............ *paintings* | | | $550 |
| ☐ **ESTELL, George E.** ............ *drawings* | | | $440 |
| American late 19th cent. | | | |
| ☐ **ESTES, Richard** ............ *paintings* | | $2,090 | $143,000 |
| American b. 1936 ................. *drawings* | | $88 | $29,700 |
| ☐ **ESTEVE, Maurice** ............ *drawings* | | | $7,150 |
| ☐ **ESTEVE YMARQUES, Augustin** ........ *paintings* | | | $36,300 |
| Spanish 1753-c. 1809 | | | |
| ☐ **ESTIENNE, Giovanni** ............ *paintings* | | $770 | $1,870 |
| Italian b. 1870 | | | |
| ☐ **ESTIENNET** ............ *paintings* | | $330 | $467 |
| ☐ **ESTOPINAN, Roberto** ............ *drawings* | | | $715 |
| ☐ **ETCHART, Severo Rodriguez** ............ *paintings* | | | $660 |
| ☐ **ETCHELLS, Frederick** ............ *drawings* | | | $41,800 |
| English 1886-1973 | | | |
| ☐ **ETCHETA, L.** ............ *sculpture* | | $1,430 | $1,815 |

| | Current Price Range | |
|---|---|---|
| | *Low* | *High* |
| ☐ **ETCHEVERRY, Hubert Denis** ............. *paintings* | | $2,200 |
| French 1867-1950 | | |
| ☐ **ETHERIDGE, C.B.** ............................. *paintings* | | $1,650 |
| American 19th cent. | | |
| ☐ **ETIENNE, Arnold** ................................. *paintings* | | $330 |
| ☐ **ETIENNE, Ch.** ...................................... *paintings* | | $385 |
| Continental 19th cent. | | |
| ☐ **ETNIER, Stephen Morgan** ................... *paintings* | $176 | $1,650 |
| American b. 1903 | | |
| ☐ **ETROG, Sorel** ..................................... *sculpture* | $1,650 | $10,450 |
| American b. 1933 | | |
| ☐ **ETTIN, K. van** ..................................... *paintings* | | $550 |
| ☐ **ETTING, H.** .......................................... *paintings* | | $385 |
| ☐ **ETTY, William** ..................................... *paintings* | $412 | $1,980 |
| English 1787-1849 ..................................... *drawings* | | $137 |
| ☐ **EUBANKS, Tony** ................................. *paintings* | $3,740 | $11,500 |
| American b. 1939 | | |
| ☐ **EUGENE-JEAN** ................................... *paintings* | | $220 |
| Haitian 20th cent. | | |
| ☐ **EURICH, Richard** ............................... *paintings* | | $770 |
| English b. 1903 | | |
| ☐ **EUZINGER, Hans** ................................. *paintings* | | $1,430 |
| ☐ **EVANS, A.E.** ........................................ *paintings* | | $352 |
| ☐ **EVANS, Bernard Walter** ....................... *drawings* | $110 | $660 |
| English 1843/48-1922 | | |
| ☐ **EVANS, Bruce** ..................................... *paintings* | $770 | $2,970 |
| ☐ **EVANS, De Scott** ............................... *paintings* | $715 | $26,400 |
| American 1847-1898 | | |
| ☐ **EVANS, Fred M.** ................................. *drawings* | | $800 |
| British 19th cent. | | |
| ☐ **EVANS, Grace Lydia** ............................ *paintings* | | $495 |
| American b. 1877 | | |
| ☐ **EVANS, James Guy** ............................. *paintings* | | $34,100 |
| American ac. 1838-1860 | | |
| ☐ **EVANS, Jessie Benton** ......................... *paintings* | $165 | $220 |
| American 1866-1954 | | |
| ☐ **EVANS, Powys** ................................... *paintings* | | $275 |
| British b. 1899 | | |
| ☐ **EVANS, Rudolph** ............................... *paintings* | $220 | $242 |
| American 1878-1960 ................................. *sculpture* | $66 | $154 |
| ☐ **EVANS, William (of Eton)** ..................... *drawings* | | $1,760 |
| English 1798-1877 | | |
| ☐ **EVE, Jean** ......................................... *paintings* | $715 | $3,520 |
| French 1900-1968 | | |
| ☐ **EVERARD, R.** ..................................... *paintings* | $132 | $495 |
| English 19th cent. | | |
| ☐ **EVERBROECK, Frans van** ................... *paintings* | | $17,600 |
| Flemish 2nd half 17th cent. | | |

| | Current Price Range | |
|---|---|---|
| | Low | High |
| ☐ **EVERDING, Wilhelm B.** ...... *paintings* | | $1,760 |
| German b. 1863 | | |
| ☐ **EVERDINGEN, Allart van** ...... *paintings* | $5,775 | $8,800 |
| Dutch c. 1621-c. 1675 ...... *drawings* | $1,760 | $3,960 |
| ☐ **EVERDINGER, Adriaen van** ...... *drawings* | | $198 |
| Dutch 1823-1910 | | |
| ☐ **EVERETT, Walter Hunt** ...... *paintings* | | $1,100 |
| American b. 1870 | | |
| ☐ **EVERGOOD, Phillip** ...... *paintings* | $352 | $12,100 |
| American 1901-1973 ...... *drawings* | $55 | $7,150 |
| ☐ **EVERINGHAM, Millard** ...... *paintings* | | $246 |
| American b. 1912 | | |
| ☐ **EVERS, Ivar Ellis** ...... *paintings* | | $330 |
| American | | |
| ☐ **EVERS, John** ...... *paintings* | $412 | $715 |
| American 1797-1884 | | |
| ☐ **EVERSDYCK, Willem van** ...... *paintings* | | $13,200 |
| Dutch d. 1671 | | |
| ☐ **EVERSEN, Adrianus** ...... *paintings* | $330 | $19,800 |
| Dutch 1818-1897 | | |
| ☐ **EVRARD, Adele** ...... *paintings* | | $24,200 |
| Flemish 1792-1889 | | |
| ☐ **EWEN, M.** ...... *paintings* | $275 | $330 |
| ☐ **EWERS, Heinrich** ...... *paintings* | $3,300 | $3,410 |
| German 1817-1885 | | |
| ☐ **EWERT, Pieter** ...... *paintings* | | $412 |
| Dutch 20th cent. | | |
| ☐ **EWINGS, A.H.** ...... *paintings* | | $357 |
| 20th cent. | | |
| ☐ **EXCRIBE, Charles** ...... *drawings* | | $385 |
| ☐ **EXNER, Johan Julius** ...... *paintings* | | $660 |
| Danish 1825-1910 | | |
| ☐ **EXTER, Alexandra** ...... *drawings* | $495 | $8,800 |
| Russian 1884-1949 | | |
| ☐ **EXTER, Julius** ...... *paintings* | | $825 |
| ☐ **EYBEL, Franz** ...... *paintings* | $660 | $5,225 |
| Austrian 1806-1880 | | |
| ☐ **EYBERGER, A.J. van** ...... *paintings* | | $357 |
| ☐ **EYCK, Caspar van** ...... *paintings* | | $7,975 |
| Flemish 1613-1673 | | |
| ☐ **EYCK, Nicholas van** ...... *paintings* | | $6,600 |
| Flemish | | |
| ☐ **EYCKEN, Charles van den** ...... *paintings* | $1,980 | $5,500 |
| Belgian 1859-1923 | | |
| ☐ **EYCKEN, Felix van den** ...... *paintings* | | $1,100 |
| Belgian 19th cent. | | |
| ☐ **EYDEN, William Arnold (Jr.)** ...... *paintings* | | $250 |
| American b. 1893 | | |

| | | Current Price Range | |
|---|---|---|---|
| | | Low | High |
| ☐ **EYK, Abraham van der** ......................... *paintings* | | $1,210 | $5,500 |
| Dutch 18th cent. | | | |
| ☐ **EYKENS, F.** ..................................... *paintings* | | | $9,900 |
| Flemish 1627-1673 | | | |
| ☐ **EYLES, L.C.** ..................................... *paintings* | | | $1,430 |
| American | | | |
| ☐ **EYMER, Arnoldus Johannes** ................. *paintings* | | | $3,520 |
| Dutch 1803-1863 | | | |
| ☐ **EYSSAUTIER, Joseph** .......................... *drawings* | | | $1,210 |
| ☐ **EYTINGE, Solomon (Jr.)** ....................... *paintings* | | | $3,960 |
| American 1833-1905 | | | |
| ☐ **FABBI, Fabio** ..................................... *paintings* | | $550 | $12,100 |
| Italian 1861-1946 ..................................... *drawings* | | $275 | $2,475 |
| ☐ **FABER, Ludwig E.** ............................... *paintings* | | $192 | $1,265 |
| American 1855-1913 ................................. *drawings* | | $120 | $187 |
| ☐ **FABER DU FAUR, Otto von** ................. *paintings* | | | $990 |
| German 1828-1901 ................................... *drawings* | | | $467 |
| ☐ **FABER VON KREUZNACH, Konrad** ... *paintings* | | | $49,500 |
| German 1500-1552/53 | | | |
| ☐ **FABERT, Jean** ..................................... *paintings* | | $11 | $220 |
| French 20th cent. | | | |
| ☐ **FABIEN, Louis** ................................... *paintings* | | | $660 |
| French b. 1924 | | | |
| ☐ **FABIJANSKI, Erasmus Rudolf** .............. *paintings* | | $1,760 | $2,530 |
| Russian 1829-1891 | | | |
| ☐ **FABRE, H.** ......................................... *paintings* | | $165 | $302 |
| European 19th cent. | | | |
| ☐ **FABRES Y COSTA, Antonio Maria** ...... *paintings* | | $5,225 | $46,200 |
| Spanish b. 1854 ..................................... *drawings* | | $2,420 | $10,175 |
| ☐ **FABRI, C.** ......................................... *paintings* | | | $192 |
| Italian 19th cent. | | | |
| ☐ **FABRIS, Giovanni** .............................. *drawings* | | | $440 |
| Italian 18th/19th cent. | | | |
| ☐ **FABRIS, Pietro** ................................... *paintings* | | | $25,300 |
| Italian 18th cent. | | | |
| ☐ **FABRITIUS DE TENGNAGEL,** | | | |
| **Frederik Michael Ernst** ........................ *paintings* | | | $8,525 |
| Danish 1781-1849 | | | |
| ☐ **FACCIOLA, G.** ................................... *drawings* | | $176 | $440 |
| Italian 19th cent. | | | |
| ☐ **FACCIOLI, Raffaele** ........................... *drawings* | | | $302 |
| ☐ **FACCIOLI, Silvio** .............................. *paintings* | | | $990 |
| Italian 19th cent. | | | |
| ☐ **FACHINETTI, C.** ............................... *paintings* | | | $1,650 |
| Italian 19th cent. | | | |
| ☐ **FADER, Fernando** .............................. *paintings* | | | $33,000 |
| Argentinian 1882-1935 | | | |
| ☐ **FAED, John** ..................................... *paintings* | | $7,700 | $47,300 |
| British 1819/20-1902 | | | |

| | | Current Price Range | |
|---|---|---|---|
| | | Low | High |
| ☐ **FAED, Thomas** ........................ *paintings* | | $440 | $4,180 |
| Scottish 1826-1900 | | | |
| ☐ **FAES, Pieter** ........................ *paintings* | | | $44,000 |
| Flemish 1750-1814 | | | |
| ☐ **FAGAN, Betty** ........................ *paintings* | | | $2,310 |
| American 20th cent. | | | |
| ☐ **FAGNANI, Guiseppe** ........................ *paintings* | | $209 | $825 |
| ☐ **FAHNESTOCK, Wallace Weir** .............. *paintings* | | $154 | $3,575 |
| American b. 1877 | | | |
| ☐ **FAHRBACH, Carl Ludwig** ................ *paintings* | | $880 | $7,150 |
| German 1835-1902 | | | |
| ☐ **FAILLE, Carl Arthur** ........................ *paintings* | | $132 | $385 |
| American 1883/84-1952? | | | |
| ☐ **FAILLOT, Edme Nicolas** ................ *sculpture* | | | $1,320 |
| French 19th cent. | | | |
| ☐ **FAIRCHILD, Elizabeth** ........................ *drawings* | | | $440 |
| American | | | |
| ☐ **FAIRCHILD, Mary** ........................ *drawings* | | | $440 |
| American 19th cent. | | | |
| ☐ **FAIRMAN, James** ........................ *paintings* | | $605 | $5,225 |
| Scottish/American 1826-1904 | | | |
| ☐ **FAISTENBERGER, Anton** ................ *paintings* | | | $3,080 |
| ☐ **FAITHFULL, Leila** ........................ *paintings* | | | $825 |
| British 19th/20th cent. | | | |
| ☐ **FAIVRE, J.A.** ........................ *paintings* | | $121 | $440 |
| French | | | |
| ☐ **FAIVRE-DUFFER, Louis Stanislas** ........ *paintings* | | | $850 |
| French 1818-1897 | | | |
| ☐ **FALANGAR, S.** ........................ *paintings* | | | $302 |
| Continental 19th/20th cent. | | | |
| ☐ **FALANGE, Enrico** ........................ *paintings* | | | $1,100 |
| ☐ **FALAT, Julian** ........................ *drawings* | | $247 | $7,700 |
| Polish b. 1853 | | | |
| ☐ **FALCHETTI, Giuseppe** ........................ *paintings* | | $1,320 | $1,870 |
| Italian 1843-1918 | | | |
| ☐ **FALCONE, Aniello** ........................ *paintings* | | $9,350 | $23,000 |
| Italian 1600/07-1656/65 | | | |
| ☐ **FALCONER, John M.** ........................ *paintings* | | | $1,800 |
| American 1820-1903 | | | |
| ☐ **FALCONET, Etienne M.** ................ *sculpture* | | $1,430 | $3,080 |
| French 1716-1791 | | | |
| ☐ **FALCUCCI** ........................ *paintings* | | $81 | $660 |
| ☐ **FALDI, Arturo** ........................ *drawings* | | | $440 |
| Italian b. 1856 | | | |
| ☐ **FALENA, P.** ........................ *drawings* | | | $495 |
| Italian 19th cent. | | | |
| ☐ **FALENS, Carel van** ........................ *paintings* | | | $5,500 |
| Flemish 1683-1733 | | | |

| | | *Current Price Range* | |
|---|---|---|---|
| | | *Low* | *High* |
| ☐ **FALERO, A.** ........................... *paintings* <br> Italian 19th cent. | | | $880 |
| ☐ **FALERO, Emilio** ............................... *paintings* <br> b. Cuba 1947 | | $22 | $2,640 |
| ☐ **FALERO, Luis Riccardo** ...................... *paintings* <br> Spanish 1851-1896 | | $2,200 | $12,100 |
| ☐ **FALGUIERE, Jean Alexandre Joseph** .... *drawings* <br> French 1831-1900 ...................................... *sculpture* | | $1,754 | $4,950 <br> $2,400 |
| ☐ **FALK, R.** ............................................. *paintings* <br> English 19th cent. | | | $297 |
| ☐ **FALK, Robert** ................................. *paintings* <br> Russian b. 1930 | | | $990 |
| ☐ **FALKENSTEIN, Claire** ................. *sculpture* <br> American b. 1908/09 | | | $550 |
| ☐ **FALKNER, Henry** ............................... *paintings* <br> American 20th cent. | | $110 | $220 |
| ☐ **FALLS, Clinton Dewitt** ......................... *paintings* <br> American 1864-1934 | | | $275 |
| ☐ **FALTER, John Philip** ........................... *paintings* <br> American b. 1910 ...................................... *drawings* | | $220 <br> $82 | $1,980 <br> $220 |
| ☐ **FANCOURT, Richard** ........................... *drawings* | | | $660 |
| ☐ **FANFANI** ......................................... *paintings* <br> Italian late 19th cent. | | $192 | $247 |
| ☐ **FANFANI, Enrico** ............................... *paintings* <br> Italian 19th cent. | | $308 | $2,200 |
| ☐ **FANGEL, Maud Tousey** ...................... *drawings* <br> American ac. 1921 | | | $357 |
| ☐ **FANGEY, Daniel** ................................. *paintings* <br> French 20th cent. | | | $176 |
| ☐ **FANGOR, Wojciech** ........................... *paintings* <br> American b. 1922 | | $385 | $2,530 |
| ☐ **FANNING, William** ............................. *paintings* <br> American 1887-1966 | | | $385 |
| ☐ **FANRASE** ......................................... *sculpture* | | | $385 |
| ☐ **FANTANGA, M.** ............................... *paintings* | | | $550 |
| ☐ **FANTIN-LATOUR,** <br>     **Ignace Henri Jean Theodore** ................. *paintings* <br> French 1836-1904 ...................................... *drawings* | | $1,650 <br> $440 | $528,000 <br> $19,800 |
| ☐ **FANTIN-LATOUR, Theodore** .............. *paintings* <br> French 1805-1872 | | | $2,200 |
| ☐ **FANTINI, Matteo** ............................... *paintings* <br> Italian | | | $275 |
| ☐ **FARAI, Gennaro** ............................... *paintings* <br> Italian b. 1882 | | | $357 |
| ☐ **FARASYN, Edgard** ............................. *paintings* <br> Belgian b. 1858 | | $770 | $1,100 |
| ☐ **FARES, William** ................................. *drawings* <br> American b. 1942 | | | $176 |

| | | Current Price Range | |
|---|---|---|---|
| | | Low | High |
| ☐ **FARETO, P.** ................................ *paintings* | | | **$1,100** |
| American 19th cent. | | | |
| ☐ **FARGUHARSON** .............................. *paintings* | | | **$248** |
| English 19th cent. | | | |
| ☐ **FARINATI, Paolo** ............................. *drawings* | | | **$2,750** |
| Italian 1524-1606 | | | |
| ☐ **FARIS, A.** ................................... *paintings* | **$247** | | **$385** |
| American late 19th cent. | | | |
| ☐ **FARIS, J.A.** .................................. *drawings* | **$500** | | **$950** |
| American 19th cent. | | | |
| ☐ **FARKNER, Edgar** ............................ *paintings* | | | **$825** |
| ☐ **FARLEY, Richard Blossom** ................... *paintings* | **$110** | | **$935** |
| American b. 1875 | | | |
| ☐ **FARLOW, Harry** ............................. *paintings* | | | **$2,420** |
| American b. 1882 | | | |
| ☐ **FARM, Gerald** ............................... *paintings* | | | **$7,000** |
| American b. 1935 | | | |
| ☐ **FARMER, Henry** ............................. *paintings* | | | **$1,045** |
| English 20th cent. | | | |
| ☐ **FARNDON, Walter** ........................... *paintings* | **$302** | | **$1,045** |
| American 1876-1964 | | | |
| ☐ **FARNES, W.M.** ............................... *paintings* | | | **$500** |
| American 19th cent. | | | |
| ☐ **FARNHAM, John** ............................ *sculpture* | | | **$660** |
| ☐ **FARNHAM, Sally James** ..................... *sculpture* | | | **$715** |
| American | | | |
| ☐ **FARNSWORTH, A.** ........................... *drawings* | **$220** | | **$247** |
| British 1858-1908 | | | |
| ☐ **FARNSWORTH, Jerry** ........................ *paintings* | | | **$880** |
| American b. 1895 | | | |
| ☐ **FARNUM, Herbert Cyrus** .................... *paintings* | **$124** | | **$550** |
| American b. 1886 | | | |
| ☐ **FARNY, Henry F.** ............................ *paintings* | **$1,980** | | **$506,000** |
| American 1847-1916 ............................ *drawings* | **$2,090** | | **$220,000** |
| ☐ **FARQUE, J. la** .............................. *paintings* | | | **$330** |
| ☐ **FARQUHARSON, David** ...................... *paintings* | **$880** | | **$2,200** |
| British 1839-1907 | | | |
| ☐ **FARQUHARSON, I.** .......................... *paintings* | | | **$770** |
| ☐ **FARQUHARSON, Joseph** ..................... *paintings* | **$600** | | **$2,200** |
| Scottish 1846-1935 | | | |
| ☐ **FARR, Helen (Mrs. John SLOAN)** ......... *paintings* | **$121** | | **$200** |
| American b. 1911 | | | |
| ☐ **FARRAR, Henry** ............................. *drawings* | **$440** | | **$4,400** |
| ☐ **FARRE, Henri** .............................. *paintings* | **$136** | | **$4,400** |
| French/American 1871-1934 | | | |
| ☐ **FARREN, Robert** ............................ *paintings* | | | **$550** |
| English School | | | |
| ☐ **FARRER, Henry** ............................. *paintings* | | | **$385** |
| American 1843-1903 ............................. *drawings* | **$286** | | **$3,080** |

| | | | *Current Price Range* | |
|---|---|---|---|---|
| | | | Low | High |
| ☐ **FARRER, Thomas Charles** ............... | *paintings* | | | $550 |
| English 1839-1891 | | | | |
| ☐ **FARRINI, E.** ........................... | *paintings* | | | $440 |
| ☐ **FARRKY, C.** ........................... | *paintings* | | | $192 |
| German early 20th cent. | | | | |
| ☐ **FARROTY, H.A.** ....................... | *paintings* | | $1,100 | $1,650 |
| Italian/French 19th cent. | | | | |
| ☐ **FARSI** ................................. | *drawings* | | | $2,860 |
| 19th cent. | | | | |
| ☐ **FARSKEY, Otto** ....................... | *paintings* | | $412 | $550 |
| ☐ **FASCE, F.** ............................. | *drawings* | | $165 | $770 |
| Italian 19th cent. | | | | |
| ☐ **FASS, Oliver** .......................... | *paintings* | | | $225 |
| French b. 1920 | | | | |
| ☐ **FASTOVSKY, J.** ....................... | *paintings* | | | $550 |
| American 20th cent. | | | | |
| ☐ **FATIGUANT, Robert** ................. | *drawings* | | | $330 |
| ☐ **FATTON, George** .................... | *paintings* | | | $192 |
| American (?) 19th cent. | | | | |
| ☐ **FATTORI, Giovanni** ................. | *paintings* | | $935 | $3,850 |
| Italian 1825-1908 | | | | |
| ☐ **FAUCONNIER, Emile Eugene** ......... | *paintings* | | | $1,430 |
| French b. 1857 | | | | |
| ☐ **FAULKNER, Benjamin** ............... | *paintings* | | | $1,870 |
| English 1787-1849 | | | | |
| ☐ **FAULKNER, C.** ....................... | *paintings* | | | $2,970 |
| British ac. 1874-1875 | | | | |
| ☐ **FAULKNER, Herbert Waldron** ......... | *paintings* | | $110 | $274 |
| American 1860-1940 | | | | |
| ☐ **FAULKNER, John** .................... | *paintings* | | $1,430 | $3,300 |
| Irish ac. 1830-1888 ..................... | *drawings* | | $324 | $4,180 |
| ☐ **FAULL** ................................. | *paintings* | | | $302 |
| ☐ **FAURE, Marie** ........................ | *paintings* | | $275 | $935 |
| American 19th cent. | | | | |
| ☐ **FAUSETT, William Dean** ........... | *paintings* | | $121 | $550 |
| American b. 1913 ........................ | *drawings* | | | $137 |
| ☐ **FAUSIO, Biggi** ....................... | *sculpture* | | | $10,450 |
| Italian 19th cent. | | | | |
| ☐ **FAUST, Heinrich** ..................... | *paintings* | | | $715 |
| German 19th cent. | | | | |
| ☐ **FAUSTINI, Modesto** ................. | *paintings* | | | $3,000 |
| Italian 1839-1893 | | | | |
| ☐ **FAUTRIER, Jean** ..................... | *paintings* | | $2,475 | $17,600 |
| French 1898-1964 ...................... | *drawings* | | $2,090 | $38,500 |
| ☐ **FAUVELET, Jean Baptiste** ........... | *paintings* | | $550 | $3,300 |
| French 1819-1883 | | | | |
| ☐ **FAUX-FROIDURE, Eugenie Juliette** ...... | *drawings* | | | $1,430 |
| French 19th cent. | | | | |

| | | Current Price Range | |
|---|---|---|---|
| | | Low | High |
| ☐ **FAVAI, Gennaro** .............................. *paintings* | | $220 | $880 |
| Italian 1879-1958 ...................................... *drawings* | | | $495 |
| ☐ **FAVELLE, R.** ....................................... *paintings* | | | $1,540 |
| ☐ **FAVERETTO, Giacomo** ....................... *paintings* | | | $2,750 |
| Italian 1849-1887 | | | |
| ☐ **FAVRE, Maurice** ............................... *sculpture* | | $770 | $797 |
| French 20th cent. | | | |
| ☐ **FAVRE DE THIERRENS, Jacques** ........ *paintings* | | $385 | $2,310 |
| French 1895-1973 | | | |
| ☐ **FAVRETTO, Giacomo** .......................... *paintings* | | $2,750 | $3,850 |
| Italian 1849-1887 ...................................... *drawings* | | | $660 |
| ☐ **FAVRY, Abel** ................................... *paintings* | | | $3,575 |
| French 19th cent. | | | |
| ☐ **FAWCETT, Robert** ............................ *drawings* | | $220 | $3,300 |
| Anglo/American 1903-1967 | | | |
| ☐ **FAXON, William Bailey** ...................... *paintings* | | | $440 |
| American b. 1849 | | | |
| ☐ **FAXSON, Richard** .............................. *paintings* | | | $1,000 |
| French 19th cent. | | | |
| ☐ **FAY, Arlene Hooker** .......................... *drawings* | | $2,100 | $3,000 |
| American 20th cent. | | | |
| ☐ **FAY, Clark** ...................................... *paintings* | | | $1,980 |
| American 20th cent. | | | |
| ☐ **FAY, Joseph** ................................... *paintings* | | | $3,300 |
| German 1813-1875 | | | |
| ☐ **FAY, Ludwig Benno** ........................... *paintings* | | | $3,300 |
| German 1859-1906 | | | |
| ☐ **FAY, William E.** ................................ *drawings* | | | $440 |
| American 1882-1967 | | | |
| ☐ **FAYARD, R.** .................................... *paintings* | | | $1,650 |
| ☐ **FAYATT** ......................................... *paintings* | | | $330 |
| English School 19th cent. | | | |
| ☐ **FAYRAL** ........................................ *sculpture* | | $143 | $1,045 |
| ☐ **FAZIA** ............................................ *paintings* | | | $412 |
| 1832-1901 | | | |
| ☐ **FAZZINI, Pericle** ............................. *drawings* | | | $308 |
| Italian b. 1913 ......................................... *sculpture* | | $1,210 | $7,150 |
| ☐ **FEBVRE, Edouard** ............................ *paintings* | | | $357 |
| ☐ **FECHIN, Nicolai** .............................. *paintings* | | $5,500 | $63,250 |
| Russian/American 1881-1955 ........................ *drawings* | | $2,310 | $5,225 |
| ................................................. *sculpture* | | | $2,000 |
| ☐ **FECHTER, Emerich** ........................... *paintings* | | | $1,430 |
| Austrian 1854-1912 | | | |
| ☐ **FEDDER, Otto** .................................. *paintings* | | $1,650 | $5,225 |
| German 1873-1919 | | | |
| ☐ **FEDELER, Carl** ............................... *paintings* | | $3,850 | $4,950 |
| German 1837-1897 | | | |
| ☐ **FEDERER, Charles A.** ........................ *paintings* | | | $1,100 |

| | | Current Price Range | |
|---|---|---|---|
| | | Low | High |
| ☐ **FEDERICO, Cavalier Michele** ............... *paintings* | | $110 | $2,200 |
| Italian b. 1884 | | | |
| ☐ **FEDERZOLI, F.** ................................. *paintings* | | | $412 |
| Italian 19th cent. | | | |
| ☐ **FEELEY, Paul** ................................. *paintings* | | $2,530 | $4,180 |
| American 1910/13-1966 | | | |
| ☐ **FEHR, Friedrich** ................................ *drawings* | | | $385 |
| German b. 1862 | | | |
| ☐ **FEINE, Ernest** .................................. *paintings* | | | $1,980 |
| American | | | |
| ☐ **FEININGER, Lyonel** ........................... *paintings* | | $24,200 | $275,000 |
| German/American 1871-1956 ......................... *drawings* | | $990 | $28,600 |
| ☐ **FEIST, Harold** .................................. *paintings* | | | $880 |
| contemporary | | | |
| ☐ **FEITO, Luis** ...................................... *paintings* | | $495 | $660 |
| contemporary | | | |
| ☐ **FEITU, Pierre** ................................... *sculpture* | | | $3,080 |
| French early 20th cent. | | | |
| ☐ **FEJES, Emerik** ................................. *paintings* | | | $2,200 |
| Yugoslavian 1904-1969 | | | |
| ☐ **FELARIK, A.** ..................................... *paintings* | | | $176 |
| Dutch 20th cent. | | | |
| ☐ **FELBER, Carl Friedrich** ...................... *paintings* | | | $1,320 |
| Swiss b. 1880 | | | |
| ☐ **FELBINGER, Franz von** ....................... *paintings* | | | $220 |
| Austrian 1844-1906 | | | |
| ☐ **FELDER, Bettie** ................................. *paintings* | | | $1,000 |
| American contemporary | | | |
| ☐ **FELDHUTTER, Ferdinand** ................... *paintings* | | $1,980 | $2,025 |
| German 1842-1898 | | | |
| ☐ **FELDMANN, Konan** .......................... *drawings* | | $330 | $660 |
| Russian b. 1870 | | | |
| ☐ **FELDTRAPPE, Henri** .......................... *paintings* | | | $2,640 |
| French 19th cent. | | | |
| ☐ **FELGENTREFF, Paul** .......................... *paintings* | | $3,080 | $4,180 |
| German b. 1854 | | | |
| ☐ **FELGUEREZ, Manuel** ......................... *sculpture* | | $165 | $385 |
| Mexican/American b. 1928 | | | |
| ☐ **FELICETTI, B.** ................................... *paintings* | | | $330 |
| ☐ **FELINGER, Jean Paul** ......................... *paintings* | | | $191 |
| American late 19th cent. | | | |
| ☐ **FELISA, O.** ...................................... *paintings* | | | $880 |
| Italian (?) 19th cent. | | | |
| ☐ **FELIX, Eugen** ................................... *paintings* | | $302 | $440 |
| Austrian 1837-1906 | | | |
| ☐ **FELIX, Giordano** ............................... *paintings* | | $209 | $495 |
| ☐ **FELIX, K.E.** ..................................... *paintings* | | $275 | $715 |
| European 19th/20th cent. | | | |
| ☐ **FELIXMULLER, Conrad** ...................... *drawings* | | | $660 |

|  | | Current Price Range | |
|---|---|---|---|
|  | | Low | High |
| ☐ **FELKEL, Joseph** .................................. *paintings* | | | $660 |
| Austrian (?) 19th cent. (?) | | | |
| ☐ **FELL, J.R.** ......................................... *paintings* | | | $302 |
| American 20th cent. | | | |
| ☐ **FELLOWES, Frank Wayland** .............. *paintings* | | | $330 |
| ☐ **FELLOWS, Byron W.** ......................... *paintings* | | | $495 |
| American? 19th/20th cent. | | | |
| ☐ **FELLOWS, Fred** ................................ *paintings* | | $1,180 | $10,000 |
| American b. 1934 ....................................... *drawings* | | | $1,650 |
| .................................................. *sculpture* | | $4,750 | $20,000 |
| ☐ **FELNER, K.** ....................................... *paintings* | | | $302 |
| German early 20th cent. | | | |
| ☐ **FELS, A.J.** ......................................... *paintings* | | | $220 |
| Dutch 19th/20th cent. | | | |
| ☐ **FELTING, H.** ...................................... *paintings* | | | $300 |
| ☐ **FENELAN** .......................................... *paintings* | | | $302 |
| ☐ **FENN, George** .................................... *paintings* | | $1,650 | $3,000 |
| ☐ **FENN, Harry** ..................................... *drawings* | | $77 | $1,980 |
| American 1845-1911 | | | |
| ☐ **FENNIMORE, Thomas J.** ..................... *paintings* | | | $825 |
| American ac. 1850 | | | |
| ☐ **FENSON, Robin** .................................. *paintings* | | $40 | $605 |
| 19th/20th cent. | | | |
| ☐ **FENTON, Hallie Champlin** .................. *paintings* | | $90 | $302 |
| American 1880-1935 | | | |
| ☐ **FENTON, J.W.** .................................... *drawings* | | | $330 |
| ☐ **FENTON, John William** ........................ *paintings* | | | $198 |
| American b. 1875 | | | |
| ☐ **FENYES, Adolf** .................................... *paintings* | | $495 | $687 |
| Hungarian 1867-1945 | | | |
| ☐ **FENZONI, Ferrau** ............................... *drawings* | | $2,640 | $2,640 |
| ☐ **FEO, Charles de** ................................ *drawings* | | | $209 |
| American 1892-1978 | | | |
| ☐ **FEOLA** .............................................. *paintings* | | | $418 |
| ☐ **FERANT, O.** ....................................... *paintings* | | | $550 |
| French 19th cent. | | | |
| ☐ **FERANTI, C.** ...................................... *paintings* | | | $935 |
| Italian 19th cent. | | | |
| ☐ **FERAT, Serge** .................................... *paintings* | | $440 | $1,320 |
| French 1881-1958 ...................................... *drawings* | | $440 | $2,530 |
| ☐ **FERBER, Herbert** ............................... *paintings* | | | $880 |
| American b. 1906 ...................................... *sculpture* | | $8,800 | $15,400 |
| ☐ **FERE, P. Fiocchi** ................................ *paintings* | | | $715 |
| ☐ **FERENZI, E.** ...................................... *paintings* | | | $450 |
| ☐ **FERETTI, F.** ...................................... *paintings* | | | $462 |
| ☐ **FEREY, Prosper** ................................. *paintings* | | | $1,100 |
| French 19th cent. | | | |
| ☐ **FERG, Franz de Paula** ......................... *paintings* | | $550 | $26,400 |
| Austrian 1689-1740 | | | |

| | | *Current Price Range* | |
|---|---|---|---|
| | | *Low* | *High* |
| ☐ **FERGUSON, Amos** ............................ *paintings* | | $1,320 | $1,540 |
| ☐ **FERGUSON, Henry A.** ......................... *paintings* | | $286 | $4,125 |
| American 1842-1911 | | | |
| ☐ **FERGUSON, Louise** ............................ *paintings* | | | $198 |
| American 19th cent. | | | |
| ☐ **FERGUSON, Nancy M.** ....................... *paintings* | | $550 | $880 |
| American 1872-1967 ................................ *drawings* | | | $40 |
| ☐ **FERGUSON, O.E.** .............................. *paintings* | | $400 | $1,870 |
| ☐ **FERNAND-TROCHAIN, Jean** ............. *paintings* | | | $350 |
| French 1879-1969 | | | |
| ☐ **FERNANDEZ, Augustin** ...................... *paintings* | | $11 | $3,025 |
| 20th cent. ................................................. *drawings* | | | $412 |
| ☐ **FERNANDEZ, Jesse** ........................... *drawings* | | | $825 |
| Puerto Rican | | | |
| ☐ **FERNANDEZ, Jose** ............................ *paintings* | | | $3,410 |
| Spanish 19th cent. | | | |
| ☐ **FERNANDEZ, Rafa** ............................ *paintings* | | | $2,750 |
| Latin American | | | |
| ☐ **FERNANDEZ CAVADA, Federico** ........ *paintings* | | | $3,520 |
| Cuban 1831-1871 | | | |
| ☐ **FERNANDEZ-MURO, Jose Antonio** ...... *paintings* | | $935 | $1,650 |
| Argentinian b. 1920 .................................. *drawings* | | | $1,100 |
| ........................................ *sculpture* | | | $2,200 |
| ☐ **FERNANDI, Francesco** | | | |
| **(called IMPERIALI)** ............................ *paintings* | | | $2,200 |
| Italian ac. 1730 | | | |
| ☐ **FERNELEY, Claude Lorraine** .............. *paintings* | | $880 | $4,950 |
| English 1822-1891/92 ................................ *drawings* | | | $357 |
| ☐ **FERNELEY, John (Jr.)** ....................... *paintings* | | $1,320 | $24,200 |
| English c. 1815-1862 | | | |
| ☐ **FERNELEY, John (Sr.)** ....................... *paintings* | | $2,750 | $82,500 |
| English 1782-1860 | | | |
| ☐ **FERNFIELD, H.H.** ............................. *paintings* | | | $1,045 |
| ☐ **FERON, Julien Hippolyte** ..................... *paintings* | | | $357 |
| French b. 1864 | | | |
| ☐ **FERONI, E.** ..................................... *paintings* | | | $1,980 |
| ☐ **FERRAND, C.** ................................... *paintings* | | $550 | $935 |
| ☐ **FERRAND, F.** ................................... *paintings* | | | $330 |
| ☐ **FERRAND, M. Plaza** ......................... *paintings* | | | $1,650 |
| ☐ **FERRANDIZ Y BADENES, Bernardo** ... *paintings* | | $1,540 | $9,900 |
| Spanish 1835-c. 1890 | | | |
| ☐ **FERRANTI** ...................................... *paintings* | | $275 | $1,540 |
| Italian 19th/20th cent. ................................ *drawings* | | $275 | $467 |
| ☐ **FERRARA, Jackie** ............................. *drawings* | | | $400 |
| ☐ **FERRARESI, F.** ................................ *drawings* | | | $3,740 |
| Italian 19th cent. | | | |
| ☐ **FERRARI, Gaudenzio** ........................ *drawings* | | | $13,200 |
| Italian c. 1484-1546 | | | |
| ☐ **FERRARI, P.** .................................... *sculpture* | | | $600 |

| | | | Current Price Range | |
| | | | Low | High |
|---|---|---|---|---|
| ☐ **FERRARINI, E.** ............... *sculpture* | | | | $4,950 |
| Italian 19th cent. | | | | |
| ☐ **FERRARIS, Arthur von** ......... *paintings* | | | | $1,430 |
| Austrian b. 1856 | | | | |
| ☐ **FERREIRA, Jesus Reyes (Chucho)** ...... *drawings* | | | $385 | $825 |
| Mexican b. 1884 | | | | |
| ☐ **FERREIRA, Manuel** ............ *drawings* | | | | $176 |
| Portugese 20th cent. | | | | |
| ☐ **FERREN, John** ............... *paintings* | | | $660 | $5,500 |
| American b. 1905 ............... *drawings* | | | $192 | $550 |
| ☐ **FERRI, A.** ............... *paintings* | | | | $385 |
| ☐ **FERRI, Ciro** ............... *paintings* | | | | $13,750 |
| Italian 1634-1689 ............... *drawings* | | | | $1,650 |
| ☐ **FERRIER, Gabriel** ............ *paintings* | | | $1,540 | $1,760 |
| French 1847-1914 | | | | |
| ☐ **FERRIER, George Stratton** ......... *drawings* | | | $275 | $357 |
| British d. 1912 | | | | |
| ☐ **FERRIER, James** ............... *drawings* | | | | $1,540 |
| English 19th cent. | | | | |
| ☐ **FERRIER,** | | | | |
| **Joseph Marie Augustin Gabriel** ......... *paintings* | | | | $1,540 |
| French b. 1847 | | | | |
| ☐ **FERRIS, Hugh** ............... *drawings* | | | | $605 |
| American | | | | |
| ☐ **FERRIS, Jean Leon Jerome** ........... *paintings* | | | $1,100 | $6,050 |
| American b. 1863 | | | | |
| ☐ **FERRO-LAGREE, Georges** ......... *paintings* | | | | $605 |
| French 20th cent. | | | | |
| ☐ **FERRONI, Egisto** ............... *paintings* | | | $242 | $440 |
| Italian | | | | |
| ☐ **FERSTEL, L.** ............... *paintings* | | | $192 | $412 |
| Austrian 19th/20th cent. | | | | |
| ☐ **FERVILLE-SUAN, Charles George** ...... *sculpture* | | | | $660 |
| French 19th cent. | | | | |
| ☐ **FERY, John** ............... *paintings* | | | $660 | $5,500 |
| Hungarian/American 1865-1934 | | | | |
| ☐ **FETTING, Rainer** ............ *paintings* | | | | $7,150 |
| contemporary | | | | |
| ☐ **FEUCHERE, Jean Jacques** ........... *sculpture* | | | $660 | $2,970 |
| French 1807-1852 | | | | |
| ☐ **FEUDEL, Arthur** ............... *paintings* | | | | $110 |
| American b. 1857 ............... *drawings* | | | $55 | $220 |
| ☐ **FEUERBACH, Anslem** ........... *paintings* | | | | $5,500 |
| German 1829-1880 ............... *drawings* | | | | $370 |
| ☐ **FEUILLET, Rene** ............... *paintings* | | | | $412 |
| French 19th cent. | | | | |
| ☐ **FEURE, Georges de** ............ *drawings* | | | $495 | $1,100 |
| French 1868-1943 | | | | |

| | | *Current Price Range* | |
| | | *Low* | *High* |
| --- | --- | --- | --- |
| ☐ **FEYEN, Jacques Eugene** ..................... *paintings* | | | **$2,400** |
| French 1815-1908 | | | |
| ☐ **FEYEN-PERRIN,** | | | |
| **Francois Nicolas Augustin** ..................... *paintings* | | **$990** | **$3,850** |
| French 1826-1888 | | | |
| ☐ **FIALA, Emmanuel** ........................... *paintings* | | **$154** | **$247** |
| Austrian b. 1892 | | | |
| ☐ **FIANI** ................................................. *paintings* | | | **$220** |
| Italian 20th cent. | | | |
| ☐ **FIASCHI, P.C.E.** ............................... *sculpture* | | **$880** | **$3,520** |
| Italian 19th/20th cent. | | | |
| ☐ **FICHEL, Benjamin Eugene** .............. *paintings* | | **$385** | **$10,450** |
| French 1826-1895 ..................................... *drawings* | | | **$132** |
| ☐ **FICHER, Jarnet** ................................. *paintings* | | | **$192** |
| American 20th cent. | | | |
| ☐ **FICHERELLI, Felice** | | | |
| **(called IL RIPOSO)** .............................. *paintings* | | | **$2,750** |
| Italian 1605-1666 | | | |
| ☐ **FIDLER, Anton** ................................. *paintings* | | | **$1,000** |
| ☐ **FIDLER, Harry** ................................. *paintings* | | | **$880** |
| ☐ **FIDLER, Michel** ................................ *paintings* | | | **$1,650** |
| ☐ **FIEDLER, Bernhard** ........................... *paintings* | | | **$1,100** |
| German 1816-1904 | | | |
| ☐ **FIEDLER, Leopold** ............................ *drawings* | | | **$247** |
| American 19th cent. | | | |
| ☐ **FIELD, Edith** .................................... *sculpture* | | | **$935** |
| American 20th cent. | | | |
| ☐ **FIELD, Edward Loyal** ........................ *paintings* | | **$247** | **$1,650** |
| American 1856-1914 ................................... *drawings* | | **$22** | **$137** |
| ☐ **FIELD, Erastus Salisbury** ................... *paintings* | | **$500** | **$26,400** |
| American 1805/07-1900 | | | |
| ☐ **FIELD, Louis Blodgett** ....................... *drawings* | | | **$250** |
| ☐ **FIELDING, Anthony Vandyke Copley** ... *paintings* | | **$165** | **$1,100** |
| English 1787-1855 ..................................... *drawings* | | **$247** | **$577** |
| ☐ **FIELDING, G.** ................................... *paintings* | | **$242** | **$605** |
| British 19th cent. | | | |
| ☐ **FIELDING, Thales** ............................ *paintings* | | **$357** | **$385** |
| English 1793-1837 ..................................... *drawings* | | | **$605** |
| ☐ **FIELDS, Chester** .............................. *sculpture* | | | **$10,500** |
| American 20th cent. | | | |
| ☐ **FIENE, Ernest** .................................. *paintings* | | **$33** | **$1,870** |
| American 1894-1965 ................................... *drawings* | | | **$418** |
| ☐ **FIERAVINO, Francesco** | | | |
| **(IL MALTESE)** ..................................... *paintings* | | | **$4,180** |
| Italian b. c. 1640; ac. 1650-1680 | | | |
| ☐ **FIESOLE, de** ..................................... *sculpture* | | | **$660** |
| French ac. c. 1925 | | | |
| ☐ **FIGARET, L.** ..................................... *drawings* | | | **$700** |
| French 19th cent. | | | |

| | | Current Price Range | |
| | | Low | High |
| --- | --- | --- | --- |
| ☐ **FIGARI, Pedro** ..................................... *paintings* | | **$500** | **$30,800** |
| Uruguayan 1861-1938 | | | |
| ☐ **FIGDOIS** ..................................... *paintings* | | | **$275** |
| French early 20th cent. | | | |
| ☐ **FILCER, Luis** ..................................... *paintings* | | **$66** | **$440** |
| Mexican 20th cent. | | | |
| ☐ **FILLA, Emil** ..................................... *paintings* | | | **$2,750** |
| Czechoslovakian b. 1882 | | | |
| ☐ **FILLANS, R.** ..................................... *paintings* | | | **$990** |
| ☐ **FILLEAU, Emery A.** ........................... *paintings* | | | **$3,300** |
| American ac. 1890-1910 | | | |
| ☐ **FILLERUP, Mel** ..................................... *paintings* | | | **$2,100** |
| American b. 1924 | | | |
| ☐ **FILLIARD, Ernest** ........................... *drawings* | | | **$576** |
| French 19th/20th cent. | | | |
| ☐ **FILLON, Arthur** ..................................... *paintings* | | **$330** | **$1,210** |
| French 1900-1974 | | | |
| ☐ **FILMUS, Tully** ..................................... *drawings* | | **$110** | **$605** |
| Russian/American b. 1903/08 | | | |
| ☐ **FILONOV, Pavel** ........................... *drawings* | | | **$2,640** |
| Russian b. 1883 | | | |
| ☐ **FILORI, G.** ..................................... *paintings* | | | **$660** |
| Italian 19th cent. | | | |
| ☐ **FILOSA, Giovanni B.** ........................... *paintings* | | | **$264** |
| Italian 1850-1935 ..................................... *drawings* | | **$825** | **$1,760** |
| ☐ **FIMA** ..................................... *paintings* | | | **$220** |
| ..................................... *drawings* | | | **$385** |
| ☐ **FINARD, J.** ..................................... *paintings* | | | **$660** |
| ☐ **FINART, Noel Dieudonne** ..................... *drawings* | | | **$1,100** |
| French 1797-1852 | | | |
| ☐ **FINCH, Alfred William (Willy)** ............. *paintings* | | **$11,000** | **$90,750** |
| Belgian 1854-1930 ..................................... *drawings* | | | **$990** |
| ☐ **FINCH, E.E.** ..................................... *paintings* | | | **$20,900** |
| American c. 1850 | | | |
| ☐ **FINCK, Furman Joseph** ....................... *paintings* | | **$66** | **$528** |
| American b. 1900 | | | |
| ☐ **FINCK, Hazel** ..................................... *paintings* | | | **$550** |
| American 1894-1977 | | | |
| ☐ **FINCKE, Hermann** ........................... *paintings* | | | **$302** |
| German b. 1845 | | | |
| ☐ **FIND, L.** ..................................... *paintings* | | | **$247** |
| Danish b. c. 1869 | | | |
| ☐ **FINDLAY, J.L.** ..................................... *paintings* | | | **$192** |
| American 19th/20th cent. ........................... *drawings* | | | **$60** |
| ☐ **FINE, Judd** ..................................... *drawings* | | | **$1,045** |
| American b. 1944 | | | |
| ☐ **FINELLI, J.R.** ..................................... *sculpture* | | | **$1,210** |
| ☐ **FINEZ, Gregoire Nicolas** ....................... *paintings* | | | **$300** |
| French ac. 1884 | | | |

| | | | Current Price Range | |
|---|---|---|---|---|
| | | | Low | High |
| ☐ **FINGESTEN, Micheal** | ............ | *drawings* | | **$440** |
| ☐ **FINI, Leonor** | ............ | *paintings* | **$825** | **$11,000** |
| Italian b. 1908 | ............ | *drawings* | **$286** | **$2,640** |
| ☐ **FINI, Umberto** | ............ | *paintings* | | **$770** |
| Italian 19th cent. | | | | |
| ☐ **FINK, August** | ............ | *paintings* | **$1,760** | **$3,850** |
| German 1846-1916 | | | | |
| ☐ **FINK, Hans** | ............ | *paintings* | | **$715** |
| ☐ **FINKELGREEN, David** | ............ | *paintings* | **$990** | **$2,420** |
| American 1888-1931 | | | | |
| ☐ **FINLAYSON, E.C.** | ............ | *paintings* | | **$495** |
| French 19th/20th cent. | | | | |
| ☐ **FINNEY, Harry** | ............ | *paintings* | | **$429** |
| American 20th cent. | | | | |
| ☐ **FIORAVANTI, Vincenzo** | ............ | *paintings* | **$264** | **$462** |
| ☐ **FIORE, Jacobello del** | ............ | *paintings* | | **$14,300** |
| Italian 1370/85-1429/39 | | | | |
| ☐ **FIORI, Ernesto de** | ............ | *sculpture* | | **$5,775** |
| German 1884-1945 | | | | |
| ☐ **FIOT, M.** | ............ | *sculpture* | | **$302** |
| ☐ **FIRANGE, Rinald** | ............ | *paintings* | | **$440** |
| European 19th cent. | | | | |
| ☐ **FIRARDOS, L. A.** | ............ | *drawings* | | **$192** |
| French 19th/20th cent. | | | | |
| ☐ **FIRENZE, Paul** | ............ | *drawings* | | **$2,750** |
| American 20th cent. | | | | |
| ☐ **FIRFIRES, Nicholas** | ............ | *paintings* | **$440** | **$7,500** |
| American b. 1917 | | | | |
| ☐ **FIRLE, Walter** | ............ | *paintings* | **$2,310** | **$7,700** |
| German 1859-1929 | | | | |
| ☐ **FIRMIN-GERARD, Marie Francois** | ...... | *paintings* | **$9,075** | **$17,600** |
| French 1838-1921 | | | | |
| ☐ **FIRSCH, Johann Christoph** | ............ | *paintings* | | **$605** |
| German 1738-1815 | | | | |
| ☐ **FIRTCH, H.** | ............ | *paintings* | | **$605** |
| ☐ **FISCHBACH, Johann** | ............ | *paintings* | | **$16,500** |
| Austrian 1797-1871 | | | | |
| ☐ **FISCHER, Anton Otto** | ............ | *paintings* | **$181** | **$4,510** |
| American 1882-1962 | | | | |
| ☐ **FISCHER, Ernst** | ............ | *paintings* | | **$1,760** |
| German | | | | |
| ☐ **FISCHER, Ernst** | ............ | *paintings* | **$4,950** | **$7,150** |
| German 1815-1874 | | | | |
| ☐ **FISCHER, Gottlob** | ............ | *paintings* | **$770** | **$1,760** |
| German 1829-1905 | | | | |
| ☐ **FISCHER, Heinrich** | ............ | *paintings* | | **$660** |
| Swiss 1820-1886 | | | | |
| ☐ **FISCHER, P.** | ............ | *paintings* | | **$11,000** |

| | | | Current Price Range | |
|---|---|---|---|---|
| | | | Low | High |
| ☐ **FISCHER, Paul** | *paintings* | | $1,980 | $7,150 |
| Danish 1860-1934 | | | | |
| ☐ **FISCHETTI, Fedele** | *paintings* | | | $7,700 |
| Italian 1734-1789 | | | | |
| ☐ **FISCHHOF, Georg** | *paintings* | | | $660 |
| Austrian 1849-1920 | | | | |
| ☐ **FISCHINGER, Oscar** | *paintings* | | | $286 |
| ☐ **FISH, George G.** | *paintings* | | | $275 |
| American 19th cent. | *drawings* | | $220 | $1,870 |
| ☐ **FISH, H.A.** | *paintings* | | | $605 |
| ☐ **FISH, Janet** | *paintings* | | $6,600 | $17,600 |
| American b. 1938 | *drawings* | | | $9,350 |
| ☐ **FISHBEIN, Jason B.** | *paintings* | | | $302 |
| American 20th cent. | *drawings* | | | $550 |
| ☐ **FISHER, Alvan** | *paintings* | | $1,100 | $5,775 |
| American 1792-1863 | *drawings* | | $250 | $4,840 |
| ☐ **FISHER, Anna S.** | *drawings* | | | $990 |
| American d. 1942 | | | | |
| ☐ **FISHER, D.A.** | *paintings* | | $65 | $500 |
| American 19th/20th cent. | | | | |
| ☐ **FISHER, Elizabeth** | *paintings* | | | $352 |
| ☐ **FISHER, Harrison** | *paintings* | | $440 | $660 |
| American 1875-1934 | *drawings* | | $55 | $3,850 |
| ☐ **FISHER, Hugo A.** | *paintings* | | $330 | $412 |
| American c. 1850/67-1916 | *drawings* | | $110 | $1,540 |
| ☐ **FISHER, Hugo Melville** | *paintings* | | $192 | $220 |
| American 1876/78-1946 | *drawings* | | $160 | $2,750 |
| ☐ **FISHER, Mac. S.** | *drawings* | | $132 | $357 |
| American 20th cent. | | | | |
| ☐ **FISHER, Melton S.** | *paintings* | | | $2,750 |
| British 1859-1939 | | | | |
| ☐ **FISHER, William Mark** | *paintings* | | $495 | $4,675 |
| English 1841-1923 | *drawings* | | | $385 |
| ☐ **FISHER, Winona (Moses)** | *paintings* | | | $990 |
| American | | | | |
| ☐ **FISK, Harry T.** | *paintings* | | | $605 |
| American ac. 1921-1948 | *drawings* | | | $44 |
| ☐ **FISK, Thomas** | *paintings* | | | $1,650 |
| ☐ **FISKE, Gertrude** | *paintings* | | $121 | $770 |
| American 1879-1961 | *drawings* | | | $80 |
| ☐ **FITLER, Harry** | *paintings* | | | $660 |
| ☐ **FITLER, William Crothers** | *paintings* | | $220 | $2,600 |
| American 1857-1915 | *drawings* | | $247 | $412 |
| ☐ **FITZ, Allee C.** | *paintings* | | $412 | $577 |
| American 19th/20th cent. | | | | |
| ☐ **FITZ, Benjamin Rutherford** | *paintings* | | | $2,200 |
| American 1855-1891 | | | | |
| ☐ **FITZ, John** | *drawings* | | | $300 |
| English early 20th cent. | | | | |

|  | | Current Price Range | |
|---|---|---|---|
|  | | *Low* | *High* |
| ☐ **FITZ, William** ............................ *paintings* | | | $220 |
| English ac. 1876-1889 | | | |
| ☐ **FITZ-GERALD, Boylan** ...................... *paintings* | | $242 | $550 |
| American 20th cent. | | | |
| ☐ **FITZGERALD, Harrington** ................. *paintings* | | | $440 |
| American b. 1847 | | | |
| ☐ **FITZGERALD, James** ........................ *paintings* | | $192 | $825 |
| American 1899-1971 ................................ *drawings* | | $165 | $165 |
| ☐ **FLACHENHAUS, H.** ......................... *paintings* | | $242 | $2,750 |
| ☐ **FLAGG, Charles Noel** ......................... *paintings* | | | $550 |
| American b. 1848 | | | |
| ☐ **FLAGG, George Washington Allston** ..... *paintings* | | | $247 |
| American 19th/20th cent. | | | |
| ☐ **FLAGG, H. Peabody** .......................... *paintings* | | $71 | $550 |
| American b. 1859 ..................................... *drawings* | | $88 | $385 |
| ☐ **FLAGG, James Montgomery** ................. *paintings* | | $825 | $7,700 |
| American 1877-1960 ................................. *drawings* | | $33 | $1,870 |
| ☐ **FLAGG, Montague** ............................. *paintings* | | $176 | $750 |
| American 1842-1915 | | | |
| ☐ **FLAHAUT, Leon Charles** ..................... *paintings* | | | $357 |
| French b. 1831 | | | |
| ☐ **FLAHERTY, J.J.** ............................. *drawings* | | | $302 |
| American 20th cent. | | | |
| ☐ **FLAHERTY, Thorpe** ........................... *paintings* | | $137 | $440 |
| American 19th/20th cent. | | | |
| ☐ **FLAMENG, Francois** ........................... *paintings* | | $467 | $9,900 |
| French 1856-1923 ..................................... *drawings* | | $165 | $275 |
| ☐ **FLANAGAN, John Richard** ................. *drawings* | | | $462 |
| Australian/American 1895-1964 | | | |
| ☐ **FLANDRIN, Jean Hippolyte** ................. *drawings* | | $385 | $990 |
| French 1809-1864 | | | |
| ☐ **FLANNAGAN, John B.** ........................ *drawings* | | | $715 |
| American 1895-1942 ................................ *sculpture* | | $4,125 | $22,000 |
| ☐ **FLATMAN, J.** ................................. *paintings* | | | $1,100 |
| British 19th cent. | | | |
| ☐ **FLATTERS, Jean Jacques** .................... *sculpture* | | | $4,950 |
| French 1796-1845 | | | |
| ☐ **FLAUGIER, Jose** ............................... *paintings* | | $3,300 | $3,300 |
| Spanish 1760-1812 | | | |
| ☐ **FLAVELLE, G.H.** .............................. *drawings* | | $90 | $412 |
| American 19th/20th cent. | | | |
| ☐ **FLAVIN, Dan** ................................. *sculpture* | | $11,000 | $31,900 |
| American b. 1933 | | | |
| ☐ **FLAVITSKY, Constantin Dmitrievich** ... *paintings* | | | $220 |
| Russian 1830-1866 | | | |
| ☐ **FLECK, Joseph Amadeus** .................... *paintings* | | $5,500 | $7,425 |
| Austrian/American 1892/3-1977 | | | |
| ☐ **FLEICHER** ..................................... *paintings* | | | $1,210 |
| German 19th cent. | | | |

|                                               | Current Price Range | |
|                                               | Low | High |
|-----------------------------------------------|-----------|-----------|
| ☐ **FLEISCHBEIN, Francois** ...... *paintings* | $385 | $2,750 |
| American c. 1804-1862                          | | |
| ☐ **FLEISCHMANN, Adolf** ...... *paintings* | $247 | $880 |
| German d. 1969                                | | |
| ☐ **FLEISCHMANN, Arthur** ...... *sculpture* | $495 | $495 |
| Hungarian b. 1896                             | | |
| ☐ **FLEISHER, Max** ...... *drawings* | | $412 |
| 1883?-1972                                     | | |
| ☐ **FLEMING, A.M.** ...... *paintings* | $495 | $660 |
| American                                      | | |
| ☐ **FLEMING, W.** ...... *paintings* | | $440 |
| ac. c. 1900                                    | | |
| ☐ **FLENAER(?), J.W.** ...... *paintings* | | $192 |
| American 19th cent.                           | | |
| ☐ **FLERS, Camille** ...... *paintings* | | $1,100 |
| French 1802-1868                              | | |
| ☐ **FLESCH, Joanne** ...... *paintings* | | $550 |
| American                                      | | |
| ☐ **FLETCHER, A.** ...... *paintings* | $187 | $198 |
| American 19th/20th cent.                      | | |
| ☐ **FLETCHER, Aaron Dean** ...... *paintings* | | $2,750 |
| American 1817-1902                            | | |
| ☐ **FLETCHER, Anne** ...... *paintings* | | $352 |
| American b. 1876                              | | |
| ☐ **FLETCHER, Blandford** ...... *paintings* | | $1,045 |
| British exhib. 1880-1918                      | | |
| ☐ **FLETCHER, C.** ...... *drawings* | | $825 |
| American                                      | | |
| ☐ **FLETCHER, Edwin** ...... *paintings* | | $990 |
| British 19th century                          | | |
| ☐ **FLETCHER, Frank Morley** ...... *paintings* | | $220 |
| English/American 1866-1949                    | | |
| ☐ **FLETCHER, L.** ...... *paintings* | | $880 |
| British 19th cent.                            | | |
| ☐ **FLEURY, Fanny** ...... *paintings* | $990 | $1,760 |
| French b. 1848                                | | |
| ☐ **FLEURY, Francois Antoine Leon** ...... *paintings* | | $660 |
| French 1804-1858                              | | |
| ☐ **FLEURY, J.V. de** ...... *paintings* | $462 | $1,045 |
| English ac.1847-68, exhib.1892/93 ...... *drawings* | | $220 |
| ☐ **FLIEHER, K.** ...... *paintings* | | $154 |
| Austrian 19th/20th cent. ...... *drawings* | $275 | $330 |
| ☐ **FLIER, Helmert R.** ...... *paintings* | | $2,310 |
| Dutch 19th cent.                              | | |
| ☐ **FLINCK, Govaert** ...... *paintings* | $19,800 | $82,500 |
| Dutch 1615/16-1660 ...... *drawings* | | $1,100 |
| ☐ **FLINT, Sir William Russell** ...... *paintings* | $7,150 | $17,600 |
| British 1880-1969 ...... *drawings* | $308 | $25,300 |

## Donor Painting

*It was common in the 15th century for wealthy families to commission altar pieces. This painting was taken from the Book of Tobit in which Tobias' father was cured of blindness. The fish carried by Tobias symbolizes this miracle. The story inspired many families to donate altar pieces representing this subject in the hope that the sight of a blind family member would be restored. The three kneeling figures at the bottom represent the donors. The painting is rich in decorative detail, including the angel's robe, the gold ground and tempera on the panel, and the architecturally ornate gothic frame. (Florentine School: 2nd quarter, 15th century, "Tobias and the Angel," tempera on panel, 62 x 28¼ in., Sotheby's, January 17, 1985, $37,400.)*

|  | | *Current Price Range* | |
|---|---|---|---|
|  | | *Low* | *High* |
| ☐ **FLOCH, Joseph** .................................. *paintings* | | **$192** | **$495** |
| Austrian/American 1895-1977 ...................... *drawings* | | **$22** | **$80** |
| ☐ **FLOGNY, Eugene Victor de** ................. *paintings* | | | **$1,650** |
| French b. 1825 | | | |
| ☐ **FLOQUET, Lucas** ............................. *paintings* | | | **$14,300** |
| Flemish 17th cent. | | | |
| ☐ **FLORENTINE SCHOOL** ...................... *paintings* | | **$11,000** | **$37,400** |
| .............................................................. *drawings* | | **$1,760** | **$3,080** |
| ☐ **FLORES, Pedro** .................................. *paintings* | | | **$1,320** |
| Spanish 1897-1967 | | | |
| ☐ **FLORSHEIM, Richard A.** ..................... *paintings* | | **$165** | **$385** |
| American 1916-1976/79 | | | |
| ☐ **FOACHE, Arthur** ............................... *paintings* | | | **$660** |
| ☐ **FOCHT, Frederic** ............................... *sculpture* | | **$1,540** | **$3,300** |
| French b. 1879 | | | |

| | | | Current Price Range | |
|---|---|---|---|---|
| | | | *Low* | *High* |
| ☐ **FOERSTER, Emil** ............................... *paintings* | | | | $10,450 |
| American 1822-1906 | | | | |
| ☐ **FOGAROLI** ........................................ *drawings* | | | | $1,760 |
| ☐ **FOGARTY, Thomas** ............................ *paintings* | | | | $770 |
| American 1873-1938 ................................... *drawings* | | | $143 | $1,870 |
| ☐ **FOGGIA, Mario Moretti** ....................... *paintings* | | | | $1,650 |
| ☐ **FOGGINI, Giovanni Battista** ................ *drawings* | | | $770 | $3,300 |
| ☐ **FOKAY, O.** ...................................... *paintings* | | | | $1,100 |
| ☐ **FOLCHI, Paulo** ................................. *paintings* | | | | $2,860 |
| ☐ **FOLEY, A.P.** .................................... *paintings* | | | | $550 |
| ☐ **FOLEY, Henry** ................................. *paintings* | | | | $1,760 |
| British 1818-1875 | | | | |
| ☐ **FOLINSBEE, John Fulton** .................. *paintings* | | | $82 | $2,640 |
| American 1892-1972 | | | | |
| ☐ **FOLLELL, B.** .................................... *drawings* | | | | $250 |
| American 19th/20th cent. | | | | |
| ☐ **FOLLETT, F.O.** ................................ *paintings* | | | $1,045 | $1,045 |
| American 19th cent. | | | | |
| ☐ **FOLLI, Luigi** ................................... *paintings* | | | | $3,300 |
| Italian 19th cent. | | | | |
| ☐ **FOLLINI, Carlo** ................................ *drawings* | | | | $412 |
| Italian 1848-1938 | | | | |
| ☐ **FOLON, Jean Michel** ......................... *drawings* | | | | $330 |
| contemporary | | | | |
| ☐ **FONDA, Harry Stuart** ....................... *paintings* | | | $110 | $247 |
| American 1863-1942/43 | | | | |
| ☐ **FONETTI, F.** .................................... *paintings* | | | | $550 |
| ☐ **FONG, Lai** ...................................... *paintings* | | | $3,000 | $4,675 |
| Chinese/American | | | | |
| ☐ **FONSECA, Reinaldo de Aquino** ........... *paintings* | | | | $9,350 |
| Brazilian b. 1925 | | | | |
| ☐ **FONT, Constantin** .............................. *paintings* | | | | $22,000 |
| French b. 1890 | | | | |
| ☐ **FONTANA, E. Sandri** ........................ *paintings* | | | | $495 |
| ☐ **FONTANA, Ernest** ............................ *paintings* | | | | $1,650 |
| Italian 19th cent. | | | | |
| ☐ **FONTANA, Giovanni** ......................... *drawings* | | | | $1,100 |
| Italian School 19th cent. | | | | |
| ☐ **FONTANA, Giuseppi** ......................... *paintings* | | | | $1,320 |
| Italian 1821-1893 | | | | |
| ☐ **FONTANA, L.** ................................... *paintings* | | | | $247 |
| American 20th cent. | | | | |
| ☐ **FONTANA, Lavinia** ........................... *paintings* | | | | $3,520 |
| Italian 1552-1614 | | | | |
| ☐ **FONTANA, Lucio** .............................. *paintings* | | | $3,850 | $12,100 |
| Italian 1899-1968 ....................................... *sculpture* | | | $1,100 | $2,750 |
| ☐ **FONTANE, A. Leonard** ....................... *paintings* | | | | $1,210 |
| European 20th cent. | | | | |

| | *Current Price Range* | |
|---|---|---|
| | *Low* | *High* |
| ☐ **FONTEBASSO, Francesco** .................... *drawings* | | $20,900 |
| Italilan 1709-1769 | | |
| ☐ **FONTENAY, Alexis Dalegie de** ............. *paintings* | | $1,760 |
| French b. 1815 | | |
| ☐ **FONTENAY, Andre** ............................ *paintings* | | $440 |
| French 20th cent. | | |
| ☐ **FONTENAY, Eugene** ........................... *paintings* | | $3,080 |
| French b. 1824 | | |
| ☐ **FONTVILLE, Alfred** .......................... *paintings* | $330 | $660 |
| English ac. 1893-1897 | | |
| ☐ **FOOTE, Edward Kilbourne** ................. *drawings* | | $2,970 |
| British 19th cent. | | |
| ☐ **FOOTE, Mary Hallock** ........................ *paintings* | | $220 |
| American 1847-1938 | | |
| ☐ **FOOTE, Will Howe** ........................... *paintings* | $137 | $2,750 |
| American 1874-1965 ................................. *drawings* | $330 | $715 |
| ☐ **FOPPIANI, Gustavo** ........................... *paintings* | $44 | $187 |
| Italian b. 1925 | | |
| ☐ **FORABOSCO, Girolamo** ...................... *paintings* | | $1,320 |
| ☐ **FORAIN, J.L.** ................................. *drawings* | | $330 |
| ☐ **FORAIN, Jean Louis** ......................... *paintings* | $1,980 | $31,900 |
| French 1852-1931 ..................................... *drawings* | $110 | $8,250 |
| ☐ **FORBES, Charles Stuart** ..................... *paintings* | | $770 |
| American | | |
| ☐ **FORBES, Edwin** ............................... *paintings* | $935 | $35,200 |
| American 1839-1895 | | |
| ☐ **FORBES, Stanhope Alexander** ............. *paintings* | $2,750 | $5,280 |
| Irish 1857-1947 | | |
| ☐ **FORBES, Stewart L.** ........................ *drawings* | | $220 |
| British 19th cent. | | |
| ☐ **FORD, A.** ..................................... *paintings* | | $1,100 |
| ☐ **FORD, Elsie May** ............................ *paintings* | $11 | $220 |
| American 20th cent. | | |
| ☐ **FORD, Henry Justice** ......................... *drawings* | | $1,430 |
| English 1860-1941 | | |
| ☐ **FORD, Neilson** ............................... *paintings* | | $385 |
| American d. 1931 | | |
| ☐ **FORD, Onslow Wolfram** ...................... *paintings* | | $220 |
| British | | |
| ☐ **FORD, W.** ..................................... *paintings* | | $1,760 |
| American | | |
| ☐ **FORD (?), E.H.** ............................... *paintings* | | $440 |
| ☐ **FORDESILLAS** ................................. *paintings* | | $250 |
| European 19th cent. | | |
| ☐ **FOREAU, Louis Henri** ......................... *paintings* | $880 | $1,650 |
| French 1866-1938/40 ................................. *drawings* | $264 | $1,430 |
| ☐ **FORETOY, A.** .................................. *sculpture* | | $797 |
| French late 19th cent. | | |
| ☐ **FORETTI, M.** .................................. *paintings* | | $528 |

| | Current Price Range | |
|---|---|---|
| | *Low* | *High* |
| ☐ **FORETTI, Paolo** ............................... *paintings* | | $264 |
| ☐ **FORIEN, J.** ........................................ *paintings* | | $275 |
| French 19th cent. | | |
| ☐ **FORILLY** ........................................... *paintings* | $605 | $825 |
| Italian 20th cent. | | |
| ☐ **FORKNER, Edgar** ............................ *paintings* | | $825 |
| ☐ **FORLENZA, D.** ................................. *paintings* | | $990 |
| Italian 19th cent. | | |
| ☐ **FORMAN, H.** .................................... *paintings* | | $275 |
| ☐ **FORMILLI, Cesare** ........................... *drawings* | | $605 |
| Italian | | |
| ☐ **FORMIS, Achille** .............................. *paintings* | $3,520 | $5,500 |
| Italian 1832-1906 | | |
| ☐ **FORMOIS, Theodore** ......................... *paintings* | | $1,100 |
| ☐ **FORNASETTI, Pierro** ........................ *paintings* | $4,620 | $35,200 |
| Italian b. 1913 ........................................ *sculpture* | | $3,850 |
| ☐ **FORNENBURGH, Jan Baptist van** ........ *paintings* | | $60,500 |
| Dutch ac. 1608-1649 | | |
| ☐ **FORNER, Raquel** .............................. *paintings* | | $3,190 |
| Argentinian b. 1902 | | |
| ☐ **FORNERO, L.** ................................... *paintings* | | $440 |
| ☐ **FORREST, Captain J. Haughton** ........... *paintings* | | $3,300 |
| British 1825-1924 | | |
| ☐ **FORREST, H.** ................................... *paintings* | $2,750 | $3,410 |
| British 19th cent. | | |
| ☐ **FORRESTAL, F.J.** ............................. *paintings* | | $522 |
| American 20th cent. | | |
| ☐ **FORRESTER, John** ............................ *paintings* | | $330 |
| contemporary | | |
| ☐ **FORRESTER, L.** ................................ *paintings* | | $385 |
| American 19th/20th cent. | | |
| ☐ **FORRESTER, Patricia Tobacco** ........... *drawings* | | $3,300 |
| American 20th cent. | | |
| ☐ **FORSTER, Berthold Paul** ..................... *paintings* | | $605 |
| German 1851-1928 | | |
| ☐ **FORSTER, George** ............................ *paintings* | $1,320 | $24,750 |
| American ac. 1861-1871 | | |
| ☐ **FORSTER, Thomas** ............................ *drawings* | | $1,210 |
| ☐ **FORSYTHE, Victor Clyde** ................... *paintings* | $137 | $1,870 |
| American 1885-1962 | | |
| ☐ **FORT, Theodore** ............................... *drawings* | | $412 |
| French 19th cent. | | |
| ☐ **FORTE, Luca** .................................... *paintings* | | $8,250 |
| Italian 18th cent. | | |
| ☐ **FORTE, S.** ........................................ *paintings* | | $302 |
| ☐ **FORTE, Vincente** .............................. *paintings* | $4,125 | $4,950 |
| Argentinian b. 1912 | | |
| ☐ **FORTESCUE, William Banks** .............. *paintings* | | $2,310 |
| British 19th cent. | | |

| | | Current Price Range | |
|---|---|---|---|
| | | Low | High |
| ☐ **FORTI, Ettore** ............................... *paintings* | | $1,180 | $8,250 |
| Italian ac. 1893-1897 | | | |
| ☐ **FORTIER, Marie Louise** ....................... *paintings* | | $1,430 | $1,870 |
| French 20th cent. | | | |
| ☐ **FORTIN, Charles** ............................... *paintings* | | | $412 |
| French 1815-1865 | | | |
| ☐ **FORTINI, A.** ..................................... *paintings* | | $154 | $2,970 |
| Italian 19th/20th cent. | | | |
| ☐ **FORTUNY, Lucia** ............................... *paintings* | | $715 | $1,430 |
| French 20th cent. | | | |
| ☐ **FORTUNY Y CARBO, Mariano** ........... *paintings* | | $2,090 | $18,700 |
| Spanish 1838-1874 ...................................... *drawings* | | $220 | $1,650 |
| ☐ **FORTUNY Y DE MADRAZO,** | | | |
| **Mariano** ............................................. *paintings* | | $715 | $3,850 |
| Spanish 1871-1949 | | | |
| ☐ **FORZI** ............................................... *paintings* | | | $1,045 |
| ☐ **FOSBURGH, James Whitney** ............... *paintings* | | $99 | $2,420 |
| American 1910-1978 ................................. *drawings* | | | $110 |
| ☐ **FOSCHI, Pier Francesco** ....................... *paintings* | | $4,675 | $24,200 |
| Italian 1502-1567 | | | |
| ☐ **FOSDICK, J. William** ........................... *paintings* | | | $770 |
| ☐ **FOSS, Olivier** ..................................... *paintings* | | $110 | $605 |
| American b. 1920 | | | |
| ☐ **FOSSATI, Emilio** ............................... *paintings* | | | $1,045 |
| Italian 20th cent. | | | |
| ☐ **FOSSOUX, Claude P.** ........................... *paintings* | | | $352 |
| ☐ **FOSTER** ............................................. *paintings* | | | $577 |
| American 19th cent. | | | |
| ☐ **FOSTER, Alan** ..................................... *paintings* | | | $4,125 |
| American b. 1892 | | | |
| ☐ **FOSTER, Arthur Turner** ....................... *paintings* | | $99 | $302 |
| American b. 1877 | | | |
| ☐ **FOSTER, Benjamin** ............................. *paintings* | | $77 | $4,400 |
| American 1852-1926 ................................. *drawings* | | $247 | $484 |
| ☐ **FOSTER, Charles** ............................... *paintings* | | $55 | $1,100 |
| American 1850-1931 | | | |
| ☐ **FOSTER, G.S.** ..................................... *paintings* | | | $660 |
| American | | | |
| ☐ **FOSTER, Gilbert** ............................... *paintings* | | | $385 |
| ☐ **FOSTER, Harold R.** ........................... *drawings* | | $220 | $1,980 |
| b. 1892 | | | |
| ☐ **FOSTER, Herbert Wilson** ................... *paintings* | | | $302 |
| English ac. 1870-1917 | | | |
| ☐ **FOSTER, J.** ......................................... *paintings* | | $330 | $715 |
| ☐ **FOSTER, Kate E.** ............................... *paintings* | | | $247 |
| English 19th cent. | | | |
| ☐ **FOSTER, Myles Birket** ......................... *paintings* | | $110 | $4,510 |
| English 1825-1899 | | | |

| | | *Current Price Range* | |
|---|---|---|---|
| | | Low | High |
| ☐ **FOSTER, Robert** ............................. *paintings* | | | $352 |
| American 20th cent. | | | |
| ☐ **FOSTER, W.G.** ............................. *paintings* | | | $275 |
| ☐ **FOSTER, William Frederick ("Will")** ..... *paintings* | | $165 | $770 |
| American b. 1882 | | | |
| ☐ **FOSTER, William Gilbert** ................... *paintings* | | $440 | $3,575 |
| British 1855-1906 | | | |
| ☐ **FOSTER, William Harnden** ................ *paintings* | | | $605 |
| 1886-1941 | | | |
| ☐ **FOTTA, L.** ......................................... *paintings* | | | $440 |
| ☐ **FOUBERT, C.** ................................... *paintings* | | | $1,320 |
| French 19th cent. | | | |
| ☐ **FOUBERT, Emile Louis** ....................... *paintings* | | $2,750 | $3,850 |
| French d. 1910 | | | |
| ☐ **FOUCHER, Luc Antoine** ...................... *drawings* | | | $660 |
| ☐ **FOUJITA, Tsuguharu** .......................... *paintings* | | $11,000 | $126,500 |
| Japanese 1886-1968 ................................. *drawings* | | $550 | $79,750 |
| ☐ **FOULKE, Captain B.F.** ........................ *paintings* | | | $220 |
| American 19th/20th cent. | | | |
| ☐ **FOULKES, Llyn** ................................. *paintings* | | $1,100 | $3,080 |
| American b. 1934 ..................................... *drawings* | | | $1,100 |
| ................................................... *sculpture* | | $1,650 | $1,650 |
| ☐ **FOUQUET, A.** ................................... *paintings* | | $440 | $1,045 |
| French 19th cent. | | | |
| ☐ **FOUQUET (?), Jacques Henri** ............... *paintings* | | | $246 |
| French 20th cent. | | | |
| ☐ **FOUQUIERES, Jacques** ....................... *paintings* | | | $35,200 |
| French 1580-1659 | | | |
| ☐ **FOUREAU, Louis-Henri** ...................... *paintings* | | | $935 |
| French 1866-1938 | | | |
| ☐ **FOURIE, Albert Auguste** ..................... *paintings* | | | $9,350 |
| French b. 1854 | | | |
| ☐ **FOURMOND, Coralyde** ....................... *paintings* | | | $302 |
| French 1803-1853 | | | |
| ☐ **FOURNIER, Alexis Jean** ...................... *paintings* | | $264 | $2,090 |
| American 1865-1948 ................................. *drawings* | | | $187 |
| ☐ **FOURNIER, Alfred Victor** ................... *paintings* | | $330 | $1,650 |
| French 1872-1924 | | | |
| ☐ **FOURNIER, J.** ................................... *paintings* | | | $660 |
| French 19th cent. | | | |
| ☐ **FOURNIER, Jean Baptiste Fortune de** ... *drawings* | | $880 | $2,090 |
| French 1798-1864 | | | |
| ☐ **FOURNIER, Louis Edouard Paul** .......... *paintings* | | | $3,300 |
| French b. 1857 | | | |
| ☐ **FOURNIER, Victor** ............................. *paintings* | | $247 | $10,450 |
| French 1872-1924 | | | |
| ☐ **FOUS, Jean** ...................................... *paintings* | | $440 | $1,210 |
| French 1901-1971 | | | |

| | | Current Price Range | |
|---|---|---|---|
| | | Low | High |
| ☐ **FOWLER, Daniel** .................................... *drawings* | | | $660 |
| English 1810-1894 | | | |
| ☐ **FOWLER, Frank** .................... *paintings* | | $137 | $700 |
| American 1852-1910 | | | |
| ☐ **FOWLER, George** .................... *paintings* | | | $1,210 |
| English 20th cent. | | | |
| ☐ **FOWLER, O.R.** .................... *paintings* | | | $1,870 |
| American 19th cent. | | | |
| ☐ **FOWLER, Robert** .................... *paintings* | | $385 | $1,100 |
| British 1853-1926 .................... *drawings* | | | $88 |
| ☐ **FOWLER, Trever Thomas** .................... *paintings* | | | $1,750 |
| American 19th cent. | | | |
| ☐ **FOWLER, William** .................... *drawings* | | $121 | $687 |
| English 19th cent. | | | |
| ☐ **FOX, Edward May** .................... *paintings* | | $1,540 | $2,000 |
| British 19th cent. | | | |
| ☐ **FOX, Fontaine Talbot (Jr.)** .................... *drawings* | | $110 | $412 |
| American 1884-1964 | | | |
| ☐ **FOX, George** .................... *paintings* | | $220 | $400 |
| English 19th cent. | | | |
| ☐ **FOX, Henry Charles** .................... *paintings* | | | $1,320 |
| English b. c. 1860 .................... *drawings* | | $121 | $660 |
| ☐ **FOX, John** .................... *paintings* | | | $412 |
| ☐ **FOX, Robert Atkinson** .................... *paintings* | | $385 | $2,475 |
| Canadian/American b. 1860; ac. c. 1898 | | | |
| ☐ **FOX, William Edward** .................... *paintings* | | | $1,870 |
| English b. 1872 | | | |
| ☐ **FRACANZANO, Francesco** .................... *paintings* | | | $7,150 |
| Italian 1612-1656 | | | |
| ☐ **FRACASSINI, Cesare** .................... *paintings* | | $1,650 | $1,760 |
| Italian 1838-1868 | | | |
| ☐ **FRADELLE, Henri Joseph** .................... *paintings* | | | $825 |
| French 1778-1865 | | | |
| ☐ **FRAGO** .................... *paintings* | | | $1,540 |
| ☐ **FRAGONARD, Alexandre Evariste** ....... *paintings* | | | $137,500 |
| French 1780-1850 .................... *drawings* | | | $1,210 |
| ☐ **FRAGONARD, Jean Honore** .................... *paintings* | | $19,800 | $264,000 |
| French 1732-1806 .................... *drawings* | | $2,200 | $88,000 |
| ☐ **FRAGONARD,** | | | |
| **Theophile Evariste Hippolyte Etienne** ..... *drawings* | | | $462 |
| French 1860-1876 | | | |
| ☐ **FRAHM** .................... *paintings* | | | $385 |
| ☐ **FRAILE, Alfonso** .................... *paintings* | | $1,100 | $1,485 |
| Spanish b. 1930 | | | |
| ☐ **FRAME, Robert Aaron** .................... *paintings* | | $110 | $191 |
| American b. 1924 | | | |
| ☐ **FRANCAIS, Francois Louis** .................... *paintings* | | | $7,150 |
| French 1814-1897 .................... *drawings* | | | $1,320 |
| ☐ **FRANCE, Charles** .................... *paintings* | | $247 | $440 |

| | | *Current Price Range* | |
|---|---|---|---|
| | | *Low* | *High* |
| ☐ **FRANCE, Eurilda Loomis** .................... *paintings* | | $60 | $4,950 |
| American 1865-1931 ................................. *drawings* | | $935 | $2,200 |
| ☐ **FRANCE, G.B.** .................................... *drawings* | | | $660 |
| ☐ **FRANCE, Jesse Leach** ......................... *paintings* | | | $356 |
| American 1862-after 1926 | | | |
| ☐ **FRANCE, Raphael** ............................. *sculpture* | | | $220 |
| French 19th/20th cent. | | | |
| ☐ **FRANCESCHI, Mariano de** ................. *paintings* | | $1,320 | $1,430 |
| Italian 1849-1896 ..................................... *drawings* | | $660 | $3,850 |
| ☐ **FRANCESCHINI, Baldassare** | | | |
| **(called IL VOLTERRANO)** .................... *paintings* | | | $1,650 |
| ................................................................ *drawings* | | | $440 |
| ☐ **FRANCESCO DI MAESTRO GIOTTO**   *paintings* | | $44,000 | $66,000 |
| Italian 14th cent. | | | |
| ☐ **FRANCESCO DI VANNI** ...................... *paintings* | | | $12,100 |
| Italian ...................................................... *drawings* | | | $880 |
| ☐ **FRANCHI, Antonio** ............................. *paintings* | | | $10,725 |
| Italian 1639-1709 | | | |
| ☐ **FRANCHI, Rossello di Jacopo** .............. *paintings* | | $9,900 | $19,800 |
| Italian c. 1377-1456 | | | |
| ☐ **FRANCHIN, A.** ..................................... *paintings* | | | $605 |
| ☐ **FRANCIA, A.T.** ................................... *drawings* | | | $1,320 |
| French 19th cent. | | | |
| ☐ **FRANCIA, Alexandre T.** ...................... *drawings* | | | $247 |
| French/Belgian c. 1815/20-1884 | | | |
| ☐ **FRANCIA, Francois Thomas Louis** ........ *drawings* | | | $467 |
| French 1772-1839 | | | |
| ☐ **FRANCIA, Giovanni de** ........................ *paintings* | | | $7,150 |
| Italian | | | |
| ☐ **FRANCIS, J.J.** ..................................... *drawings* | | | $200 |
| American 19th cent. | | | |
| ☐ **FRANCIS, John F.** .............................. *paintings* | | $1,320 | $60,500 |
| American 1808-1886 | | | |
| ☐ **FRANCIS, Sam** .................................... *paintings* | | $1,540 | $770,000 |
| American b. 1923 ...................................... *drawings* | | $990 | $60,500 |
| ☐ **FRANCISCO, John Bond** .................... *paintings* | | $385 | $3,025 |
| American 1863-1931 | | | |
| ☐ **FRANCISCO, Pietro de** ........................ *paintings* | | | $3,080 |
| Italian ac. 20th cent. | | | |
| ☐ **FRANCISY, G.** ..................................... *paintings* | | | $308 |
| ☐ **FRANCK, Pauwels** | | | |
| **(called Paolo FIAMMINGO)** ................... *paintings* | | $7,700 | $16,500 |
| Flemish 1540-1596 | | | |
| ☐ **FRANCK, Phillipp** .............................. *paintings* | | | $522 |
| German b. 1860 | | | |
| ☐ **FRANCKEN, Constantinus** ................... *paintings* | | | $2,420 |
| Flemish 1661-1717 | | | |
| ☐ **FRANCKEN, Frans (III)** ........................ *paintings* | | | $1,980 |
| Flemish 1607-1667 | | | |

| | | Current Price Range | |
|---|---|---|---|
| | | Low | High |
| ☐ **FRANCKEN, Frans (the younger)** .......... *paintings* | | $2,640 | $46,200 |
| Flemish 1581-1642 | | | |
| ☐ **FRANCKEN, Hieronymus** .................... *paintings* | | | $6,875 |
| Flemish | | | |
| ☐ **FRANCKI, Gustave de E.** ............... *paintings* | | | $330 |
| French 19th cent. | | | |
| ☐ **FRANCO, Battista** ............................. *paintings* | | | $2,300 |
| Italian 1498 or 1510-1580 | | | |
| ☐ **FRANCOIS, Alexander** ........................ *paintings* | | | $660 |
| Belgian 1824-1912 | | | |
| ☐ **FRANCOIS, Ange** ............................... *paintings* | | $2,420 | $7,920 |
| Flemish b. 1800 | | | |
| ☐ **FRANCOIS, Gustave** ........................... *paintings* | | | $605 |
| Swiss b. 1883 | | | |
| ☐ **FRANCOIS, Joseph** ............................. *paintings* | | | $1,800 |
| Belgian 20th cent. | | | |
| ☐ **FRANCOIS, Raymond** ......................... *paintings* | | $55 | $187 |
| French 20th cent. | | | |
| ☐ **FRANCOIS, Robert** ............................. *paintings* | | | $275 |
| French 20th cent. | | | |
| ☐ **FRANCUCCI, Inocenza** | | | |
| **(called Inocenza Da Imoli)** ..................... *paintings* | | | $1,320 |
| Italian 16th cent. | | | |
| ☐ **FRANDZEN, Eugene M.** ....................... *paintings* | | | $412 |
| American ac. 1930-1950 | | | |
| ☐ **FRANGIAMORE, S.** .......................... *drawings* | | | $385 |
| British 20th cent. | | | |
| ☐ **FRANGIAMORE, Salvatore** ................. *paintings* | | $1,650 | $1,760 |
| English ac. 20th cent. | | | |
| ☐ **FRANK, Friedrich** .............................. *drawings* | | $528 | $770 |
| German 19th cent. | | | |
| ☐ **FRANK, Gerald A.** ............................. *paintings* | | $247 | $770 |
| American b. 1888 | | | |
| ☐ **FRANK, Johann Andreas Joseph** .......... *paintings* | | $1,045 | $1,430 |
| German 1756-1804 | | | |
| ☐ **FRANK, Joseph** ................................. *paintings* | | $1,210 | $1,980 |
| German 19th cent. | | | |
| ☐ **FRANK, K.** ........................................ *paintings* | | | $528 |
| ☐ **FRANK, Mary** .................................... *drawings* | | $110 | $605 |
| Anglo/American b. 1933 ................................ *sculpture* | | | $1,650 |
| ☐ **FRANK-WILL** ..................................... *paintings* | | $1,100 | $4,180 |
| French 1900-1951 ..................................... *drawings* | | $150 | $1,980 |
| ☐ **FRANKE, A.J.** .................................... *paintings* | | | $3,000 |
| German 19th cent. | | | |
| ☐ **FRANKE, Albert** ............................... *paintings* | | $650 | $11,550 |
| German 1860-1924 | | | |
| ☐ **FRANKE, Bernard** ............................. *paintings* | | $324 | $357 |
| ☐ **FRANKEN, P.** ..................................... *paintings* | | | $1,100 |
| German 19th cent. | | | |

## Abstract Expressionism

American Abstract Expressionism developed in the 1940s and 1950s. It is characteristically large scale, featuring abstract shapes with some figurative and symbolic elements. The movement is associated with the New York School, which placed great stress on the process of painting. Helen Frankenthaler developed the technique of thinning paint with turpentine and pouring it directly onto unprimed canvas, allowing the diluted color to penetrate quickly into the fabric and create a purely optical image, rather than a three-dimensional form. Frankenthaler influenced many artists, including Kenneth Noland and Morris Louis. (Helen Frankenthaler, "Bay Side," oil on canvas, 74 x 81 in., Hindman, May 11, 1985, $41,800.)

| | | Current Price Range | |
| --- | --- | --- | --- |
| | | *Low* | *High* |
| ☐ **FRANKENBERG, H.** .......................... *paintings* | | | $935 |
| American 19th cent. | | | |
| ☐ **FRANKENSTEIN, Curt** ...................... *paintings* | | | $825 |
| American contemporary | | | |
| ☐ **FRANKENSTEIN, Godfrey H.** .............. *paintings* | | | $2,860 |
| ☐ **FRANKENTHALER, Helen** .................. *paintings* | | $1,540 | $88,000 |
| American b. 1928 | | | |
| ☐ **FRANKFORT, Eduard** ....................... *paintings* | | | $2,200 |
| Dutch b. 1864 ........................................ *drawings* | | | $192 |
| ☐ **FRANKFURTER, Jack** ........................ *paintings* | | $66 | $187 |
| American 20th cent. | | | |
| ☐ **FRANKL, Frank** ............................... *paintings* | | | $275 |
| ☐ **FRANKLEN, B.** ................................. *paintings* | | | $424 |
| ☐ **FRANKLIN, Ione Ruth** ....................... *sculpture* | | | $1,045 |
| American b. 1893 | | | |
| ☐ **FRANQUELIN, Jean Augustin** ............. *paintings* | | | $1,540 |
| French 1798-1839 | | | |
| ☐ **FRANQUELINE, M.** ........................... *paintings* | | | $1,980 |
| French 19th cent. | | | |
| ☐ **FRANSIOLI, Thomas Adrian** ............... *paintings* | | $1,430 | $5,225 |
| American b. 1906 | | | |
| ☐ **FRANZEN, August** ............................ *paintings* | | $6,875 | $8,525 |
| American 1863-1938 ................................ *drawings* | | | $302 |
| ☐ **FRANZIS-GLUSING** ........................... *paintings* | | | $357 |
| 20th cent. | | | |

| | | Current Price Range | |
|---|---|---|---|
| | | Low | High |
| ☐ **FRAPPA, Jose** ..................... *paintings* | | $192 | $3,575 |
| French 1854-1904 | | | |
| ☐ **FRARY, Michael** ................... *paintings* | | $33 | $495 |
| American b. 1918 ....................... *drawings* | | $220 | $247 |
| ☐ **FRASCONI, Antonio** ............. *drawings* | | $192 | $250 |
| American b. Argentina, 1919 | | | |
| ☐ **FRASER, Alexander (Jr.)** ...... *paintings* | | $174 | $6,600 |
| British 1828-1899 | | | |
| ☐ **FRASER, Alexander (Sr.)** ...... *paintings* | | $1,347 | $1,650 |
| British 1786-1865 | | | |
| ☐ **FRASER, Charles A.** ............ *paintings* | | | $275 |
| American 1782-1860 | | | |
| ☐ **FRASER, Donald Hamilton** .......... *paintings* | | $165 | $660 |
| English b. c. 1930 | | | |
| ☐ **FRASER, Douglass** ............... *paintings* | | $220 | $275 |
| American 1885-1955 | | | |
| ☐ **FRASER, E.M.** .................... *paintings* | | | $357 |
| ☐ **FRASER, Hamilton** .............. *paintings* | | $880 | $2,647 |
| contemporary | | | |
| ☐ **FRASER, James Earle** ......... *paintings* | | | $3,327 |
| American 1876-1953 ................... *sculpture* | | $136 | $82,500 |
| ☐ **FRASER, John** .................. *drawings* | | | $605 |
| British 1858-1927 | | | |
| ☐ **FRASER, John Arthur** ........ *paintings* | | | $24,200 |
| Canadian 1838-1898 | | | |
| ☐ **FRASER, Malcolm** ............. *paintings* | | $209 | $275 |
| American 1869-1949 | | | |
| ☐ **FRASER, Robert W.** ........... *drawings* | | $154 | $715 |
| English ac. 1874-1904 | | | |
| ☐ **FRATELLO, Michael San** ...... *paintings* | | | $300 |
| ☐ **FRATER, Henry** ................ *paintings* | | | $330 |
| ☐ **FRATIN, Christophe** ........... *paintings* | | | $82 |
| French c. 1800-1864 ................. *sculpture* | | $286 | $2,200 |
| ☐ **FRATTI** ........................ *drawings* | | | $660 |
| Italian 19th cent. | | | |
| ☐ **FRAUENFELDER, F.J.** ........ *paintings* | | $440 | $522 |
| Dutch 20th cent. | | | |
| ☐ **FRAZIER, Kenneth** ............ *paintings* | | $3,300 | $9,900 |
| French/American 1867-1949 .......... *drawings* | | $55 | $825 |
| ☐ **FRAZIER, Robert Winter** ..... *paintings* | | | $302 |
| English late 19th cent. | | | |
| ☐ **FRECSKAY, Laszlo von** ...... *paintings* | | | $3,080 |
| Austrian 1844-1916 | | | |
| ☐ **FREDDEN-GOLDBERG, Fred** ........ *paintings* | | $660 | $715 |
| American 20th cent. | | | |
| ☐ **FREDDIE, Wilhelm** ............ *drawings* | | | $1,045 |
| Danish b. 1909 | | | |
| ☐ **FREDERIC, Leon** ............... *paintings* | | | $880 |
| Belgian 1856-1940 | | | |

| | | Current Price Range | |
|---|---|---|---|
| | | Low | High |

☐ **FREDERICK, Frank Forrest** ............... *paintings* $66 $715
American b. 1866

☐ **FREDERICKS, Ernest** ........................... *paintings* $55 $357
American b. 1877

☐ **FREDERICKS, Marshall** ...................... *sculpture* $4,675
American 20th cent.

☐ **FREDERICKS, William** ........................ *paintings* $412
American 19th cent.

☐ **FREDOU, Jean Martial** ........................ *drawings* $2,420
French c. 1711-1795

☐ **FREE, John D.** ...................................... *sculpture* $550 $1,200
American b. 1929

☐ **FREEDLEY, Durr** ................................... *drawings* $385

☐ **FREELAND, Anna C.** ........................... *paintings* $44 $247
American 1837-1911

☐ **FREEMAN, Bradford** ............................ *paintings* $990

☐ **FREEMAN, Charles H.** ........................ *paintings* $2,750
American 1859-1918

☐ **FREEMAN, Don** .................................... *paintings* $715 $1,870
American 1908-1978

☐ **FREEMAN, Fred** ................................... *drawings* $242
American 20th cent.

☐ **FREEMAN, J.** ........................................ *drawings* $220
English 19th/20th cent.

☐ **FREEMAN, W.P.B.** .............................. *paintings* $165 $550
English 1813-1897

☐ **FREEMAN, William** ............................. *paintings* $150 $1,760
American b. 1927

☐ **FREER, Frederick Warren** ................... *paintings* $247 $2,750
American 1849-1908 ................................... *drawings* $154

☐ **FREESE, H.J.** ...................................... *paintings* $2,750

☐ **FREEZOR, W.H.M.** ............................. *paintings* $357
American 20th cent.

☐ **FREGEVIZE, Frederic** ......................... *paintings* $15,400
Swiss 1770-1849

☐ **FREIND** ............................................... *paintings* $352

☐ **FREITAG, Conrad** .............................. *paintings* $154 $935
American

☐ **FREITOSA, Roberto** ........................... *paintings* $880

☐ **FRELANT, J.** ....................................... *paintings* $385

☐ **FRELINGHUYSEN, Suzy** ..................... *drawings* $2,640 $15,400
American b. 1912

☐ **FREMIET, Emmanuel** .......................... *paintings* $330 $3,300
French 1824-1910

☐ **FREMONT, O.** ..................................... *paintings* $352

☐ **FREMONT, V.** ..................................... *paintings* $385

☐ **FRENCH, Annie** ................................... *drawings* $1,760 $5,500
Scottish ac. 1865-1924

| | | | Current Price Range | |
|---|---|---|---|---|
| | | | Low | High |
| □ **FRENCH, Daniel Chester** | .................... *sculpture* | | $2,090 | $29,700 |
| American 1850-1931 | | | | |
| □ **FRENCH, Frank** | ................................ *paintings* | | | $475 |
| American 1850-1933 | | | | |
| □ **FRENCH, Mrs. A.G.** | ........................... *paintings* | | | $400 |
| American 19th/20th cent. | | | | |
| □ **FRENTZ, Rudolf** | ................................ *paintings* | | | $3,300 |
| German 1831-1888 | | | | |
| □ **FRENZENY, Paul** | ............................... *paintings* | | | $8,250 |
| Canadian ac. 1866-1902 | ............................. *drawings* | | $495 | $880 |
| □ **FRERE, Charles Edouard** | .................... *paintings* | | $935 | $15,400 |
| French 1837-1894 | ............................................ *drawings* | | | $330 |
| □ **FRERE, Charles Theodore** | .................. *paintings* | | $605 | $7,425 |
| French 1814/15-1888 | ................................ *drawings* | | $275 | $2,640 |
| □ **FRERE, H.** | ......................................... *paintings* | | | $330 |
| French 20th cent. | | | | |
| □ **FRERE, Pierre Edouard** | ...................... *paintings* | | $247 | $30,250 |
| French 1819-1886 | | | | |
| □ **FRERICH, William Charles Anthony** | | | | |
| (or **FRERICHS**) | ..................................... *paintings* | | $605 | $5,750 |
| Belgian/American 1829-1905 | | | | |
| □ **FRESQUIS, Pedro Antonio** | ................... *paintings* | | | $220 |
| American ac. 1810-1840 | | | | |
| □ **FREUDENBERGER, Sigmund** | ............... *drawings* | | $990 | $1,100 |
| Swiss 1745-1801 | | | | |
| □ **FREUND, Fritz** | .................................. *paintings* | | $3,850 | $4,675 |
| German b. 1859 | | | | |
| □ **FREY, J.** | ......................................... *paintings* | | | $440 |
| American 20th cent. | | | | |
| □ **FREY, Johann Jakob** | ........................... *paintings* | | | $6,600 |
| Swiss 1813-1865 | | | | |
| □ **FREY, Johann Wilhelm** | ........................ *drawings* | | | $3,300 |
| Austrian b. 1830 | | | | |
| □ **FREY, Joseph** | ................................... *paintings* | | $120 | $1,430 |
| American b. 1892 | | | | |
| □ **FREY, Wilhelm** | ................................. *paintings* | | $770 | $3,080 |
| German 1826-1911 | | | | |
| □ **FREYBERG, Conrad** | ........................... *paintings* | | $3,300 | $20,350 |
| German b. 1842 | | | | |
| □ **FREYBERG, Edgar** | ............................. *paintings* | | | $330 |
| □ **FREYBERG, Maria Electrina von** | ......... *paintings* | | | $330 |
| □ **FRICK, Paul de** | ................................. *paintings* | | $495 | $3,300 |
| French 1864-1935 | | | | |
| □ **FRIED, Otto** | .................................... *paintings* | | | $220 |
| Dutch 20th cent. | | | | |
| □ **FRIED, Pal** | ...................................... *paintings* | | $110 | $1,760 |
| Hungarian 1893-1976 | ................................. *drawings* | | $198 | $550 |
| □ **FRIEDEBERG, Pedro** | ........................... *drawings* | | | $1,980 |
| Mexican b. 1937 | | | | |

|  | | Current Price Range | |
|--|--|--|--|
|  | | Low | High |
| ☐ **FRIEDENSON, Arthur A.** .................... *paintings* | | $165 | $440 |
| English b. 1872 | | | |
| ☐ **FRIEDENTHAL, David** ....................... *drawings* | | | $187 |
| American 20th cent. | | | |
| ☐ **FRIEDLAENDER, Alfred** .................... *paintings* | | | $605 |
| German b. 1860 | | | |
| ☐ **FRIEDLAENDER, Friedrich** ................ *paintings* | | | $3,080 |
| ☐ **FRIEDLAENDER, Julius** .................... *paintings* | | | $1,350 |
| Danish 1810-1861 | | | |
| ☐ **FRIEDLANDER, Arthur** ...................... *paintings* | | $770 | $770 |
| ☐ **FRIEDLANDER, Friedrich** ................... *paintings* | | $2,090 | $3,500 |
| Austrian 1825-1901 | | | |
| ☐ **FRIEDLANDER, Hedwig** ...................... *paintings* | | | $825 |
| Austrian b. 1863 | | | |
| ☐ **FRIEDLANDER, Maurice** .................... *paintings* | | | $320 |
| American b. 1899 | | | |
| ☐ **FRIEDLANDER VON MALHEIM,** | | | |
| **Camilla** ................................................. *paintings* | | | $2,420 |
| Austrian b. 1856 | | | |
| ☐ **FRIEDLINGEN** ..................................... *paintings* | | $175 | $440 |
| German 20th cent. | | | |
| ☐ **FRIEDLINGER, John** ........................... *paintings* | | $275 | $687 |
| 20th cent. | | | |
| ☐ **FRIEDMAN, Arnold** ............................ *paintings* | | $308 | $9,350 |
| American 1879-1946 | | | |
| ☐ **FRIEDRICH** ........................................ *paintings* | | | $1,320 |
| Austrian 19th cent. | | | |
| ☐ **FRIEDRICH, F.G. Behl** ....................... *sculpture* | | | $352 |
| ☐ **FRIEDRICH, Johann Heinrich August** .. *drawings* | | | $7,150 |
| German 1789-1843 | | | |
| ☐ **FRIEDRICH, Johann Nepomuk** ........... *paintings* | | | $1,980 |
| German 1817-1895 | | | |
| ☐ **FRIEDRICH, M.G.** ............................. *paintings* | | | $350 |
| ☐ **FRIEDRICHSEN, Ernestine** ................. *paintings* | | | $3,300 |
| German 1824-1892 | | | |
| ☐ **FRIEND, Washington F.** ....................... *drawings* | | $110 | $330 |
| American c. 1820-c. 1881/86 | | | |
| ☐ **FRIERS(?), W.F.** ................................ *drawings* | | | $1,045 |
| ☐ **FRIES, Charles Arthur** ...................... *paintings* | | $110 | $660 |
| American 1854-1940 | | | |
| ☐ **FRIESEKE, Frederick Carl** ................. *paintings* | | $4,125 | $93,500 |
| American 1874-1939 ................................. *drawings* | | $412 | $3,575 |
| ☐ **FRIESZ, Achille Emile Othon** .............. *paintings* | | $770 | $132,000 |
| French 1879-1949 ..................................... *drawings* | | $136 | $990 |
| ☐ **FRIGERIO** ......................................... *paintings* | | $275 | $1,210 |
| Italian 19th/20th cent. | | | |
| ☐ **FRIIS, Hans Gabriel** ........................... *paintings* | | | $8,250 |
| Danish 1838-1892 | | | |

| | | *Current Price Range* | |
|---|---|---|---|
| | | *Low* | *High* |
| ☐ **FRINK, Elizabeth** ............... *paintings* | | | $209 |
| British b. 1930 ............... *sculpture* | | $660 | $1,430 |
| ☐ **FRIPP, Alfred Downing** ......... *drawings* | | $132 | $797 |
| English 1822-1895 | | | |
| ☐ **FRIPP, George Arthur** ......... *drawings* | | $165 | $2,420 |
| English 1813-1896 | | | |
| ☐ **FRIPP, Thomas W.** ............ *drawings* | | | $1,430 |
| Canadian 1864-1931 | | | |
| ☐ **FRISCH, Johann Christoph** ........ *paintings* | | $220 | $3,850 |
| German 1738-1815 | | | |
| ☐ **FRISHMUTH, Harriet Whitney** ......... *sculpture* | | $1,210 | $35,750 |
| American 1880-1979 | | | |
| ☐ **FRISTON, David Henry** ......... *paintings* | | | $1,650 |
| British ac. 1853-69 | | | |
| ☐ **FRITH, William Powell** ......... *paintings* | | $440 | $2,750 |
| English 1819-1909 ............... *drawings* | | | $165 |
| ☐ **FRITZ, A.** ............... *paintings* | | | $715 |
| ☐ **FRITZ, Johan Ludwig** ......... *paintings* | | | $462 |
| ☐ **FRITZE, Louis** ............... *paintings* | | | $550 |
| ☐ **FRITZSCHE, Theobald Otto Wilhelm** ... *sculpture* | | $522 | $550 |
| ☐ **FRMER (?), C.** ............... *paintings* | | | $3,520 |
| ☐ **FROEHLICH** ............... *paintings* | | $2,475 | $4,675 |
| American 19th/20th cent. | | | |
| ☐ **FROELICH, Maren M.** ......... *paintings* | | | $330 |
| 20th cent. | | | |
| ☐ **FROHLICH, Lorenz** ............ *paintings* | | $880 | $2,090 |
| Danish 1820-1908 | | | |
| ☐ **FROMANTIOU, Hendrick** ......... *paintings* | | | $14,300 |
| Dutch 1633-1694 | | | |
| ☐ **FROMENTIN, Eugene** ......... *paintings* | | $412 | $126,500 |
| French 1820-1876 ............... *drawings* | | $440 | $1,210 |
| ☐ **FROMKES, Maurice** ......... *paintings* | | $11 | $880 |
| Russian/American 1872-1931 | | | |
| ☐ **FROMMHOLD, C.** ............ *paintings* | | | $440 |
| ☐ **FROOD, Hester** ............... *drawings* | | $55 | $220 |
| English 20th cent. | | | |
| ☐ **FROSSE** ............... *paintings* | | $325 | $350 |
| ☐ **FROST** ............... *paintings* | | | $352 |
| ............... *drawings* | | | $60 |
| ☐ **FROST, Annie S.R.** ............ *paintings* | | | $357 |
| American 20th cent. | | | |
| ☐ **FROST, Arthur Burdett** ......... *paintings* | | $440 | $17,600 |
| American 1851-1928 ............... *drawings* | | $45 | $17,000 |
| ☐ **FROST, George Albert** ......... *paintings* | | $176 | $1,320 |
| American b. 1843 | | | |
| ☐ **FROST, John** ............... *paintings* | | $192 | $2,420 |
| American b. 1890 | | | |
| ☐ **FROST, K.** ............... *paintings* | | | $396 |
| American late 19th cent. | | | |

| | | | Current Price Range | |
|---|---|---|---|---|
| | | | *Low* | *High* |
| ☐ **FROST, William Edward** | ................ *paintings* | | $1,540 | $2,750 |
| English 1810-1877 | ................ *drawings* | | $165 | $550 |
| ☐ **FROTHINGHAM, James** | ................ *paintings* | | | $825 |
| American | | | | |
| ☐ **FRUMM, A.C.** | ................ *sculpture* | | | $357 |
| Italian late 19th cent. | | | | |
| ☐ **FRUTER(?), G.** | ................ *paintings* | | | $330 |
| ☐ **FRY, S.** | ................ *paintings* | | | $301 |
| ☐ **FRYER, C.W.** | ................ *paintings* | | $137 | $302 |
| American 19th/20th cent. | | | | |
| ☐ **FRYER, George L.** | ................ *paintings* | | | $1,430 |
| 19th cent. | | | | |
| ☐ **FRYMIRE, Jacob** | ................ *paintings* | | | $9,900 |
| 1765/74-1822 | | | | |
| ☐ **FUCAS** | ................ *drawings* | | | $247 |
| 19th/20th cent. | | | | |
| ☐ **FUCHS, Daniel** | ................ *paintings* | | $2,200 | $2,200 |
| ☐ **FUCHS, Emil** | ................ *sculpture* | | | $330 |
| ☐ **FUCHS, Ernest** | ................ *paintings* | | | $330 |
| American | | | | |
| ☐ **FUCHS, Ernst** | ................ *paintings* | | | $22,000 |
| 20th cent. | | | | |
| ☐ **FUCHS, K.** | ................ *paintings* | | | $935 |
| ☐ **FUCHS, Karl** | ................ *paintings* | | | $440 |
| ☐ **FUCHS, Ludwijk Juliaan** | ................ *paintings* | | | $1,300 |
| Dutch 1814-1873 | | | | |
| ☐ **FUCHS, Therese** | ................ *paintings* | | | $440 |
| German b. 1849 | | | | |
| ☐ **FUECHSEL, Hermann** | ................ *paintings* | | $412 | $11,550 |
| German/American 1833-1915 | | | | |
| ☐ **FUERTES, Louis Agassiz** | ................ *paintings* | | | $550 |
| American 1874-1927 | ................ *drawings* | | $880 | $16,500 |
| ☐ **FUES, Christian Friedrich** | ................ *paintings* | | | $1,375 |
| German 1772-1836 | | | | |
| ☐ **FUGER, Friedrich Heinrich** | ................ *paintings* | | | $2,860 |
| German 1751-1818 | | | | |
| ☐ **FUGERE, Henry** | ................ *sculpture* | | $363 | $1,980 |
| French b. 1872 | | | | |
| ☐ **FUGLISTER, Fritz** | ................ *paintings* | | | $700 |
| American 20th cent. | | | | |
| ☐ **FUHR, Ernest** | ................ *drawings* | | $154 | $770 |
| American 1874-1933 | | | | |
| ☐ **FUHRKEN, Sophie** | ................ *paintings* | | | $1,210 |
| ☐ **FUHRMANN, M.** | ................ *paintings* | | | $495 |
| ☐ **FUITON, H.** | ................ *paintings* | | | $1,320 |
| French 19th cent. | | | | |
| ☐ **FUKUI, Ryonosuke** | ................ *paintings* | | $2,200 | $10,450 |
| Japanese b. 1922 | | | | |

|                                              | Current Price Range |          |
|----------------------------------------------|---------------------|----------|
|                                              | Low                 | High     |
| ☐ **FULDA, H.** .......................................... *paintings* |                     | **$192** |
| American 20th cent.                          |                     |          |
| ☐ **FULDE, Edward B.** ............................ *paintings* |                     | **$2,200** |
| American 19th/20th cent.                     |                     |          |
| ☐ **FULLER, Alfred** ................................ *paintings* | **$55**             | **$440** |
| American 20th cent.                          |                     |          |
| ☐ **FULLER, Arthur D.** ........................... *paintings* | **$302**            | **$1,320** |
| b. 1889 .................................................... *drawings* | **$176**            | **$660** |
| ☐ **FULLER, Buckminster** ........................ *sculpture* |                     | **$11,000** |
| American 1895-1983                           |                     |          |
| ☐ **FULLER, Caroline C.** .......................... *drawings* |                     | **$275** |
| 19th cent.                                   |                     |          |
| ☐ **FULLER, George** ............................... *paintings* | **$440**            | **$1,650** |
| American 1822-1884 ............................... *drawings* |                     | **$412** |
| ☐ **FULLER, Henry Brown** ....................... *paintings* |                     | **$2,200** |
| American 1867-1934                           |                     |          |
| ☐ **FULLER, S.W.** .................................... *paintings* | **$440**            | **$660** |
| American 19th/20th cent.                     |                     |          |
| ☐ **FULLER, Sue** ................................... *drawings* | **$302**            | **$330** |
| American                                     |                     |          |
| ☐ **FULLICK, E.** ...................................... *paintings* |                     | **$330** |
| ☐ **FULLWOOD, John** .............................. *drawings* | **$220**            | **$302** |
| English ac. 1881-1915; d. 1931               |                     |          |
| ☐ **FULLYLOVE, John** ............................ *drawings* |                     | **$715** |
| English 1845-1908                            |                     |          |
| ☐ **FULOP, Karoly** ................................. *paintings* | **$1,100**          | **$1,760** |
| Hungarian b. 1898 ..................................... *drawings* |                     | **$55** |
| ☐ **FULOR, Elisabeth Weber** ..................... *paintings* | **$450**            | **$1,100** |
| Austrian 19th/20th cent.                     |                     |          |
| ☐ **FULTON, David** ................................. *paintings* | **$450**            | **$650** |
| Scottish 1850-1930                           |                     |          |
| ☐ **FULTON, Fitch** ................................. *paintings* |                     | **$412** |
| American 20th cent.                          |                     |          |
| ☐ **FULTON, H.D.** ................................... *paintings* |                     | **$176** |
| American early 20th cent.                    |                     |          |
| ☐ **FULVIS, De** ..................................... *paintings* |                     | **$522** |
| Italian 20th cent.                           |                     |          |
| ☐ **FUMAGALLI** .................................... *sculpture* |                     | **$475** |
| ☐ **FUMARIA** ....................................... *drawings* |                     | **$330** |
| Italian 19th/20th cent.                      |                     |          |
| ☐ **FUMIANI, Giovanni Antonio** ............... *paintings* |                     | **$8,800** |
| Italian 1643-1710                            |                     |          |
| ☐ **FUNGAI, Bernardino** ........................... *paintings* |                     | **$26,400** |
| Italian c. 1460-1516                         |                     |          |
| ☐ **FUNK, Wilhelm Heinrich** ..................... *paintings* |                     | **$400** |
| ☐ **FUNKE, Bernard** ............................... *paintings* |                     | **$325** |
| German 20th cent.                            |                     |          |
| ☐ **FURCY DE LAVAULT, Albert Tibule** ... *paintings* |                     | **$8,250** |
| French 19th cent.                            |                     |          |

| | | Current Price Range | |
|---|---|---|---|
| | | *Low* | *High* |

☐ **FURET, Francois** ............................... *drawings*  $550
Swiss 1842-1919

☐ **FURINI, Francesco** ........................... *paintings*  $11,000
Italian 1604-1646

☐ **FURLONG, Charles Wellington** ............ *paintings*  $660  $6,600
American b. 1874

☐ **FUSELI, Henry** ................................... *drawings*  $3,300  $8,800
Swiss

☐ **FUSSEL, Katherine Barker** ................... *paintings*  $495
American

☐ **FUSSELL, Charles Lewis** ...................... *drawings*  $12,100
American 1840-1909

☐ **FUSSMANS, Klaus** ............................... *paintings*  $660  $715
German b. 1938

☐ **FUSTER, A. Torres** ............................. *paintings*  $1,045
Spansih 19th cent.

☐ **FYFE, William** ................................... *paintings*  $2,200
British 1836-1882

☐ **FYT, Jan** ........................................... *paintings*  $4,180  $14,300
Flemish 1611-1661 ................................. *drawings*  $3,850

☐ **GABANI, A.** ...................................... *paintings*  $1,320
late 19th cent.

☐ **GABANI, Guiseppe** ............................ *paintings*  $8,800
Italian 1846-1899 ................................. *drawings*  $176  $1,430

☐ **GABBIANI, Antonio Domenico** ............ *paintings*  $990
Italian 1652-1726

☐ **GABE, Nicholas Edward** ...................... *paintings*  $605  $6,325
French 1814-1865

☐ **GABELINT, J.** .................................... *drawings*  $2,860
Continental School 19th cent.

☐ **GABINO, Amadeo** .............................. *sculpture*  $242
Spanish b. 1922

☐ **GABL, Alois** ..................................... *paintings*  $1,430
Swiss 1845-1893

☐ **GABO, Naum** .................................... *sculpture*  $78,100
Russian 1890-1977

☐ **GABRIEL, Herman** ............................. *paintings*  $55  $357

☐ **GABRIEL, Paul Joseph Constantin** ....... *paintings*  $7,150
Dutch 1828-1903

☐ **GABRIEL, Paulus Joseph** ..................... *paintings*  $650

☐ **GABRINI, Pietro** ................................ *paintings*  $797  $4,400
Italian b. 1856 ..................................... *drawings*  $220  $1,760

☐ **GABRIS, B.** ...................................... *paintings*  $357
Hungarian b. 1912

☐ **GABRON, Willem** ............................... *paintings*  $18,150
Belgian 1619-1678

☐ **GADCHAUX, Roger** ............................ *sculpture*  $495

☐ **GADDI, Taddeo** ................................. *paintings*  $44,000
Italian 1300-1366

| | | Current Price Range | |
|---|---|---|---|
| | | Low | High |
| ☐ **GADES** ............................................ *paintings* | | | $440 |
| ☐ **GAEL, Barend (or GAAL)** ..................... *paintings* | | $1,760 | $13,750 |
| Dutch c. 1620-1687 or 1703 | | | |
| ☐ **GAEL, G.** ........................................... *sculpture* | | $220 | $412 |
| ☐ **GAELEN, Alexander van** ...................... *paintings* | | | $385 |
| Dutch 1670-1728 | | | |
| ☐ **GAENSSLEN, Robert** ........................... *paintings* | | | $522 |
| American 1876-1915 | | | |
| ☐ **GAERTNER, Carl F.** ............................ *paintings* | | $220 | $900 |
| American 1898-1952 ................................. *drawings* | | $198 | $825 |
| ☐ **GAG, Wanda H.** .................................. *drawings* | | $275 | $825 |
| American 1893-1946 | | | |
| ☐ **GAGE, George** .................................... *paintings* | | $770 | $1,897 |
| American 1887-1957 | | | |
| ☐ **GAGEL (?), Bemit** ............................... *paintings* | | $440 | $1,320 |
| Dutch 20th cent. | | | |
| ☐ **GAGLIARDINI, Julien Gustave** ............ *paintings* | | $1,045 | $1,980 |
| French 1846-1927 | | | |
| ☐ **GAGNI, P.** .......................................... *paintings* | | $176 | $935 |
| European | | | |
| ☐ **GAIFIER, H.** ....................................... *paintings* | | | $4,950 |
| ☐ **GAIGNERON, Jean de** ......................... *paintings* | | | $660 |
| French b. 1890 | | | |
| ☐ **GAILLARD, Francois** .......................... *paintings* | | | $2,750 |
| French b. 1766 | | | |
| ☐ **GAILLIARD, Ch.** ................................. *paintings* | | | $385 |
| ☐ **GAINSBOROUGH, Thomas** ................. *paintings* | | $3,960 | $330,000 |
| English 1727-1788 ..................................... *drawings* | | $19,250 | $21,450 |
| ☐ **GAISER, Raimond** .............................. *paintings* | | | $990 |
| French 19th cent. | | | |
| ☐ **GAISSER, Jakob Emmanuel** ................. *paintings* | | $1,100 | $5,500 |
| German 1825-1899 | | | |
| ☐ **GAISSER, Max** ................................... *paintings* | | $550 | $2,640 |
| German 1857-1922 | | | |
| ☐ **GALAN, Julio** .................................... *paintings* | | $770 | $1,210 |
| Latin American | | | |
| ☐ **GALANT, Rene** ................................... *paintings* | | | $440 |
| French 20th cent. | | | |
| ☐ **GALE, William** .................................. *paintings* | | $605 | $2,530 |
| British 1823-1909 | | | |
| ☐ **GALEOTTI, Sebastiano** ........................ *drawings* | | | $1,650 |
| ☐ **GALES, W.H.** ..................................... *paintings* | | | $302 |
| Continental School late 19th cent. | | | |
| ☐ **GALIANI, E.** ....................................... *paintings* | | | $1,430 |
| ☐ **GALIARDI, Giovanni** ........................... *paintings* | | | $330 |
| Italian 19th cent. | | | |
| ☐ **GALIEN-LALOUE, Eugene** .................. *paintings* | | | $9,075 |
| French 1854-1941 ...................................... *drawings* | | $1,650 | $28,600 |

## Thomas Gainsborough

*Thomas Gainsborough began his career as a landscape painter. His contemporaries, however, had little taste for landscape art, and Gainsborough achieved fame as a painter of portraits. He was a favorite of British high society, and his subjects included King George III and Queen Charlotte. His most famous portrait, "The Blue Boy," hangs in the Huntington Art Gallery in San Marino, California.*

*Gainsborough never really strayed from his love of landscape. Some of his greatest portraits depict gentlemen relaxing in landscape settings, and at his death his house was found stacked with unsold landscapes. Gainsborough would have been pleased to attend Doyle's sale in early 1985 when, 200 years after it was completed, one of his small chalk landscapes sold for $21,450. (Thomas Gainsborough, "A Wooded Landscape With Sheep," black and white chalk over grey wash on tan paper, 10½ x 15 in., Doyle, January 23, 1985, $21,450.)*

|  | | *Current Price Range* | |
|---|---|---|---|
|  | | *Low* | *High* |
| ☐ **GALIMBERTI, Silvio** ............................ *paintings* | | **$400** | **$880** |
| Italian b. 1878 | | | |
| ☐ **GALL, A.** ............................................. *paintings* | | | **$264** |
| American | | | |
| ☐ **GALL, Francois** ................................... *paintings* | | **$88** | **$4,675** |
| French 1912-1945 ...................................... *drawings* | | **$412** | **$715** |
| ☐ **GALL, G.** ............................................. *paintings* | | | **$577** |
| American 1855-1919 | | | |
| ☐ **GALLAGAN, H.R.** ............................... *paintings* | | | **$1,700** |
| Australian 19th cent. | | | |
| ☐ **GALLAGHER, R.** ............................... *paintings* | | **$45** | **$450** |
| American | | | |

| | | Current Price Range | |
|---|---|---|---|
| | | Low | High |
| ☐ **GALLAGHER, Sears** .......................... *paintings* | | **$2,000** | **$2,500** |
| American 1869-1955 ................................ *drawings* | | **$88** | **$1,540** |
| ☐ **GALLAIT, Louis** ............................... *paintings* | | | **$7,150** |
| Belgian 1810-1887 | | | |
| ☐ **GALLAND, Pierre Victor** ..................... *paintings* | | **$275** | **$302** |
| French 1822-1892 ..................................... *drawings* | | | **$165** |
| ☐ **GALLARD-LEPINAY,** | | | |
| **Paul Charles Emmanuel** ........................ *paintings* | | **$1,760** | **$1,980** |
| French 1842-1885 | | | |
| ☐ **GALLATIN, Albert Eugene** ................. *paintings* | | **$1,430** | **$7,500** |
| American 1881/82-1952 | | | |
| ☐ **GALLE, Hieronymous** ......................... *paintings* | | | **$3,850** |
| Flemish | | | |
| ☐ **GALLEGOS Y ARNOSA, Jose** ............. *paintings* | | **$2,640** | **$13,200** |
| Spanish 1859-1917 | | | |
| ☐ **GALLELLI, Massimiliano** .................... *paintings* | | **$2,860** | **$4,950** |
| Italian b. 1863 | | | |
| ☐ **GALLEN-KALLELA,** | | | |
| **Akseli Valdemar** ................................... *paintings* | | **$3,850** | **$6,600** |
| Finnish 1865-1931 .................................... *drawings* | | | **$990** |
| ☐ **GALLI, G.** .......................................... *paintings* | | **$1,320** | **$4,400** |
| Italian 19th cent. | | | |
| ☐ **GALLI, Giacomo** | | | |
| **(called LO SPADARINO)** ........................ *paintings* | | | **$57,750** |
| Italian 18th cent. | | | |
| ☐ **GALLI, Leopoldo** ............................... *paintings* | | | **$412** |
| Italian 19th cent. | | | |
| ☐ **GALLIAC, Louis** ............................... *paintings* | | | **$4,950** |
| French 1849-1934 | | | |
| ☐ **GALLIANY, J.** .................................... *paintings* | | | **$880** |
| ☐ **GALLIARI, Bernardino** ....................... *drawings* | | | **$2,970** |
| Italian 1704-1792 | | | |
| ☐ **GALLIARI, Gaspare** ........................... *drawings* | | | **$605** |
| Italian 1760-1818/23 | | | |
| ☐ **GALLICE, A.** ..................................... *drawings* | | | **$3,410** |
| Mexican 19th cent. | | | |
| ☐ **GALLINGS** ........................................ *drawings* | | | **$440** |
| American 20th cent. | | | |
| ☐ **GALLIOT, M.** .................................... *drawings* | | | **$286** |
| ☐ **GALLIS, Pieter** ................................. *paintings* | | | **$18,700** |
| Dutch 1633-1697 | | | |
| ☐ **GALLISON, Henry Hammond** .............. *paintings* | | **$357** | **$1,540** |
| American 1850-1910 | | | |
| ☐ **GALLO, Frank** .................................... *drawings* | | **$220** | **$275** |
| American b. 1933 ..................................... *sculpture* | | **$330** | **$7,150** |
| ☐ **GALLO, Ignacio** ................................ *sculpture* | | | **$1,155** |
| Spanish fl. 20th cent. | | | |
| ☐ **GALLON, Robert** ............................... *paintings* | | **$247** | **$4,125** |
| English 19th cent. | | | |

|  | | *Current Price Range* | |
|---|---|---|---|
|  | | *Low* | *High* |
| ☐ **GALLT, I. D.** ...................................... *paintings* | | | $440 |
| ☐ **GALOFRE Y GIMENEZ, Baldomero** .... *paintings* | | $1,540 | $41,800 |
| Spanish 1848/49-1902 ................................ *drawings* | | $577 | $1,320 |
| ☐ **GALSWORTHY, Frank** ....................... *drawings* | | $192 | $605 |
| British b. 1863 | | | |
| ☐ **GALT, Alexander** .............................. *sculpture* | | | $4,000 |
| American 1827-1863 | | | |
| ☐ **GALTON, S.A.** ................................... *paintings* | | $605 | $770 |
| English 19th cent. | | | |
| ☐ **GALVAN, Jesus Guerrero** ................... *paintings* | | $2,750 | $6,600 |
| Mexican 1910-early 1970's .......................... *drawings* | | $1,210 | $1,980 |
| ☐ **GAMBA** ............................................. *drawings* | | | $495 |
| Italian 19th cent. | | | |
| ☐ **GAMBARINI, Giuseppe** ...................... *paintings* | | $3,300 | $28,600 |
| Italian 1680-1725 | | | |
| ☐ **GAMBIER, M.** ................................... *paintings* | | | $385 |
| American 19th cent. | | | |
| ☐ **GAMBINO, Guiseppe** ......................... *paintings* | | $110 | $220 |
| Italian 20th cent. | | | |
| ☐ **GAMBLE, Edna** ................................. *paintings* | | | $220 |
| American 19th/20th cent. ............................. *drawings* | | $88 | $247 |
| ☐ **GAMBLE, John Marshall** ..................... *paintings* | | $247 | $2,860 |
| American 1863-1957 | | | |
| ☐ **GAMBLE, Roy C.** ............................... *paintings* | | $95 | $1,155 |
| American 1887-1972 | | | |
| ☐ **GANAI** ............................................. *paintings* | | | $1,320 |
| European 19th cent. | | | |
| ☐ **GANDOLFI, Gaetano** ......................... *paintings* | | $1,980 | $25,300 |
| Italian 1734-1802 ....................................... *drawings* | | $1,540 | $3,300 |
| ☐ **GANDOLFI, Mauro** ........................... *paintings* | | | $5,500 |
| Italian 1764-1834 | | | |
| ☐ **GANDOLFI, Ubaldo** ........................... *paintings* | | | $19,800 |
| Italian 1728-1781 ....................................... *drawings* | | $1,045 | $1,760 |
| ☐ **GANDY, Herbert** ............................... *paintings* | | $1,210 | $6,600 |
| English ac. 1879; d. c. 1920 | | | |
| ☐ **GANER, Henry** ................................. *drawings* | | $44 | $176 |
| American 20th cent. | | | |
| ☐ **GANGERFELT, Wilhelm von** ............... *paintings* | | | $1,870 |
| Swiss 1844-1920 | | | |
| ☐ **GANNAM, John** ................................. *drawings* | | $396 | $2,200 |
| American 1907-1965 | | | |
| ☐ **GANSO, Emil** ................................... *paintings* | | $605 | $1,980 |
| German/American 1895-1941 ........................ *drawings* | | $99 | $825 |
| ☐ **GANT, James Y.** ................................ *paintings* | | | $3,520 |
| English 19th cent. | | | |
| ☐ **GANTCHEFF** ..................................... *sculpture* | | | $550 |
| ☐ **GANTNER, Bernard** ........................... *paintings* | | $440 | $1,760 |
| French b. 1928 ......................................... *drawings* | | | $550 |

| | | Current Price Range | |
|---|---|---|---|
| | | Low | High |
| ☐ **GARAND, Gustave Cesare** ................... *paintings* <br> French 1847-1914 | | $357 | $550 |
| ☐ **GARBELL, Alexandre** ........................ *paintings* <br> Latvian/French 1903-1970 | | $247 | $550 |
| ☐ **GARBER, Daniel** ............................... *paintings* <br> American 1880-1958 | | $3,960 | $82,500 |
| ☐ **GARCIA, Gay** ..................................... *drawings* <br> b. Cuba 1928 | | | $825 |
| ☐ **GARCIA, Joaquin Torres** .................... *paintings* <br> Uraguayan 1874-1949 | | $8,800 | $33,000 |
| ☐ **GARCIA DE BENABARRE, Pedro** ....... *paintings* <br> Spanish ac. 1455-1456 | | | $12,650 |
| ☐ **GARCIA Y MENCIA, Antonio** ............. *paintings* <br> Spanish ac. 1871-1915 | | $4,400 | $15,400 |
| ☐ **GARCIA Y RAMOS, Jose** .................... *paintings* <br> Spanish b. 1852 | | $2,090 | $9,900 |
| ☐ **GARCIA Y RODRIGUEZ, Manuel** ....... *paintings* <br> Spanish b. 1863 | | $1,760 | $8,250 |
| ☐ **GARDET, Georges** ............................. *sculpture* <br> French b. 1863 | | $660 | $22,000 |
| ☐ **GARDEUR** ....................................... *paintings* <br> French 19th cent. | | $110 | $330 |
| ☐ **GARDI, Emma** .................................. *paintings* <br> Italian 19th/20th cent. | | | $3,850 |
| ☐ **GARDINER, Donald** ........................... *paintings* <br> American 20th cent. | | | $495 |
| ☐ **GARDNER, Daniel** ............................. *drawings* <br> English 1750-1805 | | $198 | $3,850 |
| ☐ **GARDNER, Gertrude** ........................... *paintings* <br> American 1878-1975 | | | $385 |
| ☐ **GARDNER, Gertrude** ........................... *paintings* <br> American 19th cent. | | | $467 |
| ☐ **GARDNER, Sheila** .............................. *drawings* <br> American | | | $1,800 |
| ☐ **GARDNER, Sidney** .............................. *paintings* <br> British ac. 1900 | | $165 | $275 |
| ☐ **GAREIS, Francis** ................................. *paintings* <br> French 19th/20th cent. | | | $302 |
| ☐ **GARET, Jedd** ...................................... *paintings* <br> American b. 1955 ..................................... *drawings* | | $3,520 | $18,700 <br> $1,650 |
| ☐ **GARGALLO, Pablo** ............................. *sculpture* <br> Spanish 1881-1934 | | $3,850 | $14,300 |
| ☐ **GARGIULLE** ..................................... *drawings* <br> Italian 19th cent. | | | $605 |
| ☐ **GARGIULO, Domenico** ........................ *drawings* <br> Italian 1612-1679 | | | $660 |
| ☐ **GARGIULO, L.** .................................... *paintings* | | | $990 |
| ☐ **GARGUILO** ........................................ *paintings* <br> Italian 19th/20th cent. | | | $660 |

| | | Current Price Range | |
|---|---|---|---|
| | | Low | High |
| ☐ GARIS, A. De ............................... *paintings* | | | $825 |
| ☐ GARLAND, George ...................... *drawings* | | | $275 |
| ☐ GARLAND, Henry ........................... *paintings* | | $715 | $3,300 |
| English ac. 1854-1892 | | | |
| ☐ GARLAND, R. ................................. *paintings* | | | $1,017 |
| British 19th cent. | | | |
| ☐ GARLAND, Valentine Thomas ............. *paintings* | | | $2,500 |
| English 19th/20th cent. | | | |
| ☐ GARLNER, L. .................................. *paintings* | | $385 | $440 |
| ☐ GARMS, Coenraad Matthias ................ *paintings* | | | $385 |
| ☐ GARNERAY, Hippolyte Jean Baptiste ... *drawings* | | | $275 |
| French 1787-1858 | | | |
| ☐ GARNIER ........................................... *sculpture* | | | $1,210 |
| French | | | |
| ☐ GARNIER, F. .................................... *sculpture* | | | $400 |
| ☐ GARNIER, V. ................................... *paintings* | | | $385 |
| French 19th cent. | | | |
| ☐ GAROLI, Pietro Francesco ................ *paintings* | | | $5,500 |
| Italian 1638-1716 | | | |
| ☐ GAROSSA ........................................ *paintings* | | | $880 |
| Czechoslovakian b. 1924 | | | |
| ☐ GARRATT, J.H. ............................... *drawings* | | $30 | $220 |
| American 19th/20th cent. | | | |
| ☐ GARRETTO, Paolo Federico ................ *drawings* | | | $825 |
| ☐ GARRICK, R. .................................. *paintings* | | | $1,540 |
| ☐ GARRIDO, Eduardo Leon ................... *paintings* | | $1,100 | $19,250 |
| Spanish 1856-1906 | | | |
| ☐ GARRISON, Edith M. ......................... *drawings* | | | $495 |
| ☐ GARRY, Charley ............................... *paintings* | | $302 | $385 |
| French b. 1891 | | | |
| ☐ GARSIDE, Thomas H. ......................... *paintings* | | | $2,090 |
| Canadian b. 1906 | | | |
| ☐ GARSON, Etta Corbett ..................... *paintings* | | $165 | $770 |
| American 1898-1968 | | | |
| ☐ GARTNER, Fritz .............................. *paintings* | | | $715 |
| German 19th/20th cent. | | | |
| ☐ GARTNER, L. .................................. *paintings* | | | $440 |
| Continental 19th cent. | | | |
| ☐ GARTO, Luis la ............................... *drawings* | | | $49,500 |
| ☐ GARZI, Luigi .................................. *paintings* | | $3,300 | $13,200 |
| Italian 1638-1721 | | | |
| ☐ GASKE, F.J. ................................... *drawings* | | $66 | $770 |
| European 19th/20th cent. | | | |
| ☐ GASKELL, George Arthur ................ *paintings* | | $605 | $1,320 |
| English ac. 1871-1900 | | | |
| ☐ GASKINS, Arthur Joseph ..................... *paintings* | | | $192 |
| English 1862-1928 | | | |
| ☐ GASPARD, Frantz ............................. *paintings* | | | $3,410 |

| | | Current Price Range | |
|---|---|---|---|
| | | *Low* | *High* |
| ☐ **GASPARD, Leon** .................................. *paintings* | | $1,100 | $104,500 |
| Russian/American 1882-1964 ......................... *drawings* | | $770 | $8,800 |
| ☐ **GASPARI, Pierre G.** ................... *sculpture* | | | $9,350 |
| American c. 1865 | | | |
| ☐ **GASSER, Henry Martin** ................... *paintings* | | $715 | $715 |
| American 1909-1981 ................................ *drawings* | | $176 | $412 |
| ☐ **GASSETTE, Grace** ............................. *drawings* | | | $990 |
| American late 19th/20th cent. | | | |
| ☐ **GASSIM, Mary W.** ............................ *paintings* | | | $209 |
| American 19th cent. | | | |
| ☐ **GASSON, Leo** ................................... *paintings* | | | $825 |
| French 1860-1944 | | | |
| ☐ **GAST, John** .................................... *paintings* | | | $22,000 |
| American | | | |
| ☐ **GASTINEAU, Henry G.** ...................... *drawings* | | | $3,300 |
| British 1791-1876 | | | |
| ☐ **GASTON, A.P.** .................................. *drawings* | | | $198 |
| French (?) 19th cent. | | | |
| ☐ **GATCH, Lee** .................................... *paintings* | | $880 | $11,550 |
| American 1902/09-1968 ............................. *drawings* | | | $2,200 |
| ☐ **GATES, E. Allsainis** ........................... *paintings* | | | $264 |
| ☐ **GATTER, Otto** ................................. *paintings* | | | $1,980 |
| American 1892-1926 | | | |
| ☐ **GATTESCHI** ...................................... *paintings* | | | $412 |
| Italian 19th cent. | | | |
| ☐ **GATTORNO, Antonio** .......................... *paintings* | | | $1,540 |
| Cuban b. 1904 | | | |
| ☐ **GAUBAULT, Alfred Emile** ................... *paintings* | | $880 | $935 |
| French d. 1895 | | | |
| ☐ **GAUDEZ, Adrien Etienne** ................... *sculpture* | | $357 | $4,125 |
| French 1845-1902 | | | |
| ☐ **GAUDFROY, Fernand** ...................... *paintings* | | $3,300 | $6,600 |
| Belgian 1885-1964 | | | |
| ☐ **GAUDI, Antonio** ............................... *sculpture* | | $5,500 | $15,400 |
| Spanish 1852-1926 | | | |
| ☐ **GAUDIER-BRZESKA, Henry** ............... *drawings* | | $308 | $1,210 |
| French 1891-1915 | | | |
| ☐ **GAUEN, M.** ..................................... *paintings* | | | $275 |
| American early 20th cent. | | | |
| ☐ **GAUERMANN, Friedrich** ..................... *paintings* | | $20,900 | $33,000 |
| Austrian 1807-1862 | | | |
| ☐ **GAUGENGIGL, Ignaz Marcel** ............. *paintings* | | $550 | $3,080 |
| German/American 1855/56-1932 | | | |
| ☐ **GAUGUIN, Paul** ............................. *paintings* | | $27,500 | $3,850,000 |
| French 1848-1903 ..................................... *drawings* | | $2,200 | $37,400 |
| .............................................................. *sculpture* | | $1,760 | $25,300 |
| ☐ **GAUL, Arrah Lee** ............................... *paintings* | | $176 | $1,650 |
| American b. 1888 | | | |

| | | *Current Price Range* | |
|---|---|---|---|
| | | Low | High |
| ☐ **GAUL, William Gilbert** ........................ *paintings* | | $132 | $30,800 |
| American 1855-1919 .............................. *drawings* | | $165 | $1,045 |
| ☐ **GAULD, David** .................................... *paintings* | | $440 | $1,650 |
| Scottish 1866-1936 | | | |
| ☐ **GAULEY, Robert David** ........................ *paintings* | | $220 | $1,045 |
| American b. 1875 .................................... *drawings* | | $275 | $286 |
| ☐ **GAULLI, Giovanni Battista** | | | |
| **(called IL BACCICCIO)** ........................ *drawings* | | $4,950 | $5,720 |
| ☐ **GAULT, Mary D.** ................................ *drawings* | | | $5,225 |
| American | | | |
| ☐ **GAUQUIE, Henri Desire** ........................ *sculpture* | | $1,320 | $2,750 |
| French 1858-1927 | | | |
| ☐ **GAUSSON, Leo** .................................... *paintings* | | | $7,700 |
| French 1860-1944 | | | |
| ☐ **GAUTHERIN, Jean** ............................. *sculpture* | | $1,210 | $1,320 |
| French 1840-1890 | | | |
| ☐ **GAUTHIER, G.** .................................... *paintings* | | | $1,430 |
| ☐ **GAUTIER, Jacques Louis** ..................... *sculpture* | | | $3,080 |
| ☐ **GAUTIER, Lucien** ............................... *paintings* | | | $418 |
| ☐ **GAVAGNIN, Natale** ............................ *paintings* | | | $495 |
| Italian b. 1851 ..................................... *drawings* | | $60 | $192 |
| ☐ **GAVANI, Giuseppe** ............................. *drawings* | | | $935 |
| Italian 1849-1899 | | | |
| ☐ **GAVARDIE, Jean de** ........................ *paintings* | | | $660 |
| French 1909-1961 | | | |
| ☐ **GAVARNI,** | | | |
| **Sulpice-Guillaume Chevalier** | | | |
| **(called Paul)** ........................................ *drawings* | | $242 | $1,760 |
| French 1804-1866 | | | |
| ☐ **GAVERE, Cornelia de** ........................ *paintings* | | $165 | $715 |
| American b. 1877 | | | |
| ☐ **GAW, William A.** ................................ *paintings* | | $88 | $495 |
| American 1891-1973 | | | |
| ☐ **GAWYER, Roswell Douglas** ................... *paintings* | | | $495 |
| American 19th/20th cent. | | | |
| ☐ **GAY, Edward B.** ............................... *paintings* | | $165 | $4,400 |
| Irish/American 1837-1928 ........................ *drawings* | | $165 | $330 |
| ☐ **GAY, George Howell** ........................ *paintings* | | $110 | $1,500 |
| American 1858-1931 .................................... *drawings* | | $110 | $3,080 |
| ☐ **GAY, Walter** ................................... *paintings* | | $330 | $15,400 |
| American 1856-1937 .................................... *drawings* | | $275 | $2,640 |
| ☐ **GAY, Winkworth Allan** ...................... *paintings* | | $330 | $1,650 |
| American 1821-1910 .................................... *drawings* | | $110 | $132 |
| ☐ **GAYER, A.** ........................................ *paintings* | | | $880 |
| 19th cent. | | | |
| ☐ **GAYLER, L.** ...................................... *paintings* | | | $2,420 |
| German (?) 19th cent. | | | |
| ☐ **GAYLOR, Samuel Wood** ...................... *paintings* | | $93 | $220 |
| American b. 1883 ...................................... *drawings* | | $55 | $154 |

|  | *Current Price Range* | |
|---|---|---|
| | *Low* | *High* |
| ☐ **GAYRARD, Paul Joseph Raymond** ........ *sculpture* | $385 | $1,540 |
| French 1807-1855 | | |
| ☐ **GAZE, Harold** ..................................... *drawings* | $550 | $1,320 |
| American | | |
| ☐ **GEBAUER, Christian David** ................ *paintings* | | $550 |
| German 1777-1831 | | |
| ☐ **GEBHARDT, Eduard von** ................... *paintings* | | $1,650 |
| German 1838-1925 | | |
| ☐ **GEBHARDT, Johann** ........................... *paintings* | $220 | $275 |
| German 20th cent. | | |
| ☐ **GEBHARDT, Ludwig** .......................... *paintings* | | $990 |
| German 1830-1908 | | |
| ☐ **GEBLER, Friedrich Otto** ..................... *paintings* | $6,600 | $22,550 |
| German 1838-1917 | | |
| ☐ **GECHTER, Jean Francois Theodore** ..... *sculpture* | $528 | $605 |
| French | | |
| ☐ **GECHTOFF, Leonid** ........................... *paintings* | $154 | $275 |
| American 20th cent. .................................. *drawings* | | $55 |
| ☐ **GECHTOFF, Sonia** ............................. *paintings* | $1,320 | $2,420 |
| American b. 1926 | | |
| ☐ **GEDDES, Norman Bel** ......................... *paintings* | | $7,975 |
| American 1893-1958 | | |
| ☐ **GEDDES, W.** ...................................... *paintings* | | $462 |
| ☐ **GEDIKE, Roman** ................................ *drawings* | | $330 |
| ☐ **GEDLEK, Ludwig** ............................... *paintings* | $3,300 | $6,050 |
| Polish b. 1847 | | |
| ☐ **GEEFS, C.K. De** ................................ *sculpture* | | $1,045 |
| ☐ **GEENS, Louis** ................................... *paintings* | $192 | $6,608 |
| Belgian 19th cent. | | |
| ☐ **GEER, Grace Woodbridge** .................... *paintings* | | $550 |
| American b. 1854 | | |
| ☐ **GEERAERTS, Marten** .......................... *paintings* | | $4,400 |
| Flemish 1709-1791 .................................. *drawings* | | $192 |
| ☐ **GEERTS, Julius** ................................. *paintings* | $4,070 | |
| German 1837-1902 | | |
| ☐ **GEEST, Julien Franciscus de** ............... *paintings* | | $1,650 |
| Flemish d. 1699 | | |
| ☐ **GEFFKEN, Walter** .............................. *paintings* | | $660 |
| German 1872-1950 | | |
| ☐ **GEGERFELT, Wilhelm von** ................... *paintings* | $1,870 | $7,700 |
| Swedish 1844-1920 | | |
| ☐ **GEHRY, P.** ........................................ *paintings* | | $357 |
| American 19th cent. | | |
| ☐ **GEIBEL, Casimir** ............................... *paintings* | | $15,400 |
| German 1839-1896 | | |
| ☐ **GEIBEL, H.** ....................................... *paintings* | | $330 |
| German 19th cent. | | |
| ☐ **GEIBEL, Isaac** .................................. *paintings* | | $770 |

| | Current Price Range | |
|---|---|---|
| | *Low* | *High* |
| ☐ **GEIGER, Conrad** .................. *paintings* <br> German 1751-1808 | | **$2,860** |
| ☐ **GEIGER, R.** .................. *paintings* <br> 20th cent. | **$440** | **$550** |
| ☐ **GEIRNAERT, Josef** .................. *paintings* <br> Belgian 1791-1859 | **$1,870** | **$3,520** |
| ☐ **GEISSER, T. E.** .................. *paintings* <br> German 19th cent. | | **$1,100** |
| ☐ **GEISSLER, M.S.** .................. *paintings* | | **$550** |
| ☐ **GEITNER, Otto** .................. *drawings* <br> German 19th cent. | | **$357** |
| ☐ **GELANZE, Giuseppe** .................. *paintings* <br> Italian b. 1867 | | **$495** |
| ☐ **GELDORP, Gortzius** .................. *paintings* <br> Flemish 1553-c. 1618 | **$330** | **$1,210** |
| ☐ **GELECTDS, Flore** .................. *paintings* | | **$1,650** |
| ☐ **GELHAY, Edouard** .................. *paintings* <br> French b. 1856 | | **$2,310** |
| ☐ **GELIBERT, Jules Bertrand** .................. *paintings* <br> French b. 1834 .................. *sculpture* | | **$770** <br> **$297** |
| ☐ **GELLI, Edoardo** .................. *paintings* <br> Italian 1852-1933 | | **$3,080** |
| ☐ **GEMEINERT, C.G.** .................. *paintings* | | **$275** |
| ☐ **GEMIN, Louise Adele** .................. *paintings* <br> French 1817-1897 | | **$275** |
| ☐ **GEMITO, Vincenzo** .................. *drawings* <br> Italian 1852-1929 .................. *sculpture* | **$660** | **$200** <br> **$7,700** |
| ☐ **GEN, Lucien** .................. *drawings* <br> French 1894-1958 | | **$200** |
| ☐ **GEN PAUL** .................. *paintings* <br> French 1895-1975 .................. *drawings* | **$770** <br> **$242** | **$7,700** <br> **$2,200** |
| ☐ **GENDREAU** .................. *paintings* <br> French 20th cent. | | **$330** |
| ☐ **GENEGEN(?), Joseph van** .................. *paintings* <br> Dutch 19th/20th cent. | | **$275** |
| ☐ **GENERALIC, Ivan** .................. *paintings* <br> Yugoslavian b. 1914 | | **$9,350** |
| ☐ **GENEVE, C. Barriot** .................. *paintings* <br> Austrian 19th cent. | | **$467** |
| ☐ **GENIN, Lucien** .................. *drawings* <br> French b. 1894 | **$412** | **$550** |
| ☐ **GENINE** .................. *paintings* <br> French 20th cent. | | **$220** |
| ☐ **GENIS, Rene** .................. *paintings* | | **$275** |
| ☐ **GENISSON, Jules Victor** .................. *paintings* <br> Belgian 1805-1860 | **$4,000** | **$7,975** |
| ☐ **GENNARELLI, Amedeo** .................. *sculpture* <br> French ac. 1913-1930 | **$2,750** | **$11,000** |

| | | *Current Price Range* | |
|---|---|---|---|
| | | Low | High |
| ☐ **GENNARI, Benedetto (the younger)** ....... *paintings* | | $3,080 | $4,620 |
| Italian 1633-1715 | | | |
| ☐ **GENNARI, G.** ..................................... *paintings* | | | $797 |
| Italian 19th cent. | | | |
| ☐ **GENNERELLI, A.** ............................... *sculpture* | | | $330 |
| ☐ **GENNO, Lucien** ............................... *drawings* | | | $308 |
| ☐ **GENOD, Michel Philibert** ..................... *paintings* | | $418 | $3,300 |
| French 1795-1862 | | | |
| ☐ **GENOELS, Abraham** .......................... *drawings* | | $660 | $1,210 |
| Flemish | | | |
| ☐ **GENTH, Lillian Matilde** ....................... *paintings* | | $220 | $12,500 |
| American 1876-1953 | | | |
| ☐ **GENTILESCHI, Artemisia** ................... *paintings* | | | $7,150 |
| Italian 1597-c. 1651 | | | |
| ☐ **GENTILI, Angelo** ............................... *drawings* | | | $467 |
| German 19th cent. | | | |
| ☐ **GENTILINI, Frederico** ......................... *paintings* | | | $7,150 |
| ☐ **GENTILZ, Jean Louis Theodore** ........... *paintings* | | | $3,080 |
| American 1819/20-1906 | | | |
| ☐ **GENTZ, Ismael** .................................... *paintings* | | | $275 |
| German 1862-1914 | | | |
| ☐ **GENUNG, J.E.** ..................................... *paintings* | | | $250 |
| ☐ **GEOFFROI, Harry** ............................... *paintings* | | | $1,100 |
| ☐ **GEOFFROY, Henri Jules Jean** .............. *paintings* | | $4,950 | $7,150 |
| French 1853-1924 | | | |
| ☐ **GEORG, Edouard** ............................... *paintings* | | | $5,500 |
| ☐ **GEORGE, A.** ....................................... *paintings* | | | $192 |
| Swiss 20th cent. | | | |
| ☐ **GEORGE, A.** ....................................... *paintings* | | | $301 |
| American late 19th cent. | | | |
| ☐ **GEORGE, Frances** ............................... *paintings* | | $33 | $385 |
| ☐ **GEORGE, M.J.** ..................................... *paintings* | | | $660 |
| American | | | |
| ☐ **GEORGE, Thomas** ............................... *drawings* | | | $300 |
| American 20th cent. | | | |
| ☐ **GEORGES, Joannes** ............................. *paintings* | | | $7,150 |
| French 19th cent. | | | |
| ☐ **GEORGES, Paul** ................................... *paintings* | | | $275 |
| ☐ **GEORGET, Charles Jean** ...................... *paintings* | | | $550 |
| French d. 1895 | | | |
| ☐ **GEORGI, Edwin** ................................... *paintings* | | $577 | $935 |
| American 1896-1964 ..................................... *drawings* | | | $275 |
| ☐ **GEORGI, Friedrich-Traugott** ................ *paintings* | | | $3,520 |
| German 1783-1838 | | | |
| ☐ **GEOTZ, Gottfried Bernhard** ................. *drawings* | | | $715 |
| ☐ **GERA, Zorad** ....................................... *paintings* | | | $302 |
| Hungarian 20th cent. | | | |
| ☐ **GERARD, Esteval Grand** ...................... *paintings* | | | $1,045 |

| | Current Price Range | |
| | Low | High |
|---|---|---|
| ☐ **GERARD,** | | |
| **Francois Pascal Simon Baron** ............... *paintings* | | **$4,620** |
| French 1770-1837 | | |
| ☐ **GERARD, J.** ........................................... *paintings* | | **$275** |
| ☐ **GERARD, Lucien** .................................. *paintings* | **$1,760** | **$3,850** |
| Belgian 1852-1935 | | |
| ☐ **GERARD, Marguerite** ......................... *paintings* | **$12,000** | **$41,800** |
| French 1761-1837 | | |
| ☐ **GERARD, Paul** ..................................... *paintings* | | **$440** |
| American 20th cent. | | |
| ☐ **GERARD, Pierre Petit** ........................ *paintings* | | **$440** |
| ☐ **GERARD, Ron** ................................... *paintings* | | **$314** |
| ☐ **GERARD, S.** ........................................ *paintings* | | **$1,320** |
| ☐ **GERARD, Theodore** ............................ *paintings* | **$715** | **$38,500** |
| Belgian 1829-1895 | | |
| ☐ **GERARD, Z.A.** .................................... *paintings* | | **$660** |
| French 19th cent. | | |
| ☐ **GERASCH, August** ............................ *paintings* | | **$2,640** |
| Austrian b. 1822 | | |
| ☐ **GERBAUD, Abel** ................................ *paintings* | | **$330** |
| French 1888-1954 | | |
| ☐ **GERBER, A.** ....................................... *paintings* | | **$330** |
| ☐ **GERBINO, Rosario U.** ......................... *paintings* | **$165** | **$770** |
| American 20th cent. | | |
| ☐ **GERBOUX, Auguste Charles** ............... *paintings* | | **$1,320** |
| Belgian 1838-1878 | | |
| ☐ **GERCHMAN, Rubens** ........................ *drawings* | | **$1,320** |
| Brazilian b. 1942 | | |
| ☐ **GERDAGO** ......................................... *sculpture* | **$990** | **$1,210** |
| ☐ **GERDERES, Jeanne** ........................... *drawings* | | **$550** |
| French 19th/20th cent. | | |
| ☐ **GERDME, Fr.** ..................................... *paintings* | | **$330** |
| French 20th cent. | | |
| ☐ **GERE, Nellie Huntington** ..................... *paintings* | | **$880** |
| American 1859-1949 | | |
| ☐ **GERHARD, George** ........................... *paintings* | | **$715** |
| German 1830-1902 | | |
| ☐ **GERHARDT, B.** ................................... *paintings* | | **$400** |
| ☐ **GERICAULT,** | | |
| **Jean Louis Andre Theodore** ................... *paintings* | | **$6,050** |
| French 1791-1824 ..................................... *drawings* | **$1,210** | **$5,500** |
| ☐ **GERINI, Lorenzo di Niccolo** ............... *paintings* | **$39,600** | **$66,000** |
| Italian 14th/15th cent. | | |
| ☐ **GERINI, Niccolo di Pietro** ..................... *paintings* | | **$18,700** |
| Italian d. 1415 | | |
| ☐ **GERLASH, Anthony** ........................... *paintings* | | **$2,200** |
| American ac. 1860-1880 | | |
| ☐ **GERMAIN, Jean Baptiste** ..................... *sculpture* | | **$3,080** |
| French d. 1910 | | |

|  | | *Current Price Range* | |
|---|---|---|---|
|  | | *Low* | *High* |
| ☐ **GERMAIN, Louis** ........................ *paintings* | | | $660 |
| French 19th cent. | | | |
| ☐ **GERNON, V.** ........................ *paintings* | | | $275 |
| French 20th cent. | | | |
| ☐ **GEROME, Jean Leon** ..................... *paintings* | | $1,320 | $440,000 |
| French 1824-1904 ........................ *drawings* | | $275 | $5,500 |
| ........................ *sculpture* | | $550 | $7,150 |
| ☐ **GERONE, F.** ........................ *paintings* | | $66 | $700 |
| French 19th/20th cent. | | | |
| ☐ **GERRARD, H.** ........................ *paintings* | | | $308 |
| ☐ **GERRY, Samuel Lancaster** ............... *paintings* | | $330 | $16,500 |
| American 1813-1891 ........................ *drawings* | | $100 | $550 |
| ☐ **GERSHAL, G. J.** ........................ *paintings* | | | $357 |
| European 19th cent. | | | |
| ☐ **GERSON, Hendrik** ........................ *paintings* | | $466 | $1,045 |
| ☐ **GERSTMAYER, A.F.** ........................ *paintings* | | | $330 |
| ☐ **GERVAIS, Paul Jean Louis** ............... *paintings* | | | $2,420 |
| French b. 1859 | | | |
| ☐ **GERVEX, Henri** ........................ *paintings* | | $990 | $19,800 |
| French 1852-1929 ........................ *drawings* | | | $3,300 |
| ☐ **GERZSO, Gunther** ..................... *paintings* | | $1,210 | $30,250 |
| Mexican b. 1915 ........................ *drawings* | | | $1,430 |
| ☐ **GESCHUTZ** ........................ *sculpture* | | $495 | $660 |
| ☐ **GESMAR, Charles** ..................... *drawings* | | $77 | $1,760 |
| 20th cent. | | | |
| ☐ **GESSING, Roland** ..................... *paintings* | | | $1,320 |
| Canadian 1895-1967 | | | |
| ☐ **GESSNER, Johann Conrad** ............... *drawings* | | | $1,430 |
| Swiss | | | |
| ☐ **GESSNER, Reinard** ..................... *paintings* | | | $192 |
| German 19th/20th cent. | | | |
| ☐ **GESSNITZER, T.C.** ..................... *paintings* | | | $825 |
| ☐ **GESTEL, Leo van** ..................... *drawings* | | | $770 |
| Continental 20th cent. | | | |
| ☐ **GETL, G.** ........................ *paintings* | | | $770 |
| ☐ **GEVERS, Helene** ..................... *paintings* | | | $605 |
| Flemish 19th cent. | | | |
| ☐ **GEYER, Alexius** ..................... *paintings* | | $770 | $5,500 |
| German 1816-1883 | | | |
| ☐ **GEYER, Hermann** ..................... *paintings* | | $165 | $1,210 |
| 19th cent. | | | |
| ☐ **GEYP, Andriaan Marinus** ............... *paintings* | | $1,100 | $1,100 |
| Dutch 1855-1926 | | | |
| ☐ **GEZZARD, J.W.** ..................... *paintings* | | | $495 |
| ☐ **GHEDUZZI, Giuseppe** ..................... *paintings* | | $2,750 | $2,860 |
| Italian 1889-1957 | | | |
| ☐ **GHERARD, P.** ..................... *sculpture* | | | $550 |
| ☐ **GHERARDI, Giuseppe** ..................... *paintings* | | | $3,850 |
| Italian ac. c. 1850 | | | |

| | Current Price Range | |
|---|---|---|
| | *Low* | *High* |
| ☐ **GHEZZI, Pier Leone** .............. *paintings* | $4,400 | $48,400 |
| Italian 1674-1755 ........................ *drawings* | $247 | $2,750 |
| ☐ **GHIGLION-GREEN, Maurice** ........... *paintings* | $418 | $1,760 |
| ☐ **GHIRLANDAJO, Ridolfi di Domenico** ... *paintings* | $5,500 | $9,350 |
| Italian 1483-1561 | | |
| ☐ **GHISLANDI, Vittore** | | |
| **(called Fra Galgario)** ................ *paintings* | | $3,850 |
| Italian 1655-1743 | | |
| ☐ **GHISOLFI, Giovanni** ............... *paintings* | $11,000 | $11,000 |
| Italian 1632-1683 | | |
| ☐ **GIACHI, E.** ....................... *paintings* | | $3,410 |
| Italian 19th cent. | | |
| ☐ **GIACOMELLI, F.** ................... *paintings* | | $550 |
| ☐ **GIACOMELLI, Vincenco** .............. *paintings* | | $962 |
| Italian 1841-1890 | | |
| ☐ **GIACOMETTI, Alberto** ............... *paintings* | $24,200 | $181,500 |
| Swiss 1901-1966 ....................... *drawings* | $990 | $38,500 |
| ................................... *sculpture* | $3,300 | $1,430,000 |
| ☐ **GIACOMETTI, Diego** ............... *sculpture* | $9,900 | $46,200 |
| Swiss b. 1902 | | |
| ☐ **GIALLINA, Angelos** ............... *drawings* | $192 | $2,200 |
| Italian b. 1857 | | |
| ☐ **GIAMPIETRI, Settimio** ............. *drawings* | | $550 |
| Italian 1852-1924 | | |
| ☐ **GIANAKOS, Steve** ................. *drawings* | | $990 |
| contemporary | | |
| ☐ **GIANI, Felice** ................... *drawings* | $264 | $4,180 |
| Italian c. 1760-1823 | | |
| ☐ **GIANI, Ugo** ...................... *paintings* | $99 | $275 |
| Italian 19th/20th cent. ................. *drawings* | | $99 |
| ☐ **GIANNACCINI** .................... *paintings* | | $495 |
| Italian b. 1897 | | |
| ☐ **GIANNELLI, Enrico** ............... *paintings* | | $1,320 |
| Italian b. 1854 | | |
| ☐ **GIANNETTI, Raffaele** ............. *paintings* | $1,045 | $3,300 |
| Italian 1832-1916 | | |
| ☐ **GIANNI, Gian** ................... *paintings* | $220 | $7,150 |
| Italian b. 1866 ....................... *drawings* | $165 | $495 |
| ☐ **GIANNI, Giuseppe** ............... *drawings* | | $356 |
| Italian 1829-1885 | | |
| ☐ **GIANNI, M.** ...................... *drawings* | $165 | $330 |
| ☐ **GIANNI, R.** ...................... *paintings* | | $1,980 |
| Italian 19th cent. | | |
| ☐ **GIANNIS, U.** ..................... *paintings* | | $275 |
| Italian 19th cent. | | |
| ☐ **GIANOLI, Louis** .................. *drawings* | | $220 |
| Swiss b. 1868 | | |
| ☐ **GIAQUINTO, Corrado** ............. *paintings* | $14,300 | $82,500 |
| Italian c. 1690-1765 | | |

| | | Current Price Range | |
|---|---|---|---|
| | | *Low* | *High* |
| ☐ **GIARDIELLO** ..................................... *paintings* | | $400 | $2,200 |
| Italian 19th/20th cent. | | | |
| ☐ **GIBB, Th.** ............................................ *paintings* | | | $440 |
| ☐ **GIBBARD, John** .............................. *paintings* | | | $3,025 |
| British 19th cent. | | | |
| ☐ **GIBBS, George** .................................... *paintings* | | $220 | $880 |
| American 1870-1942 ................................. *drawings* | | $192 | $220 |
| ☐ **GIBBS, Mary Ann** .............................. *drawings* | | | $1,210 |
| American 19th cent. | | | |
| ☐ **GIBSON, Charles Dana** ...................... *paintings* | | $247 | $1,650 |
| American 1867-1944 ................................. *drawings* | | $77 | $5,225 |
| ☐ **GIBSON, Lydia** .................................... *paintings* | | $352 | $495 |
| American b. 1891 | | | |
| ☐ **GIBSON, William Alfred** ...................... *paintings* | | | $495 |
| English 19th cent. | | | |
| ☐ **GIERYMSKI, Aleksander** ..................... *paintings* | | | $990 |
| Polish 1850-1901 | | | |
| ☐ **GIERYMSKI, Maksymilian** .................. *paintings* | | | $1,320 |
| Polish 1846-1874 | | | |
| ☐ **GIES, Joseph W.** ................................. *paintings* | | $55 | $2,200 |
| American 1860-1935 ................................. *drawings* | | | $80 |
| ☐ **GIESSEL, W.** ....................................... *paintings* | | | $550 |
| ☐ **GIETL, Josua von** ............................... *paintings* | | $935 | $2,350 |
| German 1847-1922 | | | |
| ☐ **GIFFORD, Charles Henry** .................... *paintings* | | $125 | $7,500 |
| American 1839-1904 ................................. *drawings* | | $77 | $3,000 |
| ☐ **GIFFORD, John** ................................... *paintings* | | $2,420 | $6,050 |
| English 19th cent. | | | |
| ☐ **GIFFORD, Robert Gregory** .................. *drawings* | | $74 | $220 |
| American 1895-after 1934 | | | |
| ☐ **GIFFORD, Robert Swain** ...................... *paintings* | | $330 | $7,700 |
| American 1840-1905 ................................. *drawings* | | $154 | $1,760 |
| ☐ **GIFFORD, Sanford Robinson** .............. *paintings* | | $1,650 | $203,500 |
| American 1823-1880 ................................. *drawings* | | | $3,520 |
| ☐ **GIFFORD, W.B.** ................................... *paintings* | | | $231 |
| English late 19th cent. | | | |
| ☐ **GIGANTE, Giacinto** ............................ *paintings* | | $2,310 | $6,050 |
| Italian 1806-1876 | | | |
| ☐ **GIGGS, Samuel W.** ............................. *paintings* | | | $742 |
| American 1848-98 | | | |
| ☐ **GIGLI, R.** ............................................ *drawings* | | $660 | $1,100 |
| Italian School 19th cent. | | | |
| ☐ **GIGLIO, Carlo** .................................... *drawings* | | | $990 |
| Italian 1804-1840 | | | |
| ☐ **GIGNOUX, Regis Francis** ..................... *paintings* | | $1,760 | $26,400 |
| French/American 1816-1882 | | | |
| ☐ **GIHON, Albert Dakin** .......................... *paintings* | | $357 | $440 |
| American b. 1876 | | | |

| | | Current Price Range | |
|---|---|---|---|
| | | Low | High |
| ☐ **GIHON, Clarence Montfort** ............... *paintings* | | $330 | $6,050 |
| American 1871-1929 | | | |
| ☐ **GIKOW, Ruth** ...................... *paintings* | | $198 | $357 |
| American d. 1983 | | | |
| ☐ **GIL, Antonio By** ............................... *paintings* | | | $3,850 |
| ☐ **GIL, Gomez** ............................ *paintings* | | | $2,200 |
| ☐ **GILARDI, Pier Celestino** .................. *paintings* | | $6,050 | $7,700 |
| Italian 1837-1905 | | | |
| ☐ **GILBAULT, Joseph Eugene** ............... *paintings* | | | $2,860 |
| French 19th cent. | | | |
| ☐ **GILBERT, Alfred** ........................... *drawings* | | $176 | $275 |
| English 1854-1934 ............................. *sculpture* | | | $1,430 |
| ☐ **GILBERT, Arthur** ........................... *paintings* | | $500 | $1,540 |
| British 1819-1895 | | | |
| ☐ **GILBERT, Arthur Hill** ....................... *paintings* | | $357 | $800 |
| American 1893/94-1970? | | | |
| ☐ **GILBERT, C. Ivar** ............................ *paintings* | | $55 | $600 |
| American 20th cent. ................................ *drawings* | | $27 | $82 |
| ☐ **GILBERT, C.B.G.** ......................... *drawings* | | | $495 |
| ☐ **GILBERT, Charles Allan** ..................... *drawings* | | | $440 |
| American b. 1873 | | | |
| ☐ **GILBERT, Francis** ......................... *drawings* | | | $357 |
| British 19th cent. | | | |
| ☐ **GILBERT, Frank** ............................. *paintings* | | | $825 |
| English 19th cent. | | | |
| ☐ **GILBERT, Josiah** ........................... *paintings* | | | $825 |
| English 1814-1892 ...................... *drawings* | | | $165 |
| ☐ **GILBERT, Sir Alfred** ..................... *sculpture* | | $550 | $3,190 |
| English 1854-1934 | | | |
| ☐ **GILBERT, Sir John** ........................ *drawings* | | $495 | $935 |
| English 1817-1897 | | | |
| ☐ **GILBERT, Victor Gabriel** ................... *paintings* | | $880 | $8,800 |
| French 1847-1933 | | | |
| ☐ **GILBERT, W.B.** ............................. *paintings* | | $220 | $605 |
| British 19th cent. | | | |
| ☐ **GILBERT, W.J.** ............................. *paintings* | | | $990 |
| British 19th cent. ...................... *drawings* | | | $495 |
| ☐ **GILCHRIST, Herbert H.** ..................... *paintings* | | | $4,400 |
| English ac. 1880-1914 | | | |
| ☐ **GILCHRIST, William Wallace** ............. *paintings* | | $220 | $3,300 |
| American 1879-1926 | | | |
| ☐ **GILDER, Robert Fletcher** ................... *paintings* | | $264 | $715 |
| American 1856-1940 | | | |
| ☐ **GILES, Geoffrey Douglas** ................... *paintings* | | $19,800 | $34,100 |
| English 1857-1923/24 | | | |
| ☐ **GILES, Horace P.** ........................... *paintings* | | $88 | $700 |
| American ............................................. *drawings* | | $60 | $99 |
| ☐ **GILKERSON, William** ...................... *drawings* | | | $1,400 |
| American contemporary | | | |

|  | | Current Price Range | |
|---|---|---|---|
|  | | *Low* | *High* |
| ☐ **GILL, Ann** .......................................... *drawings* | | | **$660** |
| American early 19th cent. | | | |
| ☐ **GILL, Delancey W.** ............................. *paintings* | | **$27** | **$1,210** |
| American 1859-1940 ................................. *drawings* | | **$84** | **$495** |
| ☐ **GILL, Edmund** ................................... *paintings* | | **$495** | **$4,675** |
| British 1820-1894 | | | |
| ☐ **GILL, Eric** ...................................... *drawings* | | | **$385** |
| English 1882-1940 | | | |
| ☐ **GILL, Margaret W. Mellor** .................... *paintings* | | **$60** | **$330** |
| American 20th cent. | | | |
| ☐ **GILL, Mariquita** ............................... *paintings* | | **$467** | **$605** |
| American 20th cent. | | | |
| ☐ **GILL, Paul Ludwig** ............................ *drawings* | | | **$192** |
| American b. 1894 | | | |
| ☐ **GILLE, R.** ....................................... *paintings* | | | **$242** |
| German 19th cent. | | | |
| ☐ **GILLEMANS, Jan Pauwel (the elder)** ..... *paintings* | | **$2,640** | **$6,050** |
| Flemish 1618-1675 | | | |
| ☐ **GILLEMANS, Jan Pauwel** | | | |
| **(the younger)** ...................................... *paintings* | | | **$5,060** |
| Flemish 1651-1704 | | | |
| ☐ **GILLES, J.A.** ...................................... *paintings* | | | **$2,420** |
| Haitian | | | |
| ☐ **GILLES, Nicolas** ................................. *paintings* | | | **$250** |
| German b. 1870 | | | |
| ☐ **GILLES, P.** ......................................... *sculpture* | | | **$1,210** |
| French | | | |
| ☐ **GILLESPIE, Dorothy** ........................... *drawings* | | | **$330** |
| ☐ **GILLESPIE, George** ............................. *paintings* | | | **$440** |
| American 20th cent. | | | |
| ☐ **GILLET, Frank** ................................... *drawings* | | | **$1,870** |
| ☐ **GILLETT, Violet A.** ............................. *drawings* | | | **$330** |
| ☐ **GILLIAM, Sam** ................................... *paintings* | | **$352** | **$715** |
| American b. 1933 ..................................... *drawings* | | **$440** | **$440** |
| ☐ **GILLIG, Jacob** ................................... *paintings* | | | **$825** |
| ☐ **GILLISEN, K.** ..................................... *paintings* | | | **$550** |
| Danish (?) 19th cent. | | | |
| ☐ **GILLOT, Eugene-Louis** ........................ *drawings* | | | **$385** |
| French 1868-1925 | | | |
| ☐ **GILLOT, Gustave** .............................. *sculpture* | | | **$935** |
| ☐ **GILMAN, Harold** ............................... *paintings* | | | **$770** |
| British 1876-1919 | | | |
| ☐ **GILOT, Francoise** ............................. *paintings* | | **$220** | **$1,760** |
| French b. 1921 ....................................... *drawings* | | **$275** | **$1,760** |
| ☐ **GILPIN, Rev. William** ......................... *drawings* | | | **$440** |
| ☐ **GILPIN, Sawrey** ................................. *paintings* | | **$3,500** | **$88,000** |
| British 1733-1807 | | | |
| ☐ **GILPIN, William Sawrey** ..................... *paintings* | | | **$19,800** |
| English 1762-1843 | | | |

| | | Current Price Range | |
|---|---|---|---|
| | | Low | High |
| ☐ **GILSON, Roger E.** ............... *paintings* | | | $192 |
| American 20th cent. | | | |
| ☐ **GILTE, Selden Connor** ............ *paintings* | | | $418 |
| American | | | |
| ☐ **GIMENEZ, F. Fernandez** ......... *paintings* | | | $462 |
| ☐ **GIMINEZ Y MARTIN, Juan** ........... *paintings* | | | $1,100 |
| Spanish b. 1858 ........................... *drawings* | | | $2,200 |
| ☐ **GINGELIN, Jacques van** ........ *paintings* | | | $1,089 |
| Belgian b. 1801 | | | |
| ☐ **GINILIANI, G.** ............... *paintings* | | | $418 |
| ☐ **GINNETT, Louis** ............... *paintings* | | $220 | $522 |
| English 20th cent. | | | |
| ☐ **GINNTOTARDI, F.** ............ *drawings* | | | $187 |
| Italian early 19th cent. | | | |
| ☐ **GINTSENBERG, Karl Yakovievich** ....... *paintings* | | | $2,200 |
| Russian 19th cent. | | | |
| ☐ **GIOBBI, Edward** ............... *drawings* | | $352 | $495 |
| American b. 1926 | | | |
| ☐ **GIOJA, Belisario** ............... *paintings* | | | $220 |
| Italian 1829-1906 ........................ *drawings* | | $110 | $3,190 |
| ☐ **GIOJA, Gaetana** ............... *drawings* | | | $495 |
| ☐ **GIOLFINO, Niccolo** ............ *paintings* | | | $104,500 |
| Italian | | | |
| ☐ **GIOLI, Francesco** ............... *paintings* | | | $286 |
| ☐ **GIONICOSO, V.** ............... *drawings* | | | $825 |
| ☐ **GIONIMO, Antonio** ............ *paintings* | | | $10,450 |
| Italian 1697-1732 ........................ *drawings* | | | $880 |
| ☐ **GIORDANE, Halo** ............ *paintings* | | | $660 |
| ☐ **GIORDANO, Felice** ............ *paintings* | | | $330 |
| Italian b. 1880 | | | |
| ☐ **GIORDANO, Luca** ............ *paintings* | | $1,980 | $30,800 |
| Italian 1632-1705 ........................ *drawings* | | $880 | $6,050 |
| ☐ **GIORDIO** ............... *drawings* | | | $220 |
| Italian 19th/20th cent. | | | |
| ☐ **GIORGIO, S.** ............... *sculpture* | | | $990 |
| ☐ **GIOT, Maurice** ............... *paintings* | | | $660 |
| 19th cent. | | | |
| ☐ **GIOVANNI, N.** ............... *paintings* | | | $357 |
| American 20th cent. | | | |
| ☐ **GIOVANNI DI SER GIOVANNI GUIDI** | | | |
| **(Master Adimari Cassone),** | | | |
| **(called LO SCHEGGIA)** ............ *paintings* | | | $44,000 |
| Italian | | | |
| ☐ **GIOVENNETTI, Rafael** ............ *paintings* | | | $1,595 |
| Italian 19th cent. | | | |
| ☐ **GIR, C.** ............... *sculpture* | | | $1,320 |
| ☐ **GIRADELLI, C.** ............... *paintings* | | | $660 |
| ☐ **GIRADET, Edouard Henri** ............ *paintings* | | | $4,180 |
| Swiss 1819-1880 | | | |

| | | Current Price Range | |
|---|---|---|---|
| | | Low | High |
| ☐ **GIRADET, Karl** ................................. *paintings* | | | $1,000 |
| ☐ **GIRAN, Emile Georges** ........................ *paintings* | | | $385 |
| French b. 1870 | | | |
| ☐ **GIRARD, F.** ................................... *paintings* | | | $935 |
| ☐ **GIRARD, Marie Francois Firmin** ......... *paintings* | | $2,310 | $20,350 |
| French 1838-1921 | | | |
| ☐ **GIRARD, Paul Albert** .......................... *paintings* | | $3,025 | $8,250 |
| French 1839-1920 | | | |
| ☐ **GIRARD, Theodore** ............................ *paintings* | | | $2,475 |
| French 19th cent. | | | |
| ☐ **GIRARDET, Eugene Alexis** ................... *paintings* | | $5,225 | $63,250 |
| French 1853-1907 | | | |
| ☐ **GIRARDET, Jules** ............................. *paintings* | | $600 | $14,300 |
| French b. 1856 | | | |
| ☐ **GIRARDET, Karl** ............................. *paintings* | | $2,475 | $8,800 |
| Swiss 1813-1871 | | | |
| ☐ **GIRARDIN, Frank J.** ......................... *paintings* | | $247 | $825 |
| American b. 1856 | | | |
| ☐ **GIRARDOT, E. Gustave** ....................... *paintings* | | | $3,300 |
| British 19th/20th cent. | | | |
| ☐ **GIRARDOT, Louis Auguste** .................. *paintings* | | | $1,320 |
| French 1856-1933 ................................. *drawings* | | | $247 |
| ☐ **GIRAUD, Pierre Francois Eugene** ......... *paintings* | | | $176 |
| French 1806-1881 ................................. *drawings* | | | $66 |
| ☐ **GIRAULT, L.C.** ................................. *drawings* | | | $440 |
| ☐ **GIRBAL, Gaston** ............................... *drawings* | | | $286 |
| ☐ **GIRL, Helisena (Mme. KOCH)** ............. *paintings* | | | $12,100 |
| German 1831-1916 | | | |
| ☐ **GIRLECKE, Ed** ................................. *paintings* | | $275 | $330 |
| ☐ **GIROLAMO DI BENVENUTO DI** | | | |
| **GIOVANNI DEL GUASTA** ................... *paintings* | | | $9,350 |
| Italian 1470-1524 | | | |
| ☐ **GIRONIERE, Yves Benoist** ................... *sculpture* | | $770 | $770 |
| French 20th cent. | | | |
| ☐ **GIROTTO, N.** ..................................... *drawings* | | | $275 |
| Italian 19th cent. | | | |
| ☐ **GIROUX, Ernest** ............................. *paintings* | | | $5,500 |
| French/Italian b. 1851; ac. 1883-1887 | | | |
| ☐ **GIRTIN, Thomas** ............................. *drawings* | | $385 | $38,500 |
| English 1775-1802 | | | |
| ☐ **GISBERT, Antonio** ............................. *paintings* | | $1,430 | $4,180 |
| Spanish b. 1835 | | | |
| ☐ **GISELLE, H.** ..................................... *paintings* | | | $1,870 |
| Austrian 19th cent. | | | |
| ☐ **GISEVIUS, Gerhard** ............................. *paintings* | | | $192 |
| American 20th cent. | | | |
| ☐ **GISIKE, Ida** ................................. *paintings* | | | $275 |
| American 20th cent. | | | |

| | | Current Price Range | |
|---|---|---|---|
| | | Low | High |
| ☐ **GISSON, Andre** ............... *paintings* | | $525 | $4,400 |
| French b. 1910 ....................... *drawings* | | | $275 |
| ☐ **GISSON, Andre** ............... *paintings* | | $880 | $2,090 |
| American b. 1928 | | | |
| ☐ **GISZINGER, Imre** ............ *paintings* | | | $1,870 |
| Austrian 1895-1935 | | | |
| ☐ **GITTARD, Alexandre Charles Joseph** ... *paintings* | | | $200 |
| French 1832-1904 | | | |
| ☐ **GIUDICI, Rinaldo** ............ *paintings* | | | $4,950 |
| Italian 19th cent. | | | |
| ☐ **GIULIANO, Bartholomeo** .......... *paintings* | | | $3,520 |
| Italian 1825-1909 | | | |
| ☐ **GIULLI, L.** .................. *drawings* | | | $440 |
| Italian 19th cent. | | | |
| ☐ **GIULTI, G.** .................. *drawings* | | | $1,980 |
| ☐ **GIURGOLA, Romaldo** ........... *drawings* | | | $550 |
| ☐ **GIUSTI, Guglielmo** ............ *drawings* | | $192 | $550 |
| Italian 1824-c. 1916 | | | |
| ☐ **GIUSTO, Fausto** .............. *paintings* | | $467 | $825 |
| Italian 19th cent. | | | |
| ☐ **GLACKENS, Louis M.** ........... *drawings* | | | $385 |
| American 1870-1938 | | | |
| ☐ **GLACKENS, William James** ........ *paintings* | | $7,700 | $380,000 |
| American 1870-1938 ................. *drawings* | | $150 | $24,200 |
| ☐ **GLADBEECK, Jan van** .......... *paintings* | | | $14,300 |
| Dutch ac. 1630-1653 | | | |
| ☐ **GLADENBECK, H.** .............. *sculpture* | | | $700 |
| ☐ **GLAIZE, Pierre Paul Leon** ......... *paintings* | | $825 | $1,100 |
| French 1842-1932 | | | |
| ☐ **GLARNER, Fritz** .............. *paintings* | | $1,540 | $74,800 |
| American b. 1899 ..................... *drawings* | | | $1,430 |
| ☐ **GLASCO, Joseph** .............. *paintings* | | $1,100 | $1,210 |
| American b. 1925 .................... *sculpture* | | | $880 |
| ☐ **GLASER, Elizabeth** ............ *drawings* | | | $6,050 |
| American ac. c. 1830 | | | |
| ☐ **GLASGOW, Berni** .............. *paintings* | | | $1,100 |
| American | | | |
| ☐ **GLASS, James William** .......... *paintings* | | $1,540 | $1,980 |
| American 1825-1857 | | | |
| ☐ **GLASS, John Hamilton** .......... *paintings* | | | $385 |
| ................................. *drawings* | | $110 | $110 |
| ☐ **GLATTE, Adolf** ............... *paintings* | | | $1,870 |
| German 1866-1920 | | | |
| ☐ **GLATZ, Oscar** ............... *paintings* | | $715 | $1,760 |
| Hungarian 1872-1958 | | | |
| ☐ **GLAVE, C.L.** ................. *paintings* | | $220 | $220 |
| American 20th cent. | | | |
| ☐ **GLEASON, Joe Duncan** .......... *paintings* | | $165 | $1,430 |
| American 1881-1959 ................. *drawings* | | | $220 |

| | *Current Price Range* | |
|---|---|---|
| | *Low* | *High* |
| ☐ **GLEHN, Wilfrid Gabriel von** ............... *paintings* | | **$6,600** |
| German b. 1870 | | |
| ☐ **GLEIZES, Albert** ........................... *paintings* | **$7,150** | **$154,000** |
| French 1881-1953 ..................................... *drawings* | **$605** | **$9,900** |
| ☐ **GLEN, Malcom** ............................... *paintings* | | **$577** |
| English 19th cent. | | |
| ☐ **GLENDENING, Alfred** ........................ *paintings* | **$110** | **$6,600** |
| British ac. 1860-1903 | | |
| ☐ **GLENDENING, Alfred Augustus (Jr.)** .... *paintings* | **$2,860** | **$3,080** |
| British d. 1907 ...................................... *drawings* | | **$1,870** |
| ☐ **GLENN, Willam** ............................... *paintings* | | **$990** |
| ☐ **GLINDONI, Henry Gillard** ................. *paintings* | **$715** | **$3,300** |
| English 1852-1912/13 ............................... *drawings* | | **$192** |
| ☐ **GLINTENKAMP, Henry** ..................... *paintings* | **$165** | **$990** |
| American 1887-1946 ................................. *drawings* | **$110** | **$198** |
| ☐ **GLISENTI, Achille** ........................... *paintings* | | **$550** |
| Italian 1848-1906 | | |
| ☐ **GLIUETTI, Luigi** ............................. *drawings* | | **$330** |
| Italian early 20th cent. | | |
| ☐ **GLORIEU, A.** ................................... *sculpture* | | **$990** |
| French | | |
| ☐ **GLOVER, John** ................................. *paintings* | | **$2,310** |
| British 1767-1849 | | |
| ☐ **GLOWER, W.** ................................... *paintings* | | **$440** |
| ☐ **GLUCKMANN, Grigory** ..................... *paintings* | **$605** | **$13,200** |
| Russian b. 1898 ..................................... *drawings* | **$330** | **$4,950** |
| ☐ **GLUSING, Francis** ............................. *paintings* | | **$770** |
| ☐ **GLUSQUIER** ................................... *paintings* | | **$605** |
| ☐ **GNATEK, Michael (Jr.)** ...................... *drawings* | | **$4,000** |
| American | | |
| ☐ **GNOLI, Domenico** ............................. *paintings* | | **$22,000** |
| Italian 1933-1970 ................................... *drawings* | **$1,430** | **$2,090** |
| ☐ **GOBAUT, Gaspard** ........................... *drawings* | | **$770** |
| French 1814-1882 | | |
| ☐ **GOBBI, Adriano** ............................... *paintings* | | **$990** |
| ☐ **GOBBIS, Giuseppe** ............................ *paintings* | | **$16,500** |
| Italian 18th cent. | | |
| ☐ **GOBL, Camilla** ................................. *paintings* | **$1,100** | **$1,430** |
| Austrian b. 1871 | | |
| ☐ **GOBLE, Warwick** ............................. *drawings* | | **$1,540** |
| English ac. 1893-1924 | | |
| ☐ **GOBLET, J. R.** ................................. *paintings* | | **$1,210** |
| French 19th cent. | | |
| ☐ **GODARD, C.** ................................... *paintings* | | **$300** |
| French 19th cent. | | |
| ☐ **GODCHAUX, A.** ............................... *paintings* | | **$605** |
| ☐ **GODDARD, A.** ................................. *sculpture* | **$825** | **$2,310** |
| ☐ **GODDARD, George Bouverie** ............... *paintings* | **$1,760** | **$19,800** |
| British 1832-1886 | | |

| | Current Price Range | |
|---|---|---|
| | *Low* | *High* |
| ☐ **GODERIS, Hans** ................................ *paintings* | | **$11,000** |
| Dutch ac. 1625-1645 | | |
| ☐ **GODET, Henri** ................................ *sculpture* | **$220** | **$3,300** |
| French b. 1863 | | |
| ☐ **GODFREY, E.** ................................ *paintings* | **$150** | **$250** |
| American 19th cent. | | |
| ☐ **GODFREY, John** ................................ *paintings* | | **$550** |
| British 1817-1889 | | |
| ☐ **GODOY** ................................ *paintings* | | **$742** |
| Spanish 20th cent. | | |
| ☐ **GODWARD, John William** ................... *paintings* | **$3,850** | **$30,800** |
| British 1861-1922 | | |
| ☐ **GODWIN, Karl** ................................ *paintings* | | **$385** |
| Canadian/American b. 1893 | | |
| ☐ **GOEBEL, Carl** ................................ *drawings* | | **$1,650** |
| Austrian 1824-1899 | | |
| ☐ **GOEBEL, Herman** ................................ *paintings* | | **$660** |
| German 1885-1945 | | |
| ☐ **GOEBEL, Rod** ................................ *paintings* | | **$2,475** |
| American 20th cent. | | |
| ☐ **GOENEUTTE, Norbert** ................... *paintings* | **$990** | **$23,100** |
| French 1854-1894 | | |
| ☐ **GOERBE, R.** ................................ *sculpture* | | **$275** |
| ☐ **GOERG, Edouard** ................................ *paintings* | **$550** | **$7,700** |
| French 1893-1968/69 | | |
| ☐ **GOERTZ, F.** ................................ *paintings* | **$192** | **$275** |
| ☐ **GOETSCH, Gustav** ................................ *paintings* | **$99** | **$375** |
| American 1877-1969 ................................ *drawings* | **$176** | **$264** |
| ☐ **GOETZ, Gottfried Bernhard** ............... *drawings* | | **$330** |
| ☐ **GOETZ, Henri** ................................ *paintings* | **$220** | **$302** |
| ................................ *drawings* | | **$247** |
| ☐ **GOETZELMANN, Edward** ................... *paintings* | | **$1,320** |
| ☐ **GOFF, Col. Robert Charles** ................. *drawings* | | **$220** |
| British 1837-1922 | | |
| ☐ **GOFF, Frederick Edward** ................ *drawings* | | **$180** |
| English 19th/20th cent. | | |
| ☐ **GOFFREDO, Bosisio** ................................ *paintings* | | **$715** |
| ☐ **GOGEIFELDT, W. de** ................................ *paintings* | | **$4,840** |
| French 19th cent. | | |
| ☐ **GOGH, Vincent van** ................................ *paintings* | **$93,500** | **$9,900,000** |
| Dutch 1853-1890 ................................ *drawings* | **$4,675** | **$319,000** |
| ☐ **GOGLER, L.** ................................ *paintings* | | **$176** |
| German 19th cent. | | |
| ☐ **GOINGS, F.** ................................ *paintings* | | **$220** |
| American 19th cent. | | |
| ☐ **GOINGS, Ralph** ................................ *paintings* | **$1,980** | **$22,000** |
| American b. 1928 | | |
| ☐ **GOITIA, Francisco** ................................ *paintings* | | **$3,300** |
| b. Mexico 1884-1960 | | |

## Post-Impressionism

The reaction to Impressionism was, predictably, Post-Impressionism, a movement which began in France in the late 1880s. While the Impressionists were concerned with the depiction of nature in light, the Post-Impressionists sought a deeper emotional content in their work, bolder and more specific color, and more expressive form. Some of the most illustrious names in 19th-century painting are associated with this movement, which included Paul Cezanne, Georges Seurat, Paul Gauguin, and Vincent van Gogh.

Dutch born, Van Gogh (1853–1890) did not begin painting until he was twenty-seven, and his career spanned only ten years to the time of his suicide in 1890. His most famous works date from the last two years of his life, which he spent in Arles in the south of France. Some of these canvases, including "Paysage au Soleil Levant," were completed while he was hospitalized in the asylum in St. Remy. This landscape was the view from the window of his room. Owned by the late Florence J. Gould, it was one of the 180 pieces in her collection sold at Sotheby's in April, 1985, for a total of $34 million. This work was purchased by an anonymous telephone bidder for $9.9 million, a record for a painting of the period. (Vincent van Gogh, "Paysage au Soleil Levant," oil on canvas, 28¾ x 36¼ in., Sotheby's, April 24, 1985, $9,900,000.)

| | | *Current Price Range* | |
|---|---|---|---|
| | | *Low* | *High* |
| ☐ **GOLD, Albert** ...................................... *paintings* | | | $247 |
| American b. 1916 ...................................... *drawings* | | | $275 |
| ☐ **GOLD, E.** .......................................... *paintings* | | | $525 |
| English 19th cent. | | | |
| ☐ **GOLDBERG, Michael** ........................ *paintings* | | $220 | $6,600 |
| American b. 1924 ...................................... *drawings* | | $132 | $1,760 |
| ☐ **GOLDBERG, Rube** ........................... *drawings* | | $495 | $550 |
| American 1883-1970 ............................... *sculpture* | | $242 | $770 |
| ☐ **GOLDEN, E.A.** ................................... *paintings* | | | $385 |
| ☐ **GOLDEN, Rolland** ............................. *paintings* | | $660 | $880 |
| American b. 1931 ...................................... *drawings* | | $16 | $605 |
| ☐ **GOLDENDEARTH, Henry** ................. *paintings* | | | $350 |
| ☐ **GOLDFARB, Shirley** ........................... *paintings* | | | $180 |
| American 20th cent. | | | |
| ☐ **GOLDING, Tomas** ............................. *paintings* | | $715 | $1,650 |
| Venezuelan b. 1909 | | | |
| ☐ **GOLDING, William O.** ....................... *drawings* | | $880 | $990 |
| American | | | |
| ☐ **GOLDSMITH, Wallace** ....................... *drawings* | | $60 | $275 |
| ☐ **GOLDSMITH, Walter H.** .................... *paintings* | | | $302 |
| English ac. 1880-1898 | | | |
| ☐ **GOLDSTEIN, Arnold** .......................... *sculpture* | | $220 | $880 |
| American | | | |
| ☐ **GOLDSTEIN, Jack** ............................. *paintings* | | | $3,850 |
| American b. 1945 | | | |
| ☐ **GOLDTHWAITE, Anne** ....................... *paintings* | | $220 | $605 |
| 1875-1944 | | | |
| ☐ **GOLDTHWAITE, Harold** .................... *paintings* | | $132 | $412 |
| British | | | |
| ☐ **GOLLINGS, Elling William** ................. *paintings* | | $770 | $32,500 |
| American 1878-1932 ................................. *drawings* | | $550 | $6,500 |
| ☐ **GOLOVIN, Alexander** ......................... *drawings* | | | $440 |
| ☐ **GOLTZ, Alexandre Demetrius** ............. *paintings* | | | $1,760 |
| Hungarian b. 1857 | | | |
| ☐ **GOLTZIUS, Hendrik** ........................... *paintings* | | | $742,500 |
| Dutch 1558-1616 | | | |
| ☐ **GOLTZLOFF, Karl W.** ........................ *drawings* | | | $330 |
| German 1799-1866 | | | |
| ☐ **GOLUB, Leon** ................................... *paintings* | | $770 | $6,875 |
| American b. 1922 ...................................... *drawings* | | | $935 |
| ☐ **GOLWIG, T.** ...................................... *paintings* | | $1,045 | $2,310 |
| German 19th cent. | | | |
| ☐ **GOMEZ, H.** ...................................... *paintings* | | | $550 |
| Spanish 19th cent. | | | |
| ☐ **GOMEZ, Juan** .................................. *paintings* | | | $330 |
| ☐ **GOMEZ, L.** ...................................... *paintings* | | | $385 |
| ☐ **GOMEZ, Marco Antonio** ..................... *paintings* | | $192 | $550 |
| Mexican/American 1910-1972 | | | |

## The Find in the Warehouse

*Everyone's favorite fantasy took a new twist when an IRS official asked the Butterfield Gallery to estimate the value of a large oil painting which had been seized for back taxes of $28,000. It was a major discovery, one of only forty-five known oils by 17th-century Dutch artist Hendrik Goltzius, who is noted primarily for his engravings. Titled "Danae," the work was signed and dated 1603, and had last been seen in public when it was auctioned in Stockholm, Sweden, in 1935. After fierce bidding, it was sold to the Los Angeles County Museum. (Hendrik Goltzius, "Danae," oil on canvas, 68 x 78 in., Butterfield, November 8, 1984, $742,500.)*

|  |  | Current Price Range | |
|---|---|---|---|
|  |  | *Low* | *High* |
| ☐ **GOMIEN, Paul** .................... *drawings* | | | **$440** |
| French 1799-1846 | | | |
| ☐ **GOMUCHIAN, K.M.** ........................ *paintings* | | | **$825** |
| European 19th/20th cent. | | | |
| ☐ **GONCALVES, Francisco Rebolo** ........... *paintings* | | | **$4,675** |
| Portugese | | | |
| ☐ **GONDI, Thomas** ............................ *paintings* | | | **$1,100** |
| ☐ **GONGORA, Leonel** ......................... *paintings* | | $154 | **$1,650** |
| Columbian b. 1932 ..................... *drawings* | | $605 | **$935** |
| ☐ **GONORO, Isabel** ........................... *paintings* | | | **$495** |
| Spanish 19th cent. | | | |

| | | Current Price Range | |
|---|---|---|---|
| | | *Low* | *High* |
| ☐ **GONSKE, Walt** .................................. *paintings* | | | **$660** |
| American 20th cent. | | | |
| ☐ **GONTCHAROVA, Natalia** ................... *paintings* | | **$700** | **$4,620** |
| Russian 1881-1962 ....................................... *drawings* | | **$44** | **$39,600** |
| ☐ **GONTIER, C.** .................................... *paintings* | | | **$935** |
| ☐ **GONZAGA, Pietro di Gottardo** ............. *drawings* | | | **$9,075** |
| Italian 1751-1831 | | | |
| ☐ **GONZALES, Juan Antonio** ................... *paintings* | | | **$15,950** |
| Spanish b. 1842 | | | |
| ☐ **GONZALES, Julio** .............................. *drawings* | | | **$7,150** |
| Spanish 1876-1942 ....................................... *sculpture* | | **$7,150** | **$20,900** |
| ☐ **GONZALES, Xavier** ........................... *paintings* | | | **$550** |
| American 20th cent. ..................................... *drawings* | | | **$250** |
| ☐ **GONZALEZ, Angel** ............................ *paintings* | | **$220** | **$1,100** |
| ☐ **GONZALEZ, Carmelo** .......................... *paintings* | | | **$3,520** |
| American ac. c. 1970 | | | |
| ☐ **GONZALEZ, Felipe** ............................ *paintings* | | | **$1,500** |
| ☐ **GONZALEZ, Juan Antonio** ................... *paintings* | | **$990** | **$14,300** |
| Spanish b. 1842 | | | |
| ☐ **GONZALEZ, Louis** ............................. *drawings* | | | **$306** |
| American(San Ild.) | | | |
| ☐ **GONZALEZ, Yuan A.** ........................... *paintings* | | | **$605** |
| ☐ **GOOCH, John** .................................. *paintings* | | | **$330** |
| English | | | |
| ☐ **GOOCH, Thomas** ............................... *paintings* | | **$4,950** | **$5,500** |
| English 1750-1802 | | | |
| ☐ **GOOD, John Willis** ............................ *sculpture* | | **$1,210** | **$2,420** |
| English ac. 1870-1878 | | | |
| ☐ **GOODALE** ....................................... *paintings* | | | **$412** |
| ☐ **GOODALL, Frederick** ......................... *paintings* | | **$253** | **$26,400** |
| English 1822-1904 ....................................... *drawings* | | **$352** | **$2,090** |
| ☐ **GOODE, Joe (Jose BUENO)** ................. *paintings* | | | **$5,500** |
| American b. 1937 ......................................... *drawings* | | **$330** | **$715** |
| ☐ **GOODE, John** ................................... *paintings* | | | **$7,480** |
| ☐ **GOODE, Tom** .................................... *paintings* | | | **$2,420** |
| ☐ **GOODELMAN, A.J.** ........................... *sculpture* | | | **$605** |
| ☐ **GOODEN, Olive** ............................... *sculpture* | | **$264** | **$495** |
| American | | | |
| ☐ **GOODMAN, Maude** ........................... *paintings* | | | **$550** |
| English 19th cent. | | | |
| ☐ **GOODMAN, Rima** ............................. *paintings* | | | **$605** |
| American 20th cent. | | | |
| ☐ **GOODMAN, Sidney** ........................... *paintings* | | **$1,540** | **$4,950** |
| American b. 1936 | | | |
| ☐ **GOODNOUGH, Robert** ......................... *paintings* | | **$275** | **$3,850** |
| American b. 1917 ......................................... *drawings* | | **$82** | **$715** |
| ☐ **GOODWIN, Albert** ............................. *drawings* | | **$990** | **$4,400** |
| English 1845-1932 | | | |

| | *Current Price Range* | |
|---|---|---|
| | *Low* | *High* |
| ☐ **GOODWIN, Arthur Clifton** ................. *paintings* | **$302** | **$28,600** |
| American 1866-1929 ................................... *drawings* | **$137** | **$6,600** |
| ☐ **GOODWIN, Belle** ............................... *paintings* | | **$1,100** |
| American 19th cent. | | |
| ☐ **GOODWIN, Edwin Weyburn** ............... *paintings* | **$165** | **$825** |
| American 1800-1845 | | |
| ☐ **GOODWIN, Harry** ........................... *paintings* | | **$605** |
| British 19th cent. ....................................... *drawings* | | **$332** |
| ☐ **GOODWIN, L.G.** ............................... *paintings* | | **$357** |
| British 19th cent. | | |
| ☐ **GOODWIN, Philip Russell** ................... *paintings* | **$825** | **$14,300** |
| American 1881/82-1935 ............................... *drawings* | | **$220** |
| ☐ **GOODWIN, Richard La Barre** ............. *paintings* | **$302** | **$56,100** |
| American 1840-1910 ................................... *drawings* | **$50** | **$220** |
| ☐ **GOODWOOD, K. J.** ........................... *paintings* | | **$192** |
| American 20th cent. | | |
| ☐ **GOODYEAR, C.** ................................ *drawings* | | **$176** |
| American 19th cent. | | |
| ☐ **GOOKINS, T.F.** ................................ *paintings* | | **$412** |
| European 19th/20th cent. | | |
| ☐ **GOOL, Jan van** ............................... *paintings* | | **$2,200** |
| ☐ **GORA, F.J.** ................................... *paintings* | | **$1,760** |
| ☐ **GORA, J.** ...................................... *paintings* | | **$2,640** |
| Italian 19th cent. | | |
| ☐ **GORBATOFF, Konstantin** ................... *paintings* | **$66** | **$1,870** |
| Russian 20th cent. | | |
| ☐ **GORBINO, Rosario** ........................... *paintings* | | **$330** |
| American 20th cent. | | |
| ☐ **GORCHOV, Ron** ............................... *paintings* | | **$5,500** |
| American b. 1930 | | |
| ☐ **GORDER, Luther Emerson van** ............. *paintings* | **$121** | **$1,045** |
| American 1861-1931 | | |
| ☐ **GORDIGIANI, Michele** ....................... *paintings* | | **$660** |
| Italian 1830-1909 | | |
| ☐ **GORDIN, Sidney** ............................... *drawings* | | **$220** |
| American | | |
| ☐ **GORDINE, Dora** ............................... *sculpture* | | **$990** |
| British b. 1906 | | |
| ☐ **GORDON** ...................................... *sculpture* | | **$440** |
| American 20th cent. | | |
| ☐ **GORDON, Aaron Henry** ....................... *paintings* | | **$880** |
| 1872-1933 | | |
| ☐ **GORDON, John S.** ............................. *drawings* | | **$192** |
| Canadian 20th cent. | | |
| ☐ **GORDON, Sir John Watson** ................. *paintings* | **$275** | **$12,100** |
| English 1790-1864 | | |
| ☐ **GORDON, William** ............................. *paintings* | | **$220** |
| American 20th cent. | | |

| | Current Price Range | |
|---|---|---|
| | *Low* | *High* |

☐ **GORDON-CRAIG, Edward** ................ *drawings* | | **$1,100**
Irish 1872-1966

☐ **GOREY, Edward** ............................... *drawings* | | **$418**
American

☐ **GORGET-FAURE, Henri** .................... *paintings* | | **$1,980**
French ac. 1905

☐ **GORGNEROR (?), J. de** ..................... *paintings* | | **$302**
French 20th cent.

☐ **GORGUET, Auguste Francois** ............. *paintings* | | **$660**
French 1862-1927

☐ **GORI, A.** .............................................. *sculpture* | **$770** | **$2,475**
European 19th/20th cent.

☐ **GORI, Georges** ................................... *sculpture* | | **$1,100**
French 20th cent.

☐ **GORKY, Arshile** .............................. *paintings* | **$5,500** | **$88,000**
Armenian/American 1904-1948 ..................... *drawings* | **$220** | **$308,000**
.............................................................. *sculpture* | | **$2,640**

☐ **GORL, C.** .......................................... *paintings* | | **$220**
German 20th cent.

☐ **GORLICH, Sophie** ............................ *paintings* | | **$8,800**
American 1855-1893

☐ **GORMAN, R.C.** ................................ *drawings* | **$1,430** | **$3,500**
American b. 1933

☐ **GORRA, Giulio** .................................. *paintings* | | **$2,420**
Italian 1832-84

☐ **GORSON, Aaron Henry** ...................... *paintings* | **$66** | **$14,000**
American 1872-1933

☐ **GORSTKIN-WYWIORSKI, Michael** ..... *paintings* | **$1,850** | **$15,400**
Polish 1861-1926

☐ **GORTER, Arnold Marc** ....................... *paintings* | **$550** | **$9,900**
Dutch 1866-1933 ........................................ *drawings* | **$660** | **$1,540**

☐ **GORTHELF, Victor** ........................... *sculpture* | **$137** | **$275**

☐ **GORY** ................................................ *sculpture* | **$495** | **$2,860**
French 19th/20th cent.

☐ **GOS, Albert** ..................................... *paintings* | | **$770**

☐ **GOSER, J.** ......................................... *paintings* | | **$770**
German late 19th cent.

☐ **GOSLING, William** ............................ *drawings* | | **$424**
English 1824-1883

☐ **GOSMINSKI, Richard** ......................... *paintings* | **$55** | **$550**
.............................................................. *drawings* | **$27** | **$110**

☐ **GOSSAERT, Jan** ................................ *paintings* | | **$29,700**
Flemish c. 1478-c. 1536

☐ **GOSSELIN, Charles** ........................... *paintings* | | **$2,640**
French 1834-1892

☐ **GOSSIN, Louis** .................................. *sculpture* | | **$1,320**
late 19th cent.

☐ **GOTCH, Caroline Burland Yates** .......... *paintings* | | **$1,320**
British 19th cent.

| | | *Current Price Range* | |
| | | Low | High |
| --- | --- | --- | --- |
| ☐ **GOTLEIB, Jules** ................................. *paintings* | | $55 | $275 |
| American b. 1897 | | | |
| ☐ **GOTT, J. van** ..................................... *paintings* | | | $4,950 |
| Dutch 18th cent. | | | |
| ☐ **GOTTFREDSON, Floyd** ...................... *drawings* | | $247 | $550 |
| b. 1907 | | | |
| ☐ **GOTTLIEB, Adolph** ........................... *paintings* | | $4,950 | $242,000 |
| American 1903-1974 ................................ *drawings* | | $3,080 | $16,500 |
| ☐ **GOTTLIEB, Leopold** ........................ *paintings* | | $550 | $3,575 |
| Polish 1883-before 1930 ............................. *drawings* | | | $605 |
| ☐ **GOTTLIEB, Moritz** ........................... *paintings* | | $14,300 | $55,000 |
| Polish 1856-1879 | | | |
| ☐ **GOTTWALD, Frederic C.** .................... *paintings* | | $302 | $550 |
| American 1860-1941 | | | |
| ☐ **GOTZELMANN, E.** ............................ *paintings* | | $550 | $660 |
| Austrian 19th cent. | | | |
| ☐ **GOTZINGER, Hans** ............................ *drawings* | | | $1,100 |
| Austrian b. 1867 | | | |
| ☐ **GOUBAUD, Innocent Louis** ................. *paintings* | | | $23,100 |
| French 1780-1847 | | | |
| ☐ **GOUBIE, Jean Richard** ....................... *paintings* | | $3,575 | $8,800 |
| French 1842-1899 | | | |
| ☐ **GOUGH, M.** ....................................... *paintings* | | | $412 |
| Continental School early 20th cent. | | | |
| ☐ **GOUJON, Theodore** ............................ *sculpture* | | | $2,420 |
| French early 20th cent. | | | |
| ☐ **GOULD, Chester** ................................. *drawings* | | $176 | $440 |
| American b. 1900 | | | |
| ☐ **GOULD, R.** ....................................... *paintings* | | | $330 |
| ☐ **GOULD, T.R.** .................................... *sculpture* | | | $250 |
| ☐ **GOULD, Walter** ................................. *paintings* | | $16,500 | $79,750 |
| American 1829-1893 | | | |
| ☐ **GOULDEN, Jean** ................................. *sculpture* | | | $26,400 |
| French | | | |
| ☐ **GOUPIL, F.** ....................................... *drawings* | | | $220 |
| French 19th cent. | | | |
| ☐ **GOUPIL, Jules Adolphe** ....................... *paintings* | | $440 | $6,325 |
| French 1839-1883 | | | |
| ☐ **GOURDON, R.** ................................... *paintings* | | | $2,090 |
| French 19th cent. | | | |
| ☐ **GOURFAIN, Peter** ............................. *drawings* | | | $330 |
| ☐ **GOURGUE, Jacques Enguerrand** .......... *paintings* | | $137 | $28,600 |
| Haitian b. 1930 | | | |
| ☐ **GOURNSEY, C.** ................................. *drawings* | | | $300 |
| American 19th cent. | | | |
| ☐ **GOVAERTS, Abraham** ........................ *paintings* | | | $8,000 |
| Flemish 1589-1626 | | | |
| ☐ **GOVANITTI, G.** ................................. *paintings* | | | $330 |
| ☐ **GOW, J.** .......................................... *paintings* | | | $880 |

| | | *Current Price Range* | |
| --- | --- | --- | --- |
| | | *Low* | *High* |
| ☐ **GOWTY-BAKER, Elizabeth** ............... *drawings* | | | **$440** |
| ☐ **GOYA, Francisco Jose de** ............... *paintings* | | | **$187,000** |
| Spanish 1746-1828 ..................................... *drawings* | | | **$242,000** |
| ☐ **GOYEN, Jan Josefsz van** ............... *paintings* | | **$11,000** | **$203,500** |
| Dutch 1596-1656 ..................................... *drawings* | | **$605** | **$16,500** |
| ☐ **GRAAF, Josua de** ............................. *drawings* | | | **$1,045** |
| Dutch d. c. 1712 | | | |
| ☐ **GRABACH, John R.** ........................... *paintings* | | **$275** | **$8,800** |
| American 1880/86-1981 | | | |
| ☐ **GRABAR, Igor** ................................... *paintings* | | | **$605** |
| Russian b. 1872 | | | |
| ☐ **GRABONE, Arnold** ........................... *paintings* | | | **$880** |
| German b. 1895 | | | |
| ☐ **GRABOWSKI, L.** ............................... *paintings* | | | **$440** |
| ☐ **GRACE, A.L.** ..................................... *paintings* | | **$385** | **$660** |
| English 20th cent. | | | |
| ☐ **GRACEAN, Edmund S.** ....................... *paintings* | | | **$2,200** |
| American 1876-1949 | | | |
| ☐ **GRAEF, Gustav** ................................. *paintings* | | | **$440** |
| German 1821-1895 | | | |
| ☐ **GRAEFFE, A.** ..................................... *paintings* | | | **$990** |
| ☐ **GRAEME, Colin** ................................. *paintings* | | | **$5,500** |
| British 19th cent. | | | |
| ☐ **GRAESSEL, Franz** ............................. *paintings* | | | **$15,400** |
| German b. 1861 | | | |
| ☐ **GRAF, Gerhard** ................................. *paintings* | | **$357** | **$495** |
| German 1883-1960 | | | |
| ☐ **GRAF, Hermann** ................................. *paintings* | | | **$1,100** |
| Austrian b. 1873 | | | |
| ☐ **GRAF, Paul Edmund** ........................... *paintings* | | **$1,100** | **$7,425** |
| Swedish 1866-1903 | | | |
| ☐ **GRAFSTROM, Olof Jonas** ................... *paintings* | | | **$3,025** |
| Swedish b. 1855 | | | |
| ☐ **GRAHAM, Colin** ................................. *paintings* | | | **$1,045** |
| English 19th cent. | | | |
| ☐ **GRAHAM, J. S.** ................................. *paintings* | | | **$247** |
| English 19th cent. | | | |
| ☐ **GRAHAM, James Lillie** ....................... *paintings* | | | **$2,420** |
| Canadian b. 1873 | | | |
| ☐ **GRAHAM, John D.** ............................. *paintings* | | **$495** | **$154,000** |
| Russian/American 1881-1961 ...................... *drawings* | | **$3,080** | **$11,000** |
| ☐ **GRAHAM, Peter** ................................. *paintings* | | **$330** | **$4,675** |
| British 1836-1921 | | | |
| ☐ **GRAHAM, Ralph W.** ........................... *drawings* | | | **$495** |
| ☐ **GRAHAM, Robert** ............................. *sculpture* | | | **$8,250** |
| American b. 1938 | | | |
| ☐ **GRAHAM, Robert Alexander** ............... *paintings* | | **$220** | **$8,250** |
| American b. 1873 ..................................... *drawings* | | **$165** | **$715** |
| ☐ **GRAHAM, T.A.** ................................... *drawings* | | | **$352** |

| | | Current Price Range | |
|---|---|---|---|
| | | Low | High |
| ☐ **GRAHAM, William** ............................ *paintings* | | $220 | $1,320 |
| American 1841-1910 ..................................... *drawings* | | | $45 |
| ☐ **GRAILLY, Victor de** ............................ *paintings* | | $352 | $4,400 |
| French 1804-1899 | | | |
| ☐ **GRAINGER, Th.** ................................. *paintings* | | | $220 |
| British 19th cent. | | | |
| ☐ **GRAME, Colin** ..................................... *paintings* | | $495 | $990 |
| German 19th cent. | | | |
| ☐ **GRANBERY, H.A.** ............................. *paintings* | | | $330 |
| ☐ **GRANBERY, V.** ................................. *paintings* | | | $550 |
| British 19th cent. | | | |
| ☐ **GRANDEE, Joe** ..................................... *paintings* | | | $2,200 |
| American 20th cent. | | | |
| ☐ **GRANDGERARD, Lucien Henri** .......... *paintings* | | $330 | $350 |
| ☐ **GRANDI, Francesco** ............................ *drawings* | | $82 | $363 |
| Italian 1831-1891 | | | |
| ☐ **GRANDIN, Eugene** ............................ *drawings* | | | $825 |
| French 18th/19th cent. | | | |
| ☐ **GRANDIN, J.** ..................................... *paintings* | | | $770 |
| ☐ **GRANDJEAN, Edmond Georges** .......... *paintings* | | $22,000 | $121,000 |
| French 1844-1908/09 | | | |
| ☐ **GRANDPRE, Pierre Emile Gigoux de** .... *paintings* | | | $715 |
| French b. 1826 | | | |
| ☐ **GRANDVILLE, M.** ............................ *paintings* | | | $220 |
| Italian 19th/20th cent. | | | |
| ☐ **GRANEAU, H.** ................................. *paintings* | | | $418 |
| ☐ **GRANER, Ernest** ............................ *drawings* | | | $1,210 |
| ☐ **GRANER Y ARRUFI, Luis** ................... *paintings* | | $165 | $2,750 |
| Spanish 1867-1929 | | | |
| ☐ **GRANET, Francois Marius** ................... *paintings* | | | $4,400 |
| French 1775-1849 | | | |
| ☐ **GRANT, Charles Henry** ........................ *paintings* | | $165 | $715 |
| American 1866-1938 ..................................... *drawings* | | $44 | $385 |
| ☐ **GRANT, Clement Rollins** ....................... *paintings* | | $385 | $7,975 |
| American 1849-1893 ..................................... *drawings* | | | $300 |
| ☐ **GRANT, Colin** ..................................... *paintings* | | | $302 |
| Scottish 19th cent. | | | |
| ☐ **GRANT, Donald** ............................... *paintings* | | $605 | $990 |
| ☐ **GRANT, Duncan** ............................... *paintings* | | | $935 |
| English 1885-1978 | | | |
| ☐ **GRANT, Dwinell** ................................. *paintings* | | $2,200 | $3,300 |
| American | | | |
| ☐ **GRANT, Frederick M.** .......................... *paintings* | | $77 | $1,045 |
| American b. 1886 ..................................... *drawings* | | $110 | $192 |
| ☐ **GRANT, Gordon Hope** ........................ *paintings* | | $110 | $6,050 |
| American 1875-1962 ................................. *drawings* | | $49 | $1,430 |
| ☐ **GRANT, J. Jeffrey** ............................... *paintings* | | $50 | $1,870 |
| American 1883-1960 | | | |
| ☐ **GRANT, Marie** ................................... *paintings* | | | $275 |

| | Current Price Range | |
|---|---|---|
| | Low | High |
| ☐ **GRANT, Mimi** ............................ *paintings* | | $850 |
| American | | |
| ☐ **GRANT, Sir Francis** ........................ *paintings* | | $6,600 |
| English 1803/10-1878 | | |
| ☐ **GRANT, Theodore** ........................ *paintings* | | $600 |
| European 19th cent. | | |
| ☐ **GRANT, William** ............................ *drawings* | | $1,320 |
| American | | |
| ☐ **GRANVILLE-SMITH, Walter** ............. *paintings* | $330 | $33,000 |
| American 1870-1938 ............................ *drawings* | $10 | $2,640 |
| ☐ **GRAS, J.M.** .................................... *paintings* | | $440 |
| ☐ **GRASE, D.C.** .................................. *paintings* | | $264 |
| ☐ **GRASHOF, Otto** ............................ *paintings* | | $9,350 |
| Latin American | | |
| ☐ **GRASSEL, Franz** ............................ *paintings* | | $6,600 |
| German b. 1861 | | |
| ☐ **GRATCHEFF, Alexei** ....................... *sculpture* | $847 | $2,035 |
| Russian c. 1780-after 1850 | | |
| ☐ **GRATCHEFF, Lep** ........................... *sculpture* | $1,100 | $2,200 |
| ☐ **GRATCHER** .................................... *sculpture* | | $935 |
| late 19th cent. | | |
| ☐ **GRATCHEV** .................................... *sculpture* | $660 | $3,300 |
| Russian late 19th/early 20th cent | | |
| ☐ **GRATCHEV, Vasili** .......................... *sculpture* | | $1,870 |
| ☐ **GRATECHEFF** ................................. *sculpture* | | $1,980 |
| Russian 19th cent. | | |
| ☐ **GRAU, Enrique** ............................... *paintings* | $3,300 | $24,200 |
| Colombian b. 1920 ............................ *drawings* | $1,320 | $4,950 |
| ☐ **GRAU-SALA, Emile** ......................... *paintings* | $556 | $11,000 |
| Spanish 1911-1975 ............................ *drawings* | $165 | $4,620 |
| ☐ **GRAUTSEHOLD, M.** ......................... *paintings* | | $301 |
| ☐ **GRAVELOT,** | | |
| **(Hubert F. Bourguignon d' ANVILLE)** ... *drawings* | $1,045 | $1,980 |
| French 1699-1773 | | |
| ☐ **GRAVES, Abbott Fuller** ................... *paintings* | $160 | $40,000 |
| American 1859-1936 ............................ *drawings* | $770 | $990 |
| ☐ **GRAVES, Etta Merrick** ................... *paintings* | | $247 |
| American b. 1882 | | |
| ☐ **GRAVES, H.C.** ................................. *drawings* | | $250 |
| ☐ **GRAVES, Henry Richard** ................. *paintings* | | $1,980 |
| British 19th cent. | | |
| ☐ **GRAVES, Michael** ........................... *drawings* | | $1,540 |
| American b. 1934 | | |
| ☐ **GRAVES, Morris** ............................. *paintings* | | $27,500 |
| American b. 1910 ............................ *drawings* | $110 | $6,050 |
| ☐ **GRAVES, Nancy** .............................. *paintings* | $2,420 | $18,700 |
| American b. 1940 ............................ *drawings* | | $330 |
| ☐ **GRAVES, O.E.L.** .............................. *paintings* | $80 | $423 |
| American b. 1912 ............................ *sculpture* | | $385 |

| | | Current Price Range | |
|---|---|---|---|
| | | *Low* | *High* |
| ☐ **GRAY, Alphonse** ............................ *paintings* | | | $2,090 |
| British 19th cent. | | | |
| ☐ **GRAY, Charles A.** ............................ *paintings* | | $192 | $440 |
| 1857-1933 | | | |
| ☐ **GRAY, Cleve** ............................ *paintings* | | $55 | $1,100 |
| American b. 1918 | | | |
| ☐ **GRAY, G.** ............................ *paintings* | | | $1,320 |
| ☐ **GRAY, George** ............................ *paintings* | | | $462 |
| British ac. 1880-1909 ............................ *drawings* | | | $165 |
| ☐ **GRAY, Grace** ............................ *drawings* | | $165 | $176 |
| American | | | |
| ☐ **GRAY, Henry Percy** ............................ *paintings* | | $990 | $6,600 |
| American 1869-1952 ............................ *drawings* | | $247 | $10,450 |
| ☐ **GRAY, Henry Peters** ............................ *paintings* | | $330 | $1,045 |
| American 1819-1877 | | | |
| ☐ **GRAY, Jack L.** ............................ *paintings* | | | $4,125 |
| Canadian b. 1927 | | | |
| ☐ **GRAY, John** ............................ *paintings* | | | $825 |
| British active 1885-1904 | | | |
| ☐ **GRAY, Mary M.** ............................ *paintings* | | $33 | $198 |
| American 20th cent. | | | |
| ☐ **GRAY, Nicholas Henry de** ............................ *paintings* | | | $825 |
| French b. 1822 | | | |
| ☐ **GRAY, Tom** ............................ *drawings* | | $440 | $660 |
| English 19th cent. | | | |
| ☐ **GRAY, U.L.** ............................ *paintings* | | | $990 |
| American 19th cent. | | | |
| ☐ **GRAY, U.L.** ............................ *paintings* | | | $440 |
| American 20th cent. | | | |
| ☐ **GRAY, Urban** ............................ *paintings* | | | $500 |
| ☐ **GRAYSTON, F.** ............................ *paintings* | | | $418 |
| ☐ **GRAZIANI, Ercole** ............................ *paintings* | | | $6,600 |
| Italian | | | |
| ☐ **GREACEN, Edmund William** ............................ *paintings* | | $550 | $12,100 |
| American 1877-1949 | | | |
| ☐ **GREASON, William** ............................ *paintings* | | $175 | $385 |
| American/Canadian b. 1884 | | | |
| ☐ **GREATOREX, Kathleen Honora** ............................ *paintings* | | | $1,650 |
| American b. 1851 | | | |
| ☐ **GREAVES, E.L.** ............................ *drawings* | | | $350 |
| ☐ **GREAVES, Harry E.** ............................ *paintings* | | $154 | $264 |
| American 1854-1919 | | | |
| ☐ **GREAVES, Walter** ............................ *paintings* | | | $9,350 |
| English 1846-1930 ............................ *drawings* | | | $165 |
| ☐ **GREAVES, William** ............................ *paintings* | | $495 | $741 |
| English 19th/20th cent. | | | |
| ☐ **GREB, Nam** ............................ *sculpture* | | $495 | $2,750 |
| Austrian 20th cent. | | | |

| | | Current Price Range | |
| --- | --- | --- | --- |
| | | Low | High |
| ☐ **GREBBER, Pieter de** ............................ *paintings* | | $5,500 | $13,200 |
| Dutch c. 1600-before 1692 | | | |
| ☐ **GREBLER, W.** .................................... *sculpture* | | | $650 |
| ☐ **GRECHOV, Ivanovitch** .................... *paintings* | | | $176 |
| Russian ac. 1860-1890 ................................ *sculpture* | | | $1,595 |
| ☐ **GRECO, Emilio** ................................ *drawings* | | $242 | $2,475 |
| Italian b. 1913 ........................................ *sculpture* | | $6,600 | $34,100 |
| ☐ **GRECO, S.** ........................................ *drawings* | | | $220 |
| 20th cent. | | | |
| ☐ **GREELEY, Charles** ............................ *paintings* | | | $1,430 |
| ☐ **GREEN, A. H.** .................................... *paintings* | | | $220 |
| American 20th cent. | | | |
| ☐ **GREEN, Alfred H.** ............................ *paintings* | | | $660 |
| English 19th century | | | |
| ☐ **GREEN, Charles** ................................ *drawings* | | | $3,960 |
| British 1840-1898 | | | |
| ☐ **GREEN, Charles Edwin Lewis** .............. *paintings* | | $165 | $2,695 |
| American b. 1844 | | | |
| ☐ **GREEN, Chiglion** ................................ *paintings* | | | $302 |
| .................................................... *drawings* | | | $440 |
| ☐ **GREEN, Denise** .................................... *paintings* | | | $6,050 |
| Australian/American b. 1946 | | | |
| ☐ **GREEN, Edith Jackson** ........................ *paintings* | | | $191 |
| American 1876-1934 | | | |
| ☐ **GREEN, Frank Russell** ........................ *paintings* | | $154 | $2,860 |
| American 1856/59-1940 | | | |
| ☐ **GREEN, George** ................................ *drawings* | | | $3,025 |
| contemporary | | | |
| ☐ **GREEN, Jasha** .................................... *drawings* | | $110 | $3,080 |
| .................................................... *sculpture* | | | $330 |
| ☐ **GREEN, Roland** ................................ *paintings* | | $137 | $2,860 |
| English 1896-1971 .................................... *drawings* | | | $850 |
| ☐ **GREEN, Saya** .................................... *sculpture* | | | $1,760 |
| ☐ **GREEN, William Bradford** .................... *paintings* | | | $231 |
| American 1871-1945 | | | |
| ☐ **GREENAWAY, Kate** ............................ *drawings* | | $165 | $3,850 |
| English 1846-1901 | | | |
| ☐ **GREENBAUM, Dorothea** ........................ *sculpture* | | | $3,300 |
| American b. 1893 | | | |
| ☐ **GREENE, Albert van Neese** .................. *paintings* | | | $385 |
| American 1887-1972 | | | |
| ☐ **GREENE, Balcomb** ............................ *paintings* | | $825 | $3,575 |
| American b. 1904 .................................... *drawings* | | $1,100 | $1,100 |
| ☐ **GREENE, J. Barry** ............................ *paintings* | | | $1,650 |
| American 1895-1926 | | | |
| ☐ **GREENE, LeRoy E.** ............................ *paintings* | | | $467 |
| ☐ **GREENE, Stephen** ............................ *paintings* | | $990 | $2,970 |
| American b. 1918 .................................... *drawings* | | $495 | $550 |

| | | | Current Price Range | |
|---|---|---|---|---|
| | | | Low | High |
| ☐ **GREENE, Walter L.** | ............................ | *drawings* | $330 | $330 |
| American b. 1898 | | | | |
| ☐ **GREENLAW, Emma V.** | ....................... | *paintings* | | $385 |
| American | | | | |
| ☐ **GREENLEAF, Jacob** | ........................... | *paintings* | $30 | $550 |
| American 1887-1968 | ................................... | *drawings* | | $220 |
| ☐ **GREENOUGH, Horatio** | ....................... | *sculpture* | | $16,500 |
| American 1805-1852 | | | | |
| ☐ **GREENOUGH, Richard Saltonstall** | ....... | *sculpture* | $1,430 | $8,800 |
| American 1819-1904 | | | | |
| ☐ **GREENWOOD, Ethan Allen** | ................. | *paintings* | $750 | $1,870 |
| American 1779-1856 | | | | |
| ☐ **GREENWOOD, Joseph H.** | .................... | *paintings* | $192 | $2,090 |
| American 1857-1927 | | | | |
| ☐ **GREENWOOD, Marion** | ....................... | *paintings* | $88 | $1,980 |
| American 1907-1970 | ................................... | *drawings* | | $143 |
| ☐ **GREENWOOD, Orlando** | ....................... | *paintings* | | $176 |
| English 19th/20th cent. | | | | |
| ☐ **GREER, A.D.** | ..................................... | *paintings* | | $495 |
| American 20th cent. | | | | |
| ☐ **GREER, James Emery** | .......................... | *paintings* | $121 | $231 |
| American 19th/20th cent. | | | | |
| ☐ **GREGOIRE, Alexandre** | ....................... | *paintings* | $440 | $715 |
| ☐ **GREGOIRE, Jean Louis** | ...................... | *sculpture* | $660 | $2,722 |
| French 1840-1890 | | | | |
| ☐ **GREGOIRE, Jos** | ................................. | *paintings* | | $990 |
| ☐ **GREGOIRE, Paul** | .............................. | *drawings* | $275 | $356 |
| French ac. 1781-1823 | | | | |
| ☐ **GREGOIRI, C.** | .................................. | *sculpture* | | $605 |
| Italian 19th/20th cent. | | | | |
| ☐ **GREGOR, Harold** | .............................. | *paintings* | | $8,800 |
| American b. 1929 | | | | |
| ☐ **GREGORITSCH, Toni (Anton)** | ............. | *paintings* | $880 | $1,210 |
| Austrian b. 1868 | | | | |
| ☐ **GREGORY, Anne** | .............................. | *paintings* | | $220 |
| American b. 1868 | | | | |
| ☐ **GREGORY, Eliot** | ............................... | *paintings* | $165 | $357 |
| American 1854-1915 | | | | |
| ☐ **GREGORY, John** | .............................. | *sculpture* | $3,850 | $5,280 |
| English/American 1879-1958 | | | | |
| ☐ **GREGORY, W.** | .................................. | *sculpture* | | $1,045 |
| American | | | | |
| ☐ **GREIFFENHAGEN, Maurice** | .............. | *drawings* | $20 | $223 |
| English 1862-1931 | | | | |
| ☐ **GREIG, Donald** | ................................. | *paintings* | | $302 |
| American 20th cent. | | | | |
| ☐ **GREINER, Otto** | ................................. | *drawings* | | $187 |
| German 1869-1916 | | | | |

| | | *Current Price Range* | |
|---|---|---|---|
| | | Low | High |

| | | | Low | High |
|---|---|---|---|---|
| ☐ **GRELL, Louis Frederick** ..................... *paintings* | | | $165 | $2,860 |
| American b. 1887 | | | | |
| ☐ **GRELLE, Martin** ............................... *paintings* | | | $4,500 | $15,000 |
| American b. 1954 | | | | |
| ☐ **GREMKE, Dick** ............................... *paintings* | | | | $880 |
| American 20th cent. | | | | |
| ☐ **GREMKE, M.D.** ............................... *paintings* | | | | $1,100 |
| American 20th cent. | | | | |
| ☐ **GREMKE, Richard** ............................ *paintings* | | | | $550 |
| American 19th cent. | | | | |
| ☐ **GRENDEL, Gerrit de** .......................... *paintings* | | | | $1,980 |
| Dutch 1719-1741 | | | | |
| ☐ **GRENIER, P.** ................................... *paintings* | | | | $880 |
| French 19th/20th cent. | | | | |
| ☐ **GRENNWOOD, Joseph H.** ................... *paintings* | | | | $220 |
| American 1857-1927 | | | | |
| ☐ **GRESELY, Gabriel** ............................ *paintings* | | | | $5,280 |
| French 1712-1756 | | | | |
| ☐ **GRETHE, Carlos** ............................... *paintings* | | | | $1,540 |
| German b. 1864 | | | | |
| ☐ **GREUZE, Jean Baptiste** ........................ *paintings* | | | $14,300 | $24,200 |
| French 1725-1805 ..................................... *drawings* | | | $1,650 | $24,750 |
| ☐ **GREVENBROECK, Orazio** ................. *paintings* | | | $3,300 | $7,150 |
| Dutch ac. 1670-1730 | | | | |
| ☐ **GREVIN, A.** ..................................... *sculpture* | | | | $352 |
| ☐ **GREY, Cleve** ................................... *paintings* | | | | $935 |
| American b. 1918 | | | | |
| ☐ **GREY, Gregor** ................................. *paintings* | | | | $495 |
| British ac. 1880-1911 | | | | |
| ☐ **GREYER, E.** ..................................... *paintings* | | | | $357 |
| ☐ **GRIEF, Harriet** ............................... *paintings* | | | | $495 |
| ☐ **GRIENAUER** ..................................... *sculpture* | | | | $550 |
| ☐ **GRIERSON, Charles Iver** ................... *paintings* | | | | $1,320 |
| British 1864-1939 | | | | |
| ☐ **GRIFFEN, Thomas B.** ......................... *paintings* | | | | $198 |
| American | | | | |
| ☐ **GRIFFIER, Robert** ............................ *paintings* | | | $5,225 | $8,800 |
| Dutch 1688-1750 | | | | |
| ☐ **GRIFFIN, Amrose Sylvester** ................. *paintings* | | | | $462 |
| ☐ **GRIFFIN, James Martin** ....................... *paintings* | | | $70 | $550 |
| American b. 1850 | | | | |
| ☐ **GRIFFIN, T. Bartholemew** ................... *paintings* | | | $330 | $495 |
| American 19th cent. | | | | |
| ☐ **GRIFFIN, Thomas B.** .......................... *paintings* | | | $325 | $1,045 |
| American b. 1861 | | | | |
| ☐ **GRIFFIN, Thomas Bailey** ................... *paintings* | | | $275 | $1,980 |
| American ac. 1875 | | | | |
| ☐ **GRIFFIN, W.** ................................... *paintings* | | | | $253 |

| | | *Current Price Range* | |
|---|---|---|---|
| | | Low | High |
| ☐ **GRIFFIN, Walter** .................... *paintings* | | **$165** | **$7,700** |
| American 1861-1935 ..................... *drawings* | | **$220** | **$550** |
| ☐ **GRIFFIN, Worth Dickman** ............ *paintings* | | | **$275** |
| American b. 1892 | | | |
| ☐ **GRIFFITH, Bill** ....................... *drawings* | | | **$330** |
| 20th cent. | | | |
| ☐ **GRIFFITH, Conway** ................... *paintings* | | | **$192** |
| American d. 1924 | | | |
| ☐ **GRIFFITH, Louis K.** .................. *drawings* | | | **$247** |
| American 20th cent. | | | |
| ☐ **GRIFFITH, Louis O.** .................. *paintings* | | **$165** | **$330** |
| American 1875-1956 ...................... *drawings* | | | **$110** |
| ☐ **GRIFFITH, Marie** .................... *paintings* | | | **$374** |
| American | | | |
| ☐ **GRIFFITH, Moses** .................... *drawings* | | | **$330** |
| English 1749-1819 | | | |
| ☐ **GRIFFITH, William Alexander** ......... *paintings* | | | **$2,090** |
| American 1866-1940 | | | |
| ☐ **GRIFFITHS, John** .................... *paintings* | | | **$11,000** |
| British 1837-1918 | | | |
| ☐ **GRIFFON, Gabriel** ................... *paintings* | | | **$1,210** |
| French b. 1866 | | | |
| ☐ **GRIG, Alex** ......................... *paintings* | | | **$220** |
| ...................................... *drawings* | | | **$275** |
| ☐ **GRIGGS, Samuel W.** .................. *paintings* | | **$220** | **$2,200** |
| American 1827-1898 | | | |
| ☐ **GRIGNARD, G.** ...................... *paintings* | | | **$495** |
| French 19th cent. | | | |
| ☐ **GRIGORESCO, Nicolas** ............... *paintings* | | **$302** | **$1,045** |
| Rumanian 1838-1907 | | | |
| ☐ **GRIGORIEFF, Boris** .................. *paintings* | | | **$4,180** |
| Russian 1886-1939 ...................... *drawings* | | **$82** | **$700** |
| ☐ **GRILL, Oswald** ..................... *paintings* | | | **$192** |
| Austrian b. 1878 | | | |
| ☐ **GRILLEY, Robert** .................... *paintings* | | | **$247** |
| American b. 1920 | | | |
| ☐ **GRILLO, John** ...................... *paintings* | | | **$192** |
| American b. 1917 ....................... *drawings* | | | **$440** |
| ☐ **GRILO, Sarah** ...................... *paintings* | | **$467** | **$2,420** |
| Argentinian b. 1921 | | | |
| ☐ **GRIMALDI, Giovanni Francesco** ......... *drawings* | | **$1,760** | **$2,200** |
| Italian 1606-1680 | | | |
| ☐ **GRIMAMI** .......................... *paintings* | | | **$666** |
| Italian 19th/20th cent. | | | |
| ☐ **GRIMAUD** .......................... *paintings* | | **$110** | **$660** |
| French 20th cent. | | | |
| ☐ **GRIMELUND, Johannes Martin** .......... *paintings* | | **$3,520** | **$3,850** |
| Norwegian 1842-1917 | | | |

| | | Current Price Range | |
|---|---|---|---|
| | | Low | High |
| □ **GRIMER, Jacob** .................................. *paintings* | | | **$49,500** |
| Flemish c. 1526-1589 | | | |
| □ **GRIMES** ............................................. *paintings* | | | **$330** |
| American 19th/20th cent. | | | |
| □ **GRIMM, Paul** .................................... *paintings* | | **$110** | **$1,760** |
| American 20th cent. | | | |
| □ **GRIMMER, Abel** ............................... *paintings* | | **$6,050** | **$462,000** |
| Flemish 1570/73-1619/40 | | | |
| □ **GRIMSHAW, John Atkinson** ............... *paintings* | | **$4,125** | **$19,800** |
| English 1836-1893 | | | |
| □ **GRINNELL, G. Victor** ....................... *paintings* | | **$330** | **$495** |
| American d. 1934 | | | |
| □ **GRINNELL, Roy** ............................... *paintings* | | **$3,500** | **$15,000** |
| American contemporary | | | |
| □ **GRIPS, Charles Joseph** ....................... *paintings* | | **$6,050** | **$6,050** |
| Belgian 1852-1920 | | | |
| □ **GRIS, Juan** ..................................... *paintings* | | **$68,750** | **$352,000** |
| Spanish 1887-1927 ..................................... *drawings* | | **$5,500** | **$266,112** |
| □ **GRISET, Ernest Henry** ....................... *drawings* | | **$110** | **$850** |
| French/English 1844-1907 | | | |
| □ **GRISON, Francois Adolphe** .................. *paintings* | | **$6,050** | **$38,500** |
| French 1845-1914 | | | |
| □ **GRISOT, Pierre** ............................... *paintings* | | | **$330** |
| French 20th cent. | | | |
| □ **GRISWOLD, Casimir Clayton** ............. *paintings* | | **$88** | **$400** |
| American 1834-1918 | | | |
| □ **GRISWOLD, Victor Moreau** ................ *paintings* | | | **$440** |
| American 1819-1872 | | | |
| □ **GRITCHENKO, Alexis** ....................... *paintings* | | **$495** | **$850** |
| Russian b. 1883 ..................................... *drawings* | | **$280** | **$420** |
| □ **GRIVAZ, Eugene** ............................. *paintings* | | **$742** | **$770** |
| French 1852-1915 ..................................... *drawings* | | **$220** | **$715** |
| □ **GRIVELLI, A.** ................................. *paintings* | | | **$330** |
| Italian 20th cent. | | | |
| □ **GROAT, George Hugh de** ..................... *paintings* | | **$137** | **$247** |
| American b. 1917 | | | |
| □ **GROBE** .......................................... *paintings* | | **$770** | **$2,420** |
| German b. 1857 | | | |
| □ **GROENEVELD, Tademan** ................... *paintings* | | | **$770** |
| Dutch 19th/20th cent. | | | |
| □ **GROENEWEGEN, Adrianus Johannes** .. *paintings* | | **$424** | **$825** |
| ..................................................... *drawings* | | **$462** | **$770** |
| □ **GROESBECK, Daniel Sayre** ................ *drawings* | | **$220** | **$220** |
| American 20th cent. | | | |
| □ **GROGLER, Wilhelm** ........................... *paintings* | | | **$715** |
| German 1830-1897 | | | |
| □ **GROLL, Albert Lorey** ......................... *paintings* | | **$165** | **$4,125** |
| American 1866-1952 ..................................... *drawings* | | **$132** | **$220** |

| | *Current Price Range* | |
|---|---|---|
| | *Low* | *High* |
| ☐ **GROLLERON, Paul Louis Narcisse** ....... *paintings* | $300 | $4,400 |
| French 1848-1901 ...................................... *drawings* | $220 | $550 |
| ☐ **GROMAIRE, Marcel** .......................... *paintings* | $4,180 | $27,500 |
| French 1892-1971 ...................................... *drawings* | $440 | $1,650 |
| ☐ **GRONINGEN, Jan Swart van** .............. *drawings* | | $1,650 |
| Flemish 1469-1535 | | |
| ☐ **GRONLAND, Rene** ............................. *drawings* | | $1,760 |
| German b. 1849 | | |
| ☐ **GRONLAND, Theude** .......................... *paintings* | $4,400 | $19,800 |
| German 1817-1876 | | |
| ☐ **GRONVOLD, Marcus** .......................... *paintings* | | $19,800 |
| Norwegian b. 1845 | | |
| ☐ **GROOME, M.** .................................... *paintings* | | $192 |
| American 19th/20th cent. | | |
| ☐ **GROOMS, Frank R.** ........................... *paintings* | | $175 |
| American 19th cent. | | |
| ☐ **GROOMS, Red** ................................. *paintings* | $990 | $3,850 |
| American b. 1937 ..................................... *drawings* | $528 | $9,350 |
| .......................................................... *sculpture* | $3,300 | $4,400 |
| ☐ **GROON, T.F.** .................................... *drawings* | | $528 |
| ☐ **GROOT, Adriann Milton de** ................ *paintings* | | $385 |
| American late 19th/early 20th cent | | |
| ☐ **GROOT, G. de** .................................. *paintings* | $82 | $357 |
| ☐ **GROOT, Joseph de** ............................ *paintings* | | $440 |
| Dutch b. 1840 | | |
| ☐ **GROOT, M. de** .................................. *paintings* | | $715 |
| Dutch 19th/20th cent. | | |
| ☐ **GROOT, Mozes de (Maurits)** .............. *paintings* | | $850 |
| Dutch School 1880-1934 | | |
| ☐ **GROOTEVELT, J.H. van** ...................... *paintings* | | $1,210 |
| Dutch 19th cent. | | |
| ☐ **GROPPER, William** ........................... *paintings* | $715 | $13,200 |
| American 1897-1977 .................................. *drawings* | $66 | $2,860 |
| ☐ **GROS, Baron Jean Louis** ..................... *paintings* | $6,050 | $55,000 |
| French 1793-1879 | | |
| ☐ **GROS, Ernest M.** .............................. *paintings* | $935 | $1,760 |
| French 19th cent. | | |
| ☐ **GROS, Jean Antoine Baron** ................. *paintings* | | $3,080 |
| French 1771-1835 | | |
| ☐ **GROS, Lucien Alphonse** ...................... *paintings* | | $385 |
| French 1845-1913 | | |
| ☐ **GROSCHOLSKY, Stanislaus** ................ *paintings* | | $522 |
| Polish 19th cent. | | |
| ☐ **GROSCLAUDE, Louis Frederic** ............ *drawings* | | $440 |
| French 19th cent. | | |
| ☐ **GROSE, D.C.** .................................... *paintings* | $110 | $3,850 |
| American ac. 1860-1880 | | |
| ☐ **GROSPIETSCH, Florian** ...................... *paintings* | | $7,700 |
| German 1789-1830 | | |

| | | | *Current Price Range* | |
| | | | Low | High |
|---|---|---|---|---|
| ☐ **GROSS, Chaim** | ............................ | *drawings* | **$143** | **$990** |
| American b. 1904 | ............................. | *sculpture* | **$440** | **$17,050** |
| ☐ **GROSS, G.** | ............................ | *paintings* | **$220** | **$385** |
| American 20th cent. | | | | |
| ☐ **GROSS, Juliet White** | .................... | *paintings* | | **$1,760** |
| American 1882-1934 | | | | |
| ☐ **GROSS, Oskar** | ............................ | *paintings* | | **$1,375** |
| American b. 1871 | | | | |
| ☐ **GROSS, Peter Alfred** | ................... | *paintings* | **$137** | **$522** |
| American 1849-1914 | | | | |
| ☐ **GROSS, Sidney** | ............................ | *paintings* | | **$385** |
| American b. 1921 | | | | |
| ☐ **GROSSENHEIDER, Richard P.** | ........... | *drawings* | **$1,100** | **$4,180** |
| American 1911-1975 | | | | |
| ☐ **GROSSMAN, Edwin Booth** | ................ | *paintings* | **$80** | **$440** |
| American b. 1887 | | | | |
| ☐ **GROSSMAN, Nancy** | ....................... | *sculpture* | | **$12,100** |
| ☐ **GROSVENOR, Richard** | .................... | *paintings* | | **$200** |
| American 20th cent. | | | | |
| ☐ **GROSZ, George** | ............................ | *paintings* | **$880** | **$9,075** |
| German/American 1893-1959 | ................. | *drawings* | **$308** | **$28,600** |
| ☐ **GROTIUS, Hugo** | ............................ | *paintings* | | **$220** |
| British 19th/20th cent. | | | | |
| ☐ **GROUX, Henri-Jules de** | .................. | *drawings* | | **$286** |
| Belgian 1867-1930 | | | | |
| ☐ **GROUZINSKY, P.** | ........................... | *paintings* | | **$2,200** |
| Russian 19th cent. | | | | |
| ☐ **GROVE, David** | ............................ | *drawings* | | **$660** |
| American 20th cent. | | | | |
| ☐ **GROVE, Nordhael Peter Frederick** | ........ | *paintings* | | **$3,850** |
| Danish 1822-1885 | | | | |
| ☐ **GROVER, Oliver Dennet** | ................... | *paintings* | **$715** | **$1,760** |
| American 1861-1927 | ............................. | *drawings* | | **$275** |
| ☐ **GRUBACS, Giovanni** | ....................... | *paintings* | **$770** | **$5,610** |
| Italian d. 1919 | | | | |
| ☐ **GRUBE, F.** | ............................ | *sculpture* | | **$440** |
| American 20th cent. | | | | |
| ☐ **GRUBER, Francis** | .......................... | *paintings* | **$3,960** | **$6,050** |
| French 1912-1948 | | | | |
| ☐ **GRUBER, R. W.** | ............................ | *paintings* | | **$440** |
| German 19th/20th cent. | | | | |
| ☐ **GRUBERSKI, Ladislas** | ..................... | *sculpture* | | **$1,320** |
| Polish 20th cent. | | | | |
| ☐ **GRUE, Frederick** | .......................... | *paintings* | | **$357** |
| ☐ **GRUELLE, Richard Buckner** | .............. | *paintings* | | **$385** |
| American 1851-1914 | | | | |
| ☐ **GRUGER, Frederic Roderigo** | .............. | *drawings* | **$165** | **$550** |
| Austrian 1871-1953 | | | | |

| | Current Price Range | |
|---|---|---|
| | *Low* | *High* |
| ☐ **GRUILLY, De** ...................................... *paintings* | | **$2,860** |
| French | | |
| ☐ **GRUMIEAU, Emil J.** ........................... *paintings* | | **$825** |
| American b. 1897 | | |
| ☐ **GRUN, Jules Alexandre** ........................ *paintings* | **$550** | **$12,100** |
| French 1868-1934 | | |
| ☐ **GRUN, Moritz** ................................... *paintings* | | **$2,200** |
| French b. 1869 | | |
| ☐ **GRUNENWALD, Jacob** ........................ *paintings* | | **$48,400** |
| German 1822-1896 | | |
| ☐ **GRUNER, Carl** .................................... *paintings* | **$715** | **$1,320** |
| American ac. 1859 | | |
| ☐ **GRUNEWALD, F.** .............................. *paintings* | | **$302** |
| ☐ **GRUNLER, Louis** ................................ *paintings* | | **$14,300** |
| German b. 1809 | | |
| ☐ **GRUNWALD, Carl Friedrich** ............... *drawings* | | **$330** |
| ☐ **GRUPPE, Charles Paul** ........................ *paintings* | **$150** | **$9,900** |
| Canadian/American 1860-1940 ...................... *drawings* | **$55** | **$825** |
| ☐ **GRUPPE, Emile Albert** ........................ *paintings* | **$110** | **$8,250** |
| American 1896-1978 ................................... *drawings* | **$99** | **$522** |
| ☐ **GRUPPE, Karl H.** ............................... *sculpture* | | **$990** |
| American b. 1893 | | |
| ☐ **GRUTZNER, E.J.** ................................ *paintings* | | **$1,705** |
| German 19th cent. | | |
| ☐ **GRUTZNER, Eduard von** ..................... *paintings* | **$7,700** | **$71,500** |
| German 1846-1925 | | |
| ☐ **GRUYTER, Jacob Willem** ..................... *paintings* | **$2,640** | **$4,400** |
| Dutch 1817-1880 ...................................... *drawings* | **$660** | **$715** |
| ☐ **GRUZALSKI, J.** ................................. *sculpture* | **$2,000** | **$2,250** |
| American | | |
| ☐ **GRYEFF, Adriaen de** ........................... *paintings* | **$660** | **$4,400** |
| Flemish 1670-1715 | | |
| ☐ **GRYP (?), N.M.** ................................. *paintings* | | **$357** |
| Dutch 19th cent. | | |
| ☐ **GSCHOSMANN, Ludwig** ..................... *paintings* | | **$467** |
| German b. 1901 | | |
| ☐ **GSELL, Laurent Lucien** ....................... *paintings* | | **$4,950** |
| French 1860-1944 | | |
| ☐ **GSUR, Karl Friedrich** .......................... *paintings* | **$467** | **$825** |
| Austrian 1871-1939 | | |
| ☐ **GUACCIMANNI, Vittorio** ................... *drawings* | | **$660** |
| Italian ac.1880-1900 | | |
| ☐ **GUAGUIE, H.** ................................... *sculpture* | | **$3,025** |
| ☐ **GUALDI, Pedro** ................................. *paintings* | | **$24,200** |
| Italian/American 1810-1859 | | |
| ☐ **GUARANA, Jacopo** ............................ *paintings* | | **$29,700** |
| Italian 1720-1808 | | |
| ☐ **GUARDABASSI, Guerrino** ................... *paintings* | | **$1,980** |
| Italian b. 1841 ......................................... *drawings* | **$220** | **$495** |

|                                                          | Current Price Range | |
|----------------------------------------------------------|---------:|---------:|
|                                                          | *Low* | *High* |
| ☐ **GUARDERAS, Sergio** .......................... *paintings* | | $495 |
| Mexican 20th cent. | | |
| ☐ **GUARDI, Francesco** ........................... *paintings* | $33,000 | $352,000 |
| Italian 1712-1793 ....................................... *drawings* | $11,000 | $28,600 |
| ☐ **GUARDI, Giacomo** ........................... *paintings* | $2,200 | $77,000 |
| Italian 1764-1835 ....................................... *drawings* | $1,210 | $4,400 |
| ☐ **GUARDI, Giovanni Antonio** .................. *paintings* | | $13,200 |
| Italian c. 1698-1760 | | |
| ☐ **GUARDIA, W. de la** ........................... *paintings* | | $4,400 |
| Spanish 19th cent. | | |
| ☐ **GUARDIA, Wenceslaw de la** ................. *paintings* | | $467 |
| American b. 1861 | | |
| ☐ **GUARINI, Antonio** ............................ *paintings* | | $2,475 |
| Italian b. 1846 | | |
| ☐ **GUARINO, Francesco** ......................... *paintings* | | $2,640 |
| Italian 1611-1654 | | |
| ☐ **GUARNERIO, Pietro** .......................... *sculpture* | | $2,860 |
| Italian late 19th cent. | | |
| ☐ **GUAY, Gabriel** .................................... *paintings* | | $880 |
| French b. 1848 | | |
| ☐ **GUAYASAMIN, Oswaldo** ...................... *paintings* | $770 | $9,350 |
| Ecuadorian b. 1919 ..................................... *drawings* | $385 | $5,775 |
| ☐ **GUBANI, G.** ...................................... *drawings* | | $440 |
| Italian 19th cent. | | |
| ☐ **GUDE, Hans Fredrik** ......................... *paintings* | $935 | $17,050 |
| Norwegian 1825-1903 ................................. *drawings* | $220 | $880 |
| ☐ **GUDIN, H.** ....................................... *paintings* | | $627 |
| French 19th cent. | | |
| ☐ **GUDIN, Henriette** ............................. *paintings* | $440 | $2,200 |
| French 19th cent. | | |
| ☐ **GUDIN, Theodore Jean Antoine** ............ *paintings* | $660 | $2,750 |
| French 1802-1880 | | |
| ☐ **GUE, David John** ................................ *paintings* | $137 | $1,650 |
| American 1836-1917 | | |
| ☐ **GUELDRY, F.** ................................... *paintings* | | $825 |
| ☐ **GUELDRY, Ferdinand Joseph** .............. *paintings* | $4,125 | $6,600 |
| French b. 1858 | | |
| ☐ **GUELLOW, W.** .................................. *paintings* | | $330 |
| American 19th cent. | | |
| ☐ **GUELPA, Clelio** ................................. *paintings* | | $192 |
| Italian b. 1900 | | |
| ☐ **GUERBE, Raymond** ........................... *sculpture* | $660 | $5,280 |
| French early 20th cent. | | |
| ☐ **GUERELSON, A.M.** ........................... *paintings* | | $1,210 |
| American | | |
| ☐ **GUERIN, Armand** ............................... *paintings* | $165 | $770 |
| French b. 1913 | | |
| ☐ **GUERIN, Charles** ............................... *paintings* | | $522 |
| ☐ **GUERIN, Ernest** ................................ *drawings* | | $330 |

| | *Current Price Range* | |
|---|---|---|
| | *Low* | *High* |
| ☐ **GUERIN, Joseph** .................. *paintings* <br> American b. 1889 | $770 | $1,210 |
| ☐ **GUERIN, Jules** .................. *paintings* <br> American 1866-1946 .................. *drawings* | $412 <br> $308 | $1,210 <br> $6,150 |
| ☐ **GUERIN, Pierre Narcisse** ........ *paintings* <br> French 1774-1833 | | $13,200 |
| ☐ **GUERMACHEFF, Michel** ......... *paintings* <br> Russian b. 1867 | | $770 |
| ☐ **GUERRA** .................. *paintings* | | $385 |
| ☐ **GUERRERO, Jose** .............. *paintings* <br> Spanish/American b. 1914 | $330 | $5,775 |
| ☐ **GUERRERO, Manuel Ruiz** ......... *paintings* <br> Spanish 19th cent. | | $1,980 |
| ☐ **GUERRERO, Xavier** ............ *drawings* <br> Mexican b. 1896 | | $880 |
| ☐ **GUERRERO GALVAN, Jesus** .......... *drawings* <br> Mexican 1910-1973 | $825 | $2,640 |
| ☐ **GUERRIER, Raymond** .......... *paintings* <br> French b. 1920 | $220 | $495 |
| ☐ **GUERRIERO, Henry** ........... *sculpture* <br> American b. 1929 | | $1,430 |
| ☐ **GUESNET, Georges** ............ *sculpture* <br> French | | $308 |
| ☐ **GUETIN, V.O.** .................. *paintings* | | $528 |
| ☐ **GUEVARA, Luis Herrera** ......... *paintings* | | $3,300 |
| ☐ **GUGEL, G.** .................. *paintings* | | $880 |
| ☐ **GUGGENBERGER, Thomas** ......... *paintings* <br> German 1817-1887 | $275 | $825 |
| ☐ **GUGGENHEIM, Pegeen** ......... *drawings* <br> American 20th cent. | $192 | $220 |
| ☐ **GUGLIELMI, O. Louis** .......... *paintings* <br> American 1906-1956 | $19,800 | $26,400 |
| ☐ **GUICHARD, Joseph** ............ *paintings* <br> French 19th cent. | | $250 |
| ☐ **GUIDI, Giuseppe** ............. *drawings* <br> Italian 1881/84-1931 | $880 | $9,350 |
| ☐ **GUIDI, Virgilio** .................. *paintings* <br> Italian b. 1892 | | $4,070 |
| ☐ **GUIDOTTI, A.** .................. *paintings* <br> Italian 19th cent. | | $192 |
| ☐ **GUIFFRE, H.** .................. *paintings* | | $352 |
| ☐ **GUIFON, Leon** .................. *paintings* <br> American 19th cent. | | $605 |
| ☐ **GUIGNARD, Alberto da Veiga** ......... *paintings* <br> Brazilian 1893/96-1962 | | $13,200 |
| ☐ **GUIGNARD, Alexandre Gaston** ......... *paintings* <br> French b. 1848 | | $1,870 |
| ☐ **GUIGNET, Jean Adrien** ......... *drawings* <br> French 1816-1854 | | $660 |

| | | Current Price Range | |
|---|---|---|---|
| | | Low | High |

☐ **GUIGOU, Paul Camille** .................. *paintings* | | | **$19,800** |
French 1834-1871

☐ **GUILBERT, E.** ................................. *paintings* | **$247** | **$275** |
French 19th cent.

☐ **GUILBERT, Ernest** ............................ *sculpture* | | **$1,540** |
French b. 1848

☐ **GUILBERT, Octave** ........................... *paintings* | | **$550** |
French 20th cent.

☐ **GUILLAUME, H.** ............................ *drawings* | | **$300** |
☐ **GUILLAUME, L.** ............................. *drawings* | | **$220** |
American

☐ **GUILLAUME, P.** .............................. *paintings* | | **$220** |
Dutch b. 1908

☐ **GUILLAUMET, Gustave Achille** .......... *paintings* | | **$20,900** |
French 1840-1887 .................................... *drawings* | **$495** | **$880** |

☐ **GUILLAUMIN, Jean Baptiste Armand** .. *paintings* | **$1,430** | **$93,500** |
French 1841-1927 ................................... *drawings* | **$1,045** | **$15,400** |

☐ **GUILLEMET, Jean Baptiste Antoine** ..... *paintings* | **$330** | **$5,390** |
French 1843-1918

☐ **GUILLEMIN, Alexandre Marie** ........... *paintings* | **$385** | **$2,750** |
French 1817-1880 .................................... *drawings* | **$33** | **$1,760** |

☐ **GUILLEMIN, Emile** .......................... *sculpture* | **$495** | **$4,400** |
French 1841-1907

☐ **GUILLEMINET, Claude** ...................... *paintings* | **$500** | **$3,080** |
French b. 1821

☐ **GUILLERMIC, Yves** ........................... *paintings* | | **$302** |
French 20th cent.

☐ **GUILLERMOT, G.T.** .......................... *paintings* | | **$33,000** |
French 19th/20th cent.

☐ **GUILLOD, Thomas Walker** ................. *paintings* | | **$5,225** |
British ac. 1839-1860

☐ **GUILLON, Adolphe Irenee** ................. *paintings* | | **$1,430** |
French 1829-96

☐ **GUILLON, Alfred** ............................. *paintings* | | **$1,870** |
French 19th cent.

☐ **GUILLON, Eugene Antoine** ................. *paintings* | | **$1,045** |
French b. 1834

☐ **GUILLONNET, Octave Denis Victor** ..... *paintings* | | **$687** |
French 1872-1967

☐ **GUILLOT** ...................................... *paintings* | **$330** | **$605** |
French 20th cent.

☐ **GUILLOT, Anatole** ........................... *sculpture* | | **$990** |
French 1865-1911

☐ **GUILLOT, Donat** ............................. *paintings* | | **$605** |
French 19th cent.

☐ **GUILLOT, J.** ................................... *sculpture* | | **$1,760** |
French 19th cent.

☐ **GUILLOUX, Charles** .......................... *paintings* | | **$275** |
French 20th cent.

|                                                         | Current Price Range | |
|---------------------------------------------------------|---------|------------|
|                                                         | Low     | High       |
| ☐ **GUILLVIN, Ch.** ................. *paintings*<br>French 19th/20th cent. |         | **$467**   |
| ☐ **GUILMANT, Felix** .............. *paintings*<br>French 19th cent. | **$220** | **$412**   |
| ☐ **GUINZBURG, Frederic Victor** ............. *sculpture*<br>American b. 1897 |         | **$330**   |
| ☐ **GUION, Molly** ...................... *paintings*<br>American b. 1910 | **$11** | **$220**   |
| ☐ **GUIRAND DE SCEVOLA, Lucien** ........ *paintings*<br>French 1871-1950 .................... *drawings* | **$2,200** | **$4,400**<br>**$990** |
| ☐ **GUIRANDE, J.D.** ............................. *sculpture*<br>French early 20th cent. |         | **$1,980** |
| ☐ **GUIRAUD-RIVIERE, Maurice** ............. *sculpture*<br>French b. 1881 | **$231** | **$12,100** |
| ☐ **GUISTI, Girolamo** ............................. *drawings*<br>Italian 19th cent. |         | **$330**   |
| ☐ **GUISTO, E. de** ..................................... *sculpture* |         | **$264**   |
| ☐ **GUITERMAN, H.** ............................. *paintings*<br>American late 19th cent. |         | **$687**   |
| ☐ **GULAGER, Charles** .......................... *paintings*<br>ac. 1860-1880 |         | **$935**   |
| ☐ **GULDI, G.** ........................................ *drawings*<br>Italian 19th cent. |         | **$550**   |
| ☐ **GULLAGER, Christian** ....................... *paintings*<br>American 1762-1826 |         | **$6,000** |
| ☐ **GUMMER, Don** ................................. *sculpture*<br>American b. 1946 |         | **$3,300** |
| ☐ **GUNDELFINGER, John** ....................... *paintings*<br>American b. 1937 |         | **$4,620** |
| ☐ **GUNISCHEIM, J.** ............................... *paintings*<br>German 19th cent. |         | **$825**   |
| ☐ **GUNN, Archibald** ............................. *paintings*<br>British 1849-1871 |         | **$1,210** |
| ☐ **GUNN, Archie** ................................... *drawings*<br>American 1863-1910 |         | **$200**   |
| ☐ **GUNNEWEG,**<br>**Hermanus Petrus Antonius** .................... *paintings*<br>Dutch 1846-1904 |         | **$880**   |
| ☐ **GUNTEN, Roger von** ........................... *paintings* |         | **$1,760** |
| ☐ **GUNTER, Randolph** ............................ *drawings* |         | **$495**   |
| ☐ **GUNTHER, Erwin** ............................. *paintings*<br>German 1864-1927 | **$154** | **$605**   |
| ☐ **GUNTHER, Max** ................................ *paintings*<br>German b. 1935 |         | **$220**   |
| ☐ **GURIN, Herminie** ............................. *paintings* |         | **$650**   |
| ☐ **GURLITT, Louis** ............................... *paintings*<br>European 19th cent. |         | **$9,900** |
| ☐ **GURSCHNER, Gustav** ........................ *sculpture*<br>Austrian b. 1873 | **$198** | **$4,400** |

| | | *Current Price Range* | |
|---|---|---|---|
| | | *Low* | *High* |
| ☐ GUSSOW, Roy ..................... *sculpture* | | $825 | $1,760 |
| American b. 1918 | | | |
| ☐ GUSTAVSON, Henry .......................... *paintings* | | $247 | $522 |
| American 1864-1912 | | | |
| ☐ GUSTAVSON, Herman ........................ *paintings* | | $165 | $330 |
| American 20th cent. | | | |
| ☐ GUSTAVSON, Lealand R. .................... *paintings* | | | $302 |
| ☐ GUSTEMER, G. ................................ *paintings* | | | $21,450 |
| American 19th cent. | | | |
| ☐ GUSTON, Philip ............................. *paintings* | | $9,350 | $242,000 |
| Canadian/American 1913-1980 ..................... *drawings* | | $1,100 | $12,100 |
| ☐ GUTEMAN, Gustave ........................... *paintings* | | | $660 |
| ☐ GUTFREUND, Otto .......................... *drawings* | | $550 | $1,430 |
| Czechoslovakian 1889-1927 | | | |
| ☐ GUTHRAM, Worm ........................... *paintings* | | | $1,650 |
| ☐ GUTIERREZ, Ernesto ........................ *paintings* | | $467 | $1,320 |
| Spanish 19th/20th cent. | | | |
| ☐ GUTIERREZ, Fernando ....................... *paintings* | | | $1,100 |
| ☐ GUTMANN, Bernhard ........................ *paintings* | | $88 | $880 |
| American 1869-1936 | | | |
| ☐ GUTMANN, Ida ................................. *paintings* | | | $605 |
| German 19th cent. | | | |
| ☐ GUTTUSO, Renato ............................. *paintings* | | | $30,250 |
| Italian b. 1912 ........................................ *drawings* | | $467 | $2,090 |
| ☐ GUY, Jean Baptiste Louis ..................... *paintings* | | $605 | $1,980 |
| French 1824-1888 | | | |
| ☐ GUY, Seymour Joseph ......................... *paintings* | | $2,200 | $121,000 |
| Anglo/American 1824-1910 | | | |
| ☐ GUYET, J. Louise .............................. *paintings* | | | $550 |
| French 19th cent. | | | |
| ☐ GUYILLAN, D. ................................... *paintings* | | | $577 |
| Continental 19th cent. | | | |
| ☐ GUYNEMER ...................................... *drawings* | | | $275 |
| ☐ GUYON, Maximilienne ........................ *drawings* | | | $495 |
| French 1868-1903 | | | |
| ☐ GUYOT, Georges Lucien ...................... *sculpture* | | $715 | $2,200 |
| French 1885-1973 | | | |
| ☐ GUYOT, Louise ................................. *paintings* | | $770 | $3,850 |
| French 19th cent. | | | |
| ☐ GUYS, Constantin .............................. *drawings* | | $165 | $9,900 |
| French 1802-1892 | | | |
| ☐ GUYSI, Alice V. ................................. *paintings* | | | $220 |
| American d. c. 1940 | | | |
| ☐ GUZZARDI, Giuseppe ........................ *paintings* | | $357 | $1,760 |
| Italian 1845-1914 | | | |
| ☐ GWATHMEY, Robert .......................... *paintings* | | $1,650 | $6,600 |
| American b. 1903 ..................................... *drawings* | | $715 | $1,760 |
| ☐ GYBERSON, Indiana .......................... *paintings* | | $330 | $440 |
| American 20th cent. | | | |

| | | Current Price Range | |
|---|---|---|---|
| | | Low | High |
| ☐ **GYSBRECHTS, Franciscus** ................ *paintings* | | $4,290 | $8,800 |
| Dutch ac. 1674-1677 | | | |
| ☐ **GYSELINCKX, Joseph** .............. *paintings* | | $1,485 | $2,750 |
| Belgian 19th cent. | | | |
| ☐ **GYSIS, Nicolas** ............................ *paintings* | | $2,200 | $14,300 |
| Greek 1842-1901 | | | |
| ☐ **GYZEMAN, W.A.** ........................... *paintings* | | | $302 |
| Dutch school 19th cent. | | | |
| ☐ **HAAG, Carl** ................................. *paintings* | | | $385 |
| German 1820-1915 ........................... *drawings* | | $1,540 | $1,760 |
| ☐ **HAAG, Charles** ......................... *sculpture* | | | $660 |
| American | | | |
| ☐ **HAAG, Jean Paul** ....................... *paintings* | | | $1,760 |
| French 19th cent. | | | |
| ☐ **HAAGEN, Joris van der** ............. *paintings* | | $7,150 | $7,700 |
| Dutch 1615-1669 | | | |
| ☐ **HAANEN, Adriana Johanna** ......... *paintings* | | $3,080 | $8,800 |
| Dutch 1814-1895 | | | |
| ☐ **HAANEN, Cecil van** ................. *paintings* | | | $7,700 |
| Dutch 1844-1885 | | | |
| ☐ **HAANEN, Remi van** ................. *paintings* | | | $495 |
| Dutch 1812-1894 | | | |
| ☐ **HAAPANEN, John Nichols** ........... *paintings* | | $242 | $450 |
| American b. 1891 | | | |
| ☐ **HAARLEM, Cornelis van** | | | |
| **(Cornelis CORNELISZ)** ............. *paintings* | | $7,150 | $14,300 |
| Dutch 1562-1638 | | | |
| ☐ **HAAS** ........................................ *paintings* | | $308 | $2,200 |
| Flemish 1832-1908 | | | |
| ☐ **HAAS, Alice Preble Tucker de** ........ *paintings* | | | $220 |
| American ac. 1890-1920 ..................... *drawings* | | | $137 |
| ☐ **HAAS, Frederik Hendrick de** ........ *paintings* | | $220 | $12,100 |
| Dutch/American 1832-1898 ................. *drawings* | | $165 | $660 |
| ☐ **HAAS, William Frederick de** ........ *paintings* | | $1,320 | $3,630 |
| Dutch 1830-1880 | | | |
| ☐ **HAASE, Carl** ............................... *paintings* | | | $1,210 |
| ☐ **HAASE, Curt** ............................... *paintings* | | | $1,100 |
| ☐ **HAASE, Herman** ........................ *sculpture* | | | $880 |
| German early 20th cent. | | | |
| ☐ **HAASS, E.D.** ............................... *paintings* | | | $357 |
| ☐ **HAAXMAN, Pieter** ..................... *paintings* | | | $6,325 |
| Dutch 1854-1937 | | | |
| ☐ **HABER, Leonard V.** ..................... *paintings* | | $110 | $231 |
| American 20th cent. | | | |
| ☐ **HABERLE, John** ........................... *paintings* | | | $55,000 |
| American 1853/56-1933 ..................... *drawings* | | $466 | $3,575 |
| ☐ **HABERLY** ................................... *paintings* | | | $8,250 |
| ☐ **HABERMANN, Hugo von** ............. *paintings* | | $467 | $2,200 |
| German 1849-1921 ........................... *drawings* | | $605 | $770 |

| | Current Price Range | |
|---|---|---|
| | Low | High |

☐ **HABERT, Eugene** .............................. *paintings* | | **$1,870**
French d. 1916

☐ **HABICHT, Jane** .................................. *paintings* | | **$770**
American 20th cent.

☐ **HACHMANN, Franz** ........................... *paintings* | | **$467**

☐ **HACKAERT, Jacob Philip** .................... *paintings* | | **$8,000**
German 1737-1807

☐ **HACKER, Arthur** .............................. *paintings* | **$528** | **$26,400**
British 1858-1919

☐ **HACKERT, Carl Ludwig** ...................... *drawings* | | **$3,575**
German 1740-1796

☐ **HACKERT, Jacob Philippe** .................. *drawings* | | **$990**
German 1737-1807

☐ **HACKLIN, Allan** ................................ *paintings* | | **$275**
American b. 1943

☐ **HADAMARD, Auguste** ....................... *paintings* | | **$2,750**
French 1823-1886

☐ **HADDELSEY, Vincent** ......................... *paintings* | | **$302**
English b. 1829

☐ **HADDEN, D.W.** .................................. *paintings* | | **$550**

☐ **HADDOCK, A.J.** ................................ *paintings* | | **$750**

☐ **HADDOCK, Arthur E.** ........................ *paintings* | | **$1,540**
American b. 1895

☐ **HADDON, Arthur Trevor** .................... *paintings* | **$137** | **$14,300**
British 1864-1941 ................................ *drawings* | **$357** | **$605**

☐ **HADLER, Robert** ............................... *paintings* | | **$990**
Hungarian 20th cent.

☐ **HAECHT, Tobias van** ......................... *paintings* | | **$79,750**
Flemish 1561-1631

☐ **HAECKEN, W. van** ............................. *paintings* | | **$500**
American

☐ **HAELEN, John A.** .............................. *paintings* | | **$385**
American 19th/20th cent.

☐ **HAERST, F.** ....................................... *paintings* | | **$412**
American 19th/20th cent.

☐ **HAERST, G.** ...................................... *paintings* | | **$770**
American 19th cent.

☐ **HAES JANVIER, Frances de** ............... *paintings* | | **$605**
American 1775-1824

☐ **HAESAERT, Paul** ............................... *paintings* | | **$3,850**
Belgian 1813-1893

☐ **HAESELER, Alice P. Smith** ................. *drawings* | | **$412**
American ac. 1899-1913

☐ **HAFFERKAMP, Theresa** ...................... *drawings* | **$191** | **$247**
American 20th cent.

☐ **HAGAMAN, James** ............................. *paintings* | **$165** | **$467**
American 20th cent.

☐ **HAGAN, John C.** ................................ *paintings* | | **$330**
American ac. 1839-1882

| | Current Price Range | |
|---|---|---|
| | Low | High |

☐ **HAGAR, Charles** ................................. *sculpture* | | **$2,200**
Belgian early 20th cent.

☐ **HAGARTY, Parker** .............................. *paintings* | | **$1,100**
Canadian 19th cent.

☐ **HAGBORG, August Wilhelm Nikolaus** .. *paintings* | **$1,320** | **$6,050**
Swedish 1852-1925

☐ **HAGE, Reynier de la** ........................... *paintings* | | **$2,860**

☐ **HAGEDORN, Friedrich** ........................ *paintings* | | **$12,100**
German 1814-1889 ..................................... *drawings* | | **$4,730**

☐ **HAGEFUL, H.** ...................................... *paintings* | **$275** | **$330**
American 19th/20th cent.

☐ **HAGEKAWA, T.** ............................... *drawings* | | **$192**
Japanese School 20th cent.

☐ **HAGEL, Frank** .................................... *paintings* | | **$2,700**
American contemporary ................................. *drawings* | | **$800**

☐ **HAGEMANN, Godefroy de** ................. *paintings* | **$990** | **$2,860**
French d. 1877

☐ **HAGEMANN, Oskar H.** ....................... *paintings* | | **$880**
German b. 1888

☐ **HAGEMANS, Paul** ............................. *paintings* | **$330** | **$385**

☐ **HAGEN, Theodor Josef** ........................ *paintings* | | **$2,090**
German 1842-1919

☐ **HAGENBAUMER, David** ..................... *drawings* | **$825** | **$1,540**
contemporary

☐ **HAGER, Eduard von** ........................... *paintings* | | **$495**

☐ **HAGERMANS, Maurice** ...................... *drawings* | | **$715**
Belgian 1852-1917

☐ **HAGERUP, Nels** ................................. *paintings* | **$33** | **$3,025**
American 1864-1922

☐ **HAGHE, Louis** ..................................... *paintings* | | **$1,430**
Belgian b. 1806,d. London 1885 ..................... *drawings* | **$33** | **$10,450**

☐ **HAGIWARA, T.** ................................... *drawings* | | **$275**
Japanese 20th cent.

☐ **HAGRRUD, N.** .................................... *paintings* | | **$440**

☐ **HAGUE, Joshua Anderson** .................... *paintings* | **$330** | **$550**
English 1850-1916

☐ **HAGUE, Michael** ............................... *drawings* | | **$660**

☐ **HAGY, M.** .......................................... *paintings* | | **$1,430**
American 19th/20th cent.

☐ **HAHN, Gustave** ................................. *paintings* | | **$300**
German 1811-1872

☐ **HAHN, J.M.** ....................................... *paintings* | | **$660**

☐ **HAHN, Karl Wilhelm** ........................... *paintings* | **$4,400** | **$49,500**
German/American 1829-1887

☐ **HAHN, William** .................................. *paintings* | **$1,100** | **$31,900**
American 1840-1890

☐ **HAIER, J.** .......................................... *paintings* | | **$650**

☐ **HAIGH, Alfred G.** .............................. *paintings* | **$660** | **$2,200**

☐ **HAIMAN, G.** ...................................... *paintings* | | **$550**

| | | Current Price Range | |
|---|---|---|---|
| | | *Low* | *High* |
| ☐ **HAINES, George W.** ............ *paintings* | | | $495 |
| American 19th cent. | | | |
| ☐ **HAINES, John** ............ *paintings* | | | $356 |
| ☐ **HAINES, Richard** ............ *paintings* | | $302 | $522 |
| American b. 1906 | | | |
| ☐ **HAINES, William Henry** ............ *paintings* | | $400 | $1,650 |
| English 1812-1884 ............ *drawings* | | $70 | $176 |
| ☐ **HAITE, J.C.** ............ *paintings* | | | $4,180 |
| ☐ **HAJDU, Etienne** ............ *drawings* | | | $396 |
| French b. 1907 ............ *sculpture* | | $880 | $17,600 |
| ☐ **HALBACH, David** ............ *drawings* | | | $7,500 |
| American b. 1931 | | | |
| ☐ **HALBERG-KRAUSS, Fritz** ............ *paintings* | | $1,650 | $3,850 |
| German b. 1874 | | | |
| ☐ **HALBY** ............ *paintings* | | | $605 |
| ☐ **HALDNER, Knute** ............ *paintings* | | | $1,430 |
| American 19th/20th cent. | | | |
| ☐ **HALE, Ellen Day** ............ *paintings* | | $165 | $12,100 |
| American 1855-1940 | | | |
| ☐ **HALE, Lillian Westcott** ............ *drawings* | | $165 | $220 |
| American 1881-1953 | | | |
| ☐ **HALE, Philip Leslie** ............ *paintings* | | $357 | $9,900 |
| American 1865-1931 | | | |
| ☐ **HALFPENNY, Joseph S.** ............ *paintings* | | | $6,600 |
| ............ *drawings* | | | $605 |
| ☐ **HALKO, Joe** ............ *sculpture* | | $750 | $2,800 |
| American b. 1940 | | | |
| ☐ **HALL, E.W.** ............ *paintings* | | | $600 |
| American 19th cent. | | | |
| ☐ **HALL, Frederick** ............ *paintings* | | $301 | $1,870 |
| English 1860-1948 | | | |
| ☐ **HALL, Frederick Garrison** ............ *paintings* | | $220 | $605 |
| American b. 1879 | | | |
| ☐ **HALL, George Henry** ............ *paintings* | | $385 | $19,800 |
| American 1825-1913 | | | |
| ☐ **HALL, George Lothian** ............ *drawings* | | | $352 |
| English 1825-1888 | | | |
| ☐ **HALL, H.R.** ............ *paintings* | | $302 | $1,320 |
| English ac. 1895-1902 | | | |
| ☐ **HALL, Harry** ............ *paintings* | | $1,430 | $25,300 |
| English ac. 1838-1886 | | | |
| ☐ **HALL, Henry Hammond** ............ *paintings* | | | $440 |
| ☐ **HALL, Horace** ............ *paintings* | | | $3,190 |
| American | | | |
| ☐ **HALL, Howard Hill** ............ *paintings* | | | $8,800 |
| American 1887-1933 | | | |
| ☐ **HALL, Lee** ............ *paintings* | | | $1,650 |
| American b. 1934 | | | |
| ☐ **HALL, Sidney** ............ *paintings* | | | $522 |

|  | | Current Price Range | |
|--|--|:---:|:---:|
|  | | Low | High |
| ☐ **HALL, Susan** ................................ *drawings* | | | $286 |
| ☐ **HALL, Thomas P.** .............................. *paintings* | | | $1,100 |
| English 19th cent. | | | |
| ☐ **HALL, Thomas Victor** ......................... *drawings* | | | $220 |
| American 20th cent. | | | |
| ☐ **HALL, W. Honywill** ............................. *paintings* | | | $1,100 |
| English 19th cent. | | | |
| ☐ **HALL, W.E.** ...................................... *paintings* | | | $192 |
| American 19th cent. | | | |
| ☐ **HALLE, Charles Edward** ...................... *paintings* | | | $1,870 |
| English 1846-1914 | | | |
| ☐ **HALLE, Noel** .................................... *paintings* | | | $4,620 |
| French 1711-1781 ................................ *drawings* | | | $770 |
| ☐ **HALLE, Samuel Baruch** ....................... *paintings* | | $4,400 | $6,050 |
| British 1824-1889 | | | |
| ☐ **HALLER, G.** ..................................... *paintings* | | | $440 |
| German 20th cent. | | | |
| ☐ **HALLER, Herman** ............................. *sculpture* | | | $300 |
| ☐ **HALLETT, Hendricks A.** ..................... *paintings* | | $100 | $4,950 |
| American 1847-1921 ................................ *drawings* | | $88 | $660 |
| ☐ **HALLEZ, Jaccques** ............................ *paintings* | | | $302 |
| ☐ **HALLEZ, Joseph** | | | |
| **(called Le Petit Borain)** ..................... *paintings* | | | $330 |
| French 1769-1840 | | | |
| ☐ **HALLEZ, Paul Antoine** ........................ *paintings* | | | $357 |
| French 19th cent. | | | |
| ☐ **HALLMAN** ........................................ *drawings* | | | $192 |
| American 20th cent. | | | |
| ☐ **HALLMARK, George** ........................... *paintings* | | $4,500 | $6,500 |
| American b. 1949 | | | |
| ☐ **HALLOWELL, Anna D.** ........................ *drawings* | | $200 | $1,500 |
| American 19th cent. | | | |
| ☐ **HALLOWELL, George Hawley** ............. *paintings* | | | $770 |
| American b. 1871 | | | |
| ☐ **HALLOWELL, Robert** ........................ *drawings* | | $44 | $770 |
| American 1886-1939 | | | |
| ☐ **HALLOWELL, W.R.** ........................... *paintings* | | $110 | $176 |
| 19th cent. | | | |
| ☐ **HALMI, Arthur** ................................. *paintings* | | | $467 |
| ........................................ *drawings* | | | $192 |
| ☐ **HALOU, Alfred Jean** ........................... *sculpture* | | | $1,760 |
| French b. 1829 | | | |
| ☐ **HALOWAY, Edward Stratton** ............... *paintings* | | | $374 |
| American d. 1939 | | | |
| ☐ **HALPEN, Francis** .............................. *paintings* | | | $2,800 |
| English 19th cent. | | | |
| ☐ **HALPERN, E.** .................................... *paintings* | | | $715 |
| British 19th cent. | | | |

| | | *Current Price Range* | |
|---|---|---|---|
| | | *Low* | *High* |
| ☐ **HALPERT, Samuel T.** ........................ *paintings* | | $330 | $7,425 |
| American 1884-1930 ..................................... *drawings* | | $220 | $440 |
| ☐ **HALS, Dirk** ......................................... *paintings* | | $8,800 | $22,000 |
| Dutch 1591-1656 | | | |
| ☐ **HALS, Jan Fransz.** ............................. *paintings* | | | $4,400 |
| Dutch d. 1650 | | | |
| ☐ **HALSALL, William Formby** ................ *paintings* | | $165 | $2,200 |
| American 1841-1919 | | | |
| ☐ **HALSTON, H.** ..................................... *paintings* | | | $385 |
| English 19th cent. | | | |
| ☐ **HALSWELLE, Keeley** ......................... *paintings* | | | $660 |
| English 1832-1891 | | | |
| ☐ **HALTER, Jean** ................................... *paintings* | | | $385 |
| ☐ **HALVERSON, Jean** ............................ *drawings* | | | $750 |
| American | | | |
| ☐ **HALVOET, H.** ..................................... *paintings* | | | $495 |
| Belgian 19th cent. | | | |
| ☐ **HALZ, Van der** ................................... *paintings* | | | $275 |
| Dutch 19th cent. | | | |
| ☐ **HALZER, E.** ......................................... *paintings* | | | $770 |
| ☐ **HAM, A.** .............................................. *paintings* | | | $198 |
| British 19th cent. | | | |
| ☐ **HAMACHER, Willy** ............................ *paintings* | | $550 | $990 |
| German 1865-1909 | | | |
| ☐ **HAMBLETT, Theora** ........................... *paintings* | | | $275 |
| ☐ **HAMBOURG, Andre** ........................... *paintings* | | $418 | $5,280 |
| French b. 1909 ......................................... *drawings* | | | $275 |
| ☐ **HAMBRIDGE, Jay** ............................. *paintings* | | $385 | $1,045 |
| American 1867-1924 ................................... *drawings* | | | $220 |
| ☐ **HAME, E.** ........................................... *paintings* | | | $275 |
| Europe late 19th cent. | | | |
| ☐ **HAMEL, Otto** ..................................... *paintings* | | | $825 |
| German 1866-1950 | | | |
| ☐ **HAMEN Y LEON, Juan van der** ........... *paintings* | | | $145,000 |
| Spanish 1596-1632 | | | |
| ☐ **HAMILTON, Carl Wilhelm de** .............. *paintings* | | | $10,450 |
| Austrian 1668-1754 | | | |
| ☐ **HAMILTON, Edgar Scudder** ................ *paintings* | | | $700 |
| American 1869-1903 | | | |
| ☐ **HAMILTON, Edward W.D.** ................... *paintings* | | $330 | $2,310 |
| American 1862/64-1943 | | | |
| ☐ **HAMILTON, Ferdinand Philipp de** ....... *paintings* | | $2,860 | $8,800 |
| Belgian 1664-1750 | | | |
| ☐ **HAMILTON, Franz de** ........................ *paintings* | | $462 | $2,200 |
| German 17th cent. | | | |
| ☐ **HAMILTON, George** ........................... *drawings* | | $165 | $330 |
| ☐ **HAMILTON, Hamilton** ........................ *paintings* | | $192 | $13,200 |
| Anglo/American 1847-1928 | | | |

|  | | Current Price Range | |
|---|---|---|---|
|  | | Low | High |
| ☐ HAMILTON, Helen ................... *paintings* | | $550 | $1,100 |
| American | | | |
| ☐ HAMILTON, Hugh Douglas ............ *paintings* | | $1,430 | $18,700 |
| Irish 1736/39-1806/08 .................... *drawings* | | | $990 |
| ☐ HAMILTON, James .................. *paintings* | | $440 | $11,550 |
| Irish/American 1819-1878 ................ *drawings* | | $200 | $275 |
| ☐ HAMILTON, John Mclure ............. *paintings* | | $137 | $825 |
| American 1853-1936 ..................... *drawings* | | $275 | $825 |
| ☐ HAMILTON, M.E. ................... *paintings* | | | $440 |
| ☐ HAMILTON, Philipp Ferdinand de ...... *paintings* | | $5,500 | $7,150 |
| Flemish c. 1664-1750 | | | |
| ☐ HAMILTON, R. ..................... *paintings* | | $242 | $440 |
| American 1877-1954 | | | |
| ☐ HAMILTON, Robert .................. *paintings* | | | $225 |
| Irish 20th cent. | | | |
| ☐ HAMILTON, S. ..................... *paintings* | | | $330 |
| ☐ HAMILTON, William ................ *paintings* | | $1,760 | $1,870 |
| English 1751-1801 | | | |
| ☐ HAMILTON, William R. .............. *paintings* | | | $3,300 |
| American b. 1910 | | | |
| ☐ HAMMAN, Edouard Jean Conrad ....... *paintings* | | | $660 |
| Belgian 1819-1888 | | | |
| ☐ HAMME, A. L. van ................. *paintings* | | | $1,045 |
| Dutch 19th cent. | | | |
| ☐ HAMME, Alexis van ................ *paintings* | | $3,630 | $5,500 |
| Belgian 1818-1875 | | | |
| ☐ HAMME, G. de .................... *paintings* | | $6,325 | $8,250 |
| Flemish 17th cent. | | | |
| ☐ HAMMER, Christian Gottlob .......... *drawings* | | | $2,640 |
| German 1779-1864 | | | |
| ☐ HAMMER, Johann J. ................ *paintings* | | $605 | $770 |
| German/American 1842-1906 ............ *drawings* | | | $385 |
| ☐ HAMMER, William ................. *paintings* | | $3,850 | $6,875 |
| Danish 1821-1889 | | | |
| ☐ HAMMERSTAD, John H. .............. *paintings* | | $110 | $1,320 |
| American 19th/20th cent. | | | |
| ☐ HAMMERSTARK ................... *paintings* | | | $550 |
| Continental 19th/20th cent. | | | |
| ☐ HAMMERSTED, H. .................. *paintings* | | | $330 |
| ☐ HAMMITT, Clawson S.L. ............ *paintings* | | | $2,750 |
| American 1857-1927 | | | |
| ☐ HAMMOCK, Earl Garland ............ *paintings* | | | $330 |
| American 1896-1974 | | | |
| ☐ HAMMOND, Arthur J. ............... *paintings* | | $55 | $825 |
| American 1875-1947 ..................... *drawings* | | $40 | $110 |
| ☐ HAMMOND, C. ..................... *drawings* | | | $1,320 |
| ☐ HAMMOND, F. ..................... *paintings* | | | $715 |
| American/English 19th cent. | | | |

| | | Current Price Range | |
|---|---|---|---|
| | | *Low* | *High* |
| ☐ **HAMMOND, John** .......................... *paintings* <br> Canadian 1843-1939 | | | $192 |
| ☐ **HAMMOND, Robert John** ................... *paintings* <br> British 19th cent. | | | $660 |
| ☐ **HAMON, Jean Louis** .......................... *paintings* <br> French 1821-1874 | | | $770 |
| ☐ **HAMPE, Guido** .......................... *paintings* <br> German b. 1839 | | $82 | $3,080 |
| ☐ **HAMPTON, John W.** .......................... *paintings* <br> American 1918-1976 ............................. *drawings* | | $137 <br> $1,400 | $9,500 <br> $5,000 |
| ☐ **HAMZA, Johann** .......................... *paintings* <br> German b. 1850 | | $3,575 | $18,700 |
| ☐ **HAN** .......................... *paintings* | | | $3,520 |
| ☐ **HANCOCK, Charles** .......................... *paintings* <br> English 1795-1868 | | $660 | $7,700 |
| ☐ **HAND, Thomas** .......................... *paintings* <br> English d. c. 1804 | | | $3,300 |
| ☐ **HANDWRIGHT, George** ................... *drawings* <br> American 1873-1951 | | | $880 |
| ☐ **HANES, E.** .......................... *paintings* | | | $880 |
| ☐ **HANGER, Max** .......................... *paintings* <br> German b. 1874 | | | $1,430 |
| ☐ **HANKE, Hans** .......................... *paintings* <br> Austrian 19th/20th cent. | | | $1,100 |
| ☐ **HANKEY, William Lee** .......................... *paintings* <br> English 1869-1952 ............................. *drawings* | | $825 | $4,730 <br> $247 |
| ☐ **HANKS, Lon** .......................... *paintings* <br> American | | | $550 |
| ☐ **HANLEN, John** .......................... *paintings* <br> b. 1922 | | | $275 |
| ☐ **HANLEY, J.B.** .......................... *paintings* <br> American ac. c. 1880 | | $1,870 | $1,980 |
| ☐ **HANLEY, N.H.** .......................... *paintings* <br> American mid 19th cent. | | $440 | $660 |
| ☐ **HANLEY, Sarah E.** .......................... *paintings* <br> d. 1958 | | $55 | $880 |
| ☐ **HANNAFORD, C.E.** .......................... *drawings* <br> British 19th cent. | | | $246 |
| ☐ **HANNEFOND, C.** .......................... *paintings* <br> French 19th cent. | | | $605 |
| ☐ **HANNEMAN, Adriaen** .......................... *paintings* <br> Dutch b. c. 1601-1671 | | $3,575 | $22,000 |
| ☐ **HANNEMANN, Walter** .......................... *paintings* <br> German b. 1863 | | | $935 |
| ☐ **HANNLEY, T.** .......................... *paintings* <br> English 19th cent. | | | $385 |
| ☐ **HANSCH, Anton** .......................... *paintings* <br> Austrian 1813-1876 | | | $4,675 |

| | | Current Price Range | |
|---|---|---|---|
| | | Low | High |
| ☐ **HANSEN, Armin Carl** ............................ *paintings* | | $1,100 | $27,500 |
| American 1886-1957 ................................ *drawings* | | $2,750 | $3,250 |
| ☐ **HANSEN, Carl Lodewyk** ...................... *paintings* | | | $4,180 |
| Dutch 1765-1840 | | | |
| ☐ **HANSEN, Ejnar** ................................... *paintings* | | $192 | $1,760 |
| Danish/American 1884-1965 | | | |
| ☐ **HANSEN, Frederick** ............................ *paintings* | | | $880 |
| American | | | |
| ☐ **HANSEN, Hans Peter** ......................... *paintings* | | $70 | $1,210 |
| Danish 1829-1899 ...................................... *drawings* | | $9 | $35 |
| ☐ **HANSEN, Harold** ............................... *drawings* | | | $247 |
| American 20th cent. | | | |
| ☐ **HANSEN, Herman W.** ........................ *drawings* | | $13,200 | $47,500 |
| American 1854-1924 | | | |
| ☐ **HANSEN, James Lee** .......................... *sculpture* | | | $935 |
| ☐ **HANSEN, Louis R.** ............................. *paintings* | | | $418 |
| ☐ **HANSEN, Niels** .................................. *paintings* | | $550 | $550 |
| Danish 1880-1946 | | | |
| ☐ **HANSEN, Sigvard Marius** .................... *paintings* | | | $3,850 |
| Danish b. 1859 | | | |
| ☐ **HANSEN, Theodor** ............................. *paintings* | | | $330 |
| German 20th cent. | | | |
| ☐ **HANSON, Duane** ............................... *drawings* | | $35,200 | $121,000 |
| American b. 1925 | | | |
| ☐ **HANSON, J.** ...................................... *paintings* | | | $385 |
| ☐ **HANSON, R.** ..................................... *paintings* | | | $220 |
| American 19th cent. | | | |
| ☐ **HANTMAN, Carl** ............................... *paintings* | | $330 | $2,200 |
| American contemporary | | | |
| ☐ **HAPPEL, T.H.** ................................... *paintings* | | | $1,045 |
| ☐ **HAQUETTE, Georges Jean Marie** ......... *drawings* | | $225 | $825 |
| French 1854-1906 | | | |
| ☐ **HARARI, Hananiah** ............................ *paintings* | | | $440 |
| American | | | |
| ☐ **HARBERT, J.** .................................... *paintings* | | | $770 |
| ☐ **HARBESON, Georgiana Brown** ............ *drawings* | | | $660 |
| American b. 1894 | | | |
| ☐ **HARBORGER, C.W.** ........................... *paintings* | | | $715 |
| Dutch 19th/20th cent. | | | |
| ☐ **HARBUTT, W.** ................................... *paintings* | | | $1,540 |
| British 19th cent. | | | |
| ☐ **HARDEGG, L.** .................................... *paintings* | | | $1,320 |
| German 19th cent. | | | |
| ☐ **HARDENBERGH, Gerard Rutgers** ....... *drawings* | | | $192 |
| American 1856-1915 | | | |
| ☐ **HARDERS, J.** .................................... *paintings* | | $450 | $5,500 |
| ☐ **HARDIE, Charles Martin** .................... *paintings* | | $330 | $1,650 |
| Scottish 1858-1917 | | | |

| | | Current Price Range | |
|---|---|---|---|
| | | *Low* | *High* |
| ☐ **HARDIE, Martin** ............................. *drawings* | | $330 | $330 |
| English 1875-1952 | | | |
| ☐ **HARDIME, Pieter** ............................. *paintings* | | $4,070 | $14,300 |
| Flemish 1677/78-c. 1758 | | | |
| ☐ **HARDING, George** ............................. *paintings* | | | $440 |
| American b. 1882 | | | |
| ☐ **HARDING, George Perfect** ................... *drawings* | | $99 | $660 |
| British 1777-1853 | | | |
| ☐ **HARDING, James Duffield** ................... *drawings* | | $77 | $605 |
| English 1798-1863 | | | |
| ☐ **HARDING, John L.** ............................. *paintings* | | $935 | $2,420 |
| American ac. 1835-1882 | | | |
| ☐ **HARDING, Joshua** ............................. *paintings* | | | $1,650 |
| English 1880-1940 | | | |
| ☐ **HARDING, Sylvester** ......................... *drawings* | | | $605 |
| ☐ **HARDING, W.** ................................. *paintings* | | | $308 |
| ☐ **HARDON, G.C.** ................................. *paintings* | | | $412 |
| American late 19th/early 20th cent | | | |
| ☐ **HARDT, Ernst** ................................. *paintings* | | | $1,430 |
| German 1869-1917 | | | |
| ☐ **HARDWICK, Melbourne Havelock** ....... *paintings* | | $137 | $3,700 |
| American 1857-1916 ................................. *drawings* | | $110 | $660 |
| ☐ **HARDY, Anna E.** ............................. *paintings* | | $330 | $1,870 |
| b. 1839 | | | |
| ☐ **HARDY, C.K.** ................................. *paintings* | | | $247 |
| English 19th cent. | | | |
| ☐ **HARDY, DeWitt** ............................. *drawings* | | $154 | $242 |
| American b. 1940 | | | |
| ☐ **HARDY, Dudley** ............................. *drawings* | | $715 | $2,750 |
| English c. 1866-1922 | | | |
| ☐ **HARDY, Frederick Daniel** ................... *paintings* | | | $3,300 |
| British 1826-1911 | | | |
| ☐ **HARDY, George** ............................. *paintings* | | | $1,430 |
| English 1822-1909 | | | |
| ☐ **HARDY, Heywood** ............................. *paintings* | | $550 | $71,500 |
| English 1843-1932 | | | |
| ☐ **HARDY, James** ............................. *paintings* | | $330 | $12,100 |
| British 1832-1889 | | | |
| ☐ **HARDY, L.** ................................. *drawings* | | | $356 |
| ☐ **HARDY, R.** ................................. *paintings* | | | $418 |
| ☐ **HARDY, Thomas Bush** ....................... *paintings* | | $800 | $1,320 |
| English 1842-1897 ................................. *drawings* | | $247 | $1,870 |
| ☐ **HARDY, Walter Manly** ....................... *drawings* | | $154 | $357 |
| American b. 1877 | | | |
| ☐ **HARDY, William F.** ......................... *paintings* | | $132 | $576 |
| American 19th/20th cent. | | | |
| ☐ **HARDY, William J.** ......................... *paintings* | | | $880 |
| English ac. 1845-1856 | | | |

| | | | Current Price Range | |
| --- | --- | --- | --- | --- |
| | | | Low | High |
| ☐ HARE, David | .................................... | sculpture | | $2,860 |
| American b. 1917 | | | | |
| ☐ HARE, John Knowles | ........................... | drawings | $71 | $200 |
| American b. 1884 | | | | |
| ☐ HARE, Julius | ..................................... | paintings | | $605 |
| British 1859-1932 | | | | |
| ☐ HARE, William | ................................... | paintings | | $12,100 |
| American ac. 1820s | | | | |
| ☐ HARENCZ, Josef | ................................ | paintings | | $220 |
| Hungarian 20th cent. | | | | |
| ☐ HARGITT, Edward | ............................ | paintings | $440 | $2,530 |
| English 1835-1895 | ................................ | drawings | $275 | $330 |
| ☐ HARGREAVES, L. | ............................ | paintings | | $220 |
| English 19th cent. | | | | |
| ☐ HARGROVE, Charles (Jr.) (Koor) | ......... | paintings | | $660 |
| contemporary | | | | |
| ☐ HARING, Keith | .................................... | paintings | $2,640 | $8,800 |
| American b. 1958 | ..................................... | drawings | $1,100 | $4,675 |
| ☐ HARINGH, Daniel | ............................. | paintings | | $2,310 |
| Flemish 1636-c. 1711/16 | | | | |
| ☐ HARIS, T. | ..................................... | paintings | $247 | $357 |
| American 19th/20th cent. | | | | |
| ☐ HARISSON, G.O. | ............................. | paintings | | $935 |
| ☐ HARKAVY, Minna R. | ......................... | sculpture | | $400 |
| ☐ HARLOFF, Guy | ................................... | drawings | $44 | $236 |
| Dutch b. 1933 | | | | |
| ☐ HARLOW, George Henry | ................... | paintings | $121 | $15,400 |
| English 1787-1819 | | | | |
| ☐ HARLOW, Louis Kinney | ...................... | drawings | $25 | $385 |
| American 1850-1930? | | | | |
| ☐ HARMAN, Fred | ................................ | paintings | | $7,000 |
| American b. 1902 | ................................... | drawings | $1,000 | $3,200 |
| ☐ HARMER, Alexander F. | ....................... | paintings | $605 | $8,800 |
| American 1856-1915 | ................................ | drawings | $440 | $3,300 |
| ☐ HARMON, Charles H. | ......................... | paintings | $165 | $412 |
| American d. 1936 | ................................... | drawings | $77 | $110 |
| ☐ HARMON, Sidney | ............................... | sculpture | | $301 |
| ☐ HARMS, A. | ..................................... | paintings | | $330 |
| ☐ HARNETT, William Michael | ............... | paintings | $1,100 | $159,500 |
| American 1848/51-1892 | .............................. | drawings | $770 | $2,860 |
| ☐ HARNEY, Paul E. | .............................. | paintings | $302 | $1,210 |
| American 1850-1915 | | | | |
| ☐ HARNISCH, Albert E. | ......................... | sculpture | | $605 |
| ☐ HARO, P. | ..................................... | paintings | | $1,210 |
| 19th/20th cent. | | | | |
| ☐ HARPER, Henry Andrew | ..................... | drawings | | $467 |
| English 1835-1900 | | | | |
| ☐ HARPER, M. | ..................................... | paintings | $330 | $356 |

## Trompe l'oeil (A Find in Maine)

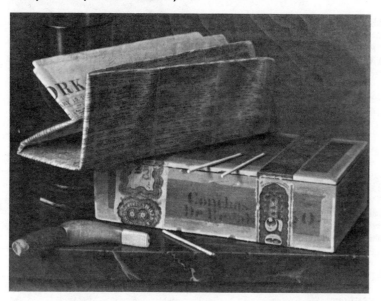

*Trompe l'oeil, literally translated as "tricking the eye," is the French term for the technique of painting so realistically that the viewer believes he or she is actually seeing the object.*

*In 1983, an attorney representing the estate of a Maine woman was asked by her children to have its contents appraised. Auctioneer James Julia was called in to do the job and spotted this painting, which he thought was the work of William Michael Harnett, the outstanding 19th-century American trompe l'oeil painter. Julia, a knowledgeable country auctioneer, took the painting to New York where a Harnett expert authenticated it as a long-lost work. (William Michael Harnett, "Still Life With Cigar Box," oil on canvas, 9½ x 13⅝ in., James Julia Auction Galleries, August 17, 1983, $82,500.)*

| | | *Current Price Range* | |
|---|---|---|---|
| | | *Low* | *High* |
| ☐ **HARPER, Margaret** ............................ *paintings* | | | **$220** |
| 20th cent. | | | |
| ☐ **HARPER, Thomas P.** ......................... *paintings* | | **$357** | **$412** |
| English 19th cent. | | | |
| ☐ **HARPIGNIES, Henri Joseph** ............... *paintings* | | **$715** | **$26,400** |
| French 1819-1916 ..................................... *drawings* | | **$88** | **$6,600** |
| ☐ **HARRADEN, Richard Banks** ............... *drawings* | | | **$330** |
| English 1778-1862 | | | |
| ☐ **HARRINGTON, E.** ............................ *paintings* | | **$44** | **$264** |
| American 20th cent. | | | |

| | Current Price Range | |
|---|---|---|
| | *Low* | *High* |
| ☐ **HARRINGTON, George** ........................ *paintings* | | $825 |
| American 1832-1911 | | |
| ☐ **HARRINGTON, James** ........................ *paintings* | | $2,800 |
| ☐ **HARRINGTON, Rufus** ........................ *paintings* | | $275 |
| American 20th cent. | | |
| ☐ **HARRIS, Charles Gordon** .................... *paintings* | $275 | $1,650 |
| American b. 1891 | | |
| ☐ **HARRIS, Charles X.** .......................... *paintings* | $1,870 | $6,050 |
| American b. 1856 | | |
| ☐ **HARRIS, E. A.** ................................. *paintings* | | $302 |
| British 19th cent. | | |
| ☐ **HARRIS, Henry** ................................ *paintings* | $220 | $1,100 |
| English 1805-1865 | | |
| ☐ **HARRIS, John Oliver** ........................ *paintings* | | $605 |
| ☐ **HARRIS, Lawren Stewart** .................... *paintings* | | $8,800 |
| Canadian 1885-1970 | | |
| ☐ **HARRIS, Robert George** ...................... *paintings* | $286 | $2,860 |
| American b. 1911 | | |
| ☐ **HARRIS, Sam Hyde** .......................... *paintings* | $275 | $850 |
| American 1889-1977 | | |
| ☐ **HARRIS, T.** ..................................... *paintings* | | $715 |
| American 19th/20th cent. | | |
| ☐ **HARRISON, Alexander** ....................... *paintings* | $440 | $5,500 |
| American 1853-1930 | | |
| ☐ **HARRISON, J.** ................................. *paintings* | | $385 |
| English 19th cent. | | |
| ☐ **HARRISON, Lowell Birge** .................... *paintings* | $176 | $27,500 |
| American 1854-1929 ................................. *drawings* | $99 | $2,750 |
| ☐ **HARRISON, Thomas Alexander** ............ *paintings* | $220 | $5,500 |
| American 1853-1930 | | |
| ☐ **HARRITON, Abraham** ........................ *paintings* | $400 | $440 |
| ☐ **HARRY, Philip** ................................ *paintings* | | $20,900 |
| Canadian ac. 1833-1857 | | |
| ☐ **HARSBURG, Carl** ............................. *paintings* | | $1,320 |
| Dutch 19th cent. | | |
| ☐ **HARSHE, Robert Bartholomew** ............ *paintings* | $137 | $935 |
| ☐ **HART, Adrian** ................................. *paintings* | | $550 |
| German 19th/20th cent. | | |
| ☐ **HART, George Overbury (Pop HART)** ... *paintings* | | $770 |
| American 1868-1933 .................................. *drawings* | $165 | $2,060 |
| ☐ **HART, James MacDougal** .................... *paintings* | $82 | $23,100 |
| American 1828-1901 | | |
| ☐ **HART, Joel Tanner** ............................ *sculpture* | | $2,200 |
| American 1810-1877 | | |
| ☐ **HART, Letitia Bennet** ........................ *paintings* | | $715 |
| American b. 1867 | | |
| ☐ **HART, Solomon Alexander** .................. *paintings* | | $467 |
| English 1806-1881 | | |

| | | *Current Price Range* | |
| --- | --- | --- | --- |
| | | Low | High |
| ☐ **HART, Thomas** ................... *paintings* | | | **$1,870** |
| English b. 1820 ......................... *drawings* | | **$88** | **$440** |
| ☐ **HART, William Howard** ..................... *paintings* | | | **$1,210** |
| American 1863-1934 | | | |
| ☐ **HART, William M.** ................. *paintings* | | **$1,650** | **$38,500** |
| American 1823-1894 ................... *drawings* | | **$75** | **$935** |
| ☐ **HARTE, Leon** ..................... *paintings* | | | **$357** |
| French 20th cent. | | | |
| ☐ **HARTFORD, William** ......................... *drawings* | | | **$467** |
| British ac. 1874-1878 | | | |
| ☐ **HARTIGAN, Grace** .......................... *paintings* | | **$1,870** | **$9,900** |
| American b. 1922 ....................... *drawings* | | **$396** | **$1,540** |
| ☐ **HARTING, G.W.** ................... *paintings* | | | **$495** |
| ☐ **HARTING, Lloyd** .............................. *drawings* | | | **$1,320** |
| American | | | |
| ☐ **HARTINGER, Gustave** ...................... *paintings* | | | **$275** |
| ☐ **HARTLAND, Henry Albert** ................ *drawings* | | **$385** | **$462** |
| Irish 1840-1893 | | | |
| ☐ **HARTLEY, Jonathan Scott** ................... *sculpture* | | **$121** | **$9,350** |
| American 1845-1912 | | | |
| ☐ **HARTLEY, Marsden** ......................... *paintings* | | **$2,750** | **$88,000** |
| American 1877-1943 ................... *drawings* | | **$550** | **$10,000** |
| ☐ **HARTLEY, Rachel V.** ......................... *paintings* | | **$121** | **$660** |
| American b. 1884 | | | |
| ☐ **HARTMAN, Bertram** ......................... *paintings* | | **$27** | **$2,640** |
| American 1882-1960 ................... *drawings* | | **$55** | **$1,000** |
| ☐ **HARTMAN, Emil Alvin** ...................... *drawings* | | **$418** | **$418** |
| American 20th cent. | | | |
| ☐ **HARTMANN, B.** ................... *paintings* | | | **$825** |
| German 19th cent. | | | |
| ☐ **HARTMANN, Friedrich Hermann** ......... *drawings* | | | **$825** |
| German School 19th cent. | | | |
| ☐ **HARTMANN, Karl** ............................ *paintings* | | | **$1,000** |
| German b. 1861 | | | |
| ☐ **HARTMANN, Ludwig** ......................... *paintings* | | **$22,000** | **$71,500** |
| German 1835-1902 | | | |
| ☐ **HARTRATH, Lucile** ......................... *paintings* | | **$418** | **$1,100** |
| American 19th/20th cent. ............................. *drawings* | | | **$110** |
| ☐ **HARTSHORNE, Howard Morton** ......... *paintings* | | | **$1,100** |
| American 19th cent. | | | |
| ☐ **HARTSON, Walter C.** ......................... *paintings* | | **$220** | **$605** |
| German b. 1866 ....................... *drawings* | | **$22** | **$275** |
| ☐ **HARTUNG, Hans** ............................ *paintings* | | **$6,600** | **$23,100** |
| German b. 1904 ....................... *drawings* | | **$1,600** | **$4,675** |
| ☐ **HARTUNG, Heinrich** ......................... *paintings* | | | **$4,070** |
| German 1851-1919 | | | |
| ☐ **HARTUNG, Johann** ............................ *paintings* | | **$660** | **$797** |
| German 19th cent. | | | |

|  | | *Current Price Range* | |
| --- | --- | --- | --- |
| | | *Low* | *High* |
| ☐ **HARTWELL** ....................... *paintings* | | | $2,475 |
| 19th cent. | | | |
| ☐ **HARTWICH, George** .......................... *paintings* | | $220 | $357 |
| ☐ **HARTWICH, Herman** .......................... *paintings* | | $137 | $3,080 |
| American 1853-1926 | | | |
| ☐ **HARTWICK, Gunther** .......................... *paintings* | | | $5,225 |
| American 1847-1857 | | | |
| ☐ **HARTWIG, Heinie** .............................. *paintings* | | $357 | $1,760 |
| American 20th cent. | | | |
| ☐ **HARVEY, A.T.** ...................................... *paintings* | | $137 | $220 |
| American 19th cent. | | | |
| ☐ **HARVEY, Eli** ....................................... *paintings* | | | $192 |
| American 1860-1957 ................................. *sculpture* | | | $1,980 |
| ☐ **HARVEY, Elisabeth** ............................ *drawings* | | | $660 |
| English ac. 1802-1812 | | | |
| ☐ **HARVEY, George** .......................... *paintings* | | $1,650 | $9,900 |
| American c. 1800-1878 ............................. *drawings* | | $2,250 | $4,400 |
| ☐ **HARVEY, George** .............................. *drawings* | | $104 | $440 |
| English 19th cent. | | | |
| ☐ **HARVEY, Gerald** | | | |
| (Gerald Harvey JONES) .......................... *paintings* | | $5,000 | $100,000 |
| American b. 1933 ...................................... *sculpture* | | $3,500 | $17,000 |
| ☐ **HARVEY, Harold** ............................... *paintings* | | | $192 |
| English 1874-1941 | | | |
| ☐ **HARVEY, Henry T.** ............................. *paintings* | | $143 | $467 |
| American 19th cent. | | | |
| ☐ **HARVEY, Henry T.** ........................... *paintings* | | | $1,210 |
| English 19th/20th cent. | | | |
| ☐ **HARVEY, James** ................................. *paintings* | | | $275 |
| American b. 1830 | | | |
| ☐ **HARVEY, Sir George** ........................... *paintings* | | | $900 |
| Scottish 1806-1876 | | | |
| ☐ **HARVEY, W.** ....................................... *paintings* | | | $330 |
| English 20th cent. | | | |
| ☐ **HASBROUCK, Du Bois Fenelon** ....... *paintings* | | $77 | $2,310 |
| American b. 1860 ...................................... *drawings* | | $77 | $308 |
| ☐ **HASCH, Carl** ....................................... *paintings* | | $2,310 | $6,325 |
| Austrian 1834/35-1897 | | | |
| ☐ **HASELEER, Frans** ............................ *paintings* | | $2,750 | $5,500 |
| Belgian 1804-1869 | | | |
| ☐ **HASELTINE, Charles Field** .................. *paintings* | | | $495 |
| American b. 1840 | | | |
| ☐ **HASELTINE, Herbert** ......................... *sculpture* | | $825 | $24,200 |
| American 1877-1962 | | | |
| ☐ **HASELTINE, William Stanley** .............. *paintings* | | $132 | $15,400 |
| American 1835-1900 ................................. *drawings* | | $467 | $5,225 |
| ☐ **HASENCLEVER, Johann Peter** ............ *paintings* | | | $2,200 |
| German 1810-1853 | | | |

| | | | Current Price Range | |
|---|---|---|---|---|
| | | | *Low* | *High* |
| ☐ **HASENETT, A.V.** ............ *paintings* | | | | $1,430 |
| American 20th cent. | | | | |
| ☐ **HASKELL, Ernest** ............ *drawings* | | | | $440 |
| 1876-1925 | | | | |
| ☐ **HASKELL, I.C.** ............ *paintings* | | | | $1,540 |
| American 19th/20th cent. | | | | |
| ☐ **HASKELL, Joseph Allen** ............ *paintings* | | | | $198 |
| American 1808-1894 | | | | |
| ☐ **HASKINS, Gayle Porter** ............ *paintings* | | | | $2,530 |
| American 1887-1962 | | | | |
| ☐ **HASSALL, John** ............ *drawings* | | | | $1,100 |
| English 1868-1948 | | | | |
| ☐ **HASSAM, Frederick Childe** ............ *paintings* | | $5,500 | | $187,000 |
| American 1859-1935 ............ *drawings* | | $3,080 | | $121,000 |
| ☐ **HASSEBUSCH, Louis** ............ *paintings* | | | | $440 |
| American b. 1863 | | | | |
| ☐ **HASSELHORST, Johann** ............ *paintings* | | | | $175 |
| 19th cent. | | | | |
| ☐ **HASSENTEUFEL, H.** ............ *paintings* | | | | $474 |
| ☐ **HASSEVENT-BACQUE, A.H.** ............ *paintings* | | | | $935 |
| ☐ **HASSMAN, Karl** ............ *drawings* | | | | $1,100 |
| American | | | | |
| ☐ **HASTINGS, George** ............ *paintings* | | | | $1,100 |
| British 19th cent. | | | | |
| ☐ **HASTINGS, Matthew** ............ *paintings* | | $110 | | $467 |
| American 1834-1919 | | | | |
| ☐ **HASTINGS, Rafael** ............ *drawings* | | $137 | | $385 |
| Peruvian b. 1945 | | | | |
| ☐ **HASWELL, C.B.** ............ *paintings* | | | | $324 |
| ☐ **HATANO, Tamajiro** ............ *paintings* | | | | $1,100 |
| Japanese 20th cent. | | | | |
| ☐ **HATCH, Alfred P.** ............ *paintings* | | | | $220 |
| American 20th cent. | | | | |
| ☐ **HATCH, Emily Nichols** ............ *paintings* | | | | $275 |
| American 20th cent. | | | | |
| ☐ **HATCH, J.F.** ............ *paintings* | | | | $302 |
| ☐ **HATFIELD, Joseph Henry** ............ *paintings* | | | | $1,210 |
| Canadian b. 1863 | | | | |
| ☐ **HATHAWAY, George M.** ............ *paintings* | | $110 | | $1,600 |
| American c. 1852-1903 ............ *drawings* | | | | $467 |
| ☐ **HATHAWAY, Rufus** ............ *paintings* | | | | $6,600 |
| 1770-1822 | | | | |
| ☐ **HAUBTMANN, Michael** ............ *paintings* | | $275 | | $2,970 |
| Czechoslovakian 1843-1921 | | | | |
| ☐ **HAUCK, Auguste C.** ............ *paintings* | | | | $357 |
| German 1742-1801 | | | | |
| ☐ **HAUEISEN, Albert** ............ *paintings* | | | | $1,650 |
| German b. 1872 | | | | |
| ☐ **HAUGENAUER, Franz** ............ *sculpture* | | $77 | | $3,960 |

| | Current Price Range | |
| --- | --- | --- |
| | Low | High |
| ☐ **HAUGHTON, Moses** .......................... *paintings* | | $1,900 |
| ☐ **HAUPT, Erik Guide** ........................... *paintings* | $121 | $4,400 |
| American b. 1891 | | |
| ☐ **HAUPT, Theodore** ............................. *paintings* | $330 | $715 |
| American b. 1902 ..................................... *drawings* | $715 | $825 |
| ☐ **HAUS, G.** ........................................... *paintings* | | $550 |
| ☐ **HAUSDORF, George** .......................... *paintings* | | $550 |
| American 20th cent. | | |
| ☐ **HAUSER, John** ................................... *paintings* | $770 | $17,000 |
| American 1858/59-1913/18 ......................... *drawings* | $935 | $15,400 |
| ☐ **HAUSER, Ludwig** .............................. *paintings* | $275 | $900 |
| German late 19th cent. | | |
| ☐ **HAUSHALTER, George M.** ................. *paintings* | | $250 |
| American b. 1862 | | |
| ☐ **HAUSKNECHT, O.** ............................ *paintings* | | $412 |
| ☐ **HAUSNER, M.** .................................... *paintings* | | $1,210 |
| ☐ **HAUTRIVE, Mathilde Marguerite** ......... *paintings* | | $550 |
| French 1881-1963 | | |
| ☐ **HAVARD, James Pinkney** ................... *paintings* | $825 | $34,100 |
| American b. 1937 | | |
| ☐ **HAVELL, Alfred Charles** .................... *paintings* | $1,045 | $1,650 |
| British ac. 1878-1884 | | |
| ☐ **HAVELL, Edmund (Jr.)** ....................... *paintings* | $6,000 | $8,250 |
| English 1819-after 1895 | | |
| ☐ **HAVELL, Robert** ............................... *paintings* | $1,760 | $33,000 |
| American 1793-1878 | | |
| ☐ **HAVENITH, Hugo** ............................. *paintings* | | $385 |
| ☐ **HAVERMAN, Hendrick Johannes** ......... *paintings* | $495 | $1,760 |
| Dutch 1857-1928 | | |
| ☐ **HAW** ................................................ *paintings* | | $467 |
| English 19th cent. | | |
| ☐ **HAWKER, Thomas** ............................ *paintings* | | $1,100 |
| English c. 1640-c. 1725 | | |
| ☐ **HAWKINS, Henry** .............................. *paintings* | | $6,325 |
| British ac. 1820-1881 | | |
| ☐ **HAWKINS, J.** ..................................... *paintings* | | $330 |
| British 19th cent. | | |
| ☐ **HAWKINS, John** ............................... *paintings* | | $300 |
| American 20th cent. | | |
| ☐ **HAWKINS, Lewis Weldon** ................... *paintings* | | $1,650 |
| British d. 1910 ........................................ *drawings* | $275 | $1,100 |
| ☐ **HAWLEY, Hughson** .......................... *drawings* | | $2,200 |
| American 1850-1936 | | |
| ☐ **HAWORTH, T. (?)** ............................. *paintings* | | $2,090 |
| English 19th cent. | | |
| ☐ **HAWTHORNE, Charles Webster** ......... *paintings* | $467 | $93,500 |
| American 1872-1930 ................................. *drawings* | $385 | $770 |
| ☐ **HAY, Bernardo** ................................. *paintings* | | $412 |
| British b. 1864 | | |

| | | | Current Price Range | |
|---|---|---|---|---|
| | | | Low | High |
| ☐ **HAYDEN, Carl** ............................ *paintings* | | | | $715 |
| 19th cent. | | | | |
| ☐ **HAYDEN, Charles H.** ...................... *paintings* | | | $220 | $2,970 |
| American 1856-1901 ........................... *drawings* | | | | $110 |
| ☐ **HAYDEN, Edward Parker** .............. *paintings* | | | $275 | $1,100 |
| American d. 1922 | | | | |
| ☐ **HAYDEN, Henri** ........................... *paintings* | | | $495 | $22,000 |
| French 1883-1970 ............................. *drawings* | | | $192 | $4,840 |
| ☐ **HAYDON, Benjamin Robert** ............ *drawings* | | | | $495 |
| English 1786-1846 | | | | |
| ☐ **HAYERDAHL, Hans** ...................... *paintings* | | | | $7,480 |
| 19th cent. | | | | |
| ☐ **HAYES, Barton S.** ......................... *paintings* | | | $2,090 | $8,250 |
| American 19th/20th cent. | | | | |
| ☐ **HAYES, Claude** ........................... *drawings* | | | $242 | $275 |
| Irish 1852-1922 | | | | |
| ☐ **HAYES, Edwin** ............................ *paintings* | | | $220 | $3,080 |
| Irish 1819/20-1904 ........................... *drawings* | | | | $385 |
| ☐ **HAYES, Ernest** ........................... *paintings* | | | | $522 |
| ☐ **HAYES, George A.** ....................... *paintings* | | | | $275 |
| American ac. 1860 | | | | |
| ☐ **HAYES, Michael Angelo** ............... *drawings* | | | | $550 |
| Irish 1820-1877 | | | | |
| ☐ **HAYES, W. J.** .............................. *paintings* | | | | $935 |
| ☐ **HAYLLAR, James** ......................... *paintings* | | | $990 | $17,600 |
| British b. 1829 | | | | |
| ☐ **HAYNES, John William** .................. *paintings* | | | | $3,960 |
| British ac. 1852-82 | | | | |
| ☐ **HAYNES-WILLIAMS, John** ............. *paintings* | | | $110 | $1,100 |
| English 1836-1908 | | | | |
| ☐ **HAYS, George Arthur** ................... *paintings* | | | $110 | $850 |
| American b. 1854 ............................. *drawings* | | | | $132 |
| ☐ **HAYS, J.H.** ................................ *paintings* | | | | $1,980 |
| American 19th cent. | | | | |
| ☐ **HAYS, William Jacob** ................... *paintings* | | | $357 | $31,900 |
| American 1830-1875 .......................... *drawings* | | | | $220 |
| ☐ **HAYTER, Charles** ........................ *paintings* | | | | $286 |
| ................................................. *drawings* | | | | $825 |
| ☐ **HAYTER, George** ......................... *paintings* | | | $2,200 | $2,750 |
| English 1792-1871 | | | | |
| ☐ **HAYTER, Stanley William** .............. *paintings* | | | $550 | $1,210 |
| English b. 1901 .............................. *drawings* | | | $308 | $1,320 |
| ☐ **HAYWARD, Peter** ........................ *paintings* | | | $165 | $247 |
| American b. 1905 | | | | |
| ☐ **HAYWARD, Roger** ........................ *paintings* | | | $44 | $330 |
| American 20th cent. .......................... *drawings* | | | $110 | $385 |
| ☐ **HAYWOOD, W.C.** ......................... *paintings* | | | | $330 |
| British 19th cent. | | | | |

| | | Current Price Range | |
|---|---|---|---|
| | | Low | High |
| □ **HAZARD, Arthur Merton** ............ *paintings* | | **$192** | **$3,575** |
| American 1872-1930 ............ *drawings* | | | **$220** |
| □ **HAZARD, W.** ............ *paintings* | | **$247** | **$275** |
| European 19th cent. | | | |
| □ **HAZELTINE, Herbert** ............ *sculpture* | | | **$5,280** |
| 1877-1962 | | | |
| □ **HAZELTON, Mary Brewster** ............ *paintings* | | **$110** | **$550** |
| American early 20th cent. | | | |
| □ **HAZELZET** ............ *paintings* | | **$198** | **$231** |
| American 20th cent. | | | |
| □ **HEAD, H. Lilian** ............ *paintings* | | | **$300** |
| □ **HEAD, J.** ............ *paintings* | | | **$220** |
| American 19th cent. | | | |
| □ **HEADE, Martin Johnson** ............ *paintings* | | **$2,640** | **$341,000** |
| American 1819-1904 | | | |
| □ **HEALY, George Peter Alexander** ............ *paintings* | | **$220** | **$22,000** |
| American 1808/13-1894 | | | |
| □ **HEARD, James** ............ *paintings* | | **$1,815** | **$3,500** |
| British 1799-1859 | | | |
| □ **HEARTLEY, Rachel** ............ *paintings* | | | **$275** |
| American b. 1884 | | | |
| □ **HEATH, E. Howell** ............ *paintings* | | **$330** | **$330** |
| □ **HEATH, Frank Gascoigne** ............ *paintings* | | | **$880** |
| □ **HEATH, Frank L.** ............ *paintings* | | **$275** | **$935** |
| American 1857-1921 | | | |
| □ **HEATH, W.A.** ............ *paintings* | | | **$275** |
| American 19th cent. | | | |
| □ **HEATH, William (called Paul PRY)** ....... *drawings* | | **$330** | **$1,540** |
| English 1795-1840 | | | |
| □ **HEATON, Augustus George Goodyear** .. *paintings* | | | **$2,640** |
| American 1844-1930 | | | |
| □ **HEATON, John** | | | |
| **(of Albany) (The Wendell Limner)** ......... *paintings* | | | **$2,750** |
| American 18th cent. | | | |
| □ **HEBALD, Milton Ebling** ............ *drawings* | | | **$247** |
| American b. 1917 ............ *sculpture* | | **$352** | **$1,430** |
| □ **HEBERT, Georges** ............ *paintings* | | | **$770** |
| French 1837-84 | | | |
| □ **HEBERT, Jules** ............ *paintings* | | | **$246** |
| Swiss 1812-1878 ............ *drawings* | | | **$247** |
| □ **HECHEIM, J.** ............ *paintings* | | | **$175** |
| German 20th cent. | | | |
| □ **HECHT, Joseph** ............ *paintings* | | | **$220** |
| German 20th cent. | | | |
| □ **HECHT, Zoltan** ............ *paintings* | | | **$192** |
| Hungarian/American 1890-1968 ............ *drawings* | | | **$220** |
| □ **HECKEL, August von** ............ *paintings* | | | **$2,750** |
| German 1824-1883 | | | |

| | | Current Price Range | |
|---|---|---|---|
| | | Low | High |
| ☐ **HECKEL, Erich** ................................. *paintings* | | | $60,500 |
| German 1883-1970 ................................ *drawings* | | $440 | $13,200 |
| ☐ **HECKENDORF, Franz** ...................... *paintings* | | | $3,250 |
| German 1888-1962 | | | |
| ☐ **HECKMAN, Albert** .......................... *paintings* | | | $286 |
| ☐ **HEDA, Gerrit Willemsz** ..................... *paintings* | | | $14,300 |
| Dutch b. before 1702 | | | |
| ☐ **HEDEGAARD** ................................... *paintings* | | | $250 |
| ☐ **HEDGES, Danforth** ........................... *paintings* | | | $300 |
| American b. 1878 | | | |
| ☐ **HEDGES, W.S.** .................................. *paintings* | | $26,400 | $37,400 |
| American | | | |
| ☐ **HEDING, G.** ...................................... *paintings* | | | $522 |
| ☐ **HEDLEY, F.** ...................................... *paintings* | | | $192 |
| English 19th/20th cent. | | | |
| ☐ **HEDOUIN, Edmond** ........................... *paintings* | | | $880 |
| French 1820-1889 | | | |
| ☐ **HEELSTONE, B.** ................................ *paintings* | | | $495 |
| ☐ **HEEM, Cornelis de** ............................ *paintings* | | $11,000 | $44,000 |
| Dutch 1631-1695 | | | |
| ☐ **HEEM, Jan Davidsz de** ...................... *paintings* | | $6,600 | $220,000 |
| Dutch 1606-c. 1684 | | | |
| ☐ **HEEMSKERCK, Egbert van** ................ *paintings* | | $165 | $5,500 |
| Dutch 1634-1704 | | | |
| ☐ **HEEMSKERCK VAN BEEST,** | | | |
| **Jacob Eduard van** ............................. *paintings* | | | $2,640 |
| Dutch 1828-1894 | | | |
| ☐ **HEEREMANS, Thomas** ...................... *paintings* | | $2,310 | $38,000 |
| Dutch c. 1640-1697 | | | |
| ☐ **HEEREN, Minna** ............................... *paintings* | | | $9,075 |
| German 1823-1898 | | | |
| ☐ **HEERSCHOP, Hendrik** ...................... *paintings* | | $1,980 | $3,300 |
| Flemish 1620-1672 | | | |
| ☐ **HEERUP, Henry** ............................... *sculpture* | | | $466 |
| ☐ **HEES, Gerrit van** ............................. *paintings* | | $6,050 | $11,000 |
| Flemish 1629-before 1702 | | | |
| ☐ **HEFFNER, Karl** ................................ *paintings* | | $550 | $6,600 |
| German 1849-1925 | | | |
| ☐ **HEGENBARTH, Emanuel** ................... *paintings* | | | $3,850 |
| German b. 1868 | | | |
| ☐ **HEGENBARTH, Ernst** ........................ *sculpture* | | | $632 |
| Austrian | | | |
| ☐ **HEGER, Heinrich Anton** ..................... *paintings* | | $1,100 | $2,860 |
| German 1832-1888 | | | |
| ☐ **HEIDE, Johannes Wilhelm van der** ....... *paintings* | | | $990 |
| ☐ **HEIDEPRIEM, Johannes** ..................... *sculpture* | | | $935 |
| German late 19th/early 20th cent | | | |
| ☐ **HEIGH, William Robinson** ................... *paintings* | | | $1,210 |
| American early 20th cent. | | | |

| | | Current Price Range | |
|---|---|---|---|
| | | Low | High |
| ☐ **HEIKKA, Earle E.** ............................ *sculpture* | | $550 | $7,150 |
| American 1910-1941 | | | |
| ☐ **HEIL, Charles Emile** ......................... *paintings* | | $55 | $253 |
| American 1870-1953 ................................. *drawings* | | $77 | $660 |
| ☐ **HEILAND, Max** ................................... *paintings* | | | $600 |
| ☐ **HEILBUTH, Ferdinand** ....................... *paintings* | | $1,100 | $4,950 |
| French 1826-1889 ..................................... *drawings* | | $715 | $8,800 |
| ☐ **HEILMAYER, Karl** ............................ *paintings* | | $2,420 | $3,080 |
| German 1829-1908 | | | |
| ☐ **HEIM, Heinz** ........................................ *paintings* | | | $1,980 |
| German 1859-1895 | | | |
| ☐ **HEIMER, C.** ........................................ *paintings* | | | $550 |
| German 19th cent. | | | |
| ☐ **HEIMERDINGER, Friedrich** ............... *paintings* | | $1,210 | $3,850 |
| German 1817-82 | | | |
| ☐ **HEIMERL, Josef** ................................. *paintings* | | $154 | $495 |
| Austrian 19th/20th cent. | | | |
| ☐ **HEIMIG, Walter** ................................. *paintings* | | | $605 |
| German b. 1881 | | | |
| ☐ **HEIN, Alois Raimond** ......................... *paintings* | | | $880 |
| Austrian b. 1852 | | | |
| ☐ **HEIN, E.** ............................................. *paintings* | | | $356 |
| German late 19th cent. | | | |
| ☐ **HEIN, Heindrik Jan** ............................ *paintings* | | | $825 |
| Dutch 1822-1866 | | | |
| ☐ **HEINE, F.** ........................................... *paintings* | | | $2,420 |
| Belgian/Dutch 19th cent. | | | |
| ☐ **HEINE, Friedrich Wilhelm** ................... *drawings* | | | $412 |
| German/American 1845-1921 | | | |
| ☐ **HEINE, Johann Adalbert** ..................... *paintings* | | | $2,200 |
| German 19th cent. | | | |
| ☐ **HEINE, Wilhelm Josef** ......................... *paintings* | | | $2,200 |
| German 1813-1839 | | | |
| ☐ **HEINEFETTER, Johannn** .................... *paintings* | | $1,200 | $2,750 |
| German 1815-1902 | | | |
| ☐ **HEINEKEN, Maria** ............................. *paintings* | | | $660 |
| Dutch 19th/20th cent. | | | |
| ☐ **HEINEL, Eduard** ................................. *paintings* | | | $4,400 |
| German 1835-1895 | | | |
| ☐ **HEINISCH, Karl Adam** ........................ *paintings* | | $2,640 | $9,900 |
| German 1847-1927 | | | |
| ☐ **HEINRICH, Franz** ............................... *paintings* | | | $2,200 |
| Austrian 1802-1890 ..................................... *drawings* | | $1,100 | $8,250 |
| ☐ **HEINRICH, Roy F.** ............................. *drawings* | | | $495 |
| ☐ **HEINSBERGEN, A.B.** ........................... *paintings* | | $302 | $412 |
| American 20th cent. | | | |
| ☐ **HEINSIUS, Joseph** ............................. *paintings* | | | $3,575 |
| ☐ **HEINTZ, Joseph (the younger)** .............. *paintings* | | | $33,000 |
| Swiss c. 1600- c. 1678 | | | |

| | Current Price Range | |
|---|---|---|
| | *Low* | *High* |
| ☐ **HEINTZ, Joseph (the elder)** ................. *paintings* <br> Swiss 1564-1609 | $1,210 | $5,500 |
| ☐ **HEINTZELMAN, Cranston** ................. *sculpture* <br> American 20th cent. | | $440 |
| ☐ **HEINZ, Bruno** .................................... *paintings* <br> British 19th/20th cent. | | $715 |
| ☐ **HEINZ, Charles Lloyd** .......................... *drawings* <br> American b. 1885 | | $192 |
| ☐ **HEINZ, D.** .......................................... *paintings* | $935 | $2,750 |
| ☐ **HEINZMAN, Louis** ............................. *paintings* <br> American 20th cent. | $357 | $357 |
| ☐ **HEISS, G.** ........................................... *paintings* <br> German 19th cent. | | $522 |
| ☐ **HEISS, Johann** .................................. *paintings* <br> German 1640-1704 | $880 | $3,300 |
| ☐ **HEITH, V.** .......................................... *paintings* <br> American | | $275 |
| ☐ **HEIZER, Michael** ............................... *sculpture* <br> American b. 1944 | | $66,000 |
| ☐ **HEKKING, Joseph Antonio** ................. *paintings* <br> American 1859-1885 | $250 | $3,575 |
| ☐ **HELBIG, Bud** ..................................... *paintings* <br> American b. 1915 ..................................... *drawings* | <br> $250 | $3,000 <br> $800 |
| ☐ **HELBIG, J.R.** ...................................... *paintings* | | $495 |
| ☐ **HELBURN, Armand F.J.** ..................... *paintings* | | $450 |
| ☐ **HELCK, Peter** ................................... *drawings* <br> American b. 1893 | $220 | $1,760 |
| ☐ **HELD, Al** ........................................... *paintings* <br> American b. 1928 ..................................... *drawings* | $2,860 <br> $715 | $33,000 <br> $4,180 |
| ☐ **HELD, Anne** ..................................... *drawings* <br> American 20th cent. | | $247 |
| ☐ **HELD, John (Jr.)** ............................... *paintings* <br> American 1889-1958 ............................. *drawings* <br> ................................................. *sculpture* | <br> $82 | $3,300 <br> $1,430 <br> $247 |
| ☐ **HELDER, Johannes** ............................ *paintings* <br> Dutch 1842-1913 | | $522 |
| ☐ **HELDNER, Collette** ........................... *paintings* <br> American 20th cent. | $357 | $357 |
| ☐ **HELDNER, Knute** .............................. *paintings* <br> American 1886-1952 | $577 | $2,475 |
| ☐ **HELFENSTELLER, Veronica** .............. *drawings* | $71 | $302 |
| ☐ **HELFFERICH, Francois** ...................... *paintings* | | $1,760 |
| ☐ **HELIGE** ............................................. *paintings* <br> German 19th cent. | | $440 |
| ☐ **HELIKER, John Edward** ...................... *paintings* <br> American b. 1909 ..................................... *drawings* | $300 <br> $176 | $1,925 <br> $605 |
| ☐ **HELION, Jean** .................................... *paintings* <br> French b. 1904 ....................................... *drawings* | $2,420 <br> $1,870 | $4,400 <br> $13,200 |

| | | Current Price Range | |
|---|---|---|---|
| | | Low | High |
| ☐ **HELL, Louis** ......................... *drawings* | | $550 | $935 |
| French 19th/20th cent. | | | |
| ☐ **HELLBUSCH, H.** ........................... *paintings* | | | $528 |
| ☐ **HELLEMANS, Pierre Jean** ................... *paintings* | | | $3,850 |
| Belgian 1787-1845 | | | |
| ☐ **HELLEN, Carl von der** ......................... *paintings* | | | $1,210 |
| Dutch 1843-1902 | | | |
| ☐ **HELLER, Edward** ............................... *paintings* | | $440 | $550 |
| European 19th cent. | | | |
| ☐ **HELLER, John M.** ............................... *paintings* | | $357 | $1,760 |
| American ac. 1928-1962 | | | |
| ☐ **HELLER, S.** ......................................... *paintings* | | | $176 |
| American 20th cent. | | | |
| ☐ **HELLESEN, Thorvald** ...................... *paintings* | | | $3,300 |
| ☐ **HELLEU, Paul Cesar** ......................... *paintings* | | $4,950 | $55,000 |
| French 1859-1927 ................................ *drawings* | | $220 | $34,100 |
| ☐ **HELLGREWE, Rudolph** ...................... *paintings* | | | $605 |
| ................................................................ *drawings* | | | $154 |
| ☐ **HELLMAN, S.** ...................................... *paintings* | | | $495 |
| ☐ **HELLNER, J.** ...................................... *paintings* | | | $357 |
| German 19th cent. | | | |
| ☐ **HELLWAG, Rudolf** ............................ *paintings* | | | $550 |
| German 1867-1842 | | | |
| ☐ **HELMICK, Howard** ............................ *paintings* | | $550 | $3,300 |
| American 1845-1907 | | | |
| ☐ **HELMONT, Lucas van Gassel** .............. *paintings* | | | $5,500 |
| Flemish 1480/1500-c. 1570 | | | |
| ☐ **HELMONT, Matthew van** ................... *paintings* | | | $3,520 |
| Flemish 17th cent. | | | |
| ☐ **HELSBY, Alfredo** ............................... *paintings* | | $880 | $8,800 |
| Chilean ac. c. 1889-1931 ............................ *drawings* | | | $1,045 |
| ☐ **HELST, Bartholomeus van der** .............. *paintings* | | | $2,500 |
| Dutch 1611/13-1670 | | | |
| ☐ **HELYI, Vasar** ...................................... *paintings* | | | $325 |
| Hungarian b. 1908 | | | |
| ☐ **HEMESSEN, Jan van** ........................ *paintings* | | | $22,000 |
| Flemish c. 1504-1566 | | | |
| ☐ **HEMING, Arthur** ............................... *drawings* | | | $357 |
| Canadian b. 1870 | | | |
| ☐ **HEMSLEY, William** ............................ *paintings* | | $990 | $3,300 |
| English b. 1819; ac. 1848-1893 | | | |
| ☐ **HEMY, Bernard Benedict** ................... *paintings* | | $210 | $7,150 |
| English ac. 1875-1910; d. 1913 | | | |
| ☐ **HEMY, Charles Napier** ....................... *paintings* | | $495 | $8,250 |
| British 1841-1917 | | | |
| ☐ **HENDERSON, Arthur E.** ................... *paintings* | | | $6,050 |
| British 19th cent. | | | |
| ☐ **HENDERSON, Charles Cooper** ............. *paintings* | | $495 | $16,500 |
| English 1803-1877 ...................................... *drawings* | | $286 | $330 |

| | Current Price Range | |
|---|---|---|
| | *Low* | *High* |
| ☐ **HENDERSON, John** .......................... *paintings* | | $1,430 |
| ☐ **HENDERSON, W.S.P.** ........................ *paintings* | $165 | $450 |
| English 19th cent. | | |
| ☐ **HENDON, S.** ......................................... *paintings* | | $770 |
| ☐ **HENDRICH, Hermann** ...................... *paintings* | | $1,320 |
| German 1856-1931 | | |
| ☐ **HENDRICKS, T.** ................................. *paintings* | | $275 |
| Dutch 19th cent. | | |
| ☐ **HENDRICKX, J.** ................................. *paintings* | | $1,600 |
| ☐ **HENDRIKS, Gerardus** ........................ *paintings* | $2,475 | $3,300 |
| Dutch 19th cent. | | |
| ☐ **HENDRIKS, Johannes** ......................... *paintings* | | $275 |
| Dutch 19th cent. | | |
| ☐ **HENDRIKS, Willem** ............................ *paintings* | $660 | $1,320 |
| Dutch 1828-1891 | | |
| ☐ **HENDRIX, Jimi** ................................... *drawings* | | $2,500 |
| American 1942-1970 | | |
| ☐ **HENDSCHEL, Ottomar** ........................ *paintings* | | $605 |
| German b. 1845 | | |
| ☐ **HENE, A.** ............................................ *paintings* | | $1,320 |
| ☐ **HENKES, Gerke** ................................ *paintings* | | $330 |
| ☐ **HENLEY, Henry W.** ............................ *paintings* | | $880 |
| British ac. 1891-1894 | | |
| ☐ **HENLEY, W.B.** ................................... *paintings* | | $660 |
| English ac. 1854-1856 | | |
| ☐ **HENN, M.R.** ....................................... *drawings* | | $495 |
| Continental 19th cent. | | |
| ☐ **HENNEBICQ, Andre** ........................... *paintings* | | $8,250 |
| Belgian 1836-1904 | | |
| ☐ **HENNER, Jean Jacques** ....................... *paintings* | $605 | $29,700 |
| French 1829-1905 | | |
| ☐ **HENNESSEY, J.** .................................. *paintings* | | $11,000 |
| 19th cent. | | |
| ☐ **HENNESSY, William John** ................... *paintings* | $550 | $24,200 |
| Irish/American 1839-1917 | | |
| ☐ **HENNING, Albin** ............................... *paintings* | | $605 |
| American 20th cent. | | |
| ☐ **HENNINGS, Ernest Martin** .................. *paintings* | $880 | $75,000 |
| American 1886-1956 ................................... *drawings* | $8,000 | $20,000 |
| ☐ **HENNINGS, Johann Friedrich** ............. *paintings* | | $1,870 |
| German 1838-1899 | | |
| ☐ **HENRI, Jules** ..................................... *paintings* | | $302 |
| French 20th cent. | | |
| ☐ **HENRI, Robert** ................................... *paintings* | $522 | $68,750 |
| American 1865-1929 ................................. *drawings* | $132 | $12,100 |
| ☐ **HENRICI, John H.** .............................. *paintings* | $247 | $2,750 |
| American b. 1839 ..................................... *drawings* | $330 | $522 |
| ☐ **HENRION, Armand Francois Joseph** ..... *paintings* | $308 | $2,310 |
| French b. 1875 | | |

| | Current Price Range | |
|---|---|---|
| | *Low* | *High* |
| ☐ **HENRIOT, Camille** ............... *paintings* | | $330 |
| ☐ **HENRY, Bernard Benedict** ............ *paintings* | | $2,420 |
| English ac. 1875 | | |
| ☐ **HENRY, D.M.** ............ *drawings* | $770 | $2,420 |
| British 20th cent. | | |
| ☐ **HENRY, Edward Lamson** ............ *paintings* | $440 | $176,000 |
| American 1841-1919 ............ *drawings* | $44 | $15,400 |
| ☐ **HENRY, John** ............ *sculpture* | | $1,760 |
| American b. 1943 | | |
| ☐ **HENRY, Michel** ............ *paintings* | $247 | $2,090 |
| French b. 1928 | | |
| ☐ **HENRY, William** ............ *paintings* | | $770 |
| British 1812-1884 | | |
| ☐ **HENSHAW, Fredrich Henry** ............ *paintings* | | $847 |
| 1807-1891 | | |
| ☐ **HENSHAW, Glen Cooper** ............ *drawings* | $192 | $550 |
| American 1885-1946 | | |
| ☐ **HENZELL, Isaac** ............ *paintings* | | $3,850 |
| British ac. 1854-1875 | | |
| ☐ **HEPPER, G.** ............ *paintings* | | $605 |
| British 19th cent. | | |
| ☐ **HEPPLE, Wilson** ............ *paintings* | | $412 |
| English 19th cent. | | |
| ☐ **HEPWORTH, Barbara** ............ *drawings* | | $1,980 |
| English 1903-1975 ............ *sculpture* | $6,600 | $26,400 |
| ☐ **HERBE, Tim** ............ *paintings* | | $880 |
| Belgian 19th cent. | | |
| ☐ **HERBERER, C.** ............ *paintings* | | $440 |
| ☐ **HERBERT, Alfred** ............ *paintings* | | $1,045 |
| British d. 1861 | | |
| ☐ **HERBERT, Emile** ............ *sculpture* | | $1,430 |
| ☐ **HERBERT, Harold B.** ............ *drawings* | | $495 |
| Australian 20th cent. | | |
| ☐ **HERBERT, James** ............ *drawings* | | $286 |
| ☐ **HERBERT, John Robert** ............ *paintings* | | $1,430 |
| British 1810-1890 | | |
| ☐ **HERBERT, Sidney** ............ *paintings* | | $357 |
| ............ *drawings* | | $50 |
| ☐ **HERBERTE, E.B.** ............ *paintings* | $385 | $8,250 |
| British ac. c. 1870-1880 ............ *drawings* | | $467 |
| ☐ **HERBIG, Otto** ............ *paintings* | | $3,300 |
| German b. 1889 | | |
| ☐ **HERBIN, Auguste** ............ *paintings* | $4,400 | $36,300 |
| French 1882-1960 ............ *drawings* | $1,320 | $8,800 |
| ☐ **HERBO, Leon** ............ *paintings* | $495 | $3,000 |
| Belgian 1850-1907 ............ *drawings* | | $27 |
| ☐ **HERBST, Frank** ............ *paintings* | | $440 |
| American 20th cent. | | |

| | | Current Price Range | |
|---|---|---|---|
| | | *Low* | *High* |
| ☐ **HERBSTHOFFER, Charles Peter** .......... *paintings* <br> Austrian 1821-1876 | | $660 | $2,970 |
| ☐ **HERBSTOFFER, Peter Rudolph Carl** ... *paintings* <br> French 1821-1876 | | | $1,870 |
| ☐ **HERDLE, George** ............................... *drawings* | | | $385 |
| ☐ **HEREAU, Jules** ................................... *paintings* <br> French 1839-1879 ........................................ *drawings* | | | $2,860 <br> $187 |
| ☐ **HERGENRODER, Emile** ...................... *paintings* <br> American d. 1925 | | $440 | $880 |
| ☐ **HERGER, Edmund** ............................ *paintings* <br> German 1860-1907 | | | $4,675 |
| ☐ **HERGESHEIMER, Ella S.** .................. *paintings* <br> American 1873-1943 | | $247 | $250 |
| ☐ **HERGET, H.** ...................................... *paintings* <br> 20th cent. | | $275 | $385 |
| ☐ **HERING, George Edwards** .................. *paintings* <br> English 1805-1879 | | $1,870 | $19,800 |
| ☐ **HERING, Harry** ................................. *paintings* <br> American b. 1887 | | $165 | $192 |
| ☐ **HERING, W. H.** ............................... *paintings* <br> English 19th cent. | | | $1,650 |
| ☐ **HERINK, F.** ...................................... *paintings* | | | $742 |
| ☐ **HERKELMAN, Rudolf** ........................ *paintings* <br> Dutch 20th cent. | | $825 | $1,100 |
| ☐ **HERKOMER, Hubert von** .................... *paintings* <br> German/English 1849-1914 ........................... *drawings* | | $1,100 <br> $286 | $2,860 <br> $2,420 |
| ☐ **HERMANN, Emil** ............................ *drawings* <br> American 19th/20th cent. | | | $302 |
| ☐ **HERMANN, Hans** ............................. *paintings* <br> German 1813-1890 | | | $3,300 |
| ☐ **HERMANN, Heinrich** ........................ *paintings* <br> German b. 1831 | | | $2,090 |
| ☐ **HERMANN, Leo** ............................... *paintings* <br> French 1853-1927 | | $550 | $12,000 |
| ☐ **HERMANN, Ludwig** ......................... *paintings* <br> German 1812-1881 | | $3,080 | $9,900 |
| ☐ **HERMANNS, Heinrich** ...................... *paintings* <br> German 1862-1942 ..................................... *drawings* | | $4,950 | $16,500 <br> $825 |
| ☐ **HERMANS, Charles** ........................... *paintings* <br> Belgian b. 1839 | | | $1,650 |
| ☐ **HERMELIN, Olaf** ............................. *paintings* <br> Swedish 1820-1913 | | $605 | $770 |
| ☐ **HERMISTON, Haig J.** .......................... *paintings* <br> French 19th cent. | | | $495 |
| ☐ **HERNANDEZ, Daniel** .......................... *paintings* <br> Peruvian 1856-1932 | | $385 | $27,500 |
| ☐ **HERNANDEZ, J.** ............................... *paintings* | | | $2,200 |
| ☐ **HERNANDEZ, Manuel** ........................ *paintings* <br> b. Colombia 1928 | | | $2,200 |

| | Current Price Range | |
|---|---|---|
| | Low | High |
| ☐ **HERNANDEZ CRUZ, Luis** ............... *paintings* <br> Puerto Rican b. 1936 | $770 | $880 |
| ☐ **HEROLD, Wilhelm** ........................... *paintings* <br> Danish b. 1865 | | $742 |
| ☐ **HERON, James** ................................ *paintings* | | $330 |
| ☐ **HERON, Patrick** ............................... *drawings* <br> English b. 1920 | $192 | $275 |
| ☐ **HERP, William van (the elder)** .............. *paintings* <br> Flemish 1614-1677 | $2,200 | $18,700 |
| ☐ **HERPEL, Franz** ............................... *paintings* | | $880 |
| ☐ **HERPFER, Carl** ............................... *paintings* <br> German 1836-1897 | $3,080 | $28,600 |
| ☐ **HERRAN, Pedro Alcantara** .................. *drawings* <br> Latin American | | $990 |
| ☐ **HERRAN, Saturnino** .......................... *drawings* <br> Mexican 1887-1918 | | $3,300 |
| ☐ **HERRERA, M.** ................................ *paintings* | | $3,410 |
| ☐ **HERRERA, Velino Shije** ...................... *paintings* <br> American Indian 1902-1973 | $396 | $770 |
| ☐ **HERREROS, C.** ............................... *paintings* <br> Spanish 19th/20th cent. | $1,045 | $1,540 |
| ☐ **HERRICK, Henry W.** ......................... *paintings* <br> b. 1824 ........................................ *drawings* | | $330 <br> $550 |
| ☐ **HERRICK, Margaret Cox** .................... *paintings* <br> American b. 1865 ............................... *drawings* | $165 <br> $137 | $275 <br> $330 |
| ☐ **HERRIMAN, George** .......................... *drawings* <br> 1880-1944 | $275 | $1,980 |
| ☐ **HERRING, Adolf** .............................. *paintings* <br> German b. 1863 | | $330 |
| ☐ **HERRING, Benjamin** ......................... *paintings* <br> British 19th cent. | $1,980 | $41,800 |
| ☐ **HERRING, James** ............................ *paintings* <br> American b. 1796 | | $3,025 |
| ☐ **HERRING, John Frederick (Jr.)** ............ *paintings* <br> British 1815-1907 | $1,210 | $33,000 |
| ☐ **HERRING, John Frederick (Sr.)** ............ *paintings* <br> British 1795-1865 | $1,760 | $375,000 |
| ☐ **HERRLEIN, J. Andreas** ...................... *paintings* <br> German d. 1817 | | $1,650 |
| ☐ **HERRMANN, Frank S.** ....................... *drawings* <br> American 1866-1942 | $137 | $825 |
| ☐ **HERRMANN, Hans** ........................... *paintings* <br> Dutch 1858-1942 | | $2,090 |
| ☐ **HERRMANN, Karl Gustav** ................... *paintings* <br> German b. 1857 | | $1,210 |
| ☐ **HERRMANN-LEON, Charles** .............. *paintings* <br> French 1838-1908 | $880 | $1,045 |
| ☐ **HERRMANSTORFER, Joseph** ............. *paintings* <br> German 1817-1901 | $2,860 | $3,850 |

| | Current Price Range | |
|---|---|---|
| | *Low* | *High* |
| ☐ **HERSCH, Eugen** ................................ *paintings* | | **$462** |
| ☐ **HERSCH, Lee F.** ................................ *paintings* | | **$4,620** |
| American | | |
| ☐ **HERSCHEL, Otto** ............................... *paintings* | **$412** | **$2,200** |
| German b. 1871 | | |
| ☐ **HERTER, Adele** ............................... *paintings* | **$385** | **$1,650** |
| American 1869-1946 ................................ *drawings* | | **$121** |
| ☐ **HERTER, Albert** ............................... *paintings* | **$220** | **$6,050** |
| American 1871-1950 ................................ *drawings* | | **$1,210** |
| ☐ **HERTERICH, Johann** .......................... *paintings* | | **$253** |
| German 1843-1905 | | |
| ☐ **HERTIO, L.** ...................................... *sculpture* | | **$220** |
| French School 19th/20th cent. | | |
| ☐ **HERVE, Jules R.** ............................... *paintings* | **$110** | **$1,980** |
| French 1887-1981 ................................... *drawings* | | **$209** |
| ☐ **HERVIER, Louis Adolphe** .................... *paintings* | **$100** | **$2,200** |
| French 1818-1879 ................................... *drawings* | | **$121** |
| ☐ **HERWOOD, T.** .................................. *paintings* | | **$385** |
| English 19th cent. | | |
| ☐ **HERZ, G.** ........................................ *paintings* | | **$352** |
| ☐ **HERZEL, Paul** .................................. *paintings* | **$324** | **$352** |
| American b. 1876 ................................... *sculpture* | | **$5,500** |
| ☐ **HERZOG, A.** ..................................... *paintings* | | **$770** |
| American 19th/20th cent. | | |
| ☐ **HERZOG, Hermann** ............................ *paintings* | **$220** | **$49,500** |
| German/American 1832-1932 ....................... *drawings* | **$330** | **$1,540** |
| ☐ **HERZOG, Louis** ................................ *paintings* | | **$400** |
| American b. 1868 | | |
| ☐ **HERZOG, Max** ................................. *paintings* | | **$660** |
| American 19th/20th cent. | | |
| ☐ **HESS, Benedikt Franz** ....................... *paintings* | | **$2,420** |
| Swiss b. 1817 | | |
| ☐ **HESS, J.N.** ...................................... *paintings* | **$350** | **$990** |
| American 19th cent. | | |
| ☐ **HESS, Peter** .................................... *paintings* | | **$1,980** |
| ................................................... *drawings* | | **$275** |
| ☐ **HESSE, Alexandre Jean Baptiste** .......... *drawings* | | **$308** |
| French 1806-1879 | | |
| ☐ **HESSE, Eva** ..................................... *drawings* | **$3,740** | **$16,500** |
| American 1936-1970 | | |
| ☐ **HESSE, Henri Joseph** ......................... *drawings* | | **$770** |
| French 1781-1849 | | |
| ☐ **HESSING, Valjean** ............................. *drawings* | | **$1,100** |
| American (Choctaw) | | |
| ☐ **HESSL, Gustav August** ....................... *paintings* | | **$2,530** |
| Austrian 1849-1926 | | |
| ☐ **HESSLER, Otto** ................................. *paintings* | | **$880** |
| ☐ **HESSMERT, Karl** .............................. *paintings* | **$2,750** | **$3,300** |
| German b. 1869 | | |

| | | Current Price Range | |
|---|---|---|---|
| | | Low | High |
| ☐ **HETHERINGTON, Charles** ............... *paintings* | | $99 | $264 |
| American 20th cent. .................................... *drawings* | | | $88 |
| ☐ **HETZ, Karl** ......................................... *paintings* | | $1,430 | $12,100 |
| German 1828-1899 | | | |
| ☐ **HETZEL, George** ............................... *paintings* | | $440 | $12,100 |
| French/American 1826-1906 | | | |
| ☐ **HEUREY, B.** ........................................ *sculpture* | | | $385 |
| ☐ **HEUSCH, Jacob de** ............................ *paintings* | | $6,875 | $17,600 |
| Dutch 1657-1701 | | | |
| ☐ **HEUSCH, Willem de** .......................... *paintings* | | $2,000 | $25,300 |
| Dutch 1638-1692 | | | |
| ☐ **HEUSER, Carl** ................................... *paintings* | | $1,540 | $4,180 |
| German 19th cent. | | | |
| ☐ **HEUSTON, Frank Zell** ........................ *paintings* | | $247 | $275 |
| American 1880-1966 | | | |
| ☐ **HEUVEL, Theodore Bernard de** ............ *paintings* | | | $1,870 |
| Flemish 1817-1906 | | | |
| ☐ **HEUZE, Edmond Amedee** ..................... *drawings* | | $55 | $550 |
| French 1884-1967 | | | |
| ☐ **HEWES, H.G.** ..................................... *paintings* | | | $247 |
| American late 19th cent. | | | |
| ☐ **HEWINS, Amasa** ................................. *paintings* | | | $4,400 |
| American | | | |
| ☐ **HEWITT, Henry** ................................. *paintings* | | | $935 |
| British 19th cent. | | | |
| ☐ **HEY, Paul** ........................................ *drawings* | | | $4,400 |
| German 1867-1952 | | | |
| ☐ **HEYD, C.** ........................................... *paintings* | | | $605 |
| ☐ **HEYDEL, Paul** ................................... *drawings* | | | $242 |
| German b. 1854 | | | |
| ☐ **HEYDEN, Jan van der** ......................... *paintings* | | $12,100 | $28,600 |
| Dutch 1637-1712 | | | |
| ☐ **HEYDENDAHL,** | | | |
| **Friedrich Joseph Nicolai** ........................ *paintings* | | | $6,600 |
| Swedish 1857-1913 | | | |
| ☐ **HEYER, Arthur** ................................. *paintings* | | $220 | $2,090 |
| German b. 1872 | | | |
| ☐ **HEYERDAHL, Hans** ........................... *paintings* | | $880 | $3,850 |
| Swedish 1857-1913 | | | |
| ☐ **HEYERMANS, Jean Arnould** ............... *paintings* | | $550 | $990 |
| Belgian 1837-1892 | | | |
| ☐ **HEYLIGERS, Gustaaf A.F.** ................. *paintings* | | $880 | $1,100 |
| Dutch 19th cent. | | | |
| ☐ **HEYMANN, Martin** ........................... *sculpture* | | $1,650 | $3,850 |
| American 19th cent. | | | |
| ☐ **HEYN, August** ................................. *paintings* | | $3,410 | $11,000 |
| German b. 1837 | | | |
| ☐ **HEYNEN-DUMONT, K.** ....................... *sculpture* | | | $220 |
| French late 19th cent. | | | |

| | | Current Price Range | |
|---|---|---|---|
| | | *Low* | *High* |
| ☐ **HIBBARD, Aldro Thompson** ................. *paintings* | | $200 | $10,450 |
| American 1886-1972 | | | |
| ☐ **HIBBARD, Mary** ................................ *paintings* | | | $220 |
| American 19th/20th cent. | | | |
| ☐ **HIBEL, Edna** ................................... *paintings* | | $385 | $4,180 |
| American b. 1917 | | | |
| ☐ **HICKEL, Anton** ................................ *paintings* | | | $800 |
| ☐ **HICKEY, Thomas** .............................. *paintings* | | $1,100 | $13,200 |
| Irish 1741-1824 | | | |
| ☐ **HICKOK, Conde Wilson** ...................... *paintings* | | | $1,210 |
| 19th/20th cent. | | | |
| ☐ **HICKS, David** ................................. *paintings* | | | $302 |
| English 19th/20th cent. | | | |
| ☐ **HICKS, Edward** ............................... *paintings* | | $44,000 | $297,000 |
| American 1780-1849 | | | |
| ☐ **HICKS, George Edgar** ........................ *paintings* | | $521 | $2,420 |
| British 1824-1914 | | | |
| ☐ **HICKS, John H.** ............................... *paintings* | | | $412 |
| American 19th cent. | | | |
| ☐ **HICKS, Sidney S.** .............................. *drawings* | | | $330 |
| American 19th cent. | | | |
| ☐ **HICKS, Thomas** ............................... *paintings* | | $425 | $3,300 |
| American 1823-1890 ............................... *drawings* | | | $110 |
| ☐ **HIDE, J. van** ................................... *paintings* | | | $660 |
| ☐ **HIDLEY, Joseph** .............................. *paintings* | | | $71,500 |
| American 1830-1872 | | | |
| ☐ **HIENL-MERRE, Franz** ........................ *paintings* | | $137 | $275 |
| Austrian 20th cent. | | | |
| ☐ **HIEPES, Tomas** ................................ *paintings* | | | $5,500 |
| Spanish d. 1674 | | | |
| ☐ **HIERSCH-MINERBI, Joachim** | | | |
| **(called van HIER)** .............................. *paintings* | | $605 | $825 |
| Austrian 1834-1905 | | | |
| ☐ **HIFTER, M.** ................................... *paintings* | | | $2,200 |
| Continental School 19th cent. | | | |
| ☐ **HIGGINS, Carleton** ........................... *paintings* | | | $1,320 |
| American 1848-1932 | | | |
| ☐ **HIGGINS, Eugene** ............................. *paintings* | | $110 | $3,300 |
| American 1874-1958 ................................ *drawings* | | $33 | $880 |
| ☐ **HIGGINS, George F.** .......................... *paintings* | | $275 | $1,760 |
| American ac. 1850-1884 | | | |
| ☐ **HIGGINS, Harry** .............................. *paintings* | | | $357 |
| ☐ **HIGGINS, Michael** ............................ *paintings* | | $100 | $290 |
| American b. 1946 | | | |
| ☐ **HIGGINS, William Victor** ..................... *paintings* | | $357 | $35,200 |
| American 1884-1949 ................................ *drawings* | | $2,750 | $9,350 |
| ☐ **HIGHMORE, Joseph** ........................... *paintings* | | $1,650 | $6,875 |
| English 1692-1780 | | | |
| ☐ **HIGHWOOD, Charles** .......................... *paintings* | | | $880 |

| | | | Current Price Range | |
|---|---|---|---|---|
| | | | Low | High |
| ☐ **HIKKING, J.A.** | paintings | | | $800 |
| American 19th cent. | | | | |
| ☐ **HILAIRE, Camille** | paintings | | $137 | $550 |
| French b. 1916 | | | | |
| ☐ **HILAIRE, Jean Baptiste** | paintings | | | $2,750 |
| French 1753-1822 | drawings | | | $605 |
| ☐ **HILDA, E. Baily** | paintings | | $990 | $1,540 |
| Austrian 19th/20th cent. | | | | |
| ☐ **HILDEBRAND, Ernst** | paintings | | $550 | $880 |
| German b. 1833 | drawings | | | $110 |
| ☐ **HILDEBRANDT, Eduard** | paintings | | $522 | $1,100 |
| German 1817-1868 | | | | |
| ☐ **HILDEBRANDT, Ferdinand-Theodor** | paintings | | | $2,640 |
| German 1804-1874 | | | | |
| ☐ **HILDEBRANDT, Howard Logan** | paintings | | $110 | $4,675 |
| American 1872-1958 | | | | |
| ☐ **HILDER, Richard** | paintings | | $990 | $1,320 |
| English exhib. 1830-1851 | | | | |
| ☐ **HILDER, Rowland** | drawings | | $352 | $418 |
| ☐ **HILER, Hilaire** | paintings | | $110 | $770 |
| American b. 1898 | | | | |
| ☐ **HILGERS, Carl** | paintings | | $2,420 | $12,100 |
| German 1818-1890 | | | | |
| ☐ **HILL, Andrew P.** | paintings | | | $605 |
| American 19th cent. | | | | |
| ☐ **HILL, Anna Gilman** | paintings | | $137 | $770 |
| American 20th cent. | | | | |
| ☐ **HILL, Arthur** | paintings | | $605 | $2,750 |
| British ac. 1858-1893 | | | | |
| ☐ **HILL, Arthur Thurnbull** | paintings | | $825 | $1,760 |
| American 1868-1929 | | | | |
| ☐ **HILL, C.M.** | paintings | | | $385 |
| ☐ **HILL, Carl Frederik** | paintings | | | $247 |
| Swedish 1849-1911 | | | | |
| ☐ **HILL, D.A.** | paintings | | | $2,200 |
| ☐ **HILL, Edward** | paintings | | $357 | $1,430 |
| American 1843-1923 | | | | |
| ☐ **HILL, Edward Rufus** | paintings | | $495 | $2,750 |
| American 1852-c. 1908 | | | | |
| ☐ **HILL, F.S.** | paintings | | | $440 |
| ☐ **HILL, Howard** | paintings | | $275 | $5,225 |
| American ac. 1860-1870 | | | | |
| ☐ **HILL, James John** | paintings | | $825 | $5,500 |
| British 1811-1882 | | | | |
| ☐ **HILL, James Stevens** | paintings | | | $935 |
| British 19th cent. | | | | |
| ☐ **HILL, John Henry** | drawings | | $143 | $2,860 |
| American 1839-1922 | | | | |

**Artist of the Yosemite**

*Thomas Hill is best known for his majestic landscapes of California. Born in England, he moved to Massachusetts while he was still in his teens and remained in the East until health problems prompted a move to a milder climate. He settled in California in 1861 and continued his largely self-taught career as a painter.*

*By the 1870s he had achieved a considerable reputation, and for two decades his panoramic landscapes commanded high prices. In 1883, he built a studio in Yosemite where he lived for the rest of his life, painting over 5,000 landscapes of what is now a major national park. During the latter part of his life, his works fell out of fashion and sales dropped. (Thomas Hill, "Panoramic View of Yosemite Valley," oil on canvas, 16 x 24 in., Butterfield, November 8, 1984, $19,800.)*

|  |  | *Current Price Range* | |
|---|---|---|---|
|  |  | *Low* | *High* |
| ☐ **HILL, John William** .......................... *paintings* | | **$1,100** | **$1,430** |
| Anglo/American 1812-1879 ......................... *drawings* | | **$143** | **$55,000** |
| ☐ **HILL, Thomas** .................................. *paintings* | | **$440** | **$70,000** |
| American,b.England 1829-1908 .................... *drawings* | | | **$275** |
| ☐ **HILL, Thomas (Jr.)** ............................. *paintings* | | **$715** | **$1,430** |
| American 1871-1922 | | | |
| ☐ **HILL, Tom** ...................................... *drawings* | | **$110** | **$250** |
| American contemporary | | | |
| ☐ **HILLBOM, Henrik** ............................. *paintings* | | | **$330** |
| Sweden 19th cent. .................................... *drawings* | | **$154** | **$154** |
| ☐ **HILLERN, Bertha von** ........................ *paintings* | | | **$550** |
| American 19th cent. | | | |
| ☐ **HILLEVELD, Adrianus David** .............. *paintings* | | | **$1,870** |
| Dutch b. 1838 | | | |

| | | Current Price Range | |
|---|---|---|---|
| | | Low | High |
| ☐ **HILLIARD, F. John** .............................. *paintings* | | | **$1,870** |
| American b. 1886 | | | |
| ☐ **HILLIARD, William Henry** ................. *paintings* | | **$192** | **$2,860** |
| American 1836-1905 .................................... *drawings* | | **$66** | **$165** |
| ☐ **HILLIER, H.D.** ...................................... *paintings* | | | **$660** |
| ☐ **HILLIER, Tristram** ............................. *paintings* | | | **$1,760** |
| English b. 1905 | | | |
| ☐ **HILLINGFORD, Robert Alexander** ....... *paintings* | | **$770** | **$5,500** |
| English 1825-1904 | | | |
| ☐ **HILLS, Anna** ....................................... *paintings* | | **$605** | **$1,980** |
| American 20th cent. | | | |
| ☐ **HILLS, Laura Coombs** ......................... *drawings* | | **$165** | **$3,410** |
| American b. 1859 | | | |
| ☐ **HILLSMITH, F.** ..................................... *paintings* | | | **$550** |
| ☐ **HILLYARD, J.W.** ............................... *paintings* | | **$1,430** | **$1,760** |
| British ac. 1833-1861 | | | |
| ☐ **HILLYER, D.** ....................................... *paintings* | | | **$1,760** |
| British 19th cent. | | | |
| ☐ **HILLYER, William (Jr.)** ......................... *paintings* | | | **$900** |
| American c. 1834 | | | |
| ☐ **HILTON, John William** ......................... *paintings* | | **$275** | **$2,090** |
| American b. 1904 | | | |
| ☐ **HILTON, Roy** ....................................... *paintings* | | | **$4,180** |
| American b. 1891 | | | |
| ☐ **HILVERDINK, Eduard Alexander** ........ *paintings* | | | **$2,860** |
| Dutch 1846-1891 | | | |
| ☐ **HILVERDINK, F.H.** ........................... *paintings* | | **$220** | **$412** |
| Dutch 20th cent. | | | |
| ☐ **HILVERDINK, Johann Jakob Anton** ..... *paintings* | | **$1,980** | **$3,850** |
| Dutch 1837-1884 | | | |
| ☐ **HILVERDINK, Johannes** ...................... *paintings* | | | **$660** |
| Dutch 1813-1902 | | | |
| ☐ **HINCHCLIFF, Woodbine** ...................... *paintings* | | | **$1,045** |
| British 20th cent. | | | |
| ☐ **HINCKLEY, Robert** ............................. *paintings* | | | **$330** |
| English 19th/20th cent. | | | |
| ☐ **HINCKLEY, Thomas Hewes** ................. *paintings* | | **$600** | **$6,600** |
| American 1813-1896 | | | |
| ☐ **HIND, William G.R.** ........................... *drawings* | | **$110** | **$1,430** |
| Canadian 1833-1888/89 | | | |
| ☐ **HINE, Henry George** ........................... *drawings* | | | **$880** |
| English 1811-1895 | | | |
| ☐ **HINES, Frederick C.** ............................ *paintings* | | **$330** | **$605** |
| English 19th cent. ...................................... *drawings* | | **$99** | **$275** |
| ☐ **HINES, John** ....................................... *paintings* | | | **$440** |
| ☐ **HINES, Paul** ....................................... *paintings* | | | **$1,320** |
| ☐ **HINES, Theodore** ............................... *paintings* | | **$357** | **$1,320** |
| British ac. 1876-1889 | | | |
| ☐ **HINGLER, A.** ....................................... *paintings* | | | **$1,045** |

**Illustration Art**

*Illustration art — artwork commissioned to illustrate stories and articles in books and magazines — is growing in popularity among collectors. The work of noted 19th-century illustrators such as Arthur Rackham, Edmund Dulac, Kate Greenaway, and Beatrice Potter commands high prices. Lesser-known 20th-century illustrators are much more affordable. Among the many magazines which commissioned illustration art during the 1940s and 1950s were "Woman's Home Companion," "Good Housekeeping," "Saturday Evening Post," and "Boy's Life." Harry Hintermeister is an example of a 20th-century American illustrator whose work has appeared at auction. (Harry Hintermeister, "This One's Going to Break the Scale, Spot!," oil on canvas, 22 x 30 in., Phillips, March 30, 1985, $880.)*

|  | | *Current Price Range* | |
|---|---|---|---|
|  | | *Low* | *High* |
| ☐ **HINKLE, Clarence K.** ........................ *paintings* | | $55 | $825 |
| American 1880-1960 ................................. *drawings* | | | $192 |
| ☐ **HINMAN, Charles B.** ........................... *paintings* | | $1,650 | $6,600 |
| American b. 1932 | | | |
| ☐ **HINTERMEISTER, Henry** .................. *paintings* | | $247 | $4,125 |
| American b. 1897 | | | |
| ☐ **HINTERREITER, Hans** ........................ *paintings* | | | $1,650 |
| Swiss b. 1902 ............................................. *drawings* | | | $1,000 |
| ☐ **HINTLEY (?), G.H.** ............................. *paintings* | | | $275 |
| ☐ **HINTON, W.H.** ................................... *paintings* | | | $330 |
| American 20th cent. | | | |
| ☐ **HINZ, Jorg** ....................................... *paintings* | | | $825 |
| German 17th cent. | | | |

| | | Current Price Range | |
|---|---|---|---|
| | | Low | High |
| ☐ **HIOLIN, Louis Auguste** *sculpture* | | $3,080 | $3,740 |
| French 1846-1912 | | | |
| ☐ **HIPPOLYTE-LUCAS, F.** *paintings* | | | $1,760 |
| ☐ **HIRAGA, Kamesky** *paintings* | | | $302 |
| Japanese b. 1890 | | | |
| ☐ **HIRD, W.** *paintings* | | | $825 |
| Continental 19th cent. | | | |
| ☐ **HIRSCH, Joseph** *paintings* | | $1,430 | $19,800 |
| American 1910-1981 *drawings* | | $77 | $462 |
| ☐ **HIRSCHBERG, Carl** *paintings* | | $30 | $660 |
| American 1854-1923 | | | |
| ☐ **HIRSCHFELD, Al** *paintings* | | | $880 |
| American b. 1903 *drawings* | | $302 | $1,320 |
| ☐ **HIRSH, Alice** *paintings* | | $110 | $528 |
| ☐ **HIRSH, Stefan** *paintings* | | | $2,420 |
| American 20th cent. | | | |
| ☐ **HIRSHFIELD, Morris** *paintings* | | | $33,000 |
| American 1872-1946 | | | |
| ☐ **HIRST, Claude Raguet** *paintings* | | $132 | $9,625 |
| American 1855-1942 *drawings* | | $605 | $8,800 |
| ☐ **HIRT, Heinrich** *paintings* | | $7,425 | $16,500 |
| German 19th cent. | | | |
| ☐ **HIS, Rene** *paintings* | | | $440 |
| ☐ **HISS, John M.** *paintings* | | | $770 |
| 20th cent. | | | |
| ☐ **HITCH, Samuel** *paintings* | | | $467 |
| American 19th cent. | | | |
| ☐ **HITCHCOCK, David Howard** *paintings* | | $330 | $1,100 |
| American 1861-1943 | | | |
| ☐ **HITCHCOCK, George** *paintings* | | $330 | $66,000 |
| American 1850-1913 | | | |
| ☐ **HITCHCOCK, Lucius Wolcott** *paintings* | | $605 | $1,430 |
| American 1868-1942 | | | |
| ☐ **HITCHENS, Alfred** *paintings* | | | $660 |
| British b. 1861 | | | |
| ☐ **HITCHENS, Ivon** *paintings* | | | $2,420 |
| English b. 1893 | | | |
| ☐ **HITCHINGS, Henry** *drawings* | | $38 | $2,200 |
| American c. 1902 | | | |
| ☐ **HITLER, Adolf** *drawings* | | | $7,150 |
| German 1889-1945 | | | |
| ☐ **HIXON, W.** *paintings* | | | $3,850 |
| ☐ **HO, Paul Prou** *paintings* | | | $4,400 |
| ☐ **HOAG, Zack** *paintings* | | | $935 |
| ☐ **HOARE, J.** *drawings* | | | $385 |
| ☐ **HOARE, Prince** *drawings* | | | $275 |
| ☐ **HOARE, William (of Bath)** *drawings* | | | $1,540 |
| English 1706-1799 | | | |

| | | Current Price Range | |
|---|---|---|---|
| | | Low | High |
| ☐ **HOBAN, R.** ......................................... *paintings* | | | $385 |
| Austrian 19th cent. | | | |
| ☐ **HOBART, Clark** ............................... *paintings* | | $385 | $1,870 |
| American b. 1880? ...................................... *drawings* | | $605 | $770 |
| ☐ **HOBBEMA, Meindert** ......................... *paintings* | | $60,500 | $107,250 |
| Dutch 1638-1709 | | | |
| ☐ **HOBBS, George T.** ............................. *paintings* | | $330 | $440 |
| American b. 1846 ...................................... *drawings* | | $198 | $301 |
| ☐ **HOBBS, Morris Henry** ......................... *paintings* | | $522 | $550 |
| American b. 1892 | | | |
| ☐ **HOBDAY, William Armsfield** .............. *paintings* | | | $192 |
| English 1771-1831 | | | |
| ☐ **HOCH, Johann Jakob** ......................... *drawings* | | | $880 |
| German 1750-1829 | | | |
| ☐ **HOCHHEIM, M.** .................................. *paintings* | | | $1,155 |
| ☐ **HOCHSTEIN** ....................................... *paintings* | | | $325 |
| American 19th cent. | | | |
| ☐ **HOCKNEY, David** ............................... *paintings* | | $38,500 | $275,000 |
| English b. 1937 ........................................ *drawings* | | $1,100 | $159,500 |
| ☐ **HODGDON, Sylvester Phelps** .............. *paintings* | | $495 | $2,860 |
| American 1830-1906 | | | |
| ☐ **HODGES, William Merritt** .................. *paintings* | | | $1,980 |
| English 20th cent. | | | |
| ☐ **HODGKIN, Howard** ............................ *paintings* | | | $29,700 |
| English b. 1932 | | | |
| ☐ **HODGKINS, Samuel** ........................... *paintings* | | $130 | $330 |
| American ac. 1899-1916 | | | |
| ☐ **HODGKINS, William** .......................... *drawings* | | | $700 |
| ☐ **HODGSON, David** .............................. *paintings* | | $330 | $1,100 |
| ☐ **HODGSON, John Evan** ....................... *paintings* | | $5,775 | $7,150 |
| British 1831-1895 | | | |
| ☐ **HODGSON, S.** ..................................... *paintings* | | | $308 |
| ☐ **HODGSON, W.** ................................... *drawings* | | | $990 |
| ☐ **HODICKE, K.H.** ................................. *paintings* | | | $7,425 |
| contemporary | | | |
| ☐ **HODLER, Ferdinand** ........................... *paintings* | | | $55,000 |
| ........................................ *drawings* | | | $3,520 |
| ☐ **HODRIDGE, R.D.** .............................. *paintings* | | $550 | $770 |
| American 19th/20th cent. | | | |
| ☐ **HOEBER, Arthur** ............................... *paintings* | | $160 | $3,575 |
| American 1854-1915 | | | |
| ☐ **HOECKE, Jan van den** ........................ *paintings* | | | $16,500 |
| Flemish 1611-1651 | | | |
| ☐ **HOECKER, Paul** ................................. *paintings* | | | $990 |
| German 1854-1910 | | | |
| ☐ **HOEFF, Abraham van der** ..................... *paintings* | | | $3,740 |
| ☐ **HOEFFLER, Adolf** .............................. *paintings* | | | $600 |
| German b. 1826 | | | |

| | Current Price Range | |
|---|---|---|
| | Low | High |

|  |  | Low | High |
|---|---|---|---|
| ☐ **HOEKKOECK, Jan H.B.** ............... *paintings* | | | $1,925 |
| Dutch 1840-1912 | | | |
| ☐ **HOENIGER, Paul** ......................... *paintings* | | | $3,300 |
| German b. 1865 | | | |
| ☐ **HOENING, Julius Robert** ............... *paintings* | | $55 | $605 |
| American 1835-1904 ............................... *drawings* | | $247 | $550 |
| ☐ **HOEPPNER, Frann** ..................... *paintings* | | | $5,750 |
| 19th cent. | | | |
| ☐ **HOERLE, Heinrich** ........................ *paintings* | | | $6,600 |
| ........................................................ *drawings* | | | $2,640 |
| ☐ **HOERMAN, Carl** ......................... *paintings* | | | $192 |
| American b. 1885 | | | |
| ☐ **HOERTZ, Fred J.** ......................... *paintings* | | | $1,100 |
| ☐ **HOESE, Jean de la** ...................... *paintings* | | $660 | $1,210 |
| Belgian 1846-1917 | | | |
| ☐ **HOESSLIN, George von** ............... *paintings* | | $220 | $1,210 |
| German 1851-1923 | | | |
| ☐ **HOET, Gerard** ............................ *paintings* | | $1,870 | $17,600 |
| Dutch 1648-1733 | | | |
| ☐ **HOEVER, Arthur** ......................... *paintings* | | | $880 |
| American 1854-1915 | | | |
| ☐ **HOFELICH, Ludwig Friedrich** ......... *paintings* | | | $385 |
| ☐ **HOFENRICHTER, F.H.** .................. *sculpture* | | | $330 |
| ☐ **HOFER, Andre** .......................... *paintings* | | $275 | $715 |
| ☐ **HOFER, Heinrich** ....................... *paintings* | | | $12,100 |
| German 1825-1878 | | | |
| ☐ **HOFER, J.** ................................ *paintings* | | | $385 |
| German 19th cent. | | | |
| ☐ **HOFER, Karl** ............................. *paintings* | | $7,700 | $16,500 |
| German 1878-1955 ............................. *drawings* | | $357 | $1,320 |
| ☐ **HOFFBAUER, Charles C.J.** ............ *paintings* | | $110 | $4,620 |
| French/American 1875-1957 .................. *drawings* | | $110 | $825 |
| ☐ **HOFFMAN, Frank B.** .................... *paintings* | | $1,430 | $4,950 |
| American 1888-1958 | | | |
| ☐ **HOFFMAN, Hans** ....................... *paintings* | | | $302 |
| ☐ **HOFFMAN, Irwin D.** .................... *paintings* | | $605 | $880 |
| American | | | |
| ☐ **HOFFMAN, Malvina** .................... *sculpture* | | $33 | $10,450 |
| American 1887-1966 | | | |
| ☐ **HOFFMAN, Richard** ..................... *drawings* | | $220 | $302 |
| ☐ **HOFFMANN, Anton** ..................... *paintings* | | | $1,210 |
| German b. 1863 | | | |
| ☐ **HOFFMANN, Arnold** .................... *paintings* | | | $1,870 |
| American b. 1886 | | | |
| ☐ **HOFFMANN, C. Heinrich** ............... *paintings* | | | $2,200 |
| German 19th cent. | | | |
| ☐ **HOFFMANN, Josef** ...................... *drawings* | | $700 | $4,950 |
| Austrian 1870-1956 | | | |

| | | Current Price Range | |
|---|---|---|---|
| | | Low | High |
| ☐ **HOFFMANN, Oscar Adolfovitch** .......... *paintings* | | | $12,100 |
| Russian 1851-1913 | | | |
| ☐ **HOFFMANS** ..................................... *paintings* | | | $247 |
| Austrian 19th cent. | | | |
| ☐ **HOFFMEISTER, Adolf** ......................... *drawings* | | $440 | $605 |
| ☐ **HOFFNER** ..................................... *paintings* | | | $330 |
| ☐ **HOFLAND, Jan van** .......................... *paintings* | | | $330 |
| Dutch 19th cent. | | | |
| ☐ **HOFLINGER, Albert** ......................... *paintings* | | | $1,925 |
| German 1855-1936 | | | |
| ☐ **HOFMAN, F.** ................................... *paintings* | | $247 | $330 |
| ☐ **HOFMAN, H.** ................................... *paintings* | | | $1,650 |
| German 19th cent. | | | |
| ☐ **HOFMANN** ..................................... *sculpture* | | $385 | $1,100 |
| German 19th/20th cent. | | | |
| ☐ **HOFMANN, A.** ................................. *paintings* | | | $3,300 |
| German 19th/20th cent. | | | |
| ☐ **HOFMANN, Charles C.** ...................... *paintings* | | $88,000 | $93,500 |
| American 1821-1882 | | | |
| ☐ **HOFMANN, Hans** ............................. *paintings* | | $1,650 | $275,000 |
| German/American 1880-1966 ..................... *drawings* | | $550 | $12,100 |
| ☐ **HOFMANN, Karl** ............................. *paintings* | | | $1,430 |
| Austrian b. 1852 | | | |
| ☐ **HOFMANN, Rudolf** ........................... *paintings* | | | $2,530 |
| German 1820-1882 | | | |
| ☐ **HOFNER, Johann Baptist** .................. *paintings* | | $275 | $22,000 |
| German 1832-1913 | | | |
| ☐ **HOFTRUP, Julius Lars** ..................... *drawings* | | $33 | $220 |
| American 1874-1954 | | | |
| ☐ **HOGAN, Jean** ................................. *paintings* | | | $330 |
| American 20th cent. | | | |
| ☐ **HOGARTH** ..................................... *drawings* | | | $660 |
| ☐ **HOGARTH, William** .......................... *paintings* | | $143,000 | $440,000 |
| English 1697-1764 | | | |
| ☐ **HOGER, Joseph** ............................... *paintings* | | | $700 |
| ☐ **HOGER, Rudolf A.** ........................... *paintings* | | $330 | $1,760 |
| Austrian 1876-1928 | | | |
| ☐ **HOGLEY, Stephen E.** ........................ *paintings* | | | $467 |
| ☐ **HOGNER, Nils** ................................ *paintings* | | | $412 |
| American | | | |
| ☐ **HOGUE, Kate** ................................. *paintings* | | | $275 |
| American 19th/20th cent. | | | |
| ☐ **HOGUET, Charles** ........................... *paintings* | | | $528 |
| ☐ **HOHENBERG, Wagner** ...................... *paintings* | | $1,870 | $3,300 |
| ☐ **HOHENREIN** .................................. *paintings* | | | $1,100 |
| ☐ **HOHENSTEIN, Adolf** ........................ *paintings* | | | $742 |
| German 1854-1917 | | | |
| ☐ **HOHNSTEDT, P.L.** ........................... *paintings* | | $192 | $770 |
| 20th cent. | | | |

|  | | *Current Price Range* | |
|---|---|---|---|
|  | | *Low* | *High* |
| ☐ **HOHS, Liselotte** ............................... *paintings* | | **$165** | **$385** |
| Austrian b. 1939 ...................................... *drawings* | | **$137** | **$302** |
| ☐ **HOIN, Claude** .................................. *drawings* | | | **$3,300** |
| French 1750-1817 | | | |
| ☐ **HOIT, Albert Gallatin** ...................... *paintings* | | | **$9,625** |
| American 1809-1856 | | | |
| ☐ **HOKINSON, Helen E.** ...................... *drawings* | | **$27** | **$176** |
| American 20th cent. | | | |
| ☐ **HOKUSAI** ......................................... *drawings* | | **$192** | **$412** |
| Japanese 18th/19th cent. | | | |
| ☐ **HOLBEIN, Edward** ........................... *paintings* | | | **$324** |
| ☐ **HOLBEIN, Hans** ............................... *paintings* | | | **$352** |
| ☐ **HOLBERG, Richard A.** ..................... *paintings* | | **$192** | **$495** |
| American 1889-1942 ................................. *drawings* | | | **$137** |
| ☐ **HOLBERTON, William** ...................... *paintings* | | **$302** | **$385** |
| American 19th cent. | | | |
| ☐ **HOLBROOK, L.T.** ............................. *paintings* | | | **$220** |
| American 19th cent. | | | |
| ☐ **HOLD, Abel** ..................................... *paintings* | | | **$521** |
| English 1830-1910 | | | |
| ☐ **HOLD, Abel** ..................................... *paintings* | | | **$247** |
| English 1849-1871 | | | |
| ☐ **HOLD, B.** ......................................... *paintings* | | | **$220** |
| English 19th/20th cent. | | | |
| ☐ **HOLDEN, James Albert** ..................... *paintings* | | **$165** | **$220** |
| American 19th/20th cent. | | | |
| ☐ **HOLDER, Edward Henry** ................... *paintings* | | **$357** | **$605** |
| 19th/20th cent. | | | |
| ☐ **HOLDING, Harold** ........................... *paintings* | | | **$192** |
| English 19th cent. | | | |
| ☐ **HOLDREDGE, Ransom Gillet** ............ *paintings* | | **$110** | **$7,425** |
| American 1836-1899 | | | |
| ☐ **HOLDSTOCK, Alfred Worsley** ........... *drawings* | | | **$660** |
| Canadian 1820-1901 | | | |
| ☐ **HOLGATE, J.** .................................... *paintings* | | | **$231** |
| English 20th cent. | | | |
| ☐ **HOLIDAY, Henry** ............................. *drawings* | | | **$522** |
| English 1839-1927 | | | |
| ☐ **HOLL, H.H.** ..................................... *paintings* | | | **$192** |
| American 19th cent. | | | |
| ☐ **HOLLAMS, Mabell** ........................... *paintings* | | | **$550** |
| ☐ **HOLLAND, James** ............................ *paintings* | | **$660** | **$6,050** |
| English 1800-1870 | | | |
| ☐ **HOLLAND, John** ............................... *paintings* | | | **$3,300** |
| English ac. 1831-1879 | | | |
| ☐ **HOLLAND, John (Jr.)** ......................... *paintings* | | | **$880** |
| British 19th cent. | | | |
| ☐ **HOLLAND, John Joseph** ..................... *paintings* | | | **$825** |
| English b. 1776 | | | |

| | Current Price Range | |
|---|---|---|
| | *Low* | *High* |
| ☐ **HOLLAND, Raymond** ........................... *paintings*<br>American 20th cent. | $38 | $1,430 |
| ☐ **HOLLAND, Samuel Sebastopol** ............. *paintings*<br>British 19th cent. | $200 | $385 |
| ☐ **HOLLAND, Tom** ................................... *drawings*<br>American b. 1936 | | $4,400 |
| ☐ **HOLLANDER, Hendrik** ....................... *paintings*<br>Dutch 1823-1884 | $550 | $3,850 |
| ☐ **HOLLAR, Wenceslaus** ......................... *drawings*<br>Bohemian 1607-1677 | | $4,510 |
| ☐ **HOLLERN, Mike** ................................ *sculpture*<br>American | | $500 |
| ☐ **HOLLIS, S.** ......................................... *paintings*<br>British 19th cent. | | $495 |
| ☐ **HOLLOWAY, Charles** ......................... *drawings*<br>ac. c. 1900 | $275 | $660 |
| ☐ **HOLLOWAY, Charles** ......................... *paintings*<br>British(?) ac. early 20th cent. | | $2,310 |
| ☐ **HOLLOWAY, Charles Edward** ............. *drawings*<br>English 1838-1897 | $165 | $247 |
| ☐ **HOLLOWAY, Edward Stratton** ............. *paintings*<br>American d. 1939 | $200 | $1,300 |
| ☐ **HOLLS, I.T.** ........................................ *paintings*<br>English 19th cent. | | $330 |
| ☐ **HOLLYER, Maud** ............................... *paintings*<br>Scottish 19th/20th cent. ...................... *drawings* | $150 | $176<br>$313 |
| ☐ **HOLLYER, W.P.** ................................. *paintings*<br>British 19th cent. | | $715 |
| ☐ **HOLM, Gustav** ................................... *paintings* | | $770 |
| ☐ **HOLMAN, Francis** ............................. *paintings*<br>English late 18th cent. | | $6,050 |
| ☐ **HOLMAN, J.C.** ................................... *paintings*<br>British 18th cent. | | $330 |
| ☐ **HOLMAN, William** ............................. *drawings*<br>b. 1903 | $165 | $192 |
| ☐ **HOLMBOE, Thorolf** ........................... *paintings* | | $330 |
| ☐ **HOLMES, Charles** ............................. *paintings*<br>American 19th/20th cent. | | $275 |
| ☐ **HOLMES, Edward** ............................. *paintings*<br>English 19th cent. | | $495 |
| ☐ **HOLMES, Elizabeth** ........................... *drawings* | | $275 |
| ☐ **HOLMES, George Augustus** ................. *paintings*<br>British 19th cent. | $209 | $330 |
| ☐ **HOLMES, Grace** ............................... *paintings*<br>British 19th cent. | | $550 |
| ☐ **HOLMES, P.A.** ................................... *paintings*<br>American 19th/20th cent. | | $247 |
| ☐ **HOLMES, Ralph** ............................... *paintings*<br>American 1876-1963 ...................... *drawings* | $66<br>$165 | $2,750<br>$165 |

| | *Current Price Range* | |
|---|---|---|
| | *Low* | *High* |
| ☐ **HOLMES, Robert H.** ............................ *paintings* | | **$1,980** |
| Canadian 1861-1930 | | |
| ☐ **HOLMES, William Henry** ..................... *paintings* | | **$357** |
| American 1846-1933 ................................ *drawings* | **$50** | **$797** |
| ☐ **HOLMGREN, Fritz** ............................ *paintings* | | **$1,016** |
| Swedish 1777-1857 | | |
| ☐ **HOLMSTEDT, J.** ............................... *paintings* | | **$1,760** |
| ☐ **HOLSLAG, Edward J.** ........................ *paintings* | **$110** | **$522** |
| American 1870-1925 | | |
| ☐ **HOLSOE, Carl Vilhelm** ....................... *paintings* | **$1,320** | **$6,050** |
| Danish late 19th/early 20th cent | | |
| ☐ **HOLST, Hermann V. von** ..................... *drawings* | | **$440** |
| ☐ **HOLST, Laurits Bernhard** ................... *paintings* | | **$495** |
| ☐ **HOLSTEIN, Schenck von** ..................... *paintings* | | **$352** |
| ☐ **HOLSTEYN, Pieter** ............................ *drawings* | | **$660** |
| ☐ **HOLSTON, George** ............................ *drawings* | | **$550** |
| 19th cent. | | |
| ☐ **HOLT, Edwin Frederick** ...................... *paintings* | **$88** | **$14,300** |
| English ac. 1850-1886 | | |
| ☐ **HOLT, Geoffrey** ............................... *paintings* | **$110** | **$192** |
| American 20th cent. | | |
| ☐ **HOLT, Neil** ..................................... *drawings* | | **$770** |
| American | | |
| ☐ **HOLTE, A. Brandish** ........................... *paintings* | **$246** | **$1,540** |
| British 19th cent. | | |
| ☐ **HOLTY, Carl Robert** ........................... *paintings* | **$121** | **$3,575** |
| American 1900-1973 ................................ *drawings* | **$220** | **$2,310** |
| ☐ **HOLTZ, Frank** ................................. *paintings* | | **$462** |
| European | | |
| ☐ **HOLWEG, Gustav** ............................ *paintings* | | **$1,100** |
| ☐ **HOLYOAK, Rowland E.** ..................... *paintings* | | **$357** |
| English 19th cent. | | |
| ☐ **HOLZ, Johann Daniel** .......................... *paintings* | | **$1,430** |
| German 1867-1945 | | |
| ☐ **HOLZER, Johann Evangelist** ............... *drawings* | | **$605** |
| ☐ **HOLZER, L.** ...................................... *paintings* | | **$1,210** |
| Austrian (?) 19th cent. | | |
| ☐ **HOMER, Winslow** ............................ *paintings* | **$16,500** | **$1,870,000** |
| American 1836-1910 ................................ *drawings* | **$522** | **$561,000** |
| ☐ **HOMME, J.L.** ................................... *paintings* | | **$1,870** |
| Continental School 19th cent. | | |
| ☐ **HONDECOETER, Gilles Claesz** ........... *paintings* | | **$18,700** |
| 17th cent. | | |
| ☐ **HONDECOETER, Gysbert de** ............... *paintings* | | **$3,300** |
| Dutch 1604-1653 | | |
| ☐ **HONDECOETER, Melchior de** ............. *paintings* | **$7,425** | **$319,000** |
| Dutch 1636-1695 | | |

## Pawn Shop Discovery

In the 1950s, a young actor browsing in a pawn shop paused to examine a water-color of a beach scene. Dated 1874, and inscribed "East Hampton Beach, Long Island," the work was initialled "W.H." While he thought that the picture was reminiscent of the work of Winslow Homer, the young man was reluctant to pay the $45 the owner was asking, and went off to the library to research Homer's career and study his signature. Discovering that Homer had, indeed, been in New York in the 1870s, he returned to the shop and bargained the price down to $35 (without the frame). He then took the work to the Whitney Museum's Lloyd Goodrich, an authority on Homer, who authenticated it.

In the 1960s, the actor sold the watercolor to a private collector. In 1981 it was consigned as part of the estate of an "anonymous private collector" to Sotheby's, where it sold for $577,500! (Winslow Homer, "East Hampton Beach, Long Island," oil on canvas, 10 x 21½ in., Sotheby's, October 22, 1981, $577,500.)

|  |  | *Current Price Range* | |
| --- | --- | --- | --- |
|  |  | *Low* | *High* |
| ☐ **HONDIUS, Abraham** ............................ *paintings* | | **$1,650** | **$9,350** |
| Dutch 1625-1695 | | | |
| ☐ **HONDIUS, Gerrit** ............................... *paintings* | | **$50** | **$1,320** |
| Dutch/American b. 1891 ............................... *drawings* | | | **$55** |
| ☐ **HONDT, Lambert de** ........................... *paintings* | | **$1,540** | **$2,200** |
| Flemish d. after 1665 | | | |
| ☐ **HONE, Nathaniel** ............................... *paintings* | | **$3,025** | **$41,800** |
| Irish | | | |
| ☐ **HONEGGER, Gottfried** ...................... *paintings* | | **$275** | **$770** |
| contemporary | | | |
| ☐ **HONICH** .............................................. *paintings* | | | **$418** |
| ☐ **HONORE, Paul** .................................... *paintings* | | | **$275** |

| | Current Price Range | |
|---|---|---|
| | Low | High |
| ☐ **HONTHORST, Gerrit van** .................. *paintings* | $412 | $15,400 |
| Dutch 1590-1656 | | |
| ☐ **HOOCH, Horatius de** .......................... *paintings* | | $4,400 |
| Dutch 17th cent. | | |
| ☐ **HOOCH, Pieter de** ............................. *paintings* | | $12,100 |
| Dutch 1629-1681 | | |
| ☐ **HOOFT, Vissert** ................................. *paintings* | | $385 |
| ☐ **HOOG, Bernard de** ........................... *paintings* | $1,210 | $8,800 |
| Dutch 1867-1943 ...................................... *drawings* | $301 | $330 |
| ☐ **HOOG, Rudolf** .................................... *paintings* | | $495 |
| Dutch 19th cent. | | |
| ☐ **HOOGSTRATEN, Samuel van** ............. *paintings* | $990 | $21,000 |
| Flemish 1627-1678 | | |
| ☐ **HOOK, James Clarke** .......................... *paintings* | | $1,650 |
| British 1819-1907 | | |
| ☐ **HOOM, Karl van** ............................... *paintings* | | $660 |
| Dutch 19th/20th cent. | | |
| ☐ **HOOPER, John Horace** ........................ *paintings* | $715 | $4,620 |
| English ac. 1870-1891; d. 1899 | | |
| ☐ **HOOPER, Luther** ............................... *paintings* | | $412 |
| British 1849-1932 | | |
| ☐ **HOOPER, P. Sylvester** ........................ *paintings* | | $330 |
| British 19th cent. | | |
| ☐ **HOOPES, Elizabeth** ............................. *drawings* | $44 | $200 |
| American b. 1908 | | |
| ☐ **HOOVER, Charles D.** .......................... *paintings* | | $275 |
| American b. 1897 | | |
| ☐ **HOOY, Van** ....................................... *paintings* | $176 | $412 |
| Dutch 19th cent. | | |
| ☐ **HOPE, James** ................................... *paintings* | $550 | $13,500 |
| American 1818-1892 | | |
| ☐ **HOPE, Robert** ................................... *paintings* | | $467 |
| British 19th cent. | | |
| ☐ **HOPE, Thomas H.** ............................. *paintings* | $357 | $4,675 |
| American,b.England d. 1926 | | |
| ☐ **HOPKIN, Robert** ............................... *paintings* | $250 | $2,750 |
| Scottish/American 1832-1909 ....................... *drawings* | $121 | $660 |
| ☐ **HOPKINS, Arthur** ............................. *drawings* | $275 | $12,100 |
| English 1848-1930 | | |
| ☐ **HOPKINS, Budd** ............................... *paintings* | $49 | $880 |
| American b. 1931 ...................................... *drawings* | $176 | $308 |
| ☐ **HOPKINS, C.E.** ................................ *drawings* | | $250 |
| American ac. 1886 | | |
| ☐ **HOPKINS, E.** ................................... *paintings* | | $467 |
| American 19th cent. | | |
| ☐ **HOPKINS, George Edward** .................. *paintings* | $121 | $550 |
| American b. 1855 | | |
| ☐ **HOPKINS, William H.** ........................ *paintings* | $2,750 | $3,000 |
| English ac. 1853-1890, d. 1892 | | |

| | | Current Price Range | |
|---|---|---|---|
| | | *Low* | *High* |
| ☐ **HOPKINSON, Charles Sidney** ............... *paintings* | | $440 | $16,500 |
| American 1869-1962 | | | |
| ☐ **HOPKINSON, Glen** ............................ *paintings* | | $950 | $4,000 |
| American contemporary | | | |
| ☐ **HOPKINSON, Harold** ......................... *paintings* | | | $700 |
| American | | | |
| ☐ **HOPLEY, Edward William John** ........... *paintings* | | | $605 |
| British 1816-1869 | | | |
| ☐ **HOPPE, C.A.W.** .............................. *paintings* | | | $1,100 |
| German 19th cent. | | | |
| ☐ **HOPPE, Ferdinand B.** ......................... *paintings* | | | $302 |
| ☐ **HOPPENBROUWERS,** | | | |
| **Johannes Franciscus** ............................ *paintings* | | | $1,210 |
| Dutch 1816-1866 | | | |
| ☐ **HOPPENRATH, C.** ............................ *paintings* | | | $192 |
| American 20th cent. | | | |
| ☐ **HOPPER, Edward** ............................. *paintings* | | $18,700 | $330,000 |
| American 1882-1967 ................................ *drawings* | | $990 | $82,500 |
| ☐ **HOPPNER, John** ............................... *paintings* | | $1,540 | $52,800 |
| British 1758-1810 | | | |
| ☐ **HOPWOOD, Henry S.** ......................... *drawings* | | | $330 |
| ☐ **HOQUET, Charles** ............................. *paintings* | | $2,420 | $4,290 |
| French 1821-1870 | | | |
| ☐ **HORACIO** ....................................... *paintings* | | $3,300 | $7,700 |
| Mexican b. 1912 | | | |
| ☐ **HORD, Donal** .................................. *paintings* | | | $66 |
| American 1902-1966 .............................. *sculpture* | | $300 | $700 |
| ☐ **HORDE, F.** ..................................... *paintings* | | | $990 |
| Dutch 19th cent. | | | |
| ☐ **HORDIJK, Gerard** ............................. *drawings* | | | $275 |
| ☐ **HOREMANS, Jan Josef (the elder)** ......... *paintings* | | $3,850 | $4,400 |
| Flemish 1682-1759 ................................. *drawings* | | | $550 |
| ☐ **HOREMANS, Jan Josef (the younger)** .... *paintings* | | $880 | $8,800 |
| Flemish 1714-c. 1790 .............................. *drawings* | | $660 | $1,045 |
| ☐ **HOREMANS, Petrus** ........................... *paintings* | | | $3,850 |
| Flemish b. 1714 | | | |
| ☐ **HOREMANS, Pieter Jacob** ................... *paintings* | | | $35,200 |
| Flemish 1700-1776 | | | |
| ☐ **HORLOR, George W.** .......................... *paintings* | | $1,320 | $4,950 |
| British ac. 1849-1890 | | | |
| ☐ **HORLOR, Joseph** .............................. *paintings* | | $330 | $2,640 |
| British 19th cent. | | | |
| ☐ **HORMANN, Theodor von** ..................... *paintings* | | | $34,100 |
| German 1840-1895 | | | |
| ☐ **HORN, J.P.** ..................................... *paintings* | | | $632 |
| ☐ **HORN, Johannes Casparus** .................. *paintings* | | | $385 |
| Dutch 18th cent. | | | |
| ☐ **HORN, Julius** .................................. *paintings* | | | $522 |
| 20th cent. | | | |

| | *Current Price Range* | |
|---|---|---|
| | *Low* | *High* |

| | | Low | High |
|---|---|---|---|
| ☐ **HORNEL, Edward Atkinson** ............... *paintings* English 1864-1933 | | | $1,925 |
| ☐ **HORNEMANN, Friedrich Adolf** ........... *paintings* German 1813-1890 | | | $28,600 |
| ☐ **HORNEMANN, P.** ............................ *paintings* | | | $385 |
| ☐ **HOROWITZ, Frank** ........................... *paintings* American b. 1889 | | | $330 |
| ☐ **HORSFALL, Robert Bruce** ............... *drawings* American b. 1869 | | $88 | $176 |
| ☐ **HORSFORD, A.J.** ............................ *paintings* | | | $385 |
| ☐ **HORSLEY, John Callcott** .................... *paintings* British 1817-1903 | | $687 | $2,420 |
| ☐ **HORSLEY, Walter Charles** ............... *drawings* British b. 1855 | | | $3,850 |
| ☐ **HORST, Gerrit Willemsz** .................... *paintings* Dutch 1612-1652 | | | $7,150 |
| ☐ **HORST, Giter** ................................. *paintings* | | | $550 |
| ☐ **HORST, Gustav August** ..................... *paintings* German 19th cent. | | | $2,000 |
| ☐ **HORST, L.** ...................................... *paintings* | | | $2,200 |
| ☐ **HORTER, Earl** ................................. *paintings* | | $880 | $7,425 |
| American 1881-1940 .................................. *drawings* | | $88 | $700 |
| ☐ **HORTON, Etty** ................................ *paintings* British ac. 1892-1903 | | $275 | $880 |
| ☐ **HORTON, William Samuel** ................ *paintings* | | $356 | $40,700 |
| American 1865-1936 .................................. *drawings* | | $100 | $1,045 |
| ☐ **HORVATH, Andor** ............................ *paintings* Hungarian b. 1876 | | | $246 |
| ☐ **HORVATH, George A.** ........................ *paintings* American | | | $500 |
| ☐ **HORWARTER, J.E.** ........................... *paintings* | | | $1,870 |
| ☐ **HORWITZ, B.** .................................. *paintings* American 20th cent. | | | $605 |
| ☐ **HORWOOD, John** ............................ *paintings* English 20th cent. | | | $220 |
| ☐ **HOSCHEDE-MONET, Blanche** ........... *paintings* French 1865-1947 | | | $2,420 |
| ☐ **HOSIASSON, Philippe** ......................... *paintings* | | $275 | $1,430 |
| French b. 1898 ....................................... *drawings* | | | $165 |
| ☐ **HOSKINS, Gayle Porter** ..................... *paintings* American 1887-1962 | | $66 | $2,090 |
| ☐ **HOSMER, Harriet Goodhue** ............... *sculpture* American 1830-1908 | | $2,887 | $8,250 |
| ☐ **HOSSE, Adolph** ............................... *paintings* German b. 1875 | | | $550 |
| ☐ **HOTCHKIS, Anna Mary** .................... *drawings* British 20th cent. | | | $330 |
| ☐ **HOUBEN, Henri** ............................. *paintings* Belgian 20th cent. | | $418 | $2,750 |

| | Current Price Range | |
|---|---|---|
| | Low | High |
| □ **HOUBRON, Frederic Anatole** ............... *drawings* <br> French 1851-1908 | $330 | $1,430 |
| □ **HOUD, Douglas van** ............................ *paintings* <br> American contemporary | | $3,300 |
| □ **HOUDIAKOFF, Andrei** ........................ *drawings* <br> Russian 20th cent. | $220 | $3,850 |
| □ **HOUDON, Jean Antoine** ........................ *sculpture* <br> French 1741-1828 | | $242,000 |
| □ **HOUDT, C.T.** ...................................... *paintings* | | $1,100 |
| □ **HOUEL, Jean Pierre Louis Laurent** ....... *drawings* <br> French 1735-1813 | $1,540 | $2,200 |
| □ **HOUGH, William** ................................ *drawings* <br> English 19th cent. | $550 | $1,210 |
| □ **HOUGHTON, F.** ................................. *drawings* <br> English 19th cent. | | $880 |
| □ **HOUME, S.** ........................................ *paintings* <br> French 20th cent. | | $192 |
| □ **HOUSER** ............................................. *paintings* <br> American (Apache) | | $1,430 |
| □ **HOUSTON, Cody** ................................ *sculpture* <br> American contemporary | | $3,600 |
| □ **HOUSTON, Frances C.** ........................ *drawings* <br> American 1867-1906 | | $1,650 |
| □ **HOUSTON, George** ............................ *paintings* <br> British 1869-1947 ..................................... *drawings* | $440 | $605 <br> $330 |
| □ **HOUSTON, John Adam** ........................ *drawings* <br> British 1812/13-1884 | | $302 |
| □ **HOUSTON, John R.** ............................ *paintings* | | $308 |
| □ **HOUSTON, William W.** ........................ *drawings* | | $935 |
| □ **HOUTEN, Sientze Mesdag van** .............. *paintings* <br> Dutch 1834-1909 | | $465 |
| □ **HOUZE, Florentin** ............................... *paintings* <br> Belgian b. 1812 | | $550 |
| □ **HOVE, Bartholomeus Johannes van** ...... *paintings* <br> 1790-1880 | $1,100 | $13,200 |
| □ **HOVE, Victor van** ................................ *paintings* <br> Belgian 1825-1891 | $1,045 | $6,600 |
| □ **HOVENDEN, Thomas** ........................ *paintings* <br> Irish 1840-1895 ....................................... *drawings* | $1,430 <br> $385 | $22,000 <br> $385 |
| □ **HOW, Julia Beatrice** ........................... *paintings* <br> English 1867-1932 ................................... *drawings* | <br> $220 | $1,045 <br> $275 |
| □ **HOW, Kenneth G.** .............................. *paintings* <br> American 20th cent. | $77 | $770 |
| □ **HOW, William** ................................... *paintings* <br> British (?) 19th cent. | | $2,310 |
| □ **HOWAD, Henry M.** ........................... *paintings* <br> American b. 1873 | | $440 |
| □ **HOWARD** ......................................... *sculpture* | $825 | $935 |

|                                                         | Current Price Range |         |
|---------------------------------------------------------|---------------------|---------|
|                                                         | Low                 | High    |
| ☐ **HOWARD, B.K.** ............................ *paintings* | $110 | $770 |
| American late 19th cent. | | |
| ☐ **HOWARD, Charles** ........................... *paintings* | $275 | $550 |
| American b. 1899 | | |
| ☐ **HOWARD, Henry Mowbray** ............... *paintings* | $110 | $1,430 |
| American b. 1873 | | |
| ☐ **HOWARD, Hugh Huntington** ............... *paintings* | | $330 |
| American b. 1859 | | |
| ☐ **HOWARD, J.** ...................................... *paintings* | $275 | $385 |
| English 19th/20th cent. | | |
| ☐ **HOWARD, Lucille** ........................... *paintings* | $16 | $200 |
| American 20th cent. | | |
| ☐ **HOWARD, Marion** ........................... *paintings* | | $203 |
| American 19th/20th cent. | | |
| ☐ **HOWARD, William** ........................... *paintings* | | $495 |
| ☐ **HOWARTH, B.M.** ........................... *paintings* | | $246 |
| English 19th cent. | | |
| ☐ **HOWE, E.R.** ...................................... *paintings* | | $375 |
| American 19th cent. | | |
| ☐ **HOWE, H.** ......................................... *paintings* | $30 | $225 |
| American 19th/20th cent. | | |
| ☐ **HOWE, Richard** ............................... *paintings* | $220 | $440 |
| ☐ **HOWE, Theodore J.** ........................... *paintings* | $110 | $330 |
| American early 20th cent. | | |
| ☐ **HOWE, William Henry** ........................ *paintings* | $412 | $1,300 |
| American 1846-1929 | | |
| ☐ **HOWELL, B.K.** .................................. *paintings* | | $2,530 |
| American | | |
| ☐ **HOWELL, Felicie Waldo** ...................... *paintings* | | $3,025 |
| American b. 1897 ...................................... *drawings* | | $440 |
| ☐ **HOWELL, William H.** ........................... *paintings* | | $1,320 |
| American 1860-1925 | | |
| ☐ **HOWELLS, Maud** ............................... *paintings* | | $900 |
| British 19th cent. ...................................... *drawings* | | $88 |
| ☐ **HOWES** ............................................. *paintings* | | $1,210 |
| British 19th cent. | | |
| ☐ **HOWITT, John Newton** ........................ *paintings* | $132 | $1,100 |
| American 1885-1958 | | |
| ☐ **HOWITT, Samuel William** .................... *drawings* | $220 | $3,000 |
| English 1765-1822 | | |
| ☐ **HOWLAND, Alfred Cornelius** ............... *paintings* | $220 | $4,125 |
| American 1838-1909 ................................. *drawings* | $40 | $220 |
| ☐ **HOYLAND, John** ............................... *paintings* | $605 | $1,760 |
| English b. 1934 ...................................... *drawings* | | $495 |
| ☐ **HOYLE, Mary E.** ............................... *paintings* | | $209 |
| English 19th/20th cent. | | |
| ☐ **HOYLE, Raphael** ............................... *paintings* | $1,045 | $1,430 |
| American 1804-1838 | | |

| | Current Price Range | |
|---|---|---|
| | *Low* | *High* |

☐ **HOYT, Edith** ..................................... *paintings* | | $247
American b. 1890

☐ **HOYT, G.E.** ...................................... *paintings* | | $522

☐ **HOYT, Mrs. E.C.** ............................. *paintings* | | $357

☐ **HOYT, William F.** ............................ *paintings* | | $356
American b. 1910

☐ **HSU, Hsiao Yew** ............................... *paintings* | | $247
Chinese contemporary

☐ **HUBACEK, William** ........................... *paintings* | $88 | $1,000
American 19th/20th cent.

☐ **HUBARD, William James** .................... *paintings* | | $11,000
American 1807-1862

☐ **HUBBARD, F.M.B.** ........................... *paintings* | $300 | $800
American 1869-1930

☐ **HUBBARD, John** ................................ *paintings* | | $330
American early 20th cent.

☐ **HUBBARD, Richard William** ............... *paintings* | $440 | $3,300
American 1817-1888

☐ **HUBBELL, Charles H.** ....................... *paintings* | $33 | $350
American 20th cent.

☐ **HUBBELL, Henry Salem** ...................... *paintings* | $825 | $35,200
American 1870-1949

☐ **HUBER, Ed** ...................................... *paintings* | | $275

☐ **HUBER, Ernst** .................................. *paintings* | | $160
Austrian 1895-1935 .................................... *drawings* | | $242

☐ **HUBER, Leon Charles** ......................... *paintings* | $3,025 | $7,150
French 1858-1928

☐ **HUBER, Wilhelm** ............................... *paintings* | | $3,300
Swiss 1787-1871

☐ **HUBERT, Jean Baptiste Louis** .............. *drawings* | | $330

☐ **HUBERT-GAUTHIER** ......................... *paintings* | | $990

☐ **HUBERT-ROBERT, Marius** ................. *paintings* | $605 | $632
French 19th/20th cent.

☐ **HUBNER, Carl** ................................... *paintings* | $7,750 | $8,250
German 1797-1831

☐ **HUBNER, Carl Wilhelm** ...................... *paintings* | $1,100 | $11,000
German 1814-1879

☐ **HUBNER, Julius** ................................ *paintings* | | $6,050
German 1842-1874

☐ **HUBOT, Louis Charles** ........................ *sculpture* | | $3,025
French 1815-1865

☐ **HUBRECHT, Amalda Bramine Louise** .. *paintings* | $1,760 | $2,750
Dutch 1855-1913

☐ **HUCHE, Chenard** .............................. *paintings* | | $330

☐ **HUCHTENBURG, Jan van** ................. *paintings* | $8,800 | $14,850
Dutch c. 1646-1733

☐ **HUDSON, Charles Bradford** ................ *paintings* | $137 | $495
American 1865-1934

| | | | Current Price Range | |
|---|---|---|---|---|
| | | | Low | High |
| ☐ **HUDSON, Charles W.** | ............... | drawings | $198 | $495 |
| American b. 1871 | | | | |
| ☐ **HUDSON, Grace Carpenter** | ............... | paintings | $660 | $36,300 |
| American 1865-1937 | | | | |
| ☐ **HUDSON, John Bradley (Jr.)** | ............... | paintings | $440 | $2,100 |
| American 1832-1903 | ............... | drawings | $110 | $750 |
| ☐ **HUDSON, Thomas** | ............... | paintings | $247 | $12,650 |
| English 1701-1779 | | | | |
| ☐ **HUE, Charles Desire** | ............... | paintings | $660 | $4,400 |
| French 19th cent. | | | | |
| ☐ **HUE, Theodore Bermond** | ............... | paintings | | $2,420 |
| ☐ **HUET, Christophe** | ............... | paintings | | $7,700 |
| French d. 1759 | | | | |
| ☐ **HUET, Jean Baptiste** | ............... | paintings | | $38,500 |
| French 1745-1811 | ............... | drawings | $253 | $1,980 |
| ☐ **HUET, Leon Armand** | ............... | paintings | | $4,400 |
| French 19th cent. | | | | |
| ☐ **HUET, Paul** | ............... | paintings | $6,875 | $8,525 |
| French 1803-1869 | ............... | drawings | $242 | $605 |
| ☐ **HUFFINGTON, John C.** | ............... | paintings | $44 | $165 |
| American 1864-1929 | ............... | drawings | | $800 |
| ☐ **HUGE, Jurgen Frederick** | ............... | paintings | $7,150 | $7,150 |
| American 1809-1878 | | | | |
| ☐ **HUGGINS, M.W.** | ............... | paintings | $242 | $302 |
| American contemporary | | | | |
| ☐ **HUGGINS, William** | ............... | paintings | $825 | $5,500 |
| British 1820-1884 | ............... | drawings | | $220 |
| ☐ **HUGGINS, William John** | ............... | paintings | | $2,420 |
| English 1781-1845 | | | | |
| ☐ **HUGHES, Arthur** | ............... | paintings | $253 | $7,700 |
| English 1832-1915 | | | | |
| ☐ **HUGHES, Arthur Foord** | ............... | drawings | $130 | $522 |
| English 1856-1914 | | | | |
| ☐ **HUGHES, Daisy Marguerite** | ............... | paintings | $82 | $605 |
| American 1883-1968 | | | | |
| ☐ **HUGHES, Edward Robert** | ............... | drawings | | $1,210 |
| English 1851-1914 | | | | |
| ☐ **HUGHES, G.F.** | ............... | paintings | | $550 |
| ☐ **HUGHES, George** | ............... | paintings | $143 | $880 |
| American b. 1907 | | | | |
| ☐ **HUGHES, John Joseph** | ............... | paintings | $440 | $3,025 |
| British ac. 1838-1867 | | | | |
| ☐ **HUGHES, John Thomas** | ............... | paintings | $77 | $440 |
| English 19th cent. | | | | |
| ☐ **HUGHES, Renne** | ............... | sculpture | | $275 |
| American contemporary | | | | |
| ☐ **HUGHES, Robert Ball** | ............... | sculpture | | $9,000 |
| English/American 1806-1868 | | | | |

| | | Current Price Range | |
|---|---|---|---|
| | | Low | High |
| ☐ **HUGHES, Stanley C.** ........................... *drawings* | | $1,250 | $1,400 |
| American contemporary | | | |
| ☐ **HUGHES, Talbot** ............................... *paintings* | | | $7,700 |
| English 19th cent. | | | |
| ☐ **HUGHES, William** ............................... *paintings* | | $825 | $3,080 |
| British 1842-1901 | | | |
| ☐ **HUGHES-STANTON, Sir Herbert** ......... *paintings* | | | $550 |
| English 1870-1937 | | | |
| ☐ **HUGHSON, W.A.** ............................... *paintings* | | $165 | $192 |
| American 19th cent. | | | |
| ☐ **HUGHTO, Darryl** ............................... *paintings* | | $1,650 | $1,980 |
| American b. 1943 | | | |
| ☐ **HUGO, Jean** ................................... *paintings* | | $308 | $2,200 |
| French b. 1894 ..................................... *drawings* | | $150 | $935 |
| ☐ **HUGO, Len** ................................... *paintings* | | | $7,700 |
| ☐ **HUGONNEL** ................................... *sculpture* | | | $1,430 |
| ☐ **HUGUES, Paul** ................................ *paintings* | | | $302 |
| French b. 1891 | | | |
| ☐ **HUGUET, Victor Pierre** ..................... *paintings* | | $990 | $18,700 |
| French 1835-1902 | | | |
| ☐ **HUI, Wang** ................................... *paintings* | | | $192 |
| Chinese 1632-1717 | | | |
| ☐ **HUIERGLIO, Merio** ............................ *paintings* | | | $605 |
| French 20th cent. | | | |
| ☐ **HULBERT, Charles Allen** ..................... *paintings* | | $300 | $330 |
| American 19th/20th cent. ......................... *drawings* | | | $357 |
| ☐ **HULBERT, Katherine Allmond** ............. *paintings* | | | $385 |
| ☐ **HULBERT, Lylian Root** ....................... *paintings* | | | $302 |
| French 19th/20th cent. | | | |
| ☐ **HULDAH** ..................................... *paintings* | | $77 | $1,430 |
| American 20th cent. ............................... *drawings* | | | $165 |
| ☐ **HULINGS, Clark** ............................. *paintings* | | $27,500 | $60,000 |
| American b. 1922 ................................. *drawings* | | | $3,500 |
| ☐ **HULK, Abraham (Jr.)** ......................... *paintings* | | $385 | $3,630 |
| English 1851-1922 ................................. *drawings* | | | $242 |
| ☐ **HULK, Abraham (Sr.)** ......................... *paintings* | | $2,090 | $5,500 |
| English 1813-1897 | | | |
| ☐ **HULK, F.** ................................... *paintings* | | | $440 |
| Dutch 19th cent. | | | |
| ☐ **HULK, Hendrik** ............................... *paintings* | | $467 | $1,320 |
| Dutch 1842-1937 | | | |
| ☐ **HULK, Johannes Frederick** ................. *paintings* | | $440 | $5,775 |
| Dutch 1829-1911 | | | |
| ☐ **HULK, William Frederick** ..................... *paintings* | | $357 | $1,100 |
| English b. 1852; ac. 1875-1906 | | | |
| ☐ **HULL, Edward** ............................... *paintings* | | | $1,700 |
| English 19th cent. ................................. *drawings* | | | $231 |
| ☐ **HULL, Marie Atkinson** ....................... *paintings* | | | $605 |
| American 1890-1980 ............................... *drawings* | | | $110 |

| | Current Price Range | |
|---|---|---|
| | Low | High |

| | | Low | High |
|---|---|---|---|
| ☐ **HULL, Wm.** .......................... *paintings* | | | $385 |
| British 19th cent. | | | |
| ☐ **HULLENKREMER, Odon** .................. *paintings* | | | $770 |
| American 20th cent. | | | |
| ☐ **HULME, Frederick William** ................. *paintings* | | $715 | $4,400 |
| English 1816-1884 | | | |
| ☐ **HULME, Jesse** ...................... *paintings* | | | $935 |
| ☐ **HULSDONCK, Jacob van** .................. *paintings* | | $28,600 | $82,500 |
| Flemish 1582-1647 | | | |
| ☐ **HULSEBUSCH** ...................... *paintings* | | | $1,320 |
| German 19th cent. | | | |
| ☐ **HULSMAN, Johann** ........................... *paintings* | | | $3,850 |
| ☐ **HULST, Frans de** .............................. *paintings* | | $3,300 | $15,750 |
| Flemish 1610-1661 | | | |
| ☐ **HULTBERG, John** ........................... *drawings* | | | $605 |
| American b. 1922 | | | |
| ☐ **HUMBERT, Andre Louis Maxime** ......... *paintings* | | | $1,320 |
| French b. 1879 | | | |
| ☐ **HUMBERT, Jacques Fernand** ............... *paintings* | | $466 | $1,100 |
| French b. 1842 | | | |
| ☐ **HUMBERT, Jean Charles Ferdinand** ..... *paintings* | | $2,420 | $3,520 |
| Swiss 1813-1881 | | | |
| ☐ **HUMBLOT, Robert** ........................... *paintings* | | | $522 |
| French 20th cent. | | | |
| ☐ **HUMBOLDT** ...................... *paintings* | | | $385 |
| American 19th/20th cent. | | | |
| ☐ **HUMBORG, Adolf** ........................... *paintings* | | $330 | $12,100 |
| Austrian b. 1847 | | | |
| ☐ **HUME, Edith** ........................... *paintings* | | | $1,760 |
| ☐ **HUMMEL, Carl Maria Nicolaus** ........... *paintings* | | $1,100 | $2,750 |
| German 1821-1907 | | | |
| ☐ **HUMPHREY, Ralph** ........................... *paintings* | | $825 | $2,640 |
| American b. 1932 ...................... *drawings* | | | $385 |
| ...................... *sculpture* | | $8,800 | $9,900 |
| ☐ **HUMPHREY, Walter Beach** ................. *paintings* | | $1,000 | $2,600 |
| American b. 1892 ...................... *drawings* | | | $165 |
| ☐ **HUMPHREYS, Charles S.** ................... *paintings* | | | $6,600 |
| American ac. 1854-1876 | | | |
| ☐ **HUMPHREYS, M.** ........................... *paintings* | | | $462 |
| ☐ **HUMPHRISS, Charles Harry** ................ *sculpture* | | $3,850 | $9,075 |
| American 1867-1934/40 | | | |
| ☐ **HUNCK, George** ...................... *paintings* | | | $990 |
| ☐ **HUNDERTWASSER,** | | | |
| **(Fritz STOWASSER)** ........................... *drawings* | | $19,800 | $31,900 |
| Austrian b. 1928 | | | |
| ☐ **HUNDLEY** ...................... *paintings* | | | $198 |
| American 20th cent. | | | |
| ☐ **HUNN, Thomas H.** ........................... *drawings* | | | $577 |
| English ac. 1878-1910 | | | |

| | | *Current Price Range* | |
|---|---|---|---|
| | | *Low* | *High* |
| ☐ **HUNS, Js.** .......................................... *drawings* | | | $301 |
| ☐ **HUNT, Alfred William** ......................... *drawings* | | $110 | $253 |
| English 1830-1896 | | | |
| ☐ **HUNT, Andrew** ................................... *paintings* | | | $330 |
| English 1790-1861 | | | |
| ☐ **HUNT, Bryan** ..................................... *sculpture* | | $6,600 | $26,400 |
| American b. 1947 | | | |
| ☐ **HUNT, Cecil Arthur** ........................... *drawings* | | | $550 |
| English 1873-1965 | | | |
| ☐ **HUNT, Charles** ................................... *paintings* | | $242 | $19,800 |
| English 1803-1877 | | | |
| ☐ **HUNT, Charles D.** ............................... *paintings* | | $246 | $825 |
| American 1840-1914 ................................... *drawings* | | $132 | $220 |
| ☐ **HUNT, Edgar** ..................................... *paintings* | | $1,320 | $17,600 |
| English 1876-1953 | | | |
| ☐ **HUNT, Edward Aubrey** ......................... *paintings* | | $220 | $3,960 |
| English 1855-1922 | | | |
| ☐ **HUNT, Esther** ..................................... *drawings* | | | $1,540 |
| American 1885-1951 | | | |
| ☐ **HUNT, Henry P.** ................................. *paintings* | | $1,210 | $1,320 |
| American 19th cent. | | | |
| ☐ **HUNT, Lynn Bogue** ............................. *paintings* | | $935 | $2,530 |
| American 1878-1960 ................................... *drawings* | | $121 | $4,800 |
| ☐ **HUNT, Peter** ..................................... *paintings* | | $25 | $400 |
| American 20th cent. | | | |
| ☐ **HUNT, Reuben** ................................... *paintings* | | | $3,850 |
| British 19th cent. | | | |
| ☐ **HUNT, Richard** ................................... *paintings* | | | $121 |
| American b. 1935 ...................................... *drawings* | | | $99 |
| ...................................................... *sculpture* | | $1,210 | $1,760 |
| ☐ **HUNT, Walter** ................................... *paintings* | | | $5,775 |
| British 19th cent. | | | |
| ☐ **HUNT, Wayne** ................................... *sculpture* | | | $3,000 |
| American b. 1904 | | | |
| ☐ **HUNT, William Henry** ......................... *paintings* | | $1,100 | $1,500 |
| British 1790-1864 ..................................... *drawings* | | $154 | $2,530 |
| ☐ **HUNT, William Morris** ......................... *paintings* | | $990 | $58,300 |
| American 1824-1879 ................................... *drawings* | | $500 | $4,840 |
| ☐ **HUNT, Wolf Robe** ............................... *drawings* | | | $1,430 |
| American (Acoma) | | | |
| ☐ **HUNTEN, Emile** ................................. *paintings* | | | $742 |
| German 1827-1902 | | | |
| ☐ **HUNTER, Ada** ................................... *drawings* | | | $440 |
| American late 19th cent. | | | |
| ☐ **HUNTER, Clementine** ......................... *paintings* | | $137 | $715 |
| American b. 1882 ...................................... *drawings* | | | $550 |
| ☐ **HUNTER, Colin** ................................. *paintings* | | $187 | $770 |
| Scottish,d. London 1841-1904 | | | |
| ☐ **HUNTER, D.J.** ................................... *drawings* | | | $302 |

| | | | Current Price Range | |
|---|---|---|---|---|
| | | | Low | High |
| ☐ **HUNTER, Frederick Leo** ..................... | *paintings* | | $60 | $825 |
| American 1858-1943 | | | | |
| ☐ **HUNTER, G.** ....................................... | *paintings* | | | $330 |
| English 19th cent. | | | | |
| ☐ **HUNTER, John Young** ........................ | *paintings* | | $1,485 | $11,000 |
| American 1874-1955 | | | | |
| ☐ **HUNTER, Leslie M.** ........................... | *drawings* | | | $412 |
| ☐ **HUNTER, Lizabeth C.** ......................... | *drawings* | | $55 | $577 |
| American b. 1868 | | | | |
| ☐ **HUNTER, Max** ................................... | *paintings* | | | $88 |
| American 19th/20th cent. ............................. | *drawings* | | | $286 |
| ☐ **HUNTER, Robert** ............................... | *paintings* | | | $1,760 |
| Irish 18th cent. | | | | |
| ☐ **HUNTER (?), W.H.** ............................. | *paintings* | | | $1,210 |
| English 19th cent. | | | | |
| ☐ **HUNTINGTON, Anna Vaughn Hyatt** .... | *sculpture* | | $650 | $9,900 |
| American 1876-1973 | | | | |
| ☐ **HUNTINGTON, C. Lyman** .................. | *paintings* | | | $467 |
| American 19th cent. | | | | |
| ☐ **HUNTINGTON, Daniel** ........................ | *paintings* | | $350 | $6,270 |
| American 1816-1906 ................................ | *drawings* | | $400 | $1,650 |
| ☐ **HUNTINGTON, Margaret Wendell** ....... | *paintings* | | | $660 |
| American 20th cent. | | | | |
| ☐ **HUNTINGTON, Sarah S.** ..................... | *paintings* | | | $605 |
| American 19th cent. | | | | |
| ☐ **HUNTINGTON, Susan Terpning** .......... | *paintings* | | $2,750 | $4,000 |
| American b. 1953 ...................................... | *drawings* | | $2,300 | $2,500 |
| ☐ **HUPCHER, F.** ................................... | *paintings* | | | $1,760 |
| American | | | | |
| ☐ **HUPIN, Jacques** ............................... | *paintings* | | | $15,400 |
| ☐ **HUQUIER, Gabriel** ............................ | *drawings* | | | $385 |
| ☐ **HURD, Peter** ................................... | *paintings* | | $1,540 | $4,950 |
| American 1904-1984 ................................. | *drawings* | | $330 | $5,500 |
| ☐ **HURDLE, George Linton** ..................... | *drawings* | | | $302 |
| American 1868-1922 | | | | |
| ☐ **HURDLEBRINK, Robert** ...................... | *sculpture* | | | $220 |
| American b. 1937 | | | | |
| ☐ **HURE, C.L.** ..................................... | *paintings* | | | $825 |
| ☐ **HURENBOUT, J.** ............................... | *paintings* | | | $990 |
| Continental 19th cent. | | | | |
| ☐ **HURL, Van der** ................................. | *paintings* | | | $412 |
| Dutch contemporary | | | | |
| ☐ **HURLEY, Wilson** ............................... | *paintings* | | $522 | $20,000 |
| American b. 1924 | | | | |
| ☐ **HURLSTONE, Frederick Yeates** .......... | *paintings* | | | $800 |
| 1800-1869 | | | | |
| ☐ **HURST, M.E.** ................................... | *paintings* | | | $440 |
| ☐ **HURT, Louis Bosworth** ...................... | *paintings* | | $440 | $9,900 |
| English 1856-1929 | | | | |

| | | Current Price Range | |
|---|---|---|---|
| | | Low | High |
| ☐ **HURTT, Arthur R.** .......................... *paintings* | | | $550 |
| American b. 1861 | | | |
| ☐ **HUSSA, Theodore (Jr.)** .......................... *paintings* | | | $220 |
| American 20th cent. | | | |
| ☐ **HUSSAR, Joseph P.** ............................ *paintings* | | $120 | $250 |
| ☐ **HUSTON, William** .......................... *paintings* | | $400 | $1,650 |
| American 19th cent. | | | |
| ☐ **HUSTWICK, E.** .......................... *paintings* | | | $1,980 |
| ☐ **HUSZAR, Vilmos** .......................... *paintings* | | | $495 |
| ☐ **HUTCHENS, Frank Townsend** ............. *paintings* | | $192 | $6,600 |
| American 1869-1937 ............................ *drawings* | | $192 | $440 |
| ☐ **HUTCHINSON, D.C.** .......................... *paintings* | | | $605 |
| ☐ **HUTCHINSON, Frederick W.** .............. *paintings* | | | $1,045 |
| American d. 1953 | | | |
| ☐ **HUTCHINSON, Robert Gemmell** .......... *paintings* | | $88 | $2,750 |
| English 1855-1936 | | | |
| ☐ **HUTCHISON, Ellen Wales** .................. *paintings* | | $77 | $275 |
| American 1867-1937 | | | |
| ☐ **HUTCHISON, Frederick William** .......... *paintings* | | $302 | $2,090 |
| American 1871-1953 | | | |
| ☐ **HUTHER, Julius** ................................ *drawings* | | | $247 |
| American | | | |
| ☐ **HUTSCHENREUTHER, Victor-Max** ..... *paintings* | | | $412 |
| Austrian b. 1828 | | | |
| ☐ **HUTSEBUSCH** .......................... *paintings* | | | $3,300 |
| ☐ **HUTSON, William** .......................... *paintings* | | $165 | $220 |
| contemporary | | | |
| ☐ **HUTT, Henry** ....................................... *drawings* | | $154 | $385 |
| American b. 1875 | | | |
| ☐ **HUTTON, T. Fawcett** .......................... *paintings* | | $1,100 | $1,540 |
| British 19th/20th cent. | | | |
| ☐ **HUTTY, Alfred Heber** .......................... *paintings* | | $660 | $1,210 |
| American 1877/78-1954 ............................ *drawings* | | $330 | $1,265 |
| ☐ **HUVE, Jean-Jacques** .......................... *drawings* | | | $3,630 |
| French 1742-1808 | | | |
| ☐ **HUYGEN, L.** .......................... *paintings* | | | $300 |
| ☐ **HUYGENS, Francois Joseph** ................ *paintings* | | | $4,400 |
| Belgian 1820-1908 | | | |
| ☐ **HUYGENS, Johannes** .......................... *paintings* | | | $1,045 |
| Dutch 19th cent. | | | |
| ☐ **HUYOT, C.** .......................... *paintings* | | | $264 |
| ☐ **HUYSMANS, Cornelis** .......................... *paintings* | | $385 | $4,000 |
| Flemish 1648-1727 | | | |
| ☐ **HUYSMANS, Jan Baptist** .................. *paintings* | | $1,650 | $31,900 |
| ☐ **HUYSUM, Jan van** .......................... *paintings* | | $24,200 | $88,000 |
| Dutch 1682-1749 ............................ *drawings* | | | $1,650 |
| ☐ **HUYSUM, Justus van** .......................... *paintings* | | $3,300 | $20,900 |
| ☐ **HUZEC** ................................................. *paintings* | | | $550 |
| American | | | |

| | | Current Price Range | |
|---|---|---|---|
| | | Low | High |
| ☐ **HYDE, George** ........................ *paintings* | | $275 | $605 |
| English 19th cent. | | | |
| ☐ **HYDE, Henry James** ............... *paintings* | | | $467 |
| British 19th cent. | | | |
| ☐ **HYDE, William Henry** ............ *paintings* | | $88 | $1,430 |
| American 1858-1943 ..................... *drawings* | | $77 | $352 |
| ☐ **HYETT, William J.** ................ *paintings* | | $385 | $467 |
| American b. 1876 ........................ *drawings* | | | $143 |
| ☐ **HYNAIS, Voytech** ................. *drawings* | | $4,510 | $4,675 |
| Czechoslovakian 1854-1925 | | | |
| ☐ **HYNEMAN, Herman N.** ......... *paintings* | | $137 | $2,420 |
| American 1859-1907 | | | |
| ☐ **HYNEMAN, Julia** ................. *paintings* | | | $660 |
| American 20th cent. | | | |
| ☐ **HYNER, Arend** .................... *paintings* | | | $1,100 |
| Dutch 1866-1916 | | | |
| ☐ **HYON, Georges Louis** ........... *paintings* | | $715 | $2,200 |
| French b. 1855 | | | |
| ☐ **HYPPOLITE, Hector** ............. *paintings* | | $1,540 | $36,300 |
| Haitian 1894-1948 | | | |
| ☐ **HYPPOLITE, L.** .................... *paintings* | | | $356 |
| Haitian 20th cent. | | | |
| ☐ **IACOVLEFF, Alexandre** ........ *paintings* | | $200 | $1,320 |
| French 1887-1938 ....................... *drawings* | | $200 | $825 |
| ☐ **IANELLI, Arcangelo** ............. *paintings* | | | $2,860 |
| Brazilian b. 1922 | | | |
| ☐ **IANELLI, Thomas** ................ *paintings* | | | $1,100 |
| Latin American | | | |
| ☐ **IAZAREV, V.** ...................... *paintings* | | | $660 |
| ☐ **IBANEZ, Manuel Ramirez** ...... *paintings* | | | $7,150 |
| Spanish 1856-1925 | | | |
| ☐ **IBBETSON, Julius Caesar** ....... *paintings* | | $660 | $18,700 |
| English 1759-1817 ...................... *drawings* | | | $7,150 |
| ☐ **IBOS, Jean Francoise** ............ *drawings* | | | $1,650 |
| ☐ **ICART, Louis** ..................... *paintings* | | $209 | $19,800 |
| French 1888-1950 ....................... *drawings* | | $77 | $6,380 |
| ☐ **ICAZA, Ernesto** .................. *paintings* | | $4,400 | $4,620 |
| b. Mexico 1866-1935 | | | |
| ☐ **ICAZA, Francisco de** ............ *paintings* | | $44 | $302 |
| Mexican b. 1930 ........................ *drawings* | | $110 | $165 |
| ........................................ *sculpture* | | $137 | $1,375 |
| ☐ **IFFLAND, Franz** .................. *sculpture* | | | $1,100 |
| German 19th cent. | | | |
| ☐ **IGLER, Gustav** .................... *paintings* | | $23,100 | $24,200 |
| Austrian 1842-1908 | | | |
| ☐ **IHLEE, Eduard Johann** ......... *paintings* | | | $4,400 |
| German 1812-1885 | | | |
| ☐ **IHLEFELD, Henry** ................ *drawings* | | | $770 |
| American 1859-1932 | | | |

| | | Current Price Range | |
|---|---|---|---|
| | | Low | High |
| ☐ **IHLY, Daniel** .................... *paintings* <br> Swiss 1854-1910 | | $192 | $247 |
| ☐ **ILIGAN, Ralph W.** .................... *paintings* <br> American early 20th cent. | | | $1,540 |
| ☐ **ILLES, Aladar Edvi** .................... *paintings* <br> Hungarian b. 1870 | | $220 | $3,850 |
| ☐ **ILSLEY, Frederick J.** .................... *paintings* <br> American 1855-1933 .................... *drawings* | | $74 | $280 <br> $121 |
| ☐ **ILYIN, Gleb** .................... *paintings* <br> American 1889-1968 | | $66 | $605 |
| ☐ **ILYIN, Peter A.** .................... *paintings* <br> Russian/American 1887-1950 .................... *drawings* | | $137 | $385 <br> $192 |
| ☐ **IMHOF, Joseph A.** .................... *drawings* <br> American 1871-1955 | | $700 | $5,500 |
| ☐ **IMMER, F.H.** .................... *paintings* | | | $450 |
| ☐ **IMPENS, Josse** .................... *paintings* <br> Belgian 1840-1905 | | | $715 |
| ☐ **IMSCHOOT, Jules A. van** .................... *paintings* <br> Belgian 1821-1824 | | | $1,650 |
| ☐ **INCE, Joseph Murray** .................... *paintings* <br> British 1806-1859 | | | $1,650 |
| ☐ **INDIANA, Robert** .................... *paintings* <br> American b. 1928 .................... *drawings* <br> .................... *sculpture* | | $2,420 | $25,300 <br> $1,540 <br> $7,700 |
| ☐ **INDONI** .................... *drawings* | | | $330 |
| ☐ **INDONI, Filippo** .................... *paintings* <br> Italian 19th cent. .................... *drawings* | | $605 <br> $192 | $1,650 <br> $1,540 |
| ☐ **INDONI, S.** .................... *paintings* <br> Continental 19th/20th cent. | | | $825 |
| ☐ **INDUNO, Domenico** .................... *paintings* <br> Italian 1815-1878 | | $1,100 | $2,640 |
| ☐ **INDUNO, Girolamo** .................... *paintings* <br> Italian 1827-1890 | | | $3,200 |
| ☐ **INGALLS, Walter** .................... *paintings* <br> Canadian 1805-1874 | | $121 | $2,200 |
| ☐ **INGANNATI, Pietro degli** .................... *paintings* <br> Italian ac. 1529-1548 | | | $1,210 |
| ☐ **INGANNI, E.** .................... *paintings* | | | $550 |
| ☐ **INGEN, Henry van** .................... *paintings* <br> Dutch 1833-1898 .................... *drawings* | | $550 | $2,750 <br> $110 |
| ☐ **INGERMANN, Keith** .................... *paintings* <br> 20th cent. | | | $192 |
| ☐ **INGHAM, Elizabeth Howell** .................... *drawings* <br> American | | | $275 |
| ☐ **INGLIS, Johnstone J.** .................... *paintings* <br> British 19th cent. | | $880 | $1,210 |
| ☐ **INGRAM, William** .................... *paintings* | | | $357 |

## Pop Art

Robert Indiana, together with Jim Dine, Claes Oldenburg, Roy Lichtenstein, Andy Warhol, James Rosenquist, and Tom Wesselmann, are the names most often linked with the Pop Art movement which dominated American art during the 1960s.

Pop artists often painted everyday objects larger than life, a reaction, some critics think, against the withdrawal from the real world that is implied by Abstract Impressionism.

Indiana is best known for his large-scale paintings and many variations on "Love." Two years after his first solo show in 1962, he collaborated with Andy Warhol on the film "EAT." His first public commission was a twenty-foot tall EAT sign for the New York State Pavilion at the 1964 World's Fair. Characteristically, he used pure intense color and optical effects.

In his "Love" paintings, figure and ground seem to be equivalent. Red and green, the colors of Phillips Petroleum and the Indiana company for which his father worked, dominate this series. Painted in 1966, this work was exhibited at the Philadelphia Museum in 1968. (Robert Indiana, "Love," oil on canvas, 48 x 48 in., Sotheby's, May 2, 1985, $20,900.)

|  |  | *Current Price Range* | |
|---|---|---|---|
|  |  | *Low* | *High* |
| ☐ **INGRES, Jean Auguste Dominique** ........ *drawings* | | **$1,320** | **$165,000** |
| French 1780-1867 | | | |
| ☐ **INGRES, Maurice** .............................. *paintings* | | | **$1,400** |
| ☐ **INJALBERT, Jean Antoine** ................... *sculpture* | | **$1,760** | **$2,475** |
| French 1845-1933 | | | |
| ☐ **INMAN, Henry** ..................................... *paintings* | | **$450** | **$11,000** |
| American 1801-1846 | | | |
| ☐ **INMAN, John O'Brien** ......................... *paintings* | | **$440** | **$4,400** |
| American 1828-1896 | | | |
| ☐ **INMAN, Tempest** ............................... *drawings* | | | **$1,210** |
| ☐ **INNES, John** ....................................... *paintings* | | | **$198** |
| American | | | |
| ☐ **INNESS, George** ............................... *paintings* | | **$605** | **$132,000** |
| American 1825-1894 ................................. *drawings* | | **$660** | **$10,450** |
| ☐ **INNESS, George (Jr.)** .......................... *paintings* | | **$330** | **$11,000** |
| American 1853-1926 ................................. *drawings* | | **$495** | **$1,650** |
| ☐ **INNOCENTI, Camillo** ......................... *paintings* | | **$385** | **$1,210** |
| Italian b. 1861 ........................................... *drawings* | | | **$11,000** |

|  | | *Current Price Range* | |
|---|---|---|---|
|  | | *Low* | *High* |
| ☐ **INO, Pierre** .......................................... *paintings* | | | $1,320 |
| French b. 1909 | | | |
| ☐ **INSLEY, Albert** ................................. *paintings* | | $88 | $3,300 |
| American 1842-1937 | | | |
| ☐ **IODE, Gerard de** ................................. *drawings* | | | $700 |
| Dutch | | | |
| ☐ **IOHFRA,** | | | |
| **Francisco Johannes Gijsbertus** ............... *paintings* | | $440 | $1,100 |
| Spanish 20th cent. | | | |
| ☐ **ION** ........................................................ *drawings* | | | $770 |
| ☐ **IPOLD, R.** ............................................. *drawings* | | $935 | $990 |
| ☐ **IPOUSTEGUY, Jean** ........................... *sculpture* | | $1,100 | $5,500 |
| French b. 1920 | | | |
| ☐ **IPPOLITO, Angelo** .............................. *drawings* | | | $220 |
| American b. 1922 | | | |
| ☐ **IPSEN, Ernest L.** ................................. *paintings* | | $302 | $990 |
| American 1869-1951 | | | |
| ☐ **IRA-MONTE, ******* ......................... *paintings* | | | $495 |
| Spanish 20th cent. | | | |
| ☐ **IRELAND, L.F.** .................................... *paintings* | | | $440 |
| ☐ **IRELAND, Leroy** ................................. *paintings* | | $577 | $1,760 |
| American b. 1889 | | | |
| ☐ **IRIARTE, Ignacio de** ........................... *paintings* | | | $2,200 |
| Spanish 1621-1685 | | | |
| ☐ **IROLLI, Vincenzo** ............................... *paintings* | | $1,650 | $31,900 |
| Italian 1860-c. 1937/42 | | | |
| ☐ **IRONSIDE, Robin** ............................... *drawings* | | $150 | $220 |
| English 20th cent. | | | |
| ☐ **IRVINE, Wilson Henry** ....................... *paintings* | | $176 | $14,300 |
| American 1869-1936 .................................... *drawings* | | $176 | $528 |
| ☐ **IRVING, John Beaufain** ....................... *paintings* | | | $700 |
| American 1825/26-1877 | | | |
| ☐ **IRVING, Washington** ........................... *paintings* | | | $550 |
| American 19th cent. | | | |
| ☐ **IRWIN, Benoni** ..................................... *paintings* | | | $1,100 |
| Canadian 1840-1896 .................................... *drawings* | | | $1,650 |
| ☐ **IRWIN, H.J.** ......................................... *paintings* | | | $385 |
| British 19th cent. | | | |
| ☐ **IRWIN, John E.** .................................... *paintings* | | $192 | $330 |
| ☐ **IRWIN, Robert** ..................................... *paintings* | | | $20,900 |
| American b. 1928 ...................................... *sculpture* | | | $49,500 |
| ☐ **ISABEY, Jean Baptiste** ........................ *paintings* | | | $1,100 |
| French 1767-1855 ........................................ *drawings* | | $522 | $550 |
| ☐ **ISABEY, Louis Gabriel Eugene** ............. *paintings* | | $220 | $19,800 |
| French 1803-1886 ....................................... *drawings* | | $495 | $880 |
| ☐ **ISAMBERT, A.** ..................................... *paintings* | | | $880 |
| French 19th cent. | | | |
| ☐ **ISELIN, Belinda** .................................... *sculpture* | | | $2,860 |

| | | *Current Price Range* | |
|---|---|---|---|
| | | Low | High |
| ☐ **ISENBRANT, Adriaen** .......................... *paintings* | | $52,800 | $110,000 |
| Flemish c. 1490-1551 | | | |
| ☐ **ISENBURGER, Eric** ........................... *paintings* | | $275 | $1,650 |
| German/American b. 1902 | | | |
| ☐ **ISHAM, Samuel** ................................. *paintings* | | $1,925 | $2,750 |
| American 1855-1914 | | | |
| ☐ **ISHIGAKI, Eitaro** .............................. *paintings* | | | $1,430 |
| Japanese/American  20th cent. | | | |
| ☐ **ISMAILOVITCH, D.** .......................... *paintings* | | | $220 |
| Russian early 20th cent. | | | |
| ☐ **ISRAEL, Daniel** ................................. *paintings* | | $2,090 | $16,500 |
| Austrian 1859-1901 | | | |
| ☐ **ISRAELS, Isaac** ................................. *paintings* | | $209 | $20,900 |
| Dutch 1865-1934 ....................................... *drawings* | | $275 | $1,760 |
| ☐ **ISRAELS, Josef** ................................. *paintings* | | $950 | $11,000 |
| Dutch 1824-1911 ....................................... *drawings* | | $715 | $1,650 |
| ☐ **ISSACHS, Joseph** .............................. *paintings* | | | $522 |
| ☐ **ISSUPOFF, Alessio** ............................. *paintings* | | $4,125 | $10,450 |
| Russian 1889-1957 | | | |
| ☐ **ISTVANFFY, Gabrielle Rainer** .............. *paintings* | | | $660 |
| Hungarian b. 1877 | | | |
| ☐ **ITASSE, Adolphe** ............................... *sculpture* | | | $1,760 |
| French 1830-1893 | | | |
| ☐ **ITTENBACH, Franz** ........................... *paintings* | | | $1,870 |
| German 1813-1879 | | | |
| ☐ **IVANOF, A.** ....................................... *paintings* | | | $302 |
| ☐ **IVANOFF, Michail Matveievitch** ........... *drawings* | | | $1,760 |
| Russian 1748-1823 | | | |
| ☐ **IVANOFF, Michail Philippovitch** ........... *paintings* | | | $935 |
| Russian b. 1869 | | | |
| ☐ **IVANOVITCH, Paul** ........................... *paintings* | | | $6,600 |
| Austrian b. 1859 | | | |
| ☐ **IVANOVITCH, Paul** ........................... *paintings* | | | $6,600 |
| Austrian b. 1859 | | | |
| ☐ **IVERD, Eugene** ................................. *paintings* | | | $880 |
| ☐ **IVERSEN, Helen** ................................ *paintings* | | | $528 |
| ☐ **IVES, Chauncey Bradley** ...................... *sculpture* | | $1,650 | $46,200 |
| American 1810/12-1894 | | | |
| ☐ **IVES, Norman** .................................. *paintings* | | | $385 |
| ☐ **IVES, Percy** ...................................... *paintings* | | $66 | $4,000 |
| American b. 1864 | | | |
| ☐ **IVY, Evelyn** ...................................... *paintings* | | | $357 |
| American 20th cent. | | | |
| ☐ **IWILL, Joseph** | | | |
| **(Marie Joseph Leon CLAVEL)** .............. *paintings* | | $440 | $1,760 |
| French 1850-1923 ....................................... *drawings* | | $2,420 | $3,520 |
| ☐ **IZAGUIRRE, Leandro** ........................ *drawings* | | $1,980 | $2,420 |
| Mexican 1867-1941 | | | |

## Neo-Classical Sculpture

*Chauncey Bradley Ives was a 19th-century American portrait sculptor whose works may be seen at the United States Capitol and the Connecticut State Capitol.*

*In the fall of 1984, Frank H. Boos Gallery discovered "Undine Receiving Her Soul" in the basement of a church in Michigan, where it had been placed in 1956, the bequest of a prominent state resident. Ives is known to have executed fourteen versions of Undine. The location of eight of these is unknown. (Chauncey Bradley Ives, "Undine Receiving Her Soul," marble, height, 35½ in., Frank H. Boos Gallery, January 25, 1985, $44,000.)*

|  | Current Price Range | |
| --- | --- | --- |
|  | *Low* | *High* |
| ☐ **IZOYKORVSKY, F. von** ............. *paintings* <br> Polish 20th cent. |  | **$385** |
| ☐ **IZQUIERDO, Maria** ............. *paintings* <br> Mexican b. 1908 ............. *drawings* | **$2,640** | **$6,600** <br> **$11,000** |
| ☐ **JACKSON, A.Y.** ............. *paintings* |  | **$28,600** |
| ☐ **JACKSON, Alexander Young** ....... *drawings* <br> Canadian b. 1882 |  | **$1,045** |
| ☐ **JACKSON, Charles Akerman** ....... *paintings* <br> American b. 1857 |  | **$220** |
| ☐ **JACKSON, Elbert McGran** ......... *paintings* <br> American b. 1896 | **$357** | **$2,640** |
| ☐ **JACKSON, Elizabeth Lesley** ....... *drawings* <br> American 1867-1934 |  | **$275** |
| ☐ **JACKSON, Elsbeth S.** ............. *paintings* <br> American 20th cent. |  | **$275** |

| | | Current Price Range | |
|---|---|---|---|
| | | Low | High |
| ☐ **JACKSON, G.** .................... *paintings* | | $715 | $1,650 |
| British 19th cent. | | | |
| ☐ **JACKSON, Harry** ...................... *drawings* | | | $137 |
| American b. 1924 .................... *sculpture* | | $935 | $40,000 |
| ☐ **JACKSON, James R.** ................ *paintings* | | | $990 |
| Australian 1886-1975 | | | |
| ☐ **JACKSON, John Edwin** ............ *drawings* | | | $247 |
| American b. 1876 | | | |
| ☐ **JACKSON, Joseph** ................... *paintings* | | | $412 |
| American d. 1850 | | | |
| ☐ **JACKSON, M.** ......................... *paintings* | | $100 | $176 |
| English 19th cent. | | | |
| ☐ **JACKSON, Martin** .................. *paintings* | | $110 | $1,000 |
| American contemporary | | | |
| ☐ **JACKSON, Samuel Phillips** ......... *drawings* | | | $880 |
| British 1830-1904 | | | |
| ☐ **JACKSON, T.J.** ....................... *paintings* | | | $308 |
| ☐ **JACKSON, W.F.** ...................... *paintings* | | | $1,540 |
| American 19th cent. | | | |
| ☐ **JACKSON, William Franklin** ........... *paintings* | | $770 | $935 |
| American 1850-1936 | | | |
| ☐ **JACKSON, William Henry** ............ *paintings* | | | $1,650 |
| American 1843-1942 | | | |
| ☐ **JACOB, Alexandre Louis** .............. *paintings* | | $880 | $990 |
| French b. 1876 | | | |
| ☐ **JACOB, J.** ........................... *paintings* | | $385 | $467 |
| Continental School 19th cent. | | | |
| ☐ **JACOB, Max** ......................... *paintings* | | | $3,850 |
| French 1876-1944 ...................... *drawings* | | $357 | $3,300 |
| ☐ **JACOB, Ned** ......................... *paintings* | | $10,000 | $27,500 |
| American b. 1938 ...................... *drawings* | | $2,250 | $2,500 |
| ☐ **JACOB, Stephen** ..................... *paintings* | | | $1,650 |
| French b. 1846 | | | |
| ☐ **JACOBI, M.M.** ....................... *paintings* | | $302 | $440 |
| ☐ **JACOBI, Otto R.** ..................... *drawings* | | $385 | $550 |
| German/Canadian 1814-1901 | | | |
| ☐ **JACOBS, Jacobus Albertus Michael** ...... *paintings* | | | $2,750 |
| Belgian 1812-79 | | | |
| ☐ **JACOBS, L.A.E.** ..................... *paintings* | | | $1,980 |
| Belgian 19th cent. | | | |
| ☐ **JACOBS, M.** ......................... *paintings* | | | $1,100 |
| American | | | |
| ☐ **JACOBS, Michel** ..................... *paintings* | | | $302 |
| American b. 1877 | | | |
| ☐ **JACOBS, Paul Emil** .................. *paintings* | | | $6,050 |
| German 1802-1866 | | | |
| ☐ **JACOBS, Ted Seth** .................. *paintings* | | $467 | $5,170 |
| American b. 1927 | | | |

## Ship Portraitist

Antonio Jacobsen, who emigrated to the United States from Denmark when he was twenty-one, was one of America's most prolific marine artists, painting more than 5,000 portraits of ships during his forty-year career. Many of his pictures were commissioned by shipping lines or the captains of vessels to commemorate the launching of a new ship. The popularity of yacht racing during the prosperous 1870s spurred the demand for yacht portraits and kept the artist busy at his easel, sometimes painting a picture a day. On a rush job, his children were pressed into service to finish the sky or sea.

Unlike many artists, Jacobsen made no attempt to incorporate his name into the design of a picture but boldly printed it, along with his street and city address. The price for Jacobsen paintings varies, depending on their quality. Other marine painters of the period included Fred Pansing, James Buttersworth, James Bard, Frederick Ward Stanton, and Frederick S. Cozzens. (Antonio Jacobsen, "Portrait of the Steamship Sequranca," oil on canvas, 18 x 30 in., Bourne, November 24, 1984, $4,250.)

|  | | *Current Price Range* | |
|---|---|---|---|
|  | | *Low* | *High* |
| ☐ **JACOBSEN, Antonio** .......................... *paintings* | | **$200** | **$18,150** |
| American 1850-1921 ................................. *drawings* | | **$1,100** | **$1,100** |
| ☐ **JACOBSEN, Carl** ........................... *paintings* | | | **$1,870** |
| ☐ **JACOBSEN, David** ........................... *paintings* | | | **$14,300** |
| ☐ **JACOBSEN, Sophus** ........................... *paintings* | | | **$2,200** |
| Norwegian 1833-1912 | | | |
| ☐ **JACOBSON, Oscar Brousse** ................ *paintings* | | **$192** | **$770** |
| American 1882-1934 | | | |
| ☐ **JACOBSSON, Edward Gustave** ............ *paintings* | | | **$275** |
| ☐ **JACOMB-HOOD, G.P.** ....................... *drawings* | | | **$247** |
| English early 20th cent. | | | |
| ☐ **JACOMIN, Alfred Louis Vigny** ............ *paintings* | | **$220** | **$3,575** |
| French 1842-c. 1913 | | | |

|                                                               |           | *Current Price Range* |           |
|---------------------------------------------------------------|-----------|-----------|-----------|
|                                                               |           | *Low*     | *High*    |
| ☐ **JACOPIN, Achille Emile** ............... *sculpture*        |           |           | **$660**  |
| French 19th/20th cent.                                        |           |           |           |
| ☐ **JACOT, Marie Paul** ................... *paintings*         |           | **$1,320** | **$1,650** |
| French 1842-1893                                              |           |           |           |
| ☐ **JACOT, Paul** ..................... *drawings*              |           | **$440**  | **$4,950** |
| French 1798-1893                                              |           |           |           |
| ☐ **JACOVACCI, Francesco** ............. *paintings*            |           |           | **$4,950** |
| Italian 19th cent.                                            |           |           |           |
| ☐ **JACOVLEFF, Alexandre** ............. *drawings*             |           |           | **$550**  |
| Russian 19th/20th cent.                                       |           |           |           |
| ☐ **JACQUAND, Claudius** ............... *paintings*            |           |           | **$4,400** |
| French 1804-1878                                             |           |           |           |
| ☐ **JACQUE, Charles Emile** ............. *paintings*           |           | **$247**  | **$52,800** |
| French 1813-1894 ..................... *drawings*             |           | **$220**  | **$3,080** |
| ☐ **JACQUE, Emile** ................... *paintings*             |           | **$660**  | **$1,100** |
| French 1848-1912 ..................... *drawings*             |           |           | **$165**  |
| ☐ **JACQUEMART, A.** ................. *sculpture*              |           |           | **$500**  |
| ☐ **JACQUEMART, Henri Alfred Marie** ..... *sculpture*          |           |           | **$550**  |
| French 19th cent.                                            |           |           |           |
| ☐ **JACQUET, Alain** ................... *paintings*            |           | **$660**  | **$770**  |
| French b. 1939                                                |           |           |           |
| ☐ **JACQUET, Gustave Jean** ............. *paintings*           |           | **$330**  | **$9,900** |
| French 1846-1909 ..................... *drawings*             |           |           | **$880**  |
| ☐ **JACQUET, Maurice** ............... *paintings*              |           |           | **$990**  |
| French b. 1877                                                |           |           |           |
| ☐ **JACQUIN, Georges Arthur** ............. *paintings*         |           |           | **$4,675** |
| French b. 1851                                                |           |           |           |
| ☐ **JADIN, Charles-Emmanuel** ............. *paintings*         |           |           | **$2,200** |
| French 19th cent.                                            |           |           |           |
| ☐ **JADIN, Louis Godefroy** ............. *paintings*           |           |           | **$1,320** |
| French 1805-1882                                             |           |           |           |
| ☐ **JAECKEL, Henry** ................... *paintings*            |           | **$1,320** | **$4,125** |
| German ac. 1853                                               |           |           |           |
| ☐ **JAEGER, Carl** ..................... *paintings*            |           | **$1,650** | **$1,650** |
| German 1833-1887                                             |           |           |           |
| ☐ **JAEGERS, Albert** ................... *sculpture*           |           |           | **$286**  |
| ☐ **JAENISCH, Hans** ................... *paintings*            |           | **$55**   | **$440**  |
| German b. 1907                                                |           |           |           |
| ☐ **JAGERSPACHER, Helene Hafliger** ....... *paintings*         |           |           | **$770**  |
| Swiss b. 1885                                                 |           |           |           |
| ☐ **JAHAM, M. de** ..................... *paintings*            |           |           | **$220**  |
| American 20th cent.                                           |           |           |           |
| ☐ **JAHN, A.** ........................ *sculpture*             |           |           | **$467**  |
| ☐ **JAHN, Louis** ..................... *paintings*             |           |           | **$412**  |
| German 1839-1911                                             |           |           |           |
| ☐ **JAHNKE, William** ................... *paintings*           |           | **$77**   | **$220**  |
| American b. 1937                                              |           |           |           |
| ☐ **JAMBOR, Louis** ................... *paintings*             |           | **$132**  | **$605**  |
| Hungarian/American 1884-1954?                                 |           |           |           |

|  | | *Current Price Range* | |
| --- | --- | --- | --- |
|  | | *Low* | *High* |
| ☐ **JAMES, David** ................................. *paintings* | | $302 | $6,050 |
| English 19th/20th cent. | | | |
| ☐ **JAMES, Frederick** ............................. *paintings* | | $825 | $5,500 |
| American 1845-1907 | | | |
| ☐ **JAMES, H.** ..................................... *drawings* | | | $660 |
| American/British 19th cent. | | | |
| ☐ **JAMES, John Wells** ............................ *paintings* | | | $275 |
| ☐ **JAMES, Paul** .................................... *paintings* | | | $192 |
| English 19th cent. | | | |
| ☐ **JAMES, Walter Charles** | | | |
| **(called Lord Northbourne)** ..................... *paintings* | | | $660 |
| English 1816-1893 | | | |
| ☐ **JAMES, William** ............................... *paintings* | | $275 | $825 |
| American 1882-after 1934 | | | |
| ☐ **JAMES, William** ............................... *paintings* | | $1,650 | $90,750 |
| British 18th cent. | | | |
| ☐ **JAMESON, Paul** ................................ *paintings* | | | $220 |
| British 19th cent. | | | |
| ☐ **JAMIESON, F.E.** ............................... *paintings* | | $385 | $770 |
| 19th/20th cent. | | | |
| ☐ **JAMISON, Philip** .............................. *drawings* | | $176 | $3,300 |
| American b. 1925 | | | |
| ☐ **JAMOR, Armand** ............................... *paintings* | | | $275 |
| Belgian b. 1870 | | | |
| ☐ **JANCK, Angelo (or JANK)** .................... *paintings* | | $1,100 | $4,620 |
| German b. 1868 | | | |
| ☐ **JANCO, Marcel** ............................... *drawings* | | | $627 |
| ☐ **JANESCH, Albert** ............................. *paintings* | | | $6,050 |
| Austrian 1889-1973 | | | |
| ☐ **JANKOWSKI, J.W.** ........................... *paintings* | | $1,210 | $2,000 |
| Austrian ac. 1825-1861 | | | |
| ☐ **JANLE** ........................................ *sculpture* | | $352 | $440 |
| ☐ **JANNECK, Franz Christoph** ................. *paintings* | | $3,080 | $23,100 |
| Austrian 1703-1761 | | | |
| ☐ **JANS, Edouard de** ............................ *paintings* | | $550 | $1,650 |
| Belgian 1855-1919 | | | |
| ☐ **JANSEM, Jean** ................................. *paintings* | | $400 | $6,050 |
| b. Armenia, French b. 1920 ........................ *drawings* | | $220 | $1,870 |
| ☐ **JANSEN, Alfred** .............................. *paintings* | | | $2,090 |
| ☐ **JANSEN, Hendrik Willebrord** .............. *paintings* | | | $2,420 |
| Dutch 1855-1908 | | | |
| ☐ **JANSEN, J.C.** .................................. *paintings* | | | $3,850 |
| ☐ **JANSEN, Joseph** .............................. *paintings* | | $550 | $7,700 |
| German 1829-1905 | | | |
| ☐ **JANSEN, Willem George Frederik** ........ *paintings* | | $220 | $3,300 |
| Dutch 1871-1949 | | | |
| ☐ **JANSER, A.R.** ................................. *paintings* | | | $440 |
| American 20th cent. | | | |
| ☐ **JANSON, Johannes** ............................ *paintings* | | | $4,400 |

| | | Current Price Range | |
|---|---|---|---|
| | | *Low* | *High* |
| ☐ **JANSON, Louis Charles** ........ *sculpture* | | | $2,530 |
| French 1823-1881 | | | |
| ☐ **JANSSEN, Louis** ............. *paintings* | | | $474 |
| Dutch 19th cent. | | | |
| ☐ **JANSSENS, Abraham** ......... *paintings* | | $4,400 | $28,600 |
| Flemish | | | |
| ☐ **JANSSENS, Hieronymus** ....... *paintings* | | | $8,250 |
| Dutch 1624-1693 | | | |
| ☐ **JANSSON, Alfred** ........... *paintings* | | $187 | $2,500 |
| Swedish/American 1863-1931 | | | |
| ☐ **JANUSKI, A.** ............ *paintings* | | | $715 |
| Continental School 19th cent. | | | |
| ☐ **JAPY, Louis Aime** ......... *paintings* | | $440 | $4,125 |
| French 1840-1916 ............ *drawings* | | $82 | $550 |
| ☐ **JAQUEMIN** ............ *sculpture* | | | $3,080 |
| French early 20th cent. | | | |
| ☐ **JAQUES, Jean Pierre** ........ *paintings* | | $66 | $825 |
| Swiss 20th cent. | | | |
| ☐ **JARAMILLO, Alipio** ......... *paintings* | | $770 | $990 |
| Latin American | | | |
| ☐ **JARAMILLO, Ignacio Gomez** ....... *paintings* | | | $1,760 |
| Colombian 20th cent. | | | |
| ☐ **JARAY, Sandor** ........... *sculpture* | | | $577 |
| Hungarian b. 1870 | | | |
| ☐ **JARDINE, Aeta** ............ *paintings* | | | $440 |
| ☐ **JARDINES, Jose Maria** ....... *paintings* | | $176 | $2,530 |
| Spanish b. 1862 | | | |
| ☐ **JARL, Otto** ............ *sculpture* | | | $1,650 |
| Austrian 19th cent. | | | |
| ☐ **JARPA, O.** ............ *paintings* | | | $274 |
| South American 20th cent. | | | |
| ☐ **JARREN, M.** ............ *paintings* | | $440 | $440 |
| German early 20th cent. | | | |
| ☐ **JARVIS, John** ........... *drawings* | | | $3,850 |
| American b. 1946 | | | |
| ☐ **JARVIS, John Wesley** ........ *paintings* | | $1,430 | $30,250 |
| American 1780-1839/40 ......... *drawings* | | | $264 |
| ☐ **JARVIS, W. Frederick** ....... *paintings* | | | $660 |
| ☐ **JASCHKE, Franz** ........... *drawings* | | $550 | $550 |
| Austrian 1775-1842 | | | |
| ☐ **JASINSKA, Wiestowa** ......... *paintings* | | | $301 |
| 20th cent. | | | |
| ☐ **JATIVA MASTER** .......... *paintings* | | | $20,900 |
| Spanish 16th cent. | | | |
| ☐ **JAUDON, Valerie** ........... *paintings* | | $11,000 | $15,400 |
| American b. 1945 | | | |
| ☐ **JAWLENSKY, Alexej von** ....... *paintings* | | $7,150 | $297,000 |
| German 1864-1941 ............ *drawings* | | $2,200 | $7,150 |

|  | | Current Price Range | |
|---|---|---|---|
|  | | Low | High |
| ☐ JAWLENSKY, Andreas ............... *paintings* | | $3,025 | $4,400 |
| Russian 20th cent. | | | |
| ☐ JAZET, Paul Leon .................... *paintings* | | | $605 |
| French b. 1848 | | | |
| ☐ JEAN, Eugene ..................... *paintings* | | $302 | $550 |
| Haitian b. 1950 | | | |
| ☐ JEAN, Fielix ........................ *paintings* | | $22 | $209 |
| Haitian 20th cent. | | | |
| ☐ JEAN, Marcel ...................... *paintings* | | $330 | $495 |
| ☐ JEAN-LOUIS, Eric ............... *paintings* | | | $715 |
| ☐ JEANMAIRE, Edouard .......... *paintings* | | $6,050 | $11,000 |
| Swiss 1847-1916 | | | |
| ☐ JEANNIN, Georges .............. *paintings* | | $660 | $13,200 |
| French 1841-1925 | | | |
| ☐ JEANNIOT, Pierre Alexandre ......... *paintings* | | | $2,420 |
| French 1826-1892 | | | |
| ☐ JEAURAT, Etienne ............. *paintings* | | | $1,980 |
| French 1699-1789 .................... *drawings* | | | $495 |
| ☐ JECT-KEY, D. Wu ............... *paintings* | | | $191 |
| American 20th cent. | | | |
| ☐ JEFFERS, V. ...................... *paintings* | | | $770 |
| English 19th cent. | | | |
| ☐ JEFFERSON, Joseph ........... *paintings* | | $275 | $770 |
| American 1829-1905 | | | |
| ☐ JEFFERY, George .............. *drawings* | | $33 | $220 |
| British 19th/20th cent. | | | |
| ☐ JEFFERY, James H. ............ *paintings* | | | $462 |
| ☐ JEGART, Artemis ............... *paintings* | | | $231 |
| American 20th cent. | | | |
| ☐ JEHOLEI, W. ...................... *paintings* | | $55 | $187 |
| German 20th cent. | | | |
| ☐ JELAUUK, A. ...................... *paintings* | | | $302 |
| ☐ JELINEK, Rudolph .............. *paintings* | | | $1,430 |
| Austrian b. 1880 | | | |
| ☐ JENKINS, George Washington ...... *paintings* | | $247 | $275 |
| American 1816-1907 | | | |
| ☐ JENKINS, J. LeBrun ........... *paintings* | | $88 | $440 |
| American 1876-1951 | | | |
| ☐ JENKINS, John Elliot .......... *paintings* | | | $231 |
| American b. 1868 | | | |
| ☐ JENKINS, Paul ................... *paintings* | | $356 | $27,500 |
| American b. 1923 .................... *drawings* | | $385 | $3,960 |
| ☐ JENKINS, Paul Ripley .......... *paintings* | | $1,540 | $11,550 |
| American 1940-1974 ................. *drawings* | | | $1,650 |
| ☐ JENKINS, Wilfred ............... *paintings* | | | $660 |
| ................................. *drawings* | | | $247 |
| ☐ JENKINSON, Geoffrey .......... *paintings* | | | $2,750 |
| American contemporary | | | |

|                                            |           | Current Price Range |          |
|--------------------------------------------|-----------|---------------------|----------|
|                                            |           | Low                 | High     |
| ☐ **JENNER, W.**  ............................ *paintings*<br>British 19th cent. |           |                     | $550     |
| ☐ **JENNEWEIN, Carl Paul**  ................. *sculpture*<br>American 1930-1978 |           | $4,400              | $10,450  |
| ☐ **JENNIN, Jonathan**  ........................... *drawings*<br>American c. 1830 |           |                     | $3,300   |
| ☐ **JENNY, Joseph**  ................................. *paintings* |           |                     | $264     |
| ☐ **JENNYS, William**  ............................. *paintings*<br>American ac. 1795-1810 |           | $1,400              | $15,400  |
| ☐ **JENSEN, Alfred**  ............................... *paintings*<br>American 1903-1981 |           | $3,520              | $60,500  |
| ☐ **JENSEN, Alfred**  ............................... *paintings*<br>Danish b. 1859 |           | $165                | $6,050   |
| ☐ **JENSEN, George**  .............................. *paintings*<br>American b. 1878 |           | $70                 | $1,650   |
| ☐ **JENSEN, Johan Laurents**  ..................... *paintings*<br>Danish 1800-1856 |           | $495                | $30,800  |
| ☐ **JENSEN, Louis Isak Napoleon**  ............. *paintings*<br>Danish 1858-1908 |           |                     | $880     |
| ☐ **JENSEN, Thomas M.**  .......................... *paintings*<br>American 1831-1916 |           |                     | $1,600   |
| ☐ **JENSEN, Williem George Frederick**  ...... *paintings*<br>Dutch 1871-1949 |           |                     | $1,650   |
| ☐ **JEQUIER, Jules**  ............................... *paintings* |           |                     | $500     |
| ☐ **JEREMEAUX, T.**  ............................... *drawings* |           |                     | $330     |
| ☐ **JEROME, G.**  .................................... *paintings*<br>American 19th cent. |           |                     | $1,540   |
| ☐ **JERRES, Antony**  ............................... *paintings* |           |                     | $660     |
| ☐ **JESSUP, F.N.**  ................................... *paintings* |           |                     | $275     |
| ☐ **JETTEL, Eugen**  ................................ *paintings*<br>Austrian 1845-1901 |           | $2,750              | $14,300  |
| ☐ **JEVTOVIC, Dusan**  ............................. *paintings*<br>Yugoslavian b. 1925 |           |                     | $1,650   |
| ☐ **JEWELL, Elizabeth G.**  ........................ *paintings*<br>American 20th cent. |           |                     | $220     |
| ☐ **JEWETT, F.S.**  .................................. *paintings*<br>1819-1864 |           |                     | $71,500  |
| ☐ **JEWETT, Maude Sherwood**  .................. *paintings*<br>American b. 1873 |           | $680                | $2,200   |
| ☐ **JEX, Garnet W.**  ................................ *paintings*<br>American b. 1895 |           | $82                 | $605     |
| ☐ **JEYDEL, Ed**  .................................... *paintings*<br>Continental 19th cent |           |                     | $1,210   |
| ☐ **JHEM, E.J.**  ..................................... *paintings* |           |                     | $528     |
| ☐ **JICHA, Joseph**  ................................. *drawings* |           | $82                 | $324     |
| ☐ **JIG, Fritz**  ...................................... *paintings*<br>Continental 19th cent. |           |                     | $550     |
| ☐ **JIKUS, K.**  ...................................... *paintings*<br>European 19th/20th cent. |           |                     | $330     |

| | | *Current Price Range* | |
|---|---|---|---|
| | | Low | High |
| ☐ **JIMENEZ Y ARANDA, Jose** ............... *paintings* | | $275 | $7,750 |
| Spanish 1837-1903 ...................................... *drawings* | | | $275 |
| ☐ **JIMENEZ Y ARANDA, Luis** ............... *paintings* | | $770 | $19,800 |
| Spanish b. 1845 ...................................... *drawings* | | | $550 |
| ☐ **JIMENEZ Y FERNANDEZ, Federico** .... *paintings* | | | $825 |
| Spanish b. 1841 | | | |
| ☐ **JIMINEZ, Alfredo** ............................. *paintings* | | | $990 |
| ☐ **JIROUCH, Frank** ............................. *paintings* | | | $274 |
| ☐ **JOBERT, Paul C. F.** ........................... *paintings* | | | $605 |
| ☐ **JOBSON, E. Winifred** ....................... *drawings* | | | $192 |
| American 20th cent. | | | |
| ☐ **JOCHEMSZ, P.F.** ............................. *paintings* | | $40 | $440 |
| Dutch 20th cent. | | | |
| ☐ **JOCHINSON** ....................................... *paintings* | | | $275 |
| ☐ **JOE, ZUCKER** ................................. *paintings* | | $990 | $6,600 |
| American b. 1941 ...................................... *drawings* | | | $1,650 |
| ☐ **JOHANSEN, John C.** ........................ *paintings* | | $209 | $880 |
| American b. 1876 | | | |
| ☐ **JOHANSSON, Carl** ........................... *paintings* | | | $825 |
| Swedish 1863-1944 | | | |
| ☐ **JOHANSSON, Johan** ......................... *paintings* | | | $990 |
| Swedish b. 1879 | | | |
| ☐ **JOHFRA** ............................................. *paintings* | | | $1,430 |
| Dutch ac. 1919-1936 | | | |
| ☐ **JOHFRA,** | | | |
| **Franciscos Johannes Gijsbertus** ............. *paintings* | | | $385 |
| ☐ **JOHN, Augustus** ............................... *paintings* | | $2,860 | $33,000 |
| British 1878-1961 ...................................... *drawings* | | $302 | $1,980 |
| ☐ **JOHN, Gwen** ..................................... *drawings* | | $715 | $5,280 |
| English 1876-1939 | | | |
| ☐ **JOHN, J. Allen St.** ............................. *paintings* | | | $900 |
| ☐ **JOHNS, Jasper** ................................. *paintings* | | $110,000 | $363,000 |
| American b. 1930 ...................................... *drawings* | | $15,400 | $66,000 |
| .................................................. *sculpture* | | $4,950 | $38,500 |
| ☐ **JOHNSEN, Johann** ............................. *paintings* | | | $28,600 |
| Swedish? b. after 1650-d. c. 1705 | | | |
| ☐ **JOHNSON, Arthur** ............................. *paintings* | | $4,400 | $10,450 |
| American 1874-1954 | | | |
| ☐ **JOHNSON, B.J.** ................................. *paintings* | | | $385 |
| British 19th cent. | | | |
| ☐ **JOHNSON, Caroline Rixford** ............... *paintings* | | $165 | $467 |
| American 1873-1961 | | | |
| ☐ **JOHNSON, Charles Edward** ................. *paintings* | | | $2,750 |
| English 1832-1913 | | | |
| ☐ **JOHNSON, David** ............................. *paintings* | | $231 | $31,900 |
| American 1827-1908 ................................... *drawings* | | $660 | $1,100 |
| ☐ **JOHNSON, Eastman** ........................... *paintings* | | $1,100 | $82,500 |
| American 1824-1906 ................................... *drawings* | | $550 | $104,500 |

|                                              |           | *Current Price Range* | |
|----------------------------------------------|-----------|-----------|-----------|
|                                              |           | Low       | High      |
| ☐ **JOHNSON, Edward Killingworth** .......... *drawings* | | $3,080 | $4,300 |
| British 1825-1896                            |           |           |           |
| ☐ **JOHNSON, Francis Norton** ................... *paintings* | | | $605 |
| American 1878-1931                           |           |           |           |
| ☐ **JOHNSON, Frank Tenney** ................... *paintings* | | $1,100 | $132,000 |
| American 1874-1939 ................................. *drawings* | | $770 | $18,000 |
| ..................................................... *sculpture* | | $900 | $1,430 |
| ☐ **JOHNSON, Grace Mott** ................... *sculpture* | | | $467 |
| American 1882-1967                           |           |           |           |
| ☐ **JOHNSON, Guy** ............................... *paintings* | | $319 | $1,210 |
| American b. 1927 ...................................... *drawings* | | $70 | $1,600 |
| ☐ **JOHNSON, Hal F.** .............................. *paintings* | | | $357 |
| American 19th/20th cent.                     |           |           |           |
| ☐ **JOHNSON, Harry John** ........................ *paintings* | | | $605 |
| English School 1826-1884                     |           |           |           |
| ☐ **JOHNSON, Harvey** ............................. *paintings* | | $3,300 | $25,000 |
| American b. 1920/21                          |           |           |           |
| ☐ **JOHNSON, J. William** ......................... *paintings* | | $165 | $550 |
| American 19th cent.                          |           |           |           |
| ☐ **JOHNSON, Larry** ............................... *drawings* | | | $247 |
| contemporary                                 |           |           |           |
| ☐ **JOHNSON, Lester** ............................. *paintings* | | $220 | $14,300 |
| American b. 1919 ..................................... *drawings* | | $264 | $3,190 |
| ☐ **JOHNSON, Marie** ............................... *paintings* | | | $330 |
| American b. 1861                             |           |           |           |
| ☐ **JOHNSON, Marshall** .......................... *paintings* | | $160 | $3,300 |
| American 1846/50-1915/21 .......................... *drawings* | | $1,600 | $2,100 |
| ☐ **JOHNSON, Nevill** ............................... *paintings* | | | $412 |
| English 20th cent.                           |           |           |           |
| ☐ **JOHNSON, Percy** ............................... *paintings* | | $44 | $192 |
| English exhib. 1921                          |           |           |           |
| ☐ **JOHNSON, Percy D.** ........................... *paintings* | | $132 | $1,540 |
| American contemporary                        |           |           |           |
| ☐ **JOHNSON, R.F.** ................................. *paintings* | | | $385 |
| ☐ **JOHNSON, Ray** ................................. *drawings* | | $137 | $1,760 |
| American b. 1927                             |           |           |           |
| ☐ **JOHNSON, Robert** ............................. *paintings* | | | $1,650 |
| Australian 1890-1964                         |           |           |           |
| ☐ **JOHNSON, Samuel Frost** ...................... *paintings* | | $440 | $825 |
| American b. 1835                             |           |           |           |
| ☐ **JOHNSON, Sidney Y.** .......................... *paintings* | | $231 | $330 |
| English 19th cent.                           |           |           |           |
| ☐ **JOHNSON, Steve** ............................... *drawings* | | $300 | |
| American                                     |           |           |           |
| ☐ **JOHNSTON, David Claypoole** ............... *paintings* | | $1,980 | $3,850 |
| American 1797-1867                           |           |           |           |
| ☐ **JOHNSTON, Inez** ................................. *drawings* | | | $412 |
| contemporary                                 |           |           |           |

|  | | *Current Price Range* | |
|---|---|---|---|
|  | | Low | High |
| ☐ **JOHNSTON, John Humphreys** ............. *paintings* | | | $2,420 |
| American b. 1857 | | | |
| ☐ **JOHNSTON, John R.** .......................... *paintings* | | $82 | $2,970 |
| American b. 1820's, ac. to 1872 | | | |
| ☐ **JOHNSTON, Joshua** ........................... *paintings* | | | $4,400 |
| American ac. 1796-1824 | | | |
| ☐ **JOHNSTON, P.D.** .............................. *paintings* | | | $742 |
| ☐ **JOHNSTON, Reuben le Grande** ............ *paintings* | | $160 | $2,200 |
| American 1850-1918/19 ............................... *drawings* | | $165 | $385 |
| ☐ **JOHNSTON, Richard T.** ....................... *paintings* | | | $605 |
| American 20th cent. | | | |
| ☐ **JOHNSTON, Robert E.** ........................ *paintings* | | | $935 |
| American 1885-1933 | | | |
| ☐ **JOHNSTON, T.** ................................. *paintings* | | | $605 |
| English 19th cent. | | | |
| ☐ **JOHNSTON, W.R.** ............................. *paintings* | | | $1,650 |
| 19th cent. | | | |
| ☐ **JOINER, Harvey** ................................ *paintings* | | $125 | $1,200 |
| American 1852-1932 | | | |
| ☐ **JOINER, L.E. de** ............................... *paintings* | | | $220 |
| American 20th cent. | | | |
| ☐ **JOLI, Antonio** ................................... *paintings* | | $15,400 | $77,000 |
| Venetian 1700?-1777 | | | |
| ☐ **JOLIN, Einar** ................................... *paintings* | | | $550 |
| Swedish 1890-1976 | | | |
| ☐ **JOLLEY, Gwilt** ................................. *paintings* | | $55 | $231 |
| American b. 1859 | | | |
| ☐ **JOLLIVET** ....................................... *paintings* | | $385 | $550 |
| French 19th cent. | | | |
| ☐ **JOLLY, Henri Jean Baptist** ................. *paintings* | | | $1,430 |
| Belgian 1812-1853 | | | |
| ☐ **JOLYET, Philippe** ............................. *paintings* | | | $7,150 |
| French 1832-1908 | | | |
| ☐ **JONAS, Louis Paul** ............................ *sculpture* | | $1,100 | $1,540 |
| American | | | |
| ☐ **JONCHERIE, Hector Francois** ............. *paintings* | | | $440 |
| ☐ **JONCHERY, Charles** .......................... *sculpture* | | | $4,180 |
| French early 20th cent. | | | |
| ☐ **JONCIERES, Leonce J.V. de** ............... *paintings* | | | $1,320 |
| French b. 1871 | | | |
| ☐ **JONES, A.R.** ................................... *paintings* | | | $1,100 |
| British 1806-1874 | | | |
| ☐ **JONES, Adrian** ................................ *paintings* | | $247 | $330 |
| English b. 1845 | | | |
| ☐ **JONES, Albertus Eugene** ..................... *paintings* | | | $550 |
| American 1882-1957 | | | |
| ☐ **JONES, Allen** ................................... *paintings* | | | $1,100 |
| British b. 1937 ....................................... *sculpture* | | | $12,100 |

| | | Current Price Range | |
|---|---|---|---|
| | | Low | High |
| ☐ **JONES, C.** ....................................... *paintings* | | | $550 |
| English 19th cent. | | | |
| ☐ **JONES, C.S.** ..................................... *paintings* | | | $1,430 |
| American 19th cent. | | | |
| ☐ **JONES, Charles** ............................... *paintings* | | $357 | $5,500 |
| English 1836-1892 | | | |
| ☐ **JONES, F. Eastman** ........................ *paintings* | | $165 | $1,320 |
| American 19th cent. | | | |
| ☐ **JONES, Francis Coates** .................... *paintings* | | $80 | $18,700 |
| American 1857-1932 ................................ *drawings* | | | $242 |
| ☐ **JONES, Franklin** .............................. *paintings* | | | $770 |
| ☐ **JONES, George W.** ........................... *paintings* | | | $660 |
| English ac. 1885 | | | |
| ☐ **JONES, H.F.** ...................................... *paintings* | | | $7,700 |
| ☐ **JONES, Herbert H.** ........................... *paintings* | | | $275 |
| ☐ **JONES, Hugh Bolton** ........................ *paintings* | | $330 | $21,780 |
| American 1848-1927 ................................ *drawings* | | | $100 |
| ☐ **JONES, J. Ford** ................................ *paintings* | | | $522 |
| ☐ **JONES, Jeff** ...................................... *paintings* | | | $440 |
| ☐ **JONES, Joe Cranston** ....................... *drawings* | | $1,012 | $14,300 |
| American early 20th cent. | | | |
| ☐ **JONES, Joseph John** ......................... *paintings* | | $550 | $880 |
| American | | | |
| ☐ **JONES, Josiah Clinton** ..................... *paintings* | | | $1,100 |
| British 1848-1936 | | | |
| ☐ **JONES, Margaret Atwater** ................ *drawings* | | | $302 |
| American b. 1864 | | | |
| ☐ **JONES, Mary E.H.** ............................ *drawings* | | | $990 |
| American mid 19th cent. | | | |
| ☐ **JONES, Maud Raphael** ...................... *paintings* | | | $660 |
| English 19th/20th cent. | | | |
| ☐ **JONES, Nell Choate** .......................... *paintings* | | $66 | $715 |
| American b. 1879 | | | |
| ☐ **JONES, Nora** ................................... *drawings* | | | $224 |
| English exhib. 1928 | | | |
| ☐ **JONES, Paul** .................................... *paintings* | | $770 | $3,300 |
| British 1856-1879 | | | |
| ☐ **JONES, Robert Edmond** ..................... *drawings* | | $522 | $7,425 |
| American b. 1887 | | | |
| ☐ **JONES, Samuel John Egbert** ............... *paintings* | | $2,200 | $8,800 |
| English ac. 1820-1845 | | | |
| ☐ **JONES, Seth C.** ................................. *paintings* | | | $165 |
| American 1853-1930 ................................ *drawings* | | $137 | $500 |
| ☐ **JONES, W.H.** ................................... *paintings* | | | $990 |
| American 19th cent. | | | |
| ☐ **JONES, William** ............................... *paintings* | | | $495 |
| English 18th cent. | | | |
| ☐ **JONG, Jacobus Frederik Sterre de** ........ *paintings* | | | $302 |
| Dutch 1866-1920 | | | |

| | | *Current Price Range* | |
|---|---|---|---|
| | | *Low* | *High* |
| ☐ **JONG, Jan de** .................... *paintings* | | | $600 |
| ☐ **JONG, W. de** .................... *paintings* | | | $880 |
| ☐ **JONGE, Jan Antonie de** .................... *paintings* Dutch 1864-1927 | | | $2,310 |
| ☐ **JONGE, L.V.D.** .................... *paintings* | | | $4,620 |
| ☐ **JONGERE, Marinus de** .................... *paintings* Dutch b. 1912 | | | $605 |
| ☐ **JONGERS, M. De** .................... *paintings* | | | $385 |
| ☐ **JONGH, Ludolf de** **(called Lieve de Jongh)** .................... *paintings* Dutch 1616-1679 | | | $18,700 |
| ☐ **JONGH, Oene Romkes de** .................... *paintings* Dutch 1812-1896 | | $600 | $3,300 |
| ☐ **JONGHE, Gustave Leonhard de** .................... *paintings* Belgian 1828/29-1893 | | $990 | $55,000 |
| ☐ **JONGHE, Jan Baptiste de** .................... *paintings* Flemish 1785-1844 | | $605 | $1,760 |
| ☐ **JONGKIND, H. J.** .................... *paintings* | | | $440 |
| ☐ **JONGKIND, Johan Barthold** .................... *paintings* Dutch 1819-1891 .................... *drawings* | | $2,200 $302 | $55,000 $9,350 |
| ☐ **JONNES, A.** .................... *paintings* | | | $550 |
| ☐ **JONNEVOLD, Carl Hendrik** .................... *paintings* American 1856-1930 | | $174 | $1,540 |
| ☐ **JONNIAUX, Alfred** .................... *paintings* Belgian/American b. 1882 | | $137 | $2,475 |
| ☐ **JONSON, Raymond** .................... *paintings* American b. 1891 .................... *drawings* | | $4,180 $1,430 | $7,920 $2,640 |
| ☐ **JONTINEL, J.H.R.** .................... *paintings* American 19th cent. | | | $2,860 |
| ☐ **JOODALE** .................... *paintings* American 20th cent. | | | $319 |
| ☐ **JOORS, Eugene** .................... *paintings* Belgian 1850-1910 | | | $7,150 |
| ☐ **JOPLING, J.** .................... *drawings* | | | $300 |
| ☐ **JORDAENS, Hans** .................... *paintings* | | $3,410 | $6,050 |
| ☐ **JORDAENS, Jacob** .................... *paintings* Flemish 1593-1678 | | | $1,980 |
| ☐ **JORDAN, Andrew** .................... *drawings* American | | $500 | $550 |
| ☐ **JORDAN, Gus** .................... *paintings* 19th/20th cent. | | | $1,430 |
| ☐ **JORDAN, Marguerite** .................... *drawings* American 20th cent. | | $110 | $220 |
| ☐ **JORDAN, Rudolf** .................... *paintings* German 1810-1887 | | | $2,640 |
| ☐ **JORDE, Lars** .................... *paintings* Norwegian b. 1865 | | | $880 |
| ☐ **JOREL, A.** .................... *sculpture* | | | $1,320 |

| | | | Current Price Range | |
|---|---|---|---|---|
| | | | *Low* | *High* |
| ☐ **JORGENSEN, Christian** | .............. | *paintings* | $770 | $3,850 |
| Norwegian/American 1860-1935 | .............. | *drawings* | $55 | $2,090 |
| ☐ **JORIS, Pio** | .............. | *drawings* | $825 | $2,420 |
| Italian 1843-1921 | | | | |
| ☐ **JORN, Asger** | .............. | *paintings* | $2,200 | $44,000 |
| Danish 1914-1973 | .............. | *drawings* | $3,080 | $7,150 |
| ☐ **JOS, Julien** | .............. | *paintings* | | $550 |
| ☐ **JOSEF, Stoitzmer** | .............. | *paintings* | | $1,400 |
| ☐ **JOSEPH, Antonio** | .............. | *paintings* | $550 | $1,210 |
| ☐ **JOSEPH, Jasmin** | .............. | *paintings* | $440 | $1,650 |
| Haitian b. 1923 | | | | |
| ☐ **JOSEPH, Julian** | .............. | *paintings* | | $1,210 |
| ☐ **JOSEPH-VALCIN, Pierre** | .............. | *paintings* | | $660 |
| ☐ **JOSHACH, A.E.** | .............. | *paintings* | | $198 |
| American 20th cent. | | | | |
| ☐ **JOUETT, Matthew Harris** | .............. | *paintings* | $440 | $2,090 |
| American 1787/88-1827 | | | | |
| ☐ **JOUFFROY, P.** | .............. | *paintings* | | $1,100 |
| French 18th cent. | | | | |
| ☐ **JOULLIN, Amedee** | .............. | *paintings* | $124 | $4,000 |
| American 1862-1917 | | | | |
| ☐ **JOULLIN, Lucile** | .............. | *paintings* | | $330 |
| ☐ **JOURDAIN, Henri** | .............. | *drawings* | $82 | $715 |
| French 1864-1931 | | | | |
| ☐ **JOURDAIN, Jean** | .............. | *paintings* | | $220 |
| American b. 1912 | | | | |
| ☐ **JOURDAIN, Roger Joseph** | .............. | *drawings* | $209 | $605 |
| French 1845-1918 | | | | |
| ☐ **JOURDAN, Adolphe** | .............. | *paintings* | | $1,430 |
| French 1825-1889 | | | | |
| ☐ **JOY, George William** | .............. | *paintings* | | $4,950 |
| English 1844-1925 | | | | |
| ☐ **JOYANT, Jules Romain** | .............. | *paintings* | | $1,650 |
| French 1803-1854 | | | | |
| ☐ **JOYOU** | .............. | *sculpture* | | $1,430 |
| ☐ **JUAN, Ronaldo de** | .............. | *paintings* | $2,200 | $2,750 |
| Argentinian b. 1930 | | | | |
| ☐ **JUAREZ, Heriberto** | .............. | *sculpture* | | $1,100 |
| Mexican 20th cent. | | | | |
| ☐ **JUAREZ, Luis** | .............. | *paintings* | | $13,200 |
| Mexican active c. 1600-1632 | | | | |
| ☐ **JUAREZ, Roberto** | .............. | *paintings* | | $4,950 |
| contemporary | | | | |
| ☐ **JUDD, Donald** | .............. | *sculpture* | $3,850 | $18,150 |
| American b. 1928 | | | | |
| ☐ **JUDSON, Alice** | .............. | *paintings* | | $2,860 |
| American d. 1948 | .............. | *drawings* | | $110 |
| ☐ **JUDSON, C. Chapel** | .............. | *paintings* | $165 | $770 |
| American 1864-1946 | | | | |

| | | *Current Price Range* | |
|---|---|---|---|
| | | *Low* | *High* |
| ☐ **JUDSON, Minnie Lee** .............. *paintings* | | | $330 |
| American | | | |
| ☐ **JUDSON, William Lees** ............. *paintings* | | $440 | $1,870 |
| Anglo/American 1842-1928 ............. *drawings* | | $110 | $440 |
| ☐ **JUEL, Jens** ............................ *drawings* | | | $1,980 |
| Danish 1745-1802 | | | |
| ☐ **JUERGENS, Alfred** ................... *paintings* | | $137 | $5,775 |
| American 1866-1934 | | | |
| ☐ **JUERSEN, Helen** ...................... *paintings* | | | $330 |
| ☐ **JUGLARIS, Tommaso** ............... *paintings* | | | $440 |
| b. 1845 | | | |
| ☐ **JUILL, A.E.** ............................ *paintings* | | | $495 |
| European 19th cent. | | | |
| ☐ **JULES, F.** .............................. *paintings* | | | $270 |
| ☐ **JULES, Mervin** ....................... *paintings* | | | $462 |
| ☐ **JULIANA Y ALBERT, Jose** ........ *drawings* | | | $330 |
| Spanish fl. 1866-1921 | | | |
| ☐ **JULIEN, Joseph** ...................... *paintings* | | $4,400 | $4,950 |
| Belgian 19th cent. | | | |
| ☐ **JULIO, E.B.D. Fabrino** ............ *paintings* | | | $990 |
| American 1843-1879 | | | |
| ☐ **JULLIARD, L.** ......................... *paintings* | | | $1,045 |
| Belgian 19th cent. | | | |
| ☐ **JULLIOTT, Made** ..................... *paintings* | | | $550 |
| ☐ **JUMP** ................................... *paintings* | | | $495 |
| American 19th/20th cent. | | | |
| ☐ **JUNCKER, Justus** ................... *paintings* | | $3,850 | $8,250 |
| German 1703-1767 | | | |
| ☐ **JUNGBLUT, Johann** ................. *paintings* | | $2,640 | $6,600 |
| German 1860-1912 | | | |
| ☐ **JUNGBLUTH, Mimi** ................. *drawings* | | | $9,500 |
| American contemporary | | | |
| ☐ **JUNGLING, J.F.** ...................... *drawings* | | $242 | $770 |
| German 19th cent. | | | |
| ☐ **JUNGMANN, Nico W.** ............. *drawings* | | $1,100 | |
| Dutch 1872-1935 | | | |
| ☐ **JUNGNICKEL, Ludwig Heinrich** ......... *paintings* | | | $1,870 |
| German b. 1881 | | | |
| ☐ **JUNYER, Joan** ....................... *drawings* | | | $275 |
| ☐ **JURRES, Johannes Hendricus** .............. *paintings* | | $385 | $880 |
| Dutch b. 1875 | | | |
| ☐ **JUSTE, Javier** ........................ *paintings* | | | $1,650 |
| Spanish 19th cent. | | | |
| ☐ **JUSTICE, Martin** .................... *drawings* | | $275 | $385 |
| American 19th/20th cent. | | | |
| ☐ **JUTSUM, Henry** ...................... *paintings* | | $2,200 | $3,520 |
| English 1816-1869 ....................... *drawings* | | $605 | $1,540 |
| ☐ **JUTZ, Karl** ........................... *paintings* | | $9,900 | $19,800 |
| German 1838-1916 | | | |

| | | Current Price Range | |
|---|---|---|---|
| | | Low | High |
| ☐ **KAA, Jan van der** ............................... *paintings* | | | $3,575 |
| Dutch 1813-77 | | | |
| ☐ **KABOTIE, Michael** ............................ *paintings* | | | $1,870 |
| American (Hopi) | | | |
| ☐ **KACERE, John** ................................... *paintings* | | $1,045 | $12,100 |
| American b. 1920 ...................................... *drawings* | | $55 | $286 |
| ☐ **KADAR, Bela** ................................... *paintings* | | $1,430 | $5,225 |
| Hungarian 1877-1955 ................................ *drawings* | | $66 | $12,100 |
| ☐ **KADISHMAN, Menashe** ...................... *paintings* | | $13,200 | $20,350 |
| Israeli b. 1932 | | | |
| ☐ **KADMEYER, G.F.** ............................ *paintings* | | | $350 |
| ☐ **KAELIN, Charles Salis** ...................... *paintings* | | $385 | $7,150 |
| American 1858-1929 ................................. *drawings* | | $110 | $4,950 |
| ☐ **KAEMMERER, Frederik Hendrik** ........ *paintings* | | $1,210 | $28,600 |
| Dutch 1839-1902 ..................................... *drawings* | | $330 | $770 |
| ☐ **KAERCHER, Amalie** ........................... *paintings* | | | $24,200 |
| American 19th cent. | | | |
| ☐ **KAESELAU, Charles** ........................... *paintings* | | | $412 |
| b. 1889 | | | |
| ☐ **KAFKA, Richard** ............................... *drawings* | | | $357 |
| ☐ **KAGAN, Rod** .................................... *sculpture* | | | $3,520 |
| ☐ **KAHILL, Joseph B.** ........................... *paintings* | | | $522 |
| American b. 1882 | | | |
| ☐ **KAHLEN, Wolf** ................................. *drawings* | | | $275 |
| contemporary | | | |
| ☐ **KAHLER, Carl** ................................. *paintings* | | $715 | $3,025 |
| Austrian b. 1855 ..................................... *drawings* | | | $418 |
| ☐ **KAHLO, Frida** .................................. *paintings* | | $16,500 | $258,500 |
| Mexican 1910-1954 .................................. *drawings* | | $3,575 | $13,200 |
| ☐ **KAHN, Wolf** .................................... *paintings* | | $715 | $990 |
| German/American b. 1927 ........................... *drawings* | | $247 | $990 |
| ☐ **KAISER, Friedrich** ............................ *paintings* | | | $2,970 |
| German 1815-1890 | | | |
| ☐ **KALBACH, F.** .................................... *paintings* | | | $1,485 |
| German late 19th cent. | | | |
| ☐ **KALCKREUTH,** | | | |
| **Karl Walter Leopold von** ....................... *paintings* | | | $357 |
| German 1855-1925 | | | |
| ☐ **KALCKREUTH, Patrick von** ................ *paintings* | | $1,210 | $1,760 |
| German 19th/20th cent. | | | |
| ☐ **KALI, Mrs. Henry K. Weynerowski** ...... *paintings* | | $220 | $825 |
| Polish/American 20th cent. | | | |
| ☐ **KALIN, Victor** ................................... *paintings* | | $330 | $330 |
| American 20th cent. | | | |
| ☐ **KALINOWSKI, Horst Egon** ................ *sculpture* | | | $880 |
| ☐ **KALISH, Max** ................................... *sculpture* | | $495 | $5,500 |
| Polish/American 1891-1945 | | | |
| ☐ **KALLEM, Henry** ............................... *paintings* | | | $246 |
| American b. 1912 .................................... *drawings* | | $121 | $181 |

| | | Current Price Range | |
|---|---|---|---|
| | | Low | High |
| ☐ **KALLEM, Herbert** ............................... *sculpture* | | $55 | $302 |
| American b. 1909 | | | |
| ☐ **KALLIS** ............................................. *paintings* | | | $550 |
| American 20th cent. | | | |
| ☐ **KALLMORGAN, Friedrich** .................. *paintings* | | $935 | $1,540 |
| ☐ **KALLOS, Paul** ................................... *paintings* | | | $440 |
| contemporary ........................................... *drawings* | | | $110 |
| ☐ **KALMENOFF, Matthew** ...................... *paintings* | | $44 | $467 |
| American b. 1905 | | | |
| ☐ **KAMPF, Arthur** .................................. *paintings* | | $44 | $2,200 |
| German 1864-1950 | | | |
| ☐ **KAN, George** ...................................... *paintings* | | | $605 |
| Austrian b. 1870 | | | |
| ☐ **KANDINSKY, Wassily** ....................... *paintings* | | $33,000 | $1,210,000 |
| Russian 1866-1944 ................................... *drawings* | | $550 | $121,000 |
| ☐ **KANDLER, Ludwig** ............................ *paintings* | | | $1,870 |
| German b. 1856 | | | |
| ☐ **KANE, Catherine Richardson** ............... *paintings* | | | $400 |
| American 20th cent. | | | |
| ☐ **KANE, John** ...................................... *paintings* | | $2,475 | $25,300 |
| American 1860-1934 ................................. *drawings* | | | $300 |
| ☐ **KANE, Morgan** ................................. *drawings* | | | $440 |
| ☐ **KANELBA** ......................................... *paintings* | | | $605 |
| ☐ **KANN, L.** ......................................... *sculpture* | | | $352 |
| ☐ **KANOLDT, Alexander** ........................ *paintings* | | | $3,850 |
| German 1881-1939 | | | |
| ☐ **KANOLDT, Edmund** ........................... *paintings* | | | $2,200 |
| German 1839-1904 | | | |
| ☐ **KANTOR, Morris** ............................... *paintings* | | $165 | $1,100 |
| American 1896-1974 ................................. *drawings* | | $88 | $440 |
| ☐ **KAPFHAMER** .................................... *paintings* | | | $275 |
| German 19th/20th cent. | | | |
| ☐ **KAPP, Gary** ...................................... *paintings* | | $3,000 | $3,600 |
| American contemporary | | | |
| ☐ **KAPPES, Alfred** ................................ *paintings* | | | $1,045 |
| ☐ **KAPPES, K.** ...................................... *paintings* | | | $192 |
| American 20th cent. | | | |
| ☐ **KAPPIS, Albert** ................................ *paintings* | | | $7,480 |
| German 1836-1914 | | | |
| ☐ **KAPPO, Karlo** ................................... *paintings* | | | $275 |
| ☐ **KARAS, E.** ........................................ *paintings* | | | $660 |
| American 20th cent. | | | |
| ☐ **KARFIOL, Bernard** ............................. *paintings* | | $187 | $3,800 |
| Hungarian/American 1866/86-1955 ................. *drawings* | | $82 | $220 |
| ☐ **KARGER, Carl** ................................... *paintings* | | $1,100 | $1,540 |
| Austrian 1848-1913 | | | |
| ☐ **KARISSE** .......................................... *paintings* | | | $550 |
| ☐ **KARLINSKY, Anton Hans** ................... *paintings* | | | $302 |

| | | | *Current Price Range* | |
|---|---|---|---|---|
| | | | *Low* | *High* |
| ☐ **KARLOVSZKY, Bertalan** | ...................... | *paintings* | **$1,650** | **$11,000** |
| Hungarian 1858-1939 | | | | |
| ☐ **KARNEC, J.E.** | ..................................... | *paintings* | | **$462** |
| ☐ **KAROLY, Dozsa** | .................................. | *paintings* | | **$385** |
| ☐ **KARPATHY, Kus (?)** | ........................... | *paintings* | | **$275** |
| ☐ **KARPFF, Jean Jacques** | | | | |
| **(called CASIMIR)** | ................................ | *drawings* | **$1,650** | **$2,970** |
| French 1770-1829 | | | | |
| ☐ **KARRAS, Spiros John** | ........................... | *paintings* | | **$192** |
| American 20th cent. | | | | |
| ☐ **KARS, George (KARPELES)** | ............... | *drawings* | **$66** | **$308** |
| French 1882-1945 | | | | |
| ☐ **KARSEN, Kaspar** | ............................... | *drawings* | | **$440** |
| ☐ **KARSSEN, Anton** | ............................... | *paintings* | **$1,430** | **$2,750** |
| Dutch 20th cent. | | | | |
| ☐ **KASHITZ** | ........................................... | *paintings* | | **$500** |
| ☐ **KASPARIDES, Edouard** | ...................... | *paintings* | **$192** | **$462** |
| German 1858-1926 | | | | |
| ☐ **KASTEL, Roger K.** | ............................. | *paintings* | **$247** | **$357** |
| American b. 1931 | | | | |
| ☐ **KAT, Anne Pierre de** | ............................ | *paintings* | | **$550** |
| ☐ **KATCHADOURIAN, Sarkis** | ................ | *paintings* | | **$660** |
| | ................................................................ | *drawings* | | **$27** |
| ☐ **KATO, Kentaro** | ................................... | *paintings* | | **$440** |
| ☐ **KATZ, Alex** | ........................................ | *paintings* | **$1,430** | **$44,000** |
| American b. 1927 | ...................................... | *drawings* | **$1,045** | **$6,050** |
| ☐ **KAUBA, Carl** | ..................................... | *sculpture* | **$165** | **$17,600** |
| Austrian 1865-1922 | | | | |
| ☐ **KAUFFMAN, Angelica** | ....................... | *paintings* | **$275** | **$2,750** |
| Swiss 1740-1807 | | | | |
| ☐ **KAUFFMAN, Hugo** | ........................... | *paintings* | **$1,430** | **$6,050** |
| German 1868-1919 | | | | |
| ☐ **KAUFFMAN, Orgela** | ........................... | *paintings* | | **$900** |
| ☐ **KAUFFMAN, Robert** | ........................... | *paintings* | | **$1,430** |
| American 20th cent. | | | | |
| ☐ **KAUFFMANN, Angela** | ....................... | *paintings* | | **$605** |
| ☐ **KAUFFMANN, Hermann** | ..................... | *paintings* | **$3,190** | **$8,800** |
| German 1808-1889 | | | | |
| ☐ **KAUFFMANN, Hugo Wilhelm** | .............. | *paintings* | **$5,280** | **$37,400** |
| German 1844-1915 | | | | |
| ☐ **KAUFFMANN, Max** | ........................... | *paintings* | **$440** | **$3,025** |
| German 19th cent. | | | | |
| ☐ **KAUFMAN, Robert** | ............................ | *paintings* | | **$302** |
| American 20th cent. | | | | |
| ☐ **KAUFMANN, Adolf** | ........................... | *paintings* | **$605** | **$2,200** |
| Austrian 1848-1916 | | | | |

**New Realism**

*Bright colors, hard edges, and a sharp focus characterize the paintings of the New Realists. Alex Katz is a leading member of this 20th-century school. Katz studied at Cooper Union in New York and the Skowhegan School of Painting and Sculpture in Maine.*

*At the outset of his career, Katz painted, created paper collages, and worked on murals. From the late 1950s, he moved toward realism, concentrating on portraiture. In the early 1960s, he began to create increasingly large-scale works, which like other works of the New Realist School, are considered to be a reaction to Abstract Expressionism. (Alex Katz, "Caroline," oil on canvas, 34 x 48 in., Sotheby's, May 2, 1985, $25,850.)*

|                                    |          | *Current Price Range* | |
|------------------------------------|----------|----------|----------|
|                                    |          | *Low*    | *High*   |
| ☐ **KAUFMANN, Arthur** ............ *paintings* |          |          | **$440** |
| German b. 1888                     |          |          |          |
| ☐ **KAUFMANN, Ferdinand** ........ *paintings* |          | **$154** | **$440** |
| German/American 1864-after 1934    |          |          |          |
| ☐ **KAUFMANN, Isidor** ........... *paintings* |          | **$1,430** | **$49,500** |
| Austrian 1853-1921                 |          |          |          |
| ☐ **KAUFMANN, Karl** ............. *paintings* |          | **$418** | **$2,200** |
| Austrian b. 1843                   |          |          |          |
| ☐ **KAUFMANN, R.C.** ............. *paintings* |          |          | **$264** |
| ☐ **KAUFMANN, Wilhelm** ......... *paintings* |          | **$190** | **$990** |
| Austrian 1895-1945 ............... *drawings* |          |          | **$120** |
| ☐ **KAULA, Lee Lufkin** .......... *paintings* |          | **$412** | **$4,675** |
| American 1865-1957 ............... *drawings* |          | **$136** | **$440** |

## Judaica

In the late 19th and early 20th centuries, Isidor Kaufmann painted life in the ghettos of Galicia, Hungary, and Poland, meticulously depicting Jewish ritual and customs. After Austrian Emperor Franz Josef bought "The Rabbi's Visit" and presented it to Vienna's Museum of Fine Art, his career soared. Kaufmann's small genre paintings of everyday Jewish life appealed to the increasingly assimilated and cosmopolitan Jewish bourgeoisie of Vienna. A skillful portraitist, he was much in demand.

Prices for Kaufmann's paintings have risen sharply in the last ten years. His pictures often appear at Sotheby's and Christie's sales of Judaica, which include decorative works of art, books, and manuscripts, as well as paintings. Yet his work may go unnoticed in a 19th-century paintings sale and bring considerably less. (Isidor Kaufmann, "A Rabbi and His Student," oil on canvas, 15½ x 12¼ in., Doyle, May 19, 1983, $49,500.)

| | | Current Price Range | |
|---|---|---|---|
| | | *Low* | *High* |
| ☐ **KAULA, William Jurian** .............. *paintings* | | **$137** | **$7,260** |
| American 1871-1953 .................. *drawings* | | **$77** | **$1,540** |
| ☐ **KAULBACH, Friedrich (Sr.)** .............. *paintings* | | | **$6,050** |
| German 1822-1903 | | | |
| ☐ **KAULBACH, Friedrich August von** | | | |
| **(Jr.)** .................................. *paintings* | | **$770** | **$2,860** |
| German 1850-1920 .................. *drawings* | | **$770** | **$1,650** |
| ☐ **KAULBACH, Hermann** .............. *paintings* | | **$11,000** | **$40,700** |
| German 1846-1909 | | | |
| ☐ **KAUMEYER, G.F.** .............. *paintings* | | | **$192** |
| American early 20th cent. | | | |
| ☐ **KAUTSKY, Hans** .............. *drawings* | | | **$330** |
| German b. 1864 | | | |

| | Current Price Range | |
|---|---|---|
| | Low | High |
| ☐ **KAUTZKY, Theodore** .......................... *drawings* | $308 | $440 |
| American b. 1935 | | |
| ☐ **KAVANAGH, Joseph Malachy** .............. *paintings* | $110 | $4,675 |
| Irish 1856-1918/19 | | |
| ☐ **KAVEL, Martin** .................................. *paintings* | $2,090 | $2,420 |
| French 19th cent. | | |
| ☐ **KAWAMURA, Gozo** ........................... *sculpture* | | $825 |
| Japanese b. 1875 | | |
| ☐ **KAY, James** ...................................... *paintings* | | $4,620 |
| English 1858-1942 ..................................... *drawings* | $154 | $495 |
| ☐ **KAY, W.** ........................................... *paintings* | | $440 |
| ☐ **KAYN, Hilde B.** .................................. *paintings* | $286 | $605 |
| American 1906-1950 .............................. *drawings* | $220 | $275 |
| ☐ **KAYSER, J.** ....................................... *paintings* | $412 | $440 |
| Dutch 20th cent. | | |
| ☐ **KAZ, Nathaniel** ................................. *drawings* | $77 | $110 |
| American 20th cent. .................................. *sculpture* | $825 | $1,430 |
| ☐ **KAZPP, W.A.** ..................................... *paintings* | | $550 |
| American 20th cent. | | |
| ☐ **KEANE, Margaret** ............................. *paintings* | | $650 |
| ☐ **KEANEY, P.** ....................................... *paintings* | | $825 |
| ☐ **KEARNEY, John Walter** ...................... *sculpture* | $411 | $1,760 |
| American b. 1924 | | |
| ☐ **KEATING, Bill** .................................. *sculpture* | | $1,650 |
| ☐ **KEATS, C.J.** ...................................... *drawings* | $192 | $467 |
| English ac. 1885 | | |
| ☐ **KEBER, C.P.** ...................................... *paintings* | | $275 |
| ☐ **KECK, George Fred** ........................... *paintings* | $220 | $440 |
| American 1895-1980 | | |
| ☐ **KECK, H.** .......................................... *sculpture* | $357 | $800 |
| ☐ **KEELING, Michael** ............................. *paintings* | | $1,320 |
| English d. 1820 | | |
| ☐ **KEELING, Sydney** ............................. *paintings* | | $302 |
| British 19th cent. | | |
| ☐ **KEENAN, B.** ...................................... *paintings* | | $192 |
| English 19th cent. | | |
| ☐ **KEENER, Anna** ................................. *paintings* | | $302 |
| American b. 1895 | | |
| ☐ **KEEP, A.L.** ........................................ *paintings* | $80 | $632 |
| ☐ **KEFFER, Frances** ............................. *paintings* | $301 | $357 |
| American 1881-1954 | | |
| ☐ **KEIL, Bernhardt** | | |
| **(called Monsu Bernardo)** ...................... *paintings* | $2,860 | $9,350 |
| Danish 1624-1687 | | |
| ☐ **KEINHOLZ, Edward** .......................... *drawings* | | $330 |
| American 20th cent. | | |
| ☐ **KEINZ, E.** ......................................... *paintings* | | $247 |
| German 19th cent. | | |

| | | Current Price Range | |
|---|---|---|---|
| | | *Low* | *High* |
| ☐ **KEIRINCX, Alexander** .......................... *paintings* | | | $104,500 |
| Flemish 1600-1652 | | | |
| ☐ **KEIRSBILCK, Jules van** ................... *paintings* | | $4,400 | $9,350 |
| Belgian 1833-1896 | | | |
| ☐ **KEISERMAN, Franz** ........................... *drawings* | | | $2,750 |
| Swiss 1765-1833 | | | |
| ☐ **KEISTER** ............................................ *paintings* | | | $330 |
| early 20th cent. | | | |
| ☐ **KEISTER, Steve** .................................. *sculpture* | | $440 | $1,045 |
| American b. 1886 | | | |
| ☐ **KEITH, Elizabeth** ............................... *paintings* | | $495 | $3,300 |
| American b. 1887 ...................................... *drawings* | | | $187 |
| ☐ **KEITH, William** ................................. *drawings* | | $110 | $550 |
| American 1839-1911 | | | |
| ☐ **KEITH, William** ................................. *paintings* | | $302 | $30,250 |
| ☐ **KELETY, Alexandre** ........................... *sculpture* | | $990 | $9,900 |
| French early 20th cent. | | | |
| ☐ **KELLEHER, Hilda M.** ........................ *sculpture* | | $33 | $440 |
| American | | | |
| ☐ **KELLER, Arthur Ignatious** .................. *paintings* | | $660 | $1,100 |
| American 1866-1924 .................................. *drawings* | | $110 | $3,080 |
| ☐ **KELLER, Carl** ................................... *paintings* | | | $2,200 |
| German 19th cent. | | | |
| ☐ **KELLER, Charles Frederick** ................ *paintings* | | | $466 |
| American ac. 1852-1928 | | | |
| ☐ **KELLER, Clyde Leon** .......................... *paintings* | | $247 | $385 |
| American 1872-1941 | | | |
| ☐ **KELLER, Ferdinand** ........................... *paintings* | | | $4,950 |
| German 1842-1922 | | | |
| ☐ **KELLER, Frank** ................................. *paintings* | | $418 | $2,310 |
| American contemporary | | | |
| ☐ **KELLER, Friedrich von** ...................... *paintings* | | | $14,300 |
| German 1840-1914 | | | |
| ☐ **KELLER, Henry G.** ............................. *paintings* | | $330 | $550 |
| American 1870-1949 ................................. *drawings* | | $11 | $522 |
| ☐ **KELLER, Maximillian** ........................ *paintings* | | | $192 |
| German 19th cent. | | | |
| ☐ **KELLER-REUTLINGEN,** | | | |
| **Paul Wilhelm** ....................................... *paintings* | | $15,400 | $19,250 |
| German 1854-1920 | | | |
| ☐ **KELLEY, Ramon** ............................... *paintings* | | | $3,000 |
| American b. 1939 ...................................... *drawings* | | $770 | $15,000 |
| ☐ **KELLEY, Sue E.** ................................. *paintings* | | | $385 |
| American 19th cent. | | | |
| ☐ **KELLOGG, A.G.** ................................ *paintings* | | | $357 |
| ☐ **KELLOGG, Harry J.** ........................... *paintings* | | | $825 |
| 19th. cent. | | | |
| ☐ **KELLY, Ellsworth** ............................. *paintings* | | $27,500 | $115,500 |
| American b. 1923 ...................................... *drawings* | | $5,500 | $14,300 |

| | | | Current Price Range | |
|---|---|---|---|---|
| | | | Low | High |
| ☐ **KELLY, James Edward** | ............... | drawings | | **$440** |
| American 1855-1933 | ............... | sculpture | **$220** | **$330** |
| ☐ **KELLY, Julia Fielding** | ............... | paintings | | **$440** |
| ☐ **KELLY, Leon** | ............... | drawings | **$66** | **$1,100** |
| Franco/American b. 1901 | | | | |
| ☐ **KELLY, Robert Talbot** | ............... | paintings | | **$440** |
| English 1861-1934 | ............... | drawings | **$605** | **$4,180** |
| ☐ **KELLY, Sir Gerald Festus** | ............... | paintings | | **$9,625** |
| English 1879-1972 | | | | |
| ☐ **KELLY, W.** | ............... | paintings | | **$1,100** |
| American 19th cent. | | | | |
| ☐ **KELLY, Walt Crawford (Jr.)** | ............... | drawings | **$385** | **$1,595** |
| 1913-1973 | | | | |
| ☐ **KELPE, Paul** | ............... | paintings | | **$9,075** |
| American b. 1902 | | | | |
| ☐ **KELSEY, Charles J. Samuel** | ............... | sculpture | | **$220** |
| English 19th cent. | | | | |
| ☐ **KEMBLE, Edward Windsor** | ............... | drawings | **$165** | **$330** |
| American 1861-1933 | | | | |
| ☐ **KEMENDY, Jeno Eugen** | ............... | paintings | **$2,750** | **$17,600** |
| Hungarian 1860-1925 | | | | |
| ☐ **KEMENYFFI, Jeno** | ............... | paintings | | **$192** |
| Hungarian 1875-1920 | | | | |
| ☐ **KEMEYS, Edward** | ............... | sculpture | **$165** | **$2,860** |
| American 1843-1907 | | | | |
| ☐ **KEMM, Robert** | ............... | paintings | **$220** | **$5,500** |
| English ac. 1874-91 | | | | |
| ☐ **KEMMEL, Julien van** | ............... | paintings | | **$660** |
| Belgian b. 1834 | | | | |
| ☐ **KEMP, Oliver** | ............... | paintings | **$715** | **$1,430** |
| 1887-1934 | | | | |
| ☐ **KEMPER, Henry W.** | ............... | paintings | **$300** | **$3,190** |
| American 19th cent. | | | | |
| ☐ **KEMPF, Gottlieb** | ............... | drawings | | **$5,775** |
| Austrian b. 1871 | | | | |
| ☐ **KEMPSON, Julie (nee HART)** | ............... | paintings | | **$385** |
| American 1835-1913 | | | | |
| ☐ **KENDAHL (?), A.J.** | ............... | paintings | | **$990** |
| German 19th cent. | | | | |
| ☐ **KENDRICK, Alfred** | ............... | paintings | | **$935** |
| ☐ **KENDRICK, Daniel** | ............... | paintings | | **$302** |
| American 20th cent. | | | | |
| ☐ **KENDRICK, Sydney** | ............... | paintings | | **$880** |
| British 1874-1955 | | | | |
| ☐ **KENNARD** | ............... | paintings | | **$467** |
| British 19th cent. | | | | |
| ☐ **KENNEDY, A.** | ............... | paintings | | **$522** |
| ☐ **KENNEDY, Cecil** | ............... | paintings | **$440** | **$1,760** |
| British b. 1905 | | | | |

| | | Current Price Range | |
|---|---|---|---|
| | | Low | High |
| ☐ **KENNEDY, Edward Sherard** ............... *paintings* | | $770 | $2,750 |
| English ac. 1862-1910 | | | |
| ☐ **KENNEDY, Norman** ........................... *paintings* | | | $275 |
| ☐ **KENNEDY, William Denholm** ............... *paintings* | | | $385 |
| British 1813-1865 | | | |
| ☐ **KENNEDY, William W.** ....................... *paintings* | | $770 | $38,500 |
| American 1817-1871 | | | |
| ☐ **KENNEY, John T.** ............................. *paintings* | | | $1,100 |
| English 20th cent. | | | |
| ☐ **KENNON, C.H.** ................................ *paintings* | | | $330 |
| American 19th cent. | | | |
| ☐ **KENSALA, R.M.** .............................. *paintings* | | | $1,045 |
| Swiss (?) 19th cent. | | | |
| ☐ **KENSETT, John Frederick** ................... *paintings* | | $935 | $594,000 |
| American 1816/18-1872 | | | |
| ☐ **KENT, Frank W.** .............................. *paintings* | | | $1,430 |
| American 20th cent. | | | |
| ☐ **KENT, H.** ...................................... *paintings* | | | $302 |
| English 19th cent. | | | |
| ☐ **KENT, H.H.** ................................... *paintings* | | | $935 |
| American 19th cent. | | | |
| ☐ **KENT, Rockwell** ............................. *paintings* | | $1,100 | $33,000 |
| American 1882-1971 ............................. *drawings* | | $55 | $3,250 |
| ☐ **KEPES, Gyorgy** ............................... *paintings* | | | $1,430 |
| American b. Hungary 1906 | | | |
| ☐ **KEPETS, Hugh** ................................ *paintings* | | $1,210 | $2,090 |
| American b. 1946 | | | |
| ☐ **KERBER** ...................................... *paintings* | | $385 | $1,700 |
| German | | | |
| ☐ **KERCHER, Robert** ........................... *drawings* | | | $700 |
| American | | | |
| ☐ **KERKAM, Earl** ............................... *paintings* | | $330 | $1,430 |
| American c. 1890-1965 ........................... *drawings* | | $66 | $308 |
| ☐ **KERKHOVE, Jan van de** ..................... *paintings* | | | $330 |
| Belgian 1822-1881 | | | |
| ☐ **KERN, Anton** ................................. *paintings* | | | $275 |
| ☐ **KERN, Melchoir** ............................. *paintings* | | | $550 |
| German b. 1872 ................................... *drawings* | | | $297 |
| ☐ **KERN, Hermann** .............................. *paintings* | | $770 | $7,150 |
| Hungarian 1839-1912 | | | |
| ☐ **KERNAN, Joseph F.** .......................... *paintings* | | $935 | $1,650 |
| American b. 1878 ................................. *drawings* | | $137 | $385 |
| ☐ **KERNER, Glaus** .............................. *paintings* | | | $440 |
| Austrian 20th cent. | | | |
| ☐ **KERR, George Edward** ....................... *drawings* | | | $400 |
| American 20th cent. | | | |
| ☐ **KERR, James P.** .............................. *paintings* | | | $275 |
| American 20th cent. | | | |

| | Current Price Range | |
|---|---|---|
| | Low | High |
| ☐ **KERR, Robert** ............... *drawings* <br> English 1777-1842 | | $350 |
| ☐ **KERR-LAWSON, James** ............... *paintings* <br> English/Canadian 1865-1939 | $1,100 | $6,600 |
| ☐ **KERRUISH, Shirley Wells** ............... *paintings* | | $385 |
| ☐ **KERSON, O.R.** ............... *paintings* | | $264 |
| ☐ **KERSTING, George Frederick** ............... *paintings* | | $440 |
| ☐ **KESSEL, Jan van (I)** ............... *paintings* <br> Dutch 1626-1679 | $3,300 | $25,300 |
| ☐ **KESSEL, Jan van (III)** ............... *paintings* <br> Dutch 1641/42-1680 | | $2,090 |
| ☐ **KESTER, H.** ............... *paintings* | | $1,210 |
| ☐ **KESZLHELY, E. J.** ............... *paintings* <br> 20th cent. | | $1,210 |
| ☐ **KETT, Emile** ............... *paintings* <br> American 1828-1880 | | $1,650 |
| ☐ **KETTEMANN, Erwin** ............... *paintings* <br> German b. 1897 | $660 | $660 |
| ☐ **KETTLE, Tilly** ............... *paintings* <br> English 1735-1786 | $1,100 | $3,300 |
| ☐ **KEUHNE, Max** ............... *paintings* <br> American b. 1880 | $192 | $1,100 |
| ☐ **KEUN, Hendrik** ............... *paintings* | | $3,575 |
| ☐ **KEVER, Jacob Simon Hendrik** ............... *paintings* <br> Dutch 1854-1922 ............... *drawings* | $385 <br> $605 | $22,000 <br> $2,090 |
| ☐ **KEY, Adriaen Thomas** ............... *paintings* | $2,000 | $3,080 |
| ☐ **KEY, John Ross** ............... *paintings* <br> American 1832-1920 ............... *drawings* | $605 <br> $440 | $12,650 <br> $550 |
| ☐ **KEYES, Bernard M.** ............... *paintings* <br> b. 1898 | | $357 |
| ☐ **KEYES, W.E.** ............... *drawings* <br> American 19th cent. | | $302 |
| ☐ **KEYSER, Auguste Paul de** ............... *paintings* <br> Belgian 1829-1890 | | $935 |
| ☐ **KEYSER, Emil** ............... *paintings* <br> Swiss 1846-1923 | $650 | $7,150 |
| ☐ **KEYSER, Ernest Wise** ............... *sculpture* <br> American 1875-1951 | | $3,850 |
| ☐ **KEYSER, Thomas de** ............... *paintings* <br> Dutch 1596-1667 | $5,500 | $26,400 |
| ☐ **KHARLAMOV, Alexei Alexe'evich** ............... *paintings* <br> Russian b. 1824 | | $990 |
| ☐ **KHAYLL, A.** ............... *paintings* <br> European 19th cent. | | $550 |
| ☐ **KHIMONA, Nikolai Petrovich** ............... *paintings* | | $11,000 |
| ☐ **KHITH, Robert** ............... *paintings* <br> Norwegian 19th cent. | | $880 |
| ☐ **KHNOPFF, Fernand** ............... *drawings* <br> Belgian 1858-1912 | $9,900 | $22,000 |

|  | | | *Current Price Range* | |
|--|--|--|--------|---------|
|  | | | Low | High |
| ☐ **KIDD, A.S.H.** .............................. *paintings* | | | | $209 |
| English 19th cent. | | | | |
| ☐ **KIEFER, Anselm** ................................ *drawings* | | | | $11,550 |
| German b. 1945 | | | | |
| ☐ **KIELMANN, M.** ........................................ *paintings* | | | | $522 |
| ☐ **KIEMLEN, Emil** ................................ *sculpture* | | | | $1,320 |
| German early 20th cent. | | | | |
| ☐ **KIENBOCK, R.** ......................................... *paintings* | | | | $330 |
| ☐ **KIENBUSCH, William** ........................ *drawings* | | $33 | | $220 |
| American b. 1914 | | | | |
| ☐ **KIENER, M.** ......................................... *paintings* | | | | $385 |
| American 19th cent. | | | | |
| ☐ **KIENHOLZ, Edward** .......................... *paintings* | | $1,760 | | $6,600 |
| American b. 1927 ..................................... *drawings* | | $286 | | $770 |
| ☐ **KIESEL, Conrad** ................................ *paintings* | | $1,100 | | $33,000 |
| German 1846-1921 | | | | |
| ☐ **KIESELWETTER, Nilhelm** ................... *paintings* | | | | $330 |
| ☐ **KIESLER, Frederick** ........................... *sculpture* | | | | $2,420 |
| American 1896-1965 | | | | |
| ☐ **KIETH, Dora Wheeler** ......................... *paintings* | | | | $440 |
| b. 1857 | | | | |
| ☐ **KIHN, William Langdon** ....................... *paintings* | | | | $9,075 |
| American 1898-c. 1957 | | | | |
| ☐ **KIKOINE, Michel** ................................ *paintings* | | $330 | | $4,400 |
| French 1892-1968 ..................................... *drawings* | | | | $550 |
| ☐ **KILBOURNE, Samuel A.** .................... *paintings* | | $935 | | $412 |
| American 1836-1881 ................................. *drawings* | | | | $550 |
| ☐ **KILBURNE, George Goodwin** .............. *paintings* | | $660 | | $4,400 |
| English 1839-1924 ................................... *drawings* | | | | $1,045 |
| ☐ **KILLGORE, Charles P.** ...................... *paintings* | | | | $577 |
| American 20th cent. | | | | |
| ☐ **KILLIKTEE, Simata** ........................... *sculpture* | | | | $275 |
| Eskimo | | | | |
| ☐ **KILM, W. L.** ....................................... *paintings* | | | | $220 |
| American? 19th cent. | | | | |
| ☐ **KILNER, P.** ......................................... *paintings* | | | | $330 |
| ☐ **KILPIN, Legh Mulhall** ...................... *drawings* | | | | $660 |
| ☐ **KILVERT, B. Cory** ............................. *drawings* | | $110 | | $660 |
| 1881-1946 | | | | |
| ☐ **KIM, Po** ........................................... *drawings* | | | | $1,520 |
| ☐ **KIMBALL, Charles Frederick** .............. *paintings* | | $220 | | $1,900 |
| American 1835/36-1907 ............................. *drawings* | | $99 | | $242 |
| ☐ **KIMBEL, Richard M.** ......................... *paintings* | | $132 | | $357 |
| American 1865-1942 | | | | |
| ☐ **KIMMEL, Lu** ..................................... *paintings* | | | | $220 |
| American 1905-1973 ................................. *drawings* | | | | $110 |
| ☐ **KIMPFEL, J.C.** .................................. *paintings* | | | | $440 |
| ☐ **KINCH, Henry** ................................... *paintings* | | | | $4,180 |
| English 19th cent. | | | | |

| | Current Price Range | |
|---|---|---|
| | Low | High |
| ☐ **KINDERMANS, Jean Baptiste** .............. *paintings* | | **$4,125** |
| Belgian 1822-1876 | | |
| ☐ **KINDERSLEY, H.W.** ........................... *paintings* | | **$260** |
| ☐ **KING, Albert F.** ................................... *paintings* | **$220** | **$20,900** |
| American 1854-1945 | | |
| ☐ **KING, Baragwanath** ........................... *paintings* | | **$1,705** |
| British 1864-1939 | | |
| ☐ **KING, Charles Bird** ........................... *paintings* | **$550** | **$3,520** |
| American 1785-1862 ................................... *drawings* | **$3,575** | **$4,400** |
| ☐ **KING, Edward R.** ............................... *paintings* | **$1,100** | **$1,760** |
| ☐ **KING, Ethel** ........................................ *drawings* | | **$192** |
| British 19th/20th cent. | | |
| ☐ **KING, Fanny Manon** ........................... *paintings* | | **$220** |
| American 20th cent. | | |
| ☐ **KING, Frank O.** ................................... *drawings* | **$88** | **$550** |
| American 1883-1969 | | |
| ☐ **KING, George W.** ............................... *paintings* | **$192** | **$1,650** |
| American 1836-1922 | | |
| ☐ **KING, Gunning** ................................... *paintings* | **$466** | **$825** |
| English 1859-1940 | | |
| ☐ **KING, H. Elizabeth** ........................... *paintings* | | **$412** |
| ☐ **KING, Haynes** ................................... *paintings* | | **$715** |
| ☐ **KING, J.L.** ........................................ *paintings* | | **$264** |
| ☐ **KING, J.W.** ........................................ *paintings* | **$385** | **$440** |
| American 20th cent. | | |
| ☐ **KING, Jessie Marion** ........................... *drawings* | **$88** | **$4,950** |
| Scottish 1875-1949 | | |
| ☐ **KING, Joe (called "Vinciata")** ................ *paintings* | **$990** | **$1,100** |
| American 20th cent. | | |
| ☐ **KING, John William** ........................... *paintings* | | **$4,290** |
| American ac. 1855-1865 | | |
| ☐ **KING, Paul** ........................................ *paintings* | **$66** | **$9,350** |
| American 1867-1947 | | |
| ☐ **KING, T.V.** ........................................ *paintings* | | **$275** |
| ☐ **KING, Tony** ........................................ *paintings* | | **$4,950** |
| contemporary | | |
| ☐ **KING, W.A.** ........................................ *paintings* | | **$275** |
| American ac. 1870 | | |
| ☐ **KING, William** ................................... *drawings* | | **$330** |
| American b. 1925 ................................... *sculpture* | **$385** | **$3,080** |
| ☐ **KING, William J.** ............................... *paintings* | | **$550** |
| British 19th cent. | | |
| ☐ **KINGMAN, Dong** ............................... *drawings* | **$110** | **$5,775** |
| American b. 1911 | | |
| ☐ **KINGMAN, Eduardo** ........................... *paintings* | **$440** | **$5,775** |
| Ecuadorian b. 1911 | | |
| ☐ **KINGSLEY, C.** ................................... *paintings* | **$187** | **$550** |

## Streets of San Francisco

*Dong Kingman is a noted contemporary artist whose favorite subject is the city of San Francisco. Kingman studied in China and had his first one-man show at the Hoover Gallery in San Francisco in 1935, when he was just twenty-four years old. Primarily an illustration artist, Kingman uses watercolor and wash to create line sketches. He has worked for major corporate clients as well as for television and movies. (Dong Kingman, "Tanks," watercolor on paper, 17 x 23 in., Butterfield, April 25, 1985, $660.)*

| | | Current Price Range | |
| --- | --- | --- | --- |
| | | Low | High |
| ☐ **KINGWELL, M. Amber** ...................... *drawings* | | | **$605** |
| British 20th cent. | | | |
| ☐ **KINNAIRD, F.G.** ................................ *paintings* | | | **$2,200** |
| ☐ **KINNAIRD, Frederick Gerald** ............... *paintings* | | **$412** | **$770** |
| British 19th cent. | | | |
| ☐ **KINNAIRD, Henry J.** ........................... *paintings* | | **$440** | **$1,320** |
| English ac. 1880-c. 1920 ............................. *drawings* | | **$143** | **$880** |
| ☐ **KINNAIRD, J. Wiggs** .......................... *paintings* | | | **$385** |
| ☐ **KINNARD, H.** .................................... *paintings* | | | **$302** |
| American 19th/20th cent. | | | |
| ☐ **KINSBURGER, S.** ............................... *sculpture* | | | **$800** |
| ☐ **KINSEY, Alberta** ............................... *paintings* | | **$22** | **$825** |
| American 1875-1955 | | | |
| ☐ **KINSTLER, Everett Raymond** .............. *drawings* | | **$247** | **$1,760** |
| American b. 1926 | | | |

| | | Current Price Range | |
| --- | --- | --- | --- |
| | | *Low* | *High* |
| ☐ **KINZEL, Josef** ................................... *paintings* | | $3,850 | $17,600 |
| Austrian 1852-1925 | | | |
| ☐ **KIPNESS, Robert** ............................. *paintings* | | | $440 |
| American b. 1931 | | | |
| ☐ **KIRBERG, Otto Karl** .......................... *paintings* | | $1,650 | $3,080 |
| German 1850-1926 | | | |
| ☐ **KIRCHNER** ...................................... *drawings* | | | $55 |
| ..................................... *sculpture* | | | $550 |
| ☐ **KIRCHNER, Ernst Ludwig** ................... *paintings* | | $49,500 | $203,500 |
| German 1880-1938 ..................................... *drawings* | | $224 | $15,950 |
| ☐ **KIRCHNER, Otto** ............................. *paintings* | | $385 | $2,420 |
| German b. 1887 | | | |
| ☐ **KIRCHNER, Raphael** .......................... *drawings* | | $275 | $605 |
| Austrian 1867-1917 | | | |
| ☐ **KIRK, Pietr van** ................................ *paintings* | | | $1,320 |
| Belgian b. 1834 | | | |
| ☐ **KIRKHAM, J.W.** ............................... *paintings* | | | $220 |
| British 19th/20th cent. | | | |
| ☐ **KIRKMANN, Augustus Josepha** ............ *paintings* | | | $440 |
| ☐ **KIRKPATRICK, Frank LeBrun** ............ *paintings* | | $2,200 | $3,025 |
| American 1853-1917 ..................................... *drawings* | | $121 | $192 |
| ☐ **KIRKPATRICK, H.** ............................ *paintings* | | | $440 |
| American 19th/20th cent. | | | |
| ☐ **KIRKPATRICK, J. L.** .......................... *paintings* | | | $418 |
| European | | | |
| ☐ **KIRMSE, Marguerite** ......................... *paintings* | | $286 | $462 |
| English/American 1885-1954 ........................ *drawings* | | | $330 |
| ..................................... *sculpture* | | | $220 |
| ☐ **KIRSCH** ...................................... *sculpture* | | | $550 |
| ☐ **KIRTLEY, F. W.** ............................. *paintings* | | $137 | $220 |
| American 19th cent. | | | |
| ☐ **KIRWAN, William Burke** .................... *drawings* | | | $850 |
| Irish b. c. 1814 | | | |
| ☐ **KIRZINGER, Marianne** ........................ *paintings* | | $1,100 | $2,200 |
| ☐ **KISCHINEZSKY, Solomon** ................. *paintings* | | | $605 |
| ☐ **KISCHKA, Isis** ................................ *paintings* | | | $550 |
| French 20th cent. | | | |
| ☐ **KISLING, Moise** ............................... *paintings* | | $3,300 | $71,500 |
| Polish/French 1891-1953 ............................. *drawings* | | $990 | $3,960 |
| ☐ **KISS, Carl Auguste Eduard** ................. *sculpture* | | | $880 |
| German c. 1860 | | | |
| ☐ **KISS, Casaba** ................................... *paintings* | | | $907 |
| Hungarian b. 1945 | | | |
| ☐ **KISSEL, Eleanora** ............................. *paintings* | | $275 | $3,740 |
| American 1891-1966 ...................................... *drawings* | | $137 | $880 |
| ☐ **KIST, Frederick** ............................... *paintings* | | | $247 |
| American 1865-1923 | | | |
| ☐ **KITAGAWA, Tamiji** ........................... *paintings* | | $82 | $176 |
| Japanese b. 1894 | | | |

## Price Ranges

A German/Swiss painter who experimented with lines, perspective, and shape, Paul Klee was a part of some of the most important movements in 20th-century art. Klee's works appear frequently at auctions, with prices for watercolors ranging from $8,250 to $275,000, and oils from $60,500 to $467,000. (Paul Klee, "Mola," gouache on paper, 6 x 14½ in., Doyle, September 24, 1980, $79,750.)

| | | Current Price Range | |
|---|---|---|---|
| | | *Low* | *High* |
| ☐ **KITAJ, R.B.** ....................... *paintings* | | **$1,210** | **$10,450** |
| American b. 1933 | | | |
| ☐ **KITCHELL, Hudson Mindell** ............... *paintings* | | **$110** | **$825** |
| American 1862-1944 | | | |
| ☐ **KITCHEN, Tella** ................... *paintings* | | | **$2,420** |
| contemporary | | | |
| ☐ **KITTLESON, John** ............................ *sculpture* | | | **$1,100** |
| ☐ **KIUSBURGER, S.** ............................. *sculpture* | | | **$1,760** |
| ☐ **KIVAS, A.** ......................................... *paintings* | | | **$495** |
| Italian 19th cent. | | | |
| ☐ **KLAGSTAD, Arnold** ........................... *paintings* | | | **$247** |
| American b. 1898 | | | |
| ☐ **KLAPHECK, Konrad** .......................... *paintings* | | | **$19,800** |
| German b. 1935 | | | |
| ☐ **KLAUSS, Hans** ................................... *paintings* | | | **$2,790** |
| German b. 1867 | | | |
| ☐ **KLECZYNSKI, Bodhan von** ................ *paintings* | | **$4,125** | **$14,850** |
| Polish 1851-1916 | | | |
| ☐ **KLEE, Paul** ....................................... *paintings* | | **$13,200** | **$467,500** |
| Swiss 1879-1940 ..................................... *drawings* | | **$2,200** | **$275,000** |
| ☐ **KLEEMAN, Ron** .................................. *paintings* | | **$1,760** | **$4,400** |
| American b. 1937 ....................................... *drawings* | | | **$220** |
| ☐ **KLEIBER, Hans** ................................. *drawings* | | **$308** | **$330** |
| American b. 1887 | | | |
| ☐ **KLEIJN, Lodewijk Johannes** ................ *paintings* | | **$137** | **$9,900** |
| Dutch 1817-1897 ....................................... *drawings* | | | **$1,100** |

| | Current Price Range | |
|---|---|---|
| | *Low* | *High* |

☐ **KLEIN, Johann Adam** ..................... *drawings* | | $1,100
German 1792-1875

☐ **KLEIN, Kathy M.** ........................... *drawings* | | $247
American 20th cent.

☐ **KLEIN, W.** ....................................... *paintings* | | $440
German 19th cent.

☐ **KLEIN, Yves** .................................... *sculpture* | | $2,310
French 1928-1962

☐ **KLEINERT, Joseph** ........................... *paintings* | | $1,100
Austrian 19th cent.

☐ **KLEINMICHEL,**
 **Ferdinand Julius Theodor** ............ *paintings* | | $6,600
German 1846-1892

☐ **KLEINSCHMIDT, Paul** .................... *paintings* | $550 | $8,250
German b. 1883 ...................................... *drawings* | $715 | $1,100

☐ **KLEM, E.** ........................................ *paintings* | | $495

☐ **KLEMKE** ......................................... *paintings* | | $605
German 19th cent.

☐ **KLEMPNER, Sigmund** ...................... *paintings* | | $385

☐ **KLENE, Bern** .................................. *paintings* | $286 | $357
Dutch 1870-1930

☐ **KLENGEL, Johann Christian** ............ *paintings* | | $1,650
German 1751-1824 ................................... *drawings* | | $605

☐ **KLEPPER, Max Francis** ..................... *paintings* | | $5,775
American 1861-1907

☐ **KLERK, Willem de** ........................... *paintings* | $1,210 | $4,400
Dutch b. 1800

☐ **KLEVER, Julius Sergius von** ............. *paintings* | $825 | $6,600
Russian 1850-1924

☐ **KLEY, C.** ........................................ *paintings* | | $220
German 19th/20th cent.

☐ **KLEY, Heinrich** ............................... *drawings* | $440 | $990

☐ **KLEY, Louis** ................................... *sculpture* | | $242
French 19th cent.

☐ **KLIENHOLZ, Frank** .......................... *paintings* | | $550
American

☐ **KLIMT, Gustav** ............................... *paintings* | | $55,000
Austrian 1862-1918 ................................. *drawings* | $650 | $15,400

☐ **KLINCKENBERG, Eugen** .................. *paintings* | | $1,540
German b. 1858

☐ **KLINE, Edith H.** .............................. *sculpture* | | $330
American 19th/20th cent.

☐ **KLINE, Franz** ................................. *paintings* | $3,850 | $880,000
American 1910-1962 ................................. *drawings* | $412 | $39,600

☐ **KLINE, William Fair** ....................... *paintings* | | $2,200
1870-1931

☐ **KLINGEBUGL, Rudolph** .................... *paintings* | | $495

☐ **KLINGER, Julius** ............................. *drawings* | $440 | $770

| | | Current Price Range | |
|---|---|---|---|
| | | Low | High |
| ☐ **KLINGER, Max** .................................. *drawings* | | | $220 |
| German 1857-1920 | | | |
| ☐ **KLINGSBEGEL** ................................. *paintings* | | | $1,100 |
| ☐ **KLINGSBOCK, Rudolf** ....................... *paintings* | | | $495 |
| ☐ **KLINKENBERG,** | | | |
| **Johannes Karel Christian** .................. *paintings* | | $880 | $11,000 |
| Dutch 1852-1924 ..................................... *drawings* | | | $165 |
| ☐ **KLITGAARD, Georgina** ....................... *paintings* | | $55 | $66 |
| ................................................................ *drawings* | | $198 | $528 |
| ☐ **KLIUN, Ivan** ...................................... *drawings* | | $1,540 | $5,500 |
| Russian 1873-1943 | | | |
| ☐ **KLOMBEEK, Johann Bernard** ............. *paintings* | | | $27,500 |
| Dutch 1815-1893 | | | |
| ☐ **KLOMP, Albert Jansz** ......................... *paintings* | | | $13,200 |
| Dutch 1618-1688 | | | |
| ☐ **KLOSS, Gene** ..................................... *drawings* | | $88 | $385 |
| American b. 1903 | | | |
| ☐ **KLOSS, P.** ......................................... *sculpture* | | | $544 |
| ☐ **KLOSSOWSKI, Erich** ......................... *drawings* | | | $385 |
| German 1875-1949 | | | |
| ☐ **KLOTS, Trafford** ............................... *paintings* | | $110 | $286 |
| ☐ **KLUGE, Constantin** ........................... *paintings* | | $330 | $2,200 |
| French b. 1912 | | | |
| ☐ **KLUTH, P.** ........................................ *paintings* | | | $440 |
| ☐ **KLUTH, Robert** .................................. *paintings* | | $412 | $1,100 |
| German/American 1854-1921 | | | |
| ☐ **KLUTSCHAK, Henry W.** ..................... *drawings* | | | $440 |
| 19th cent. | | | |
| ☐ **KLUYVER, Pieter Lodewyk Francisco** .. *paintings* | | $2,200 | $6,600 |
| Dutch 1816-1900 | | | |
| ☐ **KNAB, Ferdinand** ............................... *paintings* | | | $2,750 |
| German 1834-1902 | | | |
| ☐ **KNAPER, G.H.** ................................... *paintings* | | | $300 |
| American | | | |
| ☐ **KNAPP, Charles W.** ........................... *paintings* | | $990 | $4,675 |
| American 1822-1900 | | | |
| ☐ **KNAPP, F.O.** ..................................... *paintings* | | | $495 |
| German 19th cent. | | | |
| ☐ **KNAPP, K.** ........................................ *paintings* | | $330 | $1,760 |
| German 19th/20th cent. | | | |
| ☐ **KNAPP, Thomas** ................................ *sculpture* | | | $550 |
| American | | | |
| ☐ **KNAPTON, George** ............................. *paintings* | | | $935 |
| English 1698-1778 | | | |
| ☐ **KNARREN, Petrus Renier Hubertus** ..... *paintings* | | | $7,425 |
| Dutch 1826-1896 | | | |
| ☐ **KNATH, Arnold W.** ............................. *paintings* | | | $225 |
| American | | | |

| | Current Price Range | |
|---|---|---|
| | Low | High |
| ☐ **KNATHS, Karl** ............................... *paintings* | $330 | $8,250 |
| American 1891-1971 ........................ *drawings* | $110 | $1,100 |
| ☐ **KNAUERHASE, Paul** ...................... *paintings* | $1,320 | $1,540 |
| ☐ **KNAUS, F.** ....................................... *paintings* | | $1,760 |
| German 19th cent. | | |
| ☐ **KNAUS, Ludwig** ............................ *paintings* | $550 | $60,500 |
| German 1829-1910 ............................ *drawings* | | $880 |
| ☐ **KNEBEL, Franz (the younger)** ........ *paintings* | $4,180 | $4,950 |
| Swiss 1809-1877 | | |
| ☐ **KNEBEL, Leopold** .......................... *paintings* | | $357 |
| German b. 1810 | | |
| ☐ **KNEBEL, Tito** ............................... *paintings* | | $3,850 |
| Swiss (?) 19th cent. | | |
| ☐ **KNEIP, Robert Frank** ..................... *paintings* | | $1,100 |
| German 20th cent. | | |
| ☐ **KNEIPP, Georg** .............................. *paintings* | $165 | $220 |
| German 1793-1862 | | |
| ☐ **KNELL, Adolphus** ........................... *paintings* | | $385 |
| American 20th cent. | | |
| ☐ **KNELL, William Adolphus** ............. *paintings* | $880 | $38,500 |
| English c. 1805-1875 | | |
| ☐ **KNELL, William Callcott** ............... *paintings* | $140 | $1,760 |
| English ac. 1848-1871 | | |
| ☐ **KNELLER, Sir Godfrey** ................... *paintings* | $286 | $3,740 |
| German/English 1646-1723 | | |
| ☐ **KNERR, Harold** ............................ *paintings* | $220 | $302 |
| 1883-1949 | | |
| ☐ **KNICKER, Jan** ............................... *paintings* | | $412 |
| Dutch 19th cent. | | |
| ☐ **KNIGHT** ........................................ *paintings* | | $1,815 |
| British 19th cent. | | |
| ☐ **KNIGHT, A. Roland** ........................ *paintings* | | $1,760 |
| ☐ **KNIGHT, Charles Robert** ................ *paintings* | $165 | $687 |
| American 1874-1953 ......................... *drawings* | | $4,800 |
| ................................................ *sculpture* | | $880 |
| ☐ **KNIGHT, Clayton** ........................... *drawings* | | $247 |
| American 1891 | | |
| ☐ **KNIGHT, Dame Laura** ..................... *drawings* | $165 | $1,430 |
| English 1877-1970 | | |
| ☐ **KNIGHT, Daniel Ridgway** ............... *paintings* | $1,210 | $33,000 |
| American 1839-1924 ......................... *drawings* | $605 | $3,300 |
| ☐ **KNIGHT, George** ........................... *paintings* | $165 | $1,430 |
| British 19th cent. | | |
| ☐ **KNIGHT, John Buxton** ..................... *paintings* | | $2,200 |
| British 1843-1908 | | |
| ☐ **KNIGHT, Louis Aston** ...................... *paintings* | $66 | $11,550 |
| American 1873-1948 ......................... *drawings* | $137 | $1,100 |
| ☐ **KNIGHT, William Henry** ................. *paintings* | | $990 |
| British 1823-63 | | |

| | | *Current Price Range* | |
|---|---|---|---|
| | | *Low* | *High* |
| ☐ **KNIP, August** ....................... *paintings* | | | **$660** |
| ☐ **KNIP, Henri** ....................... *drawings* | | | **$1,100** |
| ☐ **KNIP, Henriette Ronner** ...................... *paintings* | | | **$4,290** |
| Dutch 1821-1909 | | | |
| ☐ **KNIP, Josephus Augustus** ..................... *drawings* | | | **$1,540** |
| Dutch 1777-1847 | | | |
| ☐ **KNIP, William Alexander** ..................... *paintings* | | **$495** | **$880** |
| Dutch 1883-1967 | | | |
| ☐ **KNOBLAUCH, L.V.** ................... *paintings* | | **$22** | **$800** |
| American 20th cent. | | | |
| ☐ **KNOOP, August** ................... *paintings* | | **$275** | **$2,000** |
| German 1856-1900 | | | |
| ☐ **KNOPF, Nellie A.** .................... *paintings* | | **$55** | **$770** |
| American b. 1875 | | | |
| ☐ **KNOPFF, Adolph** ............................ *paintings* | | **$3,300** | **$4,675** |
| German 1851-1917 | | | |
| ☐ **KNOPTON, George** ..................... *paintings* | | **$715** | **$797** |
| English 18th cent. | | | |
| ☐ **KNOWLES, F. McGillvray** .................. *paintings* | | | **$220** |
| American 1860-1932 | | | |
| ☐ **KNOWLES, George Sheridan** .............. *paintings* | | **$440** | **$4,675** |
| English 1863-1931 | | | |
| ☐ **KNOWLES, Joseph** ............................ *paintings* | | **$220** | **$1,650** |
| American 19th cent. | | | |
| ☐ **KNOWLTON, Grace** ....................... *drawings* | | | **$495** |
| ☐ **KNOWLTON, Helen Mary** .................. *paintings* | | | **$385** |
| 1832-1918 | | | |
| ☐ **KNOWLTON, J.H.** ........................... *paintings* | | | **$1,650** |
| American c. 1844 | | | |
| ☐ **KNOX, George John** ..................... *drawings* | | **$70** | **$467** |
| English 1810-1897 | | | |
| ☐ **KNOX, Susan Ricker** ........................... *paintings* | | **$66** | **$2,310** |
| American 1875-1959 ..................................... *drawings* | | **$154** | **$440** |
| ☐ **KNOX, W.** ..................................... *drawings* | | | **$275** |
| ☐ **KNUPFER, B.** ............................... *paintings* | | | **$264** |
| ☐ **KNUPFER, Nicolaus** ............................ *paintings* | | | **$16,500** |
| German b.c. 1603-c. 1660 | | | |
| ☐ **KNYFF, Wouter** ..................... *paintings* | | **$3,850** | **$26,400** |
| Dutch c. 1607-c. 1693 | | | |
| ☐ **KOBASHI** ............................... *drawings* | | **$81** | **$275** |
| ☐ **KOBELL, Ferdinand** ........................... *paintings* | | | **$990** |
| German 1740-1799 ...................................... *drawings* | | | **$137** |
| ☐ **KOBELL, Franz** ........................... *drawings* | | | **$1,870** |
| ☐ **KOBELL, Jan Baptist** ........................... *paintings* | | | **$1,430** |
| Dutch 1778-1814 ...................................... *drawings* | | | **$200** |
| ☐ **KOBZDEJ, Aleksander** ..................... *paintings* | | | **$330** |
| ☐ **KOCH, George** ....................... *paintings* | | | **$7,700** |
| German b. 1878 ...................................... *drawings* | | **$825** | **$1,210** |

| | | *Current Price Range* | |
|---|---|---|---|
| | | *Low* | *High* |
| ☐ **KOCH, Heinrich** .............................. *paintings* | | | $825 |
| German 1806-1893 | | | |
| ☐ **KOCH, John** ............................... *paintings* | | $2,750 | $51,700 |
| American 1909/10-1978 .............................. *drawings* | | | $1,100 |
| ☐ **KOCH, Josef Anton** ........................ *drawings* | | | $1,760 |
| ☐ **KOCH, Ludwig** ............................. *paintings* | | $935 | $3,575 |
| Austrian 1866-1934 | | | |
| ☐ **KOEGL, E.** ......................................... *paintings* | | | $687 |
| German 19th/20th cent. | | | |
| ☐ **KOEHLER, Henry** ............................ *paintings* | | $242 | $715 |
| American 20th cent. ................................. *drawings* | | $77 | $715 |
| ☐ **KOEHLER, Paul R.** ............................ *paintings* | | | $650 |
| American 1866-1909 ................................. *drawings* | | $60 | $220 |
| ☐ **KOEHLER, R.** .................................... *paintings* | | | $412 |
| American 19th/20th cent. | | | |
| ☐ **KOEKKOEK, Barend Cornelis** ............. *paintings* | | $17,600 | $38,500 |
| Dutch 1803-1862 ....................................... *drawings* | | | $2,310 |
| ☐ **KOEKKOEK, Hendrik Barend** ............. *paintings* | | $1,540 | $4,950 |
| Dutch 1849-1909 | | | |
| ☐ **KOEKKOEK, Hendrik Pieter** ............... *paintings* | | $1,600 | $16,500 |
| Dutch 1843-1890 | | | |
| ☐ **KOEKKOEK, Hermanus** | | | |
| **(Jr.called Jan van Couve)** ...................... *paintings* | | $1,980 | $4,400 |
| Dutch 1836-1909 ...................................... *drawings* | | $198 | $605 |
| ☐ **KOEKKOEK, Hermanus (Sr.)** ............... *paintings* | | $900 | $17,600 |
| Dutch 1815-1882 | | | |
| ☐ **KOEKKOEK, Hermanus Willem** .......... *paintings* | | $1,320 | $4,400 |
| Dutch 1867-1929 | | | |
| ☐ **KOEKKOEK,** | | | |
| **Johannes Hermanus Barend** ................. *paintings* | | $880 | $9,625 |
| Dutch 1840-1912 | | | |
| ☐ **KOEKKOEK, Marianus Adrianus** ......... *paintings* | | $6,600 | $22,000 |
| Dutch 1807-1870 | | | |
| ☐ **KOEKKOEK, Willem** .......................... *paintings* | | $3,850 | $30,800 |
| Dutch 1839-1895 | | | |
| ☐ **KOENIG, Fritz** ............................... *sculpture* | | | $1,650 |
| German b. 1924 | | | |
| ☐ **KOENIG, Johann** ............................. *paintings* | | $1,100 | $38,500 |
| German c. 1586-c. 1642 | | | |
| ☐ **KOENIG, Jules Raymond** ................. *paintings* | | | $440 |
| ☐ **KOENIGE, Ferdinand** ......................... *sculpture* | | | $440 |
| German 19th cent. | | | |
| ☐ **KOENIGER, W.** ............................... *paintings* | | | $880 |
| Continental 20th cent. | | | |
| ☐ **KOENIGER, Walter** ......................... *paintings* | | $99 | $6,325 |
| American b. 1881 | | | |
| ☐ **KOERLE, Pancraz** .............................. *paintings* | | | $1,430 |
| German 1823-1875 | | | |

| | | Current Price Range | |
|---|---|---|---|
| | | *Low* | *High* |
| ☐ **KOERNER, Ernst** .............................. *paintings* | | | **$3,850** |
| German b. 1846 | | | |
| ☐ **KOERNER, P.K.** ............................... *paintings* | | | **$220** |
| American 19th cent. | | | |
| ☐ **KOERNER, William Henry Dethlef** ....... *paintings* | | **$550** | **$30,000** |
| German/American 1878-1938 ......................... *drawings* | | **$467** | **$1,980** |
| ☐ **KOESTER, Alexander Max** ................. *paintings* | | **$11,000** | **$52,250** |
| German 1864-1932 | | | |
| ☐ **KOETS, Roelof** ............................... *paintings* | | | **$10,450** |
| Dutch | | | |
| ☐ **KOGL, Benedict** ............................. *paintings* | | **$1,265** | **$1,980** |
| German 19th cent. | | | |
| ☐ **KOHEN, Linda** ............................... *paintings* | | **$880** | **$2,200** |
| b. Italy 1924 | | | |
| ☐ **KOHL, Ludwig** ............................... *paintings* | | | **$440** |
| Austrian 1746-1821 | | | |
| ☐ **KOHLER, Carl** ............................... *paintings* | | **$440** | **$715** |
| ☐ **KOHLER, Gustav** ........................... *paintings* | | **$660** | **$1,870** |
| German b. 1859 | | | |
| ☐ **KOHLER, William Eiffe V.R.** .............. *paintings* | | | **$1,320** |
| American 19th cent. | | | |
| ☐ **KOHLHAUM** ...................................... *paintings* | | | **$220** |
| German 18th/19th cent. | | | |
| ☐ **KOHRL, Ludwig** .............................. *paintings* | | **$385** | **$3,300** |
| German b. 1858 | | | |
| ☐ **KOKEN, Paul** ................................... *paintings* | | | **$2,200** |
| German b. 1853 ........................................ *drawings* | | | **$330** |
| ☐ **KOKINUS** ......................................... *paintings* | | **$165** | **$1,100** |
| American | | | |
| ☐ **KOKO-MICOLETZKY, Friedrich A.** .... *paintings* | | **$660** | **$1,430** |
| ☐ **KOKOSCHKA, Øskar** ........................ *paintings* | | **$26,400** | **$220,000** |
| Austrian 1886-1980 ...................................... *drawings* | | **$577** | **$14,300** |
| ☐ **KOLAR, Jiri** ..................................... *drawings* | | **$220** | **$2,090** |
| Czechoslovakian b. 1919 ............................ *sculpture* | | **$880** | **$5,280** |
| ☐ **KOLBE, Ernest** ................................ *paintings* | | **$275** | **$770** |
| German 1876-1945 | | | |
| ☐ **KOLBE, Georg** ................................ *drawings* | | **$412** | **$1,650** |
| German 1877-1947 ..................................... *sculpture* | | **$2,090** | **$20,900** |
| ☐ **KOLBERG, Anton** ............................ *paintings* | | | **$935** |
| Polish 1816-1882 | | | |
| ☐ **KOLESSNIKOFF, Sergei** ..................... *paintings* | | **$220** | **$1,760** |
| Russian b. 1889 | | | |
| ☐ **KOLLOCK, Mary** ............................... *paintings* | | | **$1,540** |
| American 1840-1911 | | | |
| ☐ **KOLLWITZ, Kathe** ............................ *drawings* | | **$3,300** | **$34,100** |
| German 1867-1945 ..................................... *sculpture* | | **$6,600** | **$9,900** |
| ☐ **KOLNER, August** ............................ *drawings* | | **$143** | **$1,430** |
| American 1812-1906 | | | |

| | | Current Price Range | |
|---|---|---|---|
| | | *Low* | *High* |

☐ **KOLOSVOLRY** .................................. *paintings* | | | $775
Hungarian 19th cent.

☐ **KOLOSZERING, L.** ........................... *paintings* | | | $275
Hungarian 19th/20th cent.

☐ **KOLOZ** ............................................. *paintings* | | $264 | $286

☐ **KOLOZSVARY, Lajos** ....................... *paintings* | | | $660
European

☐ **KOMAROMI-KACZ, Endre** ............... *paintings* | | $220 | $418

☐ **KONARSKY, Josef** ............................ *paintings* | | | $4,400
Polish 19th cent.

☐ **KONI, Nick** ..................................... *sculpture* | | $522 | $550

☐ **KONIG, Franz Niklaus** ...................... *drawings* | | | $605

☐ **KONIG, Johann** ................................ *paintings* | | | $26,400
German 1586-1642

☐ **KONINCK, Salomon** .......................... *paintings* | | $8,800 | $11,000
Dutch 1609-1656

☐ **KONINGH** ........................................ *paintings* | | | $2,420
Dutch School mid 19th cent.

☐ **KONINGH, Leendert de** ...................... *paintings* | | | $2,420
Dutch 1810-1887

☐ **KONRAD, Adolf Ferdinand** ................ *paintings* | | | $330
American b. 1915

☐ **KONTI, Isidore** ................................. *sculpture* | | $660 | $3,300
Austrian/American 1862-1938

☐ **KOOKE, William John** ....................... *paintings* | | | $192
Irish 19th cent.

☐ **KOOL, Sipke** ................................... *paintings* | | $550 | $2,090
Dutch 1836-1902

☐ **KOOL, Willem Gillesz** ....................... *paintings* | | | $9,900
Dutch c. 1608-1666

☐ **KOON, John Lansing** ......................... *drawings* | | | $385
American c. 1830

☐ **KOONING, Elaine de** ......................... *paintings* | | $88 | $2,860
American b. 1920

☐ **KOONING, Willem de** ....................... *paintings* | | $8,250 | $1,980,000
American b. 1904 ................................... *drawings* | | $2,000 | $154,000
.......................................................... *sculpture* | | | $275,000

☐ **KOOPMAN, Augustus** ....................... *paintings* | | $352 | $2,970
American 1869-1914

☐ **KOPMAN, Benjamin** .......................... *paintings* | | $330 | $715
American 1887-1965 ................................ *drawings* | | $66 | $247

☐ **KOPMAN, Leonard** ........................... *paintings* | | | $192
American 20th cent.

☐ **KOPPENOL, Cornelis** ........................ *paintings* | | | $1,430
Dutch 1865-1946

☐ **KOPPENOL, Edward** .......................... *paintings* | | | $330
Dutch 20th cent.

☐ **KORAB, Karl** ................................... *paintings* | | $13,750 | $16,500
.......................................................... *drawings* | | | $2,310

# Childhood

*Childhood, a time of innocence, discovery, and playfulness, is a frequent choice of subject for many artists. Children are often depicted with their pets or with prized possessions. Favorite settings include gardens or idealized landscapes. Other works show idealized family scenes — tender welcomes and tearful departures. Less romanticized views of childhood show young people working at difficult or tedious chores, selling newspapers, or bending over their sewing.*

*A happier image is conveyed by Dutch artist Cornelis Koppenol's "Beach Scene With Children Playing," a painting that recalls memories of a carefree time by bringing together two popular images, that of youth and the seashore. (Cornelis Koppenol, "Beach Scene With Children Playing," oil on panel, 9½ x 14¼ in., Weschler's, June 6, 1985, $1,430.)*

|  |  | *Current Price Range* | |
|---|---|---|---|
|  |  | *Low* | *High* |
| ☐ **KORBEL, Mario Joseph** .................. *sculpture* | | **$418** | **$4,950** |
| American 1882-1954 | | | |
| ☐ **KORENCE, F.V.** .............................. *paintings* | | | **$220** |
| Polish 19th cent. | | | |
| ☐ **KORFF, F. De** ............................... *paintings* | | **$1,100** | **$1,540** |
| German 19th cent. | | | |
| ☐ **KORMAN, Harriet** ........................... *drawings* | | | **$286** |
| American b. 1947 | | | |
| ☐ **KORMITE, G.** ................................. *paintings* | | | **$825** |
| Italian | | | |
| ☐ **KORN, James** ................................ *paintings* | | | **$770** |
| ☐ **KORNER, F.** .................................. *paintings* | | | **$192** |
| German 19th cent. | | | |
| ☐ **KOROVINE, Constantin Alexeievitch** .... *paintings* | | **$374** | **$3,300** |
| Russian 1861-1939 ............................. *drawings* | | **$66** | **$1,100** |

| | Current Price Range | |
|---|---|---|
| | Low | High |

☐ **KORSAKOFF, S. de** ........................ *paintings* | | $330
American(?) 20th cent.

☐ **KORSCHANN, Charles** .................. *sculpture* | $577 | $1,650
Czechoslovakian b. 1872

☐ **KORTHALS, Johannes** ...................... *paintings* | $246 | $301
Dutch b. 1916

☐ **KORVER, John** .............................. *paintings* | | $302
American 20th cent.

☐ **KORWAN, Franz** ............................ *paintings* | | $825

☐ **KOSA, Emil (Jr.)** ........................... *paintings* | $660 | $1,980
American 1903-1968 ................................ *drawings* | | $522

☐ **KOSAK, F. Viktor** .......................... *paintings* | | $467
German 19th/20th cent.

☐ **KOSHIN** ..................................... *sculpture* | | $440
Japanese

☐ **KOSLER, Franz** .............................. *paintings* | | $12,100

☐ **KOSLOW, Howard** .......................... *paintings* | | $990

☐ **KOSLOWSKY, Jacques** ...................... *paintings* | $33 | $242
French 20th cent.

☐ **KOSSAK, Jerzy** .............................. *paintings* | $396 | $700
Polish 1890-1963

☐ **KOSSAK, Tony** ............................... *paintings* | | $1,540

☐ **KOSSAK, Woiciech von** ...................... *paintings* | $385 | $3,850
Polish 1857-1942 ................................... *drawings* | | $665

☐ **KOST, Frederick W.** ......................... *paintings* | $154 | $990
American 1865-1923

☐ **KOSTA, Alex** ................................ *sculpture* | | $8,800
American b. 1925

☐ **KOSTAN, Barbara** ........................... *paintings* | | $275
French 20th cent.

☐ **KOSTER, A.** .................................. *drawings* | | $770
Dutch 19th cent.

☐ **KOSTER, Alexander Max** .................... *paintings* | | $550
German 1864-1932

☐ **KOSTER, Paul** ............................... *paintings* | | $275

☐ **KOTASZ, Karoly** ............................ *paintings* | | $176
Hungarian b. 1872

☐ **KOTCHAR, E.** ............................... *sculpture* | | $440

☐ **KOTCHAR, Ervand** .......................... *paintings* | | $357

☐ **KOTSCHENREITER, Hugo** ................ *paintings* | $2,420 | $11,000
German 1854-1908

☐ **KOTZ, Daniel** ............................... *paintings* | | $220
American 1848-1933

☐ **KOTZEBUE, Alexander von** ................ *paintings* | | $1,100
German 1815-1889

☐ **KOUTNETZOFF** .............................. *paintings* | | $484
Russian School 20th cent.

| | | Current Price Range | |
|---|---|---|---|
| | | Low | High |
| ☐ **KOVACH, George** ............................ *paintings* | | | $330 |
| American 20th cent. | | | |
| ☐ **KOVACS, I.** ........................................ *paintings* | | | $440 |
| Hungarian d. 1930 | | | |
| ☐ **KOVEN, Mark** .................................. *drawings* | | | $440 |
| American 20th cent. | | | |
| ☐ **KOVESY, J.** ..................................... *paintings* | $150 | $250 |
| ☐ **KOWALCZEWSKI, Piotr** .................... *sculpture* | $440 | $495 |
| Polish b. 1927 | | | |
| ☐ **KOWALCZWESKI, Karl** ..................... *sculpture* | | $1,210 |
| b. 1876 | | | |
| ☐ **KOWALSKI, Ivan Ivanovich** ............... *drawings* | $55 | $220 |
| Russian | | | |
| ☐ **KOWALSKI-WIERUSZ, Alfred von** ...... *paintings* | $412 | $71,500 |
| Polish 1849-1915 | | | |
| ☐ **KOWALSKI-WIERUSZ, Karol** ............. *paintings* | | $1,430 |
| Polish | | | |
| ☐ **KOYANAGUI, Sei** .............................. *paintings* | | $1,760 |
| Japanese b. 1896 | | | |
| ☐ **KRAEMER, Peter** ............................. *paintings* | | $1,320 |
| German 1823-1907 | | | |
| ☐ **KRAEMER, Peter** ............................. *paintings* | $1,650 | $3,300 |
| German 1857-1941 | | | |
| ☐ **KRAFFT, Carl Rudolph** ..................... *paintings* | $88 | $6,050 |
| American 1884-1930 | | | |
| ☐ **KRAMER, Esther Miller von** ............... *paintings* | | $330 |
| ☐ **KRAMER, James** .............................. *drawings* | | $8,500 |
| American b. 1927 | | | |
| ☐ **KRAMM, Willibard** ........................... *paintings* | | $247 |
| German 20th cent. | | | |
| ☐ **KRANTZ, F.** ..................................... *paintings* | | $440 |
| European 19th cent. | | | |
| ☐ **KRASNER, Lee** .................................. *paintings* | $14,300 | $60,500 |
| American b. 1912 ...................................... *drawings* | | $7,700 |
| ☐ **KRASNOW, Peter** .............................. *paintings* | | $1,320 |
| American 20th cent. | | | |
| ☐ **KRATKE, Charles Louis** ..................... *paintings* | $220 | $4,675 |
| French 1848-1921 | | | |
| ☐ **KRATKY, A.** ..................................... *paintings* | | $2,750 |
| ☐ **KRATSCHKOWSKI,** | | | |
| **Jossif Jevstatjevich** .............................. *paintings* | $1,210 | $2,750 |
| Russian 1854-1914 | | | |
| ☐ **KRAUEL, B.** ...................................... *paintings* | | $440 |
| German 20th cent. | | | |
| ☐ **KRAUS, August** ................................. *paintings* | $495 | $2,420 |
| German 1852-1917 | | | |
| ☐ **KRAUS, August** ................................. *paintings* | | $4,950 |
| German 1803-1864 | | | |

|                                                      | Current Price Range | |
|------------------------------------------------------|---------|----------|
|                                                      | Low     | High     |
| ☐ **KRAUS, Friedrich** ............................ *paintings* |         | **$1,430** |
| German 1826-1894                                     |         |          |
| ☐ **KRAUS, Georg Melchior** ..................... *paintings* |         | **$3,960** |
| German 1737-1806                                     |         |          |
| ☐ **KRAUSCHE, G.** ............................ *paintings* |         | **$385** |
| ☐ **KRAUSE, Emil A.** ......................... *paintings* |         | **$825** |
| ☐ **KRAUSE, F.E.** ............................. *paintings* | **$286** | **$1,045** |
| German 1836-1900                                     |         |          |
| ☐ **KRAUSE, Felix** ........................... *paintings* |         | **$1,540** |
| German b. 1873                                       |         |          |
| ☐ **KRAUSE, Franz** ........................... *paintings* |         | **$990** |
| German 1823-1878                                     |         |          |
| ☐ **KRAUSE, T.** ............................... *paintings* |         | **$550** |
| ☐ **KRAUSKOPF, Bruno** ..................... *paintings* | **$660** | **$1,540** |
| German 1892-1962 ............................ *drawings* |         | **$165** |
| ☐ **KRAUSZ, Simon Andreas** .................... *paintings* |         | **$1,870** |
| Dutch 1760-1825                                      |         |          |
| ☐ **KRAUSZ, Wilhelm** ......................... *paintings* |         | **$522** |
| German 1878-1959                                     |         |          |
| ☐ **KRAUTH, Charles Philip** .................... *paintings* |         | **$275** |
| American b. 1893                                     |         |          |
| ☐ **KRAY, Wilhelm** ........................... *paintings* | **$1,430** | **$8,800** |
| German 1828-1889                                     |         |          |
| ☐ **KREGTEN, Fedor van** ...................... *paintings* |         | **$412** |
| Dutch 1871-1937                                      |         |          |
| ☐ **KREHBIEL, Albert H.** ...................... *paintings* | **$247** | **$990** |
| American 1875-1945                                   |         |          |
| ☐ **KREJCA, O.** ............................... *paintings* |         | **$275** |
| ☐ **KRELING, August von** ..................... *paintings* |         | **$2,090** |
| German 1819-1876                                     |         |          |
| ☐ **KREMEDEK** ................................ *paintings* |         | **$440** |
| Hungarian 19th cent.                                 |         |          |
| ☐ **KREMEGNE, Pinchus** ...................... *paintings* | **$880** | **$6,050** |
| Russian/French b. 1890 ........................ *drawings* |         | **$192** |
| ☐ **KREMER, P.** ............................... *paintings* |         | **$467** |
| ☐ **KREMP, E.** ................................ *paintings* | **$275** | **$880** |
| 20th cent.                                           |         |          |
| ☐ **KRENTZIN, Earl** .......................... *sculpture* |         | **$192** |
| American 20th cent.                                  |         |          |
| ☐ **KREPP, Friedrich** ......................... *paintings* |         | **$330** |
| Austrian 19th cent.                                  |         |          |
| ☐ **KRESTIN, Lazar** .......................... *paintings* | **$6,600** | **$30,800** |
| Russian 19th cent.                                   |         |          |
| ☐ **KRETSCHMAR, J.** ......................... *paintings* |         | **$2,090** |
| 19th cent.                                           |         |          |
| ☐ **KRETSCHMAR,** |         |          |
| **Johann Carl Heinrich** ..................... *paintings* |         | **$1,100** |
| German 1769-1847                                     |         |          |

| | Current Price Range | |
|---|---|---|
| | *Low* | *High* |
| ☐ **KRETZINGER, Clara Josephine** ........... *paintings* | | $264 |
| American b. 1883 | | |
| ☐ **KRETZSCHMER, Johann Hermann** ..... *paintings* | $4,950 | $49,500 |
| German 1811-1890 | | |
| ☐ **KREUTZER, B.** .................................. *paintings* | $440 | $1,100 |
| German 19th cent. | | |
| ☐ **KREUTZER, Felix** ............................. *paintings* | | $2,310 |
| German 1835-1876 | | |
| ☐ **KREYDER, Alexis Joseph** ................... *paintings* | $880 | $6,875 |
| French 1839-1912 | | |
| ☐ **KREYSSIG, Hugo** .............................. *paintings* | | $330 |
| German b. 1873 .................................. *drawings* | $385 | $605 |
| ☐ **KRIEGHOFF, Cornelius** ..................... *paintings* | $2,200 | $40,700 |
| Canadian 1815-1872 | | |
| ☐ **KRIEGHOFF, W.G.** ........................... *paintings* | $44 | $242 |
| American 20th cent. | | |
| ☐ **KRIEHUBER, Josef** ........................... *paintings* | | $7,700 |
| Austrian 1800-1876 .............................. *drawings* | $286 | $440 |
| ☐ **KRILOFF** ...................................... *drawings* | | $385 |
| ☐ **KRIMMEL, I.L.** ................................. *paintings* | | $2,035 |
| German School 19th cent. | | |
| ☐ **KRIMMEL, John Lewis** ....................... *paintings* | | $308,000 |
| American 1787-1821 ............................... *drawings* | | $7,700 |
| ☐ **KRIMOV, Nicolai P.** .......................... *paintings* | | $770 |
| ☐ **KRIPPENDORF, William** .................... *paintings* | | $522 |
| German 19th cent. | | |
| ☐ **KRISCHKE, Franz** ............................. *paintings* | $522 | $1,650 |
| Austrian 19th/20th cent. | | |
| ☐ **KRODEL, Wolfgang** ........................... *paintings* | | $13,200 |
| ☐ **KROGH, Per** ................................... *paintings* | $198 | $550 |
| Norwegian/American b. 1889 ..................... *drawings* | | $110 |
| ☐ **KROLL, Abraham** ............................. *paintings* | | $1,980 |
| American | | |
| ☐ **KROLL, Leon** .................................. *paintings* | $411 | $26,400 |
| American 1884-1974/75 ............................ *drawings* | $110 | $2,420 |
| ☐ **KRONBERG, Julius** ........................... *paintings* | | $1,980 |
| Swedish 1850-1921 | | |
| ☐ **KRONBERG, Louis** ............................ *paintings* | $224 | $5,500 |
| American 1872-1965 ............................... *drawings* | $44 | $4,840 |
| ☐ **KRONBERGER, Carl** .......................... *paintings* | $3,300 | $18,700 |
| Austrian 1841-1921 ............................... *drawings* | | $90 |
| ☐ **KRONBURGER, J.** ............................. *paintings* | | $605 |
| German 19th cent. | | |
| ☐ **KRONER, Christian Johann** ................. *paintings* | $2,090 | $4,675 |
| German 1861-1911 | | |
| ☐ **KRONERT, W.F.** ............................... *paintings* | | $330 |
| German | | |
| ☐ **KRONKE, Juan** ................................ *paintings* | | $412 |

| | | Current Price Range | |
|---|---|---|---|
| | | Low | High |
| ☐ **KRUEGER, E.** ....................... *paintings* | | | $715 |
| American 19th/20th cent. | | | |
| ☐ **KRUENYAK** ....................... *paintings* | | | $385 |
| ☐ **KRUGER, Carl** ....................... *paintings* | | | $700 |
| German 19th cent. | | | |
| ☐ **KRUGER, P.** ....................... *paintings* | | | $935 |
| German 19th cent. | | | |
| ☐ **KRUGER, Richard** ....................... *paintings* | | $200 | $302 |
| American 20th cent. | | | |
| ☐ **KRUGMAN, Irene** ....................... *sculpture* | | $40 | $302 |
| ☐ **KRULLOARS (?), W.** ....................... *paintings* | | | $220 |
| American 19th cent. | | | |
| ☐ **KRUMMEL, P.** ....................... *paintings* | | | $220 |
| German 19th/20th cent. | | | |
| ☐ **KRUSE, Max** ....................... *sculpture* | | $125 | $525 |
| German 1854-1942 | | | |
| ☐ **KRUSEMAN, Cornelis** ....................... *paintings* | | | $715 |
| Dutch 1797-1857 | | | |
| ☐ **KRUSEMAN, Frederik Marianus** .......... *paintings* | | $5,500 | $44,000 |
| Dutch 1817-1860 | | | |
| ☐ **KRUSEMAN VAN ELTEN,** | | | |
| **Hendrik Dirk** ....................... *paintings* | | $264 | $9,900 |
| Dutch 1829-1904 ....................... *drawings* | | $77 | $605 |
| ☐ **KRUSHENICK, Nicholas** ....................... *paintings* | | $418 | $3,850 |
| American b. 1929 ....................... *drawings* | | $550 | $1,980 |
| ☐ **KRUSMANS, A.** ....................... *paintings* | | | $660 |
| ☐ **KRUTTEN, R.** ....................... *paintings* | | | $935 |
| Dutch 20th cent. | | | |
| ☐ **KRUTZER, R.** ....................... *paintings* | | | $660 |
| ☐ **KRUYS, Cornelis** ....................... *paintings* | | | $4,950 |
| Dutch d. 1660? | | | |
| ☐ **KUBIERSCHKY, Erich** ....................... *paintings* | | $495 | $5,500 |
| German 1854-1944 ....................... *drawings* | | | $660 |
| ☐ **KUBIK, Kamie** ....................... *drawings* | | | $715 |
| American 20th cent. | | | |
| ☐ **KUBIN, Alfred** ....................... *drawings* | | $495 | $2,310 |
| Austrian 1877-1959 | | | |
| ☐ **KUBLER** ....................... *paintings* | | | $3,520 |
| German 19th cent. | | | |
| ☐ **KUCHLER** ....................... *sculpture* | | | $462 |
| ☐ **KUEHL, Gottbardt-Johann** ....................... *drawings* | | | $550 |
| ☐ **KUEHNARD, Edward A.** ....................... *paintings* | | $330 | $770 |
| European 19th cent. | | | |
| ☐ **KUEHNE, Max** ....................... *paintings* | | $412 | $6,600 |
| American 1880-1968 | | | |
| ☐ **KUELLER** ....................... *paintings* | | | $1,100 |
| ☐ **KUEN, Hendrik** ....................... *drawings* | | | $990 |
| ☐ **KUGHLER, Francis Vandeveer** .......... *paintings* | | | $550 |
| ☐ **KUGLMAYR, Max** ....................... *paintings* | | $418 | $1,045 |

| | Current Price Range | |
|---|---|---|
| | Low | High |
| ☐ **KUGLMAYZ, M.K.** ............................ *paintings* | | $220 |
| German b. 1863 | | |
| ☐ **KUHLMAN, Walter Egel** ...................... *paintings* | | $247 |
| American b. 1918 | | |
| ☐ **KUHLMANN-REGER, Emil** ................. *paintings* | $385 | $1,650 |
| German b. 1876 | | |
| ☐ **KUHN, Bernhard** .............................. *paintings* | | $302 |
| German 1850-1902 | | |
| ☐ **KUHN, F.** ........................................ *sculpture* | | $750 |
| ☐ **KUHN, J. (Jr.)** ................................. *paintings* | | $1,540 |
| ☐ **KUHN, Walt** .................................... *paintings* | $1,210 | $25,300 |
| American 1877/80-1949 .............................. *drawings* | $121 | $7,700 |
| ☐ **KUHNEN, Leopold** ............................ *paintings* | $1,320 | $1,980 |
| Belgian 1836-? | | |
| ☐ **KUHNERT, Wilhelm Friedrich Karl** ..... *paintings* | $9,900 | $34,100 |
| German 1865-1926 ..................................... *drawings* | | $1,650 |
| ☐ **KUINDJY, A.** ................................... *paintings* | | $286 |
| ☐ **KULICKE, Robert** .............................. *paintings* | | $246 |
| American b. 1924 | | |
| ☐ **KULLER, John** .................................. *paintings* | | $412 |
| ☐ **KUMMER, Carl Robert** ....................... *paintings* | | $385 |
| German 1810-1889 | | |
| ☐ **KUMMER, Julius Hermann** ................. *paintings* | $660 | $1,100 |
| ☐ **KUMMERLI, Adrian** ........................... *paintings* | | $605 |
| Swiss 1830-1894 | | |
| ☐ **KUNDERT, B.** ................................... *paintings* | | $880 |
| American 19th/20th cent. | | |
| ☐ **KUNERT, J.** ..................................... *paintings* | | $2,310 |
| German 19th cent. | | |
| ☐ **KUNIYOSHI, Yasuo** ........................... *paintings* | $2,475 | $99,000 |
| American 1893-1953 .................................. *drawings* | $132 | $4,500 |
| ☐ **KUNSTLER, B.** .................................. *paintings* | | $385 |
| ☐ **KUNSTLER, Mort** ............................. *paintings* | $132 | $7,975 |
| American b. 1931 ..................................... *drawings* | | $1,045 |
| ☐ **KUNTZ, Karl** ................................... *paintings* | | $550 |
| ☐ **KUPFERMAN, Moshe** ......................... *drawings* | | $605 |
| contemporary | | |
| ☐ **KUPKA, Frantisek** ............................. *paintings* | $2,200 | $17,600 |
| Czechoslovakian 1871-1957 .......................... *drawings* | $330 | $26,400 |
| ☐ **KUPPER, Professor W.** ....................... *paintings* | | $650 |
| German 19th cent. | | |
| ☐ **KUPPITSCH, A.** ................................ *drawings* | | $440 |
| Austrian 19th cent. | | |
| ☐ **KURT, Von Rozynski** .......................... *paintings* | | $687 |
| Polish b. 1864 | | |
| ☐ **KURTH, Herbert J.** ............................ *paintings* | $38 | $264 |
| American 19th cent. | | |
| ☐ **KURTZWELLY(?), M.** ......................... *paintings* | | $412 |
| 20th cent. | | |

| | Current Price Range | |
| --- | --- | --- |
| | Low | High |
| ☐ **KURZ, George** ..... *paintings* | | $770 |
| ☐ **KURZWEIL, Maximilian** ..... *drawings* | | $605 |
| ☐ **KUSHNER, Robert Ellis** ..... *paintings* | $3,300 | $16,500 |
| American b. 1949 | | |
| ☐ **KUSTNER, Carl** ..... *paintings* | $715 | $1,155 |
| German b. 1861 | | |
| ☐ **KUSTODIEV, Boris Mikhailovich** ..... *paintings* | | $8,250 |
| Russian 1878-1927 ..... *drawings* | $55 | $247 |
| ☐ **KUTCHER, Paul** ..... *paintings* | | $605 |
| German 19th/20th cent. | | |
| ☐ **KUTH, E.** ..... *paintings* | | $275 |
| ☐ **KUWASSEG, Charles Euphrasie (Jr.)** .... *paintings* | $165 | $12,100 |
| French 1838-1904 | | |
| ☐ **KUWAYAMA, Tadaaki** ..... *paintings* | $55 | $1,210 |
| Japanese b. 1931 | | |
| ☐ **KUYCK, Frans Pieter Lodewyk van** ..... *paintings* | | $12,100 |
| Belgian 1852-1915 | | |
| ☐ **KUYCK, Jean Louis van** ..... *paintings* | $770 | $3,500 |
| Flemish 1821-1871 | | |
| ☐ **KUYPERS, Cornelis** ..... *paintings* | $132 | $880 |
| Dutch b. 1864 | | |
| ☐ **KUZNETZOV, Nicholas Dmitrievich** ..... *paintings* | | $1,925 |
| Russian 1850-1930 | | |
| ☐ **KVAPIL, Charles** ..... *paintings* | $66 | $1,320 |
| Belgian 1884-1958 | | |
| ☐ **KWASHIKAN** ..... *drawings* | | $275 |
| Japanese 20th cent. | | |
| ☐ **KWIATOWSKI, Jean** ..... *paintings* | | $550 |
| Polish 1897-1971 | | |
| ☐ **KYLE, Joseph** ..... *paintings* | $100 | $400 |
| American 1815-1863 | | |
| ☐ **KYMLI, Franz Pieter Joseph** ..... *paintings* | | $1,760 |
| ☐ **L'AIN, Girod de** ..... *paintings* | $77 | $242 |
| French 20th cent. | | |
| ☐ **L'AINE, Louis Lagrenee** ..... *paintings* | | $3,850 |
| ☐ **L'ENGLE, William** ..... *paintings* | | $1,430 |
| American 1884-1957 | | |
| ☐ **L'HAY, Michel Eudes de** ..... *paintings* | | $15,400 |
| French ac. 1874-1898 | | |
| ☐ **L'HOSPITAL, F.D. de** ..... *paintings* | | $17,600 |
| French 18th/19th cent. | | |
| ☐ **LA ABADIA, Juan de (the younger)** ..... *paintings* | | $8,250 |
| Spanish ac. 1470-1500 | | |
| ☐ **LA BERGE, Auguste Charles de** ..... *paintings* | | $825 |
| French 1807-1842 | | |
| ☐ **LA CAULT, A.L.** ..... *paintings* | | $660 |
| ☐ **LA CHANCE, George** ..... *paintings* | $450 | $660 |
| ☐ **LA CORTE, Juan de** ..... *paintings* | | $5,000 |
| Spanish 1597-1660 | | |

|  | | *Current Price Range* | |
|---|---|---|---|
|  | | Low | High |
| ☐ **LA CROIX, Georges F. de** .................. *paintings* | | | $66,000 |
| French d. 1779/82 | | | |
| ☐ **LA FAGE, Raymond** ........................... *drawings* | | $770 | $935 |
| French 1650-1684 | | | |
| ☐ **LA FARGE, Bancel** ........................... *paintings* | | $110 | $750 |
| ☐ **LA FARGE, John** ............................. *paintings* | | $3,080 | $74,250 |
| American 1835-1910 ............................... *drawings* | | $82 | $45,100 |
| ☐ **LA FARGE, Jules** ............................ *paintings* | | | $495 |
| American | | | |
| ☐ **LA FARGUE, Jacobus Elias** ................. *paintings* | | | $22,000 |
| Dutch b. 1742 | | | |
| ☐ **LA FARGUE, Paulus Constantin** ........... *paintings* | | $12,100 | $17,600 |
| Dutch 1732-1782 | | | |
| ☐ **LA FONTAINE, Thomas Sherwood** ....... *paintings* | | | $6,050 |
| English b. 1915 | | | |
| ☐ **LA FOREST, Wesner** ........................... *paintings* | | | $3,300 |
| American 1927-1965 | | | |
| ☐ **LA FORTUNE** ................................... *sculpture* | | | $1,210 |
| ☐ **LA FOULHOUZE, Gabriel Amable de** .. *paintings* | | | $16,500 |
| French 19th cent. | | | |
| ☐ **LA FRESNAYE, Roger de** ................. *paintings* | | | $49,500 |
| French 1885-1925 ................................... *drawings* | | $660 | $3,300 |
| ................................................... *sculpture* | | | $44,000 |
| ☐ **LA GANDARA, Antonio de** ................. *paintings* | | $6,050 | $12,650 |
| French 1862-1917 | | | |
| ☐ **LA GATTA, John** ............................. *paintings* | | $440 | $2,310 |
| Italian/American b. 1894 ............................ *drawings* | | $385 | $660 |
| ☐ **LA HOESE, de** ............................... *paintings* | | | $770 |
| ☐ **LA PATELLIERE, Amedee de** ............. *paintings* | | | $3,575 |
| French 1890-1932 | | | |
| ☐ **LA ROCHENOIRE,** | | | |
| **Emile Charles Julian de** ..................... *paintings* | | $220 | $1,100 |
| French 1825-1899 | | | |
| ☐ **LA ROSA, F.** ................................... *paintings* | | | $1,650 |
| Italian 19th/20th cent. | | | |
| ☐ **LA SERNA, Ismael Gonzalez de** ........... *paintings* | | $770 | $2,970 |
| Spanish 1900-1968 ................................. *drawings* | | $66 | $330 |
| ☐ **LA THANGUE, Henry Herbert** ............. *paintings* | | $20,360 | $27,500 |
| British 1859-1929 | | | |
| ☐ **LA VEGA, Jorge De** ........................... *paintings* | | | $3,850 |
| ☐ **LA VILLEON, Emmanuel de** ............... *paintings* | | $137 | $5,500 |
| French 1858-1944 | | | |
| ☐ **LA VOLPE, Allesandro** ....................... *paintings* | | $850 | $935 |
| Italian 1820-1887 | | | |
| ☐ **LAAN, Gerard van der** ....................... *paintings* | | | $880 |
| Dutch 1844-1915 | | | |
| ☐ **LAAR, Bernardus van de** ..................... *paintings* | | | $770 |
| Dutch 1804-1872 | | | |

|                                                      | Current Price Range |          |
|                                                      | Low       | High    |
|------------------------------------------------------|-----------|---------|
| ☐ **LAAR, Pieter van** .............................. *drawings*  |           | $2,860  |
| Dutch 1582-1642                                      |           |         |
| ☐ **LABELA, H.I.** ..................................... *paintings* |           | $412    |
| Italian (?) 19th/20th cent.                          |           |         |
| ☐ **LABISSE, Felix** ............................... *paintings*   | $605      | $1,650  |
| French b. 1905                                       |           |         |
| ☐ **LABRUNIE, J.** ..................................... *paintings* |           | $440    |
| French 20th cent.                                    |           |         |
| ☐ **LABRUZZI, Carlo** ........................... *drawings*    |           | $462    |
| ☐ **LACASSE, Joseph** ............................ *paintings*  | $385      | $990    |
| Belgian 1894-1975                                    |           |         |
| ☐ **LACAVE, Peter** ................................ *paintings*  |           | $308    |
| French ac. 1769-1816                                 |           |         |
| ☐ **LACH, Andreas** ................................. *paintings* | $550      | $5,500  |
| Austrian 1817-1882                                   |           |         |
| ☐ **LACHAISE, Eugene A.** ...................... *paintings*    |           | $14,300 |
| American 1857-1925                                   |           |         |
| ☐ **LACHAISE, Gaston** ........................... *drawings*   | $550      | $3,850  |
| French 1882/86-1935 .................................. *sculpture* | $2,200    | $26,400 |
| ☐ **LACHENWITZ, F. Sigmund** ............... *paintings*       |           | $6,600  |
| German 1820-1868                                     |           |         |
| ☐ **LACHMAN, Harry B.** ........................ *paintings*   | $301      | $2,420  |
| American 1886-1974                                   |           |         |
| ☐ **LACHOU, Henri** ................................ *paintings* |           | $770    |
| ☐ **LACHTROPIUS, Nicolas** ..................... *paintings*   | $4,400    | $28,600 |
| Dutch ac. 1656-1700                                  |           |         |
| ☐ **LACOMBE, Georges** ........................... *paintings* |           | $19,800 |
| ☐ **LACOUR, Georges** ............................. *paintings* |           | $3,850  |
| French 19th cent.                                    |           |         |
| ☐ **LACROIX, Charles F. de**                         |           |         |
| **(called LACROIX de Marseilleor**                   |           |         |
| **DELACROIX)** ...................................... *paintings* | $3,300    | $33,000 |
| French d. 1782                                       |           |         |
| ☐ **LACROIX, H.** ..................................... *paintings* |           | $375    |
| ☐ **LACROIX, Paul** ................................ *paintings*  | $900      | $14,300 |
| American ac. c. 1858-1869                            |           |         |
| ☐ **LACROIX, Tristan** ............................ *paintings*  |           | $3,520  |
| French 19th cent.                                    |           |         |
| ☐ **LACROUX, H.** .................................... *paintings* |           | $990    |
| French 19th/20th cent.                               |           |         |
| ☐ **LACROY, T.** ...................................... *paintings* |           | $275    |
| Belgian 20th cent.                                   |           |         |
| ☐ **LACY, Charles J. De** ........................ *paintings*  | $440      | $1,375  |
| English 19th cent.                                   |           |         |
| ☐ **LADD, Anna Coleman** ................... *sculpture*      | $26       | $20,350 |
| American 1878-1939                                   |           |         |
| ☐ **LADD, C.** ......................................... *paintings* |           | $660    |
| American 19th/20th cent.                             |           |         |

| | | | Current Price Range | |
|---|---|---|---|---|
| | | | *Low* | *High* |
| ☐ **LADELL, Edward** | ............................... | *paintings* | $2,475 | $10,450 |
| British 1821-1886 | | | | |
| ☐ **LADELL, Ellen** | ............................... | *paintings* | | $605 |
| English 19th cent. | | | | |
| ☐ **LADEVEZE-CAUCHOIS, Louise de** | ...... | *paintings* | | $467 |
| French b. 1860 | | | | |
| ☐ **LAER, Alexander T. van** | ...................... | *paintings* | | $495 |
| American 1857-1920 | | | | |
| ☐ **LAESSIG, Robert** | ............................... | *paintings* | | $275 |
| American contemporary | | | | |
| ☐ **LAESSLE, Albert** | ............................... | *sculpture* | $374 | $1,650 |
| American 1877-1954 | | | | |
| ☐ **LAEVERENZ, Gustave** | ........................ | *paintings* | | $4,000 |
| German 1851-1909 | | | | |
| ☐ **LAFARQUE, J.** | ................................. | *paintings* | $301 | $412 |
| ☐ **LAFENESTRE, Gaston** | ........................ | *paintings* | $467 | $495 |
| French b. 1841 | | | | |
| ☐ **LAFITE, Ernest** | ................................. | *paintings* | | $357 |
| Austrian 1826-1885 | | | | |
| ☐ **LAFITTE, Louis** | ................................. | *paintings* | $660 | $660 |
| French 1770-1828 ..................................... | | *drawings* | | $154 |
| ☐ **LAFLECHE, H.** | ................................. | *paintings* | | $990 |
| American 19th cent. | | | | |
| ☐ **LAFON, Francois** | ............................... | *paintings* | | $302 |
| French ac. 1875-1911 ............................. | | *drawings* | | $660 |
| ☐ **LAFONTANT, Yves** | ............................. | *paintings* | | $715 |
| ☐ **LAFORGE, Marie** | ............................... | *paintings* | $187 | $247 |
| French b. 1865 | | | | |
| ☐ **LAFORTUNE, Felix** | ........................... | *paintings* | $605 | $990 |
| Haitian b. 1933 | | | | |
| ☐ **LAFOSSE, Charles de** | ......................... | *drawings* | $4,675 | $5,500 |
| French 1636-1716 | | | | |
| ☐ **LAGAR, Celso** | ................................... | *paintings* | | $412 |
| contemporary ......................................... | | *drawings* | | $352 |
| ☐ **LAGETSCHNIKOFF, A.L.** | ................. | *paintings* | | $935 |
| Russian 19th cent. | | | | |
| ☐ **LAGGEN, Hans** | ................................. | *paintings* | | $990 |
| ☐ **LAGNEAU, Nicolas** | ........................... | *drawings* | $1,320 | $4,675 |
| French ac. c. 1610-c. 1650 | | | | |
| ☐ **LAGOOR, Jan de** | ............................... | *paintings* | | $3,850 |
| Dutch 17th cent. | | | | |
| ☐ **LAGORIO, L.** | ................................... | *paintings* | | $286 |
| ☐ **LAGORIO, Lev Felixovich** | .................... | *paintings* | | $2,750 |
| Russian 1827-1905 | | | | |
| ☐ **LAGRANGE, Jacques** | ......................... | *paintings* | $132 | $330 |
| French b. 1917 | | | | |
| ☐ **LAGRENEE, Anthelme Francois** | ........... | *paintings* | | $1,210 |
| French 1774-1832 | | | | |

|  | | Current Price Range | |
|---|---|---|---|
|  | | Low | High |

| | | Low | High |
|---|---|---|---|
| ☐ **LAGRENEE, Jean Jacques** | | | |
| **(the younger)** ...................................... *paintings* | | | **$38,500** |
| French 1739-1821 ...................................... *drawings* | | | **$330** |
| ☐ **LAGRENEE, Louis Jean Francois** | | | |
| **(called l'aine)** ...................................... *paintings* | | **$1,100** | **$22,000** |
| French 1725-1805 | | | |
| ☐ **LAGUARDIA, Wenceslavs de** ............... *paintings* | | **$187** | **$247** |
| Spanish 19th cent. | | | |
| ☐ **LAHALLE, Charles Dominique Oscar** ... *paintings* | | | **$7,150** |
| French d. 1909 | | | |
| ☐ **LAHENS** ............................................. *paintings* | | | **$1,925** |
| French 1836-1909 | | | |
| ☐ **LAHEY, Richard Francis** ...................... *paintings* | | | **$264** |
| ☐ **LAHNER, Emil** ................................... *drawings* | | | **$302** |
| ☐ **LAHR, G.** ........................................... *paintings* | | | **$412** |
| American | | | |
| ☐ **LAING, Annie Rose** ............................ *paintings* | | **$440** | **$462** |
| British ac. 1898-1927 | | | |
| ☐ **LAING, Jomson** ................................ *paintings* | | **$165** | **$200** |
| Dutch 19th cent. | | | |
| ☐ **LAIPMAN, Ants** ................................ *paintings* | | | **$253** |
| Russian b. 1866 | | | |
| ☐ **LAIRESSE, Gerard de** ......................... *paintings* | | **$3,300** | **$28,600** |
| Flemish 1641-1711 | | | |
| ☐ **LAJOIE, M.** ....................................... *paintings* | | | **$1,650** |
| Continental School 19th cent. | | | |
| ☐ **LAJOS, Jambor** ................................ *paintings* | | | **$605** |
| ☐ **LAJOS, Ludwig Bruck** ........................ *paintings* | | | **$1,210** |
| Hungarian 1846-1910 | | | |
| ☐ **LAJOUE, Jacques de** ......................... *paintings* | | | **$6,820** |
| French 1687-1761 ...................................... *drawings* | | | **$165** |
| ☐ **LAKHOVSKY, Arnold** ........................ *paintings* | | **$375** | **$687** |
| Russian 1885-1932 | | | |
| ☐ **LALAING, Josef de** ............................ *paintings* | | | **$495** |
| Belgian | | | |
| ☐ **LALANNE, Maxime** ........................... *paintings* | | **$467** | **$770** |
| French 1827-1886 | | | |
| ☐ **LALIQUE, Rene** ................................. *drawings* | | **$132** | **$1,210** |
| French 1860-1945 ...................................... *sculpture* | | **$247** | **$3,300** |
| ☐ **LALL, Oscar de** ................................ *paintings* | | | **$220** |
| Canadian 1903-1971 | | | |
| ☐ **LALLEMAND, Georges** ........................ *paintings* | | | **$3,850** |
| French c. 1575-c. 1635 | | | |
| ☐ **LALLEMAND, Jean Baptiste** ............... *paintings* | | **$1,320** | **$4,400** |
| French c. 1710-c. 1803/1805 ........................ *drawings* | | **$825** | **$1,760** |
| ☐ **LALUNG (?), L.** ................................ *paintings* | | | **$522** |
| French 19th cent. | | | |

| | | Current Price Range | |
|---|---|---|---|
| | | Low | High |
| ☐ **LAM, Wifredo** .................. *paintings* | | $3,530 | $253,000 |
| Cuban 1902-1982 ....................... *drawings* | | $1,100 | $17,050 |
| .................. *sculpture* | | $1,650 | $10,175 |
| ☐ **LAMARRE, Henri Louis de** .......... *paintings* | | $1,760 | $3,300 |
| French b. 1829 | | | |
| ☐ **LAMASURE, Edwin** ............. *drawings* | | $55 | $357 |
| American 1866-1916 | | | |
| ☐ **LAMB, F. Mortimer** ............ *paintings* | | $330 | $4,500 |
| American b. 1861 ....................... *drawings* | | | $165 |
| ☐ **LAMB, George** ................... *drawings* | | | $275 |
| English 19th cent. | | | |
| ☐ **LAMB, Kate B.** ................... *paintings* | | | $220 |
| American 20th cent. | | | |
| ☐ **LAMB, Ruben G.** ................ *paintings* | | | $1,210 |
| American 19th cent. | | | |
| ☐ **LAMBDIN, George Cochran** ........ *paintings* | | $1,045 | $44,000 |
| American 1830-1896 | | | |
| ☐ **LAMBDIN, James R.** .......... *paintings* | | $522 | $1,540 |
| American 1807-1889 ................. *drawings* | | | $121 |
| ☐ **LAMBDIN, Robert L.** .......... *paintings* | | | $302 |
| b. 1866 ................................. *drawings* | | | $220 |
| ☐ **LAMBEAUX, Joseph Maria Thomas** | | | |
| **(called Jef)** ............ *sculpture* | | $412 | $2,420 |
| Belgian 1852-1908 | | | |
| ☐ **LAMBERT, Charles** ............ *paintings* | | $165 | $1,210 |
| ☐ **LAMBERT, Eugene** ............. *paintings* | | | $385 |
| ☐ **LAMBERT, Fernand** ........... *paintings* | | | $935 |
| French b. 1868 | | | |
| ☐ **LAMBERT, G.** ................... *paintings* | | $357 | $550 |
| 19th cent. | | | |
| ☐ **LAMBERT, J.L.** ............... *sculpture* | | | $800 |
| American 20th cent. | | | |
| ☐ **LAMBERT, Louis Eugene** ........... *paintings* | | $1,430 | $4,400 |
| French 1825-1900 | | | |
| ☐ **LAMBERT, Noel Marcel** ......... *drawings* | | | $495 |
| ☐ **LAMBERT, Ted R.** ............ *paintings* | | $4,125 | $14,300 |
| American 1905-1960 | | | |
| ☐ **LAMBERT-NAUDIN, Henri** ......... *paintings* | | $165 | $275 |
| French 20th cent. | | | |
| ☐ **LAMBERT-RUCKI, Jean** ......... *paintings* | | $1,210 | $7,975 |
| French 1888-1967 ....................... *drawings* | | $88 | $3,520 |
| .................. *sculpture* | | $385 | $4,950 |
| ☐ **LAMBINET, Emile Charles** .......... *paintings* | | $357 | $10,450 |
| French 1815-1877 | | | |
| ☐ **LAMBOURG, A.** ............... *paintings* | | | $577 |
| French 20th cent. | | | |
| ☐ **LAMBRECHTS, Jan Baptist** ........ *paintings* | | $825 | $3,080 |
| Flemish 1680-after 1731 | | | |

| | | *Current Price Range* | |
| | | Low | High |
|---|---|---|---|
| ☐ **LAMEN, Christoffel Jacobsz van der** (or LAEMEN) .......................... *paintings* Flemish 1606/15-1651 | | $825 | $9,350 |
| ☐ **LAMI, Eugene Louis** ............ *paintings* | | | $605 |
| French 1800-1890 ......................... *drawings* | | $82 | $1,760 |
| ☐ **LAMM, Albert** ..................... *paintings* German b. 1873 | | $275 | $660 |
| ☐ **LAMM, Sigrid** ..................... *paintings* | | | $302 |
| ☐ **LAMONACA, Guissepe** ......... *sculpture* French | | | $797 |
| ☐ **LAMOND, William B.** .......... *paintings* British 19th/20th cent. | | $165 | $880 |
| ☐ **LAMONT, Thomas R.** .......... *drawings* English d. 1898 | | | $1,430 |
| ☐ **LAMORINIERE, Jean Pierre Francois** .. *paintings* Belgian 1828-1911 | | | $330 |
| ☐ **LAMOTTE, Bernard** ............ *paintings* | | $44 | $2,090 |
| French b. 1903 ......................... *drawings* | | $33 | $462 |
| ☐ **LAMOURDEDIEU, Raoul** ..... *sculpture* French b. 1877 | | $990 | $1,430 |
| ☐ **LAMP, F.L.** ......................... *paintings* English 19th cent. | | | $225 |
| ☐ **LAMPE, Louis** ..................... *paintings* | | | $440 |
| ☐ **LAMPERT, E.E.** ................... *paintings* American | | | $660 |
| ☐ **LAMPI, A.** .......................... *paintings* Italian (?) 19th cent. | | | $2,200 |
| ☐ **LAMPI, Giovanni-Battista** .... *paintings* Italian 1775-1837 | | | $950 |
| ☐ **LAMPLOUGH, Antoine** ......... *drawings* 1877-1930 | | $176 | $300 |
| ☐ **LAMPLOUGH, Augustus Osborne** ........ *drawings* English 1877-1930 | | $495 | $1,980 |
| ☐ **LAMPOUGH, H.** .................. *drawings* | | | $341 |
| ☐ **LAMQUA** ......................... *paintings* Chinese 1825-1860 | | $1,900 | $2,750 |
| ☐ **LAMY, Pierre Desire Eugene Franc** ....... *paintings* French 1855-1919 | | | $7,975 |
| ☐ **LANCASTER, Mark** ............ *paintings* Anglo/American b. 1938 | | $440 | $2,310 |
| ☐ **LANCE, George** .................. *paintings* English 1802-1864 | | $247 | $34,100 |
| ☐ **LANCEDELLI, Joseph** .......... *drawings* Italian 1774-1832 | | | $467 |
| ☐ **LANCERAY, Eugene** ............ *sculpture* Russian 1848-1886 | | $385 | $6,380 |
| ☐ **LANCKEN, Frank von der** ........... *paintings* American 1872-1950 | | $165 | $2,475 |

| | *Current Price Range* | |
|---|---|---|
| | Low | High |
| ☐ **LANCKOW, Ludwig** .......................... *paintings* | $1,540 | $1,540 |
| German 19th cent. | | |
| ☐ **LANCONELLI, T.** ............................... *paintings* | | $3,520 |
| Italian 19th cent. | | |
| ☐ **LANCRET, Nicolas** ............................ *drawings* | $1,320 | $6,325 |
| French 1690-1743 | | |
| ☐ **LAND, Ernest Albert** ...................... *paintings* | $330 | $467 |
| American 20th cent. | | |
| ☐ **LANDA, B.G.** ..................................... *paintings* | | $350 |
| ☐ **LANDALUZE, Victor Patricio de** .......... *paintings* | $3,080 | $3,080 |
| Spanish d. c. 1890 | | |
| ☐ **LANDEAU, Sandor L.** ........................... *paintings* | $165 | $1,540 |
| American b. 1864 | | |
| ☐ **LANDELLE, Charles Zacharie** .............. *paintings* | $550 | $22,000 |
| French 1812-1908 ..................................... *drawings* | | $44 |
| ☐ **LANDENBURGER, Christian** ............... *paintings* | $220 | $880 |
| German 1862-1927 | | |
| ☐ **LANDERYOU, R.** ............................... *paintings* | | $330 |
| American | | |
| ☐ **LANDI, Giuseppe Antonio** ..................... *drawings* | | $440 |
| ☐ **LANDINO, Jacopo** | | |
| **(called Jacopo del Casentino)** .................. *paintings* | | $33,000 |
| Italian 1297-1358 | | |
| ☐ **LANDSBERG, Otto** ............................. *paintings* | | $330 |
| ☐ **LANDSEER, Sir Edwin Henry** .............. *paintings* | $825 | $125,000 |
| English 1802-1873 ..................................... *drawings* | $137 | $1,870 |
| ☐ **LANDTSHEER, Jean Baptiste de** .......... *paintings* | | $715 |
| Belgian 1797-1845 | | |
| ☐ **LANE, Ernest** ................................... *paintings* | | $385 |
| American 19th cent. | | |
| ☐ **LANE, Fitz Hugh** ............................... *paintings* | $29,700 | $352,000 |
| American 1804-1865 | | |
| ☐ **LANE, Katherine W.** ........................... *sculpture* | | $770 |
| American b. 1899 | | |
| ☐ **LANE, Samuel** ................................... *paintings* | | $2,200 |
| British 1780-1859 | | |
| ☐ **LANFANT, Francois Louis** | | |
| **(called Lanfant de Metz)** ........................ *paintings* | $1,100 | $7,150 |
| French 1814-1892 | | |
| ☐ **LANG, Andrew** ................................. *drawings* | | $302 |
| American 20th cent. | | |
| ☐ **LANG, Hermann** ............................... *paintings* | | $660 |
| German 1856-1899 | | |
| ☐ **LANG, Louis** ................................... *paintings* | $440 | $27,500 |
| German/American 1814/24-1893 | | |
| ☐ **LANGDALE, Marmaduke A.** ................ *paintings* | | $357 |
| British d. 1905 | | |
| ☐ **LANGDON** ....................................... *paintings* | | $302 |
| American 19th cent. | | |

| | Current Price Range | |
|---|---|---|
| | *Low* | *High* |
| ☐ **LANGDON, E.** .................... *drawings* <br> English ac. 1846-1848 | | **$209** |
| ☐ **LANGE, Johann Gustav** .............. *paintings* <br> German 1811-1887 | | **$550** |
| ☐ **LANGE, Julius** ................ *paintings* <br> German 1817-1878 | | **$2,640** |
| ☐ **LANGE, R.** .................. *sculpture* | | **$550** |
| ☐ **LANGENDOERFFER, John** .......... *drawings* | | **$440** |
| ☐ **LANGENDYK, Dirk** ............ *drawings* <br> Dutch 1748-1805 | **$935** | **$2,750** |
| ☐ **LANGENDYK, Jan Anthonie** .......... *drawings* <br> Dutch 1780-1818 | | **$2,200** |
| ☐ **LANGER, Marin** .............. *paintings* | | **$385** |
| ☐ **LANGERMANTEL** ............. *paintings* <br> German 19th cent. | | **$350** |
| ☐ **LANGEROCK, Henri** .......... *drawings* <br> Belgian b. 1885 | **$121** | **$550** |
| ☐ **LANGEVELD, Frans** .......... *paintings* <br> Dutch 1877-1939 | **$577** | **$1,430** |
| ☐ **LANGHAUS, L.** ............. *paintings* | | **$300** |
| ☐ **LANGKEY, C. D.** ............ *paintings* | | **$715** |
| ☐ **LANGLAIS, Bernard** .......... *sculpture* | **$247** | **$1,320** |
| ☐ **LANGLAN, A.** .............. *paintings* <br> English 19th cent. | | **$742** |
| ☐ **LANGLEY, C. D.** ............ *paintings* <br> English 19th cent. | | **$2,310** |
| ☐ **LANGLEY, Edward** .......... *paintings* <br> American 20th cent. .......... *drawings* | **$385** <br> **$247** | **$440** <br> **$550** |
| ☐ **LANGLEY, Walter** .......... *paintings* <br> English 1852-1922 ............ *drawings* | **$495** <br> **$1,540** | **$20,900** <br> **$2,860** |
| ☐ **LANGLEY, William** .......... *paintings* <br> English (?) 19th/20th cent. | **$176** | **$935** |
| ☐ **LANGLOIS, J.** .............. *paintings* <br> French 19th/20th cent. | **$330** | **$935** |
| ☐ **LANGLOIS, Louis** .......... *drawings* <br> French 19th cent. | | **$605** |
| ☐ **LANGLOIS, Mark W.** .......... *paintings* <br> British 19th cent. | **$385** | **$1,650** |
| ☐ **LANGLOIS, S.** .............. *paintings* <br> French 19th cent. | | **$374** |
| ☐ **LANGMOOR, Louis** .......... *paintings* <br> French 19th cent. | | **$330** |
| ☐ **LANGRONNE, Eugene Philibert** ......... *paintings* <br> French 19th cent. | | **$192** |
| ☐ **LANGRUILEN, Jacob Studer von** ........ *paintings* | | **$275** |
| ☐ **LANGWORTH, W. H.** ........ *paintings* | | **$605** |
| ☐ **LANGWORTHY, A. W.** ......... *paintings* <br> American 19th cent. | | **$440** |
| ☐ **LANIN, Marie** .............. *paintings* | | **$660** |

| | | Current Price Range | |
|---|---|---|---|
| | | *Low* | *High* |
| ☐ **LANKOUT, L.** .................................... *paintings* | | | $605 |
| ☐ **LANMAN, Charles** ............................. *paintings* | | $660 | $2,090 |
| American 1819-1895 | | | |
| ☐ **LANSIL, Walter Franklin** ................. *paintings* | | $66 | $2,640 |
| American 1846-1925 ................................. *drawings* | | | $66 |
| ☐ **LANSKOY, Andre** .............................. *paintings* | | $1,100 | $12,100 |
| Russian/French 1902-1976 ......................... *drawings* | | | $990 |
| ☐ **LANSYER, Emmanuel** ...................... *paintings* | | | $1,100 |
| French 1835-93 | | | |
| ☐ **LANYON, Ellen** ................................. *paintings* | | | $6,600 |
| American b. 1926 | | | |
| ☐ **LANZONI, P.** ..................................... *paintings* | | $1,320 | $1,430 |
| Italian 20th cent. | | | |
| ☐ **LAP, Tony de** ...................................... *sculpture* | | | $825 |
| contemporary | | | |
| ☐ **LAPEYRE, Edmund Edouard** ............... *paintings* | | | $880 |
| French 1880-1960 | | | |
| ☐ **LAPICQUE, Charles** ........................... *paintings* | | $2,350 | $3,575 |
| French b. 1898 | | | |
| ☐ **LAPINI, C.** ....................................... *sculpture* | | | $2,090 |
| Italian late 19th cent. | | | |
| ☐ **LAPIRA** ............................................ *drawings* | | $224 | $660 |
| Italian 19th/20th cent. | | | |
| ☐ **LAPITO, Auguste Louis** ...................... *paintings* | | | $3,630 |
| French 1803-1874 | | | |
| ☐ **LAPORTE, Emile** ............................... *sculpture* | | $412 | $1,210 |
| French 1858-1907 | | | |
| ☐ **LAPORTE, George Henry** .................... *paintings* | | $1,089 | $95,000 |
| German/English 1799-1873 | | | |
| ☐ **LAPORTE, Georges** ............................ *paintings* | | $88 | $192 |
| French 20th cent. | | | |
| ☐ **LAPORTE, Marcellin** ........................... *paintings* | | | $1,760 |
| French b. 1839 | | | |
| ☐ **LAPOSTOLET, Charles** ...................... *paintings* | | $550 | $5,500 |
| French 1824-1890 | | | |
| ☐ **LAPPARA, William** ............................ *paintings* | | | $242 |
| French 1873-1920 | | | |
| ☐ **LAPRADE, Pierre** ............................... *drawings* | | | $385 |
| ☐ **LAPSHINKOV, A.** ............................. *paintings* | | | $247 |
| Russian 20th cent. | | | |
| ☐ **LARA, Ernest** .................................... *paintings* | | $1,760 | $1,980 |
| ☐ **LARA, George** .................................... *paintings* | | $330 | $1,760 |
| British 19th cent. | | | |
| ☐ **LARA, Georgina** ................................. *paintings* | | | $1,100 |
| English 19th cent. | | | |
| ☐ **LARA, J. Garcia** ................................. *drawings* | | | $220 |
| Italian 19th cent. | | | |
| ☐ **LARA, W.** ......................................... *paintings* | | | $1,100 |
| British 19th cent. | | | |

|                                                              |            | Current Price Range ||
|                                                              |            | Low       | High      |
| --- | --- | --- | --- |
| ☐ **LARAIS, W.** ...... *paintings* <br> European |  |  | **$605** |
| ☐ **LARCHE, Francois Raoul** ...... *sculpture* <br> French 1860-1912 |  | **$121** | **$13,200** |
| ☐ **LARD, Francois Maurice** ...... *paintings* <br> French 1864-1908 |  |  | **$7,150** |
| ☐ **LARDERA, Berto** ...... *sculpture* <br> French b. 1911 |  | **$660** | **$1,100** |
| ☐ **LARGILLIERE, Nicolas de** ...... *paintings* <br> French 1656-1746 |  | **$60,050** | **$187,000** |
| ☐ **LARI, F.** ...... *paintings* <br> 19th cent. |  |  | **$1,870** |
| ☐ **LARI, P.** ...... *paintings* |  |  | **$880** |
| ☐ **LARINGTON, S.B.** ...... *paintings* |  |  | **$275** |
| ☐ **LARIONOV, Mikhail** ...... *paintings* <br> Russian/French 1881-1964 ...... *drawings* |  | **$7,150** <br> **$137** | **$19,800** <br> **$7,700** |
| ☐ **LAROCHE, Jaques** ...... *paintings* <br> Haitian |  |  | **$550** |
| ☐ **LAROCHE, Robert** ...... *paintings* <br> French 19th/20th cent. |  |  | **$357** |
| ☐ **LAROLLE, W.** ...... *paintings* |  |  | **$440** |
| ☐ **LAROQUE, George** ...... *paintings* |  |  | **$880** |
| ☐ **LARPENTEUR, Balthasar Charles** ...... *paintings* <br> French 18th/19th cent. |  |  | **$605** |
| ☐ **LARPENTEUR, James Desvarreux** ...... *paintings* |  | **$200** | **$275** |
| ☐ **LARRAIN, Emilio Rodriguez** ...... *paintings* <br> Peruvian b. 1928 |  |  | **$7,150** |
| ☐ **LARRAURI, Iker** ...... *paintings* |  |  | **$302** |
| ☐ **LARRAVIDE, Manuel** ...... *paintings* <br> b. Uruguay 1871-1910 |  |  | **$935** |
| ☐ **LARRAZ, Julio** ...... *paintings* <br> Cuban b. 1944 ...... *drawings* |  | **$1,100** | **$13,200** <br> **$2,200** |
| ☐ **LARSEN, Carl Frederick Emmanuel** ...... *paintings* <br> Danish 1823-1859 |  |  | **$550** |
| ☐ **LARSEN, Morten** ...... *paintings* <br> American 20th cent. |  | **$137** | **$247** |
| ☐ **LARSEN, Oscar** ...... *paintings* <br> ...... *drawings* |  | **$137** | **$462** <br> **$385** |
| ☐ **LARSON, Harold Magnus** ...... *paintings* <br> late 19th cent. |  |  | **$385** |
| ☐ **LARSON, Lotti** ...... *paintings* <br> American 19th/20th cent. |  |  | **$990** |
| ☐ **LARSSON, Marcus** ...... *paintings* <br> 1825-1864 |  |  | **$1,650** |
| ☐ **LARSSON, Virginia** ...... *drawings* |  |  | **$418** |
| ☐ **LARUE, J.** ...... *paintings* |  |  | **$330** |
| ☐ **LARWIN, Hans** ...... *paintings* <br> Austrian b. 1873 |  |  | **$1,100** |
| ☐ **LARY, Roland** ...... *paintings* |  |  | **$330** |

| | Current Price Range | |
|---|---|---|
| | *Low* | *High* |

| | | | |
|---|---|---|---|
| ☐ **LASALLE, Charles Louis** ...................... *paintings* | | | $990 |
| 1894-1958 | | | |
| ☐ **LASAR, C.** ......................................... *paintings* | | $1,100 | $1,100 |
| Lithuanian/French 19th/20th cent. | | | |
| ☐ **LASCARI, Salvatore** ........................... *paintings* | | $357 | $605 |
| American b. 1884 | | | |
| ☐ **LASCAUX, Elie** ................................. *paintings* | | $418 | $495 |
| French 1888-1969 | | | |
| ☐ **LASCELLES, Thomas W.** ................... *paintings* | | | $247 |
| British ac. 1885-1891 | | | |
| ☐ **LASELLAZ, G.** ................................... *paintings* | | | $770 |
| ☐ **LASKE, Oskar** ................................... *paintings* | | | $1,650 |
| Austrian 1874-1911 ................................. *drawings* | | $990 | $990 |
| ☐ **LASKY, L.** ......................................... *paintings* | | | $715 |
| French 19th cent. | | | |
| ☐ **LASLETT, John Pott** ........................... *paintings* | | | $1,210 |
| English 1837-1898 | | | |
| ☐ **LASSAUX, G. de** ............................... *paintings* | | | $750 |
| French 19/20th cent. | | | |
| ☐ **LASSAW, Ibram** ................................ *sculpture* | | $1,100 | $4,400 |
| American b. 1913 | | | |
| ☐ **LASSNER, N.T.** ................................. *paintings* | | | $247 |
| American 19th cent. | | | |
| ☐ **LASTMAN, Pieter** ............................. *paintings* | | | $253,000 |
| Dutch c. 1586-1625 | | | |
| ☐ **LASZLO** ............................................. *sculpture* | | | $550 |
| ☐ **LASZLO DE LOMBOS,** | | | |
| **Philip Alexius de** ................................. *paintings* | | $27 | $1,100 |
| English 1869-1937 | | | |
| ☐ **LATAPIE, Louis** ................................. *drawings* | | | $825 |
| French 1891-1972 | | | |
| ☐ **LATHAM, John** ................................. *sculpture* | | | $770 |
| British b. 1921 | | | |
| ☐ **LATHROP, Gertrude Katherine** ........... *sculpture* | | $440 | $2,500 |
| American b. 1896 | | | |
| ☐ **LATHROP, William Langson** ............... *paintings* | | $1,760 | $3,850 |
| American 1859-1938 | | | |
| ☐ **LATIMER, Lorenzo Palmer** ................. *paintings* | | $385 | $1,760 |
| American 1857-1941 ................................. *drawings* | | $137 | $1,045 |
| ☐ **LATOIX, Gaspard** ............................. *paintings* | | | $3,850 |
| American ac. 1890-1910 ........................... *drawings* | | $1,870 | $4,400 |
| ☐ **LATORTUE, Philton** ........................... *paintings* | | | $550 |
| ☐ **LATOUCHE, Gaston de** ...................... *paintings* | | $2,420 | $35,200 |
| French 1854-1913 ................................... *drawings* | | $660 | $1,045 |
| ☐ **LATOUCHE, L.** ................................... *paintings* | | | $412 |
| ☐ **LATOUR, A. de** ................................. *paintings* | | | $200 |
| French 1780-1858 | | | |
| ☐ **LATOUR, Jean** ................................... *paintings* | | $1,210 | $1,375 |
| French 19th/20th cent. | | | |

|  | | *Current Price Range* | |
|--|--|--|--|
|  | | *Low* | *High* |
| ☐ **LATOUR, Maurice Quentin de** ............. *drawings* <br> French 1704-1788 | | $550 | $66,000 |
| ☐ **LAU, Andrew** .................................... *paintings* | | | $1,320 |
| ☐ **LAUB** ................................................ *paintings* <br> French 19th cent. | | | $1,100 |
| ☐ **LAUDA, R.** ......................................... *paintings* <br> Continental 20th cent. | | | $330 |
| ☐ **LAUDEN, Margaret E.** ........................ *paintings* <br> American ac. 1899-1906 | | | $880 |
| ☐ **LAUDER, Charles James** ................... *paintings* <br> English d. 1920. | | | $1,430 |
| ☐ **LAUFMAN, Sidney** ............................ *paintings* <br> American b. 1891 | | $33 | $440 |
| ☐ **LAUGE, Achille** ................................. *paintings* <br> French 1861-1944 | | | $3,850 |
| ☐ **LAUGEE, Desire Francois** ................... *paintings* <br> French 1823-1896 ....................................... *drawings* | | $715 <br> $137 | $3,300 <br> $467 |
| ☐ **LAUGEE, Georges** ............................. *paintings* <br> French b. 1853 | | $1,210 | $4,400 |
| ☐ **LAUGHIN, M.W.** ............................... *paintings* | | | $500 |
| ☐ **LAUNAY, L.** ...................................... *paintings* | | | $286 |
| ☐ **LAUPHEIMER, Anton** ........................ *paintings* <br> German 1848-1927 | | | $7,425 |
| ☐ **LAUR, Marie Yvonne** .......................... *paintings* <br> French b. 1879 | | | $1,320 |
| ☐ **LAUR, Yo** ......................................... *paintings* | | | $990 |
| ☐ **LAUREL, Pierre** ............................... *sculpture* <br> French early 20th cent. | | | $3,300 |
| ☐ **LAURENCE, Sydney** ........................... *paintings* <br> American 1860/65-1940 .............................. *drawings* | | $385 <br> $550 | $35,750 <br> $2,750 |
| ☐ **LAURENCIN, Marie** .......................... *paintings* <br> French 1883-1956 ................................... *drawings* | | $550 <br> $99 | $176,000 <br> $52,800 |
| ☐ **LAURENCY** ....................................... *paintings* <br> French 19th cent. | | | $220 |
| ☐ **LAURENS, Henri** ............................... *drawings* <br> French 1885-1954 .................................... *sculpture* | | $1,980 <br> $13,750 | $20,900 <br> $82,500 |
| ☐ **LAURENS, Jean Paul** ......................... *drawings* <br> French 1838-1921 | | | $275 |
| ☐ **LAURENS, Jean Pierre** ....................... *paintings* <br> French 1865-1933 | | | $660 |
| ☐ **LAURENT, E. Ernest** .......................... *sculpture* <br> 19th cent. | | | $2,970 |
| ☐ **LAURENT, E. Marcel** ......................... *paintings* <br> early 20th cent. | | $180 | $350 |
| ☐ **LAURENT, Ernest Joseph** .................. *paintings* <br> French 1859-1929 ................................... *sculpture* | | $137 | $1,320 <br> $330 |
| ☐ **LAURENT, Eugene** ............................ *sculpture* <br> French 1832-1898 | | $605 | $1,210 |
| ☐ **LAURENT, Georges H.** ........................ *sculpture* | | $220 | $1,650 |

| | | | Current Price Range | |
|---|---|---|---|---|
| | | | *Low* | *High* |

| | | | Low | High |
|---|---|---|---|---|
| ☐ **LAURENT, H.J.** ............................... *paintings* | | | **$385** | **$825** |
| Haitian 1893-1976 | | | | |
| ☐ **LAURENT, John** ............................... *paintings* | | | | **$440** |
| ☐ **LAURENT, Joseph Jean** ...................... *paintings* | | | **$220** | **$412** |
| ☐ **LAURENT, Peterson** ........................... *paintings* | | | **$1,430** | **$2,970** |
| Haitian ac. 1940-1958 | | | | |
| ☐ **LAURENT, Robert** ............................. *drawings* | | | | **$220** |
| American 1890-1970 ................................. *sculpture* | | | **$1,540** | **$4,400** |
| ☐ **LAURENT, Sabon** ............................. *paintings* | | | | **$357** |
| French 20th cent. | | | | |
| ☐ **LAURENT-DESROUSSEAUX,** | | | | |
| **Henri Alphonse Louis** ........................ *paintings* | | | **$1,760** | **$7,150** |
| French 1862-1906 | | | | |
| ☐ **LAURENTANO, George Bentilo** ............ *paintings* | | | | **$825** |
| ☐ **LAURENTS, H.J.** ............................... *paintings* | | | | **$385** |
| ☐ **LAURENTY, L.** ................................... *paintings* | | | **$660** | **$3,080** |
| French 19th cent. | | | | |
| ☐ **LAURITZ, Paul** ................................. *paintings* | | | **$286** | **$3,025** |
| Norwegian/American 1889-1975 ..................... *drawings* | | | **$440** | **$467** |
| ☐ **LAURUT, Louise** ................................. *drawings* | | | | **$715** |
| French b. 1874 | | | | |
| ☐ **LAUSET, Vernet de** ............................. *paintings* | | | | **$550** |
| ☐ **LAUTERER, Arch** ............................. *drawings* | | | **$440** | **$1,100** |
| ☐ **LAUTERS, G.** ................................... *paintings* | | | | **$650** |
| ☐ **LAUVERGNE, Barthelemy** .................. *paintings* | | | | **$320** |
| French 1805-1871 | | | | |
| ☐ **LAUVRAY, Abel** ............................. *paintings* | | | | **$2,090** |
| ☐ **LAUX, August** ................................... *paintings* | | | **$660** | **$4,950** |
| American 1853-1921 | | | | |
| ☐ **LAUX, Marie** ................................... *paintings* | | | | **$605** |
| ☐ **LAVAL, Fernand** ............................. *paintings* | | | **$247** | **$577** |
| French b. 1893 | | | | |
| ☐ **LAVALLE, John** ................................. *paintings* | | | **$770** | **$3,575** |
| American b. 1896 ..................................... *drawings* | | | **$33** | **$198** |
| ☐ **LAVALLEE-POUSSIN, Etienne de** ........ *drawings* | | | | **$715** |
| French 1733-1793 | | | | |
| ☐ **LAVALLEY, Jonas Joseph** .................. *paintings* | | | **$400** | **$1,760** |
| American 1858-1930 | | | | |
| ☐ **LAVASSEUR, A.** ............................... *sculpture* | | | | **$1,375** |
| ☐ **LAVASSEUR, Henri** ........................... *sculpture* | | | | **$550** |
| ☐ **LAVAUX, George Gregoire** .................. *paintings* | | | | **$660** |
| ☐ **LAVERENT, C.** ................................... *paintings* | | | | **$1,045** |
| ☐ **LAVERGNE, Georges** ........................... *paintings* | | | | **$467** |
| ☐ **LAVERGNE, Helene** ........................... *paintings* | | | | **$660** |
| ☐ **LAVERY, Sir John** ............................. *paintings* | | | **$1,870** | **$4,840** |
| Irish 1856-1941 | | | | |
| ☐ **LAVIEILLE, Eugene** ........................... *paintings* | | | | **$935** |
| French 1820-1899 | | | | |

| | *Current Price Range* | |
|---|---|---|
| | Low | High |

☐ **LAVIGNE, Audrey Rae** ........................ *drawings* | | **$192** |
American 19th cent.

☐ **LAVILLE, Joy** ..................................... *paintings* | **$2,200** | **$12,100** |
English b. 1923 ..................................... *drawings* | **$1,100** | **$1,760** |

☐ **LAVROFF, Georges** ........................... *sculpture* | **$2,200** | **$3,080** |
Russian/French b. 1895

☐ **LAVRY, John** ..................................... *paintings* | | **$1,760** |

☐ **LAWES, Harold** ............................... *drawings* | **$192** | **$660** |
English ac. c. 1890

☐ **LAWLESS, Carl** ............................... *paintings* | **$330** | **$3,300** |
American 1894-1934

☐ **LAWLOR, George W.** ........................ *paintings* | **$165** | **$5,500** |
American 1848-1932(?)

☐ **LAWLOR, W.** ..................................... *paintings* | | **$385** |

☐ **LAWMAN, Jasper Holman** ................ *paintings* | | **$2,200** |
1825-1906

☐ **LAWRENCE, Jacob** ........................... *paintings* | **$1,100** | **$19,800** |
American b. 1917 ..................................... *drawings* | **$1,100** | **$10,450** |

☐ **LAWRENCE, R. Pearson** ................... *drawings* | | **$467** |
1883-1970

☐ **LAWRENCE, Sir Thomas** ................... *paintings* | **$357** | **$30,800** |
English 1769-1830 ..................................... *drawings* | | **$1,320** |

☐ **LAWRENCE, Sydney M.** ..................... *drawings* | | **$4,950** |
American 1860/05-1940

☐ **LAWRENSON, Charlotte Mary Rose** .... *paintings* | | **$550** |
English b. 1883

☐ **LAWRENSON, Edward Louis** .............. *paintings* | | **$1,760** |
English b. 1868

☐ **LAWRIE, (Jr.)** ..................................... *paintings* | **$770** | **$850** |
American 1828-1917

☐ **LAWSHE, Hank** ............................... *paintings* | **$880** | **$1,550** |
American contemporary

☐ **LAWSON, Cecil Gordon** ...................... *paintings* | | **$605** |
Scottish 1851-1882

☐ **LAWSON, Ernest** ............................... *paintings* | **$1,320** | **$121,000** |
American 1873-1939 ..................................... *drawings* | | **$3,025** |

☐ **LAWSON, James Kerr** ........................ *paintings* | **$2,420** | **$2,420** |
English/Canadian 1864/65-1939

☐ **LAWSON, Mark** ............................... *drawings* | **$715** | **$2,200** |

☐ **LAWSON, Mehl** ............................... *sculpture* | | **$5,000** |

☐ **LAWSON, Robert** ............................... *drawings* | | **$412** |
American early 20th cent.

☐ **LAWTON, Almira C.** ........................... *paintings* | | **$308** |
American

☐ **LAY, Cecil** ..................................... *paintings* | **$467** | **$467** |

☐ **LAYCOCK, F.** ..................................... *paintings* | | **$1,650** |

☐ **LAYOS, Lovus** ..................................... *paintings* | | **$522** |
Continental 19th cent.

☐ **LAZAREV, H.** ..................................... *paintings* | **$330** | **$357** |

## Orientalist Painting

*Fascinated by romanticized visions of life in remote places, many 19th-century European painters travelled to North Africa, the Middle East, the Far East, and other distant points. Their pictures of these exotic scenes, collectively known as "Orientalist Painting," commanded high prices during the second half of the 19th and early 20th centuries.*

*After the end of World War I, the reaction against Victorian tastes and values caused these paintings to be neglected by dealers and collectors. A major Orientalist exhibition held at the Royal Academy in London in 1981 sparked a dramatic turnaround in the market, though vascillating oil prices have caused substantial fluctuation in prices since then.*

*Paul Lazerges was typical of artists of the period. Born in France, he travelled to Algeria and lived for many years in North Africa. He specialized in Orientalist paintings and won many medals and prizes. (Jean Baptiste Paul Lazerges, "Pack Camels on the Desert," oil on panel, 5 x 7½ in., Skinner, September 13, 1984, $1,540.)*

| | | Current Price Range | |
|---|---|---|---|
| | | *Low* | *High* |
| ☐ **LAZERGES, Jean Baptiste Paul** ............ *paintings* <br> French 1845-1902 | | **$550** | **$6,600** |
| ☐ **LAZERGES, Jean Raymond Hippolyte** .. *paintings* <br> French 1817-1887 ............................... *drawings* | | **$357** | **$18,700** <br> **$352** |
| ☐ **LAZLO, Neogrady** ............................ *paintings* <br> American contemporary | | | **$880** |
| ☐ **LAZLO, P. de** ................................... *paintings* <br> Continental 19th cent. | | | **$440** |
| ☐ **LAZO, Augustin** ................................. *drawings* <br> Mexican b. 1900 | | | **$1,540** |

| | *Current Price Range* | |
|---|---|---|
| | *Low* | *High* |
| ☐ **LAZZARI, Pietro** .............................. *paintings* | | $165 |
| Italian/American 1898-1979 .......................... *drawings* | | $770 |
| ☐ **LAZZELL, Blanche** ............................. *paintings* | $242 | $770 |
| American d. 1956 ...................................... *drawings* | | $3,740 |
| ☐ **LE BARBIER, Jean Jacques Francois** | | |
| **(called Le Barbier L'Aine)** ...................... *paintings* | $605 | $2,860 |
| .............................................. *drawings* | | $990 |
| ☐ **LE BAS, Jacques Philippe** .................... *drawings* | $495 | $935 |
| French 1707-1783 | | |
| ☐ **LE BLANT, Julien** ............................... *paintings* | | $7,150 |
| French b. 1851 | | |
| ☐ **LE BOULANGER** ............................... *paintings* | | $715 |
| French 19th cent. | | |
| ☐ **LE BOURGEOIS** ............................... *drawings* | | $374 |
| ☐ **LE BRUN, Charles** ............................. *drawings* | | $3,850 |
| French 1619-1690 | | |
| ☐ **LE BUEL** ........................................... *paintings* | | $467 |
| French 19th cent. | | |
| ☐ **LE CHEVALIER, Pierre Toussaint** ....... *paintings* | | $4,950 |
| French b. 1825 | | |
| ☐ **LE CORBUSIER,** | | |
| **(Charles Edouard JEANNERET)** ............ *drawings* | $275 | $2,640 |
| French 1887-1965 | | |
| ☐ **LE DRU, Albert Ferdinand** .................. *paintings* | | $1,045 |
| French b. 1848 | | |
| ☐ **LE FAGUAYS, Pierre** .......................... *sculpture* | $660 | $7,700 |
| French b. 1892 | | |
| ☐ **LE FAUCONNIER, Henri** .................... *paintings* | | $605 |
| French 1881-1946 | | |
| ☐ **LE FLECHE, Henri** ............................. *paintings* | | $1,980 |
| French 19th cent. | | |
| ☐ **LE MAYEUR DE MERPRES, Adrien** ... *paintings* | $246 | $440 |
| ☐ **LE PARC, Julio** .................................. *paintings* | $1,320 | $2,200 |
| Argentinian b. 1928 .................................. *drawings* | $385 | $440 |
| ☐ **LE PHO** ........................................... *paintings* | $242 | $1,210 |
| French b. 1907 | | |
| ☐ **LE PRINCE, Jean Baptiste** .................. *drawings* | | $495 |
| ☐ **LE SAVARIN, Michel** .......................... *paintings* | | $466 |
| French b. 1928 | | |
| ☐ **LE SENECHAL DE KERDREORET,** | | |
| **Gustave Edouard** .................................. *paintings* | | $2,090 |
| French b. 1840 | | |
| ☐ **LE SIDANER, Henri** ........................... *paintings* | $3,300 | $71,500 |
| French 1862-1939 ...................................... *drawings* | $187 | $14,300 |
| ☐ **LE SUEUR, Louis** ............................... *drawings* | | $770 |
| ☐ **LE TRESOR** ...................................... *sculpture* | | $1,760 |
| ☐ **LE VEEL, Armond Jules** ...................... *sculpture* | | $1,694 |
| French 1821-1905 | | |
| ☐ **LE VERRIER** .................................... *sculpture* | | $990 |

|  | | Current Price Range | |
|---|---|---|---|
|  | | Low | High |
| ☐ **LEA, Tom** ............................................ *drawings* | | | $2,420 |
| b. 1907 | | | |
| ☐ **LEADER, Benjamin Edward** ................. *paintings* | | | $495 |
| British 19th/20th cent. | | | |
| ☐ **LEADER, Benjamin William** ................. *paintings* | | $247 | $28,600 |
| English 1831-1923 ..................................... *drawings* | | | $137 |
| ☐ **LEADER, Charles** ................................ *paintings* | | $302 | $330 |
| British 19th/20th cent. | | | |
| ☐ **LEADER, H.W.** ..................................... *paintings* | | | $1,045 |
| English | | | |
| ☐ **LEAKE, Eugene** .................................... *paintings* | | | $550 |
| American b. 1911 | | | |
| ☐ **LEAKE, Gerald** ..................................... *paintings* | | | $550 |
| ☐ **LEAKEY, James** .................................... *paintings* | | | $770 |
| English 1775-1865 ..................................... *drawings* | | | $165 |
| ☐ **LEAR, Edward** ..................................... *paintings* | | | $57,750 |
| English 1812-1888 ..................................... *drawings* | | $66 | $8,800 |
| ☐ **LEAVER, James** .................................... *paintings* | | | $352 |
| ☐ **LEAVER, Noel Harry** ........................... *drawings* | | $440 | $4,950 |
| English 1889-1951 | | | |
| ☐ **LEAVITT, Edward Chalmers** ............... *paintings* | | $220 | $11,000 |
| American 1842-1904 | | | |
| ☐ **LEAVITT, John F.** ............................... *drawings* | | $325 | $1,600 |
| American b. 1805 | | | |
| ☐ **LEAVITT, R.C.** ..................................... *paintings* | | | $375 |
| American | | | |
| ☐ **LEAVITT, Sheldon (Jr.)** ......................... *paintings* | | | $1,320 |
| ☐ **LEBADANG** ......................................... *paintings* | | | $522 |
| ☐ **LEBASQUE, Henri** ............................... *paintings* | | $1,320 | $49,500 |
| French 1865-1937 ..................................... *drawings* | | $220 | $4,620 |
| ☐ **LEBDUSKA, Lawrence H.** .................... *paintings* | | $137 | $2,310 |
| American b. 1894 ..................................... *drawings* | | | $220 |
| ☐ **LEBEL, Edmund** .................................. *paintings* | | | $1,900 |
| French 1834-1909 | | | |
| ☐ **LEBENSTEIN, Jan** ............................... *paintings* | | $440 | $935 |
| ☐ **LEBOT, V.** .......................................... *paintings* | | | $467 |
| French 20th cent. | | | |
| ☐ **LEBOURG, Albert Charles** ................... *paintings* | | $1,320 | $37,400 |
| French 1849-1928 ..................................... *drawings* | | $330 | $660 |
| ☐ **LEBRET, Frans** ................................... *paintings* | | $750 | $4,180 |
| Dutch 1820-1909 | | | |
| ☐ **LEBRET, Paul** ..................................... *drawings* | | $1,100 | $2,530 |
| French b. 1875; ac. 1901-1907 | | | |
| ☐ **LEBRON, Sandy** ................................... *paintings* | | | $385 |
| American b. 1951 | | | |
| ☐ **LEBRUN, Charles** ................................ *paintings* | | | $1,045 |
| French 19th cent. | | | |
| ☐ **LEBRUN, Rico** ..................................... *paintings* | | $1,540 | $2,090 |
| American 1900-1964 ................................... *drawings* | | $110 | $770 |

| | Current Price Range | |
|---|---|---|
| | Low | High |

☐ **LECADRE, Alphonse Eugene Felix** ........ *paintings* | | $30,800
French 1842-1875

☐ **LECCONI, E.** ...................................... *paintings* | | $440
American 20th cent.

☐ **LECK, Bart van der** ............................ *paintings* | | $38,500
Dutch 1876-1958

☐ **LECLAIRE, Victor** ............................... *paintings* | | $1,980
French 1830-1885

☐ **LECLEAR, Thomas** ............................. *paintings* | | $330
American 1818-1882

☐ **LECLERC, L. Jacques** ......................... *paintings* | | $4,400
French 19th/20th cent.

☐ **LECLERC, Sebastien Jacques**
**(called Leclerc Des Gobelins)** ................ *paintings* | $2,420 | $7,150

☐ **LECLERCQ, Edmund** .......................... *paintings* | | $1,650
French 1817-1853

☐ **LECOEUR, Jean Baptiste** ..................... *paintings* | | $2,750
French 1795-1838

☐ **LECOINDRE, Eugene** .......................... *paintings* | | $12,650
French 19th cent.

☐ **LECOMPTE, Louis** ............................. *paintings* | | $1,650
French 19th cent.

☐ **LECOMTE, Hippolyte** ......................... *paintings* | $1,760 | $2,640
French 1781-1857

☐ **LECOMTE, Paul** ................................ *paintings* | $880 | $5,500
French 1842-1920 ..................................... *drawings* | | $385

☐ **LECOMTE, Paul Emile** ....................... *paintings* | $660 | $2,750
French b. 1877 ....................................... *drawings* | | $143

☐ **LECOMTE, Victor** .............................. *paintings* | $275 | $880
French 1856-1920

☐ **LECOMTE DU NOUY,**
**Jean Jules Antoine** ............................... *paintings* | | $18,150
French 1842-1923

☐ **LECOQUE, Alois** ............................... *paintings* | $440 | $4,730
Czech./American 1891-1981 ......................... *drawings* | | $715

☐ **LECORNEY, Nicolas** ........................... *sculpture* | $467 | $2,530
French ac. c. 1880-1900

☐ **LECOURTIER, Prosper** ....................... *sculpture* | $300 | $1,320
French 1855-1924

☐ **LEDAIN, G.** ...................................... *drawings* | | $605
Latin American

☐ **LEDEMY, G.** ..................................... *paintings* | | $357
French 19th cent.

☐ **LEDHILL, T.G.** ................................. *paintings* | | $275
American 19th cent.

☐ **LEDOUX, Charles Picart** ..................... *paintings* | | $1,870
French 1881-1959

☐ **LEDOUX, Jeanne Philberte** .................. *paintings* | $2,200 | $4,125
French 1767-1840

| | Current Price Range | |
|---|---|---|
| | *Low* | *High* |
| ☐ **LEDRU, Auguste** ...... *sculpture* | | **$462** |
| ☐ **LEDUC, Arthur Jacques** ...... *sculpture* | | **$4,125** |
| French 1848-1918 | | |
| ☐ **LEE, Arthur** ...... *sculpture* | **$3,520** | **$4,620** |
| Norwegian/American 1881-1961 | | |
| ☐ **LEE, Bertha Stringer** ...... *paintings* | **$90** | **$500** |
| American 1873-1934/37 | | |
| ☐ **LEE, Charlie** ...... *drawings* | | **$605** |
| American (Navajo) b. 1926 | | |
| ☐ **LEE, Chee Chin S. Cheung** ...... *paintings* | | **$110** |
| Chinese/American b. 1896 ...... *drawings* | **$110** | **$247** |
| ☐ **LEE, Doris** ...... *paintings* | **$605** | **$990** |
| American b. 1905 | | |
| ☐ **LEE, Erica** ...... *sculpture* | | **$2,090** |
| English 20th cent. | | |
| ☐ **LEE, Frederick Richard** ...... *paintings* | **$450** | **$6,325** |
| British 1798-1879 | | |
| ☐ **LEE, J. Brock** ...... *paintings* | **$350** | **$750** |
| American | | |
| ☐ **LEE, James Noah** ...... *paintings* | **$385** | **$467** |
| British 19th/20th cent. | | |
| ☐ **LEE, Manning de Vileneuve** ...... *paintings* | | **$1,430** |
| American 20th cent. | | |
| ☐ **LEE, Mong R.** ...... *drawings* | | **$220** |
| American 20th cent. | | |
| ☐ **LEE, Sidney** ...... *paintings* | | **$301** |
| ☐ **LEE, Violet** ...... *paintings* | | **$825** |
| American late 19th cent. | | |
| ☐ **LEE-HANKEY, W.** ...... *paintings* | | **$2,200** |
| English 1869-1952 | | |
| ☐ **LEECH, H. Edward** ...... *paintings* | | **$192** |
| English 19th cent. | | |
| ☐ **LEECH, John** ...... *paintings* | **$132** | **$1,870** |
| English 1817-1864 ...... *drawings* | **$165** | **$1,760** |
| ☐ **LEEMANS, Johanner** ...... *paintings* | | **$3,850** |
| Dutch 1633-1688 | | |
| ☐ **LEEMPUTTEN, Cornelis van** ...... *paintings* | **$605** | **$5,500** |
| Belgian 1841-1902 | | |
| ☐ **LEEMPUTTEN, Frans van** ...... *paintings* | **$825** | **$3,850** |
| Belgian 1850-1914 | | |
| ☐ **LEEMPUTTEN, Jef Louis van** ...... *paintings* | **$440** | **$2,420** |
| Belgian 19th cent. | | |
| ☐ **LEEN, Willem van** ...... *paintings* | **$6,050** | **$7,150** |
| Dutch 1753-1825 | | |
| ☐ **LEENDERS, W. De** ...... *paintings* | | **$550** |
| Dutch 19th cent. | | |
| ☐ **LEERMANS, Pieter** ...... *paintings* | | **$3,190** |
| Dutch 1655-1706 | | |

| | | Current Price Range | |
|---|---|---|---|
| | | Low | High |
| ☐ **LEES, Charles** .................... *paintings* | | | $3,300 |
| Scottish 1800-1880 | | | |
| ☐ **LEETEC, Edgar** .................... *paintings* | | $1,760 | $1,980 |
| American 20th cent. | | | |
| ☐ **LEEUW, Alexis de** .................... *paintings* | | $1,650 | $6,000 |
| Belgian ac. 1864 | | | |
| ☐ **LEEUW, Henri van** .................... *paintings* | | | $495 |
| Dutch 1866-1918 | | | |
| ☐ **LEEUW, Pieter van der** .................... *paintings* | | $385 | $522 |
| Dutch 17th/18th cent. | | | |
| ☐ **LEFEBRE, Wilhelm Ulbert** .................... *paintings* | | | $6,600 |
| German 1873-1974 | | | |
| ☐ **LEFEBVRE, Jules Joseph** .................... *paintings* | | $880 | $19,800 |
| French 1834/36-1912 | | | |
| ☐ **LEFEUVRE, Jean** .................... *drawings* | | | $220 |
| French 19th cent. | | | |
| ☐ **LEFEVRE, Edouard** .................... *paintings* | | | $286 |
| ☐ **LEFEVRE, Laure** .................... *paintings* | | | $1,045 |
| American 19th cent. | | | |
| ☐ **LEFEVRE, M.** .................... *paintings* | | | $1,430 |
| French 19th cent. | | | |
| ☐ **LEFEVRE, Robert** .................... *paintings* | | | $715 |
| French 1755-1830 | | | |
| ☐ **LEFFER, H.** .................... *paintings* | | | $4,400 |
| Dutch 19th cent. | | | |
| ☐ **LEFLER, Franz** .................... *paintings* | | | $2,750 |
| Czechoslavakian 1831-1898 | | | |
| ☐ **LEFORT, Jean Louis** .................... *paintings* | | $495 | $1,760 |
| French b. 1875 | | | |
| ☐ **LEGA, Georgio** .................... *paintings* | | | $2,640 |
| Italian 19th cent. | | | |
| ☐ **LEGA, Giovanni** .................... *paintings* | | | $825 |
| ☐ **LEGA, Silvestro** .................... *paintings* | | | $1,210 |
| Italian 1826-1895 | | | |
| ☐ **LEGANGER, N.F.** .................... *paintings* | | | $467 |
| American 1889 | | | |
| ☐ **LEGARDA, Bernardo de** .................... *paintings* | | | $13,200 |
| b. Ecuador ac. 1730-1773 | | | |
| ☐ **LEGAT, Leon** .................... *paintings* | | $5,500 | $17,600 |
| French b. 1829 | | | |
| ☐ **LEGER, Fernand** .................... *paintings* | | $22,000 | $616,000 |
| French 1881-1955 .................... *drawings* | | $605 | $60,500 |
| .................... *sculpture* | | $4,070 | $22,000 |
| ☐ **LEGGETT, Alexander** .................... *paintings* | | | $880 |
| British 19th cent. | | | |
| ☐ **LEGGETT, H.T.** .................... *drawings* | | | $274 |
| ☐ **LEGILLON, Jean Francois** .................... *paintings* | | $935 | $990 |
| Flemish 1739-1797 .................... *drawings* | | | $357 |

|  | | | Current Price Range | |
|--|--|--|--------|--------|
|  | | | *Low* | *High* |
| ☐ **LEGLER, Thomas Joachim** ................. *paintings* | | | | $1,650 |
| Finnish 1806-1873 | | | | |
| ☐ **LEGOUT-GERARD, Fernand** ............... *paintings* | | | $935 | $9,350 |
| French 1856-1924 | | | | |
| ☐ **LEGRAND, Auguste Claude Simon** ....... *drawings* | | | | $715 |
| French 1765-1815 | | | | |
| ☐ **LEGRAND, Henry** ............................. *paintings* | | | | $1,870 |
| American | | | | |
| ☐ **LEGRAND, Louis Auguste Mathieu** ...... *drawings* | | | $440 | $11,000 |
| French 1863-1951 | | | | |
| ☐ **LEGRAND, Paul Emmanuel** ................. *paintings* | | | | $1,430 |
| French b. 1860 | | | | |
| ☐ **LEGROS, Alphonse** ............................ *paintings* | | | | $770 |
| French 1837-1911 .................................... *drawings* | | | $412 | $1,760 |
| ☐ **LEGROS, Pierre (called le jeune)** .......... *drawings* | | | | $1,650 |
| French 1666-1719 | | | | |
| ☐ **LEGUAY, Andre Guerin** ...................... *paintings* | | | | $605 |
| French b. 1872 | | | | |
| ☐ **LEGUAY, Charles Etienne** .................... *drawings* | | | | $605 |
| French 1762-1846 | | | | |
| ☐ **LEGUEULT, Raymond Jean** ................. *paintings* | | | $4,950 | $12,100 |
| French 1898-1971 ................................... *drawings* | | | $82 | $1,760 |
| ☐ **LEHMANN, Rudolf Wilhelm August** ..... *paintings* | | | $440 | $11,000 |
| German 1819-1905 | | | | |
| ☐ **LEHMBRUCK, Wilhelm** ...................... *sculpture* | | | $5,500 | $17,600 |
| German 1881-1919 | | | | |
| ☐ **LEHNER, Gilbert** ............................... *paintings* | | | | $1,540 |
| Austrian 19th cent. | | | | |
| ☐ **LEHNERT, Pierre Frederic** .................. *paintings* | | | | $825 |
| ☐ **LEHR, Adam** ...................................... *paintings* | | | $110 | $1,650 |
| American 1853-1924 | | | | |
| ☐ **LEHYMS, H.** ...................................... *paintings* | | | | $300 |
| ☐ **LEIBL, Wilhelm** ................................. *drawings* | | | | $1,100 |
| ☐ **LEICKERT, Charles Henri Joseph** ........ *paintings* | | | $385 | $31,900 |
| Belgian 1816/18-1907 ............................... *drawings* | | | | $990 |
| ☐ **LEIF, June** ........................................ *drawings* | | | | $770 |
| ☐ **LEIGH, William Robinson** ................... *paintings* | | | $770 | $148,500 |
| American 1866-1955 .................................. *drawings* | | | $247 | $12,100 |
| ☐ **LEIGHTON, Edmund Blair** ................. *paintings* | | | $1,100 | $35,200 |
| British 1853-1922 | | | | |
| ☐ **LEIGHTON, Kathryn Woodman** ........... *paintings* | | | | $1,100 |
| American 1876-1952 | | | | |
| ☐ **LEIGHTON, Lord Frederic** ................. *paintings* | | | $7,700 | $50,600 |
| British 1830-1896 ..................................... *drawings* | | | $165 | $770 |
| ☐ **LEIGHTON, Scott** ............................... *paintings* | | | $330 | $27,500 |
| American 1849-1898 ................................. *drawings* | | | | $77 |
| ☐ **LEIKER, W.** ...................................... *paintings* | | | | $320 |
| ☐ **LEIMPUTTE, Jacques** .......................... *paintings* | | | | $1,430 |

| | | *Current Price Range* | |
|---|---|---|---|
| | | Low | High |

| | | Low | High |
|---|---|---|---|
| ☐ **LEISSER, Martin B.** ............................ *paintings* | | $176 | $3,190 |
| American b. 1845 | | | |
| ☐ **LEIST, Frederick William** ...................... *paintings* | | | $4,180 |
| Austrian 1878-1946 | | | |
| ☐ **LEITCH, William Leighton** .................... *drawings* | | $198 | $330 |
| Scottish 1804-1883 | | | |
| ☐ **LEITGEB, Franz** ................................. *paintings* | | $357 | $550 |
| Austrian 19th cent. | | | |
| ☐ **LEITH-ROSS, Harry** .......................... *paintings* | | $302 | $4,730 |
| American b. 1886 ..................................... *drawings* | | | $247 |
| ☐ **LEITNER, Leander** ............................. *paintings* | | $82 | $1,045 |
| American b. 1873 | | | |
| ☐ **LEITNER, Thomas** .............................. *paintings* | | $522 | $1,210 |
| Austrian b. 1876 | | | |
| ☐ **LEJARD, G.** ....................................... *paintings* | | | $660 |
| ☐ **LEJEUNE, Eugene** ............................... *paintings* | | | $2,640 |
| French 1818-1897 | | | |
| ☐ **LEJEUNE, Henry** ................................ *paintings* | | $1,320 | $1,430 |
| British 1820-1904 | | | |
| ☐ **LELAND, Henry** ................................. *paintings* | | $528 | $4,400 |
| American 1850-1877 | | | |
| ☐ **LELIE, Adriaan de** ............................. *paintings* | | | $3,960 |
| Dutch 1755-1820 | | | |
| ☐ **LELLI, Giovanni Battista** ..................... *paintings* | | | $660 |
| Italian 1828-1887 | | | |
| ☐ **LELOIR, Alexandre Louis** .................... *paintings* | | $440 | $5,500 |
| French 1843-1884 ..................................... *drawings* | | $521 | $2,200 |
| ☐ **LELOIR, Jean Baptiste Auguste** ........... *paintings* | | $220 | $8,250 |
| French 1809-1892 | | | |
| ☐ **LELOIR, Maurice** ............................... *paintings* | | $17,600 | $19,800 |
| French 1853-1940 ..................................... *drawings* | | $352 | $1,045 |
| ☐ **LELONG** ......................................... *paintings* | | | $990 |
| French ac. 1800 ...................................... *drawings* | | $1,210 | $6,325 |
| ☐ **LELOT, V.** ....................................... *paintings* | | | $302 |
| ☐ **LELOUP DE SPA, Antoine** ................... *drawings* | | | $660 |
| French d. 1746 | | | |
| ☐ **LELY, Sir Peter** ................................ *paintings* | | $1,430 | $9,350 |
| British 1618-1680 | | | |
| ☐ **LEMAIRE, Casimir** ............................. *paintings* | | | $935 |
| French 19th/20th cent. | | | |
| ☐ **LEMAIRE, Charles** ............................. *drawings* | | $467 | $880 |
| French ac. 1756-1769 | | | |
| ☐ **LEMAIRE, Jean** ................................. *paintings* | | | $715 |
| ☐ **LEMANI, M.** ..................................... *sculpture* | | | $200 |
| mid 20th cent. | | | |
| ☐ **LEMASSON, Paul** ............................... *paintings* | | | $1,045 |
| ☐ **LEMAY, Olivier** ................................ *drawings* | | | $1,650 |
| French 1734-1797 | | | |

| | | Current Price Range | |
|---|---|---|---|
| | | Low | High |
| ☐ **LEMBECK, Jack** ............................. *paintings* | | $5,500 | $7,150 |
| American contemporary | | | |
| ☐ **LEMEN** ........................................ *drawings* | | | $1,430 |
| ☐ **LEMENOREL, Ernest Emile** .............. *paintings* | | | $1,000 |
| French b. 1848 | | | |
| ☐ **LEMIRE, Charles G.** ......................... *sculpture* | | | $850 |
| ☐ **LEMIRE, Jean Gabriel** | | | |
| **(called Sauvage)** .................................. *sculpture* | | | $935 |
| French late 18th cent. | | | |
| ☐ **LEMMEN, Georges** ........................... *paintings* | | $165 | $47,300 |
| Belgian 1865-1916 ..................................... *drawings* | | $1,400 | $14,300 |
| ☐ **LEMMENS, Theophile Victor Emile** ...... *paintings* | | $495 | $2,310 |
| French 1821-1867 | | | |
| ☐ **LEMOINE, Elisabeth Bocquet** .............. *paintings* | | $4,840 | $7,500 |
| French 18th cent. | | | |
| ☐ **LEMOINE, Francois** ......................... *drawings* | | $1,540 | $1,650 |
| French 1688-1737 | | | |
| ☐ **LEMOINE, Marie Victoire** .................... *paintings* | | $4,125 | $5,225 |
| French 1754-1820 | | | |
| ☐ **LEMON, Arthur** ............................. *paintings* | | | $440 |
| English 1850-1912 | | | |
| ☐ **LEMON, David** ............................... *sculpture* | | | $3,900 |
| American contemporary | | | |
| ☐ **LEMON, Frank** ............................... *sculpture* | | | $3,080 |
| early 20th cent. | | | |
| ☐ **LEMORDANT, Jean Julien** ................. *paintings* | | $770 | $1,870 |
| French b. 1878 | | | |
| ☐ **LEMOXII, Kyril** ............................. *paintings* | | | $1,760 |
| ☐ **LEMPICKA, Tamara de** ..................... *paintings* | | $4,950 | $242,000 |
| Polish 1898-1980 | | | |
| ☐ **LENARDEZ, P.** ............................... *sculpture* | | | $308 |
| ☐ **LENBACH, Franz Seraph von** ............. *paintings* | | $110 | $8,250 |
| German 1836-1904 ..................................... *drawings* | | $440 | $880 |
| ☐ **LENBACH, J. von** ............................. *paintings* | | | $605 |
| ☐ **LENDENSCHMIDT, Herman** ............... *paintings* | | | $275 |
| ☐ **LENDT, P.Y.R.** ............................... *paintings* | | | $220 |
| Dutch b. 1915 | | | |
| ☐ **LENDY, E.** ................................... *paintings* | | | $660 |
| European 19th cent. | | | |
| ☐ **LENGO, Francesco** ........................... *drawings* | | | $3,080 |
| ☐ **LENGO Y MARTINEZ, Horacio** ........... *paintings* | | | $1,430 |
| Spanish b. 1890 | | | |
| ☐ **LENHART, A.** ................................ *paintings* | | | $176 |
| American 20th cent. | | | |
| ☐ **LENOIR, Charles Amable** ................... *paintings* | | $660 | $30,800 |
| French b. 1861 | | | |
| ☐ **LENOIR, Felix** ............................... *paintings* | | | $385 |
| ☐ **LENOIR, Pierre Charles** ...................... *sculpture* | | $1,650 | $2,420 |
| French b. 1879 | | | |

| | Current Price Range | |
|---|---|---|
| | *Low* | *High* |
| ☐ **LENORDEZ, Pierre** .......................... *sculpture* | $990 | $1,600 |
| French 19th cent. | | |
| ☐ **LENS, Bernard (the younger)** ................ *paintings* | | $385 |
| ☐ **LENTEMAN, Hans** ............................. *paintings* | $385 | $633 |
| 20th century | | |
| ☐ **LENZ, F.** ........................................... *paintings* | | $330 |
| German 19th cent. | | |
| ☐ **LENZ, Nic** ....................................... *paintings* | $74 | $352 |
| ☐ **LENZI, Luigi** .................................... *paintings* | | $1,100 |
| Italian 19th/20th cent. | | |
| ☐ **LEON, Amanda de** ............................. *paintings* | | $264 |
| ☐ **LEON, Francisco de** .......................... *paintings* | | $9,900 |
| Mexican ac. early 18th cent. | | |
| ☐ **LEON, Noe** ....................................... *paintings* | $990 | $1,980 |
| Colombian b. 1907 ..................................... *drawings* | | $1,045 |
| ☐ **LEON, Omar de** ................................ *paintings* | $550 | $825 |
| ☐ **LEONARD** ........................................ *paintings* | | $467 |
| ☐ **LEONARD, A.** ................................... *paintings* | $1,045 | $2,640 |
| Continental 19th cent. | | |
| ☐ **LEONARD, Agathon** ......................... *sculpture* | $330 | $4,950 |
| French b. 1841 | | |
| ☐ **LEONARD, B.** ................................... *paintings* | | $264 |
| American 20th cent. | | |
| ☐ **LEONARD, Hector** ............................ *drawings* | | $192 |
| contemporary | | |
| ☐ **LEONARD, Jules** ............................... *paintings* | | $440 |
| ☐ **LEONARDI, Achille** ........................... *paintings* | | $1,760 |
| Italian School 19th cent. | | |
| ☐ **LEONARDI, Guido Reni** ...................... *paintings* | | $935 |
| ☐ **LEONARDO** ...................................... *paintings* | | $440 |
| ☐ **LEONE, John** .................................... *paintings* | $4,700 | $10,000 |
| American contemporary | | |
| ☐ **LEONE, S.** ........................................ *paintings* | $220 | $412 |
| American contemporary | | |
| ☐ **LEONELLI, Dante** ............................. *drawings* | $165 | $374 |
| Italian contemporary | | |
| ☐ **LEONG, James Chan** .......................... *paintings* | | $411 |
| American b. 1925 | | |
| ☐ **LEONI, Ramolo** ................................. *paintings* | | $286 |
| ☐ **LEONID** ........................................... *paintings* | | $424 |
| ☐ **LEONTUS, Adam** .............................. *paintings* | $110 | $1,320 |
| Haitian 20th cent. | | |
| ☐ **LEOPOLD, V.** .................................... *paintings* | | $1,320 |
| German 19th/20th cent. | | |
| ☐ **LEOUW, A. de** ................................... *paintings* | | $528 |
| ☐ **LEPAGE, Jules Bastien** ....................... *paintings* | | $17,600 |
| ☐ **LEPAPE, Georges** .............................. *drawings* | $495 | $660 |

| | | Current Price Range | |
|---|---|---|---|
| | | Low | High |
| ☐ **LEPICIE, Nicolas Bernard** ................... *drawings* | | $715 | $3,300 |
| French 1735-1784 | | | |
| ☐ **LEPINAY, Paul Gallard** ...................... *paintings* | | | $2,640 |
| French 1842-1903 | | | |
| ☐ **LEPINE, Stanislas** ............................... *paintings* | | $632 | $37,400 |
| French 1835-1892 ..................................... *drawings* | | $600 | $6,050 |
| ☐ **LEPOITEVIN,** | | | |
| **Eugene Modeste Edmond** ...................... *paintings* | | | $2,200 |
| French 1806-1870 | | | |
| ☐ **LEPOITTEVIN, Louis** ......................... *paintings* | | | $1,980 |
| French 1847-1909 | | | |
| ☐ **LEPRI, Stanislao** ................................ *paintings* | | | $880 |
| ☐ **LEPRIN, Marcel Francois** ................... *paintings* | | $935 | $990 |
| French 1891-1933 | | | |
| ☐ **LEPRINCE, Auguste Xavier** ................ *paintings* | | | $1,870 |
| French 1799-1826 ..................................... *drawings* | | | $825 |
| ☐ **LEPRINCE, Jean Baptiste** ................... *paintings* | | $7,700 | $17,600 |
| French 1734-1781 ..................................... *drawings* | | | $2,475 |
| ☐ **LEQUESNE, Eugene Louis** ................... *sculpture* | | | $1,320 |
| French late 19th cent. | | | |
| ☐ **LERAY, Prudent Louis** ........................ *paintings* | | $935 | $990 |
| French 1820-79 | | | |
| ☐ **LERAY, S.** ......................................... *paintings* | | | $1,045 |
| French 19th cent. | | | |
| ☐ **LERCHE, Vincent Stoltenberg** .............. *paintings* | | | $3,300 |
| Norwegian 1837-1892 | | | |
| ☐ **LERIN, Jean G.** ................................... *paintings* | | | $385 |
| ☐ **LERIUS, Joseph Henri Francois van** ...... *paintings* | | | $1,430 |
| Belgian 1823-1876 | | | |
| ☐ **LEROE, Jean** ...................................... *paintings* | | | $320 |
| ☐ **LEROLLE, Henry** ................................ *paintings* | | $550 | $6,600 |
| French 1848-1929 | | | |
| ☐ **LEROUX, Gaston Veuvenot** .................. *sculpture* | | $1,980 | $5,280 |
| French b. 1854 | | | |
| ☐ **LEROUX, Louis Hector** ........................ *paintings* | | $2,200 | $2,420 |
| French 1829-1900 | | | |
| ☐ **LEROY, Charles** ................................. *paintings* | | | $1,100 |
| French 19th cent. | | | |
| ☐ **LEROY, Jeanette** ................................ *drawings* | | | $990 |
| ☐ **LEROY, Jules** ..................................... *paintings* | | $412 | $6,050 |
| French 1833-1865 | | | |
| ☐ **LEROY DE LIANCOURT, Francois** ..... *drawings* | | | $4,400 |
| French 1741-1835 | | | |
| ☐ **LERSY, Roger** ..................................... *paintings* | | $110 | $521 |
| French b. 1920 | | | |
| ☐ **LERY, G.** ........................................... *sculpture* | | | $412 |
| ☐ **LESIEUR, Pierre** ................................ *paintings* | | | $220 |
| French b. 1920 | | | |

|  | | *Current Price Range* | |
|---|---|---|---|
|  | | *Low* | *High* |
| ☐ **LESIRE, Paulus** ................................ *paintings* | | | **$12,100** |
| 1611-1656 | | | |
| ☐ **LESLEY, B.** ........................................ *paintings* | | | **$424** |
| ☐ **LESLI, R.** ......................................... *paintings* | | | **$880** |
| British 19th cent. | | | |
| ☐ **LESLIE, Alfred** ................................. *paintings* | **$9,900** | **$13,200** |
| American b. 1927 ..................................... *drawings* | **$1,540** | **$3,960** |
| ☐ **LESLIE, Charles** ............................... *paintings* | **$225** | **$1,320** |
| English b. 1840 | | | |
| ☐ **LESLIE, Charles Robert** ....................... *paintings* | **$330** | **$3,630** |
| English 1794-1859 | | | |
| ☐ **LESLIE, George Dunlop** ....................... *paintings* | **$297** | **$4,180** |
| British 1835-1921 | | | |
| ☐ **LESLIE, Robert Charles** ...................... *paintings* | **$220** | **$418** |
| English 19th cent., ac. 1840-1887 | | | |
| ☐ **LESPINASSE, Louis Nicolas de** ............. *drawings* | | **$2,420** |
| ☐ **LESREL, Adolphe Alexandre** ................ *paintings* | **$1,045** | **$7,150** |
| French 1839-1921 | | | |
| ☐ **LESSER-URY** .................................... *paintings* | **$550** | **$20,900** |
| German 1861-1931 ..................................... *drawings* | **$137** | **$10,175** |
| ☐ **LESSI, Giovanni** ............................... *paintings* | | **$3,410** |
| Italian 1852-1922 | | | |
| ☐ **LESSING, Karl Friedrich** ..................... *paintings* | **$6,050** | **$29,700** |
| German 1808-1880 | | | |
| ☐ **LESSORE, Jules** ............................... *drawings* | | **$220** |
| French b. 1892 | | | |
| ☐ **LESSORE, Jules** ............................... *drawings* | | **$16,500** |
| English ac. 1864-1877 | | | |
| ☐ **LESUR, Henri Victor** .......................... *paintings* | **$2,420** | **$9,350** |
| French b. 1863 | | | |
| ☐ **LESZEZYNSKI, M.** ............................. *paintings* | | **$330** |
| ☐ **LETTERINI, Bartolomeo** ...................... *paintings* | | **$275** |
| ☐ **LEU, August Wilhelm** ......................... *paintings* | **$2,750** | **$6,325** |
| German 1819-1897 | | | |
| ☐ **LEU, Oscar** ..................................... *paintings* | | **$1,210** |
| German 1864-1942 | | | |
| ☐ **LEUERS, Jeanette** ............................. *paintings* | | **$1,320** |
| ☐ **LEURS, Jan** .................................... *paintings* | | **$1,540** |
| Dutch 19th cent. | | | |
| ☐ **LEURS, Johannes Karel** ....................... *paintings* | **$550** | **$1,650** |
| Dutch 1865-1938 | | | |
| ☐ **LEUTZE, Emanuel Gottlieb** ................ *paintings* | **$275** | **$5,500** |
| German 1816-1868 ..................................... *drawings* | | **$1,100** |
| ☐ **LEUUS, Jesus** .................................. *paintings* | | **$550** |
| Mexican 20th cent. | | | |
| ☐ **LEUZE-HIRSCHFELD, Emmy** .............. *paintings* | **$2,970** | **$6,050** |
| French b. 1884 | | | |
| ☐ **LEVASSCUR, Jean** ............................. *paintings* | | **$325** |

| | | *Current Price Range* | |
|---|---|---|---|
| | | Low | High |
| ☐ **LEVASSEUR, Henri Louis** .................... *paintings* | | **$1,210** | **$2,090** |
| French b. 1853 | | | |
| ☐ **LEVE, Samuel** ..................................... *drawings* | | | **$330** |
| ☐ **LEVECQ, Jacob** ................................... *paintings* | | | **$1,980** |
| Dutch 1634-1675 | | | |
| ☐ **LEVEE, John** ...................................... *paintings* | | **$88** | **$462** |
| American b. 1924 | | | |
| ☐ **LEVENS, Hy** ...................................... *sculpture* | | | **$1,320** |
| American b. 1922 | | | |
| ☐ **LEVEQUE, Gabriel** ............................. *paintings* | | **$275** | **$4,950** |
| Haitian b. 1923 | | | |
| ☐ **LEVER, Richard Hayley** ...................... *paintings* | | **$150** | **$39,600** |
| American 1876-1958/68 .............................. *drawings* | | **$82** | **$3,740** |
| ☐ **LEVERD, Rene** ................................... *drawings* | | | **$495** |
| French b. 1872 | | | |
| ☐ **LEVERRIER, M.** ................................. *sculpture* | | **$99** | **$1,045** |
| ☐ **LEVESQUE** ....................................... *paintings* | | | **$301** |
| French 19th/20th cent. | | | |
| ☐ **LEVEY, H.** ........................................ *drawings* | | | **$308** |
| ☐ **LEVI, Julian** ..................................... *paintings* | | **$137** | **$1,760** |
| American 1874-1982 .................................. *drawings* | | **$55** | **$880** |
| ☐ **LEVIER, Charles** ............................... *paintings* | | **$55** | **$1,430** |
| American (?) b. 1920 ................................. *drawings* | | | **$220** |
| ☐ **LEVIGNE, Theodore** ........................... *paintings* | | | **$1,430** |
| French 19th cent. | | | |
| ☐ **LEVIN, H.** ........................................ *paintings* | | | **$605** |
| American 19th cent. | | | |
| ☐ **LEVINE, David Philip** ......................... *paintings* | | **$330** | **$352** |
| American b. 1910 ..................................... *drawings* | | **$132** | **$550** |
| ☐ **LEVINE, Edmund D.** ........................... *drawings* | | | **$880** |
| American 20th cent. | | | |
| ☐ **LEVINE, Jack** ..................................... *paintings* | | **$1,300** | **$19,250** |
| American b. 1915 ..................................... *drawings* | | **$165** | **$5,500** |
| ☐ **LEVINE, Marilyn** ............................... *sculpture* | | | **$3,080** |
| American b. 1935 | | | |
| ☐ **LEVINSEN, S.** ................................... *paintings* | | | **$550** |
| French 20th cent. | | | |
| ☐ **LEVIS, D.** ........................................ *paintings* | | | **$550** |
| English 18th cent. | | | |
| ☐ **LEVIS, Maurice** ................................. *paintings* | | **$1,320** | **$11,550** |
| French 1860-after 1927 | | | |
| ☐ **LEVITAN, Isaac Ilyitch** ....................... *paintings* | | **$440** | **$10,450** |
| Lithuanian 1860-1900 ................................ *drawings* | | **$275** | **$440** |
| ☐ **LEVORATI, Ernesto** ........................... *drawings* | | **$220** | **$308** |
| European | | | |
| ☐ **LEVRAC-TOURNIERES, Robert** .......... *paintings* | | **$770** | **$6,600** |
| French 1667/68-1752 | | | |
| ☐ **LEVY, A.** ......................................... *paintings* | | | **$330** |
| French 19th cent. | | | |

| | | Current Price Range | |
|---|---|---|---|
| | | Low | High |
| ☐ **LEVY, Alexander Oscar** ...... *paintings* <br> American 1881-1947 | | $165 | $2,750 |
| ☐ **LEVY, Charles Octave** ...... *sculpture* <br> French | | | $2,310 |
| ☐ **LEVY, Emile** ...... *paintings* <br> French 1826-1890 | | $880 | $5,500 |
| ☐ **LEVY, Fanny** ...... *paintings* | | | $412 |
| ☐ **LEVY, Henri Leopold** ...... *paintings* <br> French 1840-1904 | | | $6,600 |
| ☐ **LEVY, Isidore** ...... *paintings* <br> American b. 1899 | | | $990 |
| ☐ **LEVY, Nat** ...... *drawings* <br> American 20th cent. | | | $357 |
| ☐ **LEVY, William Auerbach** ...... *paintings* <br> American 1889-1964 ...... *drawings* | | $55 | $550 <br> $110 |
| ☐ **LEVY-DHURMER, Lucien** ...... *paintings* <br> French 1865-1953 ...... *drawings* | | $1,210 <br> $88 | $31,900 <br> $11,000 |
| ☐ **LEWALLEN, Donald** ...... *paintings* | | $44 | $385 |
| ☐ **LEWANDOWSKI, Edmund D.** ...... *paintings* <br> American b. 1914 ...... *drawings* | | $1,650 | $2,200 <br> $1,980 |
| ☐ **LEWIN, James Morgan** ...... *paintings* <br> American 1836-1877 | | | $2,200 |
| ☐ **LEWIS, A.H.** ...... *paintings* | | $300 | $385 |
| ☐ **LEWIS, C.H.** ...... *drawings* | | | $700 |
| ☐ **LEWIS, Charles James** ...... *paintings* <br> British 1830-1892 | | $770 | $1,045 |
| ☐ **LEWIS, Edmund Darch** ...... *paintings* <br> American 1835-1910 ...... *drawings* | | $225 <br> $99 | $7,975 <br> $3,850 |
| ☐ **LEWIS, Emerson** ...... *paintings* <br> American b. 1892 ...... *drawings* | | $130 <br> $88 | $440 <br> $330 |
| ☐ **LEWIS, Ernest** ...... *drawings* <br> American (Navajo) | | | $605 |
| ☐ **LEWIS, Frederick Christian** ...... *paintings* <br> English 1779-1856 ...... *drawings* | | $600 <br> $88 | $1,430 <br> $550 |
| ☐ **LEWIS, Geoffrey** ...... *paintings* | | $66 | $357 |
| ☐ **LEWIS, George Jeffrey** ...... *paintings* <br> American 20th cent. | | $192 | $275 |
| ☐ **LEWIS, Henry** ...... *paintings* <br> English/German 1819-1904 | | $660 | $7,700 |
| ☐ **LEWIS, Hugo** ...... *paintings* <br> American 20th cent. | | | $176 |
| ☐ **LEWIS, J.** ...... *paintings* <br> Dutch School early 20th cent. | | | $1,155 |
| ☐ **LEWIS, J. Swing** ...... *paintings* <br> American | | | $192 |
| ☐ **LEWIS, John Frederick** ...... *paintings* <br> English 1805-1876 ...... *drawings* | | $330 <br> $660 | $1,265,000 <br> $5,720 |
| ☐ **LEWIS, L.** ...... *drawings* <br> English | | $275 | $550 |

| | Current Price Range | |
|---|---|---|
| | Low | High |
| ☐ **LEWIS, Martin** ............................... *paintings* | **$7,150** | **$7,975** |
| American 1881/83-1962 ............................ *drawings* | **$5,060** | **$5,280** |
| ☐ **LEWIS, Percy Wyndham** ...................... *drawings* | $110 | $16,500 |
| British 1884-1957 | | |
| ☐ **LEWIS, St. John** ............................... *paintings* | | $660 |
| American 19th cent. | | |
| ☐ **LEWIS, Walter** ................................. *paintings* | $412 | $660 |
| ☐ **LEWIS, William** ............................... *paintings* | $165 | $385 |
| English early 19th cent. | | |
| ☐ **LEWISOHN, Rafael** ............................ *paintings* | | $880 |
| German 1863-1923 | | |
| ☐ **LEWITT, Sol** ..................................... *drawings* | $165 | $2,640 |
| American b. 1928 ..................................... *sculpture* | $6,050 | $18,700 |
| ☐ **LEY, Van D** ..................................... *paintings* | | $1,650 |
| Dutch 19th cent. | | |
| ☐ **LEYDE, Otto** .................................... *drawings* | $209 | $275 |
| ☐ **LEYDEN, Jan van** ............................. *paintings* | | $5,060 |
| Dutch 17th cent. | | |
| ☐ **LEYENDECKER, F.A.** ......................... *paintings* | | $400 |
| ☐ **LEYENDECKER, Frank Xavier** ............ *paintings* | $880 | $5,225 |
| American 1877/78-1924 ............................. *drawings* | $220 | $495 |
| ☐ **LEYENDECKER, Joseph Christian** ....... *paintings* | $550 | $28,600 |
| American 1874-1951 ................................. *drawings* | $308 | $1,320 |
| ☐ **LEYENDECKER, Paul Joseph** .............. *paintings* | $1,540 | $3,300 |
| French b. 1842 | | |
| ☐ **LEYSTER, Judith** .............................. *paintings* | | $74,250 |
| Dutch 1600-1660 | | |
| ☐ **LHARIDON, Octave Penguilly** ............. *drawings* | | $302 |
| ☐ **LHERMITTE, Leon Augustin** .............. *paintings* | $750 | $37,400 |
| French 1844-1925 ..................................... *drawings* | $137 | $13,200 |
| ☐ **LHOTE, Andre** ................................... *paintings* | $1,650 | $55,000 |
| French 1885-1962 ..................................... *drawings* | $120 | $17,000 |
| ☐ **LHUILLIER, Charles Marie** ................ *paintings* | | $715 |
| French 1824-1898 | | |
| ☐ **LIAUTAUD, George** ........................... *sculpture* | $440 | $1,320 |
| Haitian b. 1899 | | |
| ☐ **LIBARDI, G.** .................................... *paintings* | | $220 |
| Spanish 20th cent. | | |
| ☐ **LIBBY, Francis Orville** ....................... *paintings* | $27 | $522 |
| American b. 1884 ..................................... *drawings* | | $275 |
| ☐ **LIBERI, Pietro (called LIBERTINO)** ...... *paintings* | | $2,200 |
| Italian 1614-1687 | | |
| ☐ **LIBERICH, Nicolai Ivanovich** .............. *sculpture* | $1,210 | $1,045 |
| Russian 1828-1883 | | |
| ☐ **LIBERMAN, Alexander** ....................... *paintings* | $82 | $4,400 |
| Russian/American b. 1912 ........................... *drawings* | $55 | $715 |
| ............................................................. *sculpture* | $6,050 | $3,520 |
| ☐ **LIBERTE, Jean** ................................. *paintings* | $99 | $308 |
| American 1895-1965 ................................. *drawings* | | $22 |

| | | *Current Price Range* | |
|---|---|---|---|
| | | *Low* | *High* |
| ☐ **LIBMON, J.** .................................. *paintings* | | | $385 |
| ☐ **LICHT, Hans** .................................. *paintings* | | | $550 |
| German b. 1876 | | | |
| ☐ **LICHTENAUER, Joseph Mortimer** ....... *paintings* | | $66 | $770 |
| American b. 1876 ................................ *drawings* | | | $55 |
| ☐ **LICHTENBERG, M.** ........................ *paintings* | | | $357 |
| American 20th cent. | | | |
| ☐ **LICHTENFELS, Eduard** .................... *paintings* | | | $3,300 |
| ☐ **LICHTENHELD, Wilhelm** .................. *paintings* | | | $825 |
| Austrian 1817-1891 | | | |
| ☐ **LICHTENSTEIN, Roy** ....................... *paintings* | | $3,080 | $522,500 |
| American b. 1923 ................................ *drawings* | | $1,980 | $22,000 |
| .................................................... *sculpture* | | $825 | $151,250 |
| ☐ **LIDDERDALE, Charles Sillem** ............ *paintings* | | $440 | $6,050 |
| English 1831-1895 ............................... *drawings* | | | $770 |
| ☐ **LIE, Jonas** .................................. *paintings* | | $50 | $31,900 |
| American 1880-1940 ............................. *drawings* | | $165 | $330 |
| ☐ **LIE, Robert** ................................. *paintings* | | $165 | $550 |
| American 20th cent. | | | |
| ☐ **LIEBERICH** .................................. *sculpture* | | | $3,025 |
| ☐ **LIEBERMANN, Ernst** ....................... *paintings* | | | $1,980 |
| German b. 1869 | | | |
| ☐ **LIEBERMANN, Max** ......................... *paintings* | | $6,050 | $209,000 |
| German 1847-1935 ............................... *drawings* | | $550 | $4,400 |
| ☐ **LIEBLER, Theodore August** .............. *drawings* | | | $462 |
| ☐ **LIEBMANN, Gerhardt** ...................... *paintings* | | | $330 |
| ☐ **LIEBMANN, Hans Henry** .................. *sculpture* | | | $605 |
| German | | | |
| ☐ **LIEBSCHER, Karl** ........................... *paintings* | | | $770 |
| Polish 1851-1906 | | | |
| ☐ **LIECK, Joseph** .............................. *paintings* | | $1,210 | $4,125 |
| German b. 1849 | | | |
| ☐ **LIEGEOIS, Paul** ............................. *paintings* | | | $11,550 |
| ☐ **LIENARD, E.** ................................ *sculpture* | | | $495 |
| French | | | |
| ☐ **LIENARD, Emile Desire** .................... *paintings* | | | $2,750 |
| French | | | |
| ☐ **LIENARD, Jean Baptiste** ................... *paintings* | | | $1,100 |
| ☐ **LIENDER, Paulus van** .................... *drawings* | | | $1,540 |
| Dutch 1731-1797 | | | |
| ☐ **LIESEGANG, Helmut** ....................... *paintings* | | $2,750 | $3,850 |
| German b. 1858 | | | |
| ☐ **LIESTE, Cornelis** ........................... *paintings* | | | $1,760 |
| Dutch 1817-1861 | | | |
| ☐ **LIEUWEN, L. Von** ........................... *paintings* | | | $605 |
| German 19th cent. | | | |
| ☐ **LIEVENS, Jan** ............................... *paintings* | | $16,500 | $30,800 |
| Dutch 1607-1672/74 | | | |
| ☐ **LIEVIN, Jacques** ............................ *paintings* | | | $1,100 |

| | | Current Price Range | |
|---|---|---|---|
| | | *Low* | *High* |
| ☐ **LIGGETT, A.** ..................................... *paintings* | | | $357 |
| Scottish 19th cent. | | | |
| ☐ **LIGTELIJN, Evert Jan** ....................... *paintings* | | $275 | $990 |
| Dutch 1893-1974 | | | |
| ☐ **LIL, Abraham van** ............................. *paintings* | | | $990 |
| ☐ **LILLEY, Albert E.V.** ........................... *paintings* | | $550 | $2,310 |
| American 19th/20th cent. | | | |
| ☐ **LILLIENDAHL, Johannas** .................... *paintings* | | | $275 |
| Swedish? 19th cent. | | | |
| ☐ **LILO, F. Cocu** ................................... *paintings* | | | $935 |
| Latin American | | | |
| ☐ **LIMBERGER, Gustav** ......................... *paintings* | | | $550 |
| ☐ **LIMBERT, B.** ..................................... *paintings* | | | $247 |
| English 19th cent. | | | |
| ☐ **LIMBORCH, Hendrik van** .................... *paintings* | | | $3,080 |
| Dutch 1681-1759 | | | |
| ☐ **LIMOUSIN** ........................................ *sculpture* | | $154 | $264 |
| ☐ **LINCOLN, Ephram F.** ......................... *paintings* | | $800 | $3,200 |
| American 18th/19th cent. | | | |
| ☐ **LINDE, Jan van der** ........................... *paintings* | | $220 | $385 |
| Dutch 1864-1945 ..................................... *drawings* | | | $715 |
| ☐ **LINDE, Johan van der** ........................ *paintings* | | | $1,210 |
| ☐ **LINDE, Ossip** .................................... *paintings* | | | $352 |
| ☐ **LINDENMUTH, A.M.** ......................... *paintings* | | $90 | $231 |
| American 20th cent. | | | |
| ☐ **LINDENMUTH, Tod** ........................... *paintings* | | $385 | $660 |
| American b. 1885 | | | |
| ☐ **LINDENSCHMIT, Wilhelm von** ........... *paintings* | | | $3,575 |
| German 1829-1895 | | | |
| ☐ **LINDER, Franz** ................................. *paintings* | | | $1,870 |
| German 1738-1809 | | | |
| ☐ **LINDER, Henry** ................................ *paintings* | | $165 | $220 |
| American 1854-1910 | | | |
| ☐ **LINDER, Lambert** ............................. *paintings* | | $3,300 | $5,280 |
| German 1841-1889 | | | |
| ☐ **LINDER, Philippe Jacques** .................. *paintings* | | $4,125 | $13,200 |
| French ac. 1857-1880 | | | |
| ☐ **LINDERUM, Richard** ......................... *paintings* | | $495 | $10,450 |
| German b. 1851 | | | |
| ☐ **LINDHOLM, Berndt** ......................... *paintings* | | | $467 |
| ☐ **LINDHOLM, W.** ................................ *paintings* | | | $410 |
| American 19th cent. | | | |
| ☐ **LINDLAR, Johann Wilhelm** ................. *paintings* | | | $2,090 |
| German 1816-1896 | | | |
| ☐ **LINDNER, Richard** ............................. *paintings* | | $660 | $330,000 |
| German/American 1901-1978 ........................ *drawings* | | $770 | $28,600 |
| ☐ **LINDNEUX, Robert** ............................ *paintings* | | $110 | $385 |
| American 20th cent. | | | |
| ☐ **LINDO, Francis** ................................. *paintings* | | | $440 |

| | | Current Price Range | |
|---|---|---|---|
| | | Low | High |
| ☐ **LINDON** ............................................ *paintings* | | | $600 |
| American early 20th cent. | | | |
| ☐ **LINDSAY, Thomas Corwin** ................. *paintings* | | $352 | $935 |
| American 1845-1907 | | | |
| ☐ **LINDSTROM, Bengt** ............................ *paintings* | | | $880 |
| ☐ **LINES, H. H.** ...................................... *paintings* | | | $880 |
| ☐ **LINFORD, Charles** ............................. *paintings* | | $412 | $1,760 |
| American 1846-1897 | | | |
| ☐ **LING, Paul** ....................................... *paintings* | | | $3,575 |
| Dutch 19th cent. | | | |
| ☐ **LINGELBACH, Johannes** ..................... *paintings* | | $33,000 | $56,000 |
| Dutch c. 1622-1674 ................................. *drawings* | | | $132 |
| ☐ **LINGNER, Otto Theodore Gustav** ......... *paintings* | | | $2,090 |
| German b. 1856 | | | |
| ☐ **LINK, Carl** ...................................... *drawings* | | | $1,760 |
| ☐ **LINKE, Paul Rudolf** ........................... *paintings* | | | $2,420 |
| ☐ **LINN, Steven** ................................... *sculpture* | | | $550 |
| ☐ **LINNARD, John** ................................. *paintings* | | | $350 |
| English 19th cent. | | | |
| ☐ **LINNELL, John** ................................. *paintings* | | $440 | $27,500 |
| English 1792-1882 ...................................... *drawings* | | $385 | $440 |
| ☐ **LINNELL, William** ............................. *paintings* | | | $2,860 |
| British 1826-1910 | | | |
| ☐ **LINNIG, Egidius** ................................ *paintings* | | $2,640 | $4,400 |
| Flemish 1821-1860 | | | |
| ☐ **LINNIG, J.** ....................................... *paintings* | | | $2,530 |
| Belgian 19th cent. | | | |
| ☐ **LINNIG, Willem** ................................ *paintings* | | | $4,400 |
| Belgian 1819-1885 | | | |
| ☐ **LINON, G. Felix** ................................ *paintings* | | | $600 |
| ☐ **LINSON, Corwin Knapp** ...................... *paintings* | | $242 | $1,870 |
| American b. 1864 | | | |
| ☐ **LINT, Hendrik Frans van** | | | |
| **(called Studio)** ..................................... *paintings* | | $1,320 | $41,800 |
| Flemish 1684-1763 | | | |
| ☐ **LINT, Peter van** ............................... *paintings* | | $2,750 | $4,950 |
| Flemish 1609-1690 | | | |
| ☐ **LINTHORST, Jacobus Johannes** ........... *paintings* | | $11,000 | $66,000 |
| Dutch 1745-1815 | | | |
| ☐ **LINTON, Frank Benton Ashley** ............. *paintings* | | $330 | $605 |
| American 1871-1943 | | | |
| ☐ **LINTON, Sir James Dromgole** .............. *drawings* | | | $308 |
| English 1840-1916 | | | |
| ☐ **LINTON, William** ................................ *paintings* | | | $4,675 |
| British 1791-1876 | | | |
| ☐ **LINTOTT, Edward Barnard** ................. *paintings* | | $55 | $467 |
| American 1875-1951 ................................... *drawings* | | $209 | $357 |
| ☐ **LION, Alexander Louis** ........................ *paintings* | | | $7,150 |
| Belgian 1823-1842 | | | |

| | | Current Price Range | |
|---|---|---|---|
| | | Low | High |
| ☐ **LION, Flora** .......................................... *paintings* | | $137 | $1,650 |
| British 19th/20th cent. | | | |
| ☐ **LION, Herman** ................................... *paintings* | | | $275 |
| English 19th cent. | | | |
| ☐ **LIPCHITZ, Jacques** ........................... *drawings* | | $330 | $19,800 |
| French 1891-1973 ...................................... *sculpture* | | $1,430 | $192,500 |
| ☐ **LIPPERT, Leon** ..................................... *paintings* | | $81 | $176 |
| French 19th/20th cent. | | | |
| ☐ **LIPPI, Filippo (called Filippino)** ............. *paintings* | | $6,600 | $44,000 |
| Italian 1457-1504 | | | |
| ☐ **LIPPINCOTT, William Henry** ............... *paintings* | | $357 | $15,400 |
| American 1849-1920 ................................... *drawings* | | | $242 |
| ☐ **LIPPO DI BENIVIENI** ........................ *paintings* | | | $71,500 |
| Italian 14th cent. | | | |
| ☐ **LIPSCHITZ, Samuel** ........................... *sculpture* | | | $275 |
| ☐ **LIPSCHUTZ, S.** ................................... *sculpture* | | | $1,760 |
| ☐ **LIPTON, Seymour** ............................. *sculpture* | | $2,090 | $2,640 |
| American b. 1903 | | | |
| ☐ **LIRA, Benjamin** ................................ *drawings* | | | $1,980 |
| b. Chile 1950 | | | |
| ☐ **LIRIANO, Louis** .................................. *paintings* | | | $300 |
| ☐ **LIS, Jan** ............................................... *paintings* | | | $1,430 |
| Dutch c. 1595-1629 | | | |
| ☐ **LISI, de** ................................................ *paintings* | | | $275 |
| Italian 19th cent. | | | |
| ☐ **LISIO, Arnaldo de** ............................... *drawings* | | $247 | $385 |
| Italian 19th cent. | | | |
| ☐ **LISKA, Hans** ....................................... *paintings* | | | $1,650 |
| German 20th cent. | | | |
| ☐ **LISMER, Arthur** ................................. *paintings* | | | $8,250 |
| Canadian 1885-1911 | | | |
| ☐ **LISSE, Dirck van der** ........................... *paintings* | | $2,750 | $5,280 |
| Dutch d. 1669 | | | |
| ☐ **LISSITZKY, El** ..................................... *drawings* | | | $825 |
| Russian b. 1890 | | | |
| ☐ **LITHGOW, David C.** ............................ *paintings* | | $110 | $660 |
| American | | | |
| ☐ **LITKE, Theodor** ................................... *sculpture* | | | $423 |
| German 1847-1902 | | | |
| ☐ **LITLE, Arthur** ..................................... *paintings* | | | $3,740 |
| American 20th cent. | | | |
| ☐ **LITSCHAUER, Karl Joseph** ............... *paintings* | | $660 | $1,100 |
| Austrian 1830-1871 | | | |
| ☐ **LITTLE, A.P.** ....................................... *paintings* | | | $275 |
| American 19th cent. | | | |
| ☐ **LITTLE, John Wesley** ........................... *paintings* | | $550 | $3,850 |
| American 1867-1923 ................................... *drawings* | | $100 | $302 |
| ☐ **LITTLE, Nathaniel Stanton** ................... *paintings* | | $2,090 | $3,000 |
| American b. 1893 | | | |

|  | | *Current Price Range* | |
| --- | --- | --- | --- |
|  | | Low | High |
| ☐ **LITTLE, Philip** | *paintings* | $605 | $8,800 |
| American 1857-1942 | *drawings* | $93 | $660 |
| ☐ **LITTLEFIELD, William Horace** | *paintings* | $11 | $247 |
| American b. 1902 | *drawings* | | $50 |
| ☐ **LIVEMONT, Privat** | *paintings* | | $330 |
| Belgian 1861-1936 | *drawings* | | $880 |
| ☐ **LIVENS, Henry** | *paintings* | $286 | $1,760 |
| British 1860-1885 | | | |
| ☐ **LIVENS, Horace Mann** | *paintings* | $330 | $1,980 |
| British b. 1862 | | | |
| ☐ **LIVERMORE, F.D.** | *paintings* | | $286 |
| | *drawings* | | $55 |
| ☐ **LIVESI, P.** | *drawings* | | $1,100 |
| ☐ **LIVINGS, H.** | *paintings* | | $550 |
| English 19th cent. | | | |
| ☐ **LIVINGSTON, N.C.** | *paintings* | | $300 |
| Scottish 19th cent. | | | |
| ☐ **LIZCANO Y ESTEBAN, Angel** | *paintings* | $4,675 | $9,900 |
| Spanish 1846-1929 | | | |
| ☐ **LLINAS, Guido** | *paintings* | $440 | $660 |
| b. Cuba 1930 | | | |
| ☐ **LLONA, Ramiro** | *drawings* | | $1,320 |
| Peruvian b. 1947 | | | |
| ☐ **LLOPIS, Carlos Ruano** | *paintings* | $770 | $1,980 |
| Mexican 20th cent. | | | |
| ☐ **LLOR-OS, F.** | *paintings* | | $467 |
| 20th cent. | | | |
| ☐ **LLORENS Y DAIZ, Francisco** | *paintings* | | $715 |
| ☐ **LLOYD, Cora** | *paintings* | | $275 |
| American ac. 1870-1880 | | | |
| ☐ **LLOYD, Edward** | *paintings* | $2,090 | $2,200 |
| British ac. 1866 | | | |
| ☐ **LLOYD, Henry** | *paintings* | | $330 |
| ☐ **LLOYD, Robert Malcolm** | *drawings* | | $220 |
| English ac. 1879-1900 | | | |
| ☐ **LLOYD, Sara** | *paintings* | | $880 |
| American 20th cent. | | | |
| ☐ **LLOYD, T. Ivester** | *paintings* | $770 | $5,500 |
| British 19th cent. | | | |
| ☐ **LLOYD, Thomas James** | *drawings* | $440 | $660 |
| English 1849-1910 | | | |
| ☐ **LLOYD, W. Stuart** | *paintings* | $550 | $1,870 |
| English ac. 1875-1929 | *drawings* | | $260 |
| ☐ **LLOYDS, F.** | *paintings* | | $3,520 |
| English ac. 1855 | | | |
| ☐ **LLULL, Jose Pinelo** | *paintings* | $3,300 | $4,125 |
| Spanish 1861-1922 | | | |
| ☐ **LOBO, Balthazar** | *sculpture* | | $935 |

| | Current Price Range | |
|---|---|---|
| | Low | High |
| ☐ **LOBRE, Maurice** .............................. *paintings* | $275 | $29,700 |
| French 1862-1951 | | |
| ☐ **LOBRICHON, Timoleon Marie** ............. *paintings* | | $9,350 |
| French 1831-1914 | | |
| ☐ **LOCATELLI, Andrea** ......................... *paintings* | $4,400 | $9,900 |
| Italian 1693-1741 | | |
| ☐ **LOCHER, Carl** ................................. *paintings* | $1,540 | $1,760 |
| Danish 1851-1915 | | |
| ☐ **LOCHRIE, Elizabeth Davey** ................. *paintings* | | $605 |
| American b. 1890 | | |
| ☐ **LOCK, F.W.** ..................................... *drawings* | | $1,100 |
| ☐ **LOCKE, C.H.** .................................. *paintings* | | $385 |
| ☐ **LOCKHART, David** ............................ *drawings* | | $192 |
| American 20th cent. | | |
| ☐ **LOCKHEAD, John** ............................ *paintings* | | $750 |
| British b. 1866 | | |
| ☐ **LOCKHORST, Dirk Pieter van** ............. *paintings* | | $550 |
| Dutch b. 1860 | | |
| ☐ **LOCKWOOD, John Ward** .................... *drawings* | $176 | $935 |
| American | | |
| ☐ **LOCKWOOD, Robert Wilton** ............... *paintings* | | $385 |
| American 1861-1914 | | |
| ☐ **LODATO, Peter** ................................. *paintings* | | $550 |
| American b. 1946 | | |
| ☐ **LODER, Edwin (of Bath)** ...................... *paintings* | | $3,800 |
| ☐ **LODER, James (of Bath)** ....................... *paintings* | $2,860 | $7,150 |
| English ac. 1820-1857 | | |
| ☐ **LODGE, George Edward** ..................... *paintings* | | $2,200 |
| English 1860-1954 .................................... *drawings* | $605 | $1,760 |
| ☐ **LODI, A.** .......................................... *paintings* | | $220 |
| Italian 19th cent. | | |
| ☐ **LODI, Gaetano** ................................. *paintings* | | $440 |
| ☐ **LOEB, Louis** ..................................... *paintings* | $154 | $4,125 |
| American 1866-1909 | | |
| ☐ **LOEBERS, Adrian** .............................. *paintings* | | $495 |
| ☐ **LOEFF, Jacob Gerritsz.** ....................... *paintings* | | $11,000 |
| ☐ **LOEMANS, Alexander F.** .................... *paintings* | $605 | $1,760 |
| American 19th cent. | | |
| ☐ **LOEW, Charles E.** ............................. *paintings* | | $412 |
| American 20th cent. | | |
| ☐ **LOEW, Michael** ................................. *paintings* | $275 | $495 |
| American b. 1907 | | |
| ☐ **LOFFLER, August** ............................. *paintings* | $935 | $1,870 |
| German 1822-18666 | | |
| ☐ **LOFFLER, Berthold** ........................... *paintings* | | $37,400 |
| Austrian 1874-1960 | | |
| ☐ **LOFFLER, Franz Karl** ......................... *drawings* | | $550 |
| ☐ **LOFFTZ, Ludwig von** ........................... *paintings* | | $1,760 |
| German 1845-1910 | | |

|  | | | *Current Price Range* | |
|---|---|---|---|---|
|  | | | Low | High |
| ☐ **LOFTEN, Richard** | *paintings* | | | $302 |
| American 20th cent. | | | | |
| ☐ **LOGAN, Leonard** | *sculpture* | | | $495 |
| American 20th cent. | | | | |
| ☐ **LOGAN, Maurice** | *paintings* | | $770 | $1,320 |
| American 1886-1977 | *drawings* | | $220 | $880 |
| ☐ **LOGAN, Robert Fulton** | *paintings* | | $880 | $1,320 |
| American b. 1889 | | | | |
| ☐ **LOGAN, Robert H.** | *paintings* | | $770 | $4,400 |
| American 1874-1942 | | | | |
| ☐ **LOGSDAIL, William** | *paintings* | | | $2,500 |
| English | | | | |
| ☐ **LOHR, August** | *paintings* | | $5,500 | $24,200 |
| German 19th cent. | *drawings* | | $1,210 | $4,400 |
| ☐ **LOHR, Emil Ludwig** | *paintings* | | | $4,400 |
| German 1809-1876 | | | | |
| ☐ **LOHR, Hugo** | *paintings* | | | $1,100 |
| 19th cent. | *drawings* | | | $90 |
| ☐ **LOIR, Luigi** | *paintings* | | $385 | $33,000 |
| French 1845-1916 | *drawings* | | $247 | $16,500 |
| ☐ **LOIR, Marianne** | *paintings* | | | $6,050 |
| French b.c. 1715 | | | | |
| ☐ **LOIRE, Leon** | *paintings* | | $770 | $2,420 |
| French 1821-1898 | | | | |
| ☐ **LOISEAU, Gustave** | *paintings* | | $605 | $48,400 |
| French 1865-1935 | *drawings* | | | $1,320 |
| ☐ **LOKHORST, Dirk von** | *paintings* | | $605 | $5,500 |
| Dutch 1818-1893 | | | | |
| ☐ **LOMAN, Joseph S.** | *paintings* | | | $302 |
| English 20th cent. | | | | |
| ☐ **LOMAX, C.A.** | *paintings* | | | $715 |
| ☐ **LONAT, M.** | *paintings* | | | $687 |
| French | | | | |
| ☐ **LONDONIO, Francesco** | *drawings* | | | $2,200 |
| Italian 1723-1783 | | | | |
| ☐ **LONE WOLF** | *drawings* | | $1,100 | $11,500 |
| American 1882-1970 | | | | |
| ☐ **LONG, Clara Hayward de** | *paintings* | | | $220 |
| American 19th cent. | | | | |
| ☐ **LONG, Edwin** | *paintings* | | | $1,650 |
| English 1829-1891 | | | | |
| ☐ **LONG, Stanley** | *drawings* | | $220 | $770 |
| American 1892-1972 | | | | |
| ☐ **LONGACRE, Lydia** | *paintings* | | $15 | $715 |
| American b. 1870 | | | | |
| ☐ **LONGANESI, R.** | *paintings* | | | $450 |
| Italian b. 1922 | | | | |
| ☐ **LONGFELLOW, Mark K.** | *drawings* | | | $605 |
| American 19th cent. | | | | |

| | | Current Price Range | |
|---|---|---|---|
| | | *Low* | *High* |
| ☐ **LONGHI, Alessandro** ............. *paintings* | | | $14,300 |
| Italian 1733-1813 | | | |
| ☐ **LONGHI, Barbara** ............. *paintings* | | $1,650 | $7,700 |
| Italian 1552-1638 | | | |
| ☐ **LONGHI, Luca** | | | |
| **(called Raphael de Ravenna)** ......... *paintings* | | $550 | $4,950 |
| Italian 1507-1580 | | | |
| ☐ **LONGHI, Pietro** ................. *paintings* | | | $1,650 |
| Italian 1702-1785 | | | |
| ☐ **LONGI** ................. *paintings* | | | $1,870 |
| Italian 20th cent. | | | |
| ☐ **LONGMAN, Evelyn Beatrice** ......... *sculpture* | | | $4,620 |
| American | | | |
| ☐ **LONGMORE, Ken** ............. *drawings* | | | $600 |
| American | | | |
| ☐ **LONGO, Robert** ............. *drawings* | | $440 | $2,090 |
| American b. 1923 ................. *sculpture* | | | $6,380 |
| ☐ **LONGPRE, Paul de** ............. *paintings* | | $715 | $12,100 |
| French/American 1855-1911 ......... *drawings* | | $275 | $2,860 |
| ☐ **LONGPRE, Raoul de** ............. *paintings* | | | $1,980 |
| French/American 19th/20th cent. ......... *drawings* | | $242 | $2,420 |
| ☐ **LONGSTAFF, John** ............. *paintings* | | | $550 |
| Australian 1862-1941 | | | |
| ☐ **LONGSTAFFE, Edgar** ............. *paintings* | | $715 | $770 |
| English 1849-1912 | | | |
| ☐ **LONGSTAFFE, Ernest** ............. *paintings* | | $385 | $1,540 |
| English 19th cent. | | | |
| ☐ **LONSDALE, James** ............. *paintings* | | | $1,980 |
| English 1777-1839 | | | |
| ☐ **LOO, Charles Andre** | | | |
| **(called Carle van LOO)** ............. *paintings* | | $5,500 | $25,300 |
| French 1705-1765 ................. *drawings* | | $2,860 | $6,160 |
| ☐ **LOO, Jacob van** ............. *paintings* | | | $4,950 |
| Dutch 1614-1670 | | | |
| ☐ **LOO, Jean Baptiste van** ......... *paintings* | | $1,980 | $6,050 |
| French 1684-1745 | | | |
| ☐ **LOO, Louis Michael van** ......... *paintings* | | $11,000 | $74,250 |
| French 1707-1771 | | | |
| ☐ **LOO, Pieter van** ............. *drawings* | | $2,750 | $4,125 |
| Dutch 1731-1784 | | | |
| ☐ **LOO, Pieter van** ............. *drawings* | | | $1,650 |
| Flemish 1600-1660 | | | |
| ☐ **LOOMIS, Andrew** ............. *paintings* | | | $1,650 |
| American 1892-1959 | | | |
| ☐ **LOOMIS, Charles Russell** ......... *paintings* | | $110 | $440 |
| American d. 1883 ................. *drawings* | | $33 | $357 |
| ☐ **LOOMIS, Chester R.** ............. *paintings* | | $192 | $1,430 |
| American 1852-1924 ................. *drawings* | | $82 | $137 |
| ☐ **LOOMIS, Jessie Parrott** ......... *drawings* | | | $286 |

| | | Current Price Range | |
| --- | --- | :---: | :---: |
| | | *Low* | *High* |
| ☐ **LOOMIS, Manchus C.** ........................ *paintings* | | $22 | $247 |
| American 20th cent. | | | |
| ☐ **LOOMIS, Osbert Burr** ...................... *paintings* | | | $550 |
| ☐ **LOON, Henrick Willen van** .................. *drawings* | | | $264 |
| ☐ **LOOP, Henry Augustus** ...................... *paintings* | | $220 | $462 |
| American 1831-1895 | | | |
| ☐ **LOOP, Jennie S.** ............................... *paintings* | | $191 | $550 |
| American 1840-1909 | | | |
| ☐ **LOOS, Henry** ..................................... *paintings* | | | $2,475 |
| Belgian 19th/20th cent. | | | |
| ☐ **LOOS, John** ...................................... *paintings* | | | $7,425 |
| ☐ **LOOSBROEK, J.P. van** ...................... *paintings* | | | $1,100 |
| ☐ **LOOSE, Basile de** .............................. *paintings* | | $3,850 | $16,500 |
| Dutch 1809-1885 | | | |
| ☐ **LOPEZ, Angel Chavez** ....................... *paintings* | | | $440 |
| b. Peru 1929 | | | |
| ☐ **LOPEZ, Carlos** ................................. *paintings* | | $110 | $968 |
| American 20th cent. | | | |
| ☐ **LOPEZ, Gasparo** | | | |
| **(called Gasparo Di Fiori)** ...................... *paintings* | | $4,400 | $11,000 |
| ☐ **LOPEZ Y MARTINEZ, Enrique** ........... *paintings* | | | $8,800 |
| Spanish 1853-75 | | | |
| ☐ **LOPEZ-LOZA, Luis** ........................... *paintings* | | | $1,100 |
| Latin American ......................................... *drawings* | | | $990 |
| ☐ **LORD, Elyse** .................................... *drawings* | | | $605 |
| ☐ **LORDBECK, H.A.** ............................. *paintings* | | | $605 |
| ☐ **LOREDO, T. Aceves** ........................... *paintings* | | | $2,090 |
| Spanish | | | |
| ☐ **LOREIN, A.** ...................................... *paintings* | | | $412 |
| European 20th cent. | | | |
| ☐ **LOREN, Richard** ............................... *paintings* | | | $7,700 |
| ☐ **LORENTZ, Pauline** ............................ *paintings* | | | $220 |
| American 20th cent. | | | |
| ☐ **LORENZ, A.** ..................................... *paintings* | | | $1,540 |
| ☐ **LORENZ, Carl** .................................. *paintings* | | | $495 |
| Austrian b. 1871 | | | |
| ☐ **LORENZ, Gottfried** ............................ *paintings* | | | $935 |
| German 19th cent. | | | |
| ☐ **LORENZ, Richard** ............................. *paintings* | | $192 | $28,600 |
| German/American 1858-1915 | | | |
| ☐ **LORENZL, Josef** ............................... *sculpture* | | $176 | $3,520 |
| Australian early 20th cent. | | | |
| ☐ **LORI, K.** ......................................... *drawings* | | | $2,970 |
| ☐ **LORIA, Vincenzo** .............................. *paintings* | | $242 | $8,800 |
| Italian b. 1850 ......................................... *drawings* | | $320 | $1,870 |
| ☐ **LORIMER, John Henry** ....................... *paintings* | | | $6,325 |
| British 1856-1936 | | | |
| ☐ **LORIMIER, Guillemette de** .................. *paintings* | | | $467 |

| | | Current Price Range | |
|---|---|---|---|
| | | Low | High |
| ☐ **LORING, Francis William** ...... *paintings* | | $330 | $660 |
| American 1838-1905 | | | |
| ☐ **LORING, J.A.** ...... *paintings* | | | $275 |
| American 19th cent. | | | |
| ☐ **LORING, V.** ...... *drawings* | | | $250 |
| ☐ **LORINO** ...... *sculpture* | | | $1,045 |
| French early 20th cent. | | | |
| ☐ **LORIOSE, C.** ...... *paintings* | | | $412 |
| ☐ **LORJOU, Bernard** ...... *paintings* | | $100 | $2,860 |
| French b. 1908 ...... *drawings* | | $110 | $1,540 |
| ☐ **LORME, Antonie de** ...... *paintings* | | $1,210 | $6,050 |
| ☐ **LORMIER** ...... *sculpture* | | | $308 |
| ☐ **LORRAIN, Claude (Claude GELEE)** ...... *drawings* | | $4,400 | $4,400 |
| French 1600-1682 | | | |
| ☐ **LORRAIN, Rene** ...... *paintings* | | | $275 |
| ☐ **LORTET, Leberecht** ...... *paintings* | | | $1,320 |
| French 1818-1901 | | | |
| ☐ **LOS, M. Wodzimierz** ...... *paintings* | | | $19,800 |
| 19th cent. | | | |
| ☐ **LOSE, Johann Jacob Joseph de** ...... *paintings* | | | $3,410 |
| German ac. 1755-1813 | | | |
| ☐ **LOSSOW, Heinrich** ...... *paintings* | | $220 | $450 |
| German 1843-1897 | | | |
| ☐ **LOTH, Jan Carl** ...... *paintings* | | | $4,400 |
| German 1632-1698 | | | |
| ☐ **LOTH, Johann Ulrich** ...... *paintings* | | | $2,200 |
| ☐ **LOTT, E.** ...... *paintings* | | | $605 |
| Dutch 19th cent. | | | |
| ☐ **LOTT, F.T.** ...... *paintings* | | | $605 |
| ☐ **LOTT, W.** ...... *drawings* | | | $550 |
| ☐ **LOTTEL, A.** ...... *paintings* | | | $605 |
| German 19th cent. | | | |
| ☐ **LOTZ, Matilda** ...... *paintings* | | $467 | $660 |
| American 19th cent. | | | |
| ☐ **LOTZE, Moritz Eduard** ...... *paintings* | | | $1,320 |
| German 1809-1890 | | | |
| ☐ **LOUCHET, Charles** ...... *sculpture* | | | $1,760 |
| ☐ **LOUDERBACK, Walt** ...... *paintings* | | $140 | $1,760 |
| American 1887-1941 ...... *drawings* | | | $825 |
| ☐ **LOUGHEED, Robert Elmer** ...... *paintings* | | $1,210 | $100,000 |
| American b. 1910 ...... *drawings* | | $1,870 | $27,500 |
| ☐ **LOUIS, Morris** ...... *paintings* | | $33,000 | $473,000 |
| American 1912-1962 | | | |
| ☐ **LOUND, Thomas** ...... *drawings* | | $495 | $522 |
| English 1802-1861 | | | |
| ☐ **LOUTCHANSKI, Jacques** ...... *sculpture* | | | $385 |
| French b. 1876 | | | |
| ☐ **LOUTHER, Charles Drange** ...... *paintings* | | | $632 |
| Canadian 19th/20th cent. | | | |

| | | Current Price Range | |
|---|---|---|---|
| | | Low | High |
| ☐ **LOUTHERBOURG, Philipp Jakob de** ... *paintings* | | $385 | $15,400 |
| French 1740-1812 ..................................... *drawings* | | | $1,210 |
| ☐ **LOUTTER, E.R.** ................................. *paintings* | | | $3,250 |
| ☐ **LOUYOT, Edmond** ............................ *paintings* | | $880 | $6,600 |
| German b. 1861 | | | |
| ☐ **LOVATTI, A.** ...................................... *paintings* | | | $770 |
| ☐ **LOVATTI, E.A.** .................................. *drawings* | | | $330 |
| ☐ **LOVATTI, Matteo** ........................... *paintings* | | | $2,420 |
| Italian b. 1861 | | | |
| ☐ **LOVE, Jim** ....................................... *sculpture* | | $7,150 | $7,700 |
| American b. 1927 | | | |
| ☐ **LOVE, Joseph C.** .............................. *paintings* | | $300 | $4,675 |
| American 19th cent. | | | |
| ☐ **LOVEBRIDGE, Charles** ....................... *paintings* | | | $357 |
| American 19th cent. | | | |
| ☐ **LOVEJOY, Rupert** ............................ *paintings* | | | $770 |
| American 20th cent. | | | |
| ☐ **LOVELL, Katherine** ........................... *paintings* | | $495 | $500 |
| American c. 1877-c. 1955 | | | |
| ☐ **LOVELL, Tom** ................................... *paintings* | | $935 | $100,000 |
| American b. 1909 ...................................... *drawings* | | $10,000 | $25,000 |
| ☐ **LOVEN, Frank W.** ............................. *paintings* | | $242 | $3,080 |
| American 1869-1941 ................................ *drawings* | | $330 | $352 |
| ☐ **LOVER, Samuel** ................................ *paintings* | | | $2,310 |
| Irish 1797-1868 | | | |
| ☐ **LOVERIDGE, Clinton** ........................ *paintings* | | $231 | $1,760 |
| American 1824-1902 | | | |
| ☐ **LOVET-LORSKI, Boris** ....................... *sculpture* | | $2,200 | $66,000 |
| Lithuanian/American 1894-1973 | | | |
| ☐ **LOVING, Alvin** ............................... *paintings* | | $302 | $935 |
| American b. 1935 ...................................... *drawings* | | $412 | $825 |
| ☐ **LOW, Gilman** ................................... *paintings* | | $385 | $1,210 |
| American 19th/20th cent. | | | |
| ☐ **LOW, Mary Fairchild** ........................ *paintings* | | | $687 |
| American 20th cent. | | | |
| ☐ **LOW, Will Hicok** .............................. *paintings* | | $1,320 | $4,500 |
| American 1853-1932 ................................ *drawings* | | $308 | $385 |
| ☐ **LOWE, Eugenia** ............................... *paintings* | | | $275 |
| American | | | |
| ☐ **LOWELL, Milton H.** .......................... *paintings* | | $192 | $1,000 |
| American 1848-1927 ................................ *drawings* | | | $330 |
| ☐ **LOWELL, Orson** ............................... *paintings* | | $220 | $2,640 |
| American 1871-1956 ................................ *drawings* | | $25 | $1,045 |
| ☐ **LOWENHEIM, F.** ............................... *paintings* | | $110 | $770 |
| American | | | |
| ☐ **LOWENSOHN, Julius** ......................... *paintings* | | | $1,430 |
| German 1820-1890 | | | |
| ☐ **LOWENTHAL, Julia H.** ....................... *paintings* | | $192 | $357 |

| | | Current Price Range | |
|---|---|---|---|
| | | Low | High |
| ☐ **LOWES, H.C.** ........................ *paintings* | | | $412 |
| American 19th cent. | | | |
| ☐ **LOWITH, Wilhelm** ..................... *paintings* | | $1,210 | $6,050 |
| Austrian b. 1861 | | | |
| ☐ **LOWNES, Anna** ...................... *paintings* | | | $2,090 |
| American 19th cent. | | | |
| ☐ **LOWNING, M.** ........................ *paintings* | | | $220 |
| American 19th cent. | | | |
| ☐ **LOWRY, H.U.** ........................ *drawings* | | | $308 |
| ☐ **LOWRY, William J.** .................. *paintings* | | | $450 |
| American 19th cent. | | | |
| ☐ **LOXATTI, E. Auguste** ............... *paintings* | | | $220 |
| Italian b. 1816 | | | |
| ☐ **LOYE, Charles Auguste** | | | |
| **(called MONTBARD)** ............... *drawings* | | | $352 |
| French 1841-1905 | | | |
| ☐ **LOYSEN, D. P.** ...................... *paintings* | | | $500 |
| American 19th/20th cent. | | | |
| ☐ **LOZANO, Lazaro** .................... *paintings* | | $165 | $275 |
| Portuguese b. 1906 | | | |
| ☐ **LOZOWICK, Louis** ................... *paintings* | | | $7,700 |
| American | | | |
| ☐ **LU-MING, T'Ang** .................... *drawings* | | | $605 |
| ☐ **LUBBERS, Holger Peter Svane** ....... *paintings* | | $110 | $2,310 |
| Danish b. 1850 | | | |
| ☐ **LUBER, M.** ......................... *paintings* | | | $660 |
| ☐ **LUBIN, C.** ......................... *paintings* | | | $385 |
| ☐ **LUBIN, Jules** ...................... *paintings* | | | $550 |
| ☐ **LUCA, F. de** ....................... *sculpture* | | $2,310 | $2,365 |
| Italian School | | | |
| ☐ **LUCA, G. de** ....................... *drawings* | | | $440 |
| Italian 19th/20th cent. | | | |
| ☐ **LUCARDI, P.** ....................... *paintings* | | | $440 |
| Italian 19th/20th cent. | | | |
| ☐ **LUCAS, Albert Durer** ............... *drawings* | | | $935 |
| British b. 1828, fl. 1859-1910 | | | |
| ☐ **LUCAS, Albert Pike** ................ *paintings* | | $990 | $8,800 |
| American 1862-1945 | | | |
| ☐ **LUCAS, Edward George Handel** ....... *paintings* | | | $3,850 |
| British 1863-1936 | | | |
| ☐ **LUCAS, George** ..................... *paintings* | | | $660 |
| British 19th cent. | | | |
| ☐ **LUCAS, Henry Frederick Lucas** ...... *paintings* | | $660 | $38,500 |
| British d. 1943 | | | |
| ☐ **LUCAS, John Seymour** ............... *paintings* | | | $495 |
| British 1849-1923 | | | |
| ☐ **LUCAS, John Templeton** ............. *paintings* | | $220 | $550 |
| English 1836-1880 | | | |

| | | *Current Price Range* | |
|---|---|---|---|
| | | Low | High |
| ☐ **LUCAS, Marie Felix Hippolyte** ............. *paintings* French 1854-1925 | | | $8,800 |
| ☐ **LUCAS, William** ................................... *paintings* | | | $660 |
| ☐ **LUCAS Y PADILLA, Eugenio** ............. *paintings* Spanish 1824-1870 ..................................... *drawings* | | $2,200 | $20,900 $385 |
| ☐ **LUCAS Y VILLAMIL, Eugenio** ............ *paintings* Spanish 19th cent. | | | $2,640 |
| ☐ **LUCAS-ROBIQUET, Marie Aimee** ........ *paintings* French b. 1864 | | | $3,190 |
| ☐ **LUCCHESE** ....................................... *sculpture* | | | $880 |
| ☐ **LUCCHESI, Bruno** ............................. *drawings* Italian/American b. 1926 ............................ *sculpture* | | $467 | $165 $6,050 |
| ☐ **LUCE, L.W.** ...................................... *paintings* ................................................................ *drawings* | | | $302 $165 |
| ☐ **LUCE, Marie Huxford** ....................... *drawings* American 19th cent. | | | $225 |
| ☐ **LUCE, Maximilien** ............................ *paintings* French 1858-1941 ...................................... *drawings* | | $440 $275 | $39,600 $6,600 |
| ☐ **LUCE, Molly** ................................... *paintings* American b. 1896 | | | $330 |
| ☐ **LUCE, Percival de** ............................ *paintings* American 1847-1914 | | $250 | $605 |
| ☐ **LUCEBERT, Jean** .............................. *paintings* contemporary | | $1,980 | $8,800 |
| ☐ **LUCIANO, Galeotti** ........................... *sculpture* | | | $302 |
| ☐ **LUCIANO, Spazzali** ........................... *paintings* ................................................................ *drawings* | | | $274 $110 |
| ☐ **LUCIONI, Luigi** ............................... *paintings* Italian/American b. 1900 | | $495 | $7,250 |
| ☐ **LUCKHARDT, K.** ............................. *paintings* German b. 1886 | | $726 | $880 |
| ☐ **LUCOP, Thomas** ............................... *paintings* British 19th cent. | | $450 | $1,100 |
| ☐ **LUCS, L.W.** ..................................... *paintings* | | | $440 |
| ☐ **LUDLOW, Hal** .................................. *paintings* British b. 1861 | | | $302 |
| ☐ **LUDOVIC-RODO, (Rodo PISSARRO)** ............................. *paintings* French 1878-1952 | | $385 | $2,200 |
| ☐ **LUDOVICI, Albert** ............................. *paintings* British 1820-1894 | | | $220 |
| ☐ **LUDOVICI, Albert (Jr.)** ...................... *paintings* English 1852-1932 | | | $660 |
| ☐ **LUDWIG, Auguste** ............................. *paintings* German b. 1834 | | | $9,350 |
| ☐ **LUEDERS** ........................................ *paintings* American 20th cent. | | | $385 |
| ☐ **LUEGER, Michael** ............................. *paintings* German 1804-1883 | | | $1,430 |

|                                          |           | Current Price Range |            |
|------------------------------------------|-----------|---------------------|------------|
|                                          |           | Low                 | High       |
| ☐ **LUGERTH, Ferdinand** ............. *sculpture* | $412                | $1,650     |
| Austrian early 20th cent.                |           |                     |            |
| ☐ **LUGO, Emil** .............................. *paintings* | $2,090              | $7,700     |
| German 1840-1902                         |           |                     |            |
| ☐ **LUHRIG, Otto** ............................ *paintings* |                     | $3,300     |
| ☐ **LUIGARD, F.** ............................. *paintings* |                     | $577       |
| French 20th cent.                        |           |                     |            |
| ☐ **LUIGINI, Ferdinand Jean** ............ *paintings* | $192                | $220       |
| French b. 1870                           |           |                     |            |
| ☐ **LUINI, Aurelio** .......................... *drawings* |                     | $825       |
| ☐ **LUKA, Madeleine** ...................... *paintings* | $165                | $2,310     |
| French 20th cent.                        |           |                     |            |
| ☐ **LUKE, Samuel** ........................... *paintings* |                     | $302       |
| French 19th cent.                        |           |                     |            |
| ☐ **LUKER, William** ......................... *paintings* |                     | $880       |
| British ac. 1852-1889                    |           |                     |            |
| ☐ **LUKIN, Sven** ............................. *paintings* |                     | $550       |
| Latvian b. 1934                          |           |                     |            |
| ☐ **LUKITS, Theodore Nikolai** .......... *paintings* |                     | $935       |
| American ac. 1934                        |           |                     |            |
| ☐ **LUKS, George Benjamin** ............ *paintings* | $605                | $258,500   |
| American 1867-1933                .......... *drawings* | $77                 | $6,325     |
| ☐ **LUMINAIS, Evariste Vital** ........... *paintings* | $121                | $220       |
| French 1822-1896                         |           |                     |            |
| ☐ **LUMIS, Harriet Randall** ............ *paintings* | $2,200              | $20,900    |
| American 1870-1953                       |           |                     |            |
| ☐ **LUMLEY, Arthur** ........................ *paintings* |                     | $275       |
| ☐ **LUN, E. Cole** ............................ *paintings* |                     | $330       |
| late 19th cent.                          |           |                     |            |
| ☐ **LUNA, Antonio Rodriguez** .......... *paintings* |                     | $1,540     |
| Mexican b. 1910 ........................... *drawings* |                     | $1,760     |
| ☐ **LUNA, Mariano** ........................ *drawings* | $1,100              | $2,640     |
| Italian 19th cent.                       |           |                     |            |
| ☐ **LUND, David** ............................ *drawings* | $44                 | $220       |
| American b. 1925                         |           |                     |            |
| ☐ **LUND, Frederick Christian** ......... *paintings* |                     | $3,520     |
| Dutch 1826-1901                          |           |                     |            |
| ☐ **LUND, Hal** ............................... *sculpture* |                     | $950       |
| ☐ **LUND, Johan Ludwig** ................ *paintings* |                     | $275       |
| German 1777-1867                         |           |                     |            |
| ☐ **LUND, Niels Moller** ................... *paintings* |                     | $2,090     |
| British 1863-1916                        |           |                     |            |
| ☐ **LUND, T.** ................................. *paintings* |                     | $330       |
| European 19th cent.                      |           |                     |            |
| ☐ **LUNDBERG, August F.** ............. *paintings* | $55                 | $39,600    |
| American 1878-1928                       |           |                     |            |
| ☐ **LUNDE, Raymond** ...................... *paintings* |                     | $1,100     |
| ☐ **LUNDEAN, J. Louis** ................... *paintings* | $220                | $1,650     |
| American 20th cent.                      |           |                     |            |

| | | *Current Price Range* | |
|---|---|---|---|
| | | *Low* | *High* |
| ☐ **LUNDEBERG, Helen** ........................... *paintings* | | | **$240** |
| American b. 1908 | | | |
| ☐ **LUNDEGARD, Justus** ........................ *paintings* | | **$440** | **$605** |
| Swedish 1860-1924 | | | |
| ☐ **LUNDENS, Gerrit** ............................. *paintings* | | **$1,650** | **$38,500** |
| Dutch 1622-1677 | | | |
| ☐ **LUNDMARK, Leon** ........................... *paintings* | | **$220** | **$660** |
| American 20th cent. | | | |
| ☐ **LUNDY, (or LEANDY)** ....................... *paintings* | | | **$450** |
| ☐ **LUNGE, Jeffrey** ............................... *drawings* | | **$165** | **$192** |
| American 20th cent. | | | |
| ☐ **LUNGREN, Fernand Harvey** ............... *paintings* | | | **$3,960** |
| American 1857/59-1932 .............................. *drawings* | | | **$1,430** |
| ☐ **LUNIAR, Jan Amigger** ........................ *paintings* | | | **$385** |
| Dutch late 19th cent. | | | |
| ☐ **LUNTESCHUTZ, Jules** ....................... *paintings* | | | **$462** |
| ☐ **LUNY, Thomas** ................................. *paintings* | | **$687** | **$68,200** |
| English 1759-1837 | | | |
| ☐ **LUONGO, Aldo** ................................. *paintings* | | | **$2,750** |
| Argentinian b. 1940 | | | |
| ☐ **LUONI, Romolo** ................................ *paintings* | | | **$1,045** |
| Italian 20th cent. | | | |
| ☐ **LUPO** ............................................. *paintings* | | | **$495** |
| ☐ **LUPTON, Nevil Oliver** ........................ *paintings* | | | **$1,100** |
| British b. 1828 | | | |
| ☐ **LURCAT, Andre** ............................... *paintings* | | | **$1,980** |
| ☐ **LURCAT, Jean** ................................. *paintings* | | **$137** | **$1,980** |
| French 1892-1966 .................................... *drawings* | | **$220** | **$880** |
| ☐ **LURIE, Nan** ..................................... *paintings* | | | **$466** |
| American 20th cent. | | | |
| ☐ **LUSINI, Marco** ................................. *paintings* | | | **$550** |
| ☐ **LUSTOU** ......................................... *paintings* | | | **$385** |
| ☐ **LUSTY, Otto** ................................... *paintings* | | | **$1,870** |
| German 20th cent. | | | |
| ☐ **LUTTEROLL, A.** ............................... *paintings* | | | **$1,650** |
| ☐ **LUTTEROTH, Ascan** ......................... *paintings* | | | **$3,300** |
| German 1842-1923 | | | |
| ☐ **LUTTICH, Mila von** ........................... *drawings* | | | **$550** |
| ☐ **LUTTICHUYS, Simon** ......................... *paintings* | | **$4,180** | **$14,850** |
| Dutch 1610-1662 | | | |
| ☐ **LUTTICUYS, Issac** ............................. *paintings* | | | **$2,860** |
| ☐ **LUTYENS, Charles Augustus Henry** ..... *paintings* | | | **$935** |
| ☐ **LUTZ, Dan** ..................................... *paintings* | | **$44** | **$770** |
| American 1906-1978 | | | |
| ☐ **LUTZ, L.** ......................................... *paintings* | | **$110** | **$247** |
| German/Austrian 19th cent. | | | |
| ☐ **LUTZENS** ....................................... *paintings* | | | **$385** |
| French School early 20th cent. | | | |

|                                                              | Current Price Range | |
|                                                              | Low | High |
|--------------------------------------------------------------|---------|---------|
| ☐ **LUYCX, Franz** .................................... *paintings* | | **$3,190** |
| Flemish 1604-1668 | | |
| ☐ **LUYTIES, Jan van** ............................. *paintings* | | **$350** |
| Dutch/American | | |
| ☐ **LUZZI, Ceto L.** .................................... *paintings* | | **$1,210** |
| ☐ **LUZZO, A.** .................................... *drawings* | | **$550** |
| ☐ **LYBAERT, Theophile Marie Francois** ... *paintings* | | **$825** |
| Belgian b. 1848 | | |
| ☐ **LYDIS, Mariette** ............................. *paintings* | **$1,045** | **$1,650** |
| ☐ **LYMAN, H.R.** .................................... *drawings* | | **$302** |
| ☐ **LYMAN, Joseph** ............................. *paintings* | **$550** | **$2,200** |
| American 1843-1913 | | |
| ☐ **LYNCH, Albert** ............................. *paintings* | **$495** | **$7,975** |
| Peruvian b. 1851,ac. Paris 1930 | | |
| ☐ **LYNDE, R.** .................................... *paintings* | | **$1,980** |
| ☐ **LYNDON (?), P.H.** ............................. *paintings* | | **$990** |
| English 19th cent. | | |
| ☐ **LYNE, Michael** ............................. *paintings* | **$1,600** | **$3,025** |
| English b. 1912 ......................................... *drawings* | | **$44** |
| ☐ **LYNN, David** .................................... *paintings* | | **$302** |
| American 20th cent. | | |
| ☐ **LYNTON, H.S.** .................................... *drawings* | **$81** | **$3,300** |
| 19th cent. | | |
| ☐ **LYON, David** .................................... *paintings* | | **$5,500** |
| English ac. c. 1774 | | |
| ☐ **LYON, Dustin** .................................... *drawings* | | **$250** |
| American | | |
| ☐ **LYONNEL, A.** .................................... *paintings* | | **$411** |
| American 19th/20th cent. | | |
| ☐ **LYRE, Adolphe la** ............................. *paintings* | | **$1,760** |
| French b. 1850 | | |
| ☐ **LYS, Jan van der** ............................. *paintings* | | **$1,100** |
| Belgian 19th cent. | | |
| ☐ **MAANEN, Ivan** .................................... *paintings* | | **$800** |
| ☐ **MAAR, Carl Ritter von** ........................ *paintings* | | **$715** |
| German 1858-1936 | | |
| ☐ **MAAR, Dora** .................................... *paintings* | **$110** | **$330** |
| French 20th cent. | | |
| ☐ **MAAREL, Marinus van der** ................. *paintings* | **$99** | **$521** |
| Dutch 1857-1921 | | |
| ☐ **MAAS, Aert van** ............................. *paintings* | | **$8,800** |
| Dutch c. 1620-1664 | | |
| ☐ **MAAS, Henry** .................................... *drawings* | | **$247** |
| Dutch 20th cent. | | |
| ☐ **MAAS, Johannes (the younger)** .............. *paintings* | | **$12,100** |
| Dutch 17th cent. | | |
| ☐ **MAAS, Lorenz Johann** ........................ *drawings* | | **$192** |
| German 1845-1882 | | |

|                                                                 | Current Price Range |          |
|                                                                 | Low      | High     |
|-----------------------------------------------------------------|----------|----------|
| ☐ **MABE, Manabu** .................................. *paintings* | **$1,320** | **$11,000** |
| Brazilian b. 1924 in Japan ........................... *drawings* |          | **$1,650** |
| ☐ **MABRY, Jane** ...................................... *drawings* |          | **$275** |
| ☐ **MACAULEY** ...................................... *drawings*  |          | **$825** |
| ☐ **MACAULIFFE, J.J.** ........................... *paintings*   |          | **$3,850** |
| American 1848-1921                                              |          |          |
| ☐ **MACAUSLAN, Helen** .......................... *paintings*   |          | **$191** |
| American 20th cent.                                            |          |          |
| ☐ **MACBETH, Robert Walker** .................. *drawings*      | **$1,650** | **$2,255** |
| English 1848-1910                                              |          |          |
| ☐ **MACCAMERON, Robert Lee** ............... *paintings*        | **$2,310** | **$11,000** |
| American 1866-1912                                             |          |          |
| ☐ **MACCARI, Mino** ............................... *paintings*  |          | **$528** |
| Italian b. 1898                                                |          |          |
| ☐ **MACCIO, Romulo** ............................ *paintings*    |          | **$1,540** |
| Argentinian b. 1931                                            |          |          |
| ☐ **MACCO, Georg** .................................. *drawings* |          | **$1,760** |
| German b. 1863                                                 |          |          |
| ☐ **MACCONNEL, Kim** ........................... *paintings*     | **$10,450** | **$13,200** |
| contemporary                                                   |          |          |
| ☐ **MACCORD, Charles William** .............. *paintings*        |          | **$600** |
| American 1852-1923                                             |          |          |
| ☐ **MACCORD, Mary Nicholena** ............... *paintings*        | **$1,210** | **$6,050** |
| American 20th cent.                                            |          |          |
| ☐ **MACCORMAC, A.** ............................. *paintings*    |          | **$220** |
| Scottish 19th cent.                                            |          |          |
| ☐ **MACCULLUM, H.** ............................. *paintings*    |          | **$330** |
| ☐ **MACDONALD, Grant** .......................... *paintings*    | **$6,200** | **$7,250** |
| American                                                       |          |          |
| ☐ **MACDONALD, James Edward Hervey** .. *paintings*             | **$3,850** | **$60,500** |
| Canadian 1873-1932                                             |          |          |
| ☐ **MACDONALD, Julian** ........................ *paintings*     |          | **$1,100** |
| ☐ **MACDONALD, Kevin** ......................... *drawings*      |          | **$412** |
| ☐ **MACDONALD, Manly E.** ..................... *paintings*      |          | **$880** |
| Canadian 20th cent.                                            |          |          |
| ☐ **MACDONALD, Murray** ....................... *drawings*       |          | **$176** |
| Scottish 19th cent.                                            |          |          |
| ☐ **MACDONALD, W.A.** .......................... *paintings*     |          | **$462** |
| ☐ **MACDONALD-WRIGHT, Stanton** ........ *paintings*           | **$3,850** | **$22,000** |
| American 1890-1973 ................................. *drawings*  | **$660**  | **$5,500** |
| ☐ **MACDONALL, Angus** ......................... *paintings*     |          | **$330** |
| ☐ **MACDONNELL, James** ....................... *paintings*      |          | **$330** |
| Irish d. 1911                                                  |          |          |
| ☐ **MACENTYRE, Eduardo** ...................... *paintings*      | **$880**  | **$1,980** |
| Argentinian b. 1929                                           |          |          |
| ☐ **MACEWEN, Walter** ........................... *paintings*    | **$192**  | **$7,150** |
| American 1860-1943 ................................. *drawings*  |          | **$522** |
| ☐ **MACGEORGE, William Stewart** ........... *paintings*        |          | **$5,500** |
| British 1861-1931                                             |          |          |

|                                                      | Current Price Range | |
|------------------------------------------------------|---------|-----------|
|                                                      | Low     | High      |
| ☐ **MACGILVARY, Norwood Hodge** .......... *paintings* |         | $2,750    |
| American b. 1874                                     |         |           |
| ☐ **MACGINNIS, Henry R.** ....................... *paintings* |   | $2,420    |
| American 1874-1962                                   |         |           |
| ☐ **MACGOWAN, J.P.** ............................ *paintings* |   | $660      |
| Canadian 19th cent.                                  |         |           |
| ☐ **MACGREGOR, J.C.** ........................... *paintings* |   | $1,100    |
| ☐ **MACHADO, A.G.** .............................. *paintings* | $160 | $474    |
| Azorean 20th cent.                                   |         |           |
| ☐ **MACHARD, Jules Louis** ....................... *paintings* |   | $467      |
| French 1839-1900 ..................................... *drawings* |   | $5,500 |
| ☐ **MACHEIL, Ambrose** .......................... *paintings* |   | $357      |
| Italian (?) 19th/20th cent.                          |         |           |
| ☐ **MACHEN, William Henry** ................... *paintings* | $100 | $1,870   |
| American 1832-1911                                   |         |           |
| ☐ **MACHERA, J.** .................................. *paintings* |   | $4,180  |
| ☐ **MACHESNEY, Clara Taggart** .............. *paintings* |   | $440      |
| American b. 1860                                     |         |           |
| ☐ **MACHU** ....................................... *paintings* | $136 | $356     |
| ☐ **MACINNIS, Charles** .......................... *paintings* |   | $605      |
| American 19th cent.                                  |         |           |
| ☐ **MACIVER, Loren** ............................. *paintings* | $4,400 | $11,000 |
| American b. 1909 .................................... *drawings* |   | $660   |
| ☐ **MACK, Bernhard Karl** ........................ *paintings* |   | $550      |
| German 19th cent.                                    |         |           |
| ☐ **MACK, Mark** ................................. *drawings* |   | $660      |
| ☐ **MACKAY, H.** .................................. *paintings* | $385 | $440    |
| British exhib. 1902-1906                             |         |           |
| ☐ **MACKAY, Thomas** ............................ *paintings* |   | $385      |
| ☐ **MACKAY, William Darling** ................. *paintings* |   | $385      |
| Scottish b. 1854                                     |         |           |
| ☐ **MACKE, August** ............................. *paintings* |   | $49,500   |
| German 1887-1914 ..................................... *drawings* | $1,430 | $2,400 |
| ☐ **MACKELLER, Duncan** ....................... *paintings* |   | $880      |
| Scottish 1849-1908                                   |         |           |
| ☐ **MACKENDRICK, Lilian** ..................... *paintings* | $1,300 | $2,000   |
| American b. 1906                                     |         |           |
| ☐ **MACKENZIE, Daniel** .......................... *paintings* |   | $1,540    |
| British 19th cent.                                   |         |           |
| ☐ **MACKENZIE, Frank J.** ....................... *paintings* |   | $495      |
| English/American 1865/67-1939                        |         |           |
| ☐ **MACKENZIE, Frederick** ................... *drawings* |   | $275      |
| Scottish c. 1787-1854                                |         |           |
| ☐ **MACKENZIE, P.** ............................... *paintings* |   | $1,320  |
| ☐ **MACKEPRANG, Adolf** ........................ *paintings* |   | $3,850    |
| Danish 1833-1911                                     |         |           |
| ☐ **MACKINNON, Mary** ......................... *drawings* |   | $301      |
| ☐ **MACKINTOSH, Alice E.** ..................... *paintings* | $462 | $605     |
| Scottish 19th cent.                                  |         |           |

| | | *Current Price Range* | |
|---|---|---|---|
| | | *Low* | *High* |
| ☐ **MACKNIGHT, Dodge** ............... *drawings* | | $192 | $1,760 |
| American 1860-1950 | | | |
| ☐ **MACLEARY, Bonnie** ............. *sculpture* | | | $605 |
| American 20th cent. | | | |
| ☐ **MACLEOD, Jessie** ............. *paintings* | | | $357 |
| ☐ **MACLEOD, William** ............. *paintings* | | | $4,400 |
| American ac. 1848-1864 | | | |
| ☐ **MACLET, Elisee** ............. *paintings* | | $330 | $4,950 |
| French 1881-1962 ............. *drawings* | | $192 | $1,100 |
| ☐ **MACMAHON, John** ............. *paintings* | | | $660 |
| ............. *drawings* | | | $110 |
| ☐ **MACMONNIES, Frederick William** ...... *drawings* | | | $9,350 |
| American 1863-1937 ............. *sculpture* | | $660 | $19,800 |
| ☐ **MACMONNIES, Mary Fairchild** ........... *paintings* | | | $17,600 |
| American 19th cent. | | | |
| ☐ **MACMULDROW, Edith** ............. *paintings* | | | $880 |
| British 19th cent. | | | |
| ☐ **MACNAB, Madame Marie** ............. *paintings* | | | $2,100 |
| French 1832-1911 | | | |
| ☐ **MACNEE, Robert Russell** ............. *paintings* | | | $687 |
| ☐ **MACNEIL, Hermon Atkins** ............. *sculpture* | | $1,650 | $60,500 |
| American 1866-1947 | | | |
| ☐ **MACNEIL, Carol Brooks** ............. *sculpture* | | | $935 |
| American 1871-1944 | | | |
| ☐ **MACOMBER, Mary Lizzie** ............. *paintings* | | $500 | $9,350 |
| American 1861-1916 | | | |
| ☐ **MACPHEARSON, John** ............. *paintings* | | | $1,100 |
| British ac. 1865-1884 ............. *drawings* | | | $330 |
| ☐ **MACRAE, Elmer Livingston** ............. *paintings* | | $220 | $27,500 |
| American 1875-1955 ............. *drawings* | | $275 | $522 |
| ☐ **MACRAE, Emma Fordyce** ............. *paintings* | | | $2,090 |
| American 1887-1974 | | | |
| ☐ **MACRUM, George Herbert** ............. *paintings* | | $522 | $715 |
| b. 1888 | | | |
| ☐ **MACS, Yon** ............. *paintings* | | | $3,190 |
| ☐ **MACWHINNIE, John** ............. *paintings* | | | $3,520 |
| ☐ **MACWHIRTER, Agnes Eliza** ............. *drawings* | | | $192 |
| American (?) 19th/20th cent. | | | |
| ☐ **MACWHIRTER, John** ............. *paintings* | | | $220 |
| British 1839-1911 | | | |
| ☐ **MACY, Wendell Ferdinand** ............. *paintings* | | $132 | $1,300 |
| American 19th cent. | | | |
| ☐ **MACY, William Starbuck** ............. *paintings* | | $1,210 | $5,225 |
| American 1853-1916 | | | |
| ☐ **MADDERSTEG, Michael** ............. *paintings* | | $6,600 | $12,650 |
| Dutch 1659-1709 | | | |
| ☐ **MADELAIN, Gustave** ............. *paintings* | | $605 | $3,300 |
| French 1867-1944 | | | |
| ☐ **MADELINE, Paul** ............. *paintings* | | | $4,070 |

|  | | Current Price Range | |
|---|---|---|---|
|  | | Low | High |
| ☐ **MADER, Louis** .................................... *paintings* | | **$11,000** | **$26,400** |
| 1842-after 1892 | | | |
| ☐ **MADIOL, Adrien Jean** ........................ *paintings* | | **$1,320** | **$2,200** |
| Dutch 1845-1892 | | | |
| ☐ **MADIOL, Jakob** .................................... *paintings* | | | **$990** |
| ☐ **MADOU, Jean Baptiste** ........................ *paintings* | | **$3,080** | **$4,620** |
| Belgian 1796-1877 ...................................... *drawings* | | | **$800** |
| ☐ **MADRASSI, Luca** ............................... *paintings* | | **$2,310** | **$3,960** |
| Italian 19th cent. | | | |
| ☐ **MADRAZO, Don Federigo de** .............. *paintings* | | | **$1,650** |
| Spanish 1815-1894 | | | |
| ☐ **MADRAZO, Federico de** ....................... *paintings* | | | **$5,500** |
| Spanish 1874-1935 | | | |
| ☐ **MADRAZO Y GARRETA,** | | | |
| **Raimundo de** ...................................... *paintings* | | **$2,750** | **$23,100** |
| Spanish 1841-1920 | | | |
| ☐ **MADRID, Simones** ............................... *paintings* | | | **$330** |
| ☐ **MADROZO Y GARRETA, Ricardo de** .. *drawings* | | | **$220** |
| Spanish 1852-1917 | | | |
| ☐ **MADRUGO, M.J.** ................................. *paintings* | | | **$300** |
| Azorean 20th cent. | | | |
| ☐ **MAENTEL, Jacob** ............................... *paintings* | | | **$467** |
| German/American 1763-1863 ......................... *drawings* | | **$1,100** | **$15,400** |
| ☐ **MAEROUKA** ....................................... *paintings* | | | **$660** |
| ☐ **MAES, Dirk** ....................................... *drawings* | | | **$660** |
| Dutch 1659-1717 | | | |
| ☐ **MAES, Eugene Remy** ........................... *paintings* | | **$2,475** | **$5,610** |
| Belgian 1849-1912 | | | |
| ☐ **MAES, H.** .......................................... *paintings* | | | **$660** |
| ☐ **MAES, Nicolaes** .................................. *paintings* | | **$3,300** | **$12,100** |
| Dutch 1632/34-1693 .................................... *drawings* | | **$1,045** | **$9,625** |
| ☐ **MAES, T.** .......................................... *paintings* | | | **$467** |
| Continental School 19th cent. | | | |
| ☐ **MAESTOSI, F.** .................................... *paintings* | | | **$3,520** |
| ☐ **MAESTRI, Michaelangelo** ..................... *drawings* | | | **$286** |
| Italian d. 1812 | | | |
| ☐ **MAFFEI, Francesco** ............................ *paintings* | | | **$17,600** |
| Italian c. 1600/20-1660 | | | |
| ☐ **MAGALHAES, Aloisio** ......................... *paintings* | | | **$1,430** |
| Brazilian b. 1927 | | | |
| ☐ **MAGANZA, Alessandro** ........................ *drawings* | | | **$5,280** |
| Italian 1556-1630 | | | |
| ☐ **MAGARE, Masayuki** ........................... *sculpture* | | | **$1,650** |
| contemporary | | | |
| ☐ **MAGDISH, Dennis** ............................... *paintings* | | **$220** | **$632** |
| ☐ **MAGEE, J.C.** ..................................... *paintings* | | **$275** | **$286** |
| American 20th cent. ..................................... *drawings* | | | **$110** |
| ☐ **MAGEE, James C.** ............................... *paintings* | | | **$4,675** |
| American 1846-1924 .................................... *drawings* | | | **$44** |

| | Current Price Range | |
|---|---|---|
| | Low | High |
| ☐ **MAGES** ............................................ *paintings* | | **$6,600** |
| ☐ **MAGGIORANI, Luigi** ......................... *drawings*<br>Italian 19th cent. | | **$192** |
| ☐ **MAGGIOTTO, Domenico** ..................... *paintings*<br>Italian 1713-1794 | | **$13,200** |
| ☐ **MAGGS, John Charles** ........................ *paintings*<br>English 1819-1895 | **$1,500** | **$20,000** |
| ☐ **MAGINN** ........................................... *paintings* | | **$440** |
| ☐ **MAGLAI, R.** ...................................... *paintings*<br>Hungarian 20th cent. | | **$3,300** |
| ☐ **MAGLIANO** ....................................... *sculpture* | | **$1,100** |
| ☐ **MAGNASCO, Alessandro**<br>**(called LISSANDRINO or IL**<br>**LISSANDRO)** ...................................... *paintings*<br>Italian 1667-1749 | **$13,200** | **$15,400** |
| ☐ **MAGNAVACCA, Ubaldo** ...................... *paintings*<br>Italian 20th cent. | **$77** | **$220** |
| ☐ **MAGNE, D.** ....................................... *paintings* | | **$385** |
| ☐ **MAGNELLI, Alberto** ........................... *paintings*<br>Italian 1888-1971 .................................... *drawings* | | **$6,050**<br>**$7,425** |
| ☐ **MAGNI, Giuseppe** ............................... *paintings*<br>Italian b. 1869 | **$2,420** | **$12,650** |
| ☐ **MAGNUS, Camille** .............................. *paintings*<br>French 19th cent. | **$198** | **$2,860** |
| ☐ **MAGRATH, William** ........................... *paintings*<br>Irish 1838-1918 | **$385** | **$1,540** |
| ☐ **MAGRITTE, Rene** ............................... *paintings*<br>Belgian 1898-1967 ................................... *drawings* | **$8,250**<br>**$330** | **$418,000**<br>**$82,500** |
| ☐ **MAGUET** .......................................... *sculpture* | | **$800** |
| ☐ **MAGUNA, A.** ..................................... *drawings*<br>German 19th/20th cent. | | **$357** |
| ☐ **MAHAFFEY, Noel** ............................... *paintings*<br>American b. 1944 | **$1,000** | **$11,000** |
| ☐ **MAHLER, Anna** .................................. *sculpture* | | **$385** |
| ☐ **MAHLERS (?), W.** ............................... *paintings*<br>English 19th cent. | | **$187** |
| ☐ **MAHLKNECHT, Edmund** ..................... *paintings*<br>Austrian 1820-1903 | | **$8,250** |
| ☐ **MAHONEY, Joella Jean** ....................... *paintings* | | **$1,430** |
| ☐ **MAIDMENT, Henry** ............................. *paintings*<br>British 19th/20th cent. | **$330** | **$1,870** |
| ☐ **MAIER** ............................................. *paintings* | | **$770** |
| ☐ **MAIGNAN, R.** .................................... *paintings*<br>Latin American | | **$1,320** |
| ☐ **MAIGNTONIA** .................................... *paintings*<br>Italian early 20th cent. | **$220** | **$302** |
| ☐ **MAILLARD, Emile** .............................. *paintings*<br>French b. 1846; ac. 1884-1893 | **$462** | **$495** |
| ☐ **MAILLART, Diogene** ............................ *drawings*<br>French 1840-1926 | | **$302** |

| | | Current Price Range | |
|---|---|---|---|
| | | Low | High |
| ☐ **MAILLAUD, Fernand** ............ *drawings* | | | $1,155 |
| French 1863-1948 | | | |
| ☐ **MAILLOL, Aristide** ............ *drawings* | | $825 | $38,500 |
| French 1861-1944 ............ *sculpture* | | $1,045 | $1,100,000 |
| ☐ **MAILLOT, Victoria** ............ *paintings* | | | $1,045 |
| American 20th cent. | | | |
| ☐ **MAIN, William** ............ *paintings* | | | $357 |
| English 19th cent. | | | |
| ☐ **MAINCENT, Gustave** ............ *paintings* | | | $1,210 |
| European | | | |
| ☐ **MAINELLA, Raffaele** ............ *paintings* | | | $467 |
| Italian b. 1858 ............ *drawings* | | $220 | $2,860 |
| ☐ **MAINER, Le** ............ *paintings* | | | $308 |
| ☐ **MAINO, Juan Bautista** ............ *paintings* | | | $12,000 |
| Spanish c. 1569-1649 | | | |
| ☐ **MAIORANO** ............ *paintings* | | | $440 |
| Italian 19th cent. | | | |
| ☐ **MAIRE, Andri** ............ *drawings* | | | $275 |
| ☐ **MAISIAT, Joanny** ............ *paintings* | | $192 | $275 |
| French b. 1824 | | | |
| ☐ **MAJEWICZ, George** ............ *paintings* | | $1,045 | $1,870 |
| ☐ **MAJOR, B.** ............ *paintings* | | $192 | $495 |
| American 19th/20th cent. | | | |
| ☐ **MAJOR, Ernest Lee** ............ *paintings* | | $715 | $3,080 |
| American 1864-1950 ............ *drawings* | | $165 | $191 |
| ☐ **MAKART, Hans** ............ *paintings* | | $9,075 | $79,750 |
| Austrian 1840-1884 ............ *drawings* | | | $121 |
| ☐ **MAKIELSKI, Leon A.** ............ *paintings* | | | $176 |
| American b. 1885 | | | |
| ☐ **MAKIN, T.K.** ............ *paintings* | | | $412 |
| British 19th cent. | | | |
| ☐ **MAKLOTH, Johann** ............ *paintings* | | | $1,100 |
| ☐ **MAKO, B.** ............ *paintings* | | $770 | $1,045 |
| American b. 1890 | | | |
| ☐ **MAKOHJKIU, Kaupo H.** ............ *paintings* | | | $880 |
| ☐ **MAKOVSKY, Constantin** ............ *paintings* | | $385 | $77,000 |
| Russian 1839-1915 | | | |
| ☐ **MAKOVSKY, Nikolai** ............ *paintings* | | | $3,410 |
| Russian 1842-1886 | | | |
| ☐ **MAKOVSKY, Vladimir** ............ *paintings* | | $110 | $1,320 |
| Russian 1846-1920 | | | |
| ☐ **MAKOWSKI, Zbigniew (IV)** ............ *paintings* | | | $330 |
| Poland b. 1930 | | | |
| ☐ **MALACREA, Francesco** ............ *paintings* | | | $1,017 |
| Italian 1812-1886 | | | |
| ☐ **MALAINE, Joseph Laurent** ............ *paintings* | | | $11,000 |
| French 1745-1809 | | | |
| ☐ **MALASSIS, Edmond** ............ *drawings* | | | $825 |

| | | Current Price Range | |
|---|---|---|---|
| | | Low | High |

| | | | Low | High |
|---|---|---|---|---|
| ☐ **MALATESTA, Narciso** ......................... *paintings* | | | | $2,750 |
| Italian b. 1835 | | | | |
| ☐ **MALBET, Aurelie Leontine** .................. *paintings* | | | | $330 |
| Austrian 19th cent. | | | | |
| ☐ **MALBON, William** ............................. *paintings* | | | | $495 |
| British b. 1850 | | | | |
| ☐ **MALBRANCHE** .................................. *paintings* | | | | $374 |
| ☐ **MALDAGUE, Augusta** ........................ *paintings* | | | | $192 |
| Belgian 1893-1965 | | | | |
| ☐ **MALDONADO, Estuardo** ..................... *drawings* | | | | $330 |
| Latin American | | | | |
| ☐ **MALECKI, Wladislaw** .......................... *paintings* | | | | $3,190 |
| Polish 1836-1900 | | | | |
| ☐ **MALET, Albert** .................................. *paintings* | | | | $880 |
| French b. 1902 | | | | |
| ☐ **MALEVITCH, Kasimir** ........................ *drawings* | | | $440 | $6,600 |
| Russian 1878-1935 | | | | |
| ☐ **MALFILATRE, Mademoiselle Lucie** ...... *paintings* | | | | $220 |
| French b. 1871 | | | | |
| ☐ **MALFROY, Charles** ............................ *paintings* | | | | $990 |
| French b. 1862 | | | | |
| ☐ **MALFROY, Henry** .............................. *paintings* | | | $495 | $1,650 |
| French b. 1895 | | | | |
| ☐ **MALHERBE, William** ......................... *paintings* | | | $357 | $5,500 |
| French 19th/20th cent. | | | | |
| ☐ **MALI, Christian Friedrich** ................... *paintings* | | | $11,000 | $17,050 |
| German 1832-1906 | | | | |
| ☐ **MALIAVINE, Philippe** ......................... *paintings* | | | | $990 |
| Russian 1869-1939 ..................................... *drawings* | | | $275 | $750 |
| ☐ **MALISSARD, Georges** ......................... *sculpture* | | | $1,650 | $3,025 |
| French b. 1877 | | | | |
| ☐ **MALLEBRANCHE, Louis Claude** | | | | |
| **(or MALBRANCHE)** ............................. *paintings* | | | $770 | $3,850 |
| French 1790-1838 | | | | |
| ☐ **MALLET, Jean Baptiste** ....................... *paintings* | | | $2,420 | $4,400 |
| French 1759-1835 ..................................... *drawings* | | | | $2,310 |
| ☐ **MALLIA, Rene** .................................. *paintings* | | | | $2,310 |
| French 1890-1948 | | | | |
| ☐ **MALLORY, Ronald** ............................ *sculpture* | | | $110 | $275 |
| ☐ **MALLOT** ......................................... *paintings* | | | | $247 |
| 20th cent. | | | | |
| ☐ **MALMED** ......................................... *paintings* | | | $302 | $412 |
| American contemporary | | | | |
| ☐ **MALONEY, Dave** ............................... *paintings* | | | | $900 |
| American | | | | |
| ☐ **MALOTKI, H.** ................................... *paintings* | | | | $605 |
| ☐ **MALTA, Eduardo** .............................. *paintings* | | | $550 | $935 |
| Portuguese 1900-1967 | | | | |
| ☐ **MALTAYS, Casimir** ............................ *paintings* | | | | $462 |

| | Current Price Range | |
|---|---|---|
| | Low | High |
| ☐ **MALTOLINI, A.** ................................ *drawings* | | $192 |
| Italian 19th cent. | | |
| ☐ **MALTZ, Rickey** .................................. *paintings* | | $880 |
| American 20th cent. | | |
| ☐ **MALTZMAN, Stanley** ......................... *drawings* | | $198 |
| American | | |
| ☐ **MAN, L. de** .......................................... *paintings* | | $2,860 |
| ☐ **MANAGO, Vincent** ............................. *paintings* | $880 | $1,760 |
| Italian 19th/20th cent. | | |
| ☐ **MANCINI, Antonio** ............................ *paintings* | $209 | $23,100 |
| Italian 1852-1930 ..................................... *drawings* | $1,100 | $17,600 |
| ☐ **MANCINI, Carlo** ................................. *paintings* | $150 | $9,900 |
| Italian 1829-1910 | | |
| ☐ **MANCINI, F. Franco** ........................... *drawings* | | $467 |
| Italian late 19th cent. | | |
| ☐ **MANCINI, Francesco Giovanni** ............. *paintings* | $275 | $6,050 |
| Italian 1829-1905 | | |
| ☐ **MANCINI, Francesco Longo** ................. *paintings* | | $352 |
| ☐ **MANCINI, Gualterio** ........................... *paintings* | | $1,402 |
| Italian b. 1840 | | |
| ☐ **MANCINI, L.** ....................................... *paintings* | | $495 |
| ☐ **MANDER, William Henry** .................. *paintings* | | $880 |
| British ac. 1880-1922 | | |
| ☐ **MANDEVARE, Alphonse N. Michel** ...... *drawings* | $165 | $1,100 |
| French d. 1829 | | |
| ☐ **MANDIJN, Jan** .................................... *paintings* | | $64,900 |
| Dutch 1500/02-1560 | | |
| ☐ **MANDRE, Emile Albert de** ................... *paintings* | | $1,870 |
| French 1869-1929 | | |
| ☐ **MANE-KATZ** ....................................... *paintings* | $2,860 | $36,300 |
| French/Israeli 1894-1962 .............................. *drawings* | $220 | $7,700 |
| ☐ **MANELYER, Max Muller** .................... *paintings* | | $550 |
| ☐ **MANESSIER, Alfred** ........................... *paintings* | | $6,050 |
| French b. 1941 ...................................... *drawings* | $935 | $1,100 |
| ☐ **MANET, Edouard** ............................... *paintings* | $27,500 | $3,960,000 |
| French 1832-1883 ..................................... *drawings* | $2,250 | $330,000 |
| ☐ **MANFREDI, Bartolomeo** ..................... *paintings* | | $44,000 |
| Italian c. 1580-c. 1620 | | |
| ☐ **MANGOLD, Robert** ............................. *paintings* | $2,200 | $35,200 |
| American b. 1937 ..................................... *drawings* | $1,980 | $13,200 |
| ☐ **MANGRAVITE, Peppino** ..................... *paintings* | $176 | $1,100 |
| Italian/American b. 1896 ............................ *drawings* | | $715 |
| ☐ **MANGUIN, Henri Charles** .................. *paintings* | $4,000 | $84,700 |
| French 1874-1943/49 ................................. *drawings* | $572 | $1,320 |
| ☐ **MANIGAULT, Edward Middleton** ........ *paintings* | $302 | $1,650 |
| American 1887-1922 ................................. *sculpture* | | $12,650 |
| ☐ **MANLEY, Thomas R.** ........................... *paintings* | | $330 |
| American b. 1853 | | |

| | Current Price Range | |
|---|---|---|
| | Low | High |
| ☐ **MANLY, Eleanor E.** ........................... *drawings* <br> English 19th cent. | | $880 |
| ☐ **MANN, Bezalel** ................................... *sculpture* <br> Israeli contemporary | | $600 |
| ☐ **MANN, Cathleen** ............................... *paintings* <br> English 1896-1959 | $275 | $550 |
| ☐ **MANN, Harrington** ........................... *paintings* <br> Scottish b. 1864 | | $715 |
| ☐ **MANN, James S.** ............................... *paintings* <br> English 20th cent. | | $440 |
| ☐ **MANN-WADELL, Harry** ..................... *paintings* <br> American 20th cent. | | $935 |
| ☐ **MANNERS, William** ........................... *paintings* <br> English ac. 1885-1910 | $220 | $660 |
| ☐ **MANNHEIM, Jean** ............................. *paintings* <br> German/American c. 1861/63-1945 | $133 | $3,300 |
| ☐ **MANNI, Giannicola di Paolo** ............... *paintings* <br> Italian 1460-1544 | | $15,400 |
| ☐ **MANNUCCI, Cipriano** ....................... *paintings* <br> Italian b. 1882 | $1,870 | $2,200 |
| ☐ **MANOLO, (Manuel Martinez Hugue)** .... *sculpture* <br> Cuban/Spanish 1872/76-1945 | $1,650 | $3,850 |
| ☐ **MANS, Martha** ................................... *drawings* <br> American | $500 | $650 |
| ☐ **MANSCH, Ignaz** ................................. *paintings* <br> Austrian b. 1867 | | $880 |
| ☐ **MANSFELD, Heinrich August** .............. *paintings* <br> Austrian 1816-1901 | | $1,100 |
| ☐ **MANSFELD, Moriz** ............................. *paintings* <br> Austrian ac. 1850-1890 | $1,265 | $1,980 |
| ☐ **MANSHIP, Paul Howard** ..................... *sculpture* <br> American 1885-1966 | $200 | $231,000 |
| ☐ **MANSKIRCH, Bernhard Gottfried** ....... *paintings* <br> German 1736-1817 | | $4,675 |
| ☐ **MANSOUROFF, Paul** .......................... *drawings* | | $330 |
| ☐ **MANTEGAZZA, Giacomo** ................... *drawings* <br> Italian 1853-1920 | $220 | $275 |
| ☐ **MANTEGUA, Andrea** ......................... *drawings* <br> Italian 1431-1506 | | $715 |
| ☐ **MANTEOLA** ....................................... *drawings* | | $880 |
| ☐ **MANTIEL** .......................................... *paintings* <br> American 20th cent. | | $220 |
| ☐ **MANUCE, Henri de** ............................ *paintings* <br> American | | $440 |
| ☐ **MANUEL, Victor** ............................... *paintings* <br> ..................................................... *drawings* | <br> $1,100 | $7,700 <br> $3,520 |
| ☐ **MANZANA-PISSARRO, Georges** .......... *paintings* <br> French 1871-1961 | | $2,860 |

## Art Deco Sculptor

*In the first part of this century, Paul
Howard Manship was one of the
most popular sculptors in America.
An early success, he was elected to
the National Academy of Design in
1916 when he was just thirty-one.
Manship's style matured during the
next two decades, and his work
shows the elegant stylization of Art
Deco. Manship created a
monument for the 1939 New York
World's Fair, as well as the gates to
the Metropolitan Museum and the
Children's Zoo in Central Park.
While he remained popular with the
public, by 1940 critics considered
his work dated.*

*In 1985, the centennial of
Manship's birth in St. Paul,
Minnesota, the National Museum of American Art and the Minnesota Museum of Art
marked a renewed surge of interest in Manship's work with a travelling exhibit. A
month before the exhibit opened, "Dancer and Gazelles" was offered at auction by
William Doyle Galleries. Estimated at $40,000 to $60,000, the 32½ inch bronze, which
had been cast in an edition of twelve, sold for $231,000 to a private collector. Other
castings of the work may be seen at the Art Institute of Chicago, the Cleveland
Museum of Art, the Detroit Institute of Arts, the Century Association of New York, the
Musée du Luxembourg in Paris, and the Rhode Island School of Design. (Paul
Manship, "Dancers and Gazelles," bronze, height, 32½ in., Doyle, April 24, 1985,
$231,000 Photograph, courtesy of Rhode Island School of Design.)*

|                                                   |            | *Current Price Range* | |
| ------------------------------------------------- | ---------- | Low | High |
| ☐ **MANZONI, Paul**  ................................ *paintings* |            |          | **$990** |
| French  1823-1906                                 |            |          |          |
| ☐ **MANZU, Giacomo**  .............................. *drawings* | **$715** | **$4,070** |
| Italian b. 1908  ....................................... *sculpture* | **$12,100** | **$192,500** |
| ☐ **MANZUOLI, Egisto**  ............................ *paintings* |            |          | **$440** |
| Italian  19th cent.                               |            |          |          |
| ☐ **MANZUR, David**  ................................ *paintings* | **$66** | **$3,850** |
| Colombian b. 1929                                 |            |          |          |
| ☐ **MAONTCHENU-LAIVROTTE,**                        |            |          |          |
| **Jane de**  ................................................ *paintings* |            | **$1,760** |
| French  19th cent.                                |            |          |          |
| ☐ **MAPEWI, (Velino Shije Herrera)**  .......... *drawings* |          | **$1,210** |
| Pueblo Indian  1902-1973                          |            |          |          |
| ☐ **MAPPIN, Douglas**  .............................. *drawings* |          | **$1,100** |
| British  19th/20th cent.                          |            |          |          |

| | | Current Price Range | |
| --- | --- | --- | --- |
| | | Low | High |
| ☐ **MARAIS, Adolphe Charles** .................. *paintings* | | $495 | $522 |
| French b. 1856 | | | |
| ☐ **MARAIS-MILTON, Victor** .................. *paintings* | | | $8,525 |
| French b. 1872 | | | |
| ☐ **MARANTONIA, F.** ............................ *paintings* | | | $550 |
| ☐ **MARASCO, Antonio** ........................... *paintings* | | $220 | $220 |
| Italian b. 1886 | | | |
| ☐ **MARAT** ....................................... *paintings* | | | $385 |
| ☐ **MARATTA, Carlo** ............................ *drawings* | | $1,210 | $13,200 |
| Italian 1625-1713 | | | |
| ☐ **MARATTA, Hardesty G.** ..................... *paintings* | | | $275 |
| American b. 1864 ....................................... *drawings* | | | $440 |
| ☐ **MARBOEUF, V.** ................................ *paintings* | | | $250 |
| American 20th cent. | | | |
| ☐ **MARC, Franz** ..................................... *paintings* | | $60,500 | $385,000 |
| German 1880-1916 ...................................... *drawings* | | | $341,000 |
| ☐ **MARCA-RELLI, Conrad** ...................... *paintings* | | $550 | $6,600 |
| American b. 1913 | | | |
| ☐ **MARCEAUX, Jon** ............................. *sculpture* | | | $3,300 |
| French 19th cent. | | | |
| ☐ **MARCEGLIA, F.** ................................ *paintings* | | $770 | $962 |
| Italian 19th cent. | | | |
| ☐ **MARCEL-CLEMENT, Amedee Julien** ... *paintings* | | $1,760 | $1,870 |
| French b. 1873 | | | |
| ☐ **MARCENA Y DE GHUY, Antoine de** .... *paintings* | | | $18,700 |
| French 1724-1811 | | | |
| ☐ **MARCH, Edward** ............................... *paintings* | | | $385 |
| British 19th cent. | | | |
| ☐ **MARCH, Vernon** ................................ *sculpture* | | | $1,045 |
| English 1891-1930 | | | |
| ☐ **MARCHAIS, Jean Baptiste Etienne** ....... *paintings* | | | $1,430 |
| French b. 1818 | | | |
| ☐ **MARCHAND, Charles** .......................... *paintings* | | | $2,860 |
| French (?) 19th cent. | | | |
| ☐ **MARCHAND, Jean Hippolyte** .............. *paintings* | | $160 | $4,400 |
| French 1883-1940 ...................................... *drawings* | | $137 | $660 |
| ☐ **MARCHAND, John Norval** .................. *paintings* | | $1,980 | $3,740 |
| American 1875-1921 .................................. *drawings* | | | $165 |
| ☐ **MARCHANT, Edward D.** ..................... *paintings* | | | $297 |
| American 1806-1887 | | | |
| ☐ **MARCHE, Ernest Gaston** .................... *paintings* | | | $357 |
| French 1864-1932 | | | |
| ☐ **MARCHESI, Giuseppe** | | | |
| **(called IL SANSONE)** ............................ *paintings* | | $2,860 | $5,720 |
| Italian 1699-1771 | | | |
| ☐ **MARCHETTI** ..................................... *paintings* | | | $726 |
| Italian b. 1901 | | | |
| ☐ **MARCHETTI, Ludovico** ....................... *paintings* | | $1,210 | $66,000 |
| Italian 1853-1909 ..................................... *drawings* | | $302 | $522 |

| | | Current Price Range | |
|---|---|---|---|
| | | *Low* | *High* |
| ☐ **MARCHIONNI, E.** ............................ *paintings* | | | $2,090 |
| ☐ **MARCHISIO, Andrea** ........................ *paintings* | | | $1,650 |
| Italian 1850-1927 | | | |
| ☐ **MARCIUS-SIMONS, Pinckney** ............. *paintings* | | $1,210 | $3,850 |
| American 1867-1909 | | | |
| ☐ **MARCKE, Emile van** ........................ *paintings* | | | $990 |
| Belgian 1797-1839 | | | |
| ☐ **MARCKE, Jean van** ........................... *paintings* | | | $2,750 |
| French 1798-1849 | | | |
| ☐ **MARCKE DE LUMMEN, Emile van** ..... *paintings* | | $220 | $2,475 |
| French 1827-1890 | | | |
| ☐ **MARCKS, Alexander** ......................... *paintings* | | $660 | $2,640 |
| German 1864-1909 | | | |
| ☐ **MARCKS, Gerhard** ............................ *drawings* | | $110 | $440 |
| German b. 1889 ..................................... *sculpture* | | $2,090 | $8,800 |
| ☐ **MARCOUSSIS, Louis** ........................ *paintings* | | $3,520 | $24,200 |
| French 1883-1941 ................................... *drawings* | | $522 | $46,200 |
| ☐ **MARCOUX** ....................................... *paintings* | | | $2,090 |
| French 19th cent. | | | |
| ☐ **MARCUCCI, Lucio** ........................... *drawings* | | $170 | $385 |
| Italian 19th/20th cent. | | | |
| ☐ **MARCUS, P.** ..................................... *paintings* | | | $308 |
| ☐ **MARDEN, Brice** ................................ *drawings* | | $1,760 | $13,200 |
| American b. 1938 | | | |
| ☐ **MARE** ............................................. *paintings* | | | $467 |
| ☐ **MARECHAL, Charles** ......................... *paintings* | | | $500 |
| French 1801-1887 | | | |
| ☐ **MARECHAL, Jean Baptiste** ................. *drawings* | | $770 | $6,050 |
| French late 18th cent. | | | |
| ☐ **MAREIS, A.** ...................................... *paintings* | | | $1,210 |
| Dutch late 19th cent. | | | |
| ☐ **MARESCY, Marie** ............................. *paintings* | | $880 | $1,320 |
| French 20th cent. | | | |
| ☐ **MARESHAL, C.F.** .............................. *paintings* | | | $550 |
| ☐ **MARGARITA, S.Y.** ............................ *drawings* | | | $1,045 |
| ☐ **MARGAT, Andre** ............................... *drawings* | | | $1,320 |
| French b. 1903 | | | |
| ☐ **MARGETTS, Mary** ............................ *drawings* | | $990 | $2,420 |
| English ac. 1841-1886 | | | |
| ☐ **MARGO, Boris** ................................. *paintings* | | | $192 |
| American b. 1902 | | | |
| ☐ **MARGOTTE DE QUIVIERES,** | | | |
| **Augustin Marie Paul** ........................... *paintings* | | $1,210 | $1,320 |
| French 1854-1907 | | | |
| ☐ **MARGOTTON, Rene** ........................... *paintings* | | $44 | $230 |
| French 20th cent | | | |
| ☐ **MARGULIES, Joseph** ........................ *paintings* | | $110 | $352 |
| American b. Austria 1896 ......................... *drawings* | | $44 | $385 |
| ☐ **MARIA, Ana** ..................................... *paintings* | | $935 | $1,210 |

| | | Current Price Range | |
|---|---|---|---|
| | | *Low* | *High* |
| ☐ **MARIA, Francesco de** ........................... *paintings* | | | $660 |
| Italian 1845-1908 | | | |
| ☐ **MARIA ELISA** .................................... *paintings* | | $385 | $715 |
| 20th cent. | | | |
| ☐ **MARIANI, Pompeo** ........................... *paintings* | | | $4,125 |
| Italian 1857-1927 ...................................... *drawings* | | $286 | $450 |
| ☐ **MARIANO** ......................................... *drawings* | | | $1,980 |
| Cuban b. 1912 | | | |
| ☐ **MARIDA, Carlos** ............................... *sculpture* | | | $7,700 |
| Mexican b. 1895 | | | |
| ☐ **MARIE, Jeanne** ................................... *drawings* | | | $302 |
| ☐ **MARIE-ALIX, Alice** ........................... *paintings* | | | $4,400 |
| French 20th cent. | | | |
| ☐ **MARIESCHI, Michele** ........................ *paintings* | | $11,000 | $74,250 |
| Italian 1696-1743 | | | |
| ☐ **MARIJNISSEN, A.** ............................. *paintings* | | | $385 |
| ☐ **MARIL, Herman** ................................ *drawings* | | | $209 |
| American 20th cent. | | | |
| ☐ **MARILHAT, Prosper Georges Antoine** .. *paintings* | | | $9,625 |
| French 1811-1847 | | | |
| ☐ **MARIN, Emile** .................................... *paintings* | | | $462 |
| French b. 1876 | | | |
| ☐ **MARIN, John** .................................... *paintings* | | $12,100 | $30,000 |
| American 1870-1953 ................................... *drawings* | | $275 | $39,600 |
| ☐ **MARIN GARCES, Isidoro** .................... *paintings* | | | $1,210 |
| Spanish b. 1863 | | | |
| ☐ **MARINETTI, Antonio** ........................... *paintings* | | | $4,400 |
| Italian 1710-1796 | | | |
| ☐ **MARINGER, C.** .................................... *paintings* | | | $275 |
| ☐ **MARINI, F.** ...................................... *paintings* | | | $1,320 |
| ☐ **MARINI, Marino** ................................ *paintings* | | $6,600 | $126,500 |
| Italian 1901-1980 ...................................... *drawings* | | $1,430 | $38,500 |
| ........................................................ *sculpture* | | $13,200 | $363,000 |
| ☐ **MARINO, Bepi** .................................... *paintings* | | | $192 |
| Italian b. 1906 | | | |
| ☐ **MARINUS VAN REYMERSWAELE** ..... *paintings* | | | $20,350 |
| Dutch c. 1493-c. 1597 | | | |
| ☐ **MARIOTON, Eugene** ........................... *sculpture* | | $600 | $2,420 |
| French b. 1854; ac. 1882-1922 | | | |
| ☐ **MARIOTTI, Leopoldo** ......................... *paintings* | | $495 | $880 |
| Italian 1848-1916 ...................................... *drawings* | | | $330 |
| ☐ **MARIOTTO DI NARDO** ..................... *paintings* | | $20,900 | $30,800 |
| Italian ac. 1394-1424 | | | |
| ☐ **MARIS** ............................................. *paintings* | | | $440 |
| Dutch 19th cent. | | | |
| ☐ **MARIS, Jacob Henricus** ........................ *paintings* | | $1,100 | $37,400 |
| Dutch 1837-1899 | | | |
| ☐ **MARIS, Simon** .................................... *paintings* | | | $1,650 |
| Dutch 1873-1935 | | | |

|                                          | | *Current Price Range* | |
|------------------------------------------|--------------|----------|----------|
|                                          |          | Low | High |
| ☐ **MARIS, Walter De** .............................. *paintings* | | | **$1,540** |
| b. 1877 | | | |
| ☐ **MARIS, Willem** .............................. *paintings* | | **$600** | **$8,250** |
| Dutch 1844-1910 ...................................... *drawings* | | | **$467** |
| ☐ **MARISOL** .............................................. *drawings* | | **$880** | **$880** |
| contemporary ............................................ *sculpture* | | **$1,210** | **$35,200** |
| ☐ **MARIUS** .............................................. *paintings* | | **$220** | **$550** |
| German 20th cent. | | | |
| ☐ **MARK, George Washington** ................. *paintings* | | | **$1,100** |
| American d. 1879 | | | |
| ☐ **MARK, Lajos (or Louis)** ........................ *paintings* | | **$66** | **$440** |
| Hungarian 1867-1942 | | | |
| ☐ **MARKHAM, Charles C.** ....................... *paintings* | | | **$6,050** |
| American 1837-1907 | | | |
| ☐ **MARKHAM, Kyra** .............................. *paintings* | | | **$2,420** |
| American | | | |
| ☐ **MARKHOLF** ....................................... *paintings* | | | **$770** |
| ☐ **MARKINO, Yoshio** .............................. *paintings* | | | **$242** |
| Japanese (?) 19th/20th cent. | | | |
| ☐ **MARKO, Andreas** .............................. *paintings* | | **$385** | **$6,050** |
| Austrian 1824-1895 | | | |
| ☐ **MARKO, Karl** .................................... *paintings* | | **$880** | **$3,850** |
| Hungarian 1822-1891 | | | |
| ☐ **MARKOS, Lajos** .............................. *paintings* | | **$9,500** | **$55,000** |
| American b. 1917 | | | |
| ☐ **MARKS, George** .............................. *paintings* | | | **$8,500** |
| American b. 1923 | | | |
| ☐ **MARKS, Henry Stacy** ......................... *paintings* | | **$770** | **$4,400** |
| English 1829-1898 ...................................... *drawings* | | **$220** | **$770** |
| ☐ **MARLATT, H. Irving** ......................... *paintings* | | **$55** | **$495** |
| American d. 1929 | | | |
| ☐ **MARLIER, Phillipe de** ......................... *paintings* | | | **$33,000** |
| ☐ **MARLIN, D.** ...................................... *paintings* | | | **$715** |
| ☐ **MARLIN, Karel** .............................. *paintings* | | | **$2,310** |
| American | | | |
| ☐ **MARLOW, William** ........................... *paintings* | | **$660** | **$1,210** |
| English 1740-1813 | | | |
| ☐ **MARLOWE, William** ......................... *drawings* | | | **$1,540** |
| ☐ **MARMILE** ......................................... *paintings* | | | **$800** |
| American 19th cent. | | | |
| ☐ **MARMION, Simon** ............................. *paintings* | | | **$4,400** |
| ☐ **MARNOYOBS, C.** ............................. *paintings* | | | **$935** |
| Slavic 19th cent. | | | |
| ☐ **MARNY, Paul** .................................... *drawings* | | | **$220** |
| English 1829-1914 | | | |
| ☐ **MAROHN, Ferdinand** ......................... *paintings* | | | **$1,650** |
| French 19th cent. ...................................... *drawings* | | | **$440** |
| ☐ **MAROHN, Frederick** ......................... *paintings* | | | **$1,320** |

|  | | Current Price Range | |
|---|---|---|---|
|  | | Low | High |
| ☐ **MAROLD, Ludwig** ............................. *drawings* | | | **$880** |
| Austrian 1865-1898 | | | |
| ☐ **MARONIEZ,** | | | |
| **Georges Philibert Charles** ...................... *paintings* | | **$467** | **$2,420** |
| French b. 1865 | | | |
| ☐ **MAROT, Daniel** ................................... *drawings* | | | **$4,400** |
| Franco/Dutch c. 1663-1752 | | | |
| ☐ **MAROT, Francois** .............................. *paintings* | | | **$11,000** |
| French 1666-1719 | | | |
| ☐ **MARPLE, William L.** .......................... *paintings* | | **$660** | **$2,530** |
| American 1827-1910 | | | |
| ☐ **MARQUET** ....................................... *sculpture* | | | **$1,375** |
| French c. 1925 | | | |
| ☐ **MARQUET, Albert** ........................... *paintings* | | **$3,190** | **$132,000** |
| French 1875-1947 ..................................... *drawings* | | **$412** | **$7,975** |
| ☐ **MARQUIS, Edouard** .......................... *drawings* | | | **$1,320** |
| French 1812-1894 | | | |
| ☐ **MARR, Carl** ................................... *paintings* | | **$715** | **$4,400** |
| American 1858-1936 | | | |
| ☐ **MARRE, Jules** ................................... *drawings* | | | **$192** |
| French 19th cent. | | | |
| ☐ **MARS-VALLET, Marius** ..................... *sculpture* | | | **$5,610** |
| French b. 1867 | | | |
| ☐ **MARSANO, L.A.** .............................. *paintings* | | | **$1,980** |
| ☐ **MARSDEN, Theodore** ......................... *paintings* | | | **$1,600** |
| American 19th cent. | | | |
| ☐ **MARSELLA, G.** ................................. *paintings* | | | **$550** |
| Italian late 19th cent. | | | |
| ☐ **MARSH, Frederick Dana** ...................... *paintings* | | | **$715** |
| American b. 1872 | | | |
| ☐ **MARSH, Reginald** ............................. *paintings* | | **$550** | **$46,200** |
| American 1898-1954 ................................... *drawings* | | **$165** | **$41,800** |
| ☐ **MARSHALL, Ben** ............................... *paintings* | | **$12,100** | **$253,000** |
| English 1767-1835 | | | |
| ☐ **MARSHALL, Chester** | | | |
| **(Walt Disney Studios)** ......................... *drawings* | | | **$522** |
| ☐ **MARSHALL, Clarke** .......................... *drawings* | | | **$187** |
| English 19th cent. | | | |
| ☐ **MARSHALL, Clarke S.** ....................... *paintings* | | **$137** | **$187** |
| American b. 1882 | | | |
| ☐ **MARSHALL, E.M.** ............................. *paintings* | | | **$440** |
| British 19th cent. | | | |
| ☐ **MARSHALL, Frank Howard** ................ *paintings* | | **$60** | **$200** |
| American b. 1866 | | | |
| ☐ **MARSHALL, H.** ................................. *paintings* | | **$2,200** | **$2,420** |
| English 19th cent. | | | |
| ☐ **MARSHALL, J. Fitz** .......................... *paintings* | | | **$990** |
| British 19th cent. | | | |

| | | Current Price Range | |
|---|---|---|---|
| | | Low | High |
| ☐ **MARSHALL, John** ............................ *paintings* | | | $8,250 |
| British 1840-1896 | | | |
| ☐ **MARSHALL, Lambert** ........................ *paintings* | | $2,750 | $9,350 |
| British 1810-1870 | | | |
| ☐ **MARSHALL, Mary E.** ....................... *paintings* | | | $297 |
| American 20th cent. | | | |
| ☐ **MARSHALL, T. S.** ............................ *paintings* | | | $253 |
| American 19th/20th cent. | | | |
| ☐ **MARSHALL, Thomas Falcon** .............. *paintings* | | | $2,750 |
| English 1818-1878 | | | |
| ☐ **MARSHALL, Thomas W.** ..................... *paintings* | | | $1,870 |
| American 1850-1874 | | | |
| ☐ **MARSHALL, William Edgar** ............... *paintings* | | | $6,600 |
| American 1837-1906 | | | |
| ☐ **MARSIE** ........................................... *sculpture* | | | $1,320 |
| American Indian | | | |
| ☐ **MARSZEWSKI, Josef** ......................... *paintings* | | | $880 |
| ☐ **MARTEAU, Augusto** .......................... *paintings* | | | $550 |
| b. Argentina 1890 | | | |
| ☐ **MARTEL, Jan** .................................... *sculpture* | | | $330 |
| ☐ **MARTELL, K.** .................................... *sculpture* | | | $605 |
| ☐ **MARTEN, Elliot H.** ............................ *drawings* | | | $330 |
| British ac. 1880's | | | |
| ☐ **MARTENET, Marjorie D.** .................... *paintings* | | | $302 |
| American 19th/20th cent. | | | |
| ☐ **MARTENS, Fritz** ............................... *paintings* | | | $600 |
| ☐ **MARTENS, Johann Heinrich** ............... *paintings* | | | $412 |
| German 1815-1843 | | | |
| ☐ **MARTENS, Willy** ............................... *drawings* | | | $440 |
| Dutch 1856-1927 | | | |
| ☐ **MARTEROSOV, L.** ............................. *paintings* | | | $1,100 |
| Russian 19th/20th cent. | | | |
| ☐ **MARTI Y ALSINA, Ramon** ................. *paintings* | | | $1,430 |
| Spanish 1826-1894 | | | |
| ☐ **MARTIMUS** ...................................... *sculpture* | | | $3,300 |
| ☐ **MARTIN, Agnes** ............................... *paintings* | | $5,500 | $104,500 |
| Canadian/American b. 1912 ........................ *drawings* | | $3,850 | $11,000 |
| ................................................................... *sculpture* | | | $9,900 |
| ☐ **MARTIN, Alexander** ........................... *paintings* | | | $550 |
| American b. 1931 .................................... *drawings* | | | $137 |
| ☐ **MARTIN, Anson A.** ............................ *paintings* | | $4,950 | $18,700 |
| English ac. 1840-1861 | | | |
| ☐ **MARTIN, Fletcher** ............................. *paintings* | | $242 | $3,740 |
| American 1904-1979 .................................. *drawings* | | $110 | $418 |
| ☐ **MARTIN, Fritz** ................................. *paintings* | | | $3,850 |
| German 1859-1889 | | | |
| ☐ **MARTIN, Gill** .................................... *paintings* | | | $528 |
| American 20th cent. | | | |

| | | Current Price Range | |
|---|---|---|---|
| | | Low | High |
| □ **MARTIN, Henri Jean Guillaume** | | | |
| **(called Henri MARTIN)** .......................... *paintings* | | **$1,650** | **$51,700** |
| French 1860-1943 | | | |
| □ **MARTIN, Homer Dodge** ...................... *paintings* | | **$440** | **$20,900** |
| American 1836-1897 ................................. *drawings* | | **$110** | **$1,100** |
| □ **MARTIN, J.R.** ..................................... *paintings* | | | **$34,100** |
| European 19th cent. | | | |
| □ **MARTIN, Jean Baptiste** | | | |
| **(le vieux) (Martin Des Batailles)** .............. *paintings* | | **$2,530** | **$11,000** |
| □ **MARTIN, John** .................................... *drawings* | | | **$1,980** |
| English 1789-1854 | | | |
| □ **MARTIN,** | | | |
| **Jules Leon Gabriel Alexandre** ............... *paintings* | | | **$660** |
| French 19th cent. | | | |
| □ **MARTIN, Knox** ................................... *paintings* | | **$500** | **$715** |
| Colombian/Amer. b. 1923 ............................. *drawings* | | **$88** | **$110** |
| □ **MARTIN, L.C.A.** ............................... *sculpture* | | | **$550** |
| □ **MARTIN, M. San** ............................... *paintings* | | | **$495** |
| Spanish 19th cent. | | | |
| □ **MARTIN, Maria** .................................. *paintings* | | **$352** | **$385** |
| □ **MARTIN, Pierre** ................................. *paintings* | | | **$1,650** |
| French 19th cent. | | | |
| □ **MARTIN, Scott** ................................... *drawings* | | | **$660** |
| □ **MARTIN, Sylvester** ............................. *paintings* | | **$550** | **$2,200** |
| English 19th cent. | | | |
| □ **MARTIN, Thomas Mower** .................... *drawings* | | **$220** | **$990** |
| Canadian 1838-1934 | | | |
| □ **MARTIN, W.** ...................................... *paintings* | | | **$605** |
| English 19th cent. | | | |
| □ **MARTIN-FERRIERES, Jac** ................. *paintings* | | **$550** | **$2,310** |
| French b. 1893 | | | |
| □ **MARTINEAU, Gertrude** ...................... *paintings* | | | **$3,300** |
| British ac. 1862-1894 | | | |
| □ **MARTINEAU,** | | | |
| **Louis Joseph Philadelphe** ...................... *paintings* | | | **$2,090** |
| French 1800-1868 | | | |
| □ **MARTINEAUX, Edith** ....................... *drawings* | | | **$357** |
| British 19th/20th cent. | | | |
| □ **MARTINEK** ....................................... *paintings* | | | **$605** |
| □ **MARTINELLI, Giovanni** ...................... *paintings* | | **$2,090** | **$2,200** |
| Italian 1610-1659 | | | |
| □ **MARTINELLI, Ludwig** ....................... *paintings* | | | **$1,210** |
| Austrian b. 1834 | | | |
| □ **MARTINET, Achille Louis** ................... *drawings* | | | **$1,210** |
| French 1806-1877 | | | |
| □ **MARTINET, Etienne** .......................... *paintings* | | **$17,600** | **$22,000** |
| □ **MARTINETTI, Maria** .......................... *drawings* | | **$352** | **$4,400** |
| Italian b. 1864 | | | |

| | | Current Price Range | |
| --- | --- | --- | --- |
| | | Low | High |
| ☐ **MARTINEZ, Alfredo Ramos** ................ *paintings* | | $385 | $4,950 |
| Mexican 1872-1946 ..................................... *drawings* | | $357 | $4,400 |
| ☐ **MARTINEZ, Francisco** ........................ *paintings* | | | $7,700 |
| Mexican ac. c. 1718-1755 | | | |
| ☐ **MARTINEZ, J.** ................................... *paintings* | | | $990 |
| Dutch 19th cent. | | | |
| ☐ **MARTINEZ, Julian** ............................ *drawings* | | $1,045 | $1,870 |
| American/Pueblo 1897-1943/44 | | | |
| ☐ **MARTINEZ, M.** ................................. *paintings* | | | $1,430 |
| 19th cent. | | | |
| ☐ **MARTINEZ, O.** ................................. *paintings* | | | $176 |
| Mexican 19th/20th cent. | | | |
| ☐ **MARTINEZ, Ricardo** .......................... *paintings* | | $1,045 | $12,100 |
| Mexican b. 1918 ..................................... *drawings* | | $550 | $1,320 |
| ☐ **MARTINEZ, Xavier** ............................ *paintings* | | $357 | $8,800 |
| Mexican/American 1874-1943 ........................ *drawings* | | $110 | $850 |
| ☐ **MARTINEZ CASTENADA, Baltazar** .... *sculpture* | | $1,870 | $2,090 |
| Mexican b. 1938 | | | |
| ☐ **MARTINEZ-PEDRO, Luis** ................... *drawings* | | $605 | $4,400 |
| Cuban 20th cent. | | | |
| ☐ **MARTINI, Alberto** ............................. *paintings* | | | $440 |
| Italian b. 1876 | | | |
| ☐ **MARTINI, I.R.J.** ............................... *paintings* | | $715 | $1,870 |
| Italian 20th cent. | | | |
| ☐ **MARTINO, Antonio Pietro** ................... *paintings* | | $82 | $2,530 |
| American b. 1902 | | | |
| ☐ **MARTINO, Edouardo** ......................... *paintings* | | | $330 |
| Italian 1838-1912 | | | |
| ☐ **MARTINO, Giovanni de** ....................... *sculpture* | | | $2,090 |
| Italian early 20th cent. | | | |
| ☐ **MARTINO, M.** ................................... *drawings* | | | $357 |
| Italian 19th/20th cent. | | | |
| ☐ **MARTINUS** ..................................... *sculpture* | | | $4,125 |
| ☐ **MARTINY, P.H.** ............................... *sculpture* | | | $1,650 |
| ☐ **MARUS, W.** ..................................... *paintings* | | | $522 |
| ☐ **MARX, Alphonse** ............................. *paintings* | | $935 | $935 |
| French 19th cent. | | | |
| ☐ **MARX, F.** ....................................... *drawings* | | | $253 |
| ☐ **MARX, Johann** ................................. *drawings* | | | $192 |
| German b. 1886 | | | |
| ☐ **MARX, Roberto Burle** ........................ *paintings* | | | $3,300 |
| b. Brazil 1909-1982 | | | |
| ☐ **MARX, Sam** ................................... *paintings* | | | $1,430 |
| American b. 1885 | | | |
| ☐ **MARYAN** ....................................... *drawings* | | | $440 |
| contemporary | | | |
| ☐ **MARYE, Simone** ............................... *sculpture* | | | $3,080 |
| French early 20th cent. | | | |

| | | Current Price Range | |
|---|---|---|---|
| | | Low | High |
| ☐ **MARZELLI, F.** ..................................... *paintings* | | | $715 |
| Italian 19th cent. | | | |
| ☐ **MARZI, Ezio** ....................................... *paintings* | | | $192 |
| Italian b. 1875 | | | |
| ☐ **MARZOTINO, S.** ................................. *paintings* | | | $1,760 |
| Italian 19th cent. | | | |
| ☐ **MAS Y FONDEVILA, Arcadia** .............. *paintings* | | | $880 |
| Spanish b. 1850 | | | |
| ☐ **MASCART, Gustave** ............................ *paintings* | | | $440 |
| French ac. 1880-1895 | | | |
| ☐ **MASEREEL, Frans** ............................. *paintings* | $2,310 | $3,025 |
| Belgian 1889-1971 ..................................... *drawings* | $550 | $935 |
| ☐ **MASH, H.** .......................................... *paintings* | | | $715 |
| American 19th cent. | | | |
| ☐ **MASHKOV, Ilya** ................................. *paintings* | | | $192 |
| Russian | | | |
| ☐ **MASIP, Juan Vincente** | | | |
| **(called Juan de Joanesor) (or MACIP)** ..... *paintings* | | | $7,700 |
| Spanish before 1523-1579 | | | |
| ☐ **MASON, Alice Trumbull** ...................... *paintings* | | | $2,310 |
| American 1904-1971 | | | |
| ☐ **MASON, Barry** ................................. *paintings* | $275 | $350 |
| 20th cent. | | | |
| ☐ **MASON, Frank** ................................. *paintings* | $66 | $302 |
| American b. 1921 | | | |
| ☐ **MASON, George Hemning** ................... *paintings* | | | $2,860 |
| English 1818-1872 | | | |
| ☐ **MASON, Maud Mary** .......................... *paintings* | $55 | $550 |
| American 1867-1956 | | | |
| ☐ **MASON, Robert** ................................ *paintings* | | | $440 |
| American b. 1874 | | | |
| ☐ **MASON, Sanford** .............................. *paintings* | $1,100 | $3,080 |
| American c. 1798-c. 1862 | | | |
| ☐ **MASON, William N.** .......................... *drawings* | | | $462 |
| ☐ **MASON, William Sanford** ................... *paintings* | $247 | $4,675 |
| American 1824-1864 | | | |
| ☐ **MASSANI, Pompeo** ............................ *paintings* | $137 | $15,400 |
| Italian 1850-1920 | | | |
| ☐ **MASSARD, Jean Baptiste Raphael** ........ *drawings* | | | $550 |
| ☐ **MASSARI, Lucio** ............................... *paintings* | | | $1,320 |
| Italian 1569-1633 | | | |
| ☐ **MASSE, Jean Baptiste** ........................ *paintings* | | | $4,400 |
| French 1687-1767 | | | |
| ☐ **MASSEY, Joseph** ............................... *sculpture* | | | $2,860 |
| English 19th/20th cent. | | | |
| ☐ **MASSIUS, P.** ..................................... *paintings* | | | $990 |
| ☐ **MASSOLINI, Cesare Giuseppe** ............. *paintings* | | | $275 |

|  | | Current Price Range | |
| --- | --- | --- | --- |
|  | | Low | High |
| □ **MASSON, Andre** ............................. *paintings* | | **$2,200** | **$93,500** |
| French b. 1896 ........................................ *drawings* | | **$440** | **$18,150** |
| ........................................................... *sculpture* | | | **$1,650** |
| □ **MASSON, Charles** ............................. *sculpture* | | | **$770** |
| □ **MASSON, Henri Leopold** ...................... *paintings* | | | **$3,575** |
| Canadian b. 1907 | | | |
| □ **MASSON, Jules Edmond** ...................... *sculpture* | | | **$308** |
| □ **MASSON, Paul** ............................... *paintings* | | **$800** | **$1,210** |
| Belgian 1883-1970 | | | |
| □ **MASSONA, H.** ................................. *paintings* | | | **$308** |
| □ **MASSONI, Egisto** ............................. *paintings* | | | **$2,750** |
| Italian 1854-1929 | | | |
| □ **MASSOULE, Andre Paul Arthur** .......... *sculpture* | | | **$1,430** |
| French late 19th cent. | | | |
| □ **MASSYS, Cornelis** ........................... *paintings* | | | **$6,325** |
| Flemish c. 1508-c. 1580 | | | |
| □ **MASSYS, Jan** ............................... *paintings* | | | **$5,775** |
| Flemish 1505-1575 | | | |
| □ **MAST, Thomas** ............................... *drawings* | | | **$880** |
| American 1840-1902 | | | |
| □ **MASTENBROEK, Johan Hendrik van** .. *paintings* | | **$200** | **$3,850** |
| Dutch 1875-1945 ................................. *drawings* | | **$440** | **$2,530** |
| □ **MASTER, G.** ................................. *paintings* | | | **$302** |
| □ **MASTER HB (WITH GRIFFIN'S** | | | |
| **HEAD)** ....................................... *paintings* | | | **$8,800** |
| □ **MASTER OF 1399** ........................... *paintings* | | | **$22,000** |
| □ **MASTER OF CALAMARCA** ................ *paintings* | | | **$12,100** |
| Bolivia active late 17th cent. | | | |
| □ **MASTER OF MARRADI** ...................... *paintings* | | | **$18,700** |
| □ **MASTER OF SAINT IVO** ..................... *paintings* | | | **$11,000** |
| □ **MASTER OF SAN DAVINO** ................ *paintings* | | | **$46,750** |
| □ **MASTER OF SAN FILIPPO** ................ *paintings* | | | **$4,400** |
| □ **MASTER OF SAN MINIATO** ............... *paintings* | | | **$13,200** |
| □ **MASTER OF SANTO SPIRITO** ........... *paintings* | | | **$17,600** |
| □ **MASTER OF TAMARA** ...................... *paintings* | | | **$6,600** |
| □ **MASTER OF THE 1540'S** .................... *paintings* | | | **$16,500** |
| □ **MASTER OF THE ASHMOLEAN** | | | |
| **PREDELLA** .................................... *paintings* | | | **$28,600** |
| □ **MASTER OF THE BARGELLO** ........... *paintings* | | | **$77,000** |
| □ **MASTER OF THE BERN ST. JOHN** | | | |
| **ALTAR** ....................................... *paintings* | | | **$26,400** |
| □ **MASTER OF THE EMBROIDERED** | | | |
| **FOLIAGE** .................................... *paintings* | | | **$154,000** |
| □ **MASTER OF THE FEMALE** | | | |
| **HALF-LENGTHS** .............................. *paintings* | | **$14,500** | **$101,750** |
| ac. early 16th cent. | | | |
| □ **MASTER OF THE FIESOLE** | | | |
| **EPIPHANY** ................................... *paintings* | | | **$13,200** |

|  | | Current Price Range | |
| --- | --- | --- | --- |
|  | | Low | High |
| ☐ **MASTER OF THE HELSINUS LEGEND** | | | |
| .................................... *paintings* | | | $14,300 |
| Italian ac. 1375 | | | |
| ☐ **MASTER OF THE IONI FORGERIES** .. *paintings* | | | $770 |
| ☐ **MASTER OF THE JUDGEMENT OF** | | | |
| **PARIS** .................................... *paintings* | | | $11,000 |
| ☐ **MASTER OF THE KRESS** | | | |
| **LANDSCAPES** ..................... *paintings* | | | $3,500 |
| ☐ **MASTER OF THE LIVERPOOL** | | | |
| **MADONNA** ..................... *paintings* | | | $17,600 |
| ☐ **MASTER OF THE LUCCHESE** | | | |
| **IMMACULATE CONCEPTION** ........... *paintings* | | | $17,600 |
| ☐ **MASTER OF THE NAUMBURG** | | | |
| **MADONNA** .......................... *paintings* | | | $63,250 |
| ☐ **MASTER OF THE PARROT** ............. *paintings* | | $2,200 | $40,000 |
| Flemish 16th cent. | | | |
| ☐ **MASTER OF THE PRODIGAL SON** .... *paintings* | | $4,950 | $5,225 |
| ☐ **MASUCCI, Agostino** .......................... *paintings* | | | $4,620 |
| ☐ **MASWIENS, J.** ......................... *paintings* | | | $1,210 |
| Belgian 19th cent. | | | |
| ☐ **MATAMOROS, R.J.** ........................ *paintings* | | $660 | $935 |
| Latin American | | | |
| ☐ **MATANIA, Fortunino** ........................ *paintings* | | | $825 |
| Italian b. 1881 ....................... *drawings* | | $5 | $385 |
| ☐ **MATARE, Ewald** .............................. *sculpture* | | $1,045 | $7,150 |
| German 1887-1965 | | | |
| ☐ **MATHAM, Theodor (Dirck)** ................ *drawings* | | | $2,750 |
| ☐ **MATHELIN, Lucien** ............................ *paintings* | | | $330 |
| ☐ **MATHEUS, A.** ................................... *drawings* | | | $247 |
| American 19th/20th cent. | | | |
| ☐ **MATHEW, P.H.** .................................. *paintings* | | | $385 |
| ☐ **MATHEWS, Arthur Frank** ................. *paintings* | | | $2,200 |
| American 1860-1945 .................. *drawings* | | | $2,750 |
| ☐ **MATHEWS, John Chester** ................. *paintings* | | | $2,310 |
| English ac. 1884-1900 | | | |
| ☐ **MATHEWSON, Frank Convers** ........... *paintings* | | $99 | $1,045 |
| American 1862-1941 | | | |
| ☐ **MATHEY, Paul** .................................. *paintings* | | | $385 |
| ☐ **MATHIAS, Gabriel** ............................ *paintings* | | | $412 |
| ☐ **MATHIEU, Anna Rosina** | | | |
| **(nee LISZEWSKA)** ............................ *paintings* | | $2,475 | $4,125 |
| German 1716-1783 | | | |
| ☐ **MATHIEU, Georges** .......................... *paintings* | | $4,400 | $17,600 |
| French b. 1921 ....................... *drawings* | | $990 | $1,540 |
| ☐ **MATHIEU, Lambert Joseph** ................ *drawings* | | | $176 |
| Flemish 1804-1861 | | | |
| ☐ **MATHON, Emil Louis** .......................... *paintings* | | | $440 |
| French 19th cent. | | | |

| | | | Current Price Range | |
|---|---|---|---|---|
| | | | Low | High |
| ☐ **MATISSE, Henri** | ............................... | *paintings* | $41,250 | $660,000 |
| French 1869-1954 | ..................................... | *drawings* | $1,045 | $176,000 |
| | ....................................................... | *sculpture* | $17,600 | $159,500 |
| ☐ **MATON, A.** | ........................................ | *sculpture* | | $350 |
| ☐ **MATSUDA, Koichi** | ............................ | *paintings* | $165 | $220 |
| Japanese 20th cent. | | | | |
| ☐ **MATTA, Roberto Echaurren** | ............... | *paintings* | $5,225 | $176,000 |
| Chilean b. 1911 | ......................................... | *drawings* | $1,210 | $121,000 |
| | ....................................................... | *sculpture* | | $1,320 |
| ☐ **MATTEIS, Paolo di** | ............................. | *paintings* | $2,640 | $6,600 |
| Italian 1662-1728 | | | | |
| ☐ **MATTELE, G.** | ..................................... | *paintings* | | $5,500 |
| ☐ **MATTENHEIMER, Andreas Theodor** | ... | *paintings* | | $1,870 |
| German 1752-1810 | | | | |
| ☐ **MATTESON, Tompkins Harrison** | ......... | *paintings* | $1,100 | $6,600 |
| American 1813-1884 | | | | |
| ☐ **MATTHEWS, G.B.** | ............................. | *paintings* | | $825 |
| ☐ **MATTHEWS, Marmaduke** | ................... | *paintings* | | $1,210 |
| Canadian 1837-1913 | | | | |
| ☐ **MATTHEWS, W.S.** | ............................. | *paintings* | | $687 |
| ☐ **MATTHEWS, William** | ........................ | *paintings* | | $357 |
| ☐ **MATTO** | ......................................... | *sculpture* | | $467 |
| French ac. 1915-1925 | | | | |
| ☐ **MATTSON, Henry** | ............................. | *paintings* | $121 | $330 |
| ☐ **MATULKA, Jan** | ................................. | *paintings* | $165 | $7,150 |
| Czechoslovakian/Am 1890-1972 | ..................... | *drawings* | $550 | $4,400 |
| ☐ **MATVEIEV, Nicolai Sergeievich** | .......... | *paintings* | | $3,630 |
| Russian b. 1855 | | | | |
| ☐ **MAUFRA, Maxime Emile Louis** | ........... | *paintings* | $220 | $20,900 |
| French 1861/62-1918 | | | | |
| ☐ **MAUGARD, Alfredo Best** | .................... | *paintings* | | $550 |
| ☐ **MAUGHAM, Brian** | ........................... | *sculpture* | | $550 |
| American | | | | |
| ☐ **MAUGHLIN, M.W.** | ........................... | *paintings* | | $192 |
| American 19th cent. | | | | |
| ☐ **MAUGSCH** | ..................................... | *sculpture* | | $1,045 |
| ☐ **MAULBERTSCH, Franz Anton** | ........... | *paintings* | | $23,100 |
| Austrian 1724-1796 | | | | |
| ☐ **MAULDIN, B.** | ................................... | *drawings* | | $474 |
| ☐ **MAURER, Alfred H.** | ........................ | *paintings* | $715 | $187,000 |
| American 1868-1932 | ................................. | *drawings* | $880 | $7,150 |
| ☐ **MAURER, Louis** | ............................... | *paintings* | $4,675 | $60,000 |
| American 1832-1932 | | | | |
| ☐ **MAURIN, Charles** | ........................... | *paintings* | | $4,125 |
| French 1856-1914 | ..................................... | *drawings* | | $2,750 |
| ☐ **MAURY, Francois** | ............................. | *paintings* | $275 | $770 |
| French 1861-1933 | | | | |
| ☐ **MAUTON** | ......................................... | *drawings* | $2,750 | $2,860 |

| | | Current Price Range | |
|---|---|---|---|
| | | Low | High |
| ☐ **MAUVE, Anton** ............................... *paintings* | | $88 | $4,950 |
| Dutch 1838-1888 ....................................... *drawings* | | $143 | $1,430 |
| ☐ **MAUVE, Anton Rudolf** ......................... *paintings* | | | $1,100 |
| Dutch 1876-1962 | | | |
| ☐ **MAUZAISSE, Jean Baptiste** ................. *paintings* | | | $3,080 |
| French 1784-1844 | | | |
| ☐ **MAVROGORDATO, Alexander J.** ........ *drawings* | | | $990 |
| Russian 19th/20th cent. | | | |
| ☐ **MAVRY, F.** ...................................... *paintings* | | $550 | $1,320 |
| French 19th cent. | | | |
| ☐ **MAX, Gabriel Cornelius von** ................. *paintings* | | $550 | $4,950 |
| Czechoslovakian 1840-1915 | | | |
| ☐ **MAX, Gustav** ................................... *paintings* | | | $2,090 |
| ☐ **MAX, Peter** ..................................... *paintings* | | $286 | $935 |
| German/American b. 1937 ......................... *drawings* | | $77 | $385 |
| ☐ **MAX-EHRLER, Luise** ......................... *paintings* | | | $14,300 |
| Italian b. 1850 | | | |
| ☐ **MAXENCE, Edgard** ............................ *paintings* | | $330 | $1,430 |
| French 1871-1954 ..................................... *drawings* | | | $3,300 |
| ☐ **MAXFIELD, Clara** ............................ *drawings* | | $125 | $302 |
| American 19th/20th cent. | | | |
| ☐ **MAXFIELD, G.E.** ............................. *paintings* | | | $1,650 |
| ☐ **MAXFIELD, James E.** ......................... *paintings* | | $200 | $467 |
| American b. 1848 | | | |
| ☐ **MAXWELL** ....................................... *paintings* | | | $192 |
| English 19th/20th cent. | | | |
| ☐ **MAY, A.** ......................................... *paintings* | | | $192 |
| English 19th cent. | | | |
| ☐ **MAY, Charles Jones** ............................ *drawings* | | | $192 |
| British 1834-1919 | | | |
| ☐ **MAY, Edouard** ................................... *paintings* | | | $412 |
| ☐ **MAY, Edward Harrison** ....................... *paintings* | | | $1,870 |
| English 1824-1887 | | | |
| ☐ **MAY, J.** ......................................... *paintings* | | | $495 |
| American 19th/20th cent. | | | |
| ☐ **MAY, Philip William (Phil)** ................. *drawings* | | $110 | $176 |
| English 1864-1903 | | | |
| ☐ **MAY, Sibylle** ..................................... *sculpture* | | $352 | $1,210 |
| French early 20th cent. | | | |
| ☐ **MAYER, Christian** ............................ *paintings* | | | $1,210 |
| American 1805-1851 | | | |
| ☐ **MAYER, Christian** ............................ *paintings* | | | $6,000 |
| Austrian 1812-1870 | | | |
| ☐ **MAYER, Constance** ............................ *paintings* | | | $1,980 |
| French 1775/78-1821 ................................. *drawings* | | | $3,300 |
| ☐ **MAYER, Constant** ............................ *paintings* | | $308 | $3,900 |
| French/American 1829/32-1911 | | | |
| ☐ **MAYER, Frank Blackwell** ..................... *paintings* | | $495 | $26,000 |
| American 1827-1889 | | | |

|  | | *Current Price Range* | |
|---|---|---|---|
|  | | *Low* | *High* |
| ☐ **MAYER, Franz** ................................ *paintings* | | | **$286** |
| German 20th cent. | | | |
| ☐ **MAYER, Fritz** ................................ *paintings* | | | **$990** |
| Continental School 1835-1904 | | | |
| ☐ **MAYER, Louis** ................................ *sculpture* | | | **$330** |
| American b. 1869 | | | |
| ☐ **MAYER, Luigi** ................................ *drawings* | | | **$2,860** |
| Italian 19th cent. | | | |
| ☐ **MAYER, Peter Bela** ........................ *paintings* | | **$385** | **$19,800** |
| American b. 1888 | | | |
| ☐ **MAYER-AL** ................................ *paintings* | | | **$385** |
| Austrian 19th/20th cent. | | | |
| ☐ **MAYER-CLEMY, E.** ........................ *paintings* | | | **$1,210** |
| German 19th cent. | | | |
| ☐ **MAYERNIK, Ken** ........................ *sculpture* | | | **$2,000** |
| American | | | |
| ☐ **MAYFIELD, E.** ................................ *paintings* | | | **$350** |
| ☐ **MAYFIELD, Robert B.** ........................ *paintings* | | **$110** | **$880** |
| American 1869-1934 | | | |
| ☐ **MAYHEW, A.** ................................ *paintings* | | | **$385** |
| ☐ **MAYNARD, George Willoughby** ........... *paintings* | | **$450** | **$2,200** |
| American 1843-1923 | | | |
| ☐ **MAYO** ................................ *paintings* | | | **$385** |
| ☐ **MAYODON, Jean Claude** ................... *paintings* | | **$82** | **$231** |
| French b. 1938 | | | |
| ☐ **MAYOR, L.** ................................ *paintings* | | | **$550** |
| British 19th cent. | | | |
| ☐ **MAYR, Christian** ................................ *paintings* | | | **$1,100** |
| American | | | |
| ☐ **MAYR, Franz von Paula** ........................ *drawings* | | | **$880** |
| ☐ **MAYR, Heinrich von** ........................ *paintings* | | **$2,860** | **$4,180** |
| German 1806-1871 | | | |
| ☐ **MAYR-GRAZ, Carl** ........................ *paintings* | | | **$3,025** |
| Austrian 1850-1929 | | | |
| ☐ **MAYRE, C.** ................................ *paintings* | | | **$2,860** |
| Dutch 19th cent. | | | |
| ☐ **MAYRHOFER, Johann Nepomuk** ......... *paintings* | | | **$8,800** |
| Austrian 1764-1832 | | | |
| ☐ **MAZA, Fernando** ................................ *paintings* | | | **$2,200** |
| b. Argentina 1936 | | | |
| ☐ **MAZE, Paul** ................................ *paintings* | | **$302** | **$440** |
| French 1887-1979 ................................ *drawings* | | **$165** | **$1,430** |
| ☐ **MAZINI** ................................ *drawings* | | **$110** | **$5,500** |
| Italian 19th cent. | | | |
| ☐ **MAZUR, Michael** ................................ *drawings* | | | **$3,300** |
| American b. 1935 | | | |
| ☐ **MAZURA, F.** ................................ *sculpture* | | | **$660** |
| ☐ **MAZZANOVICH, Lawrence** ................. *paintings* | | **$1,210** | **$9,900** |
| American 1872-after 1934 | | | |

| | | *Current Price Range* | |
|---|---|---|---|
| | | *Low* | *High* |
| ☐ **MAZZOLINI, Giuseppe** ......... *paintings* | | $385 | $8,250 |
| Italian 19th cent. | | | |
| ☐ **MAZZONI, Sebastiano** ......... *paintings* | | | $8,800 |
| ☐ **MAZZONI, T.** ......... *paintings* | | | $1,210 |
| ☐ **MAZZONOVICH, Lawrence** ......... *paintings* | | | $3,000 |
| American | | | |
| ☐ **MAZZOTTA, Federico** ......... *paintings* | | $10,175 | $20,900 |
| Italian 19th cent. | | | |
| ☐ **MCADAMS, T.** ......... *paintings* | | | $247 |
| American | | | |
| ☐ **MCALLISTER, Charles** ......... *drawings* | | | $770 |
| American 19th cent. | | | |
| ☐ **MCARTHY (?)** ......... *paintings* | | | $3,190 |
| American 19th cent. | | | |
| ☐ **MCAULIFFE, James J.** ......... *paintings* | | $770 | $4,675 |
| American 1848-1921 | | | |
| ☐ **MCBEY, James** ......... *drawings* | | $192 | $770 |
| British 1883-1959 | | | |
| ☐ **MCBRIDE, Henry** ......... *drawings* | | | $275 |
| British 19th cent. | | | |
| ☐ **MCBURNEY, James E.** ......... *paintings* | | | $330 |
| American 1868-1934 | | | |
| ☐ **MCCALL, Charles** ......... *paintings* | | $495 | $935 |
| American 20th cent. | | | |
| ☐ **MCCALL, Robert T.** ......... *paintings* | | $220 | $550 |
| b. 1919 | | | |
| ☐ **MCCARTAN, Edward** ......... *sculpture* | | $1,430 | $28,600 |
| American 1879-1947 | | | |
| ☐ **MCCARTER, Henry** ......... *paintings* | | | $440 |
| American b. 1866 ......... *drawings* | | $11 | $770 |
| ☐ **MCCARTHY, Frank** ......... *paintings* | | $357 | $54,000 |
| American b. 1924 | | | |
| ☐ **MCCARTHY, Kevin** ......... *sculpture* | | | $2,750 |
| American contemporary | | | |
| ☐ **MCCAY, Winsor** ......... *paintings* | | | $224 |
| American 1871-1934 ......... *drawings* | | $440 | $605 |
| ☐ **MCCLELLAN** ......... *paintings* | | | $11,000 |
| American 19th cent. | | | |
| ☐ **MCCLOSKEY, J. Burns** ......... *paintings* | | | $880 |
| American 20th cent. | | | |
| ☐ **MCCLOSKEY, Jim** ......... *paintings* | | | $935 |
| American contemporary | | | |
| ☐ **MCCLOSKEY, William John** ......... *paintings* | | | $148,500 |
| American c. 1860-early 1900's | | | |
| ☐ **MCCOLVIN, John** ......... *paintings* | | | $264 |
| English 19th cent. | | | |
| ☐ **MCCOLVINI, J.** ......... *paintings* | | $137 | $192 |
| Italian 19th cent. | | | |

| | Current Price Range | |
|---|---|---|
| | Low | High |
| ☐ **MCCOMAS, Francis John** .......... *paintings* | | $19,800 |
| American 1874-1938 ................. *drawings* | $605 | $6,930 |
| ☐ **MCCOMAS, Gene Frances** ......... *paintings* | | $247 |
| American 20th cent. ................. *drawings* | $88 | $330 |
| ☐ **MCCOMBS, Solomon** ............. *paintings* | | $3,850 |
| American (Creek) b. 1913 | | |
| ☐ **MCCONNELL, George** ........... *paintings* | $60 | $990 |
| American 1852-1929 ................. *drawings* | $77 | $80 |
| ☐ **MCCORD, Charles William** ......... *paintings* | | $247 |
| American 1852-1923 | | |
| ☐ **MCCORD, George Herbert** ......... *paintings* | $187 | $3,410 |
| American 1848-1909 ................. *drawings* | $99 | $880 |
| ☐ **MCCORD, Scott** ............... *paintings* | | $2,970 |
| late 19th cent. | | |
| ☐ **MCCORMICK, Arthur David** ......... *paintings* | $1,760 | $4,125 |
| British 1860-1943 ................. *drawings* | | $165 |
| ☐ **MCCOY, Lawrence R.** ........... *paintings* | $88 | $495 |
| American b. 1888 | | |
| ☐ **MCCRACKEN, John Harvey** ......... *paintings* | $275 | $2,530 |
| American b. 1934 ................. *drawings* | | $154 |
| ................. *sculpture* | $275 | $770 |
| ☐ **MCCREA, Samuel Harkness** ......... *paintings* | $165 | $2,475 |
| American b. 1867 | | |
| ☐ **MCCREARY, Harrison** ......... *paintings* | | $522 |
| American 20th cent. | | |
| ☐ **MCCULLEM, A.** ............... *drawings* | | $550 |
| American 19th cent. | | |
| ☐ **MCCULLOCH, Horatio** ......... *paintings* | $605 | $2,860 |
| Scottish 1805-1867 | | |
| ☐ **MCDERMOTT, A.R.** ............ *paintings* | | $357 |
| American 20th cent. | | |
| ☐ **MCDONALD, John Blake** ......... *paintings* | $412 | $935 |
| Scottish 1829-1901 | | |
| ☐ **MCDOUGAL, John** ............. *drawings* | $220 | $522 |
| British 1877-1941 | | |
| ☐ **MCDOUGALL, J.A. (Jr.)** ......... *paintings* | | $880 |
| ☐ **MCDUFF** ............... *paintings* | | $1,430 |
| ☐ **MCENTEE, Jervis** ............. *paintings* | $605 | $57,750 |
| American 1828-1891 ................. *drawings* | | $715 |
| ☐ **MCEVOY, Ambrose** ............. *drawings* | $110 | $935 |
| English 1878-1927 | | |
| ☐ **MCEWAN, Thomas** ............. *paintings* | | $2,750 |
| British 1861-1914 | | |
| ☐ **MCEWEN, Walter** ............. *paintings* | $440 | $3,080 |
| American 1860-1943 ................. *drawings* | $990 | $7,150 |
| ☐ **MCEWEN, William** ............. *paintings* | $495 | $2,640 |
| American ac. c. 1868 | | |
| ☐ **MCFARLANE, David** ............. *paintings* | $4,000 | $22,000 |
| British ac. 1840-1866 | | |

| | | Current Price Range | |
|---|---|---|---|
| | | Low | High |
| ☐ **MCFEE, Henry Lee** ............... *paintings* | | $990 | $6,050 |
| American 1886-1953 ............... *drawings* | | | $1,320 |
| ☐ **MCGILLIVARY, Florence Helena** ...... *paintings* | | $605 | $770 |
| Canadian b. 1864 | | | |
| ☐ **MCGIVEREN, Ethel** ............... *drawings* | | | $275 |
| ☐ **MCGRATH, Clarence** ............... *paintings* | | $9,000 | $10,000 |
| American b. 1938 | | | |
| ☐ **MCGREGOR, D.M.** ............... *paintings* | | | $247 |
| Scottish 19th cent. | | | |
| ☐ **MCGREGOR, Robert** ............... *paintings* | | | $1,100 |
| ☐ **MCGREGOR, Sarah** ............... *paintings* | | | $880 |
| British 19th/20th cent. | | | |
| ☐ **MCGREGOR, William York** ............... *paintings* | | | $275 |
| English 1855-1923 | | | |
| ☐ **MCGREW, Ralph Brownell** ............... *paintings* | | $12,000 | $49,000 |
| American b. 1916 ............... *drawings* | | | $10,000 |
| ☐ **MCGUINNESS, C.W.** ............... *drawings* | | | $2,500 |
| American | | | |
| ☐ **MCGUINNESS, Robert E.** ............... *paintings* | | | $247 |
| b. 1926 | | | |
| ☐ **MCGUIRE, Robert** ............... *paintings* | | | $528 |
| American 20th cent. | | | |
| ☐ **MCILHENNY, Charles Morgan** ............... *paintings* | | $330 | $7,000 |
| American 1858-1904 | | | |
| ☐ **MCINNESS, A.** ............... *paintings* | | | $2,420 |
| ☐ **MCINTOSH, Robert J.** ............... *paintings* | | | $385 |
| American 20th cent. | | | |
| ☐ **MCINTYRE, James** ............... *paintings* | | | $1,540 |
| British ac. 1867-1891 | | | |
| ☐ **MCINTYRE, Joseph Wrightson** ............... *paintings* | | | $357 |
| British 19th cent. | | | |
| ☐ **MCINTYRE, Peter** ............... *drawings* | | | $357 |
| ☐ **MCKAY, F.H.** ............... *paintings* | | $250 | $605 |
| ☐ **MCKAY, M.R.** ............... *paintings* | | | $220 |
| American 19th cent. | | | |
| ☐ **MCKEE, Ron** ............... *paintings* | | | $2,000 |
| American contemporary | | | |
| ☐ **MCKENNEY, Henrietta** ............... *paintings* | | $770 | $3,520 |
| American 1825-1887 | | | |
| ☐ **MCKENZIE, Peter** ............... *paintings* | | | $203 |
| Canadian 1886-1969 | | | |
| ☐ **MCKENZIE, Robert Tait** ............... *sculpture* | | $1,760 | $60,000 |
| Canadian/Amer. 1867-1938 | | | |
| ☐ **MCKENZIE, William** ............... *paintings* | | | $605 |
| British 19th cent. | | | |
| ☐ **MCKEWAN, David Hall** ............... *drawings* | | | $385 |
| English 1816/17-1873 | | | |
| ☐ **MCKNIGHT, Dodge** ............... *drawings* | | $275 | $400 |
| American 1860-1950 | | | |

| | | *Current Price Range* | |
|---|---|---|---|
| | | *Low* | *High* |
| ☐ **MCKNIGHT-SMITH, C.** ...................... *drawings* | | | $220 |
| American early 20th cent. | | | |
| ☐ **MCLACHLAN, Thomas Hope** ............... *paintings* | | | $220 |
| British 1845-1897 | | | |
| ☐ **MCLARGEN, A.N.** ............................ *paintings* | | | $192 |
| British 19th cent. | | | |
| ☐ **MCLAUGHLIN, John** ......................... *paintings* | | $1,650 | $15,400 |
| American b. 1898 | | | |
| ☐ **MCLEA, J. W.** ................................. *paintings* | | | $715 |
| Scottish 19th cent. | | | |
| ☐ **MCLEAN, Avis L.** ............................ *paintings* | | | $275 |
| American 20th cent. | | | |
| ☐ **MCLEAN, Bruce** .............................. *paintings* | | | $5,720 |
| contemporary | | | |
| ☐ **MCLEAN, Harold** ............................. *paintings* | | | $12,100 |
| American 19th/20th cent. | | | |
| ☐ **MCLEAN, Howard** ............................ *paintings* | | | $1,430 |
| American 20th cent. | | | |
| ☐ **MCLEAN, Richard** ............................ *paintings* | | $14,300 | $16,500 |
| American b. 1934 | | | |
| ☐ **MCLEAY, MacNeil** ........................... *paintings* | | $1,045 | $1,430 |
| Scottish 19th cent. | | | |
| ☐ **MCLELLAN, R.** ............................... *paintings* | | | $220 |
| American 19th/20th cent. | | | |
| ☐ **MCLEOD, W.** .................................. *paintings* | | | $4,950 |
| American 19th cent. | | | |
| ☐ **MCLOUGHLIN, Gregory** .................... *paintings* | | | $300 |
| American 20th cent. | | | |
| ☐ **MCMANUS, George** .......................... *drawings* | | $71 | $495 |
| American 1884-1954 | | | |
| ☐ **MCMEIN, Neysa** .............................. *drawings* | | $550 | $1,100 |
| American 1890-1949 | | | |
| ☐ **MCMINN, William Kimmins** ............... *paintings* | | $3,500 | $4,000 |
| British ac. 1854-1880 | | | |
| ☐ **MCNEIL, George** ............................. *paintings* | | | $1,100 |
| American b. 1908 | | | |
| ☐ **MCNETT, W. Brown** .......................... *paintings* | | | $275 |
| American 19th/20th cent. | | | |
| ☐ **MCNULTY, George** ........................... *sculpture* | | | $275 |
| American contemporary | | | |
| ☐ **MCNULTY, William C.** ...................... *paintings* | | | $715 |
| ☐ **MCPHERSON, J.** .............................. *drawings* | | | $440 |
| ☐ **MCSWINEY, Eugene** ......................... *paintings* | | | $990 |
| ☐ **MCTAGGERT** .................................. *paintings* | | | $495 |
| ☐ **MCWADE, Frank** ............................. *paintings* | | | $176 |
| American 20th cent. | | | |
| ☐ **MEAD, J.B.** .................................... *paintings* | | | $220 |
| English 19th cent. | | | |

| | | Current Price Range | |
| --- | --- | --- | --- |
| | | Low | High |
| ☐ MEAD, Larkin Goldsmith ........ *sculpture* | | **$1,650** | **$2,420** |
| American 1835-1910 | | | |
| ☐ MEADOR, Joshua ........ *paintings* | | | **$192** |
| American b. 1911 | | | |
| ☐ MEADOWS, Arthur Joseph ........ *paintings* | | **$495** | **$5,500** |
| British 1843-1907 | | | |
| ☐ MEADOWS, Bernard ........ *sculpture* | | **$275** | **$1,760** |
| English b. 1915 | | | |
| ☐ MEADOWS, Edwin L. ........ *paintings* | | **$990** | **$4,400** |
| English ac. 1854-1872 | | | |
| ☐ MEADOWS, James Edward ........ *paintings* | | | **$3,630** |
| ☐ MEADOWS, James Edwin ........ *paintings* | | **$1,045** | **$9,350** |
| British 1828-1888 | | | |
| ☐ MEADOWS, Jason E. ........ *paintings* | | | **$770** |
| English 19th cent. | | | |
| ☐ MEADOWS, William ........ *paintings* | | | **$1,045** |
| British 19th cent. | | | |
| ☐ MEADOWS, William G. ........ *paintings* | | | **$2,750** |
| ☐ MEAKIN, Lewis Henry ........ *paintings* | | **$440** | **$10,175** |
| English 1853-1917 | | | |
| ☐ MEARNS, A. ........ *paintings* | | | **$5,225** |
| British ac. 1855-1866 | | | |
| ☐ MEARTZ, Franz ........ *paintings* | | | **$357** |
| ☐ MECHBERG, Lev ........ *paintings* | | | **$302** |
| Russian 20th cent. | | | |
| ☐ MECKEL, Adolph von ........ *paintings* | | | **$11,000** |
| German 1856-1893 | | | |
| ☐ MECKLENBURG, Ludwig ........ *paintings* | | | **$4,400** |
| German 1820-1882 | | | |
| ☐ MEDINA, John ........ *paintings* | | | **$495** |
| English 1721-1796 | | | |
| ☐ MEDINA, Sir John ........ *paintings* | | | **$1,100** |
| Scottish 1660-1711 | | | |
| ☐ MEDLYCOTT, | | | |
| The Rev. Sir Hubert James ........ *drawings* | | **$220** | **$412** |
| English 1841-1920 | | | |
| ☐ MEDNYANSZKY, Baron Laszlo ........ *paintings* | | **$990** | **$1,210** |
| Hungarian 1852-1919 | | | |
| ☐ MEEKER, Joseph Rusling ........ *paintings* | | **$770** | **$13,200** |
| American 1827-1887/89 | | | |
| ☐ MEEN, Margaret ........ *paintings* | | | **$990** |
| English 18th/19th cent. | | | |
| ☐ MEER, Barend van der ........ *paintings* | | **$8,800** | **$9,350** |
| Dutch b. c. 1659 | | | |
| ☐ MEERHOUD, Jan ........ *paintings* | | | **$1,430** |
| Dutch d. 1677 | | | |
| ☐ MEERTENS, Abraham ........ *drawings* | | **$55** | **$1,650** |
| Dutch 1757-1823 | | | |

| | | | Current Price Range | |
|---|---|---|---|---|
| | | | Low | High |
| ☐ **MEERTS, Franz** .............. *paintings* | | | $1,045 | $1,540 |
| Belgian 1836-1896 | | | | |
| ☐ **MEESER, Lilian B.** ............ *paintings* | | | | $385 |
| American 19th/20th cent. ........... *drawings* | | | | $25 |
| ☐ **MEEYER, Edg. van** ........... *paintings* | | | | $220 |
| Dutch 20th cent. | | | | |
| ☐ **MEGAREE, Edwin** ............ *paintings* | | | $715 | $715 |
| American 20th cent. | | | | |
| ☐ **MEGARGEE, Lon** ............ *paintings* | | | $440 | $880 |
| American 1883-1960 | | | | |
| ☐ **MEGIA, N.** ..................... *drawings* | | | | $192 |
| Spanish c. 1880 | | | | |
| ☐ **MEHLE, Carl R.** ............ *paintings* | | | | $1,430 |
| ☐ **MEIDE, J.L. van der** ........... *paintings* | | | $385 | $412 |
| Belgian 20th cent. | | | | |
| ☐ **MEIDNER, Ludwig** ............ *drawings* | | | $1,210 | $1,980 |
| German 1884-1966 | | | | |
| ☐ **MEIER, Richard** ............... *drawings* | | | | $935 |
| American b. 1934 | | | | |
| ☐ **MEIHE, W.A.** ................... *paintings* | | | | $324 |
| ☐ **MEIJER, Johan** ............... *paintings* | | | | $308 |
| ☐ **MEILINK, A.** ................... *paintings* | | | | $242 |
| Dutch 20th cent. | | | | |
| ☐ **MEIN, Etienne Joseph** ......... *paintings* | | | | $715 |
| French b. 1865 | | | | |
| ☐ **MEINDL, Albert** ............... *paintings* | | | | $600 |
| Austrian 20th cent. | | | | |
| ☐ **MEINDL, Alfred** ............... *paintings* | | | $330 | $440 |
| German 20th cent. | | | | |
| ☐ **MEINERS, Pieter** ............ *paintings* | | | | $495 |
| Dutch 1857-1903 | | | | |
| ☐ **MEIREN, Jan Baptiste van der** ............ *paintings* | | | | $3,300 |
| Flemish 1664-1708 | | | | |
| ☐ **MEIRHANS, Joseph** ............ *paintings* | | | | $2,750 |
| American 1890-1981 ............... *drawings* | | | $2,090 | $2,090 |
| ☐ **MEISEL, Ernst** ............... *paintings* | | | $1,700 | $2,200 |
| German 1838-1895 | | | | |
| ☐ **MEISNER, B.** ................... *paintings* | | | | $715 |
| ☐ **MEISSEL** ..................... *paintings* | | | | $1,650 |
| German 19th cent. | | | | |
| ☐ **MEISSIONIER, Jean Charles** ............ *paintings* | | | $770 | $2,200 |
| French 1848-1917 | | | | |
| ☐ **MEISSNER, Adolf Ernst** ......... *paintings* | | | $2,420 | $15,400 |
| German 1837-1902 | | | | |
| ☐ **MEISSONIER, Jean Louis Ernest** ......... *paintings* | | | $302 | $13,200 |
| French 1815-1891 ..................... *drawings* | | | $275 | $1,430 |
| ☐ **MEISTCHANINOFF, Oscar** ............... *paintings* | | | | $1,100 |
| ☐ **MEISTER, Ernst** ............... *paintings* | | | | $3,850 |
| German 19th cent. | | | | |

| | | Current Price Range | |
| | | Low | High |
|---|---|---|---|
| ☐ **MEIXNER, Ludwig** ............... *paintings* | | | **$1,540** |
| German 1828-1885 | | | |
| ☐ **MELARSKY, M.** ................. *paintings* | | **$357** | **$385** |
| ☐ **MELBY, F.G.** .................... *paintings* | | | **$4,250** |
| Danish 19th cent. | | | |
| ☐ **MELBY, Wilhelm** ............... *paintings* | | **$3,520** | **$7,700** |
| Danish 1824-1882 | | | |
| ☐ **MELBYE, Daniel Hermann Anton** ........ *paintings* | | | **$1,980** |
| Danish 1818-1875 | | | |
| ☐ **MELCHER, Jakob** ............... *paintings* | | | **$550** |
| German 19th cent. | | | |
| ☐ **MELCHER-TILMES, Jan Hermanus** .... *paintings* | | | **$2,420** |
| ☐ **MELCHERS, Julius Gari** ........ *paintings* | | **$1,540** | **$28,600** |
| American 1860-1932 .................... *drawings* | | **$880** | **$1,045** |
| ☐ **MELE, E.** ........................ *sculpture* | | | **$1,925** |
| ☐ **MELENDEZ, Luis** ............... *paintings* | | | **$44,000** |
| Spanish 1716-1780 | | | |
| ☐ **MELIAT, Victoria** ............... *paintings* | | | **$495** |
| ☐ **MELIDA Y ALINARI, Don Enrique** ...... *paintings* | | | **$2,420** |
| Spanish 1834-1892 | | | |
| ☐ **MELIN, Joseph Herbain** ........ *paintings* | | | **$330** |
| French 1814-1886 | | | |
| ☐ **MELIS, Henricus Johannes** ............ *paintings* | | | **$3,630** |
| Dutch 1845-1923 | | | |
| ☐ **MELLAERT, G. van** ............ *paintings* | | | **$935** |
| European | | | |
| ☐ **MELLEN, Mary** ................. *paintings* | | **$200** | **$4,675** |
| American 19th cent. | | | |
| ☐ **MELLERY, Xavier** ............... *paintings* | | | **$550** |
| Belgian 1845-1921 ..................... *drawings* | | | **$209** |
| ☐ **MELLING, Antoine Ignace** ........ *drawings* | | **$4,400** | **$4,620** |
| French 1763-1931 | | | |
| ☐ **MELLINI, Paulo** ............... *paintings* | | **$220** | **$660** |
| Italian 19th/20th cent. | | | |
| ☐ **MELLINS** ...................... *paintings* | | | **$220** |
| 19th/20th cent. | | | |
| ☐ **MELLISH, Thomas** ............... *paintings* | | | **$9,350** |
| English ac. 1740-1766 | | | |
| ☐ **MELLON, Eleanor** ............... *paintings* | | | **$302** |
| American b. 1894 | | | |
| ☐ **MELLOR, J.** ..................... *paintings* | | **$165** | **$357** |
| ☐ **MELLOR, William** ............... *paintings* | | **$247** | **$3,575** |
| British 1851-1931 | | | |
| ☐ **MELOHS, Charles** ............... *paintings* | | | **$357** |
| ☐ **MELROSE, Andrew W.** ........ *paintings* | | **$440** | **$20,900** |
| American 1836-1901 .................... *drawings* | | **$357** | **$1,100** |
| ☐ **MELTZER, Anna E.** ............ *paintings* | | | **$550** |
| American 20th cent. | | | |

|  | | *Current Price Range* | |
|---|---|---|---|
|  | | *Low* | *High* |
| ☐ **MELTZER, Arthur** ............................ *paintings* | | $154 | $10,450 |
| American b. 1893 | | | |
| ☐ **MELVILL, Antonia** ............................ *paintings* | | | $192 |
| American b. 1875 | | | |
| ☐ **MELVILLE, Arthur** ............................ *paintings* | | | $1,980 |
| British 1855-1904 ................................... *drawings* | | | $550 |
| ☐ **MELVILLE, Harland** ........................ *paintings* | | | $500 |
| British 19th cent. | | | |
| ☐ **MELVILLE, J. C.** .............................. *paintings* | | | $660 |
| ☐ **MELZER, A.** ..................................... *paintings* | | | $1,045 |
| German 19th cent. | | | |
| ☐ **MELZER, Franciscus** ........................ *paintings* | | $1,760 | $2,750 |
| Belgian b. 1808 | | | |
| ☐ **MEMPES, Mortimer L.** ...................... *paintings* | | $3,520 | $5,775 |
| British 1859-1938 | | | |
| ☐ **MEMPRES, Adrian Layeur de** ............. *paintings* | | $825 | $1,870 |
| Belgian b. 1844 | | | |
| ☐ **MENABONI, Athos** ........................... *paintings* | | $104 | $2,900 |
| Italian/American b. 1895 | | | |
| ☐ **MENARD, Marie Auguste Emile Rene** ... *paintings* | | $357 | $5,500 |
| French 1862-1930 | | | |
| ☐ **MENARD, Victor Pierre** ...................... *paintings* | | | $825 |
| French b. 1857 | | | |
| ☐ **MENASCO, Milton** ............................ *paintings* | | | $5,500 |
| American | | | |
| ☐ **MENCHETTI, R.** ................................ *paintings* | | | $750 |
| ☐ **MENCONI, D.** ................................... *sculpture* | | | $1,760 |
| Italian 19th cent. | | | |
| ☐ **MENDENHALL, Jack** ......................... *paintings* | | $8,250 | $11,000 |
| American b. 1937 | | | |
| ☐ **MENDJINSKY, Serge** ......................... *paintings* | | $176 | $660 |
| French 20th cent. | | | |
| ☐ **MENDOZA, Esteban** ........................ *paintings* | | $275 | $495 |
| Spanish ac. 1630 | | | |
| ☐ **MENDOZA, Pedro** ............................ *paintings* | | | $550 |
| Spanish ac. 1593-1597 | | | |
| ☐ **MENE, Pierre Jules** ........................... *sculpture* | | $82 | $19,250 |
| French 1810-1879 | | | |
| ☐ **MENESCARDI, Giustino** ...................... *paintings* | | | $6,600 |
| Italian b. 1720 | | | |
| ☐ **MENGIN, Paul Eugene** ........................ *sculpture* | | | $4,070 |
| French ac. 19th/20th cent. | | | |
| ☐ **MENINSKY, Bernard** .......................... *paintings* | | | $412 |
| ☐ **MENIS, G.** ...................................... *paintings* | | | $1,210 |
| ☐ **MENKES, Sigmund (or Zygmunt)** .......... *paintings* | | $27 | $1,980 |
| Polish/American b. 1896 ............................ *drawings* | | $154 | $330 |
| ☐ **MENKIS** ......................................... *drawings* | | $110 | $302 |
| ☐ **MENN, Barthelemy** ........................... *paintings* | | | $1,320 |
| Swiss 1815-1893 | | | |

| | | Current Price Range | |
|---|---|---|---|
| | | Low | High |
| ☐ **MENNEVILLE, A.** ............................. *sculpture* | | | $330 |
| ☐ **MENOCAL, Armando** ........................... *paintings* | | | $3,300 |
| Cuban 1863-1942 | | | |
| ☐ **MENOTTI, P.** .................................... *paintings* | | | $2,300 |
| Italian 19th cent. | | | |
| ☐ **MENOTTI, V.A.** .................................. *paintings* | | | $2,090 |
| Italian 19th cent. | | | |
| ☐ **MENSE, Carlo** .................................... *drawings* | | | $300 |
| German 1886-1965 | | | |
| ☐ **MENZEL, Adolf Friedrich Erdmann** ..... *paintings* | | | $35,750 |
| German 1815-1905 ................................ *drawings* | | $385 | $28,600 |
| ☐ **MENZLER, Wilhelm** ........................... *paintings* | | $467 | $2,200 |
| German b. 1846 | | | |
| ☐ **MENZLER-PEYTON, Bertha S.** ........... *paintings* | | $715 | $2,530 |
| American b. 1874 | | | |
| ☐ **MEQUIGNON, Francois-Guillaume** ....... *paintings* | | | $440 |
| ☐ **MER, Gerret de** .................................... *paintings* | | $330 | $1,320 |
| Dutch 17th cent. | | | |
| ☐ **MERCIE, Marius Jean Antonin** ........... *paintings* | | | $6,050 |
| French 1845-1916 ..................................... *sculpture* | | $660 | $880 |
| ☐ **MERCIER, Charlotte** ........................... *drawings* | | | $19,800 |
| English d. 1762 | | | |
| ☐ **MERCIER, Philippe** ........................... *paintings* | | $715 | $55,000 |
| French 1689/91-1760 | | | |
| ☐ **MERCK, Jacob Frans van der** ............. *paintings* | | | $1,650 |
| Dutch 1610-1664 | | | |
| ☐ **MERCKLE, Adolph** ............................... *paintings* | | | $275 |
| ☐ **MERCULIANO** .................................... *sculpture* | | | $440 |
| ☐ **MERELUS** ......................................... *paintings* | | | $330 |
| ☐ **MERIA** .............................................. *paintings* | | | $1,650 |
| Belgian School 19th cent. | | | |
| ☐ **MERIADEC** ........................................ *sculpture* | | | $715 |
| ☐ **MERIDA, Carlos** ............................... *paintings* | | $1,320 | $28,600 |
| Guatemalan/Mexican 1891-1984 ..................... *drawings* | | $550 | $17,600 |
| ................................................................. *sculpture* | | | $7,700 |
| ☐ **MERIN, F.** ......................................... *drawings* | | | $356 |
| English 19th cent. | | | |
| ☐ **MERINO, Ignacio** ............................... *paintings* | | | $14,300 |
| Peruvian/French 1818-1876 | | | |
| ☐ **MERIOT, R.** ....................................... *paintings* | | | $715 |
| French 19th cent. | | | |
| ☐ **MERITE, Edouard Paul** ....................... *drawings* | | | $250 |
| French 1867-1941 | | | |
| ☐ **MERKEL, O.** ...................................... *paintings* | | | $550 |
| American 19th cent. | | | |
| ☐ **MERLE, Georges Hugues** ..................... *paintings* | | | $3,850 |
| French 19th cent. | | | |
| ☐ **MERLE, Hugues** ................................. *paintings* | | $1,430 | $5,500 |
| French 1823-1881 | | | |

## Latin American Paintings

Each May and November, the New York auction houses of Christie's and Sotheby's hold Latin American paintings sales. The works of Carlos Merida frequently appear at auction. Born in Guatemala, Merida studied in Paris and returned to his native country in 1914.

This painting is an example of Merida's earlier work and is connected to his study of native folklore. His later work is more abstract and shows the influence of Klee, Kandinsky, Miro, and Picasso. Merida is noted as an extraordinary colorist. He painted in oil, but also produced works in other media, among them, engravings, lithographs, and prints. (Carlos Merida, "Motivo Guatamalteco," oil on canvas, 38¾ x 28 in., Christie's, November 28, 1984, $19,800.)

|  | | Current Price Range | |
|---|---|---|---|
|  | | Low | High |
| ☐ **MERLIN, Daniel** ................................. *paintings* | | **$192** | **$3,850** |
| French 1861-1933 | | | |
| ☐ **MERLOT, Emile Justin** ........................ *paintings* | | | **$356** |
| French 1839-1900 | | | |
| ☐ **MERRIAM, J.A.** ................................. *paintings* | | | **$385** |
| ☐ **MERRILL, Frank Thayer** .................... *paintings* | | **$220** | **$440** |
| American b. 1848 ...................................... *drawings* | | **$110** | **$242** |
| ☐ **MERRILL, R.S.** ................................. *paintings* | | | **$352** |
| American | | | |
| ☐ **MERRILL, T.** ..................................... *paintings* | | | **$330** |
| German (?) 19th cent. | | | |
| ☐ **MERRITT, Anna Lea** ........................... *paintings* | | **$440** | **$1,650** |
| Anglo/American 1844-1930 | | | |
| ☐ **MERSFELDER, Jules** ......................... *paintings* | | **$220** | **$1,650** |
| American 1865-1937 | | | |
| ☐ **MERTENS, Bruno** ............................. *paintings* | | | **$550** |
| Dutch b. 1914 | | | |
| ☐ **MERTENS, Willy** ................................ *paintings* | | | **$825** |

| | | Current Price Range | |
|---|---|---|---|
| | | Low | High |
| ☐ **MERVIUS, H.** ..................................... *paintings* | | | **$2,090** |
| ☐ **MERY, A.E.** ..................................... *paintings* | | | **$605** |
| ☐ **MERY, Paul** ..................................... *paintings* | | | **$330** |
| ☐ **MESBURGER, T.** ..................................... *paintings* | | | **$880** |
| ☐ **MESDACH, Salamon** ........................... *paintings* | | | **$900** |
| Dutch 17th cent. | | | |
| ☐ **MESDAG, Hendrik Willem** .................. *paintings* | | **$1,650** | **$24,200** |
| Dutch 1831-1915 ..................................... *drawings* | | **$110** | **$4,950** |
| ☐ **MESDANG, W.** ..................................... *paintings* | | | **$412** |
| Dutch 19th/20th cent. | | | |
| ☐ **MESENS, E.L.T.** ............................... *drawings* | | | **$1,210** |
| Belgian 1903-1971 | | | |
| ☐ **MESEROLE, A.K.** ............................... *paintings* | | | **$385** |
| American 20th cent. | | | |
| ☐ **MESGRIGNY, Frank de** ....................... *paintings* | | | **$9,350** |
| French 1836-1884 ..................................... *drawings* | | | **$880** |
| ☐ **MESGRINY, Claude Francois Auguste** .. *paintings* | | | **$7,700** |
| French 1836-1884 | | | |
| ☐ **MESHBERG, Lev** ............................... *paintings* | | **$220** | **$275** |
| Russian 20th cent. | | | |
| ☐ **MESINO** ..................................... *drawings* | | | **$247** |
| Italian 20th cent. | | | |
| ☐ **MESLE, Joseph Paul** ........................... *paintings* | | **$99** | **$880** |
| French 1855-1929 | | | |
| ☐ **MESMER, G.** ..................................... *paintings* | | | **$1,400** |
| Swiss 19th cent. | | | |
| ☐ **MESPLES, Paul Eugene** ....................... *paintings* | | | **$1,100** |
| French b. 1849 | | | |
| ☐ **MESSAGIER, Jean** ........................... *paintings* | | **$990** | **$1,100** |
| French b. 1920 | | | |
| ☐ **MESSEL, Oliver** ............................... *drawings* | | **$110** | **$2,200** |
| British 20th cent. | | | |
| ☐ **MESSER, Edmund Clarence** ................ *paintings* | | **$770** | **$1,210** |
| American b. 1842 | | | |
| ☐ **MESSINA, A. (of Rome)** ....................... *sculpture* | | | **$250** |
| Italian 19th cent. | | | |
| ☐ **MESSINA, Francesco** ........................... *sculpture* | | | **$3,850** |
| Italian b. 1900 | | | |
| ☐ **MESSLET, A.** ..................................... *drawings* | | | **$330** |
| ☐ **MESTROVIC, Ivan** ........................... *drawings* | | **$330** | **$357** |
| American 1883/84-1962 | | | |
| ☐ **MESZOLY, Geza von** ........................... *paintings* | | | **$1,980** |
| Hungarian 1844-1887 | | | |
| ☐ **METCALF, Conger** ............................... *paintings* | | | **$302** |
| American 20th cent. ..................................... *drawings* | | | **$192** |
| ☐ **METCALF, Eliab** ............................... *paintings* | | | **$2,530** |
| 1785-1834 | | | |
| ☐ **METCALF, Willard Leroy** .................. *paintings* | | **$550** | **$148,500** |
| American 1858-1925 ..................................... *drawings* | | **$242** | **$4,400** |

|                                              | *Current Price Range* | |
|                                              | *Low* | *High* |
| ☐ **METCALFE, N.W.** .............. *paintings* | | $2,420 |
| American 19th cent. | | |
| ☐ **METEYARD, Sidney Harold** ............ *paintings* | $825 | $33,000 |
| British 1868-1947 ................... *drawings* | $220 | $3,850 |
| ☐ **METEYARD, Thomas B.** ........... *paintings* | | $352 |
| Anglo/American 1865-1928 .......... *drawings* | $275 | $495 |
| ☐ **METHVEN, H. Wallace** ........ *paintings* | | $302 |
| American b. 1875 | | |
| ☐ **METSU, Gabriel** ............. *paintings* | $2,200 | $7,000 |
| Dutch 1629-1667 | | |
| ☐ **METTLING, Louis** .......... *paintings* | $1,430 | $6,875 |
| French 1847-1904 | | |
| ☐ **METTRAY, H.B.** .......... *paintings* | | $528 |
| ☐ **METVEEF, Fedor** .......... *paintings* | | $2,200 |
| Russian 19th cent. | | |
| ☐ **METZ, Conrad Martin** ....... *drawings* | | $330 |
| British 1749-1827 | | |
| ☐ **METZ, Gerry** .......... *paintings* | | $550 |
| American b. 1943 | | |
| ☐ **METZINGER, Jean** .......... *paintings* | $3,960 | $50,600 |
| French 1883-1956 ........... *drawings* | $1,100 | $12,100 |
| ☐ **MEUCCI, Michelangelo** ........ *paintings* | $60 | $1,320 |
| Italian 19th cent. | | |
| ☐ **MEUGNIEZ, Jack** .......... *paintings* | | $385 |
| ☐ **MEULEMANS, Adrian** ......... *drawings* | | $275 |
| ☐ **MEULEN, Adam Frans van der** ....... *paintings* | $3,300 | $9,350 |
| Belgian 1632-1690 ............. *drawings* | | $3,850 |
| ☐ **MEULENER, Pieter** .......... *paintings* | $1,870 | $7,150 |
| Dutch 1602-1654 | | |
| ☐ **MEUNIER, Alfieri da** ......... *paintings* | | $495 |
| ☐ **MEUNIER, Constantine** ......... *sculpture* | $286 | $440 |
| French 1831-1905 | | |
| ☐ **MEURER, Charles A.** .......... *paintings* | $302 | $1,100 |
| American 1865-1955 | | |
| ☐ **MEURIS** .......... *drawings* | | $605 |
| Belgian 19th cent. | | |
| ☐ **MEUSNIER, Mathieu** ......... *sculpture* | | $900 |
| French 1824-1876 | | |
| ☐ **MEUTTMAN, William** ......... *paintings* | | $825 |
| American 19th/20th cent. ........ *drawings* | | $2,420 |
| ☐ **MEW, Thomas Millier** ......... *paintings* | | $2,500 |
| ☐ **MEY** .......... *paintings* | | $250 |
| Continental 19th cent. | | |
| ☐ **MEYER, August Eduard Nicolaus** ....... *paintings* | | $3,575 |
| German 1856-1919 | | |
| ☐ **MEYER, Christian** ......... *paintings* | | $1,650 |
| American 1838-1907 | | |
| ☐ **MEYER, Claus** .......... *paintings* | | $1,760 |
| German 1856-1919 | | |

| | Current Price Range | |
|---|---|---|
| | *Low* | *High* |
| ☐ **MEYER, Conrad** .................... *paintings* | | **$3,300** |
| ☐ **MEYER, Constans** .................... *paintings* | | **$385** |
| ☐ **MEYER, Emile** .................... *paintings* | **$7,150** | **$8,140** |
| French 19th cent. | | |
| ☐ **MEYER, Emile E.** .................... *drawings* | | **$220** |
| American 20th cent. | | |
| ☐ **MEYER, Ernest Frederick** .................... *paintings* | **$165** | **$301** |
| American 1863-1952 | | |
| ☐ **MEYER, Ernst Ludolf** .................... *paintings* | | **$1,320** |
| German b. 1848 | | |
| ☐ **MEYER, Gilles de** .................... *paintings* | | **$440** |
| Dutch 1780-1867 | | |
| ☐ **MEYER, Guillaume** .................... *paintings* | | **$2,090** |
| French 19th cent. | | |
| ☐ **MEYER, Hendrik de** .................... *paintings* | **$5,500** | **$15,400** |
| Dutch .................... *drawings* | | **$1,100** |
| ☐ **MEYER, Hendrik de (II)** .................... *drawings* | **$605** | **$880** |
| Dutch 1737-1793 | | |
| ☐ **MEYER, Herbert** .................... *paintings* | **$412** | **$2,420** |
| American 1882-1960 | | |
| ☐ **MEYER, Johann Heinrich Louis** .................... *paintings* | | **$4,620** |
| Dutch 1809-1866 | | |
| ☐ **MEYER, Johann Jakob** .................... *drawings* | | **$2,640** |
| Swiss 1749-1829 | | |
| ☐ **MEYER, L.** .................... *paintings* | | **$1,100** |
| ☐ **MEYER VON BREMEN,** | | |
| **Johann Georg** .................... *paintings* | **$412** | **$38,500** |
| German 1813-1886 .................... *drawings* | **$1,100** | **$3,575** |
| ☐ **MEYER-KASSEL, Hans** .................... *paintings* | | **$715** |
| American 20th cent. .................... *drawings* | | **$220** |
| ☐ **MEYER-WALDECK, Kunz** .................... *paintings* | **$1,760** | **$4,125** |
| German 1859-1953 | | |
| ☐ **MEYERHEIM, Friedrich Edouard** .................... *paintings* | | **$12,100** |
| German 1808-1879 | | |
| ☐ **MEYERHEIM, Hermann** .................... *paintings* | **$2,420** | **$18,700** |
| German 19th cent. | | |
| ☐ **MEYERHEIM, Paul Friedrich** .................... *paintings* | | **$1,980** |
| German 1842-1915 | | |
| ☐ **MEYERHEIM, Paul Wilhelm** .................... *paintings* | | **$3,850** |
| German ac. 1868-1895 | | |
| ☐ **MEYERHEIM, Wilhelm Alexander** .................... *paintings* | **$5,500** | **$11,000** |
| German 1814/15-1882 | | |
| ☐ **MEYERHEM, M.** .................... *paintings* | | **$2,299** |
| Dutch 19th cent. | | |
| ☐ **MEYERING, Albert** .................... *paintings* | | **$3,575** |
| Dutch 1645-1714 | | |
| ☐ **MEYEROWITZ, William** .................... *paintings* | **$220** | **$1,540** |
| Russian/American b.c. 1898, d. 1981 | | |

| | | *Current Price Range* | |
|---|---|---|---|
| | | Low | High |
| ☐ **MEYERS, A.** ........................ *paintings* | | | $825 |
| British 19th cent. | | | |
| ☐ **MEYERS, Bob** ........................ *paintings* | | $10,000 | $11,000 |
| American 1919-1970 | | | |
| ☐ **MEYERS, Frank H.** ........................ *paintings* | | | $247 |
| American 20th cent. | | | |
| ☐ **MEYERS, Harry Morse** ........................ *paintings* | | $132 | $286 |
| American | | | |
| ☐ **MEYERS, Isidore** ........................ *paintings* | | | $302 |
| Belgian 1836-1917 | | | |
| ☐ **MEYERS, Ralph** ........................ *paintings* | | | $770 |
| American 1885-1948 | | | |
| ☐ **MEYERS, Robert** ........................ *paintings* | | | $10,000 |
| American 1919-1970 | | | |
| ☐ **MEYLAN, Henry** ........................ *drawings* | | $176 | $231 |
| Swiss b. 1895 | | | |
| ☐ **MEYLIES, J.** ........................ *paintings* | | | $521 |
| Belgian 19th cent. | | | |
| ☐ **MEZA, Guillermo** ........................ *paintings* | | $330 | $4,675 |
| Mexican b. 1917 ........................ *drawings* | | $440 | $1,870 |
| ☐ **MEZA, Jose Reyes** ........................ *paintings* | | $33 | $350 |
| Mexican b. 1924 | | | |
| ☐ **MEZQUITA, Jose Maria Lopez** ........... *paintings* | | $82 | $302 |
| Spanish b. 1883 ........................ *drawings* | | $33 | $577 |
| ☐ **MEZZARA, Francois** ........................ *paintings* | | | $2,640 |
| French 19th cent. | | | |
| ☐ **MICALI, Guiseppe** ........................ *drawings* | | | $750 |
| Italian b. 1866 | | | |
| ☐ **MICALI, L.** ........................ *paintings* | | | $3,025 |
| Italian 19th cent. | | | |
| ☐ **MICHAEL, F.H.** ........................ *paintings* | | | $308 |
| ☐ **MICHAEL-HENRY** ........................ *paintings* | | | $192 |
| French b. 1928 | | | |
| ☐ **MICHAELIS, H. von** ........................ *paintings* | | | $495 |
| American 20th cent. | | | |
| ☐ **MICHAELS, Glen** ........................ *paintings* | | $224 | $250 |
| ☐ **MICHAELS, Max** ........................ *paintings* | | | $1,045 |
| German 1823-1891 | | | |
| ☐ **MICHALEK, Ludwig** ........................ *drawings* | | $132 | $330 |
| ☐ **MICHALONSKI, Herman** ........................ *paintings* | | | $825 |
| German 19th cent. | | | |
| ☐ **MICHALOWSKI, Piotr** ........................ *drawings* | | | $550 |
| Polish 1800-1855 | | | |
| ☐ **MICHAU, Theobald** ........................ *paintings* | | $484 | $8,800 |
| Flemish 1676-1765 | | | |
| ☐ **MICHAUT, A.** ........................ *paintings* | | $990 | $5,500 |
| ☐ **MICHAUX, Henri** ........................ *drawings* | | $935 | $2,090 |
| Belgian b. 1899 | | | |

| | | | Current Price Range | |
|---|---|---|---|---|
| | | | *Low* | *High* |
| ☐ **MICHEL, Claude (called Clodion)** .......... *sculpture* | | | $495 | $1,870 |
| French 19th cent. | | | | |
| ☐ **MICHEL, Emmanual L.** ...................... *paintings* | | | | $990 |
| Latin American | | | | |
| ☐ **MICHEL, Eugenie** ............................. *paintings* | | | | $357 |
| French early 20th cent. | | | | |
| ☐ **MICHEL, Georges** ............................ *paintings* | | | $770 | $12,100 |
| French 1763-1843 ...................................... *drawings* | | | $165 | $4,950 |
| ☐ **MICHEL, Robert** ............................ *drawings* | | | $1,650 | $4,125 |
| German b. 1897 | | | | |
| ☐ **MICHEL-HENRY** ............................. *paintings* | | | $192 | $1,320 |
| French b. 1928 | | | | |
| ☐ **MICHELI, Parrasio** ........................... *drawings* | | | | $5,940 |
| ☐ **MICHELSON, Leo** ........................... *paintings* | | | | $495 |
| American b. 1887 | | | | |
| ☐ **MICHETTI, Francesco Paolo** ............... *paintings* | | | $3,850 | $8,800 |
| Italian 1851/52-1929 ...................................... *drawings* | | | | $3,300 |
| ☐ **MICHETTI, Quintilio** ........................... *paintings* | | | | $8,250 |
| Italian b. 1849 | | | | |
| ☐ **MICHIE, John D.** .............................. *paintings* | | | | $3,080 |
| British ac. 1864-88 | | | | |
| ☐ **MICHIELI, Andrea Dei** | | | | |
| **(called VICENTINO)** ............................. *paintings* | | | | $3,850 |
| Italian 1539-1614 | | | | |
| ☐ **MICHIS, Pietro** ................................. *paintings* | | | | $6,050 |
| Italian 1836-1903 ...................................... *drawings* | | | | $440 |
| ☐ **MICKER, Jan Christiaensz.** ................. *paintings* | | | $8,800 | $10,175 |
| Dutch 17th cent. | | | | |
| ☐ **MICOTTA, J.** .................................. *paintings* | | | | $550 |
| ☐ **MIDDENDORF, Helmut** ...................... *paintings* | | | | $5,500 |
| German? b. 1953 ...................................... *drawings* | | | $2,200 | $3,850 |
| ☐ **MIDDLETON, Alex B.** ...................... *paintings* | | | | $330 |
| English 19th cent. | | | | |
| ☐ **MIDDLETON, Arthur** ........................... *drawings* | | | | $325 |
| American | | | | |
| ☐ **MIDDLETON, David** ........................... *paintings* | | | | $467 |
| ☐ **MIDDLETON, James Godsell** ............... *paintings* | | | $550 | $4,950 |
| English 19th cent. | | | | |
| ☐ **MIDDLETON, James Raeburn** ............. *paintings* | | | | $2,530 |
| British b. 1855 | | | | |
| ☐ **MIDDLETON, Stanley Grant** ............... *paintings* | | | $286 | $2,200 |
| American 1852-1942 ...................................... *drawings* | | | | $33 |
| ☐ **MIDJO, Christian M. S.** ...................... *paintings* | | | | $1,980 |
| Norwegian/American 1880-1973 | | | | |
| ☐ **MIDWOOD, William Henry** ................. *paintings* | | | $356 | $3,300 |
| British 19th cent. | | | | |
| ☐ **MIDY, Adolphe** .................................. *drawings* | | | | $550 |
| ☐ **MIEDUCH, Dan** ................................ *paintings* | | | $7,500 | $12,000 |
| American b. 1947 | | | | |

| | | Current Price Range | |
| --- | --- | --- | --- |
| | | *Low* | *High* |
| ☐ **MIEL, Jan** ............................................ *paintings* | | $4,400 | $8,250 |
| Flemish 1599-1663 | | | |
| ☐ **MIELATZ, Karl Friedrich Wilhelm** ....... *paintings* | | | $330 |
| American 1864-1919 ...................................... *drawings* | | | $143 |
| ☐ **MIELZINER, Jo** ................................ *drawings* | | $55 | $176 |
| American 20th cent. | | | |
| ☐ **MIELZINER, Leo** ............................... *drawings* | | $77 | $220 |
| American 1869-1935 | | | |
| ☐ **MIEREN, Jan Baptiste van der** ............. *paintings* | | | $2,090 |
| ☐ **MIEREVELT, Michiel Janszoon van** ..... *paintings* | | $3,300 | $14,300 |
| Dutch 1567-1641 | | | |
| ☐ **MIERIS, Willem van** ........................... *paintings* | | $3,850 | $11,000 |
| Dutch 1662-1747 | | | |
| ☐ **MIETH, Hugo** ...................................... *paintings* | | | $6,050 |
| German b. 1865 | | | |
| ☐ **MIFFLIN, John** .................................... *paintings* | | $880 | $3,300 |
| American 1807-1888 | | | |
| ☐ **MIFFLIN, Lloyd** ................................. *paintings* | | $220 | $880 |
| American 1846-1921 | | | |
| ☐ **MIGLIARA, Giovanni** .......................... *paintings* | | $2,750 | $12,650 |
| Italian 1785-1837 | | | |
| ☐ **MIGLIARO, Vicenzo** ........................... *paintings* | | | $5,500 |
| Italian 1858-1938 | | | |
| ☐ **MIGLIORE, Guglielmo** ....................... *paintings* | | | $605 |
| Italian b. 1922 | | | |
| ☐ **MIGNARD, Pierre** .............................. *paintings* | | | $2,200 |
| ☐ **MIGNON, Abraham** ............................ *paintings* | | | $82,500 |
| German 1640-1679 | | | |
| ☐ **MIGNON, Lucien** ................................ *paintings* | | $330 | $522 |
| French 1865-1944 | | | |
| ☐ **MIGNOT, Louis Remy** ........................ *paintings* | | $660 | $30,800 |
| American 1831-1870 | | | |
| ☐ **MIGOTTI, F.** ....................................... *paintings* | | | $550 |
| ☐ **MIHALOVITS, Miklos** ......................... *paintings* | | $275 | $605 |
| Hungarian 19th cent. | | | |
| ☐ **MIJARES, Jose** ................................... *paintings* | | $2,420 | $5,500 |
| Cuban b. 1921 | | | |
| ☐ **MIJN, Robert van der** .......................... *paintings* | | | $2,090 |
| Dutch 1724-1764 | | | |
| ☐ **MIKESCH, Fritzi** ............................... *paintings* | | | $8,800 |
| Austrian 1853-1891 | | | |
| ☐ **MIKLOS, Gustave** ............................... *sculpture* | | | $209 |
| French 1888-1967 | | | |
| ☐ **MIKOLELSKY, F. Koko** ....................... *paintings* | | | $770 |
| ☐ **MIKOTA, J.** ........................................ *paintings* | | | $220 |
| Austrian 19th/20th cent. | | | |
| ☐ **MIKUS, Eleanore** ............................... *paintings* | | | $495 |
| ☐ **MILANE, G.** ....................................... *paintings* | | | $605 |
| Italian 19th cent. | | | |

| | Current Price Range | |
|---|---|---|
| | Low | High |
| ☐ **MILBOURNE, Henri** ............................ *paintings* | | $605 |
| French 19th cent. | | |
| ☐ **MILBURN, J.** ................................ *paintings* | | $1,540 |
| American 19th cent. | | |
| ☐ **MILBURN, Oliver** ............................. *paintings* | | $1,760 |
| Canadian/American 1883-1934 | | |
| ☐ **MILCENDEAU,** | | |
| **Edmond Charles Theodore** .................... *drawings* | | $330 |
| ☐ **MILCHIER, W.** ................................ *paintings* | | $3,100 |
| Continental School 19th cent. | | |
| ☐ **MILDER, Jay** ................................ *paintings* | $66 | $1,650 |
| American b. 1934 ..................................... *drawings* | | $357 |
| ☐ **MILES, E.** ........................................ *paintings* | | $935 |
| American | | |
| ☐ **MILES, J.R.** ..................................... *paintings* | | $3,025 |
| Australian 19th/20th cent. | | |
| ☐ **MILES, Leonidas Clint** ..................... *paintings* | $1,210 | $1,760 |
| British ac. 1860-1883 | | |
| ☐ **MILES, Lewis** ................................ *paintings* | | $203 |
| American 1878-1923 | | |
| ☐ **MILES, S.S.** ..................................... *paintings* | | $500 |
| American 19th cent. | | |
| ☐ **MILES, Thomas Rose** ......................... *paintings* | $550 | $3,025 |
| English ac. 1869-1906 | | |
| ☐ **MILES, W.J.** ..................................... *paintings* | | $440 |
| English 19th/20th cent. | | |
| ☐ **MILESI, Alessandro** ......................... *paintings* | $880 | $4,950 |
| Italian 1856-1945 | | |
| ☐ **MILESI, L.** ...................................... *paintings* | | $1,210 |
| ☐ **MILIAN, Raul** ................................ *paintings* | | $1,045 |
| b. Cuba 1914 ..................................... *drawings* | $440 | $880 |
| ☐ **MILICH, Abram Adolphe** .................... *paintings* | $220 | $385 |
| Polish 1884-1964 | | |
| ☐ **MILIUS, Felix Augustin** ..................... *paintings* | $7,150 | $7,150 |
| French 1843-1894 | | |
| ☐ **MILL, John Henry** ............................ *drawings* | $825 | $7,150 |
| ☐ **MILLAIS, H. Raoul** ........................... *paintings* | | $7,150 |
| English ac. 1928-1936 | | |
| ☐ **MILLAIS, Sir John Everett** .................. *paintings* | $880 | $33,000 |
| English 1829-1896 ................................. *drawings* | $440 | $5,280 |
| ☐ **MILLAR, Addison Thomas** ................. *paintings* | $126 | $7,000 |
| American 1860-1913 ............................... *drawings* | $60 | $750 |
| ☐ **MILLARC, William** ........................... *paintings* | $110 | $192 |
| American 1920-1957 | | |
| ☐ **MILLARES, Manolo** ........................... *paintings* | $1,320 | $11,000 |
| Spanish 1926-1972 ................................. *drawings* | $850 | $10,725 |
| ☐ **MILLE, Leslie B. de** ......................... *drawings* | | $1,400 |
| ☐ **MILLER, Alfred Jacob** ....................... *paintings* | $770 | $187,000 |
| American 1810-1874 ............................... *drawings* | $825 | $101,750 |

| | | | Current Price Range | |
|---|---|---|---|---|
| | | | Low | High |
| ☐ **MILLER, Carol** ................................ | *sculpture* | | | $6,050 |
| ☐ **MILLER, Charles Henry** ..................... | *paintings* | | $110 | $2,750 |
| American 1842-1922 ................................ | *drawings* | | $198 | $220 |
| ☐ **MILLER, Evylena Nunn** ..................... | *paintings* | | $275 | $495 |
| American b. 1888 | | | | |
| ☐ **MILLER, Frank D.** ............................. | *paintings* | | | $2,310 |
| ☐ **MILLER, Henry** ............................... | *drawings* | | | $330 |
| British 20th cent. | | | | |
| ☐ **MILLER, Henry** ............................... | *drawings* | | | $495 |
| American 20th cent. | | | | |
| ☐ **MILLER, John Paul** ........................... | *drawings* | | | $825 |
| ☐ **MILLER, Joseph** .............................. | *paintings* | | $1,100 | $9,350 |
| German 19th cent. | | | | |
| ☐ **MILLER, Kenneth Hayes** .................... | *paintings* | | $330 | $10,450 |
| American 1876-1952 ............................... | *drawings* | | | $247 |
| ☐ **MILLER, Louie** .............................. | *paintings* | | | $550 |
| ☐ **MILLER, M.J.** ................................ | *paintings* | | | $495 |
| American | | | | |
| ☐ **MILLER, Melvin** ............................. | *paintings* | | | $324 |
| American b. 1937 | | | | |
| ☐ **MILLER, Oxley** .............................. | *paintings* | | | $1,210 |
| American 19th/20th cent. | | | | |
| ☐ **MILLER, Ralph Davison** ..................... | *paintings* | | $90 | $2,750 |
| American 1858-1945 ............................... | *drawings* | | | $165 |
| ☐ **MILLER, Richard Emil** ...................... | *paintings* | | $440 | $275,000 |
| American 1875-1943 ............................... | *drawings* | | | $385 |
| ☐ **MILLER, Ted** ................................ | *paintings* | | $275 | $742 |
| American School late 19th/early 20th cent. | | | | |
| ☐ **MILLER, William R.** .......................... | *paintings* | | $220 | $330 |
| American 1850-1923 | | | | |
| ☐ **MILLER, William Rickarby** ................... | *paintings* | | $275 | $26,400 |
| Anglo/American 1818-1893 ........................ | *drawings* | | $220 | $3,080 |
| ☐ **MILLES, Carl** ................................ | *sculpture* | | $2,750 | $66,000 |
| Swedish 1875-1955 | | | | |
| ☐ **MILLESON, Royal Hill** ....................... | *paintings* | | $55 | $605 |
| American b. 1849 ................................. | *drawings* | | $66 | $143 |
| ☐ **MILLET, Clarence** ........................... | *paintings* | | $990 | $6,600 |
| American 1897-1959 | | | | |
| ☐ **MILLET, Francis David** ...................... | *paintings* | | $330 | $55,000 |
| American 1846-1912 ............................... | *drawings* | | $650 | $800 |
| ☐ **MILLET, Geraldine Reed** ..................... | *paintings* | | | $935 |
| American 19th/20th cent. | | | | |
| ☐ **MILLET, Jean Francois** ...................... | *paintings* | | $522 | $605,000 |
| French 1814-1875 ................................. | *drawings* | | $605 | $330,000 |
| ☐ **MILLET, Jean Francois** | | | | |
| **(called Francisque)** ............................ | *drawings* | | | $1,045 |
| Flemish 1642-1679 | | | | |
| ☐ **MILLETT, G. van** ............................. | *paintings* | | $137 | $275 |
| American b. 1864 | | | | |

## Barbizon School

Between 1830 and 1880, a group of French painters formed an informal art colony in the village of Barbizon on the edge of the Fontainebleau Forest. They were the first French artists to paint from nature, rather than create landscapes in their studios.

Pastoral scenes were the favorite subjects of the Barbizon School, whose leaders included Theodore Rousseau and Charles Francois Daubigny. Jean Francois Millet immortalized French peasantry by adding realistic depictions of their lives to his landscapes. Millet has retained his popularity. The Boston Museum of Fine Arts has one of the largest collections of his drawings and paintings in the world, and his works are now very popular in Japan. (Jean Francois Millet, "Le Bain Des Oies," oil on canvas, 18 x 22 in., Stalker, June 23, 1984, $385,000.)

| | | Current Price Range | |
|---|---|---|---|
| | | Low | High |
| ☐ **MILLIER, Arthur** .............................. *drawings* | | **$275** | **$440** |
| English/American 1893-1975 | | | |
| ☐ **MILLINGS, A.** ................................... *paintings* | | | **$192** |
| British 19th cent. | | | |
| ☐ **MILLNER, Karl** .............................. *paintings* | | **$700** | **$7,150** |
| German 1825-1894 | | | |
| ☐ **MILLOCKER** ..................................... *paintings* | | | **$247** |
| Scottish 19th cent. | | | |
| ☐ **MILLOT, Adolphe Philippe** ................. *paintings* | | | **$192** |
| French 1857-1921 | | | |
| ☐ **MILLROSE, A.** ................................... *paintings* | | **$71** | **$192** |
| British 19th cent. | | | |
| ☐ **MILLROSE, G.** ................................... *paintings* | | | **$385** |
| ☐ **MILLS, Edward I.** ............................ *drawings* | | | **$605** |
| ☐ **MILNE, David** ................................... *paintings* | | | **$880** |
| American | | | |
| ☐ **MILNE, John MacLauchlan** ................. *paintings* | | **$605** | **$825** |
| Scottish 20th cent. | | | |
| ☐ **MILNE, Joseph** ................................... *paintings* | | | **$935** |
| British 1861-1911 | | | |
| ☐ **MILNER, George** ............................... *paintings* | | | **$440** |
| American | | | |
| ☐ **MILONE, Antonio** ............................. *paintings* | | | **$700** |
| Italian 19th cent. | | | |

|                                        |             | *Current Price Range* |          |
|                                        |             | *Low*    | *High*     |
|----------------------------------------|-------------|----------|------------|
| ☐ **MILONE, Giuseppe** .............. *paintings* | | $220     | $1,760     |
| Italian 19th cent.                     |             |          |            |
| ☐ **MILONE, Rocco** ................. *paintings* | |          | $440       |
| Italian 19th cent.                     |             |          |            |
| ☐ **MILONOPULO, Agostino** ...... *drawings* | |          | $4,180     |
| ☐ **MILOVICH, Tenasko** .......... *paintings* | |          | $385       |
| American 1900-1964                     |             |          |            |
| ☐ **MILTENBERGER, Lucia** ...... *paintings* | |          | $220       |
| American 19th cent. (?)                |             |          |            |
| ☐ **MILTON, Victor Marias** ....... *paintings* | |          | $1,430     |
| French b. 1872                         |             |          |            |
| ☐ **MIMNAUGH, Terry** ........... *sculpture* | |          | $3,000     |
| American                               |             |          |            |
| ☐ **MINARTZ, Tony** ............. *paintings* | |          | $2,750     |
| French 1870-1944                       |             |          |            |
| ☐ **MINAUX, Andre** .............. *paintings* | | $385     | $440       |
| French b. 1923                         |             |          |            |
| ☐ **MINDERHOUT, Hendrik van** ...... *paintings* | | $3,080   | $7,700     |
| Dutch 1632-1696                        |             |          |            |
| ☐ **MINE, Caspar** ............... *paintings* | | $165     | $247       |
| French b. 1905                         |             |          |            |
| ☐ **MINER, Edgar Otis** ........... *paintings* | |          | $660       |
| ☐ **MINER, Robert C.** ........... *paintings* | |          | $1,760     |
| ☐ **MINNE, George** ............. *sculpture* | | $2,860   | $2,970     |
| Belgian 1866-1941 ................. *drawings* | |          | $990       |
| ☐ **MINNELLI, Vincente** ......... *drawings* | | $385     | $1,210     |
| American b. 1910                       |             |          |            |
| ☐ **MINNIGERODE, Ludwig** ...... *paintings* | |          | $990       |
| Polish 1847-1900                       |             |          |            |
| ☐ **MINOR, Anne Rogers** ......... *paintings* | | $110     | $324       |
| American b. 1864                       |             |          |            |
| ☐ **MINOR, Ferdinand** ........... *paintings* | |          | $4,500     |
| German 1814-1883                       |             |          |            |
| ☐ **MINOR, Robert Crannel** ...... *paintings* | | $220     | $3,575     |
| American 1840-1904 ............... *drawings* | | $60      | $300       |
| ☐ **MINOZZI, Flaminio Innocenozo** ...... *drawings* | | $467     | $2,200     |
| Italian 1735-1817                      |             |          |            |
| ☐ **MINTCHINE, Abraham** ....... *paintings* | | $550     | $1,650     |
| Russian 1898-1931                      |             |          |            |
| ☐ **MINTCHINE, Isaac** ........... *drawings* | |          | $300       |
| ☐ **MIOLIO, Giorgio** ............. *paintings* | |          | $302       |
| 20th cent.                             |             |          |            |
| ☐ **MIR, Joaquin** ............... *paintings* | | $3,850   | $4,950     |
| Spanish 1873-1940                      |             |          |            |
| ☐ **MIRA, Alfred S.** ............. *paintings* | | $385     | $1,540     |
| American 20th cent.                    |             |          |            |
| ☐ **MIRABENT Y CATELL, Jose** ...... *paintings* | |          | $2,475     |
| Spanish 1831-1899                      |             |          |            |
| ☐ **MIRALLES, Enrique** ........... *paintings* | |          | $3,520     |

| | | Current Price Range | |
|---|---|---|---|
| | | Low | High |
| ☐ **MIRALLES, Francisco** ..................... *paintings* | | $1,650 | $14,300 |
| Spanish b.c. 1850 | | | |
| ☐ **MIRAM-STOCKMANN, P.V.** ............... *sculpture* | | | $1,870 |
| ☐ **MIRANDA, Leandro de** ..................... *paintings* | | | $418 |
| ☐ **MIRANDA, Miguel de** ......................... *paintings* | | | $1,100 |
| Spanish 17th cent. | | | |
| ☐ **MIRKO,** | | | |
| **(called Mirko BASALDELLA)** ............... *drawings* | | $124 | $308 |
| ..................................................... *sculpture* | | $880 | $8,800 |
| ☐ **MIRO, Joan** ......................................... *paintings* | | $22,000 | $1,480,248 |
| Spanish 1893-1983 .................................... *drawings* | | $880 | $451,000 |
| ..................................................... *sculpture* | | $55,000 | $275,000 |
| ☐ **MIROU, Antoine** ................................. *paintings* | | | $31,900 |
| Flemish 1586-1661 | | | |
| ☐ **MIRVAL, C.** ........................................ *sculpture* | | $6,600 | $10,780 |
| French early 20th cent. | | | |
| ☐ **MISERENOINO, V.** ........................... *sculpture* | | $550 | $550 |
| Italian/American 20th cent. | | | |
| ☐ **MISHER, F.** ....................................... *paintings* | | | $275 |
| ☐ **MISPISTRIS, Leonardo di** ................... *drawings* | | | $220 |
| Italian 20th cent. | | | |
| ☐ **MISSANT, A.** ..................................... *paintings* | | | $330 |
| French 20th cent. | | | |
| ☐ **MITCHELL, Alfred R.** ........................ *paintings* | | $495 | $1,980 |
| American 1886/88-1972 | | | |
| ☐ **MITCHELL, Arthur** ............................ *paintings* | | $121 | $209 |
| American b. 1864 | | | |
| ☐ **MITCHELL, Arthur R.** ....................... *paintings* | | $4,500 | $5,500 |
| American 1889-1977 | | | |
| ☐ **MITCHELL, Bleecker N.** ..................... *paintings* | | $770 | $1,100 |
| 19th cent. | | | |
| ☐ **MITCHELL, Bruce** ............................ *paintings* | | | $38 |
| American 1908-1963 .................................... *drawings* | | $88 | $275 |
| ☐ **MITCHELL, C.T.** ............................... *paintings* | | $88 | $200 |
| American 19th/20th cent. | | | |
| ☐ **MITCHELL, Charles Davis** .................. *drawings* | | $137 | $220 |
| 1887-1940 | | | |
| ☐ **MITCHELL, E.T.** ............................... *paintings* | | | $220 |
| American 19th cent. | | | |
| ☐ **MITCHELL, George Bertrand** .............. *paintings* | | $220 | $450 |
| American b. 1874 ..................................... *drawings* | | $220 | $308 |
| ☐ **MITCHELL, Glenn** ............................ *paintings* | | | $385 |
| American b. 1894 | | | |
| ☐ **MITCHELL, Joan** ............................... *paintings* | | $1,210 | $51,700 |
| American b. 1926 ..................................... *drawings* | | | $1,045 |
| ☐ **MITCHELL, John** ................................ *paintings* | | | $3,750 |
| ☐ **MITCHELL, Norman** ........................... *paintings* | | | $577 |
| ☐ **MITCHELL, Thomas John** ................... *paintings* | | | $1,210 |
| American b. 1875 | | | |

| | | Current Price Range | |
|---|---|---|---|
| | | Low | High |
| ☐ **MITCHELL, W.B.** ............... *paintings* | | | $440 |
| British 19th/20th cent. | | | |
| ☐ **MITRUCK, S.** ..................... *paintings* | | | $275 |
| American 20th cent. | | | |
| ☐ **MITTARAKIS, Lia** ............ *paintings* | | $33 | $440 |
| South American | | | |
| ☐ **MITTERFELLNER, Andreas** ........ *paintings* | | $247 | $550 |
| German 20th cent. | | | |
| ☐ **MIYAMOTO, Kaname** .......... *paintings* | | | $286 |
| American b. 1891 | | | |
| ☐ **MIZEN, Frederick Kimball** ......... *paintings* | | $247 | $715 |
| American 1888-1964/65 | | | |
| ☐ **MOB, Louis** ..................... *paintings* | | | $385 |
| American 19th cent. | | | |
| ☐ **MOBERLY, Mariquita Jenny** ......... *paintings* | | | $6,600 |
| British ac. 1855-1903 | | | |
| ☐ **MOCATTI, C.** ..................... *paintings* | | | $247 |
| Italian 19th cent. | | | |
| ☐ **MOCHEZ, H.** ..................... *paintings* | | | $2,750 |
| French (?) 19th cent. | | | |
| ☐ **MOD, J.** ..................... *paintings* | | | $302 |
| ☐ **MODERSOHN, Otto** ............ *paintings* | | $4,400 | $11,000 |
| German 1865-1943 | | | |
| ☐ **MODIGLIANI, Amedeo** ......... *paintings* | | $93,500 | $4,620,000 |
| Italian 1884-1920 ................ *drawings* | | $1,045 | $198,000 |
| ☐ **MODRA, Theodore B.** ......... *paintings* | | $33 | $242 |
| American 1873-1930 ................ *drawings* | | | $200 |
| ☐ **MODZELEVICH, Efraim** ......... *drawings* | | | $301 |
| 20th cent. | | | |
| ☐ **MOELLER, Louis Charles** ........ *paintings* | | $1,100 | $31,900 |
| American 1855-1930 ................ *drawings* | | $165 | $3,520 |
| ☐ **MOERENHOUT, E.S.** ......... *paintings* | | | $190 |
| Belgian 19th cent. | | | |
| ☐ **MOERMAN, Albert Edouard** ......... *paintings* | | | $950 |
| Flemish 1808-1857 | | | |
| ☐ **MOERMAN, E.P.** ............ *paintings* | | $357 | $385 |
| Dutch 20th cent. | | | |
| ☐ **MOESELAGEN, Jean A.** ......... *paintings* | | | $4,400 |
| German b. 1827 | | | |
| ☐ **MOEYAERT, Nicolaes Cornelisz** | | | |
| ((Claes)) ............... *paintings* | | $1,980 | $9,350 |
| Dutch 1590-1655 ................ *drawings* | | | $1,100 |
| ☐ **MOFFETT, Ross E.** ............ *paintings* | | $418 | $1,760 |
| American 1888-1971 | | | |
| ☐ **MOGFORD, John** ............ *paintings* | | $1,100 | $1,320 |
| English 1821-1885 ................ *drawings* | | $2,420 | $2,420 |
| ☐ **MOHLER, Paul** ............ *paintings* | | | $741 |
| German 19th cent. | | | |
| ☐ **MOHLER, R.M.** ............ *paintings* | | | $467 |

| | | Current Price Range | |
|---|---|---|---|
| | | *Low* | *High* |
| ☐ **MOHLTE, J. Alfred** ............... *paintings* | | | **$495** |
| British 19th/20th cent. | | | |
| ☐ **MOHOLY-NAGY, Laszlo** ............ *paintings* | | **$3,630** | **$55,000** |
| Hungarian 1895-1946 ................. *drawings* | | **$1,980** | **$3,520** |
| ☐ **MOHRMANN, Henry** ............... *paintings* | | | **$715** |
| ☐ **MOIGNE, Simone le** ............... *paintings* | | **$77** | **$715** |
| French 20th cent. | | | |
| ☐ **MOIGNIEZ, Jules** ............... *sculpture* | | **$176** | **$5,500** |
| French 1835-1894 | | | |
| ☐ **MOIR, John** ............... *paintings* | | | **$385** |
| English 1776-1857 | | | |
| ☐ **MOISSET, Marthe** ............... *paintings* | | **$302** | **$1,320** |
| French 20th cent. | | | |
| ☐ **MOIZO, B.** ............... *paintings* | | | **$2,640** |
| Spanish(?) 19th cent. | | | |
| ☐ **MOKADY, Moshe** ............... *paintings* | | | **$4,950** |
| Palestinian 20th cent. | | | |
| ☐ **MOLA, Pier Francesco** ............ *drawings* | | | **$17,050** |
| ☐ **MOLARSKY, Maurice** ............... *paintings* | | **$88** | **$1,650** |
| Russian/American 1885-1950 | | | |
| ☐ **MOLDARELLI, L.** ............... *drawings* | | | **$330** |
| ☐ **MOLE, John Henry** ............... *drawings* | | **$110** | **$1,970** |
| English 1814-1886 | | | |
| ☐ **MOLENAER, Bartholomeus** ......... *paintings* | | | **$2,640** |
| Dutch 1650 | | | |
| ☐ **MOLENAER, Cornelis** | | | |
| **(called De Scheele Neel)** ............ *paintings* | | | **$9,625** |
| ☐ **MOLENAER, Jan Miense** ............ *paintings* | | **$1,100** | **$36,300** |
| Dutch c. 1610-1668 | | | |
| ☐ **MOLENAER, Klaes** ............... *paintings* | | **$2,200** | **$44,000** |
| Dutch before 1630-1676 | | | |
| ☐ **MOLENAER, Pieter** ............... *paintings* | | | **$660** |
| ☐ **MOLES, F.** ............... *paintings* | | | **$1,210** |
| ☐ **MOLESI, E.** ............... *paintings* | | | **$522** |
| Italian 19th cent. | | | |
| ☐ **MOLIN, Oreste da** ............... *paintings* | | | **$6,050** |
| Italian 1856-1921 | | | |
| ☐ **MOLINA CAMPOS, Florencio** ......... *paintings* | | | **$6,050** |
| b. Argentina 1891-1959 ............... *drawings* | | **$1,760** | **$2,750** |
| ☐ **MOLINARI, Antonio** ............... *paintings* | | **$110** | **$7,425** |
| Italian d. 1648 | | | |
| ☐ **MOLINARY, Andre** ............... *paintings* | | **$440** | **$2,200** |
| American 1847-1915 | | | |
| ☐ **MOLINE, A. de** ............... *paintings* | | | **$10,725** |
| French 19th cent. | | | |
| ☐ **MOLINO** ............... *paintings* | | | **$275** |
| Italian 19th cent. | | | |
| ☐ **MOLITOR, Franz** ............... *paintings* | | **$1,430** | **$4,180** |
| German 1857-1929 | | | |

| | Current Price Range | |
|---|---|---|
| | *Low* | *High* |

| | | Low | High |
|---|---|---|---|
| ☐ **MOLITOR, Peter** ............... *paintings* | | | $385 |
| ☐ **MOLKE, A.** ...................... *drawings* | | | $2,500 |
| ☐ **MOLL, Carl** ................... *paintings* | | | $9,900 |
| Austrian 1861-1945 | | | |
| ☐ **MOLL, Evert** ................... *paintings* | | $660 | $1,540 |
| Dutch 1878-1955 | | | |
| ☐ **MOLL, Kim** ................... *paintings* | | | $275 |
| ☐ **MOLLER, C.** ................... *paintings* | | | $275 |
| ☐ **MOLLER, Hans** ............... *paintings* | | | $467 |
| ☐ **MOLLINGER, Gerrit Alexander** .......... *paintings* | | | $2,750 |
| Dutch 1836-1867 | | | |
| ☐ **MOLLINGER, J.W.** ............. *paintings* | | | $1,600 |
| ☐ **MOLLOY** ...................... *sculpture* | | | $440 |
| French early 20th cent. | | | |
| ☐ **MOLNAIR, J.** ................... *paintings* | | | $533 |
| ☐ **MOLNAR, Jozsef** ............... *paintings* | | $308 | $330 |
| Hungarian 1821-1899 | | | |
| ☐ **MOLOKIN** ...................... *paintings* | | | $2,750 |
| Russian 19th cent. | | | |
| ☐ **MOLYN, Petrus Marius** ........... *paintings* | | | $3,300 |
| Belgian 1819-1849 | | | |
| ☐ **MOLYN, Pieter de (the elder)** ............... *paintings* | | $3,300 | $4,400 |
| Dutch 1595-1661 | | | |
| ☐ **MOLYNEUX, Edward Frank** ............... *paintings* | | | $550 |
| American b. 1896 | | | |
| ☐ **MOMADAY, Al** ............... *paintings* | | | $3,300 |
| American (Kiowa) b. 1913 | | | |
| ☐ **MOMMERS, Hendrik** .......... *paintings* | | $1,045 | $12,000 |
| Dutch c. 1623-1693 | | | |
| ☐ **MOMPER, Frans de** .......... *paintings* | | $8,800 | $15,000 |
| Flemish 1603-1660 | | | |
| ☐ **MOMPER, Giovanni** .......... *paintings* | | | $3,300 |
| ☐ **MOMPER, Jan de** .......... *paintings* | | | $2,090 |
| ☐ **MOMPER, Joos de** .......... *paintings* | | $6,600 | $30,800 |
| Flemish 1564-1635 | | | |
| ☐ **MON, Bascha** .......... *paintings* | | $440 | $550 |
| American | | | |
| ☐ **MONACHESI, Sante** .......... *paintings* | | $330 | $440 |
| Italian b. 1910 | | | |
| ☐ **MONAGHAN, Eileen** .......... *drawings* | | $121 | $187 |
| American b. 1911 | | | |
| ☐ **MONAHAN, Hugh** .......... *paintings* | | | $330 |
| British 20th cent. | | | |
| ☐ **MONALDI, Paolo** .......... *paintings* | | $6,050 | $24,200 |
| Italian ac. c. 1760 | | | |
| ☐ **MONAMY, Peter** .......... *paintings* | | $660 | $11,000 |
| English 1670/89-1749 .......... *drawings* | | | $1,760 |
| ☐ **MONARI, Christoforo** .......... *paintings* | | $22,000 | $40,700 |

## 17th Century Landscapes

*Frans de Momper was a Flemish landscape painter popular in the 17th century, a period in which landscape paintings reflected people, both peasants and royalty, engaged in everyday life rituals. The human elements, however, were not so important as the natural scenery and composition. De Momper, together with other noted landscape painters of his time, including Jacob van Ruisdael and Meindert Hobbema, consistently displayed his fascination with nature, depicting storms, clouds, skies, and light. (Frans de Momper, "Winter View With Cathedral," oil on panel, 24 x 33 in., Fine Arts Co., October 20, 1984, $8,800.)*

|  |  | *Current Price Range* | |
|---|---|---|---|
|  |  | *Low* | *High* |
| ☐ **MONASTERIO, Luis Ortiz** .................. *sculpture* | | **$935** | **$1,320** |
| Mexican b. 1906 | | | |
| ☐ **MONATIO, S.** ..................................... *paintings* | | | **$4,000** |
| ☐ **MONCALVO, Guglielmo Caccia, Il** ....... *paintings* | | | **$4,400** |
| ☐ **MONCAYO, E.** .................................... *paintings* | | | **$715** |
| Latin American 19th/20th cent. | | | |
| ☐ **MONCH, C.** ....................................... *paintings* | | | **$990** |
| European 19th cent. | | | |
| ☐ **MONCHABLON, Edouard** .................. *paintings* | | | **$2,090** |
| French 1879-1914 | | | |

| | | Current Price Range | |
|---|---|---|---|
| | | Low | High |
| ☐ **MONCHABLON, Jean Ferdinand** ......... *paintings* <br> French 1855-1904 | | $1,210 | $5,280 |
| ☐ **MONCHET, L.** ............................... *paintings* <br> French 1850-1920 | | | $192 |
| ☐ **MONDIDIER, Devant** ........................... *paintings* <br> French 20th cent. | | | $302 |
| ☐ **MONDRIAN, Piet** .............................. *paintings* | | $9,350 | $2,328,480 |
| Dutch 1872-1944 ......................................... *drawings* | | $8,800 | $77,000 |
| ☐ **MONEGAR, Clarence Boyce** ................ *drawings* <br> American Indian 1910-1968 | | $104 | $209 |
| ☐ **MONET, Claude** ............................. *paintings* | | $25,300 | $2,640,000 |
| French 1840-1926 ......................................... *drawings* | | $2,310 | $37,400 |
| ☐ **MONFALLET, Adolphe Francois** ......... *paintings* <br> French 1816-1900 | | $1,210 | $1,210 |
| ☐ **MONFIELD, J.** ................................... *paintings* <br> British 19th cent. | | | $1,760 |
| ☐ **MONFORT, Joseph** ........................... *paintings* | | | $495 |
| ☐ **MONFREID, Georges Daniel de** ........... *paintings* | | $6,325 | $20,900 |
| French 1856-1929/30 ................................. *drawings* | | | $2,000 |
| ☐ **MONGIN, Antoine Pierre** ................ *paintings* | | | $440 |
| French 1761-1827 ......................................... *drawings* | | $1,210 | $5,225 |
| ☐ **MONGINOT, Charles** ........................... *paintings* <br> French 1825-1900 | | | $2,200 |
| ☐ **MONGINOT, Charlotte H.** ................... *sculpture* <br> French b. 1872 | | | $1,540 |
| ☐ **MONIEN, Julius** ............................. *paintings* <br> German 1842-1897 | | | $1,210 |
| ☐ **MONINCKX, Pieter** ........................... *paintings* | | | $2,200 |
| ☐ **MONKS, John Austin Sands** ................ *paintings* | | $275 | $305 |
| American 1850-1917 ................................. *drawings* | | $100 | $275 |
| ☐ **MONNARD** ......................................... *paintings* | | | $330 |
| ☐ **MONNERET, Jean** ........................... *paintings* | | | $275 |
| ☐ **MONNIER, Henry** ............................. *drawings* <br> French 1805-1877 | | $330 | $605 |
| ☐ **MONNIER, Pierre** ........................... *paintings* <br> French b. 1870 | | | $1,320 |
| ☐ **MONNOT, Maurice Louis** ................... *paintings* <br> French b. 1869 | | $605 | $880 |
| ☐ **MONNOYER, Jean Baptiste** ................ *paintings* <br> French 1636-1699 | | $4,125 | $30,000 |
| ☐ **MONOGRAMMIST GVR** ................... *paintings* <br> Dutch c. 1620 | | | $8,800 |
| ☐ **MONOTOYA, Gustavo** ........................... *paintings* <br> Latin American | | | $2,200 |
| ☐ **MONREAL, Andres** ........................... *paintings* <br> b. Chile | | | $2,200 |
| ☐ **MONRO, Hugh** ................................... *paintings* <br> British b. 1873 | | | $2,310 |

|  |  | | Current Price Range | |
|---|---|---|---|---|
|  |  | | Low | High |
| ☐ **MONROE, Gordon** ............................. *sculpture* | | | | $700 |
| American | | | | |
| ☐ **MONRONTOYI** ...................................... *paintings* | | | | $385 |
| ☐ **MONSEN, G.** ......................................... *paintings* | | | | $300 |
| American 19th cent. | | | | |
| ☐ **MONSFELD, T.** ..................................... *paintings* | | | | $935 |
| ☐ **MONSTED, Peder** ............................... *paintings* | | $330 | | $3,300 |
| Danish 1859-1941 | | | | |
| ☐ **MONT, Frances** ................................... *sculpture* | | | | $2,640 |
| ☐ **MONT, Jo du** ...................................... *paintings* | | | | $847 |
| ☐ **MONTAGNE, Louis** ............................. *paintings* | | | | $220 |
| French 20th cent. | | | | |
| ☐ **MONTAGNE, Renaud de la** .................. *paintings* | | | | $1,760 |
| Dutch 17th cent. | | | | |
| ☐ **MONTAGUE, Alfred** ........................... *paintings* | | $418 | | $1,760 |
| British ac. 1832-1883 | | | | |
| ☐ **MONTAGUE, Allen** ............................. *paintings* | | $333 | | $385 |
| American | | | | |
| ☐ **MONTAGUE, Clifford** ......................... *paintings* | | | | $356 |
| ☐ **MONTAGUE, F.L.** ............................... *paintings* | | | | $715 |
| American 19th cent. | | | | |
| ☐ **MONTALANT, I.O. de** ......................... *paintings* | | $770 | | $3,080 |
| French 19th cent. | | | | |
| ☐ **MONTALBA, Clara** ............................. *drawings* | | | | $715 |
| English 1842-1929 | | | | |
| ☐ **MONTANINI, Pietro** | | | | |
| **(IL PETRUCCIO)** ................................ *paintings* | | $2,420 | | $3,850 |
| Italian 1626-1689 | | | | |
| ☐ **MONTARDIER** ..................................... *drawings* | | | | $2,640 |
| ☐ **MONTASSIER, Henri** ......................... *paintings* | | $198 | | $825 |
| ☐ **MONTAYA, Gustavo** ........................... *paintings* | | $990 | | $1,870 |
| b. Mexico 1905 | | | | |
| ☐ **MONTE, Jose de** ................................. *paintings* | | $1,650 | | $2,640 |
| ☐ **MONTEFORTE, Edouard** .................... *paintings* | | | | $495 |
| Italian b. 1849 ........................................ *drawings* | | | | $66 |
| ☐ **MONTEGAZZA, G.** ............................. *paintings* | | $495 | | $2,200 |
| Italian 19th cent. | | | | |
| ☐ **MONTELATICI, Francesco** | | | | |
| **(called CECCO BRAVO)** ...................... *drawings* | | $220 | | $550 |
| ☐ **MONTEMEZZO, Antonio** .................... *paintings* | | $8,800 | | $12,100 |
| German 1841-1898 | | | | |
| ☐ **MONTENARD, Frederic** ...................... *paintings* | | | | $1,760 |
| French 1849-1926 | | | | |
| ☐ **MONTENEGRO, Roberto** .................... *paintings* | | $440 | | $19,250 |
| Mexican b. 1885 ..................................... *drawings* | | $110 | | $2,200 |
| ☐ **MONTERRO, P.** ................................... *paintings* | | | | $660 |
| Spanish 19th cent. | | | | |
| ☐ **MONTESUIOR, A.** ............................... *paintings* | | | | $357 |
| French 19th cent. | | | | |

| | | Current Price Range | |
|---|---|---|---|
| | | Low | High |
| ☐ **MONTEVERDE, Giulio** ..................... *sculpture* | | | $1,760 |
| Italian early 20th cent. | | | |
| ☐ **MONTEVERDE, Luigi** | | | |
| **(called Raphael des Raisins)** ................... *paintings* | | | $33,000 |
| Swiss b. 1843 | | | |
| ☐ **MONTEZIN, Pierre Eugene** ................. *paintings* | | $990 | $26,400 |
| French 1874-1946 ...................................... *drawings* | | $825 | $1,540 |
| ☐ **MONTFORT, Antoine Alphonse** ............ *paintings* | | | $1,100 |
| French 1802-1884 | | | |
| ☐ **MONTFORT, Guy de** .......................... *paintings* | | | $1,210 |
| French 19th/20th cent. | | | |
| ☐ **MONTGOMERY, Alfred** ..................... *paintings* | | $385 | $1,100 |
| American 1857-1922 | | | |
| ☐ **MONTGOMERY, M.** ........................... *paintings* | | | $275 |
| ☐ **MONTICELLI,** | | | |
| **Adolphe Joseph Thomas** ................ *paintings* | | $1,210 | $33,000 |
| French 1824-1886 | | | |
| ☐ **MONTIGANI, L.** ................................. *paintings* | | | $990 |
| Italian early 20th cent. | | | |
| ☐ **MONTOYA** ......................................... *paintings* | | | $247 |
| Spanish 19th cent. | | | |
| ☐ **MONTOYA, Gustavo** .......................... *paintings* | | $1,320 | $7,700 |
| b. Mexico 1905 | | | |
| ☐ **MONTOYA, Manuel** ........................... *paintings* | | | $357 |
| Spanish 20th cent. | | | |
| ☐ **MONTPEZAT,** | | | |
| **Henri d'Ainecy Comte de** ..................... *paintings* | | $1,045 | $18,700 |
| French 1817-1859 | | | |
| ☐ **MONTULLO, S.** ................................. *paintings* | | | $550 |
| Italian 19th cent. | | | |
| ☐ **MONTURIAL, Enrique Pascuel de** ........ *paintings* | | | $224 |
| Spanish 1878-1934 ..................................... *drawings* | | $55 | $200 |
| ☐ **MOODIE, Donald** ............................... *paintings* | | | $302 |
| British 1892-1963 | | | |
| ☐ **MOON, Carl** ..................................... *paintings* | | | $4,950 |
| American 1879-1948 | | | |
| ☐ **MOONEY, E. Hartley** .......................... *paintings* | | | $220 |
| British early 20th cent. | | | |
| ☐ **MOOR VAN DASHORST, Anthonis** ..... *paintings* | | | $30,800 |
| Dutch c. 1517-c. 1575 | | | |
| ☐ **MOORE, A.** ....................................... *paintings* | | $750 | $950 |
| British School | | | |
| ☐ **MOORE, Albert Joseph** ........................ *drawings* | | | $1,100 |
| English d. 1892 | | | |
| ☐ **MOORE, Barlow** ............................... *paintings* | | | $770 |
| English 19th cent. | | | |
| ☐ **MOORE, Benson Bond** ........................ *paintings* | | $110 | $3,300 |
| American b. 1882 ...................................... *drawings* | | | $99 |
| ☐ **MOORE, Charles** ............................... *drawings* | | | $440 |

| | | *Current Price Range* | |
|---|---|---|---|
| | | Low | High |
| ☐ **MOORE, Charles Herbert** ............... *paintings* | | | $308 |
| American b. 1840 | | | |
| ☐ **MOORE, Edwin Augustus** ............... *paintings* | | | $3,520 |
| American b. 1858 | | | |
| ☐ **MOORE, Frank Montague** ............... *paintings* | | $88 | $577 |
| American 1877/1887-1967 | | | |
| ☐ **MOORE, George Belton** ............... *paintings* | | | $440 |
| English 1805-1875 | | | |
| ☐ **MOORE, Guernsey** ............... *drawings* | | | $1,210 |
| American 1874-1925 | | | |
| ☐ **MOORE, H.** ............... *paintings* | | | $1,320 |
| English 19th cent. | | | |
| ☐ **MOORE, H.W.** ............... *paintings* | | $192 | $247 |
| American 19th/20th cent. | | | |
| ☐ **MOORE, Harry Humphrey** ............... *paintings* | | $550 | $9,900 |
| American 1844-1926 ............... *drawings* | | $55 | $1,540 |
| ☐ **MOORE, Henry** ............... *paintings* | | | $1,320 |
| English 1831-1895 | | | |
| ☐ **MOORE, Henry** ............... *paintings* | | | $1,540 |
| English b. 1898 ............... *drawings* | | $660 | $341,000 |
| ............... *sculpture* | | $2,970 | $1,265,000 |
| ☐ **MOORE, Herbert** ............... *paintings* | | | $1,100 |
| American early 20th cent. | | | |
| ☐ **MOORE, John** ............... *paintings* | | $825 | $990 |
| English 1820-1902 | | | |
| ☐ **MOORE, Nelson Augustus** ............... *paintings* | | $132 | $1,980 |
| American 1824-1902 | | | |
| ☐ **MOORE, W.J.** ............... *paintings* | | | $700 |
| ☐ **MOORE-PARK, Carton** ............... *paintings* | | | $660 |
| English b. 1877 | | | |
| ☐ **MOORMANS, Franz** ............... *paintings* | | $880 | $8,525 |
| Dutch 1831-1873/93 | | | |
| ☐ **MOOTZKA, Waldo** ............... *drawings* | | | $2,200 |
| American (Hopi) | | | |
| ☐ **MOPOPE, Stephen** ............... *drawings* | | | $1,650 |
| American (Kiowa) b. 1898 | | | |
| ☐ **MORA, Francis Luis** ............... *paintings* | | $385 | $16,500 |
| Uruguayan/American 1874-1940 ............... *drawings* | | $44 | $1,980 |
| ☐ **MORADEI, A.** ............... *paintings* | | | $700 |
| Italian 19th cent. | | | |
| ☐ **MORADEI, Arturo** ............... *paintings* | | $2,090 | $2,750 |
| ☐ **MORADO, Jose Chavez** ............... *paintings* | | $3,300 | $10,450 |
| Mexican b. 1909 ............... *drawings* | | | $467 |
| ☐ **MORAGAS Y TORRAS, Tomas** ............... *paintings* | | | $52,800 |
| Spanish 1837-1906 | | | |
| ☐ **MORALES, Armando** ............... *paintings* | | $250 | $10,450 |
| Nicaraguan/Amer. b. 1927 ............... *drawings* | | $990 | $6,050 |
| ☐ **MORALES, Dario** ............... *paintings* | | | $49,500 |
| Columbian b. 1944 ............... *drawings* | | $2,200 | $17,600 |

|                                                      |            | *Current Price Range* | |
|------------------------------------------------------|------------|---------|----------|
|                                                      |            | *Low*   | *High*   |
| ☐ **MORALES, Eduardo** .............. *paintings*    |            | $1,320  | $10,450  |
| Cuban 1868-1938                                      |            |         |          |
| ☐ **MORALES, Juane Antonio** ............... *paintings* |        |         | $330     |
| Spanish 20th cent.                                   |            |         |          |
| ☐ **MORALES, Luis de**                               |            |         |          |
| **(called EL DIVINO)** ............... *paintings*   |            | $16,500 | $49,500  |
| Spanish c. 1509/10-1586                              |            |         |          |
| ☐ **MORALES, Rodolfo** ............... *paintings*   |            |         | $880     |
| Latin American                                       |            |         |          |
| ☐ **MORALES, Ruiz Sanchez** ............... *paintings* |         |         | $2,420   |
| ☐ **MORAN, Annette** ............... *paintings*     |            | $1,540  | $2,420   |
| American 19th cent.                                  |            |         |          |
| ☐ **MORAN, Earl** ............... *drawings*         |            |         | $495     |
| ☐ **MORAN, Edward** ............... *paintings*      |            | $226    | $20,350  |
| American 1829-1901 ............... *drawings*         |            | $55     | $2,090   |
| ☐ **MORAN, Edward Percy** ............... *paintings* |           | $242    | $13,200  |
| American 1862-1935 ............... *drawings*         |            | $220    | $1,045   |
| ☐ **MORAN, G.** ............... *paintings*          |            | $180    | $850     |
| ☐ **MORAN, H.** ............... *paintings*          |            |         | $935     |
| American 19th/20th cent.                             |            |         |          |
| ☐ **MORAN, Leon (or John Leon)** ............... *paintings* |     | $143    | $8,800   |
| American 1864-1941 ............... *drawings*         |            | $88     | $385     |
| ☐ **MORAN, Paul Nimmo** ............... *paintings*  |            |         | $5,500   |
| American b. 1907                                     |            |         |          |
| ☐ **MORAN, Percy** ............... *paintings*       |            |         | $4,180   |
| American 1862-1935                                   |            |         |          |
| ☐ **MORAN, Peter** ............... *paintings*       |            | $110    | $30,800  |
| American 1841-1914 ............... *drawings*         |            | $88     | $2,200   |
| ☐ **MORAN, Thomas** ............... *paintings*      |            | $467    | $495,000 |
| American 1837-1926 ............... *drawings*         |            | $600    | $187,000 |
| ☐ **MORAN, Victor** ............... *paintings*      |            |         | $330     |
| American 19th cent.                                  |            |         |          |
| ☐ **MORANDI, Giorgio** ............... *paintings*   |            | $55,000 | $165,000 |
| Italian 1890-1964 ............... *drawings*          |            | $5,500  | $33,000  |
| ☐ **MORANI** ............... *paintings*             |            | $357    | $660     |
| Italian 19th cent.                                   |            |         |          |
| ☐ **MORANTE** ............... *sculpture*            |            |         | $356     |
| French early 20th cent.                              |            |         |          |
| ☐ **MORAS, W.** ............... *paintings*          |            |         | $357     |
| German 19th/20th cent.                               |            |         |          |
| ☐ **MORATZ, Frank** ............... *paintings*      |            | $192    | $715     |
| American 20th cent.                                  |            |         |          |
| ☐ **MORAZZONE, Pier Francesco** ............... *paintings* |      |         | $4,950   |
| Italian 1573-1626 ............... *drawings*          |            |         | $1,210   |
| ☐ **MORE, F.E.** ............... *paintings*         |            |         | $467     |
| 19th cent.                                           |            |         |          |
| ☐ **MOREAU, Adrien** ............... *paintings*     |            | $3,740  | $22,000  |
| French 1843-1906 ............... *drawings*           |            |         | $66      |
| ☐ **MOREAU, Auguste** ............... *paintings*    |            | $302    | $3,520   |
| French                                               |            |         |          |

| | | | Current Price Range |
|---|---|---|---|
| | | **Low** | **High** |
| ☐ **MOREAU, Augustin Jean** (called Moreau-Vautier) ......... *sculpture* French b. 1831 | | $2,090 | $5,500 |
| ☐ **MOREAU, Charles** ............... *paintings* French b. 1830 | | $522 | $14,300 |
| ☐ **MOREAU, Gustave** ............. *drawings* French 1826-1898 | | $1,760 | $143,000 |
| ☐ **MOREAU, Hippolyte Francois** ............. *sculpture* French 1832-1917 | | $423 | $3,740 |
| ☐ **MOREAU, J.** ...................... *sculpture* late 19th cent. | | | $6,600 |
| ☐ **MOREAU, Jean Michel** (called Moreau le jeune) ......... *drawings* French 1741-1814 | | $715 | $4,180 |
| ☐ **MOREAU, Louis Auguste** ..................... *sculpture* French 1855-1919 | | $220 | $1,650 |
| ☐ **MOREAU, Louis Gabriel** (called l'aine) ...................... *drawings* French 1740-1806 | | $660 | $4,400 |
| ☐ **MOREAU, Mathurin** ........................... *sculpture* French 1822-1912 | | $176 | $5,500 |
| ☐ **MOREAU, Max** .................................. *paintings* Belgian 20th cent. | | $330 | $400 |
| ☐ **MOREAU-VAUTHIER, Paul Gabriel Jean** ....................... *sculpture* French b. 1871 | | | $1,540 |
| ☐ **MOREELSE, Paulus** ......................... *paintings* Dutch 1571-1638 | | | $6,600 |
| ☐ **MOREL, Anton** .................................. *paintings* Dutch 20th cent. | | | $440 |
| ☐ **MOREL, Casparus Johannes** ................ *paintings* | | | $2,420 |
| ☐ **MOREL, H.** .......................................... *paintings* | | | $990 |
| ☐ **MOREL, Jan Baptiste** ......................... *paintings* | | | $4,950 |
| ☐ **MOREL, Jan Evert** ........................... *paintings* Dutch 1777-1808 | | $550 | $3,300 |
| ☐ **MOREL, Jan Evert (the younger)** .......... *paintings* Dutch 1835-1905 | | $440 | $7,700 |
| ☐ **MOREL, M. van der** ........................... *paintings* | | | $605 |
| ☐ **MOREL, P.** ......................................... *drawings* | | | $990 |
| ☐ **MORELAND, George** ........................ *paintings* British 1763-1804 | | | $2,750 |
| ☐ **MORELAND, Marylee M.** ..................... *drawings* American | | | $500 |
| ☐ **MORELFT, J.E.** ................................. *paintings* | | | $4,620 |
| ☐ **MORELLI, A.** .................................. *sculpture* Italian early 20th cent. | | | $577 |
| ☐ **MORELLI, C.** ...................................... *sculpture* Italian 19th cent. | | | $660 |

| | Current Price Range | |
|---|---|---|
| | *Low* | *High* |
| ☐ **MORELLI, Domenico** .......................... *paintings* <br> Italian 1823-1901 | **$880** | **$2,310** |
| ☐ **MORELLI, F.** ...................................... *paintings* <br> French 1768-1830 | | **$550** |
| ☐ **MORELLI, L.** ...................................... *sculpture* <br> Italian late 19th cent. | | **$1,320** |
| ☐ **MORELLO, Leandro** .......................... *drawings* <br> Italian 19th cent. | | **$1,045** |
| ☐ **MORENO, Matias** .............................. *paintings* <br> Spanish b. 1840 | | **$8,800** |
| ☐ **MORENO, Rafael** .............................. *paintings* <br> Latin American | | **$990** |
| ☐ **MORERA, Bernard** .......................... *paintings* <br> French 20th cent. | | **$825** |
| ☐ **MORERE, Rene** ............................... *paintings* | | **$550** |
| ☐ **MORET, Henry** ............................... *paintings* <br> French 1856-1913 | **$4,400** | **$22,000** |
| ☐ **MORETH, J.** ...................................... *paintings* | | **$2,310** |
| ☐ **MORETTI** ......................................... *paintings* | | **$660** |
| ☐ **MORETTI, C.** .................................... *paintings* | | **$825** |
| ☐ **MORETTI, Lucien Philippe** ................. *paintings* <br> French 20th cent. | **$220** | **$3,410** |
| ☐ **MORETTI, R.** .................................... *paintings* <br> Italian 19th cent. .................................. *drawings* | **$154** | **$700** <br> **$1,100** |
| ☐ **MOREZ, Mary** ................................... *drawings* <br> American (Navajo) | | **$660** |
| ☐ **MORGAN, Alfred** ............................ *paintings* <br> British 1868-1928 | | **$935** |
| ☐ **MORGAN, Annie Laurie** ...................... *paintings* <br> American ac. late 19th cent. | **$1,100** | **$1,540** |
| ☐ **MORGAN, Evelyn de** .......................... *paintings* <br> British 1855-1919 .................................. *drawings* | | **$15,950** <br> **$495** |
| ☐ **MORGAN, Frederick** .......................... *paintings* <br> British 1856-1927 .................................. *drawings* | **$5,500** | **$20,000** <br> **$660** |
| ☐ **MORGAN, John** ............................... *paintings* <br> British 1823-1886 | | **$550** |
| ☐ **MORGAN, Mary de Neale** .................... *paintings* <br> American 1868-1948 .................................. *drawings* | **$192** <br> **$110** | **$1,430** <br> **$247** |
| ☐ **MORGAN, Randall** ............................ *paintings* <br> American b. 1920 | **$66** | **$411** |
| ☐ **MORGAN, Robert F.** .......................... *paintings* <br> American contemporary | | **$1,400** |
| ☐ **MORGAN, T.** ...................................... *drawings* <br> American 19th/20th cent. | | **$302** |
| ☐ **MORGAN, William** ............................ *paintings* <br> American 1826-1900 | **$247** | **$3,575** |
| ☐ **MORGAN, William** ............................ *paintings* <br> d. 1948 | | **$4,180** |

| | | *Low* | *High* |
|---|---|---|---|
| ☐ **MORGAND, Madame Cecile** ............... *paintings*<br>French 19th cent. | | $500 | $1,540 |
| ☐ **MORGENSTERN, Carl** ........................ *paintings*<br>German 1811-1893 ..................................... *drawings* | | | $1,760<br>$275 |
| ☐ **MORGENSTERN,**<br>**Christian Ernst Bernhard** ...................... *paintings*<br>German 1805-1867 | | $1,650 | $3,300 |
| ☐ **MORGENTHALER, Charles** ............... *paintings*<br>American 20th cent. | | | $330 |
| ☐ **MORI, L.** .......................................... *drawings*<br>Italian 20th cent. | | | $275 |
| ☐ **MORIANI, A.** ................................... *paintings*<br>Italian 19th/20th cent. ............................... *drawings* | | | $1,100<br>$121 |
| ☐ **MORIN, G.** ...................................... *paintings*<br>European 19th cent. | | | $770 |
| ☐ **MORIN, Louis** ................................. *paintings*<br>French b. 1855 | | $55 | $1,320 |
| ☐ **MORIS, J.** ........................................ *paintings*<br>Dutch 1837-1899 | | $450 | $660 |
| ☐ **MORISEA, S.** ................................... *paintings*<br>Italian 19th/20th cent. | | $880 | $880 |
| ☐ **MORISOT, Berthe** ........................... *paintings*<br>French 1841-1895 ...................................... *drawings* | | $12,100<br>$1,320 | $429,000<br>$44,000 |
| ☐ **MORISOT, Edma** .............................. *paintings*<br>French 19th cent. | | $192 | $385 |
| ☐ **MORISSET, Francois Henri** ............... *paintings*<br>French b. 1870 | | $1,870 | $16,500 |
| ☐ **MORITZ, William** ............................. *paintings*<br>Swiss 1816-1860 | | $3,300 | $5,775 |
| ☐ **MORLAN, A.M.** ................................ *paintings*<br>Latin American | | | $1,980 |
| ☐ **MORLAND, George** ........................... *paintings*<br>English 1763-1804 ..................................... *drawings* | | $325<br>$165 | $38,500<br>$467 |
| ☐ **MORLAND, Henry** ............................ *paintings*<br>English 1730-1797 | | $1,760 | $1,980 |
| ☐ **MORLEY, C.** ..................................... *paintings*<br>19th cent. | | $325 | $935 |
| ☐ **MORLEY, F.** ..................................... *paintings*<br>British 19th cent. | | | $522 |
| ☐ **MORLEY, George** ............................. *paintings*<br>English 1832-1863 | | | $330 |
| ☐ **MORLEY, Henry** ............................... *paintings*<br>British b. 1869 | | | $880 |
| ☐ **MORLEY, Malcolm** ........................... *paintings*<br>American b. 1931 ..................................... *drawings*<br>.................................................. *sculpture* | | $2,860<br>$825<br>$660 | $27,500<br>$12,650<br>$1,800 |
| ☐ **MORLON, Paul Emile Antony** ............. *paintings*<br>French 19th cent. | | $1,045 | $13,200 |

| | Current Price Range | |
| --- | --- | --- |
| | *Low* | *High* |
| ☐ **MORMILE, Gaetano** .................... *paintings*<br>Italian 1839-1890 | **$440** | **$715** |
| ☐ **MORMILE, George** .................... *paintings* | | **$440** |
| ☐ **MORO, A. del** .................... *paintings* | | **$385** |
| ☐ **MORO, Battista del** .................... *paintings*<br>Italian 1514-1575 | | **$3,300** |
| ☐ **MOROMOLI, Pietro** .................... *sculpture*<br>Italian late 19th cent. | | **$242** |
| ☐ **MORONI, F.** .................... *paintings*<br>American (?) 20th cent. | | **$550** |
| ☐ **MORONI, Giovanni Battista** .................... *paintings*<br>Italian 1525-1578 | | **$2,860** |
| ☐ **MORONI, P.** .................... *paintings*<br>Italian 19th cent. | | **$467** |
| ☐ **MOROT, A.** .................... *paintings* | | **$715** |
| ☐ **MORQUERA, R.** .................... *drawings*<br>Italian 19th cent. | | **$192** |
| ☐ **MORREL, Owen** .................... *drawings* | **$1,540** | **$1,540** |
| ☐ **MORRELL, B. J.** .................... *paintings*<br>British (?) 19th cent. | | **$1,760** |
| ☐ **MORRELL, Wayne** .................... *paintings*<br>American 20th cent. | **$88** | **$1,870** |
| ☐ **MORRICE** .................... *paintings*<br>French 20th cent. | | **$275** |
| ☐ **MORRICE, James Wilson** .................... *paintings*<br>Canadian 1874-1924 | | **$60,500** |
| ☐ **MORRIS, Carl** .................... *paintings*<br>American b. 1911 | **$38** | **$440** |
| ☐ **MORRIS, Charles D.** .................... *paintings* | | **$605** |
| ☐ **MORRIS, G. D.** .................... *paintings*<br>American 19th/20th cent. | | **$247** |
| ☐ **MORRIS, George Ford** .................... *paintings*<br>American 1873-1960 .................... *drawings* | **$1,320**<br>**$110** | **$2,200**<br>**$330** |
| ☐ **MORRIS, George Lovett Kingsland** ...... *paintings*<br>American 1905-1975 .................... *drawings* | **$165**<br>**$220** | **$16,500**<br>**$7,425** |
| ☐ **MORRIS, Jacob** .................... *paintings*<br>Dutch b. 1837 | | **$650** |
| ☐ **MORRIS, John** .................... *paintings*<br>British 19th cent. | **$4,125** | **$4,950** |
| ☐ **MORRIS, John Floyd** .................... *paintings* | | **$275** |
| ☐ **MORRIS, Jones Fawson** .................... *paintings*<br>American ac. 1820-1845 | | **$2,750** |
| ☐ **MORRIS, Kathleen Moir** .................... *paintings*<br>Canadian b. 1893 | **$6,160** | **$15,400** |
| ☐ **MORRIS, Kaye** .................... *paintings*<br>contemporary | | **$825** |
| ☐ **MORRIS, Kyle** .................... *paintings*<br>American 1918-1979 | | **$3,080** |

| | | Current Price Range | |
|---|---|---|---|
| | | Low | High |
| ☐ **MORRIS, Philip Richard** ...... *paintings*<br>British 1836-1902 | | $550 | $605 |
| ☐ **MORRIS, Robert** ...... *sculpture*<br>American b. 1931 | | $7,425 | $27,500 |
| ☐ **MORRIS, Simon** ...... *paintings* | | | $1,100 |
| ☐ **MORRISON, William** ...... *drawings*<br>British 19th cent. | | | $247 |
| ☐ **MORSE, Edward Lind** ...... *paintings*<br>American 1857-1923 ...... *drawings* | | | $660<br>$143 |
| ☐ **MORSE, George F.** ...... *paintings*<br>American 19th cent. | | | $220 |
| ☐ **MORSE, H.S.** ...... *paintings*<br>American 19th cent. | | | $660 |
| ☐ **MORSE, Henry Dutton** ...... *paintings*<br>American 1826-1888 | | $475 | $2,750 |
| ☐ **MORSE, J.B.** ...... *paintings*<br>American 19th/20th cent. | | | $605 |
| ☐ **MORSE, J.B.** ...... *paintings*<br>American ac. 1780-1790 | | $55 | $715 |
| ☐ **MORSE, Jonathan Bradley** ...... *drawings*<br>American 1834-1898 | | | $440 |
| ☐ **MORSE, Samuel F.B.** ...... *paintings*<br>American 1791-1872 | | $2,310 | $2,860 |
| ☐ **MORSE, Sarah** ...... *drawings* | | | $880 |
| ☐ **MORSE, Vernon Jay** ...... *paintings*<br>American 1898-1965 | | | $660 |
| ☐ **MORSHEAD** ...... *paintings*<br>American 20th cent. | | $165 | $275 |
| ☐ **MORTELMANS, Frans** ...... *paintings*<br>Belgian 1865-1936 | | $3,300 | $6,875 |
| ☐ **MORTIMER, John Hamilton** ...... *paintings*<br>English 1740/41-1779 | | $1,320 | $4,840 |
| ☐ **MORTON, William E.** ...... *paintings*<br>American 1843-1916 | | | $4,400 |
| ☐ **MORVAN, Jean Jacques** ...... *paintings*<br>French b. 1928 | | $126 | $192 |
| ☐ **MORVILLER, Joseph** ...... *paintings*<br>American ac. 1855-1870 | | $605 | $1,650 |
| ☐ **MOSCO, J.** ...... *paintings*<br>Italian | | | $412 |
| ☐ **MOSCOSO, Luis** ...... *paintings*<br>Ecuadorian b. 1915 | | | $990 |
| ☐ **MOSELSIO, Simon** ...... *sculpture*<br>American b. 1890 | | $302 | $742 |
| ☐ **MOSER, Frank** ...... *paintings* | | | $385 |
| ☐ **MOSER, James Henry** ...... *paintings*<br>American 1854-1913 ...... *drawings* | | $55<br>$110 | $660<br>$412 |
| ☐ **MOSER, Julius** ...... *paintings*<br>German b. 1808 | | | $1,650 |

| | Current Price Range | |
|---|---|---|
| | Low | High |

| | | Low | High |
|---|---|---|---|
| ☐ **MOSER, Richard** ............... *drawings* | | | $6,050 |
| Austrian b. 1874 | | | |
| ☐ **MOSER-PADINA, Alexander** | | | |
| **(called Alex MOSER)** ............ *paintings* | | $220 | $275 |
| ☐ **MOSERT, Zoe** ................. *drawings* | | | $1,045 |
| American 20th cent. | | | |
| ☐ **MOSES,** | | | |
| **Anna Mary Robertson ("Grandma")** ....... *paintings* | | $1,100 | $65,000 |
| American 1860-1961 | | | |
| ☐ **MOSES, Ed** ........................ *drawings* | | $990 | $1,430 |
| American b. 1926 | | | |
| ☐ **MOSES, Forrest King** ........... *paintings* | | $385 | $2,640 |
| American 1893-1974 ............ *drawings* | | | $990 |
| ☐ **MOSES, Thomas G.** ............ *paintings* | | $440 | $550 |
| English/American 1856-1934 | | | |
| ☐ **MOSES, Walter Farrington** ........ *paintings* | | | $412 |
| American b. 1874 | | | |
| ☐ **MOSKOWITZ, Robert** ........... *paintings* | | | $4,400 |
| American b. 1935 | | | |
| ☐ **MOSLER, Gustave Henry** ........ *paintings* | | | $176 |
| American 1875-1906 | | | |
| ☐ **MOSLER, Henry** ............... *paintings* | | $375 | $11,000 |
| American 1841-1920 | | | |
| ☐ **MOSLER, John Henry** ......... *drawings* | | | $275 |
| American | | | |
| ☐ **MOSNIER, Jean Laurent** ....... *paintings* | | $6,600 | $33,000 |
| French 1743/44-1808 | | | |
| ☐ **MOSSMAN, John G.** ........... *sculpture* | | | $1,650 |
| Scottish 1817-1890 | | | |
| ☐ **MOSTEL, Zero** ................. *paintings* | | $80 | $356 |
| American 20th cent. | | | |
| ☐ **MOSTYN, Tom Edwin** ......... *paintings* | | $165 | $550 |
| English 1864-1930 | | | |
| ☐ **MOTA, J. Garriques** ......... *drawings* | | | $330 |
| ☐ **MOTE, George William** ........ *paintings* | | $495 | $1,430 |
| English 1832?-1909 | | | |
| ☐ **MOTHERWELL, Robert** ....... *paintings* | | $5,225 | $275,000 |
| American b. 1915 ................ *drawings* | | $1,100 | $41,800 |
| ☐ **MOTT, Herb** .................... *paintings* | | $137 | $330 |
| .................... *drawings* | | | $110 |
| ☐ **MOTTA, Raphael** | | | |
| **(called Rafaellino de Reggio)** .......... *paintings* | | | $12,100 |
| Italian c. 1550-1578 | | | |
| ☐ **MOTTE, Henri Paul** ......... *paintings* | | | $770 |
| French 1846-1922 | | | |
| ☐ **MOTTET, Jeanie Gallup** ...... *paintings* | | $660 | $3,300 |
| American 1864-1934 | | | |
| ☐ **MOTTET, Yvonne** ............. *paintings* | | $99 | $440 |
| French 1906-1968 | | | |

|  | | Current Price Range | |
|---|---|---|---|
|  | | Low | High |
| ☐ **MOTTEZ, Henry** ................................ *paintings* | | | $3,080 |
| French b. 1855 | | | |
| ☐ **MOTTRAM, Charles** ........................... *drawings* | | | $220 |
| English 1807-1876 | | | |
| ☐ **MOTTRAM, Charles Sim** .................... *drawings* | | $220 | $1,320 |
| English ac. 1876-1903 | | | |
| ☐ **MOUCHERON, Frederick de** ............... *paintings* | | | $2,200 |
| Dutch 1633-1686 | | | |
| ☐ **MOUCHERON, Isaac de** ...................... *paintings* | | | $14,000 |
| Dutch 1667-1744 ...................................... *drawings* | | $495 | $5,775 |
| ☐ **MOUCHERON, J.D.** ............................ *paintings* | | | $1,650 |
| ☐ **MOUCHOT, Louis Claude** ................... *paintings* | | | $16,500 |
| French 1830-1891 | | | |
| ☐ **MOUETTE, Alphonse** .......................... *paintings* | | | $286 |
| ☐ **MOULIN, Hippolyte** ........................... *sculpture* | | | $3,080 |
| French 1832-1884 | | | |
| ☐ **MOULINET, Antoine Edouard Joseph** .. *paintings* | | | $1,430 |
| French 1833-1891 | | | |
| ☐ **MOULLE, Albert** ............................... *paintings* | | | $880 |
| 19th/20th cent. | | | |
| ☐ **MOULLNOT** ....................................... *paintings* | | | $990 |
| French 19th cent. | | | |
| ☐ **MOULTON, F.** .................................... *paintings* | | | $450 |
| American 19th cent. | | | |
| ☐ **MOULTON, Lillian** ............................ *drawings* | | | $220 |
| American | | | |
| ☐ **MOUNT, Charles Merrill** ..................... *paintings* | | | $352 |
| ☐ **MOUNT, Evilina** ................................ *paintings* | | | $1,430 |
| American 19th cent. | | | |
| ☐ **MOUNT, Nina** .................................... *paintings* | | | $550 |
| American 1837-1920 | | | |
| ☐ **MOUNT, Paul** ..................................... *sculpture* | | | $396 |
| ☐ **MOUNT, Shepard Alonzo** .................... *paintings* | | $935 | $16,500 |
| American 1804-1868 | | | |
| ☐ **MOUNT, Willim Sidney** ....................... *paintings* | | $4,400 | $880,000 |
| American 1807-1868 .................................. *drawings* | | $825 | $1,540 |
| ☐ **MOUNTFORD, Arnold G.** ................... *paintings* | | | $330 |
| ☐ **MOURANS, Franz** ............................. *paintings* | | | $275 |
| Dutch 1831-1873 | | | |
| ☐ **MOUTON, Grover** ............................. *drawings* | | | $440 |
| contemporary | | | |
| ☐ **MOWBRAY, A.** .................................. *paintings* | | | $275 |
| Spanish 19th/20th cent. | | | |
| ☐ **MOWBRAY, Henry Siddons** ................ *paintings* | | $1,980 | $44,000 |
| American 1858-1928 | | | |
| ☐ **MOYER, N.** ....................................... *paintings* | | $300 | $550 |
| ☐ **MOYERS, William** ............................. *paintings* | | | $5,000 |
| American b. 1916 ...................................... *sculpture* | | | $9,500 |

| | Current Price Range | |
|---|---|---|
| | *Low* | *High* |
| ☐ **MOYLAN, Lloyd** ............................ *paintings* | | $2,750 |
| American b. 1893 | | |
| ☐ **MOZIER, C.** .................................... *drawings* | | $264 |
| ☐ **MOZIER, Joseph** ............................ *paintings* | | $385 |
| American 1812-1870/90 ............................ *sculpture* | $1,430 | $6,600 |
| ☐ **MUCCINI, Marcello** .......................... *drawings* | | $385 |
| Italian b. 1926 | | |
| ☐ **MUCHA, Alphonse Maria** ................... *paintings* | $3,080 | $19,800 |
| Czechoslovakian 1860-1939 ........................... *drawings* | $330 | $60,500 |
| ☐ **MUCHE, P.** .................................... *paintings* | | $275 |
| ☐ **MUCKE, Karl Emil** .......................... *paintings* | | $9,350 |
| German 1847-1923 | | |
| ☐ **MUCKLEY, Louis Fairfax** ................... *paintings* | | $1,100 |
| ☐ **MUELLER, Alexander** ........................ *paintings* | $440 | $1,320 |
| American 1872-1935 | | |
| ☐ **MUELLER, Fritz** .............................. *paintings* | | $990 |
| German 20th cent. | | |
| ☐ **MUELLER, M.** .................................. *paintings* | | $550 |
| German 1841-1899 | | |
| ☐ **MUELLER, Otto** .............................. *paintings* | $286 | $154,000 |
| German 1874-1930 ..................................... *drawings* | $440 | $36,300 |
| ☐ **MUELLER, Stephen** .......................... *paintings* | $220 | $2,420 |
| contemporary | | |
| ☐ **MUENCH, Toni Olga** ......................... *drawings* | $88 | $462 |
| ☐ **MUENIER, Jules Alexis** ...................... *paintings* | $1,320 | $12,100 |
| French 1863-1934/1942 | | |
| ☐ **MUENTER, Gabrielle** ........................ *paintings* | $8,250 | $26,400 |
| ☐ **MUHL, Roger** ................................. *paintings* | $330 | $1,980 |
| French b. 1929 | | |
| ☐ **MUHLBERG, Georg** ........................... *paintings* | | $400 |
| German 1863-1925 | | |
| ☐ **MUHLENFELD, Otto** .......................... *paintings* | | $412 |
| American | | |
| ☐ **MUHLFELD, Joseph Molitor von** .......... *paintings* | | $2,200 |
| German 1856-1890 | | |
| ☐ **MUHLHAN** .................................... *paintings* | | $522 |
| ☐ **MUHLIG, Hugo** .............................. *paintings* | $660 | $33,000 |
| German 1854-1929 | | |
| ☐ **MUHLIG, Meno** .............................. *paintings* | $440 | $8,800 |
| German 1823-1873 | | |
| ☐ **MUHRMANN, Henry** .......................... *paintings* | | $2,750 |
| 20th cent. | | |
| ☐ **MUHRMANN, Ludwig** ........................ *paintings* | | $770 |
| German b. 1886 | | |
| ☐ **MUIR, J.** ...................................... *paintings* | | $1,540 |
| Scottish School 19th cent. | | |
| ☐ **MUIR, J.N.** .................................... *sculpture* | | $20,000 |
| American contemporary | | |

|  | | | *Current Price Range* | |
| --- | --- | --- | --- | --- |
|  | | | Low | High |
| ☐ **MUIRHEAD, David** ............................ | *paintings* | | | $605 |
| English 1867-1930 | | | | |
| ☐ **MULBE, W.** ......................................... | *paintings* | | | $385 |
| ☐ **MULERTT, Carel Eugene** ...................... | *paintings* | | $880 | $2,090 |
| American b. 1869 ...................................... | *drawings* | | $200 | $467 |
| ☐ **MULFORD, Stockton** ............................ | *paintings* | | | $302 |
| ☐ **MULHAUPT, Frederick John** ............... | *paintings* | | $200 | $5,280 |
| American 1871-1938 | | | | |
| ☐ **MULHOLLAND, Samuel A.** ................. | *drawings* | | | $440 |
| British 19th cent. | | | | |
| ☐ **MULHOLLAND, St. Clair A.** ............... | *drawings* | | | $495 |
| English 19th cent. | | | | |
| ☐ **MULIER, Pieter** | | | | |
| **(the younger, Cavaliere Tempesta)** .......... | *paintings* | | $2,090 | $5,500 |
| Dutch 1637-1701 | | | | |
| ☐ **MULLENFELD, S.L.R.** ......................... | *paintings* | | | $8,400 |
| ☐ **MULLER** ............................................... | *paintings* | | | $280 |
| ...................................................... | *sculpture* | | $467 | $660 |
| ☐ **MULLER, Adam** ............................... | *paintings* | | | $275 |
| Danish 1811-1844 | | | | |
| ☐ **MULLER, Adolf** ................................ | *sculpture* | | | $2,750 |
| German 19th cent. | | | | |
| ☐ **MULLER, Adolph** ............................... | *paintings* | | $880 | $2,310 |
| German b. 1853 | | | | |
| ☐ **MULLER, Anton** ................................ | *paintings* | | $3,300 | $23,100 |
| Austrian 1853-1897 .................................... | *drawings* | | | $165 |
| ☐ **MULLER, August** .............................. | *paintings* | | $2,420 | $5,390 |
| German 1836-1885 | | | | |
| ☐ **MULLER, C.** ...................................... | *paintings* | | | $385 |
| Austrian 1834-1892 | | | | |
| ☐ **MULLER, Carl Friedrich Moritz** | | | | |
| **(called Feuermuller)** .............................. | *paintings* | | | $8,800 |
| German 1807-65 | | | | |
| ☐ **MULLER, Charles** ............................... | *sculpture* | | | $935 |
| ☐ **MULLER, Charles Louis Lucien** .......... | *paintings* | | $990 | $3,850 |
| French 1815-1892 | | | | |
| ☐ **MULLER, Emma von** ........................... | *paintings* | | $1,320 | $1,320 |
| German b. 1859 | | | | |
| ☐ **MULLER, Erich** ................................. | *paintings* | | | $352 |
| ☐ **MULLER, Ernst** ................................ | *paintings* | | | $1,650 |
| German 1823-1875 | | | | |
| ☐ **MULLER, Ernst Emmanuel** ................. | *paintings* | | $605 | $9,500 |
| German b. 1844 | | | | |
| ☐ **MULLER, Frans Hubert** ...................... | *paintings* | | | $500 |
| German 1784-1835 | | | | |
| ☐ **MULLER, Franz** ................................ | *paintings* | | | $1,600 |
| German 1843-1929 | | | | |
| ☐ **MULLER, Friedrich** ........................... | *drawings* | | $308 | $550 |

| | | Current Price Range | |
|---|---|---|---|
| | | Low | High |
| ☐ **MULLER, Fritz** .................................. *paintings* | | $220 | $1,650 |
| German b. 1879 | | | |
| ☐ **MULLER, Fritz** .................................. *paintings* | | | $715 |
| German b. 1818 | | | |
| ☐ **MULLER, Fritz** .................................. *paintings* | | $544 | $1,815 |
| German b. 1913 | | | |
| ☐ **MULLER, Hans** .................................. *sculpture* | | $99 | $770 |
| German b. 1873 | | | |
| ☐ **MULLER, Heinrich Edouard** ................ *paintings* | | $3,300 | $25,300 |
| German 1823-1853 | | | |
| ☐ **MULLER, Jan** .................................. *drawings* | | | $880 |
| Dutch 1571-1628 | | | |
| ☐ **MULLER, Jan** .................................. *drawings* | | $1,045 | $1,540 |
| German/American 1922-1958 | | | |
| ☐ **MULLER, Karl** .................................. *paintings* | | | $500 |
| German 19th cent. | | | |
| ☐ **MULLER, Leopold Karl** ...................... *paintings* | | | $22,000 |
| Austrian 1834-1892 | | | |
| ☐ **MULLER, Ludwig Cornelius** ................ *paintings* | | $1,100 | $3,575 |
| German 19th cent. | | | |
| ☐ **MULLER, Max** .................................. *paintings* | | | $1,430 |
| German 19th cent. | | | |
| ☐ **MULLER, Moritz** | | | |
| **(called KINDERMULLER)** ...................... *paintings* | | | $1,980 |
| German 1825-1894 | | | |
| ☐ **MULLER, Moritz Karl Friedrich** .......... *paintings* | | $1,320 | $3,300 |
| German 1807-1865 | | | |
| ☐ **MULLER, N.M.** .................................. *paintings* | | | $660 |
| ☐ **MULLER, Oscar** .................................. *sculpture* | | | $1,400 |
| Swiss School 20th cent. | | | |
| ☐ **MULLER, Peter Paul** .......................... *paintings* | | | $770 |
| German b. 1853 | | | |
| ☐ **MULLER, Robert A.** ........................... *paintings* | | | $1,100 |
| ☐ **MULLER, Rosa** .................................. *paintings* | | | $770 |
| German 19th cent. | | | |
| ☐ **MULLER, Rudolph Gustave** ................ *paintings* | | | $12,100 |
| German 1858-88 | | | |
| ☐ **MULLER, William James** ...................... *paintings* | | $341 | $1,980 |
| English 1812-1845 | | | |
| ☐ **MULLER-KREFELD, Adolph** .............. *sculpture* | | | $2,475 |
| German b. 1863 | | | |
| ☐ **MULLER-LINGKE, Albert** ................... *paintings* | | $1,760 | $5,775 |
| German b. 1844 | | | |
| ☐ **MULLER-URY, Adolph** ....................... *paintings* | | $70 | $285 |
| American 1862-1947 | | | |
| ☐ **MULLIEZ, PI. R.** .............................. *paintings* | | | $220 |
| French 20th cent. | | | |
| ☐ **MULMULD, W.** .................................. *paintings* | | | $605 |

| | | | *Current Price Range* | |
| --- | --- | --- | --- | --- |
| | | | *Low* | *High* |
| ☐ **MULREADY, Augustus E.** ................... *paintings* | | | $352 | $1,100 |
| English 19th cent. | | | | |
| ☐ **MULREADY, William** ......................... *paintings* | | | $220 | $1,650 |
| Irish 1786-1863 | | | | |
| ☐ **MULTAR, C.** ...................................... *paintings* | | | | $350 |
| ☐ **MUMFORD, Claire Dana** ................... *drawings* | | | | $192 |
| American 20th cent. | | | | |
| ☐ **MUNCH, Edvard** ............................. *paintings* | | | $3,850 | $3,080,000 |
| Norwegian 1863-1944 .............................. *drawings* | | | $450 | $1,100 |
| ☐ **MUNCHEN, Lazar Binenbaum** ............. *paintings* | | | | $550 |
| German early 20th cent. | | | | |
| ☐ **MUNCHHAUSEN, A. von** ................... *drawings* | | | | $308 |
| ☐ **MUNDELL, J.** ..................................... *paintings* | | | | $440 |
| English 1818-1875 | | | | |
| ☐ **MUNDUAAN, G.Y.** ............................ *paintings* | | | | $1,430 |
| Dutch 19th cent. | | | | |
| ☐ **MUNDY, Charles** ............................... *paintings* | | | | $550 |
| ☐ **MUNGER, Gilbert** ............................. *paintings* | | | $385 | $5,500 |
| American 1836/37-1903 | | | | |
| ☐ **MUNIER, Emile** ................................. *paintings* | | | $1,430 | $23,100 |
| French b. 1810 | | | | |
| ☐ **MUNK, Jacob** ................................... *paintings* | | | $467 | $715 |
| English d. 1885 | | | | |
| ☐ **MUNKACSY, Michael von Leib** | | | | |
| **(called Mihaly)** ........................................ *paintings* | | | $577 | $5,500 |
| Hungarian 1844-1900/09 .............................. *drawings* | | | $137 | $242 |
| ☐ **MUNN, George Frederick** ................... *paintings* | | | | $5,775 |
| American 1852-1907 | | | | |
| ☐ **MUNN, P.S.** ...................................... *drawings* | | | | $522 |
| American 19th/20th cent. | | | | |
| ☐ **MUNN, Paul Sandby** .......................... *drawings* | | | | $825 |
| English 1773-1845 | | | | |
| ☐ **MUNNINGER, Ludwig** ......................... *paintings* | | | | $2,090 |
| ☐ **MUNNINGS, Sir Alfred J.** ................... *paintings* | | | $1,540 | $357,500 |
| English 1878-1959 ..................................... *drawings* | | | $450 | $41,250 |
| ☐ **MUNOZ, Oscar** ................................. *drawings* | | | | $2,530 |
| Colombian b. 1951 | | | | |
| ☐ **MUNOZ Y CUESTA, Domingo** ............. *paintings* | | | $1,100 | $20,900 |
| Spanish 1850-1912 | | | | |
| ☐ **MUNROE, Albert F.** ........................... *paintings* | | | | $770 |
| American | | | | |
| ☐ **MUNSCH, Joseph** ............................. *paintings* | | | | $4,125 |
| Austrian 1832-1896 | | | | |
| ☐ **MUNSCH, Leopold** ............................. *paintings* | | | $605 | $3,025 |
| Austrian 1826-1888 | | | | |
| ☐ **MUNSON, H. Sherrill** .......................... *paintings* | | | $110 | $440 |
| American 20th cent. | | | | |
| ☐ **MUNSON, K.** ...................................... *drawings* | | | $412 | $797 |
| American 20th cent. | | | | |

## Sporting Paintings

*In the first week of June, on the eve of New York's Belmont Stakes, Sotheby's and Christie's hold their annual sales of sporting paintings. Each year new records have been set, reflecting the increasing interest in this genre since the first specialized sale of sporting paintings in the United States was held in 1981.*

*Subject matter, provenance, and the skill and importance of the artist all have a direct bearing on the prices realized in the sporting market. The principal categories of sporting paintings are racing, hunting (fox and stag), coaching, breeding portraits, shooting (bird or big game), and fishing. As a general rule, a racing picture by a given artist is more valuable than a hunting subject by the same individual.*

*Sir Alfred Munnings is one of the best known sporting painters of the 20th century. At the sporting sale in June, 1985, this racing painting sold for nearly a quarter of a million dollars. (Sir Alfred Munnings, "A Park Meeting, The Eclipse Stakes, Sandown Park," oil on board, 20 x 26 in., Christie's, June 7, 1985, $242,000.)*

|  | *Current Price Range* | |
|---|---|---|
|  | *Low* | *High* |
| ☐ **MUNSTERFELD, F.** ............................ *paintings* | | **$550** |
| German 19th cent. | | |
| ☐ **MUNTER, Gabriele** ............................. *paintings* | **$605** | **$99,000** |
| German 1877-1962 | | |
| ☐ **MUNTHE,** | | |
| **Gerhard Arij Morgenstjerne** .................. *paintings* | **$330** | **$2,200** |
| Dutch 1875-1950 | | |
| ☐ **MUNTHE, Ludwig** .............................. *paintings* | **$3,300** | **$14,300** |
| Norwegian 1841-1896 | | |

| | | Current Price Range | |
|---|---|---|---|
| | | *Low* | *High* |
| ☐ **MURA, Angelo Della** .......................... *paintings* | | | **$1,100** |
| Italian b. 1867 | | | |
| ☐ **MURA, Francesco de** .................. *paintings* | | **$2,860** | **$33,000** |
| Italian 1696-1782 | | | |
| ☐ **MURA, Frank** .................................. *paintings* | | **$302** | **$2,200** |
| French b. 1861 | | | |
| ☐ **MURCH, Walter** .............................. *paintings* | | **$330** | **$15,950** |
| American 1907-1967 .............................. *drawings* | | **$1,650** | **$4,620** |
| ☐ **MURDOCH, John H.** ......................... *paintings* | | | **$450** |
| ☐ **MURDOCK, John** ............................ *paintings* | | | **$6,600** |
| American ac. 1854 | | | |
| ☐ **MURIEL, F.** .................................... *paintings* | | | **$990** |
| ☐ **MURILLO, Bartolome Esteban** ............. *paintings* | | **$82,500** | **$209,000** |
| Spanish 1618-1682 | | | |
| ☐ **MURILLO, Salvador** .......................... *paintings* | | | **$6,050** |
| ☐ **MUROWANA, Lorenz** .......................... *paintings* | | | **$220** |
| German 20th cent. | | | |
| ☐ **MURPHY, A.B.** ................................ *paintings* | | **$33** | **$176** |
| American 20th cent. | | | |
| ☐ **MURPHY, Adah Clifford** ...................... *paintings* | | | **$385** |
| American 20th cent. | | | |
| ☐ **MURPHY, Charles Augustus** ............... *paintings* | | | **$192** |
| America 1874-1943 | | | |
| ☐ **MURPHY, Christopher (Jr.)** .................. *paintings* | | | **$495** |
| American b. 1902 | | | |
| ☐ **MURPHY, H.C.** ................................ *paintings* | | | **$385** |
| American | | | |
| ☐ **MURPHY, Herman Dudley** ................... *paintings* | | **$220** | **$7,700** |
| American 1867-1945 .............................. *drawings* | | | **$990** |
| ☐ **MURPHY, John Francis** ...................... *paintings* | | **$385** | **$19,800** |
| American 1853-1921 .............................. *drawings* | | **$247** | **$3,300** |
| ☐ **MURRAY, Alexander Henry Hallam** ..... *drawings* | | | **$220** |
| English 1854-1934 | | | |
| ☐ **MURRAY, Alfred** ............................. *paintings* | | | **$275** |
| English 19th cent. | | | |
| ☐ **MURRAY, Charles Fairfax** ................... *drawings* | | | **$330** |
| ☐ **MURRAY, David** ............................. *paintings* | | | **$1,760** |
| English 1849-1933 | | | |
| ☐ **MURRAY, Elizabeth** ........................... *drawings* | | | **$495** |
| English 1815-1882 | | | |
| ☐ **MURRAY, H.** .................................... *drawings* | | **$275** | **$3,850** |
| English ac. 1850-1860 | | | |
| ☐ **MURRAY, Lilian** ............................... *paintings* | | **$660** | **$770** |
| British 19th cent. | | | |
| ☐ **MURRAY, Sir David** .......................... *paintings* | | **$300** | **$1,300** |
| British 1849-1933 | | | |
| ☐ **MURRY, J.E.** .................................... *paintings* | | | **$357** |
| American 19th cent. | | | |

| | | *Current Price Range* | |
|---|---|---|---|
| | | Low | High |
| ☐ **MUSCART, Gustave** ............................ *paintings* | | | **$1,100** |
| French 19th cent. | | | |
| ☐ **MUSCHAMP, F. Sydney** ..................... *paintings* | | **$137** | **$2,090** |
| English ac. 1870-1903, d. 1929 ..................... *drawings* | | **$385** | **$797** |
| ☐ **MUSCHAMP, P.** ................................. *paintings* | | | **$385** |
| ☐ **MUSCRAFT, E.G.** .............................. *paintings* | | | **$935** |
| British fl. 19th cent. | | | |
| ☐ **MUSGRAVE, Arthur F.** ...................... *paintings* | | **$522** | **$522** |
| American b. 1880 | | | |
| ☐ **MUSIC, Zoran Antonio** ...................... *paintings* | | **$770** | **$23,100** |
| Italian 1909-1952 ...................................... *drawings* | | **$55** | **$1,760** |
| ☐ **MUSIGNIE** ...................................... *paintings* | | | **$522** |
| ☐ **MUSIN, Auguste Henri** ........................ *paintings* | | **$2,200** | **$9,350** |
| Belgian 1852-1920 | | | |
| ☐ **MUSIN, Francois Etienne** ..................... *paintings* | | **$1,100** | **$3,700** |
| Belgian 1820-1888 | | | |
| ☐ **MUSLIN, I.A.** .................................... *paintings* | | | **$330** |
| ☐ **MUSS-ARNOLT, Gustav** ..................... *paintings* | | **$660** | **$6,325** |
| 1858-1927 | | | |
| ☐ **MUSSCHER, Michiel van** ..................... *paintings* | | | **$44,000** |
| Dutch 1645-1705 | | | |
| ☐ **MUSSO, Domenico** .............................. *drawings* | | | **$300** |
| South American 19th cent. | | | |
| ☐ **MUSSON, F.** ...................................... *drawings* | | | **$330** |
| French 19th/20th cent. | | | |
| ☐ **MUTER, Mela** ................................... *paintings* | | | **$3,080** |
| French 1886-1967 | | | |
| ☐ **MUTRIE, Annie Feray** ......................... *paintings* | | | **$1,045** |
| British 1826-1893 | | | |
| ☐ **MUTRIE, Martha Darlay** ..................... *paintings* | | | **$2,200** |
| British 1824-1885 | | | |
| ☐ **MUTTONI, Pietro de** | | | |
| **(called Pietro della VECCHIA)** ............... *paintings* | | **$935** | **$8,800** |
| Italian 1605-1678 | | | |
| ☐ **MUTZNER, S.** .................................... *paintings* | | | **$302** |
| German 20th cent. | | | |
| ☐ **MY, Hieronymus van der** ..................... *paintings* | | | **$412** |
| Dutch 1687-1761 | | | |
| ☐ **MYERHEIN, A.** ................................. *paintings* | | | **$357** |
| Dutch 19th cent. | | | |
| ☐ **MYERS, Ethel** ................................... *sculpture* | | **$462** | **$1,100** |
| American 19th/20th cent. | | | |
| ☐ **MYERS, Frank Harmon** ....................... *paintings* | | | **$880** |
| American 1899-1956 | | | |
| ☐ **MYERS, Harry** ................................... *paintings* | | | **$1,100** |
| American 20th cent. | | | |
| ☐ **MYERS, Irwin O.** ............................... *drawings* | | | **$247** |
| American b. 1888 | | | |

| | | Current Price Range | |
| --- | --- | --- | --- |
| | | *Low* | *High* |
| ☐ **MYERS, Jerome** ............................ *paintings* | | $154 | $7,425 |
| American 1867-1940/41 ........................ *drawings* | | $55 | $7,150 |
| ☐ **MYGATT, Robertson K.** ................ *paintings* | | $60 | $467 |
| d. 1919 | | | |
| ☐ **MYLES, W.J.** ................................. *paintings* | | | $275 |
| ☐ **MYRBACH-RHEINFELD,** | | | |
| **Felicien Baron de** ........................... *drawings* | | $33 | $300 |
| Austrian 1853-1940 | | | |
| ☐ **MYTENS, Jan** ................................. *paintings* | | | $6,600 |
| ☐ **NAAGER, Franz** ............................. *paintings* | | | $302 |
| German b. 1870 | | | |
| ☐ **NADELMAN, Elie** ........................... *drawings* | | $440 | $4,400 |
| American 1885-1946 ............................ *sculpture* | | $800 | $159,500 |
| ☐ **NADLER, Robert** ............................ *paintings* | | | $1,650 |
| Hungarian b. 1938 | | | |
| ☐ **NAEGELE, Charles Frederick** .......... *paintings* | | | $990 |
| American b. 1857 | | | |
| ☐ **NAEGLE, John** ................................ *paintings* | | | $880 |
| American 1796-1865 | | | |
| ☐ **NAGARE, Masayuki** ........................ *sculpture* | | $3,575 | $4,125 |
| Japanese b. 1923 | | | |
| ☐ **NAGEL, Herman F.** .......................... *paintings* | | | $440 |
| American b. 1876 | | | |
| ☐ **NAGEL, Pat** .................................... *paintings* | | | $880 |
| German 20th cent. | | | |
| ☐ **NAGY, Emo** ................................... *paintings* | | | $1,100 |
| Hungarian 19th/20th cent. | | | |
| ☐ **NAGY, Ernest de** ............................ *paintings* | | | $825 |
| German 20th cent. | | | |
| ☐ **NAHA, Raymond** ............................ *drawings* | | $1,650 | $2,310 |
| American (Hopi) 1933-1976 | | | |
| ☐ **NAHL, Charles Christian** .................. *paintings* | | $1,760 | $25,300 |
| American 1818-1878 | | | |
| ☐ **NAHL, Hugo Wilhelm Arthur** .......... *paintings* | | | $1,870 |
| German/American 1820/33-1881/89 | | | |
| ☐ **NAHL, Johann August** ...................... *drawings* | | $385 | $550 |
| ☐ **NAILOR, Gerald** .............................. *paintings* | | $330 | $1,320 |
| American (Navajo) 1917-1952 ................ *drawings* | | $770 | $3,080 |
| ☐ **NAIRN, George** .............................. *paintings* | | | $2,000 |
| Irish 1799-1850 | | | |
| ☐ **NAISH, John George** ...................... *drawings* | | | $1,430 |
| British 1824-1905 | | | |
| ☐ **NAIVEU, Matthys** ............................ *paintings* | | | $880 |
| ☐ **NAKACHE, Armand** ......................... *paintings* | | | $605 |
| ☐ **NAKAGAWA, Hachiro** ..................... *drawings* | | $143 | $900 |
| Japanese 1877-1922 | | | |
| ☐ **NAKHER, W. Carl** ............................ *paintings* | | | $440 |
| ☐ **NAKIAN, Reuben** ............................ *drawings* | | $242 | $528 |
| American b. 1897 ................................ *sculpture* | | $715 | $39,600 |

| | | *Current Price Range* | |
|---|---|---|---|
| | | Low | High |
| ☐ **NAKKEN, Willem Carel** ................... *paintings* | | $605 | $5,280 |
| Dutch 1835-1926 | | | |
| ☐ **NALDINI, Giovanni Battista** .............. *paintings* | | | $6,600 |
| Italian .................................................. *drawings* | | $7,150 | $14,300 |
| ☐ **NANI, Jacopo (or Giacomo)** ................ *paintings* | | $1,540 | $24,200 |
| Italian 1701-1770 | | | |
| ☐ **NANKIVELL, Frank Arthur** .............. *paintings* | | $200 | $7,700 |
| American 1869-1959 | | | |
| ☐ **NANNINI, R.** ..................................... *sculpture* | | | $440 |
| Italian 19th cent. | | | |
| ☐ **NANNINI, R.** ..................................... *sculpture* | | | $275 |
| French ac. 1870-1895 | | | |
| ☐ **NANTEUIL, L.** ................................... *sculpture* | | | $770 |
| French 19th cent. | | | |
| ☐ **NAPOLI, L. Roberto** ......................... *drawings* | | $275 | $330 |
| Italian late 19th cent. | | | |
| ☐ **NARDEUX, Henri** .............................. *paintings* | | $770 | $4,950 |
| French 19th cent. | | | |
| ☐ **NARDI, Enrico** ................................. *drawings* | | $550 | $660 |
| ☐ **NARDI, Francois** .............................. *paintings* | | | $440 |
| ☐ **NARDI, J.F.** ..................................... *paintings* | | | $1,430 |
| ☐ **NARJOT, Erneste** .............................. *paintings* | | $605 | $19,800 |
| American/French 1826-1898 ...................... *drawings* | | | $82 |
| ☐ **NARVAEZ, Francisco** .......................... *sculpture* | | | $11,000 |
| Venezuelan b. 1905/08 | | | |
| ☐ **NASH, John** ..................................... *drawings* | | | $550 |
| British b. 1895 | | | |
| ☐ **NASH, Joseph** .................................. *drawings* | | $3,025 | $3,300 |
| English 1808-1878 | | | |
| ☐ **NASMITH, Mary** ............................... *paintings* | | | $2,420 |
| ☐ **NASMYTH, Alexander** ........................ *paintings* | | $715 | $22,000 |
| Scottish 1758-1840 | | | |
| ☐ **NASMYTH, Charlotte** ........................ *paintings* | | $274 | $2,200 |
| English 19th cent. | | | |
| ☐ **NASMYTH, Margaret** ......................... *paintings* | | | $2,090 |
| British 1791-1869 | | | |
| ☐ **NASMYTH, Patrick** ........................... *paintings* | | $247 | $3,080 |
| British 1787-1831 | | | |
| ☐ **NASON, Pieter** ................................. *paintings* | | $1,650 | $3,080 |
| ☐ **NAST, Thomas** ................................. *paintings* | | $3,300 | $3,850 |
| American 1840-1902 ................................ *drawings* | | $88 | $440 |
| ☐ **NAT, Willem Hendrik van der** ............. *paintings* | | | $275 |
| Dutch 1864-1929 .................................... *drawings* | | $330 | $550 |
| ☐ **NATALI, Renato** ............................... *paintings* | | $660 | $770 |
| Italian b. 1883 | | | |
| ☐ **NATKIN, Robert** ............................... *paintings* | | $165 | $19,800 |
| American b. 1930 ................................... *drawings* | | $1,210 | $3,520 |
| ☐ **NATOIRE, Charles Joseph** ................ *drawings* | | $935 | $11,000 |
| French 1700-1777 | | | |

| | Current Price Range | |
|---|---|---|
| | *Low* | *High* |
| ☐ **NATTIER, Jean Marc** ........................ *paintings*<br>French 1685-1766 | $27,500 | $49,500 |
| ☐ **NATTONIER, C.** ............................. *paintings*<br>French 19th/20th cent. | $440 | $440 |
| ☐ **NATTONIER, R.** ............................. *paintings* | | $352 |
| ☐ **NAUER, Adolf** ............................. *paintings*<br>German b. 1886 | | $1,100 |
| ☐ **NAUMAN, Bruce** ............................. *drawings*<br>American b. 1941 ........................ *sculpture* | $6,600 | $1,540<br>$26,400 |
| ☐ **NAURWETAERT, G.** ......................... *paintings* | | $301 |
| ☐ **NAUTET, Jean** ............................. *paintings* | | $1,650 |
| ☐ **NAUWINCX, Hermann** ...................... *paintings*<br>Flemish 1624-1651 | | $440 |
| ☐ **NAVARRA, Pietro** ........................... *paintings*<br>Italian ac. 17th/18th cent. | | $22,000 |
| ☐ **NAVEZ, Arthur** ............................. *paintings*<br>Flemish 1881-1931 | | $660 |
| ☐ **NAVEZ, Francois Joseph** .................. *paintings*<br>Belgian 1787-1869 | | $880 |
| ☐ **NAVKA, J.** ................................. *paintings*<br>Italian 20th cent. | | $275 |
| ☐ **NAVLET, Joseph** ........................... *drawings* | | $770 |
| ☐ **NAVONE, Edoardo** .......................... *drawings*<br>Italian 19th cent. | | $1,650 |
| ☐ **NAY, Ernst Wilhelm** ........................ *paintings*<br>German 1902-1968 ......................... *drawings* | $9,900<br>$440 | $30,800<br>$7,150 |
| ☐ **NAYA, Dominquez** ........................... *paintings*<br>Spanish 19th/20th cent. | $302 | $385 |
| ☐ **NAZARI, Bartolomeo** ........................ *paintings*<br>Italian 1699-1758 | | $2,530 |
| ☐ **NEAGLE, John** ............................. *paintings*<br>American 1796-1865 | $495 | $1,320 |
| ☐ **NEAL, David Dalhoff** ........................ *paintings*<br>American 1837/38-1915 | | $1,800 |
| ☐ **NEAL, Reginald** ........................... *drawings*<br>American contemporary | | $187 |
| ☐ **NEALE, L. O.** .............................. *drawings*<br>American 19th cent. | | $176 |
| ☐ **NEBEKER, Bill** ............................. *sculpture*<br>American b. 1942 | | $4,500 |
| ☐ **NECK, Jan van** ............................. *paintings*<br>Dutch 1635-1714 | | $3,410 |
| ☐ **NECK, K. van** ............................. *paintings*<br>Dutch 20th cent. | $165 | $330 |
| ☐ **NECK, William** ............................. *paintings*<br>American 19th/20th cent. | | $192 |
| ☐ **NEDER, Johann Michael** .................... *paintings*<br>Austrian 1807-1882 | | $3,520 |

| | | Current Price Range | |
|---|---|---|---|
| | | *Low* | *High* |
| ☐ **NEDHAM, W.** .................................... *paintings* | | | $4,000 |
| British 19th cent. | | | |
| ☐ **NEEDHAN, D.** .................................... *paintings* | | | $330 |
| American 20th cent. | | | |
| ☐ **NEEF, Phillips H.S. de** ..................... *paintings* | | | $4,950 |
| ☐ **NEEFS, Pieter** ................................... *paintings* | | $6,600 | $29,700 |
| Flemish | | | |
| ☐ **NEEL, Alice** ..................................... *paintings* | | | $3,300 |
| American 1900-1984 .................................... *drawings* | | | $330 |
| ☐ **NEER, Aert van der** ......................... *paintings* | | $19,800 | $44,000 |
| Dutch 17th cent. | | | |
| ☐ **NEGELY, R.** ....................................... *paintings* | | $450 | $3,000 |
| Hungarian 19th/20th cent. | | | |
| ☐ **NEGRET, Edgar** ............................... *paintings* | | | $1,870 |
| Colombian b. 1920 ................................... *sculpture* | | $1,210 | $8,800 |
| ☐ **NEGUS, Nathan** ................................ *paintings* | | | $1,980 |
| American 1801-1825 | | | |
| ☐ **NEHLIG, Victor** ................................ *paintings* | | | $440 |
| French 1830-1910 | | | |
| ☐ **NEIDHARDT, Carl** ............................ *paintings* | | | $440 |
| ☐ **NEILLOT, Louis** ............................... *paintings* | | $467 | $1,650 |
| French 1898-1973 .................................... *drawings* | | | $330 |
| ☐ **NEILSON, C.P.** .................................. *drawings* | | | $412 |
| American 19th cent. | | | |
| ☐ **NEILSON, H.** .................................... *paintings* | | | $467 |
| ☐ **NEILSON, Raymond Perry Rodgers** ...... *paintings* | | $330 | $20,350 |
| American 1881-1964 .................................. *drawings* | | | $385 |
| ☐ **NEIMAN, Leroy** ............................... *paintings* | | $2,200 | $15,400 |
| American b. 1926 ..................................... *drawings* | | $275 | $12,100 |
| ☐ **NEIMANN, Edmond John** ................... *paintings* | | | $660 |
| English 19th cent. | | | |
| ☐ **NELAN, Charles** ............................... *drawings* | | | $220 |
| 1859-1904 | | | |
| ☐ **NELIG, Victor** .................................. *paintings* | | | $385 |
| ☐ **NELKE, Alexander** ............................ *paintings* | | $192 | $330 |
| American 19th/20th cent. | | | |
| ☐ **NELL, Tony** .................................... *drawings* | | | $495 |
| American | | | |
| ☐ **NELLA** ............................................ *paintings* | | $50 | $1,750 |
| ☐ **NELLE, Anthony** .............................. *drawings* | | $1,980 | $5,775 |
| ☐ **NELLIUS, Martinus** ........................... *paintings* | | | $14,300 |
| Dutch ac. 1670-1706 | | | |
| ☐ **NELSON, Anton R.** ............................ *sculpture* | | | $1,925 |
| French ac. 1880-1910 | | | |
| ☐ **NELSON, George Laurence** .................. *paintings* | | $22 | $7,700 |
| American 1887-1978 | | | |
| ☐ **NELSON, J.** ....................................... *paintings* | | | $357 |
| American late 19th cent. | | | |

|  | | Current Price Range | |
| --- | --- | --- | --- |
|  | | Low | High |
| ☐ **NELSON, Ralph Lewis** .......... *paintings* | | | $250 |
| American b. 1885 | | | |
| ☐ **NELSON, William** .......... *paintings* | | $143 | $357 |
| American 19th cent. .......... *drawings* | | | $165 |
| ☐ **NEMDI, Andt** .......... *drawings* | | | $264 |
| ☐ **NEMETH, Gyorgy** .......... *paintings* | | $440 | $880 |
| Hungarian 19th/20th cent. | | | |
| ☐ **NEMETHY, Albert** .......... *paintings* | | $55 | $2,530 |
| American 20th cent. | | | |
| ☐ **NEMON, Oscar** .......... *sculpture* | | | $275 |
| American 20th cent. | | | |
| ☐ **NEOGRADY, Antal (or Laszlo)** .......... *paintings* | | $176 | $2,420 |
| Hungarian 1861-1942 | | | |
| ☐ **NEOGRADY, Miklos** .......... *paintings* | | | $1,430 |
| Hungarian 20th cent. | | | |
| ☐ **NEPPEL, H.** .......... *paintings* | | | $1,650 |
| ☐ **NERENZ, Wilhelm** .......... *paintings* | | $440 | $1,430 |
| German 1804-1871 | | | |
| ☐ **NERI** .......... *sculpture* | | | $687 |
| ☐ **NESBITT, John** .......... *paintings* | | $770 | $1,320 |
| English 1831-1904 .......... *drawings* | | $192 | $330 |
| ☐ **NESBITT, Lowell** .......... *paintings* | | $495 | $18,700 |
| American b. 1933 .......... *drawings* | | $165 | $660 |
| ☐ **NESSI, Marie Lucie** .......... *paintings* | | | $550 |
| French contemporary | | | |
| ☐ **NETCHER, C.** .......... *paintings* | | | $522 |
| Dutch 19th cent. | | | |
| ☐ **NETHERMOND, A.** .......... *paintings* | | | $253 |
| Dutch 19th cent. | | | |
| ☐ **NETHERWOOD, A.** .......... *paintings* | | | $330 |
| ☐ **NETO, Calasans** .......... *paintings* | | | $550 |
| ☐ **NETO, Manuel Chong** .......... *paintings* | | $1,100 | $3,410 |
| Latin American | | | |
| ☐ **NETSCHER, Caspar** .......... *paintings* | | $4,000 | $45,100 |
| Dutch 1639-1684 | | | |
| ☐ **NETSCHER, Constantin** .......... *paintings* | | $2,200 | $17,600 |
| Dutch 1668-1723 | | | |
| ☐ **NETTE, Wesley van** .......... *paintings* | | | $330 |
| American | | | |
| ☐ **NETTI, Francesco** .......... *paintings* | | | $4,400 |
| Italian 1834-1894 | | | |
| ☐ **NETTLESHIP, John Trivet** .......... *paintings* | | | $467 |
| ☐ **NETTLETON, Walter** .......... *paintings* | | $350 | $1,650 |
| American 1861-1936 | | | |
| ☐ **NETZELY, H.** .......... *paintings* | | | $412 |
| European 19th cent. | | | |
| ☐ **NEUBERT, Ludwig ((or Louis))** .......... *paintings* | | $770 | $3,850 |
| German 1846-1892 | | | |

| | | *Current Price Range* | |
|---|---|---|---|
| | | *Low* | *High* |
| ☐ **NEUHAUS, Eugen** .............................. *paintings* | | $275 | $605 |
| American 1879-1963 | | | |
| ☐ **NEUHAUS, Trude** ............... *paintings* | | | $550 |
| German 20th cent. | | | |
| ☐ **NEUHUYS, Albert (or Johan Albertus)** ... *paintings* | | $302 | $5,500 |
| Dutch 1844-1914 ...................................... *drawings* | | $605 | $2,475 |
| ☐ **NEUMAN, Carl** ..................................... *paintings* | | | $495 |
| ☐ **NEUMAN, M.R.** ................................. *paintings* | | | $357 |
| ☐ **NEUMAN, Robert** ............................. *paintings* | | | $110 |
| American b. 1926 ...................................... *drawings* | | | $220 |
| ☐ **NEUMANN, Johan J.** ......................... *paintings* | | | $605 |
| Danish/German 1860-1940 | | | |
| ☐ **NEUMANS, Alphonse** ......................... *paintings* | | | $2,090 |
| Dutch 19th cent. | | | |
| ☐ **NEUMANS, P.J.** ................................. *paintings* | | | $2,200 |
| Belgian (?) 19th cent. | | | |
| ☐ **NEUMULLER, B.** ............................... *paintings* | | $308 | $330 |
| ☐ **NEUQUELMAN, Lucien** ..................... *paintings* | | $1,650 | $3,080 |
| French b. 1909 | | | |
| ☐ **NEUSTATTER, Ludwig** ..................... *paintings* | | | $11,000 |
| German 1829-1899 | | | |
| ☐ **NEUSTEIN, Joshua** ............................. *paintings* | | | $4,400 |
| Polish/American b. 1940 | | | |
| ☐ **NEUSTUCK, Maximilian** ..................... *paintings* | | $880 | $935 |
| Swiss 1756-1834 | | | |
| ☐ **NEUVILLE, Alphonse Marie de** ............ *paintings* | | $385 | $12,100 |
| French 1835-1885 ...................................... *drawings* | | $275 | $1,210 |
| ☐ **NEUVILLE,** | | | |
| **Baroness Anne Marguerite Hyde de** ....... *drawings* | | $990 | $3,080 |
| American c. 1779-1849 | | | |
| ☐ **NEUVILLE, Bruno de** ........................... *paintings* | | | $1,100 |
| French 19th/20th cent. | | | |
| ☐ **NEVELSON, Louise** ............................. *drawings* | | $176 | $3,300 |
| Russian/American b. 1900 ............................ *sculpture* | | $605 | $121,000 |
| ☐ **NEVIL, E.** ......................................... *drawings* | | | $1,045 |
| Continental School 19th cent. | | | |
| ☐ **NEVILLE-CUMMING, R.H.** ................ *drawings* | | | $1,650 |
| American | | | |
| ☐ **NEVINSON,** | | | |
| **Christopher Richard Wynne** .................. *paintings* | | | $18,700 |
| English 1889-1946 | | | |
| ☐ **NEWARK, Marilyn** ............................. *sculpture* | | | $1,100 |
| ☐ **NEWBERG, Anni** ............................... *paintings* | | | $280 |
| ☐ **NEWBOTT, John** ............................... *paintings* | | | $880 |
| British 1805-1867 | | | |
| ☐ **NEWCOMBE, Frederick Clive** ............. *paintings* | | | $275 |
| English 1847-1894 | | | |
| ☐ **NEWCOMER, Mary** ........................... *drawings* | | | $1,210 |
| American mid 19th cent. | | | |

|  | | Current Price Range | |
|---|---|---|---|
|  | | Low | High |
| ☐ **NEWELL, George Glenn** ............... *paintings* | | $77 | $3,025 |
| American 1870-1947 | | | |
| ☐ **NEWELL, Hugh** ............... *paintings* | | $247 | $27,500 |
| American 1830-1915 ............... *drawings* | | | $880 |
| ☐ **NEWELL, R. R.** ............... *drawings* | | | $440 |
| American 20th cent. | | | |
| ☐ **NEWHALL, Harriott B.** ............... *drawings* | | $110 | $220 |
| American 19th cent. | | | |
| ☐ **NEWHALL, Kate W.** ............... *paintings* | | | $550 |
| 20th cent. | | | |
| ☐ **NEWHAM, John Deeing** ............... *paintings* | | | $935 |
| ☐ **NEWHAUS** ............... *paintings* | | | $247 |
| German b. 1937 | | | |
| ☐ **NEWHOUSE, C.B.** ............... *drawings* | | | $660 |
| British 19th cent. | | | |
| ☐ **NEWMAN, Allen George** ............... *sculpture* | | | $6,600 |
| American | | | |
| ☐ **NEWMAN, B. Spencer** ............... *paintings* | | $55 | $275 |
| American 1859-1969 ............... *drawings* | | | $55 |
| ☐ **NEWMAN, B.T.** ............... *paintings* | | | $2,750 |
| American 19th/20th cent. | | | |
| ☐ **NEWMAN, Barnett** ............... *paintings* | | $60,500 | $1,595,000 |
| American 1905-1970 ............... *drawings* | | $28,600 | $55,000 |
| ☐ **NEWMAN, Carl** ............... *paintings* | | $357 | $1,320 |
| American 1858-1932 | | | |
| ☐ **NEWMAN, George A.** ............... *paintings* | | $44 | $187 |
| American 20th cent. | | | |
| ☐ **NEWMAN, Henry Roderick** ............... *drawings* | | | $275 |
| American 1833(?)-1918 | | | |
| ☐ **NEWMAN, Malcolm** ............... *paintings* | | | $302 |
| American 20th cent. | | | |
| ☐ **NEWMAN, Robert Loftin** ............... *paintings* | | | $1,540 |
| American | | | |
| ☐ **NEWMAN, Willie Betty** ............... *paintings* | | $385 | $440 |
| American b. 1864 | | | |
| ☐ **NEWMARCH, Strafford** ............... *paintings* | | | $550 |
| British 19th cent. | | | |
| ☐ **NEWMARK, Hank** | | | |
| **(Walt Disney Studios)** ............... *paintings* | | | $550 |
| ............... *drawings* | | | $770 |
| ☐ **NEWNHAM, J.** ............... *paintings* | | | $550 |
| British 19th cent. | | | |
| ☐ **NEWTON, Gilbert Stuart** ............... *paintings* | | $275 | $1,760 |
| b. Canada, d. Eng. c. 1794-1835 | | | |
| ☐ **NEWTON, Parker** ............... *paintings* | | $308 | $880 |
| American | | | |
| ☐ **NEWTON, Richard** ............... *paintings* | | $2,090 | $2,200 |
| English 1777-1798 | | | |

|                                                   | Current Price Range | |
|                                                   | Low       | High    |
| --------------------------------------------------| --------- | ------- |
| ☐ **NEYLAND, H.A.** .................................. *paintings* |           | **$400** |
| American 20th cent.                               |           |         |
| ☐ **NEYN, Pieter de** ................................. *paintings* | **$6,600** | **$6,600** |
| Dutch 1597-1639                                   |           |         |
| ☐ **NEYRAC, Guy de** ................................. *paintings* |           | **$82** |
| French 19th/20th cent. ............................... *drawings* | **$44** | **$385** |
| ☐ **NEZ, Guy (Jr.)** ................................. *paintings* |           | **$990** |
| American (Navajo)                                 |           |         |
| ☐ **NIBBRIG, Ferdinand Hart** ..................... *paintings* |           | **$12,100** |
| Dutch 1866-1915                                   |           |         |
| ☐ **NIBBS, Richard Henry** ......................... *paintings* |           | **$5,500** |
| British 1816-1893 ...................................... *drawings* |           | **$357** |
| ☐ **NIBLETT, Gary** ................................. *paintings* | **$4,500** | **$32,500** |
| American b. 1943 .................................... *drawings* | **$4,500** | **$5,500** |
| ☐ **NICCOLO DA VOLTRI** ........................ *paintings* |           | **$25,300** |
| Italian 1385-1417                                 |           |         |
| ☐ **NICHOL, John Watson** ........................ *paintings* |           | **$2,200** |
| British ac. 1875-1890                             |           |         |
| ☐ **NICHOLAS, Grace** ............................. *paintings* |           | **$230** |
| American 19th cent.                               |           |         |
| ☐ **NICHOLAS, P.** ................................. *paintings* |           | **$192** |
| American 19th cent.                               |           |         |
| ☐ **NICHOLAS, Tom** ............................... *paintings* |           | **$935** |
| American 20th cent. ................................... *drawings* |           | **$750** |
| ☐ **NICHOLL, Andrew** ............................. *drawings* | **$4,400** | **$7,700** |
| Irish 1804-1886                                   |           |         |
| ☐ **NICHOLLS, Burr H.** ............................ *paintings* | **$200** | **$990** |
| American 1848-1915                                |           |         |
| ☐ **NICHOLLS, Rhoda Holmes** ................. *drawings* | **$55** | **$3,250** |
| Anglo/American 1854-1930                          |           |         |
| ☐ **NICHOLS, C.C.** .................................... *paintings* | **$302** | **$330** |
| English 19th cent.                                |           |         |
| ☐ **NICHOLS, Celeste Bruff** ..................... *paintings* | **$302** | **$660** |
| American ac. 1887-1910                            |           |         |
| ☐ **NICHOLS, Dale William** ...................... *paintings* | **$1,045** | **$9,075** |
| American b. 1904 ...................................... *drawings* | **$550** | **$1,650** |
| ☐ **NICHOLS, G.W.** ................................. *paintings* |           | **$1,100** |
| American 19th cent.                               |           |         |
| ☐ **NICHOLS, Henry Hobart** ..................... *paintings* | **$247** | **$11,000** |
| American 1869-1962 ................................... *drawings* | **$80** | **$440** |
| ☐ **NICHOLS, Hubley** ............................. *paintings* |           | **$935** |
| ☐ **NICHOLS, Spencer Baird** .................... *paintings* |           | **$495** |
| American 1878-1950 ................................... *drawings* |           | **$220** |
| ☐ **NICHOLSON, Ben** ............................. *paintings* | **$18,700** | **$242,000** |
| British 1894-1982 ...................................... *drawings* | **$450** | **$13,200** |
| .................................................... *sculpture* | **$9,900** | **$126,500** |
| ☐ **NICHOLSON, Charles W.** ..................... *paintings* | **$165** | **$302** |
| American 19th/20th cent.                          |           |         |

| | | *Current Price Range* | |
| --- | --- | --- | --- |
| | | Low | High |
| ☐ **NICHOLSON, Edward Horace** .............. *paintings* | | $165 | $440 |
| American 1901-1966 | | | |
| ☐ **NICHOLSON, Francis** ......................... *drawings* | | $110 | $264 |
| ☐ **NICHOLSON, George Washington** ........ *paintings* | | $132 | $11,000 |
| American 1832-1912 ................................. *drawings* | | $330 | $1,980 |
| ☐ **NICHOLSON, Lillie May** ..................... *paintings* | | | $1,430 |
| American 1884-1964 | | | |
| ☐ **NICKELE, Isaak van** ........................... *paintings* | | | $3,300 |
| Dutch 1660-1703 | | | |
| ☐ **NICOL, Erskine** .................................. *paintings* | | $88 | $18,700 |
| British 1825-1904 ...................................... *drawings* | | | $440 |
| ☐ **NICOLAY, J.** ...................................... *paintings* | | $385 | $495 |
| European 19th cent. | | | |
| ☐ **NICOLET** ....................................... *sculpture* | | | $1,210 |
| ☐ **NICOLETE, Gabriel** ........................... *paintings* | | | $4,400 |
| Swiss 1856-1921 | | | |
| ☐ **NICOLIE, J.C.** ................................... *paintings* | | | $1,210 |
| ☐ **NICOLL, James Craig** ......................... *paintings* | | $121 | $935 |
| American 1846-1918 | | | |
| ☐ **NICOLL, Nicol** .................................. *drawings* | | $246 | $660 |
| American b. 1923 | | | |
| ☐ **NICOLLE, Victor Jean** ........................ *drawings* | | $220 | $2,530 |
| French 1754-1826 | | | |
| ☐ **NICOLS, Audley Dean** ........................ *paintings* | | | $660 |
| ☐ **NICORE, A. Harvey** ........................... *paintings* | | | $341 |
| English 19th/20th cent. | | | |
| ☐ **NICZKY, Eduard** ................................ *paintings* | | | $1,540 |
| German b. 1850 | | | |
| ☐ **NIEHAUS, Charles Henry** ................... *sculpture* | | | $4,000 |
| American 1855-1935 | | | |
| ☐ **NIELSEN, Kay** .................................. *drawings* | | | $4,950 |
| Danish 1886-1957 | | | |
| ☐ **NIEMANN, Edmund John** ................... *paintings* | | $220 | $15,400 |
| British 1813-1876 | | | |
| ☐ **NIEMANN, Edward H.** ........................ *paintings* | | $550 | $660 |
| British School 19th cent. | | | |
| ☐ **NIERMAN, Leonardo** ......................... *paintings* | | $356 | $1,650 |
| Mexican 20th cent. ................................... *drawings* | | $264 | $440 |
| ☐ **NIEULANDT, Adriaen van** ................... *paintings* | | $22,000 | $26,400 |
| Flemish 1587-1658 | | | |
| ☐ **NIEULANDT, Willem van (II)** .............. *paintings* | | $1,650 | $5,500 |
| ☐ **NIEUWENHOVEN, Willem van** ............ *paintings* | | $1,320 | $3,850 |
| Dutch b. 1879 | | | |
| ☐ **NIGG** .............................................. *paintings* | | $110 | $192 |
| Austrian 19th cent. | | | |
| ☐ **NIGG, Joseph** .................................. *drawings* | | | $26,400 |
| Austrian 1782-1863 | | | |
| ☐ **NIGHTINGALE, Basil** ........................ *paintings* | | $440 | $4,180 |
| English 19th cent. | | | |

| | | Current Price Range | |
|---|---|---|---|
| | | Low | High |
| ☐ **NIGHTINGALE, Leonard Charles** ........ *paintings* English ac. 1877-1913 | | | $742 |
| ☐ **NIGHTINGALE, Robert** ...................... *paintings* English 1815-1895 | | | $9,075 |
| ☐ **NIJMEGEN, Gerard van** ...................... *drawings* Dutch 1735-1808 | | | $6,050 |
| ☐ **NIKIFOR** ............................................. *drawings* | | | $660 |
| ☐ **NIKOLAKI, Z.P.** ............................... *drawings* 20th cent. | | | $220 |
| ☐ **NIKONOV, Nikolai** ........................... *paintings* Russian 20th cent. | | | $374 |
| ☐ **NIKUTOWSKI, Arthur Johann Severin** ........................ *paintings* German 1830-1888 | | | $56,100 |
| ☐ **NILES, George E.** ............................... *paintings* American 1837-1898 | | | $605 |
| ☐ **NILSON, Severin** ............................... *paintings* Swedish 1846-1918 | | | $1,155 |
| ☐ **NILSSON, Axel** ............................... *paintings* Swedish b. 1887/89 | $275 | $4,400 |
| ☐ **NILSSON, Gladys** ............................... *drawings* American b. 1940 | | | $1,650 |
| ☐ **NINI, Jean Baptiste** ........................... *sculpture* Italian 1717-1786 | | | $220 |
| ☐ **NINO, Alberto** ..................................... *paintings* | | | $352 |
| ☐ **NIRNSTEIN, Z.** ..................................... *paintings* early 20th cent. | | | $275 |
| ☐ **NIRO, Robert de** ........................... *paintings* American b. 1922 | $550 | $1,210 |
| ☐ **NISBET, Robert H.** ............................... *paintings* | $275 | $660 |
| American b. 1879 ..................................... *drawings* | $66 | $242 |
| ☐ **NISSL, Rudolph** ............................... *paintings* Austrian b. 1870 | | | $1,925 |
| ☐ **NITSCH, Richard** ............................... *paintings* German b. 1866 | $247 | $1,100 |
| ☐ **NITSCHKE** ......................................... *sculpture* | | | $286 |
| ☐ **NITTIS, Giuseppe de** ........................... *paintings* | $8,800 | $33,000 |
| Italian 1846-1884 ..................................... *drawings* | $440 | $11,550 |
| ☐ **NIVERT, Georgette** ............................... *paintings* French 20th cent. | $44 | $241 |
| ☐ **NIVERVILLE, Louis de** ...................... *paintings* Canadian b. 1933 | | | $1,430 |
| ☐ **NIVET, E.** ......................................... *sculpture* | | | $1,760 |
| ☐ **NIXON, James Henry** ........................... *paintings* English c. 1808 | | | $5,500 |
| ☐ **NIXON, W.R.** ..................................... *paintings* English 19th cent. | | | $1,430 |
| ☐ **NOBLE, Charles F.** ............................... *paintings* British 20th cent. | | | $1,100 |

| | *Current Price Range* | |
|---|---|---|
| | Low | High |
| ☐ **NOBLE, James Campbell** ............... *paintings* | | $330 |
| ☐ **NOBLE, John** ............... *paintings* | $165 | $3,850 |
| American 1874-1935 | | |
| ☐ **NOBLE, Robert** ............... *paintings* | $198 | $1,210 |
| British 1857-1917 | | |
| ☐ **NOBLE, Thomas Satterwhite** ............... *paintings* | $550 | $9,075 |
| American 1835-1907 | | |
| ☐ **NOBLE, William Clark** ............... *sculpture* | | $1,210 |
| American 1858-1938 | | |
| ☐ **NOBREGA, Nelson** ............... *paintings* | | $880 |
| b. Brazil 1900 | | |
| ☐ **NOCI, Arturo** ............... *drawings* | | $275 |
| ☐ **NOE, Luis Felipe** ............... *paintings* | | $17,600 |
| Argentinian b. 1933 | | |
| ☐ **NOEL, Alexandre Jean** ............... *drawings* | $2,090 | $3,190 |
| French 1752-1834 | | |
| ☐ **NOEL, Amelia** ............... *drawings* | | $330 |
| English 18th cent. | | |
| ☐ **NOEL, F.E.** ............... *paintings* | | $880 |
| ☐ **NOEL, Georges** ............... *drawings* | $550 | $2,200 |
| French b. 1924 | | |
| ☐ **NOEL, Gustave** ............... *drawings* | | $192 |
| French b. 1823 | | |
| ☐ **NOEL, John Bates** ............... *paintings* | $935 | $990 |
| British 19th/20th cent. ............... *drawings* | $137 | $137 |
| ☐ **NOEL, Jules Achille** ............... *paintings* | $132 | $8,800 |
| French 1813/15-1881 ............... *drawings* | | $550 |
| ☐ **NOEL, Pierre** ............... *paintings* | | $797 |
| French 19th cent. | | |
| ☐ **NOEL, R.** ............... *sculpture* | | $467 |
| French early 19th cent. | | |
| ☐ **NOELSMITH, T.** ............... *drawings* | | $467 |
| English 19th cent. | | |
| ☐ **NOGARI, Giuseppe** ............... *paintings* | | $2,200 |
| Italian 1699-1763 | | |
| ☐ **NOGARO, Charles** ............... *drawings* | | $308 |
| ☐ **NOGGERATH, Rufina** ............... *drawings* | | $550 |
| ☐ **NOGUCHI, Isamu** ............... *paintings* | $1,760 | $79,200 |
| American b. 1904 ............... *drawings* | $440 | $1,210 |
| ☐ **NOLAN, Harry** ............... *paintings* | | $330 |
| ☐ **NOLAN, Sidney** ............... *paintings* | $8,800 | $13,200 |
| Australian b. 1917 ............... *drawings* | | $495 |
| ☐ **NOLAND, Kenneth** ............... *paintings* | $4,950 | $330,000 |
| American b. 1924 | | |
| ☐ **NOLDE, Emil** ............... *paintings* | $77,000 | $330,000 |
| German 1867-1956 ............... *drawings* | $1,100 | $52,800 |
| ☐ **NOLET, A.** ............... *paintings* | | $352 |
| ☐ **NOLF, John** ............... *paintings* | | $660 |
| American 20th cent. | | |

| | | Current Price Range | |
|---|---|---|---|
| | | Low | High |
| ☐ **NOLLEKENS, Pieter** ............................. *paintings* | | $990 | $1,320 |
| Flemish 17th/18th cent. | | | |
| ☐ **NOLTEE, C.** ......................................... *paintings* | | | $550 |
| Dutch 1903-1967 | | | |
| ☐ **NOME, Francesco de** | | | |
| **(called Monsu Desiderio)** ......................... *paintings* | | $8,500 | $41,800 |
| Italian 1593-c. 1618 | | | |
| ☐ **NONAS, Richard** ................................. *sculpture* | | $308 | $1,430 |
| American contemporary | | | |
| ☐ **NONN, Carl** ......................................... *paintings* | | | $550 |
| ☐ **NONNENBRUCH, Max** ......................... *paintings* | | | $7,700 |
| German 1857-1922 | | | |
| ☐ **NOOK, Fern** ....................................... *paintings* | | | $192 |
| American 19th cent. | | | |
| ☐ **NOOMS, Renier (called Zeeman)** ............ *paintings* | | | $34,100 |
| Dutch 1623-1667 | | | |
| ☐ **NOORT, Adrianus Cornelis van** .......... *paintings* | | $440 | $880 |
| Dutch b. 1914/16 | | | |
| ☐ **NOORT, Jan van** ............................... *paintings* | | | $440 |
| Dutch 19th/20th cent. | | | |
| ☐ **NOOTEBOOM, J.H.J.** ......................... *paintings* | | | $2,200 |
| Dutch 19th cent. | | | |
| ☐ **NORBERG, C.** ..................................... *paintings* | | | $192 |
| American 19th/20th cent. | | | |
| ☐ **NORBLIN DE LA GOURDAINE,** | | | |
| **Jean Pierre** ....................................... *drawings* | | $825 | $2,200 |
| French 1745-1830 | | | |
| ☐ **NORCROSS, Emily D.** ......................... *paintings* | | | $192 |
| American 1849-1909 | | | |
| ☐ **NORDALM, Federico** ......................... *paintings* | | $1,320 | $2,200 |
| ☐ **NORDELL, Carl J.** ............................. *paintings* | | $209 | $11,000 |
| Danish/American b. 1885 | | | |
| ☐ **NORDELL, Polly (E. Parker)** ............... *drawings* | | $88 | $275 |
| American 19th/20th cent. | | | |
| ☐ **NORDENBERG, C. Hendrick** ............... *paintings* | | $2,090 | $2,200 |
| Swedish 1857-1928 | | | |
| ☐ **NORDFELDT, Bror Julius Olsson** ......... *paintings* | | $935 | $9,900 |
| Swedish/American 1878-1955 ...................... *drawings* | | $935 | $1,760 |
| ☐ **NORDGREN, Axel Wilhelm** ................. *paintings* | | $600 | $850 |
| ☐ **NORDHAGEN, Olaf** ............................. *paintings* | | | $2,310 |
| Norwegian 19th cent. | | | |
| ☐ **NORDHAUSEN, August Henry** ............. *paintings* | | $143 | $500 |
| American b. 1901 | | | |
| ☐ **NORDSTROM, Carl Harold** ................. *paintings* | | $110 | $302 |
| American b. 1876 ..................................... *drawings* | | $27 | $66 |
| ☐ **NORDSTROM, Karl F.** ......................... *paintings* | | | $301 |
| Swedish 1855-1923 ................................... *drawings* | | | $66 |
| ☐ **NORFOLK, Walter** ............................. *paintings* | | $165 | $275 |
| American 19th/20th cent. | | | |

| | Current Price Range | |
|---|---|---|
| | Low | High |

| | | Low | High |
|---|---|---|---|
| ☐ **NORIE, Orlando** .................... *drawings* | | $165 | $550 |
| Scottish 1832-1901 | | | |
| ☐ **NORMAN, F.M.** .................... *paintings* | | | $418 |
| ☐ **NORMAN, Mabel** .................... *paintings* | | | $192 |
| American 20th cent. | | | |
| ☐ **NORMAN, Philip** .................... *drawings* | | | $412 |
| British c. 1843-1931 | | | |
| ☐ **NORMAND, Adelsteen** | | | |
| **(or NORMANN)** .................... *paintings* | | $440 | $22,000 |
| Norwegian 1848-1918 | | | |
| ☐ **NORMAND, Ernest** .................... *paintings* | | | $19,800 |
| British 1857-1923 | | | |
| ☐ **NORMANN, E.P.** .................... *paintings* | | | $1,100 |
| ☐ **NORMIL, Andre** .................... *paintings* | | $385 | $3,300 |
| Haitian 20th cent. | | | |
| ☐ **NORSE, Stansbury** .................... *paintings* | | $50 | $2,200 |
| American 19th cent. | | | |
| ☐ **NORTH, Noah** .................... *paintings* | | $5,500 | $12,100 |
| American 1809-1880 | | | |
| ☐ **NORTHCOTE, H.B.** .................... *paintings* | | | $660 |
| English 19th cent. | | | |
| ☐ **NORTHCOTE, James** .................... *paintings* | | $247 | $605 |
| American 1822-1904 .................... *drawings* | | | $308 |
| ☐ **NORTHCOTE, James** | | | |
| **(or Thomas James)** .................... *paintings* | | $302 | $6,325 |
| English 1746-1831 | | | |
| ☐ **NORTHEN, Adolf** .................... *paintings* | | $1,430 | $3,300 |
| German 1828-1876 | | | |
| ☐ **NORTON, B. Cam** .................... *paintings* | | | $14,000 |
| ☐ **NORTON, Jim** .................... *paintings* | | | $900 |
| American | | | |
| ☐ **NORTON, L.D.** .................... *paintings* | | | $374 |
| American late 19th cent. .................... *drawings* | | | $605 |
| ☐ **NORTON, W. H.** .................... *drawings* | | | $715 |
| American ac. c. 1859-60 | | | |
| ☐ **NORTON, William Edward** .................... *paintings* | | $100 | $8,800 |
| American 1843-1916 .................... *drawings* | | $34 | $2,200 |
| ☐ **NORTWICK, Evan** .................... *paintings* | | | $192 |
| American 20th cent. | | | |
| ☐ **NORWELL, Graham Noble** .................... *drawings* | | $175 | $356 |
| Canadian 1901-1967 | | | |
| ☐ **NOTER, David Emil Joseph de** .................... *paintings* | | $2,750 | $14,300 |
| Belgian 1825-1880/1900 | | | |
| ☐ **NOTER, Raphael David Marie de** .................... *paintings* | | | $1,540 |
| Belgian 19th cent. | | | |
| ☐ **NOTERMANN, Zacherie** .................... *paintings* | | $605 | $6,050 |
| German 19th cent. | | | |
| ☐ **NOTT, Raymond** .................... *paintings* | | $137 | $770 |
| American 19th/20th cent. .................... *drawings* | | $55 | $385 |

| | Current Price Range | |
|---|---|---|
| | Low | High |
| ☐ **NOTT, W.E.** ........ *paintings* | | $275 |
| ☐ **NOTTERMAN, Emmanuel** ........ *paintings* | | $357 |
| Belgian 1808-1863 | | |
| ☐ **NOUQUET, Hean Michel** ........ *paintings* | | $522 |
| French contemporary | | |
| ☐ **NOURSE, Elizabeth** ........ *paintings* | $1,760 | $33,000 |
| American 1859/60-1938 ........ *drawings* | $220 | $24,200 |
| ☐ **NOURT, Andrianus Cornelius van** ........ *paintings* | | $1,760 |
| Dutch b. 1914 | | |
| ☐ **NOURY, Jacques** ........ *paintings* | | $330 |
| ☐ **NOUVILLE, B.** ........ *paintings* | | $1,375 |
| French 20th cent. | | |
| ☐ **NOVELLI, Pietro Antonio** ........ *drawings* | $440 | $1,870 |
| Italian | | |
| ☐ **NOVICE, William** ........ *paintings* | $495 | $522 |
| Scottish 19th cent. | | |
| ☐ **NOVO, Stefano** ........ *paintings* | $850 | $7,425 |
| Italian b. 1862 | | |
| ☐ **NOVOA, Gustavo** ........ *paintings* | $100 | $990 |
| ☐ **NOVOSIELSKI, Michael** ........ *drawings* | $880 | $880 |
| ☐ **NOVROS, David** ........ *paintings* | $286 | $18,700 |
| American b. 1941 ........ *drawings* | | $1,100 |
| ☐ **NOWAK, Ernst** ........ *paintings* | $1,320 | $1,980 |
| Austrian | | |
| ☐ **NOWAK, Franz** ........ *paintings* | $770 | $1,870 |
| Austrian 19th/20th cent. | | |
| ☐ **NOWAK, Otto** ........ *paintings* | $715 | $1,045 |
| Austrian 1874-1945 | | |
| ☐ **NOWEY, Adolf** ........ *paintings* | | $550 |
| 19th cent. | | |
| ☐ **NOWY, A.R.** ........ *paintings* | | $521 |
| ☐ **NOYER, Denis Paul** ........ *paintings* | $247 | $1,650 |
| French b. 1940 | | |
| ☐ **NOYER, Oliver P.** ........ *paintings* | | $330 |
| ☐ **NOYER, Philippe Henri** ........ *paintings* | $715 | $5,170 |
| French b. 1917 ........ *drawings* | $220 | $1,760 |
| ☐ **NOYES, Bertha** ........ *paintings* | | $176 |
| American 1876-1966 | | |
| ☐ **NOYES, George Loftus** ........ *paintings* | $44 | $26,400 |
| Canadian/American 1864-1951/54 ........ *drawings* | | $400 |
| ☐ **NOYES, George Loring** ........ *paintings* | | $2,310 |
| Canadian 19th/20th cent. | | |
| ☐ **NOYES, Wilbur Fisk** ........ *paintings* | | $825 |
| American 20th cent. | | |
| ☐ **NOZAL, Alexandre** ........ *paintings* | $660 | $1,320 |
| French 1852-1929 ........ *drawings* | | $330 |
| ☐ **NUDERSCHER, Frank** ........ *paintings* | $165 | $3,520 |
| American 1880-1959 ........ *drawings* | | $467 |

| | Current Price Range | |
|---|---|---|
| | Low | High |
| ☐ **NUHLER, Augustus W.** ........................ *drawings* <br> American d. 1920 | | **$192** |
| ☐ **NULJIM(?), Amaldus** ........................ *paintings* | | **$4,180** |
| ☐ **NUNAMAKER, Kenneth R.** .................. *paintings* <br> American contemporary | | **$2,750** |
| ☐ **NUNES, E.** ........................................ *paintings* <br> Portuguese 20th cent. | | **$385** |
| ☐ **NUNEZ, Fernando** ............................. *paintings* <br> Mexican 19th/20th cent. | **$770** | **$1,375** |
| ☐ **NUNEZ DE VILLAVICENZIO, Pedro** .. *paintings* <br> Spanish 1644-1700 | | **$3,300** |
| ☐ **NUNEZ DEL PRADO, Marina** .............. *sculpture* <br> Bolivian b. 1912 | **$1,430** | **$5,500** |
| ☐ **NUNNENBERG, D.** ............................. *paintings* | | **$330** |
| ☐ **NURICK, Irving** ................................ *paintings* <br> American 20th cent. | | **$275** |
| ☐ **NURSTRUM, C.** ................................. *drawings* <br> American early 20th cent. | | **$412** |
| ☐ **NUSE, Roy Cleveland** ........................ *paintings* <br> American | | **$605** |
| ☐ **NUSSBAUM, Ervin** ............................. *paintings* <br> American | | **$1,100** |
| ☐ **NUSSI, Arnaldo** ................................ *paintings* <br> Italian b. 1902 | | **$660** |
| ☐ **NUSSY, Eric de** ................................ *sculpture* <br> French late 19th cent. | | **$440** |
| ☐ **NUTT, Jim** ........................................ *sculpture* <br> American b. 1938 | | **$7,700** |
| ☐ **NUVOLONE, Giuseppe** <br> **(called Panfilo)** ...................................... *paintings* <br> Italian 1619-1703 | | **$6,050** |
| ☐ **NUZZIO, Mario** <br> **(called MARIO DA FIORI)** .................... *paintings* <br> Italian 1603-1673 | | **$2,090** |
| ☐ **NYE, Edgar** ....................................... *paintings* <br> American 1879-1943 ................................. *drawings* | **$148** <br> **$77** | **$935** <br> **$302** |
| ☐ **NYGARD** ........................................... *paintings* <br> Danish b. 1932 | | **$220** |
| ☐ **NYILASY, Sandor** .............................. *paintings* <br> Hungarian b. 1873 | | **$1,210** |
| ☐ **O'BRIEN, L.** ...................................... *paintings* <br> American 19th cent. | | **$275** |
| ☐ **O'CONNOR, James Arthur** ................ *paintings* <br> Irish 1792-1841 | **$2,200** | **$3,575** |
| ☐ **O'DONOVAN, William Rudolf** .............. *drawings* <br> American 1844-1920 | **$11** | **$220** |
| ☐ **O'GORMAN, Juan** ............................. *paintings* <br> Mexican 1905-1982 ................................. *drawings* | **$14,300** <br> **$1,650** | **$29,700** <br> **$2,090** |

|                                          | Current Price Range | |
|                                          | Low | High |
|------------------------------------------|--------|-----------|
| ☐ **O'GRADY, Donn** .................................. *paintings* | $467 | $715 |
| American 20th cent. | | |
| ☐ **O'HAGEN, John L.** ............................... *paintings* | | $275 |
| American 20th cent. | | |
| ☐ **O'HARA, Eliot** ....................................... *drawings* | $99 | $363 |
| ☐ **O'HIGGINS, Pablo** ............................. *paintings* | $990 | $4,400 |
| Mexican b. 1904 ...................................... *drawings* | | $1,210 |
| ☐ **O'KEEFFE, Georgia** ........................... *paintings* | $33,000 | $330,000 |
| American b. 1887 ..................................... *drawings* | $16,500 | $110,000 |
| ☐ **O'KELLY, Aloysius** ........................... *paintings* | $110 | $2,310 |
| Irish/American b. 1850/53 | | |
| ☐ **O'LEARY, Galbraith** ........................... *paintings* | | $1,500 |
| American 20th cent. | | |
| ☐ **O'NEIL, George Bernard** ................... *paintings* | | $2,420 |
| English 1828-1917 | | |
| ☐ **O'NEIL, Henry** ................................... *paintings* | | $1,650 |
| ☐ **O'NEIL, Thomas F.** ............................. *paintings* | $16 | $302 |
| American 1852-1922 | | |
| ☐ **O'NEILL, George Bernard** ................... *paintings* | $3,300 | $4,950 |
| British 1828-1917 | | |
| ☐ **O'NEILL, Rose** ................................... *drawings* | $385 | $825 |
| American 1874-1944 | | |
| ☐ **O'REILLY, Joseph** ............................. *paintings* | | $2,640 |
| Irish d. 1893 | | |
| ☐ **O'SHEA, John** ................................... *paintings* | | $495 |
| American ac. 1934 | | |
| ☐ **O'TOOLE, Cathal B.** ........................... *paintings* | $33 | $11,000 |
| American b. 1903 | | |
| ☐ **OAKES, Wilbur L.** ............................. *paintings* | $110 | $357 |
| American 1876-1934 | | |
| ☐ **OAKLEY, Octavius** ............................. *drawings* | | $264 |
| ☐ **OAKLEY, Thornton** ........................... *paintings* | $770 | $2,200 |
| American 1881-1953 ................................. *drawings* | $110 | $1,980 |
| ☐ **OAKLEY, Violet** ................................. *paintings* | | $77 |
| American 1874-1961 ................................. *drawings* | $45 | $385 |
| ☐ **OBAS, Charles** ................................... *drawings* | | $330 |
| ☐ **OBER, Artemi Lavrentevich** ................ *sculpture* | $1,650 | $3,190 |
| Russian 19th cent. | | |
| ☐ **OBERG, A.** ......................................... *sculpture* | | $1,870 |
| Russian 19th cent. | | |
| ☐ **OBERHAUS, F.** ................................... *paintings* | | $1,980 |
| German (?) 19th cent. | | |
| ☐ **OBERHAUSER, E.** ............................. *paintings* | | $4,400 |
| German 19th cent. | | |
| ☐ **OBERMEULLER, O.** ........................... *paintings* | | $660 |
| ☐ **OBERMULLER, Franz** ....................... *paintings* | $330 | $1,650 |
| Austrian 1869-1917 | | |
| ☐ **OBERMULLNER, Adolf** ....................... *paintings* | | $3,025 |
| Austrian 1833-1898 | | |

| | Current Price Range | |
|---|---|---|
| | *Low* | *High* |
| ☐ **OBERSTEINER, Ludwig** ...... *paintings* | | $1,650 |
| Austrian b. 1857 | | |
| ☐ **OBERT, J.** ...... *paintings* | | $275 |
| late 19th cent. | | |
| ☐ **OBERTEUFFER, George** ...... *paintings* | $385 | $14,300 |
| American 1878-1940 | | |
| ☐ **OBIN, Antoine** ...... *paintings* | $220 | $1,870 |
| Haitian b. 1929 | | |
| ☐ **OBIN, Claude** ...... *paintings* | $11 | $880 |
| b. Haiti | | |
| ☐ **OBIN, Harrison** ...... *paintings* | | $330 |
| ☐ **OBIN, Michael** ...... *paintings* | $825 | $935 |
| b. Haiti | | |
| ☐ **OBIN, Philome** ...... *paintings* | $1,870 | $18,700 |
| Haitian b. 1892 | | |
| ☐ **OBIN, Seneque** ...... *paintings* | $715 | $16,500 |
| Haitian 1893-1977 | | |
| ☐ **OBIN, Telemaque** ...... *paintings* | | $440 |
| ☐ **OBREGON, Alejandro** ...... *paintings* | $2,750 | $20,900 |
| Spanish/Colombian b. 1920 ...... *drawings* | | $1,760 |
| ☐ **OBRIST, C.** ...... *paintings* | | $605 |
| Austrian 19th cent. | | |
| ☐ **OCAMPO, Isidoro** ...... *paintings* | | $1,045 |
| Mexican 20th cent. | | |
| ☐ **OCAMPO, Miguel** ...... *paintings* | $880 | $1,760 |
| Argentinean b. 1922 | | |
| ☐ **OCHS, Konrad** ...... *paintings* | | $935 |
| Austrian | | |
| ☐ **OCHTMAN, Leonard** ...... *paintings* | $330 | $24,000 |
| Dutch/American 1854-1934 ...... *drawings* | $242 | $302 |
| ☐ **OCHTMAN, Mina Fonda** ...... *paintings* | $110 | $880 |
| American 1862-1924 ...... *drawings* | | $220 |
| ☐ **OCKERT, Carl** ...... *paintings* | $550 | $935 |
| German 1825-1899 | | |
| ☐ **OCTAVIEN, Francois** ...... *paintings* | | $10,450 |
| French 1695-1732 or 1736 | | |
| ☐ **ODDIE, Walter M.** ...... *paintings* | $4,125 | $4,400 |
| American 1808-1865 | | |
| ☐ **ODELL, Thomas Jefferson** ...... *paintings* | | $495 |
| American 1810-1849 | | |
| ☐ **ODIERNA, Guido** ...... *paintings* | $110 | $715 |
| Italian 19th/20th cent. | | |
| ☐ **ODNORALOV, Michael** ...... *paintings* | | $187 |
| Russian 20th cent. | | |
| ☐ **OECONOMO, Aristede** ...... *paintings* | | $605 |
| ☐ **OEDER, Georg** ...... *paintings* | | $1,430 |
| German 1846-1931 | | |
| ☐ **OEHMICHEN, Hugo** ...... *paintings* | | $935 |
| ☐ **OEHRENS, P.** ...... *paintings* | | $352 |

| | Current Price Range | |
|---|---|---|
| | *Low* | *High* |
| ☐ **OEHRING, Hedwig** ............................ *paintings* | | $1,650 |
| German b. 1860 | | |
| ☐ **OELWEIN, A.** ...................................... *paintings* | | $275 |
| ☐ **OER, Theobald Reinhold von** ............... *drawings* | | $880 |
| German 1807-1885 | | |
| ☐ **OERDER, Frans David** .......................... *paintings* | | $2,420 |
| Dutch 1866-1944 | | |
| ☐ **OERTEL, J.A.** ..................................... *paintings* | | $220 |
| late 19th cent. | | |
| ☐ **OF, George F.** ................................... *paintings* | $187 | $660 |
| American | | |
| ☐ **OFFERMANS, Antony Jacob** ............... *paintings* | | $1,650 |
| Dutch 1796-1872 | | |
| ☐ **OFFERMANS, Tony Lodewijk George** .. *paintings* | $200 | $990 |
| Dutch 1854-1911 | | |
| ☐ **OFFNER, Elliot** ................................. *drawings* | | $66 |
| American 20th cent. .................................. *sculpture* | $192 | $1,870 |
| ☐ **OFFORD, John S.** ............................... *paintings* | | $3,850 |
| English 19th cent. | | |
| ☐ **OFTOWN, Karl O'Lynch** ..................... *paintings* | | $357 |
| German 1869-1942 | | |
| ☐ **OGDEN, Frederick D.** .......................... *paintings* | $247 | $1,100 |
| American 19th/20th cent. | | |
| ☐ **OGDEN, J. William** ............................ *paintings* | $220 | $246 |
| Anglo/American 19th cent. | | |
| ☐ **OGE, Pierre Marie Francois** ................ *sculpture* | | $715 |
| French 19th/20th cent. | | |
| ☐ **OGER, Ferdinand** .............................. *drawings* | | $660 |
| ☐ **OGILVIE, Clinton** ............................. *paintings* | $440 | $10,450 |
| American 1838-1900 | | |
| ☐ **OGUISS, Takanari** ............................. *paintings* | $7,700 | $40,700 |
| Japanese b.c. 1900/1901 | | |
| ☐ **OHL, Gabrielle** ................................... *paintings* | | $495 |
| French b. 1928 | | |
| ☐ **OHL, L. Fritz** .................................... *paintings* | | $495 |
| ☐ **OHLSON, Doug** .................................. *paintings* | | $495 |
| ☐ **OHTAKE, Tomie** ................................ *paintings* | | $3,300 |
| Japanese/Brazilian b. 1913 | | |
| ☐ **OKADA, Kenzo** ................................... *paintings* | $2,200 | $25,300 |
| Japanese/American b. 1902 | | |
| ☐ **OKAMOTO** ......................................... *paintings* | $1,210 | $1,430 |
| Japanese | | |
| ☐ **OKAMURA, Arthur** ............................ *paintings* | $80 | $3,850 |
| American b. 1932 | | |
| ☐ **OKIMOTO, Jerry** ............................... *paintings* | | $660 |
| contemporary | | |
| ☐ **OKUN, Edward** ................................... *paintings* | $17,600 | $19,800 |
| Polish 1872-1945 | | |

| | Current Price Range | |
|---|---|---|
| | *Low* | *High* |
| ☐ **OLBERT, V.** .............................. *paintings* | | **$467** |
| Italian 19th/20th cent. | | |
| ☐ **OLBRICH, V.** .............................. *paintings* | | **$550** |
| ☐ **OLDEMAN, Hendrik** .......................... *paintings* | | **$550** |
| Dutch 19th/20th cent. | | |
| ☐ **OLDEMAN, R.H.** .............................. *paintings* | **$165** | **$191** |
| Dutch 19th/20th cent. | | |
| ☐ **OLDENBURG, Claes** .......................... *drawings* | **$825** | **$12,100** |
| Swedish/American b. 1929 .......................... *sculpture* | **$1,430** | **$181,500** |
| ☐ **OLDERSHAM, C.** .............................. *paintings* | | **$412** |
| English 19th cent. | | |
| ☐ **OLDFIELD, Fred** .......................... *paintings* | **$1,300** | **$1,600** |
| American contemporary | | |
| ☐ **OLDFIELD, Otis William** .................... *paintings* | **$247** | **$495** |
| American b. 1890 | | |
| ☐ **OLESEN, Olaf** .............................. *paintings* | | **$3,520** |
| American b. 1873 | | |
| ☐ **OLGYAY, Ferenc** .......................... *paintings* | **$275** | **$385** |
| Hungarian b. 1892 | | |
| ☐ **OLIBECK, Jacobus** .......................... *paintings* | | **$4,400** |
| Dutch 17th cent. | | |
| ☐ **OLIGAM** .............................. *paintings* | | **$264** |
| ☐ **OLINSKY, Ivan G.** .......................... *paintings* | **$286** | **$6,324** |
| Russian/American 1878-1962 .................... *drawings* | | **$605** |
| ☐ **OLIS, Jan** .............................. *paintings* | | **$3,520** |
| ☐ **OLITSKI, Jules** .......................... *paintings* | **$1,540** | **$60,500** |
| American b. 1922 .......................... *drawings* | **$308** | **$1,210** |
| ☐ **OLIVA, Alexandre Joseph** .................... *sculpture* | | **$605** |
| late 19th cent. | | |
| ☐ **OLIVA, Felix** .............................. *paintings* | **$852** | **$3,630** |
| Peruvian b. 1936 | | |
| ☐ **OLIVE, Jean Baptiste** .......................... *paintings* | | **$1,760** |
| French 1848-1936 | | |
| ☐ **OLIVEIRA, Nathan** .......................... *paintings* | **$1,100** | **$38,500** |
| American b. 1928 .......................... *drawings* | **$715** | **$3,850** |
| ☐ **OLIVER, Clark** .............................. *drawings* | | **$357** |
| American 19th/20th cent. | | |
| ☐ **OLIVER, H.** .............................. *paintings* | | **$467** |
| British 19th cent. | | |
| ☐ **OLIVER, Jean** .............................. *paintings* | | **$1,100** |
| French 20th cent. | | |
| ☐ **OLIVER, Thomas Clarkson** .................... *paintings* | **$2,310** | **$2,600** |
| American 1827-1892 | | |
| ☐ **OLIVER, William** .......................... *paintings* | **$440** | **$3,300** |
| British ac. 1867-1882 | | |
| ☐ **OLIVER, William** .......................... *paintings* | **$1,980** | **$3,025** |
| British 1805-1853 | | |
| ☐ **OLIVERIO, M. A.** .......................... *paintings* | | **$300** |
| American | | |

| | Current Price Range | |
|---|---|---|
| | Low | High |
| ☐ **OLIVETTI, Luigi** ................................ *drawings* | $330 | $770 |
| Italian 19th/20th cent. | | |
| ☐ **OLIVIER, T.** ..................................... *paintings* | | $247 |
| French contemporary | | |
| ☐ **OLLAGUE, Bolivar** ............................ *paintings* | | $2,970 |
| Ecuadorian 20th cent. | | |
| ☐ **OLLEROS Y QUINTANA, Blas** ............ *paintings* | | $2,475 |
| Italian c. 1851-1919 ..................................... *drawings* | | $44 |
| ☐ **OLLIVARY, Annette** ........................... *paintings* | $110 | $770 |
| French 20th cent. | | |
| ☐ **OLLIVIER** ........................................ *drawings* | | $1,100 |
| ☐ **OLSEN, Chr Benjamin** ...................... *paintings* | $1,540 | $4,620 |
| Danish 1818-1878 | | |
| ☐ **OLSEN, Henry** .................................. *paintings* | $70 | $687 |
| American 1902-1983 .................................. *drawings* | | $170 |
| ☐ **OLSEN, Herb** .................................... *drawings* | $191 | $220 |
| American 1905-1973 | | |
| ☐ **OLSON, Carl Gustaf Theodore** ............ *paintings* | $82 | $770 |
| American b. Sweden 1875 | | |
| ☐ **OLSON, George Wallace** ...................... *paintings* | | $275 |
| American 20th cent. | | |
| ☐ **OLSON, J. Olaf** ................................. *paintings* | $577 | $2,860 |
| American 1894-1979 ................................. *drawings* | $154 | $1,045 |
| ☐ **OLSON, R.A.** ..................................... *paintings* | | $286 |
| American 1894-1979 | | |
| ☐ **OLSSON, Julius** ............................... *paintings* | | $852 |
| British 1864-1942 | | |
| ☐ **OMERTH, Georges** ............................ *sculpture* | | $3,300 |
| ☐ **OMMEGANCK, Balthasar Paul** ............ *paintings* | $110 | $2,860 |
| Flemish 1755-1826 | | |
| ☐ **ONDANO, Celso** ................................ *drawings* | | $660 |
| ☐ **ONDERDONK, Julian** ........................ *paintings* | $150 | $18,500 |
| American 1882-1922 | | |
| ☐ **ONGANIA, Umberto** ........................... *drawings* | $176 | $192 |
| Italian 19th cent. | | |
| ☐ **ONU, Aurore** ................................... *sculpture* | | $770 |
| ☐ **OOLEN, Adriaen van** ........................ *paintings* | | $4,950 |
| Dutch d. 1694 | | |
| ☐ **OOLEN, Jacob van** ............................ *paintings* | | $22,100 |
| ☐ **OORSCHOTT, Theodore V.** ................ *paintings* | | $181 |
| Dutch c. 1926 | | |
| ☐ **OORT, Hendrik van** .......................... *paintings* | | $4,180 |
| Dutch 1775-1847 | | |
| ☐ **OOST, Jacob van** ............................... *paintings* | $2,200 | $26,400 |
| Flemish | | |
| ☐ **OOSTEN, Frans van** ........................... *paintings* | | $3,300 |
| Flemish d. 1679/1680 | | |
| ☐ **OOSTEN, Izaak van** ........................... *paintings* | $4,950 | $18,150 |
| Flemish 1613-1661 | | |

| | Current Price Range | |
|---|---|---|
| | Low | High |
| ☐ OOSTERHOUDT, Dirk van ............... *paintings* | | $3,850 |
| ☐ OPAZO, Rodolfo ................... *paintings* | | $990 |
| b. Chile 1925 | | |
| ☐ OPDENHOFF, Georg Willem ............... *paintings* | $3,520 | $13,200 |
| Dutch 1807-1873 | | |
| ☐ OPERTI, Albert Jasper .................. *paintings* | | $1,320 |
| Italian/American 1852-1927 ........................ *drawings* | $88 | $1,155 |
| ☐ OPIE, John ................................ *paintings* | $825 | $5,500 |
| English 1761-1807 | | |
| ☐ OPORTO, Dario d' ........................... *paintings* | | $605 |
| Austrian/American 20th cent. | | |
| ☐ OPPENHEIM, Dennis A. ............... *drawings* | $1,650 | $2,750 |
| American b. 1938 ...................................... *sculpture* | | $11,000 |
| ☐ OPPENHEIMER, Joseph .................... *paintings* | | $302 |
| ☐ OPPENHEIMER, Max (called Mopp) ..... *paintings* | | $8,800 |
| German 1895-1954 | | |
| ☐ OPPER, Frederick Burr ............... *drawings* | $88 | $1,045 |
| American 1857-1937 | | |
| ☐ OPPER, John ...................................... *paintings* | $49 | $550 |
| American b. 1908 ...................................... *drawings* | $55 | $1,045 |
| ☐ OPPLER, Ernst ............................... *drawings* | $330 | $660 |
| German b. 1869 | | |
| ☐ OPSTAL, Gaspard Jacques van | | |
| (the younger) ...................................... *paintings* | | $4,125 |
| Flemish | | |
| ☐ ORANGE, Maurice Henri ............... *paintings* | $880 | $1,100 |
| French 1868-1916 | | |
| ☐ ORBAN, G. ................................ *paintings* | | $825 |
| ☐ ORBERMULLER, M. ................... *paintings* | | $550 |
| ☐ ORCHARDSON ................................ *paintings* | | $302 |
| Scottish 19th cent. | | |
| ☐ ORCZY, Emma Baronne de ............... *paintings* | | $1,540 |
| British b. Hungary 1865 | | |
| ☐ ORD, Joseph Biays ........................... *paintings* | $4,950 | $7,150 |
| American 1805-1865 | | |
| ☐ ORDONEZ, David ........................... *drawings* | | $990 |
| ☐ ORETTI, A.P. ................................ *paintings* | | $4,400 |
| ☐ ORFEI, Orfeo ................................ *paintings* | $3,850 | $5,500 |
| Italian 19th cent. | | |
| ☐ ORIZANTI ........................................ *paintings* | | $1,320 |
| Dutch 17th cent. | | |
| ☐ ORLANDO, Felipe ........................... *paintings* | $2,200 | $2,750 |
| Latin American | | |
| ☐ ORLEANS, R. d' ................................ *paintings* | | $550 |
| ☐ ORLEY, Richard van (II) ...................... *drawings* | | $264 |
| ☐ ORLIK, Emil ...................................... *paintings* | $660 | $4,400 |
| German 1870-1932 ...................................... *drawings* | $200 | $550 |
| ☐ ORLOFF, Chana ............................... *sculpture* | $3,520 | $5,720 |
| Russian/French 1888-1968 | | |

| | | | *Current Price Range* | |
| --- | --- | --- | --- | --- |
| | | | Low | High |
| ☐ **ORLOFF, Nicolas Wassilievitch** | ............. | *paintings* | $770 | $9,350 |
| Russian b. 1863 | | | | |
| ☐ **OROZCO, Jose Clemente** | ................. | *paintings* | $1,320 | $77,000 |
| Mexican 1883-1949 | ..................................... | *drawings* | $1,320 | $20,350 |
| ☐ **OROZCO ROMERO, Carlos** | ............... | *paintings* | $1,100 | $8,250 |
| Mexican b. 1898 | ..................................... | *drawings* | $1,540 | $5,575 |
| ☐ **ORPEN, Sir William** | ..................... | *paintings* | $2,200 | $23,000 |
| Irish 1878-1931 | ........................................ | *drawings* | $1,540 | $990 |
| ☐ **ORR, Elliot** | ........................................ | *paintings* | $13 | $300 |
| American b. 1904 | | | | |
| ☐ **ORR, Louis** | ........................................ | *paintings* | | $330 |
| American b. 1879 | ..................................... | *drawings* | | $33 |
| ☐ **ORSELLI, Arturo** | ................................ | *drawings* | $495 | $880 |
| Italian 19th cent. | | | | |
| ☐ **ORTEGA, Jose** | ..................................... | *paintings* | $467 | $2,500 |
| Spanish | | | | |
| ☐ **ORTIZ, Emilio** | ..................................... | *paintings* | $715 | $11,000 |
| b. Mexico 1936 | | | | |
| ☐ **ORTLIEB, Friedrich** | ............................ | *paintings* | $3,850 | $22,000 |
| German 1839-1909 | | | | |
| ☐ **ORTMAN, George** | ............................. | *paintings* | | $4,125 |
| ☐ **ORTMANS, Francois Auguste** | ............... | *paintings* | $660 | $2,090 |
| French 1827-1884 | | | | |
| ☐ **ORTUZAR, Carlos** | ............................. | *paintings* | | $1,650 |
| Chilean b. 1935 | ......................................... | *drawings* | | $66 |
| ☐ **ORUTRA, C.** | ...................................... | *drawings* | | $825 |
| American | | | | |
| ☐ **OS, Georgius Jacobus Johannes van** | ...... | *paintings* | $6,600 | $9,350 |
| Dutch 1782-1861 | ..................................... | *drawings* | $1,320 | $1,760 |
| ☐ **OS, Jan van** | ........................................ | *paintings* | $29,700 | $253,000 |
| Dutch 1744-1808 | | | | |
| ☐ **OS, Maria Magrita van** | ........................ | *drawings* | $1,980 | $3,850 |
| Dutch 1780-1862 | | | | |
| ☐ **OS, Pieter Frederick van** | ........................ | *drawings* | | $990 |
| ☐ **OS, Pieter Gerardus van** | ........................ | *paintings* | $4,180 | $4,400 |
| Dutch 1776-1839 | ..................................... | *drawings* | | $660 |
| ☐ **OSAKI** | ................................................. | *paintings* | | $550 |
| ☐ **OSBERT, Alphonse** | ............................ | *paintings* | | $1,760 |
| French 1857-1939 | ..................................... | *drawings* | $174 | $264 |
| ☐ **OSBORN, K.L.** | ..................................... | *paintings* | | $1,430 |
| American | | | | |
| ☐ **OSBORNE, Emily Mary** | ........................ | *paintings* | | $2,310 |
| English 1834-1913 | | | | |
| ☐ **OSBORNE, William** | ............................ | *paintings* | | $2,090 |
| ☐ **OSBURN, Sally** | ................................... | *drawings* | | $224 |
| American 20th cent. | | | | |
| ☐ **OSCAR, Charles** | ................................ | *paintings* | | $660 |
| American | ................................................. | *drawings* | $330 | $1,540 |

| | Current Price Range | |
|---|---|---|
| | Low | High |
| ☐ **OSGOD, N.** .......................... *paintings* | | **$302** |
| European 19th cent. | | |
| ☐ **OSHOTAPIK** ....................... *sculpture* | | **$302** |
| Eskimo | | |
| ☐ **OSNAGHI, Josephine** .......................... *paintings* | **$605** | **$3,740** |
| Austrian 19th cent. | | |
| ☐ **OSNOBICHIN, I.** ...................... *paintings* | | **$660** |
| Russian 19th cent. | | |
| ☐ **OSSORIO, Alfonso A.** .................... *paintings* | **$825** | **$3,960** |
| American b. 1916 ........................ *drawings* | **$385** | **$2,970** |
| .................... *sculpture* | | **$4,400** |
| ☐ **OSSWALD, Fritz** ..................... *paintings* | **$660** | **$715** |
| ☐ **OSTADE, Adriaen van** .................. *paintings* | **$165** | **$93,500** |
| Dutch 1610-1685 ....................... *drawings* | | **$935** |
| ☐ **OSTADE, Isaac van** .................. *paintings* | | **$88,000** |
| Dutch 1621-1649 | | |
| ☐ **OSTENETZER, C.** ..................... *paintings* | | **$550** |
| ☐ **OSTERLIND, Anders** ...................... *paintings* | | **$1,100** |
| ☐ **OSTERMAYER, Ernst Ludwig** ............. *paintings* | **$137** | **$275** |
| German 1868-1918 | | |
| ☐ **OSTERSETZER, Carl** ........................ *paintings* | **$550** | **$4,180** |
| German 19th/20th cent. | | |
| ☐ **OSTERTAG, Uriel** ............................ *paintings* | **$192** | **$192** |
| German 19th cent. ...................... *drawings* | **$440** | **$9,900** |
| ☐ **OSTHAUS, Edmund Henry** ................. *paintings* | **$600** | **$15,400** |
| German/American 1858-1928 .................... *drawings* | **$440** | **$9,900** |
| ☐ **OSTRANDER, William C.** ............... *paintings* | | **$44** |
| ........................ *drawings* | | **$418** |
| ☐ **OSTROUTHOFF, Ilya Semenovich** ........ *paintings* | | **$330** |
| Russian 1858-1929 | | |
| ☐ **OSTROW, W.E.** ..................... *drawings* | | **$286** |
| American 20th cent. | | |
| ☐ **OSTROWSKY, Sam** .......................... *paintings* | **$50** | **$880** |
| American | | |
| ☐ **OSVER, Arthur** ...................... *paintings* | **$440** | **$550** |
| American b. 1912 ....................... *drawings* | | **$495** |
| ☐ **OSWALD, C.W.** ..................... *paintings* | **$412** | **$550** |
| British 19th cent. | | |
| ☐ **OSWALD, J.H.** ..................... *paintings* | | **$330** |
| English 19th cent. | | |
| ☐ **OSWALD, John H.** .......................... *paintings* | **$605** | **$632** |
| English 1843-1895 | | |
| ☐ **OTERO, Alejandro** ..................... *paintings* | | **$8,250** |
| Venezuelan b. 1921 | | |
| ☐ **OTIS, Bass** ...................... *paintings* | **$1,650** | **$1,980** |
| American 1784-1861 | | |
| ☐ **OTIS, George Demont** ......................... *paintings* | **$466** | **$6,325** |
| American 1877/79-1962 ............................ *drawings* | **$136** | **$495** |
| ☐ **OTT, Jerry** ..................... *paintings* | | **$605** |

|  | | Current Price Range | |
|---|---|---|---|
|  | | Low | High |
| ☐ **OTT, Lucien** ............................ *paintings* | | | $660 |
| French d. 1927 | | | |
| ☐ **OTTE, C.** ............................ *paintings* | | | $467 |
| English School 19th cent. | | | |
| ☐ **OTTE, William Louis** ................ *paintings* | | | $385 |
| American 20th cent. | | | |
| ☐ **OTTENFELD, Rudolf Ritter von** .......... *paintings* | | $4,125 | $9,900 |
| Italian 1856-1913 | | | |
| ☐ **OTTERSON, John** ........................ *paintings* | | | $522 |
| American 20th cent. | | | |
| ☐ **OTTESEN, Otto Diderich** .............. *paintings* | | | $3,850 |
| Danish 1816-1892 | | | |
| ☐ **OTTEVAERE, Henri** .................... *drawings* | | | $495 |
| Northern Europe 19th/20th cent. | | | |
| ☐ **OTTEWELL, B.J.** ...................... *drawings* | | $165 | $308 |
| English 19th cent. | | | |
| ☐ **OTTINGER, George M.** .................. *paintings* | | | $6,325 |
| American 1833-1917 | | | |
| ☐ **OTTMANN, Henri** ...................... *paintings* | | $577 | $1,045 |
| French 1877-1927 | | | |
| ☐ **OTTO, Carl** ............................ *paintings* | | | $3,080 |
| German 1830-1902 | | | |
| ☐ **OUDENHAVEN, Joseph van** ............ *paintings* | | | $2,200 |
| Belgium ac. 1845 | | | |
| ☐ **OUDENROGGE,** | | | |
| **Johannes Dircksz van** .............. *paintings* | | | $3,300 |
| Dutch 1622-1653 | | | |
| ☐ **OUDINOT, Achille Francois** ............ *paintings* | | $770 | $2,420 |
| French 1820-1891 | | | |
| ☐ **OUDOT, Roland** ........................ *paintings* | | $55 | $3,575 |
| French b. 1897 ............................ *drawings* | | $572 | $4,400 |
| ☐ **OUDRY, Gustave** ...................... *paintings* | | | $1,650 |
| ☐ **OUDRY, Jacques Charles** .............. *paintings* | | | $22,000 |
| French 1720-1778 | | | |
| ☐ **OUDRY, Jean Baptiste** ................ *paintings* | | | $66,000 |
| French 1686-1755 ........................ *drawings* | | $3,300 | $12,100 |
| ☐ **OUKEN, C.** ............................ *paintings* | | | $440 |
| ☐ **OULINE, A.** ............................ *sculpture* | | | $935 |
| ☐ **OUREN, Karl** .......................... *paintings* | | | $2,750 |
| Norwegian/American 1882-1934 | | | |
| ☐ **OURSLER, C. Leslie** .................. *paintings* | | | $715 |
| ............................ *drawings* | | | $330 |
| ☐ **OUTCAULT, Richard Felton** ............ *drawings* | | $715 | $6,710 |
| American 1863-1928 | | | |
| ☐ **OUTIN, Pierre** ........................ *paintings* | | $770 | $8,800 |
| French 1840-1899 | | | |
| ☐ **OUVRIE, Pierre Justin** ................ *paintings* | | $4,620 | $6,050 |
| French 1806-1879 ........................ *drawings* | | | $1,155 |

| | | Current Price Range | |
|---|---|---|---|
| | | Low | High |
| ☐ **OVENS, Jurgen** .................................... *paintings* | | **$3,300** | **$4,400** |
| German 1623-1678 | | | |
| ☐ **OVERBECK, Fritz** .............................. *paintings* | | | **$660** |
| German 1869-1909 | | | |
| ☐ **OVERBEEK, Johannes van** .................. *paintings* | | | **$385** |
| Dutch School 19th cent. | | | |
| ☐ **OVEREND, William Heysman** .............. *paintings* | | | **$660** |
| American 1851-1898 | | | |
| ☐ **OVERHOFF, R.** .................................... *paintings* | | | **$852** |
| French 19th cent. | | | |
| ☐ **OVERSTREET, Anne Aller** .................. *drawings* | | | **$450** |
| American | | | |
| ☐ **OWEN, Bill** ........................................ *paintings* | | **$2,530** | **$28,000** |
| American b. 1942 | | | |
| ☐ **OWEN, Frank** .................................... *paintings* | | | **$1,320** |
| American b. 1939 | | | |
| ☐ **OWEN, Joel** ........................................ *paintings* | | **$110** | **$385** |
| Scottish 19th/20th cent. | | | |
| ☐ **OWEN, Robert Emmett** ........................ *paintings* | | **$110** | **$3,300** |
| American 1878-1957 | | | |
| ☐ **OWEN, Samuel** .................................... *drawings* | | | **$1,100** |
| British 1768-1857 | | | |
| ☐ **OWEN, William** .................................... *paintings* | | **$880** | **$8,250** |
| British 1765-1829 | | | |
| ☐ **OWENS, Charles** .................................. *paintings* | | | **$412** |
| American 1881-1958 | | | |
| ☐ **OWLES, Alfred** .................................... *drawings* | | **$200** | **$275** |
| Anglo/American b. 1895/98 | | | |
| ☐ **OYENS, David** .................................... *paintings* | | | **$1,210** |
| ☐ **OZENFANT, Amedee** ............................ *paintings* | | | **$990** |
| French 1886-1966 | | | |
| ☐ **PAALEN, Wolfgang** ............................ *paintings* | | **$825** | **$4,400** |
| Mexican 1905/07-1959 | | | |
| ☐ **PAAR, D.** .......................................... *drawings* | | | **$550** |
| ☐ **PACCHIA, Girolamo del** ...................... *paintings* | | | **$28,600** |
| Italian 1477-1535 | | | |
| ☐ **PACE, Raineri del** .............................. *paintings* | | | **$4,620** |
| Italian 18th cent. | | | |
| ☐ **PACETTI, Michaelangelo** ...................... *paintings* | | | **$2,750** |
| Italian 1793-1855 | | | |
| ☐ **PACHECO, Maria Luisa** ...................... *paintings* | | **$550** | **$9,350** |
| Bolivian b. 1919 ...................................... *drawings* | | | **$1,045** |
| ☐ **PACHECO, Maximo** ............................ *drawings* | | **$495** | **$1,980** |
| ☐ **PACHER, Ferdinand** ............................ *paintings* | | **$4,500** | **$19,800** |
| German 1852-1911 | | | |
| ☐ **PACIEOREK (?), J.** .............................. *paintings* | | | **$264** |
| Austrian | | | |
| ☐ **PACKARD, Mabel** .............................. *paintings* | | **$550** | **$880** |
| American 19th cent. | | | |

| | | | *Current Price Range* | |
|---|---|---|---|---|
| | | | *Low* | *High* |
| ☐ **PADDOCK, Ethel Louise** | .................... | *paintings* | | $33 |
| American c. 1877-1960 | .............................. | *drawings* | $165 | $412 |
| ☐ **PADDOCK, Josephine** | .......................... | *paintings* | $30 | $506 |
| American 20th cent. | | | | |
| ☐ **PADDOCK, M.M.** | ............................... | *paintings* | | $187 |
| American 19th cent. | | | | |
| ☐ **PADILLA, Eugenio Lucas** | .................... | *paintings* | | $1,540 |
| ☐ **PADILLA, Luis H.** | ............................. | *paintings* | | $412 |
| ☐ **PADWICK, P.H.** | ................................ | *paintings* | | $880 |
| English 1876(?)-1936 | | | | |
| ☐ **PAELINCK, Joseph** | ............................ | *paintings* | | $16,500 |
| Belgian 1781-1839 | | | | |
| ☐ **PAEZ, Joseph de** | ............................... | *paintings* | | $935 |
| Mexican 18th cent. | | | | |
| ☐ **PAEZ-VILARO, Carlos** | ...................... | *drawings* | | $330 |
| b. Uruguay 1923 | | | | |
| ☐ **PAGANO, Michele** | ............................. | *paintings* | | $9,350 |
| Italian c. 1697-c. 1732 | | | | |
| ☐ **PAGE, Elizabeth Amie** | ....................... | *paintings* | $165 | $357 |
| American b. 1908 | | | | |
| ☐ **PAGE, H. Flood** | ............................... | *paintings* | | $990 |
| British School 19th cent. | | | | |
| ☐ **PAGE, Henri Maurice** | ........................ | *paintings* | $550 | $4,400 |
| English ac. 1879-1890 | | | | |
| ☐ **PAGE, Jules Bastien le** | ...................... | *drawings* | | $300 |
| French 1848-1884 | | | | |
| ☐ **PAGE, M.L.** | ...................................... | *paintings* | $357 | $400 |
| European 19th/20th cent. | | | | |
| ☐ **PAGE, Marie Danforth** | ...................... | *paintings* | $3,850 | $12,100 |
| American 1869-1940 | | | | |
| ☐ **PAGE, Walter Gilman** | ........................ | *paintings* | $192 | $1,320 |
| American 1862-1934 | | | | |
| ☐ **PAGE, William** | ................................. | *paintings* | | $4,125 |
| American 1811-1885 | | | | |
| ☐ **PAGEDAIEFF, Georges A. de** | ............. | *drawings* | | $715 |
| ☐ **PAGES, Jules Eugene** | ........................ | *paintings* | $522 | $4,950 |
| American 1867-1946 | .............................. | *drawings* | | $220 |
| ☐ **PAGET, Sidney** | ................................. | *drawings* | | $1,500 |
| ☐ **PAGI, Giorgio** | ................................. | *paintings* | | $1,100 |
| Italian b. 1913 | | | | |
| ☐ **PAGINTON** | ...................................... | *paintings* | | $275 |
| American 19th/20th cent. | | | | |
| ☐ **PAGLIACCI, Aldo** | ............................. | *paintings* | $148 | $495 |
| Italian b. 1913 | ..................................... | *drawings* | $247 | $247 |
| ☐ **PAGLIANA, Luigi** | .............................. | *paintings* | | $302 |
| Italian 19th cent. | | | | |
| ☐ **PAGLIEI, Gioacchino** | ......................... | *paintings* | | $440 |
| Italian 1852-1896 | | | | |

| | | *Current Price Range* | |
|---|---|---|---|
| | | *Low* | *High* |
| ☐ **PAICE, George** ............................. *paintings* | | $220 | $412 |
| British ac. 1887-91 | | | |
| ☐ **PAIL, Edouard** ................................ *paintings* | | $250 | $550 |
| French b. 1851 | | | |
| ☐ **PAILES, Isaac** ............................... *paintings* | | $143 | $2,310 |
| French b. 1895 | | | |
| ☐ **PAILLET, Charles** ........................... *sculpture* | | $93 | $2,200 |
| French b. 1871 | | | |
| ☐ **PAIN, William Bowyer** ..................... *drawings* | | $137 | $440 |
| American 1856-1930 | | | |
| ☐ **PAINE, H.H.** ................................. *paintings* | | | $4,400 |
| American 19th cent. | | | |
| ☐ **PAINLEO, H. Volk** .......................... *paintings* | | | $700 |
| ☐ **PAIRPOINT, Nellie M.** ..................... *paintings* | | $124 | $200 |
| American 19th/20th cent. | | | |
| ☐ **PAJOU, Augustin** ........................... *drawings* | | $550 | $2,750 |
| French 1730-1809 | | | |
| ☐ **PALACIOS, Alirio** .......................... *paintings* | | | $467 |
| Latin American ................................. *drawings* | | $2,860 | $6,600 |
| ☐ **PALADINO, Mimmo** ........................ *drawings* | | $1,100 | $20,900 |
| Italian b. 1948 | | | |
| ☐ **PALAMEDES, Anthonie** | | | |
| **(called Stevers)** ............................. *paintings* | | $1,320 | $11,000 |
| Dutch 1601-1673 | | | |
| ☐ **PALCE, George** .............................. *paintings* | | | $440 |
| ☐ **PALENCIA, Benjamin** ....................... *paintings* | | $660 | $2,420 |
| Spanish b. 1902 | | | |
| ☐ **PALEZIEUX, Edmond de** ................... *paintings* | | | $275 |
| ☐ **PALIN, William Mainwaring** ............. *paintings* | | | $1,925 |
| British 1862-1947 | | | |
| ☐ **PALING, Issac** ............................... *paintings* | | | $3,740 |
| ☐ **PALIZZA, Giuseppe** ......................... *paintings* | | $412 | $6,050 |
| Italian 1812-1888 | | | |
| ☐ **PALIZZI, Filippo** ........................... *paintings* | | $1,650 | $13,200 |
| Italian 1818-1889 | | | |
| ☐ **PALLARES Y ALLUSTANTE,** | | | |
| **Joaquin** ...................................... *paintings* | | $3,850 | $5,225 |
| Spanish 19th cent. | | | |
| ☐ **PALLENBERG, Joseph Franz** ............. *sculpture* | | $797 | $2,090 |
| German 1882-1946 | | | |
| ☐ **PALLIERE, Jean Leon** ...................... *paintings* | | | $5,500 |
| French b. 1823 | | | |
| ☐ **PALLIK, Bela** ............................... *paintings* | | | $12,650 |
| Hungarian 1845-1908 | | | |
| ☐ **PALLYA, Carolus** ........................... *paintings* | | | $440 |
| ☐ **PALMA, Jacopo** | | | |
| **(called IL GIOVANE)** ....................... *paintings* | | $4,950 | $17,050 |
| Italian 1544-1628 ............................... *drawings* | | $440 | $11,580 |
| ☐ **PALMAROLI Y GONZALEZ, Vicente** .. *paintings* | | $715 | $17,600 |
| Spanish 1834-1896 ............................... *drawings* | | $385 | $660 |

| | | *Current Price Range* | |
|---|---|---|---|
| | | Low | High |
| ☐ **PALMEIRO, Jose** ............................... *paintings* | | $247 | $412 |
| ☐ **PALMER, Adelaide** ............................ *paintings* | | $275 | $1,210 |
| American c. 1851-1928 | | | |
| ☐ **PALMER, Erastus Dow** ...................... *drawings* | | | $66 |
| American 1817-1904 ................................. *sculpture* | | $1,100 | $7,975 |
| ☐ **PALMER, Gerald** ............................... *paintings* | | | $192 |
| English 19th/20th cent. | | | |
| ☐ **PALMER, Harry Sutton** ...................... *drawings* | | $297 | $632 |
| English 1854-1933 | | | |
| ☐ **PALMER, James Lynwood** ................... *paintings* | | $605 | $20,900 |
| British 1865-1941 | | | |
| ☐ **PALMER, O.** ...................................... *paintings* | | | $330 |
| American (?) 19th/20th cent. | | | |
| ☐ **PALMER, Pauline** .............................. *paintings* | | $110 | $2,090 |
| American 1865-1938 | | | |
| ☐ **PALMER, R.** ...................................... *paintings* | | | $330 |
| American 19th/20th cent. | | | |
| ☐ **PALMER, Samuel** .............................. *drawings* | | | $495 |
| British 1805-1881 | | | |
| ☐ **PALMER, Walter Launt** ...................... *paintings* | | $412 | $14,300 |
| American 1854-1932 ................................... *drawings* | | $605 | $6,250 |
| ☐ **PALMER, William** ............................. *paintings* | | | $450 |
| English 1763-1790 | | | |
| ☐ **PALMER, William C.** .......................... *paintings* | | $385 | $660 |
| American b. 1906 | | | |
| ☐ **PALMIERI, Pietro** .............................. *paintings* | | | $550 |
| Italian 19th cent. ...................................... *drawings* | | $660 | $1,100 |
| ☐ **PALMORE, Tom** ................................ *paintings* | | $187 | $6,600 |
| American 20th cent. | | | |
| ☐ **PALMSTORFF (?), F.** .......................... *paintings* | | | $825 |
| 19th cent. | | | |
| ☐ **PALOMINO, Antonio Acislo** ................. *paintings* | | | $3,520 |
| Spanish | | | |
| ☐ **PALOTA, George** ................................ *paintings* | | $275 | $301 |
| Hungarian 19th cent. | | | |
| ☐ **PANCETTI, Jose** ................................. *paintings* | | | $4,400 |
| Latin American | | | |
| ☐ **PANCOAST, Morris Hall** ...................... *paintings* | | $165 | $495 |
| American b. 1877 ...................................... *drawings* | | | $55 |
| ☐ **PANECES, J.L.** .................................. *paintings* | | | $3,850 |
| 19th cent. | | | |
| ☐ **PANERRI, R.** ..................................... *paintings* | | | $660 |
| ☐ **PANINI, Giovanni Paolo** ...................... *paintings* | | $15,950 | $63,800 |
| Italian 1691/92-1765 | | | |
| ☐ **PANNELL, Harry** ............................... *paintings* | | | $440 |
| ☐ **PANNOLI** ........................................ *paintings* | | | $352 |
| ☐ **PANSING, Fred** .................................. *paintings* | | $325 | $4,500 |
| American ac. c. 1818 | | | |

| | *Current Price Range* | |
|---|---|---|
| | *Low* | *High* |

☐ **PANZAELLI** ....................................... *paintings* | | **$440** |
Italian 19th cent.

☐ **PAOLETTI, Antonio Ermolao** .............. *paintings* | **$550** | **$7,700** |
Italian 1834-1912

☐ **PAOLETTI, Sylvius D.** ........................ *paintings* | | **$4,675** |
Italian 1864-1921

☐ **PAOLI** ................................................ *paintings* | | **$275** |
French 20th cent.

☐ **PAOLINI, Pietro** ................................. *paintings* | | **$25,300** |
Italian 1603/05-1681/82

☐ **PAOLO, Cartaino S.** ........................... *sculpture* | | **$2,750** |
American

☐ **PAOLO DI GIOVANNI FEI** ................. *paintings* | | **$93,500** |
Italian 14th/15th cent.

☐ **PAOLOZZI, Eduardo** ......................... *drawings* | | **$450** |
British b. 1924 ......................................... *sculpture* | **$440** | **$10,450** |

☐ **PAON, Jean Baptiste Louis le** .............. *drawings* | | **$25,300** |
French c. 1735-1785

☐ **PAPACHRISTOU, Tician** ..................... *drawings* | | **$286** |

☐ **PAPADOPERAKIS, Thomas** ................ *paintings* | | **$275** |

☐ **PAPALUCA, L.** .................................. *paintings* | **$165** | **$500** |
Italian 19th/20th cent.

☐ **PAPART, Max** ................................... *paintings* | **$176** | **$1,430** |
French b. 1911

☐ **PAPE, Abraham de** ............................ *paintings* | | **$4,500** |
Dutch 1620-1666

☐ **PAPE, Hans** ...................................... *paintings* | **$110** | **$440** |
American 20th cent.

☐ **PAPELEN, Victor de** ........................... *paintings* | | **$1,650** |
French 1810-1881

☐ **PAPETY, Dominique Louis** ................... *drawings* | **$1,760** | **$3,080** |
French 1815-1849

☐ **PARADISE, John** ............................... *paintings* | | **$2,750** |
American 1783-1834

☐ **PARBOYNE** ...................................... *paintings* | | **$770** |

☐ **PAREDES, Vicenta de** ......................... *paintings* | **$605** | **$10,450** |
Spanish 19th cent. ................................... *drawings* | **$165** | **$330** |

☐ **PARENT, Aubert Joseph** ..................... *sculpture* | | **$20,900** |
French late 18th cent.

☐ **PARENTE, G.** .................................... *sculpture* | | **$440** |
Italian late 19th cent.

☐ **PARENTE, P.** ..................................... *sculpture* | | **$880** |

☐ **PARFONRY, F.** .................................. *paintings* | | **$880** |
Hungarian (?) 19th cent.

☐ **PARIS, Alfred** .................................... *paintings* | | **$15,400** |
French 1846-1908

☐ **PARIS, George de** ............................... *drawings* | | **$935** |
British 1829-1911

| | *Current Price Range* | |
|---|---|---|
| | *Low* | *High* |

| | | Low | High |
|---|---|---|---|
| ☐ **PARIS, Harry Russ** ............................ *paintings*<br>late 19th cent. | | | $220 |
| ☐ **PARIS, Pierre Adrien** ......................... *drawings* | | | $990 |
| ☐ **PARIS, Roland** ..................................... *sculpture*<br>German b. 1894 | | $935 | $1,760 |
| ☐ **PARIS, Walter** ..................................... *drawings*<br>American 1842-1906 | | | $1,540 |
| ☐ **PARISEN, J. or William** ....................... *paintings*<br>American early 19th cent. | | | $605 |
| ☐ **PARISH, Betty Waldo** .......................... *paintings* | | | $330 |
| ☐ **PARISH, Jane** ..................................... *paintings*<br>19th cent. | | | $1,760 |
| ☐ **PARK, David** ...................................... *paintings*<br>American 1911-1960 .................................. *drawings* | | $1,320 | $27,500<br>$7,150 |
| ☐ **PARK, E.** ............................................ *drawings*<br>French 20th cent. | | | $192 |
| ☐ **PARK, J.C.** ......................................... *drawings* | | | $330 |
| ☐ **PARK, J.S.** ......................................... *paintings*<br>English 19th cent. | | | $220 |
| ☐ **PARK, Richard Hamilton** ...................... *sculpture*<br>1832-after 1890 | | | $1,980 |
| ☐ **PARK, Roswell** ................................... *drawings*<br>fl. c. 1824 | | | $18,700 |
| ☐ **PARKER, C.R.** ..................................... *paintings*<br>American 19th cent. | | | $412 |
| ☐ **PARKER, Charles S.** ............................ *paintings*<br>American 1860-1930 | | $302 | $450 |
| ☐ **PARKER, Henry H.** ............................. *paintings*<br>American 1869-1917 | | | $3,300 |
| ☐ **PARKER, Henry H.** ............................. *paintings*<br>English 1858-1930 | | $600 | $6,050 |
| ☐ **PARKER, Henry Perlee** ....................... *paintings*<br>English 1795-1873 | | | $9,000 |
| ☐ **PARKER, John Adams** ......................... *paintings*<br>American 1827-1905 | | $605 | $3,300 |
| ☐ **PARKER, John F.** ............................... *paintings*<br>American b. 1884 | | | $192 |
| ☐ **PARKER, Lawton S.** ........................... *paintings*<br>American 1868-1954 ................................. *drawings* | | $385<br>$5 | $25,300<br>$770 |
| ☐ **PARKER, Ray** ..................................... *paintings*<br>American b. 1922 | | $301 | $3,960 |
| ☐ **PARKER, Robert Andrew** .................... *paintings*<br>American 20th cent. | | $82 | $440 |
| ☐ **PARKER, Tom G.** ............................... *paintings* | | | $385 |
| ☐ **PARKHURST, C.S.** .............................. *paintings*<br>American | | $385 | $550 |
| ☐ **PARKHURST, Daniel Burleigh** ............. *paintings*<br>American late 19th/early 20th cent | | | $192 |

| | | Current Price Range | |
|---|---|---|---|
| | | Low | High |
| ☐ **PARKINGTON, J.** ........................... *paintings* | | | $275 |
| American 19th cent. | | | |
| ☐ **PARKS, Bob** ..................................... *sculpture* | | $800 | $4,840 |
| American b. 1943 | | | |
| ☐ **PARMEGGIANI, Tancredi** ................... *paintings* | | | $770 |
| Italian 1927-1964 | | | |
| ☐ **PARMIGIANINO,** | | | |
| (Girolomo Francesco **MAZZOLA**) ........... *drawings* | | | $20,900 |
| Italian 1503-1540 | | | |
| ☐ **PARMIGIANINO, (Michele ROCCA)** .... *paintings* | | $2,420 | $4,180 |
| Italian 1670/75-1751 | | | |
| ☐ **PAROLARI** ....................................... *drawings* | | | $600 |
| ☐ **PARRA, Felix** ................................... *paintings* | | | $4,400 |
| ☐ **PARRA, M. de** ................................. *paintings* | | | $440 |
| ☐ **PARRAVICINI, Angelo** ....................... *drawings* | | $550 | $1,430 |
| ☐ **PARRIS, Edmund Thomas** ................. *paintings* | | | $495 |
| ☐ **PARRISH, Clara Weaver** ..................... *drawings* | | | $286 |
| American 1861-1925 | | | |
| ☐ **PARRISH, David Buchanan** ................. *paintings* | | $6,600 | $7,700 |
| American b. 1939 | | | |
| ☐ **PARRISH, Jean** ................................. *paintings* | | | $577 |
| American contemporary | | | |
| ☐ **PARRISH, Maxfield** ............................ *paintings* | | $715 | $74,800 |
| American 1870-1966 ................................. *drawings* | | $440 | $5,500 |
| ☐ **PARRISH, Stephen** .............................. *paintings* | | $220 | $2,500 |
| American 1846-1938 | | | |
| ☐ **PARROCEL, Etienne** .......................... *drawings* | | | $5,225 |
| ☐ **PARROCEL, Ignace Jacques** ............... *paintings* | | | $13,200 |
| French 1667-1722 | | | |
| ☐ **PARROCEL, Joseph** ........................... *drawings* | | | $715 |
| French 17th cent. | | | |
| ☐ **PARROCEL, Marguerite** ...................... *paintings* | | | $990 |
| ☐ **PARROT, Philippe** ............................. *paintings* | | | $3,850 |
| French 1831-1894 | | | |
| ☐ **PARROTT, William Samuel** ................. *paintings* | | $440 | $5,225 |
| American 1844-1915 | | | |
| ☐ **PARS, William** .................................. *drawings* | | | $4,180 |
| English 1742-1782 | | | |
| ☐ **PARSHALL, De Witt** .......................... *paintings* | | $550 | $880 |
| American 1864-1956 | | | |
| ☐ **PARSHALL, Douglas Ewell** ................. *paintings* | | $660 | $1,100 |
| American b. 1899 ..................................... *drawings* | | | $357 |
| ☐ **PARSON, A.** ...................................... *paintings* | | | $440 |
| American 19th cent. | | | |
| ☐ **PARSONS, Alfred** .............................. *paintings* | | | $330 |
| American 19th cent. | | | |
| ☐ **PARSONS, Alfred William** ................... *paintings* | | $825 | $2,200 |
| English 1847-1920 ..................................... *drawings* | | $825 | $3,520 |

| | | | Current Price Range | |
|---|---|---|---|---|
| | | | Low | High |
| ☐ **PARSONS, Beatrice** .............................. *drawings* | | | **$2,310** | **$2,420** |
| English 1870-1955 | | | | |
| ☐ **PARSONS, Betty B.** .............................. *drawings* | | | **$165** | **$605** |
| American 20th cent. | | | | |
| ☐ **PARSONS, Charles F.** .......................... *paintings* | | | **$440** | **$660** |
| American 1821-1910 | | | | |
| ☐ **PARSONS, Edith Baretto Stevens** .......... *sculpture* | | | **$220** | **$11,550** |
| American 1878-1956 | | | | |
| ☐ **PARSONS, J.W.** ................................. *paintings* | | | | **$198** |
| English b. 1859 | | | | |
| ☐ **PARSONS, M.A.** ................................. *drawings* | | | | **$1,650** |
| American 19th cent. | | | | |
| ☐ **PARSONS, Orrin Sheldon** ...................... *paintings* | | | **$44** | **$3,410** |
| American 1866/68-1943 | | | | |
| ☐ **PARSONS, P.B.** .................................. *drawings* | | | | **$357** |
| ☐ **PARSONS, Walter Edward** .................... *paintings* | | | | **$275** |
| American b. 1890 | | | | |
| ☐ **PARTEE, McCullough** ........................... *drawings* | | | | **$357** |
| American b. 1900 | | | | |
| ☐ **PARTINGTON, John H.E.** ................... *paintings* | | | | **$275** |
| British/American 1843-1899 | | | | |
| ☐ **PARTINGTON, Richard Langtry** .......... *paintings* | | | **$440** | **$1,210** |
| American 1868-1929 | | | | |
| ☐ **PARTON, Arthur** ............................... *paintings* | | | **$300** | **$12,650** |
| American 1842-1914 | | | | |
| ☐ **PARTON, Ernest** ............................... *paintings* | | | **$385** | **$4,125** |
| American 1845-1933 | | | | |
| ☐ **PARTON, G.** ..................................... *paintings* | | | | **$522** |
| English 19th cent. | | | | |
| ☐ **PARTON, Henry Woodbridge** ............... *paintings* | | | **$110** | **$1,100** |
| American b. 1858 | | | | |
| ☐ **PARTRIDGE, Alfred** ........................... *paintings* | | | | **$660** |
| British 19th/20th cent. | | | | |
| ☐ **PARTRIDGE, William Ordway** ............. *sculpture* | | | | **$1,980** |
| American 1861-1930 | | | | |
| ☐ **PASCAL, Paul** ................................... *drawings* | | | **$246** | **$1,298** |
| French 1832-1903 | | | | |
| ☐ **PASCAL, Paul B.** ............................... *drawings* | | | **$110** | **$1,100** |
| French b. 1867 | | | | |
| ☐ **PASCAULI, J.** ................................... *paintings* | | | | **$577** |
| late 19th cent. | | | | |
| ☐ **PASCHEK, A.J.** ................................. *paintings* | | | | **$275** |
| Czechoslovakian 19th cent. | | | | |
| ☐ **PASCIN, Jules** ................................. *paintings* | | | **$4,675** | **$55,000** |
| French/American 1885-1930 ........................ *drawings* | | | **$132** | **$9,350** |
| ☐ **PASCOE, William** ............................... *paintings* | | | | **$385** |
| British 19th cent. | | | | |
| ☐ **PASCUL, P.B.** ................................... *drawings* | | | | **$275** |
| French 19th cent. | | | | |

| | | Current Price Range | |
|---|---|---|---|
| | | *Low* | *High* |
| ☐ **PASCUTTI, Antonio** ............................ *paintings* | | | $1,980 |
| Austrian 19th cent. | | | |
| ☐ **PASERTI, T.** ...................................... *paintings* | | | $220 |
| Italian 19th cent. | | | |
| ☐ **PASINI, Alberto** ............................... *paintings* | | $715 | $25,300 |
| Italian 1826-1899 ...................................... *drawings* | | $440 | $5,225 |
| ☐ **PASKELL, William** ........................... *paintings* | | $82 | $2,500 |
| American 1866-1951 .................................. *drawings* | | $44 | $350 |
| ☐ **PASMORE, Daniel** ............................ *paintings* | | | $1,210 |
| British ac. 1830-1891 | | | |
| ☐ **PASMORE, John F.** ........................... *paintings* | | | $990 |
| British active 1841-66 | | | |
| ☐ **PASMORE, Joseph** ............................ *paintings* | | | $1,320 |
| ☐ **PASQUIER** ........................................ *drawings* | | | $440 |
| ☐ **PASSA, E.** ......................................... *paintings* | | | $1,200 |
| ☐ **PASSAROTTI, Bartolomeo** ................ *drawings* | | $605 | $2,420 |
| Italian 1529-1592 | | | |
| ☐ **PASSARRO, Camille** ......................... *drawings* | | | $2,000 |
| ☐ **PASSERI, Giuseppe** ............................ *paintings* | | | $1,100 |
| Italian 1654-1714 | | | |
| ☐ **PASSEY, Charles Henry** ..................... *paintings* | | $742 | $2,090 |
| British active 1870-85 | | | |
| ☐ **PASSINE, I.** ....................................... *paintings* | | $600 | $1,100 |
| ☐ **PASSMORE, John Frederick** ............... *paintings* | | | $1,980 |
| British 1820-1881 | | | |
| ☐ **PASTEGA, Luigi** ................................ *paintings* | | $550 | $7,150 |
| Italian 1858-1927 | | | |
| ☐ **PASTERNAK, Leonid Ossipovitsch** ....... *drawings* | | $165 | $220 |
| Russian 1862-1945 | | | |
| ☐ **PATAKY VON SOSPATAK, Laszlo** ...... *paintings* | | $935 | $1,045 |
| Hungarian 1857-1912 | | | |
| ☐ **PATALANO, Enrico** ........................... *paintings* | | | $1,430 |
| British 19th cent. | | | |
| ☐ **PATCH, Thomas** ............................... *paintings* | | | $880 |
| ☐ **PATER, Jean Baptiste** ........................ *paintings* | | $18,150 | $220,000 |
| French 1695-1736 | | | |
| ☐ **PATERNOSTO, Cesar** ......................... *paintings* | | | $880 |
| ☐ **PATERSON, Charles Robert** ................ *paintings* | | | $700 |
| ☐ **PATERSSON, Benjamin** ...................... *drawings* | | | $1,320 |
| ☐ **PATET-GERARD** ............................... *paintings* | | | $412 |
| ☐ **PATIGAN, Haig** ................................ *sculpture* | | | $1,430 |
| ☐ **PATON, Frank** ................................. *paintings* | | $605 | $7,700 |
| English 1856-1909 | | | |
| ☐ **PATON, Sir Joseph Noel** ..................... *paintings* | | | $2,200 |
| British 1821-1901 ...................................... *drawings* | | | $1,980 |
| ☐ **PATON, W. Hubert** ............................ *drawings* | | | $935 |
| Scottish 1853-1927 | | | |
| ☐ **PATON, Waller Hugh** ......................... *paintings* | | $467 | $1,760 |
| English 1828-1895 ..................................... *drawings* | | | $220 |

| | | Current Price Range | |
|---|---|---|---|
| | | Low | High |
| ☐ **PATRY, Edward**  ................................. *paintings* | | | $412 |
| English 1856-1940 | | | |
| ☐ **PATTEIN, Cesar**  ................................ *paintings* | | $3,080 | $8,800 |
| French 19th cent. | | | |
| ☐ **PATTEN, Alfred Fowler**  ...................... *paintings* | | | $330 |
| ☐ **PATTEN, George**  ............................... *paintings* | | | $750 |
| English 1801-1865 | | | |
| ☐ **PATTEN, Thomas**  ............................... *paintings* | | | $247 |
| American 20th cent. | | | |
| ☐ **PATTERSON, Ambrose**  ....................... *paintings* | | | $550 |
| ☐ **PATTERSON, Charles Robert**  ............. *paintings* | | $462 | $3,500 |
| American 1875/78-1958 | | | |
| ☐ **PATTERSON, Howard Ashman**  ........... *paintings* | | $121 | $302 |
| American b. 1891 | | | |
| ☐ **PATTERSON, Margaret Jordan**  ........... *paintings* | | | $275 |
| American b. 1887 ...................................... *drawings* | | $82 | $176 |
| ☐ **PATTERSON, Robert**  ........................... *paintings* | | $99 | $247 |
| b. 1898 | | | |
| ☐ **PATTERSON, Russell**  .......................... *paintings* | | | $110 |
| American 1896-1977 ................................... *drawings* | | | $302 |
| ☐ **PATTERSON (?), Morris**  ...................... *paintings* | | | $412 |
| American 20th cent. | | | |
| ☐ **PATTISON, James William**  ................. *paintings* | | $1,650 | $2,475 |
| American 1884-1915 | | | |
| ☐ **PATTON, Katherine**  ............................ *paintings* | | $137 | $1,200 |
| American d. 1941 | | | |
| ☐ **PATTY, William Arthur**  ....................... *paintings* | | $165 | $412 |
| American b. 1889 | | | |
| ☐ **PAU DE SAINT MARTIN, Alexandre**  ... *paintings* | | | $1,210 |
| French 18th cent. | | | |
| ☐ **PAUDISS, Christoph**  ........................... *paintings* | | | $2,750 |
| German 1618-1666/7 | | | |
| ☐ **PAUJAY (?), F.**  ................................... *paintings* | | | $357 |
| ☐ **PAUL, Damien**  ................................... *paintings* | | | $220 |
| Haitian b. 1941 | | | |
| ☐ **PAUL, Gerard**  ................................... *drawings* | | | $330 |
| Haitian | | | |
| ☐ **PAUL, Joseph H.**  ............................... *paintings* | | | $880 |
| English 19th cent. | | | |
| ☐ **PAUL, Sir John Dean**  ......................... *paintings* | | $3,520 | $6,600 |
| English | | | |
| ☐ **PAULE**  ............................................ *paintings* | | | $521 |
| ☐ **PAULI, Adolph**  .................................. *drawings* | | | $770 |
| Belgian 1820-1895 | | | |
| ☐ **PAULI, Gustav**  .................................. *paintings* | | | $264 |
| 19th/20th cent. | | | |
| ☐ **PAULI, Richard**  ................................ *paintings* | | | $522 |
| ☐ **PAULIN, Paul**  .................................. *sculpture* | | | $1,045 |
| ☐ **PAULMAN, J.**  .................................... *paintings* | | $110 | $550 |

| | Current Price Range | |
|---|---|---|
| | *Low* | *High* |
| ☐ **PAULSEN, Erich** .................... *paintings* <br> German b. 1932 | | **$325** |
| ☐ **PAULSEN, Fritz** .................... *paintings* <br> German 1838-1898 | **$577** | **$5,225** |
| ☐ **PAULSEN, Julius** .................... *paintings* <br> Danish 1860-1940 | **$220** | **$935** |
| ☐ **PAULUS, Francis Petrus** .................... *paintings* <br> American 1862-1933 .................... *drawings* <br> .................... *sculpture* | **$75** | **$1,265** <br> **$200** <br> **$3,190** |
| ☐ **PAULUS, H.** .................... *paintings* <br> German 19th/20th cent. | | **$440** |
| ☐ **PAUS, Herbert** .................... *drawings* <br> American 1880-1946 | | **$247** |
| ☐ **PAUSINGER, Clemens von** .................... *drawings* <br> Austrian 1855-1936 | | **$550** |
| ☐ **PAUSINGER, Franz Von** .................... *paintings* <br> Austrian 1839-1915 | | **$1,430** |
| ☐ **PAUTROT, Ferdinand** .................... *sculpture* <br> French 19th cent. | **$132** | **$1,320** |
| ☐ **PAUTROT, S.** .................... *sculpture* | | **$550** |
| ☐ **PAVESI, P.** .................... *drawings* <br> Italian 19th cent. | **$440** | **$5,775** |
| ☐ **PAVIL, Elie Anatole** .................... *paintings* <br> French 1873-1948 | **$935** | **$2,200** |
| ☐ **PAVLOS** .................... *sculpture* <br> Greek b. 1930 | | **$550** |
| ☐ **PAVLOVSKY, Vladimir** .................... *paintings* <br> American 20th cent. | **$246** | **$1,100** |
| ☐ **PAVONI, I.** .................... *paintings* | **$125** | **$513** |
| ☐ **PAVY, Eugene** .................... *paintings* | | **$6,050** |
| ☐ **PAXSON, Edgar Samuel** .................... *paintings* <br> American 1852-1919 .................... *drawings* | **$3,575** <br> **$242** | **$66,000** <br> **$33,000** |
| ☐ **PAXSON, Ethel** .................... *paintings* <br> American b. 1885 | **$385** | **$550** |
| ☐ **PAXTON, W.A.** .................... *paintings* <br> American 20th cent. | | **$275** |
| ☐ **PAXTON, William McGregor** .................... *paintings* <br> American 1869-1941 .................... *drawings* | **$1,210** <br> **$110** | **$66,000** <br> **$11,000** |
| ☐ **PAYNE, Albert Henry** .................... *paintings* | | **$550** |
| ☐ **PAYNE, David** .................... *paintings* <br> British 19th cent. .................... *drawings* | **$247** | **$357** <br> **$192** |
| ☐ **PAYNE, Edgar Alwin** .................... *paintings* <br> American 1882-1947 .................... *drawings* | **$467** <br> **$247** | **$12,100** <br> **$1,210** |
| ☐ **PAYNE, George Forest** .................... *paintings* | **$264** | **$385** |
| ☐ **PAYNE, Gordon** .................... *paintings* <br> Canadian b. 1891 | | **$687** |
| ☐ **PAYNE, H.C.** .................... *drawings* <br> American 20th cent. | | **$247** |

| | | *Current Price Range* | |
| | | *Low* | *High* |
|---|---|---|---|
| ☐ **PAYNE, Ken** ............................ *sculpture* | | | $1,100 |
| American b.c. 1937 | | | |
| ☐ **PAYNE, Willard** ........................ *paintings* | | $33 | $220 |
| American contemporary | | | |
| ☐ **PAYNE, William** ........................ *drawings* | | $385 | $1,100 |
| British 1760-1830 | | | |
| ☐ **PAYNE LIMNER** ........................ *paintings* | | $7,700 | $7,700 |
| American 18th cent. | | | |
| ☐ **PEABODY, Ruth** ........................ *paintings* | | | $1,600 |
| American b. 1898 .......................... *drawings* | | | $50 |
| ☐ **PEAKE, Mervyn** ........................ *paintings* | | | $550 |
| ☐ **PEAKE, Robert (the younger)** ........ *paintings* | | | $6,325 |
| ☐ **PEALE, Charles Willson** .............. *paintings* | | $18,700 | $37,400 |
| American 1741-1827 | | | |
| ☐ **PEALE, Harriet Cary** .................. *paintings* | | | $6,600 |
| American b. 1800 | | | |
| ☐ **PEALE, Henrietta** ...................... *paintings* | | | $385 |
| American 1806-1892 | | | |
| ☐ **PEALE, James** .......................... *paintings* | | $2,640 | $55,000 |
| American 1749-1831 | | | |
| ☐ **PEALE, Mary Jane** ...................... *paintings* | | $990 | $8,800 |
| American 1827-1902 ...................... *drawings* | | | $770 |
| ☐ **PEALE, Rembrandt** ...................... *paintings* | | $1,320 | $63,250 |
| American 1778-1860 | | | |
| ☐ **PEALE, Rubens** .......................... *paintings* | | | $9,000 |
| American 1784-1864/65 | | | |
| ☐ **PEALE, Sarah Miriam** .................. *paintings* | | $2,420 | $2,860 |
| American 1800-1885 ...................... *drawings* | | $300 | $352 |
| ☐ **PEALE, Titian Ramsey** ................ *paintings* | | $1,870 | $5,775 |
| American 1799-1885 | | | |
| ☐ **PEARCE, Charles Sprague** ............ *paintings* | | $660 | $247,500 |
| American 1851-1914 ...................... *drawings* | | $110 | $330 |
| ☐ **PEARCE, Edgar Lewis** .................. *paintings* | | $440 | $990 |
| American b. 1885 | | | |
| ☐ **PEARLMUTTER, Stella** ................ *paintings* | | $1,100 | $1,760 |
| American contemporary | | | |
| ☐ **PEARLSTEIN, Philip** .................. *paintings* | | $2,970 | $41,250 |
| American b. 1924 .......................... *drawings* | | $440 | $8,250 |
| ☐ **PEARN, W.** .............................. *paintings* | | | $715 |
| American | | | |
| ☐ **PEARS, Charles** ........................ *paintings* | | | $1,320 |
| British 1873-1958 | | | |
| ☐ **PEARSON, A.** ............................ *paintings* | | | $880 |
| ☐ **PEARSON, Cornelius** .................. *drawings* | | $132 | $880 |
| British 1805-1891 | | | |
| ☐ **PEARSON, Henry** ...................... *paintings* | | $467 | $715 |
| American b. 1914 | | | |
| ☐ **PEARSON, James** ...................... *paintings* | | $330 | $385 |
| American b. 1900 | | | |

| | | | Current Price Range | |
| | | | Low | High |
|---|---|---|---|---|
| ☐ **PEARSON, Joseph T. (Jr.)** | .................. | *paintings* | **$1,210** | **$1,375** |
| American b. 1876 | | | | |
| ☐ **PEARSON, Marguerite Stuber** | ............. | *paintings* | **$82** | **$8,250** |
| American 1898-1978 | | | | |
| ☐ **PEARSON, R.** | ..................................... | *paintings* | **$176** | **$242** |
| American d. 1891 | | | | |
| ☐ **PEARSON, William H.** | ........................ | *drawings* | **$77** | **$302** |
| English 19th cent. | | | | |
| ☐ **PEASE, G.M.** | ..................................... | *paintings* | | **$250** |
| American 19th cent. | | | | |
| ☐ **PEBBLES, Francis Marion** | ................. | *paintings* | **$165** | **$660** |
| American 1839-1928 | | | | |
| ☐ **PECCANSKI, F.** | ................................ | *paintings* | | **$797** |
| Polish 19th cent. | | | | |
| ☐ **PECHEUX, Laurent** | ........................... | *drawings* | | **$2,090** |
| French 1729-1821 | | | | |
| ☐ **PECHSTEIN, Max Hermann M.** | ........... | *paintings* | **$8,800** | **$57,200** |
| German 1881-1955 | ..................................... | *drawings* | **$880** | **$11,000** |
| ☐ **PECK, Charles** | ................................ | *paintings* | **$357** | **$1,210** |
| American 19th cent. | | | | |
| ☐ **PECK, Henry Jaris** | ............................. | *paintings* | **$137** | **$1,760** |
| American b. 1880 | | | | |
| ☐ **PECK, Sheldon** | ................................. | *paintings* | | **$71,500** |
| American 1797-1868 | | | | |
| ☐ **PECKHAM, Deacon Robert** | ................. | *drawings* | | **$990** |
| American | | | | |
| ☐ **PECKITT, Thomas** | ............................. | *paintings* | | **$1,980** |
| ☐ **PECRUS, Charles Francois** | .................. | *paintings* | **$550** | **$2,420** |
| French 1826-1907 | | | | |
| ☐ **PECZELY, Anton** | ............................... | *paintings* | | **$605** |
| Hungarian b. 1891 | | | | |
| ☐ **PEDERSEN, Carl Henning** | ................. | *paintings* | **$1,210** | **$13,200** |
| Danish b. 1913 | ..................................... | *drawings* | | **$1,870** |
| ☐ **PEDERSEN, Hugo** | ............................. | *paintings* | | **$220** |
| Dutch 19th/20th cent. | | | | |
| ☐ **PEDIETTI, F.** | ................................... | *paintings* | | **$1,100** |
| Italian 19th/20th cent. | | | | |
| ☐ **PEDRO, Luis Martinez** | ....................... | *drawings* | **$220** | **$2,530** |
| Cuban b. 1910 | | | | |
| ☐ **PEDROTTI, Amadeo** | .......................... | *paintings* | | **$275** |
| ☐ **PEDULLI, Federigo** | ........................... | *drawings* | | **$220** |
| Italian b. 1860 | | | | |
| ☐ **PEEL, James** | ................................... | *paintings* | **$400** | **$4,125** |
| English 1811-1906 | | | | |
| ☐ **PEEL, Paul** | ..................................... | *paintings* | | **$3,190** |
| Canadian 1861-1892 | | | | |
| ☐ **PEELE, John Thomas** | ......................... | *paintings* | **$935** | **$8,250** |
| Anglo/American 1822-1897 | | | | |

| | | Current Price Range | |
| | | Low | High |
|---|---|---|---|
| ☐ **PEEPLES, Nina** ............................ *drawings* | | | $301 |
| American d. 1979 | | | |
| ☐ **PEETERS, Bonaventura** ...................... *paintings* | | $5,500 | $45,100 |
| Flemish | | | |
| ☐ **PEETERS, Eugene P.J.** ...................... *paintings* | | $250 | $286 |
| Continental School late 19th cent. ................... *drawings* | | | $302 |
| ☐ **PEETERS, Jacob** ............................... *paintings* | | | $880 |
| ☐ **PEETERS, Jan** ............................... *paintings* | | $4,400 | $7,700 |
| ☐ **PEETORANUS, Johannes** .................... *drawings* | | | $1,540 |
| ☐ **PEGURIER, Auguste** ........................ *paintings* | | $165 | $880 |
| French 1856-1936 ..................................... *drawings* | | $110 | $990 |
| ☐ **PEINADO, Joaquin** ........................... *paintings* | | | $935 |
| Spanish 1898-1975 | | | |
| ☐ **PEIPERL, Adam** ............................... *drawings* | | | $440 |
| ☐ **PEIRCE, H. Winthrop** ...................... *paintings* | | $175 | $825 |
| American 1850-1935 ................................. *drawings* | | $325 | $1,650 |
| ☐ **PEIRCE, Waldo** ............................... *paintings* | | $110 | $3,850 |
| American 1884-1970 ................................. *drawings* | | $88 | $605 |
| ☐ **PEIXOTO, George** ........................... *paintings* | | $66 | $632 |
| American | | | |
| ☐ **PEIXOTTO, Ernest Clifford** ................ *paintings* | | $330 | $770 |
| American b. 1869 | | | |
| ☐ **PEIXOTTO, Florian** ........................... *paintings* | | | $522 |
| American 19th cent. | | | |
| ☐ **PEJEANAESCHI (?)** ........................... *paintings* | | | $275 |
| ☐ **PELAEZ, Amelia** ............................... *paintings* | | $4,950 | $23,100 |
| Cuban 1897-1968 ................................... *drawings* | | $660 | $12,100 |
| ☐ **PELESCHKA, F.** ............................... *sculpture* | | | $550 |
| ☐ **PELEZ, Fernand** ............................... *paintings* | | | $935 |
| French 1843-1913 | | | |
| ☐ **PELGROM, Jacobus** ........................... *paintings* | | | $2,750 |
| Dutch 1811-1861 | | | |
| ☐ **PELHAM, James (II)** ......................... *paintings* | | | $1,540 |
| British 1800-1874 | | | |
| ☐ **PELHAM, Thomas Kent** ...................... *paintings* | | | $1,870 |
| British ac. 1860-1891 | | | |
| ☐ **PELITI, F.** ....................................... *paintings* | | | $550 |
| ☐ **PELL, Ella** ..................................... *paintings* | | | $600 |
| ☐ **PELL, J.** ......................................... *paintings* | | | $385 |
| American 19th/20th cent. | | | |
| ☐ **PELLAR, Hans** .................................. *paintings* | | | $220 |
| German b. 1886 | | | |
| ☐ **PELLEGRIN, Honore** .......................... *drawings* | | $2,250 | $12,500 |
| French 1800-1870 | | | |
| ☐ **PELLEGRINI, Carlo** ........................... *drawings* | | | $330 |
| ☐ **PELLEGRINI, Giovanni Antonio** .......... *paintings* | | $7,150 | $24,200 |
| Italian 1675-1741 | | | |
| ☐ **PELLEGRINI, Riccardo** ...................... *paintings* | | $2,200 | $3,630 |
| Italian 1863/66-1934 | | | |

| | Current Price Range | |
|---|---|---|
| | Low | High |

| | | Low | High |
|---|---|---|---|
| ☐ PELLERIN, J.G. ............................... *drawings* | | | $352 |
| ☐ PELLETIER, Claude ........................... *paintings* | | | $1,430 |
| French 20th cent. | | | |
| ☐ PELLETIER, Pierre Jacques ............... *paintings* | | $495 | $605 |
| ☐ PELLIGRINNI ................................... *paintings* | | | $550 |
| Italian 19th cent. | | | |
| ☐ PELLINI, M. .................................... *paintings* | | | $660 |
| ☐ PELLIZZA DA VOLPEDO, Giuseppe ... *paintings* | | | $2,200 |
| Italian 1868-1907 | | | |
| ☐ PELLON, Gina .................................. *paintings* | | $770 | $1,650 |
| Cuban b. 1925 | | | |
| ☐ PELOUSE, Andre ............................... *paintings* | | | $528 |
| ☐ PELOUSE, Leon Germain ................... *paintings* | | $900 | $4,400 |
| French 1838-1891 | | | |
| ☐ PELS, Albert ................................... *paintings* | | | $440 |
| ☐ PELTON, Agnes ................................ *paintings* | | $165 | $200 |
| German/American 1881-1961 | | | |
| ☐ PELUSO, E. .................................... *paintings* | | | $495 |
| ☐ PELUSO, Francesco ........................... *paintings* | | $330 | $2,200 |
| Italian b. 1836 | | | |
| ☐ PEMBROOK, T.K. ............................. *paintings* | | | $302 |
| ☐ PENA, Tonita .................................. *drawings* | | | $880 |
| American 1895-1949 | | | |
| ☐ PENALBA ....................................... *sculpture* | | | $715 |
| ☐ PENALBA, Alicia Perez ...................... *sculpture* | | $880 | $8,800 |
| Argentinian b. 1918 | | | |
| ☐ PENCK, A.R. ................................... *paintings* | | $1,650 | $46,750 |
| German b. 1939 | | | |
| ☐ PENDL, Erwin ................................. *drawings* | | $1,980 | $2,530 |
| Austrian b. 1875 | | | |
| ☐ PENEL (?), Aime .............................. *paintings* | | | $2,200 |
| ☐ PENEN, Theodoor van ........................ *paintings* | | | $2,200 |
| ☐ PENFIELD, Edward ........................... *drawings* | | $121 | $440 |
| American 1866-1925 | | | |
| ☐ PENFOLD, Frank C. ........................... *paintings* | | | $3,100 |
| American | | | |
| ☐ PENIC, D. ...................................... *sculpture* | | | $330 |
| ☐ PENLEY, Aaron Edwin ....................... *drawings* | | $220 | $715 |
| English 1807-1870 | | | |
| ☐ PENN, Stanley ................................. *paintings* | | | $495 |
| British 19th cent. | | | |
| ☐ PENNACCHINI, Domenico ................... *paintings* | | | $1,050 |
| Italian 1860-1928 | | | |
| ☐ PENNE, Charles Olivier de ................. *paintings* | | $1,760 | $13,200 |
| French 1831-1897 ................................ *drawings* | | | $1,540 |
| ☐ PENNEL, Joseph .............................. *drawings* | | $55 | $2,090 |
| American 1860-1926 | | | |
| ☐ PENNELL, Harry .............................. *paintings* | | $220 | $2,860 |
| American 19th/20th cent. | | | |

| | | | Current Price Range | |
|---|---|---|---|---|
| | | | *Low* | *High* |
| ☐ **PENNELL, Joseph** | *drawings* | | $55 | $2,090 |
| American 1860-1926 | | | | |
| ☐ **PENNINGTON, Harper** | *paintings* | | | $2,310 |
| American 1854/55-1920 | *drawings* | | | $77 |
| ☐ **PENNOYER, Albert Sheldon** | *paintings* | | $192 | $2,310 |
| American 1888-1957 | *drawings* | | $88 | $143 |
| ☐ **PENNY, A.W.** | *paintings* | | | $192 |
| English 19th cent. | | | | |
| ☐ **PENNY, R.** | *paintings* | | | $220 |
| American 20th cent. | | | | |
| ☐ **PENNY, W.D.** | *paintings* | | $880 | $1,045 |
| English 19th cent. | | | | |
| ☐ **PENOT, Albert Joseph** | *paintings* | | $550 | $1,100 |
| French ac. 1910 | *drawings* | | | $247 |
| ☐ **PENTEWA, Dick** | *drawings* | | | $176 |
| American (Hopi) | | | | |
| ☐ **PENTZER** | *paintings* | | | $440 |
| American 19th cent. | | | | |
| ☐ **PEPIN, Emile** | *sculpture* | | | $495 |
| ☐ **PEPPER, Beverly** | *sculpture* | | $165 | $4,400 |
| American b. 1924 | | | | |
| ☐ **PEPPER, Charles Hovey** | *paintings* | | | $660 |
| American 1864-1950 | *drawings* | | | $302 |
| ☐ **PEPPERCORN, Arthur D.** | *paintings* | | | $300 |
| ☐ **PERAIRE, A.** | *paintings* | | | $1,320 |
| ☐ **PERAIRE, Paul Emmanuel** | *paintings* | | $302 | $1,320 |
| French 1829-1893 | | | | |
| ☐ **PERALTA DEL CAMPO, Francisco** | *paintings* | | | $2,750 |
| Spanish d. 1897 | *drawings* | | | $1,100 |
| ☐ **PERAUX, Lionel** | *paintings* | | | $1,320 |
| French b. 1871 | *drawings* | | | $55 |
| ☐ **PERBANDT, Carl von** | *paintings* | | $1,045 | $2,200 |
| American 1832-1911 | | | | |
| ☐ **PERBOYRE, Paul Emile Leon** | *paintings* | | $577 | $2,860 |
| French 1826-1907 | | | | |
| ☐ **PERCEVAL, Don** | *drawings* | | | $440 |
| ☐ **PERCIVAL, Edwin** | *paintings* | | | $550 |
| American b. 1793 | | | | |
| ☐ **PERCIVAL, H.** | *drawings* | | | $1,700 |
| English 19th cent. | | | | |
| ☐ **PERCONI, D.F.** | *paintings* | | | $1,650 |
| American 20th cent. | | | | |
| ☐ **PERCY, Isabelle Clark** | *drawings* | | | $275 |
| b. 1882 | | | | |
| ☐ **PERCY, Sidney Richard Williams** | *paintings* | | $715 | $13,200 |
| English 1821-1886 | | | | |
| ☐ **PEREDA, Antonio de** | *paintings* | | | $4,400 |
| Spanish 1599-1669 | | | | |

| | | *Current Price Range* | |
|---|---|---|---|
| | | *Low* | *High* |
| ☐ **PEREHUDOFF, William W.** ............... *paintings* | | $880 | $1,540 |
| Canadian b. 1919 | | | |
| ☐ **PERELLE, Nicolas** ........................... *paintings* | | | $4,180 |
| French 1631-1695 | | | |
| ☐ **PERELLI, Achille** ........................... *paintings* | | $357 | $1,540 |
| American 1829-1891 ........................... *sculpture* | | $258 | $935 |
| ☐ **PEREZ, Alonso** ........................... *paintings* | | $1,210 | $16,500 |
| Spanish ac. 1893-1914 ........................... *drawings* | | $462 | $467 |
| ☐ **PEREZ, Andre** ........................... *paintings* | | | $605 |
| ☐ **PEREZ, Bartolome** ........................... *paintings* | | $8,800 | $16,500 |
| Spanish 1634-1693 | | | |
| ☐ **PEREZ, Carlos Alonzo** ........................... *paintings* | | | $1,540 |
| Spanish b. 1858 | | | |
| ☐ **PEREZ, Eleuterio** ........................... *paintings* | | | $330 |
| ☐ **PEREZ, Pedro Felix** ........................... *paintings* | | | $440 |
| contemporary | | | |
| ☐ **PEREZ-SENET, Rafael** ........................... *drawings* | | | $1,320 |
| Spanish b. 1856 | | | |
| ☐ **PERGAULT, Dominique** ........................... *drawings* | | | $385 |
| ☐ **PERICONI, D.F.M.** ........................... *paintings* | | | $467 |
| ☐ **PERIGAL, Arthur** ........................... *paintings* | | $474 | $990 |
| British 1816-1884 ........................... *drawings* | | $132 | $385 |
| ☐ **PERIGNON, Nicolas** ........................... *drawings* | | $990 | $1,650 |
| French | | | |
| ☐ **PERILLO, Gregory** ........................... *paintings* | | $522 | $8,800 |
| American 20th cent. | | | |
| ☐ **PERK, W.D.** ........................... *paintings* | | | $1,760 |
| British 19th cent. | | | |
| ☐ **PERKINS, Granville** ........................... *paintings* | | $137 | $12,100 |
| American 1830-1895 ........................... *drawings* | | $140 | $1,870 |
| ☐ **PERKINS, John W.** ........................... *paintings* | | | $385 |
| American 19th/20th cent. | | | |
| ☐ **PERKINS, Robert A.** ........................... *paintings* | | $330 | $400 |
| American b. 1960 | | | |
| ☐ **PERKINS, Sarah** ........................... *drawings* | | | $1,430 |
| American 1771-1831 | | | |
| ☐ **PERKINS, William** ........................... *drawings* | | | $275 |
| ☐ **PERKS, J.H.** ........................... *paintings* | | | $412 |
| British 19th cent. | | | |
| ☐ **PERL, Karl** ........................... *sculpture* | | $264 | $1,210 |
| Austrian b. 1876 | | | |
| ☐ **PERLAR, L.** ........................... *paintings* | | | $990 |
| American 19th cent. | | | |
| ☐ **PERLBERG, Georg** ........................... *paintings* | | | $6,600 |
| German 1807-1884 | | | |
| ☐ **PERLMUTTER, Jack** ........................... *paintings* | | $385 | $495 |
| American 20th cent. | | | |
| ☐ **PERLROTT, Csaba Vilmos** ........................... *paintings* | | | $286 |

| | | Current Price Range | |
|---|---|---|---|
| | | Low | High |
| ☐ **PERMEKE, Constant** ........................... *paintings* | | | **$5,500** |
| Belgian 1886-1952 | | | |
| ☐ **PERMENZEL, L.** ............................... *paintings* | | | **$412** |
| ☐ **PERNAS** ............................................... *paintings* | | | **$302** |
| French 19th cent. | | | |
| ☐ **PERNET, Jean Henry Alexandre** ........... *drawings* | | **$550** | **$4,675** |
| French b. c. 1763 | | | |
| ☐ **PERON, Guy** ....................................... *paintings* | | | **$350** |
| French 20th cent. | | | |
| ☐ **PEROT, Annie L.** ............................... *paintings* | | | **$495** |
| American | | | |
| ☐ **PEROV, Vasili** ................................... *paintings* | | | **$550** |
| Russian 1833-1882 | | | |
| ☐ **PERRAULT, I. Marie** ........................ *drawings* | | | **$325** |
| ☐ **PERRAULT, Leon Jean Basile** .............. *paintings* | | **$2,200** | **$15,950** |
| French 1832-1908 | | | |
| ☐ **PERRAULT, Mire** ............................. *drawings* | | | **$330** |
| ☐ **PERRAULT-HARRY, Emile** ................. *sculpture* | | | **$385** |
| French early 20th cent. | | | |
| ☐ **PERRET, Aime** .................................... *paintings* | | **$1,045** | **$4,400** |
| French 1847-1927 | | | |
| ☐ **PERRET, Edouard** ............................... *paintings* | | | **$1,760** |
| French b. 1864 | | | |
| ☐ **PERRETTEN, E.** ................................. *paintings* | | | **$605** |
| French 19th cent. | | | |
| ☐ **PERREY, Louis** ................................... *paintings* | | **$770** | **$1,045** |
| French b. 1856 | | | |
| ☐ **PERREZ, Domingo** ............................. *paintings* | | | **$660** |
| ☐ **PERRIER, Emilio Sanchez** .................... *paintings* | | **$12,100** | **$17,600** |
| Spanish 1853-1907 | | | |
| ☐ **PERRIGARD, Hal Ross** ....................... *paintings* | | | **$264** |
| ☐ **PERRIN, Alfred Feyer** ......................... *paintings* | | **$330** | **$770** |
| British 1860-1911 | | | |
| ☐ **PERRIN, Charles** ................................... *paintings* | | | **$495** |
| French 19th cent. | | | |
| ☐ **PERRIN, G.** ....................................... *paintings* | | | **$5,225** |
| French 19th cent. | | | |
| ☐ **PERRIN, P.** ....................................... *drawings* | | | **$275** |
| French 19th/20th cent. | | | |
| ☐ **PERRINE, Van Dearing** ....................... *paintings* | | **$1,320** | **$4,125** |
| American 1869-1955 | | | |
| ☐ **PERROT, A.** ....................................... *paintings* | | **$110** | **$660** |
| French 19th cent. | | | |
| ☐ **PERRUZZINI, Giovanni Battista** ........... *paintings* | | | **$1,650** |
| ☐ **PERRY, Charles O.** ............................. *sculpture* | | | **$5,500** |
| American b. 1929 | | | |
| ☐ **PERRY, Clara Fairfield** ....................... *paintings* | | | **$330** |
| American d. 1941 | | | |

| | | *Current Price Range* | |
|---|---|---|---|
| | | Low | High |
| ☐ **PERRY, Clara G.** ................... *paintings* | | | $450 |
| American 1871-1960 | | | |
| ☐ **PERRY, Enoch Wood** .............. *paintings* | | $550 | $46,200 |
| American 1831-1915 ..................... *drawings* | | | $4,950 |
| ☐ **PERRY, F.C.** ........................ *paintings* | | | $275 |
| American late 19th cent. | | | |
| ☐ **PERRY, Lilla Cabot** ............... *paintings* | | $400 | $11,000 |
| American 1848?-1933 | | | |
| ☐ **PERRY, Roland Hilton** ........... *paintings* | | | $247 |
| American 1870-1941 | | | |
| ☐ **PERRY, William C.** ................ *paintings* | | | $440 |
| American 20th cent. | | | |
| ☐ **PERSAN, Raffy le** ................. *paintings* | | $143 | $467 |
| ☐ **PERSIN, Gustave Joseph** ........ *paintings* | | | $935 |
| ☐ **PERSOGLIA, Franz von** .......... *paintings* | | $2,750 | $4,400 |
| Austrian b. 1852 | | | |
| ☐ **PERSON, Henri** ..................... *drawings* | | | $1,870 |
| French 1876-1926 | | | |
| ☐ **PERSSON, Fritiof** .................. *paintings* | | | $302 |
| American 20th cent. | | | |
| ☐ **PERUGIA, A. del** ................... *sculpture* | | | $385 |
| Italian c. 1900 | | | |
| ☐ **PERUGINI, Charles Edward** ..... *paintings* | | $2,200 | $6,050 |
| English, b. Naples 1839-c. 1918 | | | |
| ☐ **PERUZZI, Baldassare** ............. *drawings* | | $2,750 | $19,250 |
| Italian 1481-1536 | | | |
| ☐ **PERUZZINI, Domenico** ........... *drawings* | | | $4,400 |
| ☐ **PESENTI, Domenico** ............... *paintings* | | $1,210 | $1,430 |
| Italian 1843-1918 | | | |
| ☐ **PESKE, Geza** ....................... *paintings* | | | $1,100 |
| Hungarian b. 1859 | | | |
| ☐ **PESNE, Antoine** .................... *paintings* | | $2,420 | $4,400 |
| French 1683-1757 | | | |
| ☐ **PESSENTI, D.** ...................... *paintings* | | | $1,870 |
| Italian 19th cent. | | | |
| ☐ **PESSLER, Ernst** .................... *paintings* | | | $440 |
| Austrian 1838-1900 | | | |
| ☐ **PETER, Wenceslaus** ............... *paintings* | | | $330 |
| Austrian 1742-1829 | | | |
| ☐ **PETER, Wenzel Johann** .......... *paintings* | | | $1,760 |
| ☐ **PETERDI, Gabor** ................... *drawings* | | $275 | $550 |
| Hungarian/American b. 1915 | | | |
| ☐ **PETERIS, J.H.** ..................... *paintings* | | | $412 |
| American 20th cent. | | | |
| ☐ **PETERS, Anna** .................... *paintings* | | | $5,775 |
| German 1843-1926 | | | |
| ☐ **PETERS, Bernhard** ............... *paintings* | | | $418 |
| ☐ **PETERS, C.** ....................... *drawings* | | | $1,760 |
| American | | | |

| | | Current Price Range | |
|---|---|---|---|
| | | Low | High |
| ☐ PETERS, Charles Rollo ......................... *paintings* | | $385 | $4,675 |
| American 1862-1928 | | | |
| ☐ PETERS, Pieter Francis (the younger) .... *paintings* | | | $1,320 |
| Dutch 1818-1903 ......................................... *drawings* | | | $825 |
| ☐ PETERS, Rev. Matthew William ........... *paintings* | | | $935 |
| Irish 1741/42-1814 ...................................... *drawings* | | | $88 |
| ☐ PETERS, S. ........................................... *drawings* | | | $3,190 |
| early 19th cent. | | | |
| ☐ PETERSEN, H. .................................... *paintings* | | $412 | $1,650 |
| ☐ PETERSEN, J. ..................................... *drawings* | | | $2,420 |
| ☐ PETERSEN, L. .................................... *paintings* | | | $3,750 |
| American 19th cent. | | | |
| ☐ PETERSEN, Olaf ................................. *paintings* | | | $1,100 |
| ☐ PETERSON, Jane ................................. *paintings* | | $110 | $23,100 |
| American 1876-1965/68 ............................... *drawings* | | $132 | $30,800 |
| ☐ PETERSON, Lester M. .......................... *drawings* | | $30 | $175 |
| American 20th cent. | | | |
| ☐ PETERSON, Thomas ............................ *paintings* | | $412 | $880 |
| 20th cent. | | | |
| ☐ PETERSON, V. ..................................... *paintings* | | | $350 |
| American 19th cent. | | | |
| ☐ PETHER, Abraham ............................ *paintings* | | | $10,000 |
| English 1756-1812 | | | |
| ☐ PETHYBRIDGE, Henry ....................... *paintings* | | | $308 |
| American 20th cent. | | | |
| ☐ PETICOLAS, Arthur ........................... *paintings* | | | $6,325 |
| American 1793-1853 | | | |
| ☐ PETICOV, Antonio ............................. *sculpture* | | | $2,420 |
| b. Brazil 1906 | | | |
| ☐ PETILLION, Jules .............................. *paintings* | | | $4,675 |
| French 1845-1899 | | | |
| ☐ PETIT, Adrien ...................................... *drawings* | | | $275 |
| French 19th cent. | | | |
| ☐ PETIT, Corneille .................................. *paintings* | | | $2,090 |
| Belgian 19th cent. | | | |
| ☐ PETIT, Eugene .................................... *paintings* | | $220 | $3,960 |
| French 1839-1886 | | | |
| ☐ PETIT, Francois Constant ..................... *paintings* | | $1,650 | $4,950 |
| Belgian 19th cent. | | | |
| ☐ PETIT, Jean Louis .............................. *paintings* | | | $2,200 |
| French 1795-1876 | | | |
| ☐ PETIT-GERARD, Pierre ....................... *paintings* | | | $605 |
| French b. 1852 | | | |
| ☐ PETIT-JEAN, Andre ............................ *paintings* | | | $330 |
| ☐ PETITBOIS, Agathon du ...................... *paintings* | | | $6,600 |
| ☐ PETITI, Filiberto ............................... *paintings* | | | $220 |
| Italian 1845-1924 | | | |
| ☐ PETITJEAN, Edmond Marie ................ *paintings* | | $600 | $14,300 |
| French 1844-1925 | | | |

| | | *Current Price Range* | |
|---|---|---|---|
| | | *Low* | *High* |
| ☐ **PETITJEAN, Hippolyte** ............... *paintings* | | $660 | $18,700 |
| French 1854-1929 .............................. *drawings* | | $110 | $3,300 |
| ☐ **PETO, John Frederick** ............ *paintings* | | $3,025 | $55,000* |
| American 1854-1907 ......................... *drawings* | | $44 | $411 |
| ☐ **PETRI** .............................................. *paintings* | | | $253 |
| American 20th cent. | | | |
| ☐ **PETRIDES, Konrad** ..................... *paintings* | | | $1,760 |
| Austrian 1864-1943 | | | |
| ☐ **PETRIE, Graham** ........................ *drawings* | | | $374 |
| ☐ **PETRILLI, A.** ............................... *sculpture* | | | $440 |
| ☐ **PETRILLY, H.** .............................. *sculpture* | | | $450 |
| ☐ **PETRITSKY, Anatole** ................. *drawings* | | | $2,200 |
| ☐ **PETROCELLI, Arturo** ................ *paintings* | | $440 | $2,750 |
| Italian b. 1856 | | | |
| ☐ **PETROCELLI, Vincenzo** ............ *paintings* | | | $1,100 |
| Italian 1823-1896 | | | |
| ☐ **PETROFF, Andre** ........................ *paintings* | | | $275 |
| French 19th/20th cent. ...................... *drawings* | | $88 | $99 |
| ☐ **PETRUOLO, Salvatore** ............. *paintings* | | | $3,520 |
| Italian b. 1857 | | | |
| ☐ **PETRY, A.** ..................................... *paintings* | | | $275 |
| ☐ **PETRYKOWSKI, Janusz** .......... *paintings* | | | $302 |
| Polish 20th cent. | | | |
| ☐ **PETTENKOFEN,** | | | |
| **August Carl Ritter von** ............... *paintings* | | $495 | $3,300 |
| Austrian c. 1822-1889 | | | |
| ☐ **PETTER, Franz Xavier** ............. *paintings* | | $17,600 | $30,800 |
| Austrian | | | |
| ☐ **PETTERSON, K.O.** ..................... *paintings* | | | $715 |
| ☐ **PETTES, Robert** ......................... *paintings* | | | $550 |
| ☐ **PETTET, William** ....................... *paintings* | | $302 | $302 |
| American b. 1942 | | | |
| ☐ **PETTIBONE, Richard** ............... *paintings* | | | $770 |
| American b. 1938 | | | |
| ☐ **PETTIE, Sir John** ....................... *paintings* | | | $1,100 |
| Scottish 1839-1893 | | | |
| ☐ **PETTIT, J.A. Conistan** ............. *paintings* | | $88 | $200 |
| British 19th/20th cent. | | | |
| ☐ **PETTITT, Edwin Alfred** ........... *paintings* | | $660 | $1,045 |
| British 1840-1912 | | | |
| ☐ **PETTITT, Joseph Paul** ............. *paintings* | | $660 | $2,722 |
| English 1812-1882 | | | |
| ☐ **PETTORUTI, Emilio** .................. *paintings* | | $11,000 | $209,000 |
| Argentinian 1892-1971 ...................... *drawings* | | $2,420 | $4,400 |
| ☐ **PETTY, George** ........................... *drawings* | | | $5,500 |
| American 20th cent. | | | |
| ☐ **PEURSE, Adam van** ................... *paintings* | | | $1,650 |
| Dutch b. 1814 | | | |

|                                        |           | Current Price Range |          |
|----------------------------------------|-----------|---------------------|----------|
|                                        |           | Low                 | High     |
| ☐ **PEVSNER, Antoine** ............... *sculpture* |  |          | **$93,500** |
| French 1884-1962                       |           |                     |          |
| ☐ **PEW, Gertrude** .................. *drawings* |    |          | **$275**   |
| American                               |           |                     |          |
| ☐ **PEYNOT, Emile Edmond** ........ *sculpture* |   |          | **$7,700**  |
| French late 19th cent.                 |           |                     |          |
| ☐ **PEYRAUD, Frank Charles** ....... *paintings* | **$275** | **$4,125** |
| American b. 1858                       |           |                     |          |
| ☐ **PEYRE, Raphael Charles** ....... *sculpture* | **$850** | **$7,700** |
| French b. 1872                         |           |                     |          |
| ☐ **PEYROL, Rene** .................. *paintings* |  |          | **$2,640**  |
| French 19th cent.                      |           |                     |          |
| ☐ **PEYRON, Jean Francois Pierre** ........ *drawings* | |       | **$4,125**  |
| French 1744-1814                       |           |                     |          |
| ☐ **PEYSTER, Eva de** ............... *drawings* |   |          | **$715**   |
| American                               |           |                     |          |
| ☐ **PEYTEL, Adrienne S.** .......... *paintings* |  |          | **$1,430**  |
| French School 19th cent.               |           |                     |          |
| ☐ **PEYTON, J.** ..................... *paintings* | |          | **$495**   |
| British 19th cent.                     |           |                     |          |
| ☐ **PEZANT, Aymar** ................ *paintings* | **$385** | **$1,760** |
| French 1846-after 1914                 |           |                     |          |
| ☐ **PEZENBURG, E.** ................ *paintings* |  |          | **$3,850**  |
| German 19th cent.                      |           |                     |          |
| ☐ **PEZOUS, Jean** .................. *paintings* | **$330** | **$440** |
| ☐ **PFAFF, Judy** ................... *sculpture* |  |          | **$12,100** |
| American contemporary                  |           |                     |          |
| ☐ **PFAU, Conrad** .................. *paintings* |  |          | **$605**   |
| German b. 1885                         |           |                     |          |
| ☐ **PFEIFFAR, Richard** ............ *paintings* |  |          | **$192**   |
| German b. 1878                         |           |                     |          |
| ☐ **PFEIFFER, Fritz** ............... *paintings* | |          | **$880**   |
| American                               |           |                     |          |
| ☐ **PFEIFFER, Herman** ............ *drawings* |    |          | **$330**   |
| ☐ **PFEIFFER, L.** ................... *paintings* | |          | **$467**   |
| French 19th cent.                      |           |                     |          |
| ☐ **PFEUVINDSCHMUTH, H.** ....... *paintings* |    |          | **$275**   |
| ☐ **PFIEFFER, J.** ................... *paintings* | |          | **$1,100**  |
| ☐ **PFISTER, Jean Jacques** ........ *paintings* |  |          | **$192**   |
| American 20th cent.                    |           |                     |          |
| ☐ **PFISTERER, A.** ................. *paintings* |  |          | **$880**   |
| German 19th cent.                      |           |                     |          |
| ☐ **PHARES, Frank** ................ *paintings* | **$55** | **$275** |
| American 20th cent.                    |           |                     |          |
| ☐ **PHELAN, Charles T.** .......... *paintings* | **$132** | **$440** |
| American b. 1840                       |           |                     |          |
| ☐ **PHELPS, Edith Catlin** ......... *paintings* | **$330** | **$1,100** |
| American 1875/79-1961                   |           |                     |          |

| | | Current Price Range | |
|---|---|---|---|
| | | *Low* | *High* |

☐ **PHELPS, John R.** ............... *sculpture* | | $800
American

☐ **PHELPS, Rusty** .................. *sculpture* | | $1,300
American 20th cent.

☐ **PHELPS, William Preston** .................... *paintings* | $357 | $6,500
American 1848-1923

☐ **PHILBERT** ........................................ *paintings* | | $275
19th cent.

☐ **PHILDOR, P.** ..................................... *paintings* | | $385

☐ **PHILIPP, Robert** ............................. *paintings* | $192 | $7,150
American 1895-1981 ............................. *drawings* | $192 | $2,090

☐ **PHILIPPE, A.R.** ............................... *sculpture* | | $550

☐ **PHILIPPE, Paul** ............................... *sculpture* | $935 | $8,250
Polish

☐ **PHILIPPE-AUGUSTE, Salnave** ............ *paintings* | $1,540 | $9,350
Haitian b. 1908

☐ **PHILIPPEAU, Karel Frans** .................. *paintings* | $5,500 | $8,800
Dutch 1825-1897

☐ **PHILIPPOTEAUX,**
**Henri Felix Emmanuel** ....................... *paintings* | | $7,700
French 1815-1884

☐ **PHILIPPOTEAUX, Paul Dominique** ...... *paintings* | $550 | $1,650
French 19th cent. .................................... *drawings* | | $660

☐ **PHILIPS, Charles** .............................. *paintings* | | $5,225

☐ **PHILIPS, Frank Albert** ....................... *paintings* | $825 | $1,320
British 19th cent.

☐ **PHILLIP, John** ................................. *paintings* | $495 | $1,100
English 1817-1867

☐ **PHILLIPPE, Paul** ............................... *sculpture* | $550 | $1,650
Polish

☐ **PHILLIPS, A.E.** ................................ *paintings* | | $484

☐ **PHILLIPS, Ammi** ............................... *paintings* | $3,630 | $682,000
American 1788-1865

☐ **PHILLIPS, Bert Greer** ......................... *paintings* | $1,430 | $66,000
American 1868-1956 ............................... *drawings* | $220 | $1,100

☐ **PHILLIPS, Charles** ............................ *paintings* | | $2,420
English 18th/19th cent.

☐ **PHILLIPS, Charles** ............................ *paintings* | $1,430 | $14,300
English 1708-1747

☐ **PHILLIPS, Coles** ............................... *paintings* | $5,060 | $9,350
American 1880-1927

☐ **PHILLIPS, Gail** ................................. *paintings* | $121 | $301
American 20th cent.

☐ **PHILLIPS, Gordon** ............................. *paintings* | $4,400 | $11,000
American b. 1927 .................................... *drawings* | | $825
........................................................ *sculpture* | $1,320 | $3,575

☐ **PHILLIPS, J. Campbell** ....................... *paintings* | $77 | $660
American 1873-1948/49

## American Folk Painting

*America's Bicentennial in 1976 helped popularize folk paintings. A decade later, they continue to appreciate in value, sometimes quite dramatically.*

*A Washington, D.C., resident brought this painting to a benefit appraisal day sponsored by Christie's at the Corcoran Gallery. The work of 19th-century American folk painter Ammi Phillips, it was estimated at $60,000 to $90,000 and consigned to the auction house for the January American Decorative Arts sale, which traditionally coincides with the Winter Antiques Show held each January in New York.*

*Early that month, the Museum of American Folk Art had announced that a New York collector had paid $1 million for a similar portrait by Phillips. Amidst much excitement,*

*eight telephone bidders competed for "Portrait of a Girl in a Red Dress." When the hammer came down, an anonymous bidder had secured the work for $682,000! (Ammi Phillips, "Portrait of a Girl in a Red Dress," oil on canvas, 32 x 27 in., Christie's, January 26, 1985, $682,000.)*

|  | | Current Price Range | |
|---|---|---|---|
|  | | Low | High |
| ☐ **PHILLIPS, S. George** ............... *paintings* | | **$220** | **$385** |
| American d. 1965 | | | |
| ☐ **PHIPPEN, George** ............... *paintings* | | **$25,000** | **$55,000** |
| American 1916-1966 ............... *drawings* | | **$2,000** | **$2,500** |
| ☐ **PHOENIX, George** ............... *paintings* | | | **$10,450** |
| British 1863-1935 | | | |
| ☐ **PHYSICK, William** ............... *sculpture* | | | **$5,170** |
| English 1836-1871 | | | |
| ☐ **PIACENZA, Carlo** ............... *paintings* | | | **$411** |
| Italian 1814-1887 | | | |
| ☐ **PIATKOWSKI, Henryk** ............... *paintings* | | | **$1,500** |
| Polish 1853-1932 | | | |
| ☐ **PIAZZA-CARERRA, A.** ............... *sculpture* | | | **$660** |
| Italian 19th cent. | | | |
| ☐ **PIAZZETTA, Giambattista** ............... *drawings* | | | **$1,100** |
| Italian 1682-1754 | | | |
| ☐ **PIAZZONI, Gottardo F.P.** ............... *paintings* | | **$220** | **$4,675** |
| American 1872-1945 | | | |

## 20th-Century Master

Pablo Picasso was one of the most
influential and prolific artists of the
20th century. He lived to the ripe
age of 92 and painted from virtually
the first moment that he could hold
a brush, holding his first one-man
show when he was sixteen.

In the course of his long career
Picasso passed through many
different stages of development and
was versatile in many different
media. There are Picasso ceramics,
lithographs, sculptures, drawings,
and oils. "Femme Assise au
Chapeau" is a 1923 pastel on
unprimed canvas and reveals the
artist's preoccupation with classical
imagery, which developed after his
exploration of Cubism a decade
earlier. (Pablo Picasso, "Femme
Assise au Chapeau," pastel on
unprimed canvas,
51⅛ x 38¼ in., Christie's,
November 13, 1984, $4,290,000.)

| | | Current Price Range | |
|---|---|---|---|
| | | *Low* | *High* |
| ☐ **PICABIA, Francis** ............................... *paintings* | | **$2,200** | **$88,000** |
| French 1878-1953 ..................................... *drawings* | | **$110** | **$214,500** |
| ☐ **PICABIA, Marie** ................................ *drawings* | | | **$418** |
| ☐ **PICARD, Gustave** ............................... *paintings* | | | **$3,630** |
| French 19th cent. | | | |
| ☐ **PICARD, Simon** ................................ *paintings* | | | **$495** |
| ☐ **PICARDET, L.** ................................... *paintings* | | | **$825** |
| French 19th cent. | | | |
| ☐ **PICARDIE SCHOOL, 15TH CENTURY** .. *paintings* | | | **$46,750** |
| ☐ **PICART, Bernard** ............................... *drawings* | | **$825** | **$1,430** |
| ☐ **PICASSO, Pablo** ................................ *paintings* | | **$24,200** | **$5,830,000** |
| Spanish 1881-1973 ..................................... *drawings* | | **$110** | **$4,290,000** |
| .......................................................... *sculpture* | | **$4,180** | **$104,500** |
| ☐ **PICAULT, C.E.** ................................. *paintings* | | **$1,155** | **$2,530** |
| French 19th cent. | | | |
| ☐ **PICAULT, Emile Louis** ........................ *sculpture* | | **$484** | **$3,300** |
| French ac. 1863-1909 | | | |

| | | | *Current Price Range* | |
| | | | *Low* | *High* |
| ☐ **PICCINI, Gaetano** ............................... *drawings* | | | $137 | $440 |
| Italian ac. c. 1600 | | | | |
| ☐ **PICCIRILLI, Attilio** ...................... *sculpture* | | | $770 | $3,080 |
| American 1866-1945 | | | | |
| ☐ **PICHOT, Ramon** ............................... *paintings* | | | | $550 |
| French 20th cent. | | | | |
| ☐ **PICILLO, Joseph** ............................. *paintings* | | | $1,100 | $1,430 |
| ☐ **PICK, Anton** ..................................... *paintings* | | | $330 | $2,090 |
| Austrian b. 1840 | | | | |
| ☐ **PICKARD, C.G.** ................................. *paintings* | | | | $440 |
| American School 20th cent. | | | | |
| ☐ **PICKARD, Louise** ............................. *paintings* | | | | $1,155 |
| British 1865-1928 | | | | |
| ☐ **PICKERING, Henry** ........................... *paintings* | | | $192 | $495 |
| English ac. 1745-1776 | | | | |
| ☐ **PICKERING, Joseph Langsdale** ........... *paintings* | | | $110 | $352 |
| British d. 1912 | | | | |
| ☐ **PICKERT, A.** ...................................... *paintings* | | | | $412 |
| German (?) 19th cent. | | | | |
| ☐ **PICKETT, Joseph** .............................. *paintings* | | | | $22,000 |
| American 1848-1918 | | | | |
| ☐ **PICKNELL, George W.** ....................... *paintings* | | | $154 | $1,000 |
| American b. 1864 | | | | |
| ☐ **PICKNELL, William Lamb** ................. *paintings* | | | $462 | $7,150 |
| American 1854-1897 | | | | |
| ☐ **PICOLO Y LOPEZ, Manuel** ................ *paintings* | | | $1,320 | $1,320 |
| Spanish b. 1850 | | | | |
| ☐ **PICOT, Andre** ................................... *paintings* | | | | $247 |
| French 20th cent. | | | | |
| ☐ **PICOU, Henri Pierre** .......................... *paintings* | | | $440 | $4,290 |
| French 1824-1895 ..................................... *drawings* | | | | $385 |
| ☐ **PICTU, L.** ......................................... *paintings* | | | | $440 |
| ☐ **PIECK, Philip** .................................... *paintings* | | | | $209 |
| Russian/American 20th cent. ......................... *drawings* | | | | $121 |
| ☐ **PIELER, Franz Xavier** ....................... *paintings* | | | $3,080 | $15,400 |
| Austrian 1879-1952 | | | | |
| ☐ **PIENE, Otto** .................................... *paintings* | | | $605 | $770 |
| German/American b. 1928 | | | | |
| ☐ **PIENNE, Georges** .............................. *paintings* | | | $550 | $1,210 |
| British ac. 1891-92 | | | | |
| ☐ **PIERAULT** ......................................... *paintings* | | | | $10,450 |
| c. 1875-1900 | | | | |
| ☐ **PIERAY** ............................................ *paintings* | | | | $665 |
| ☐ **PIERCE, A.W.** ................................... *drawings* | | | | $1,760 |
| American 19th cent. | | | | |
| ☐ **PIERCE, Charles Franklin** .................... *paintings* | | | $77 | $770 |
| American 1844-1920 | | | | |
| ☐ **PIERCE, John R.** ............................... *paintings* | | | | $385 |
| American 20th cent. | | | | |

| | | *Current Price Range* | |
|---|---|---|---|
| | | Low | High |

| | | Low | High |
|---|---|---|---|
| ☐ **PIERCE, R.E.** ...................................... *paintings* | | **$650** | **$1,000** |
| American | | | |
| ☐ **PIERCY, Frederick** .............................. *drawings* | | | **$2,860** |
| English fl. 1848-1880 | | | |
| ☐ **PIERDON, Francois** ............................ *paintings* | | | **$467** |
| French 1821-1904 | | | |
| ☐ **PIERO DI COSIMO** ........................... *paintings* | | | **$16,500** |
| Italian 1492-1521 | | | |
| ☐ **PIERON, Henri** .................................. *paintings* | | | **$624** |
| French 19th cent. | | | |
| ☐ **PIERRE, Andre** .................................. *paintings* | | **$301** | **$2,750** |
| Haitian b. 1914 | | | |
| ☐ **PIERRE,** | | | |
| **Edgar de Montzaigle de Saint** ................ *paintings* | | | **$2,750** |
| French b. 1867 | | | |
| ☐ **PIERRE, Fernand** ............................... *paintings* | | **$80** | **$5,500** |
| Haitian ..................................................... *drawings* | | | **$104** |
| ☐ **PIERRE, Gustave Rene** ........................ *paintings* | | | **$220** |
| French b. 1875 | | | |
| ☐ **PIERRE, Jean Baptiste Marie** .............. *drawings* | | **$2,090** | **$7,975** |
| French 1713-1789 | | | |
| ☐ **PIERSON, Alden** ................................ *paintings* | | **$1,100** | **$1,980** |
| American 1874-1921 | | | |
| ☐ **PIERVALIER** ..................................... *sculpture* | | | **$576** |
| ☐ **PIETA, A.** ......................................... *paintings* | | | **$412** |
| Italian 19th cent. | | | |
| ☐ **PIETERS, Evert** ................................. *paintings* | | **$247** | **$19,250** |
| Dutch 1856-1932 ..................................... *drawings* | | | **$1,540** |
| ☐ **PIETERSZ, Bertus** .............................. *paintings* | | | **$385** |
| Dutch/American 1869-1938 | | | |
| ☐ **PIETRI, Pietro de** .............................. *paintings* | | **$550** | **$1,100** |
| ☐ **PIETRO, A.** ....................................... *paintings* | | | **$1,045** |
| Dutch 19th cent. | | | |
| ☐ **PIETRO DI DOMENICO** ..................... *paintings* | | | **$26,400** |
| Italian 1457-c. 1506 | | | |
| ☐ **PIFBERGER, M.** ................................. *paintings* | | | **$264** |
| ☐ **PIFFARD, Harold H.** .......................... *paintings* | | | **$1,870** |
| British ac. 1895-1899 | | | |
| ☐ **PIGNON, Edouard** .............................. *paintings* | | **$605** | **$1,540** |
| French b. 1905 | | | |
| ☐ **PIGUET, Rodolphe** ............................. *drawings* | | **$110** | **$550** |
| Swiss 1840-1915 | | | |
| ☐ **PIKE, John** ....................................... *drawings* | | | **$352** |
| ☐ **PIKE, Joseph** ................................... *paintings* | | | **$198** |
| British 19th cent. | | | |
| ☐ **PIKE, Sidney** ................................... *paintings* | | | **$660** |
| British 19th/20th cent. | | | |
| ☐ **PILAET, C.B.** ..................................... *paintings* | | | **$385** |
| ☐ **PILETTI, Arturo** ............................... *paintings* | | **$187** | **$418** |

|                                                                 | *Current Price Range* | |
| --- | --- | --- |
|                                                                 | *Low* | *High* |
| ☐ **PILICHOWSKI, Leopold** ...................... *paintings* | $577 | $3,520 |
| Polish 1869-1933 ........................................ *drawings* | $1,100 | $2,400 |
| ☐ **PILL, Charles** ...................................... *paintings* | | $275 |
| ☐ **PILLEAU, Henry** ............................... *drawings* | | $192 |
| English 1815-1899 | | |
| ☐ **PILLEMENT, Jean Baptiste** ................. *paintings* | $2,400 | $15,400 |
| French 1728-1808 ...................................... *drawings* | $660 | $20,900 |
| ☐ **PILLET, L.** ......................................... *sculpture* | | $500 |
| ☐ **PILOT, Robert Wakeham** ................. *paintings* | $1,980 | $20,900 |
| Canadian 1898-1967/68 | | |
| ☐ **PILOTY, Carl Theodor von** ............... *paintings* | | $1,400 |
| German 1826-1886 | | |
| ☐ **PILOTY, Ferdinand** ........................... *paintings* | | $2,090 |
| German 1828-1895 | | |
| ☐ **PILS, Isidore Alexandre Augustin** ......... *paintings* | $770 | $6,875 |
| French 1813-1875 ...................................... *drawings* | $137 | $1,650 |
| ☐ **PILSBURY, Wilmot** ........................... *drawings* | | $462 |
| English 1840-c. 1908 | | |
| ☐ **PILTERS, Josef** ............................... *paintings* | | $440 |
| German 1877-1957 | | |
| ☐ **PILTZ, Otto** ...................................... *paintings* | $6,600 | $33,000 |
| German 1846-1910 | | |
| ☐ **PILZ, Otto** ....................................... *sculpture* | | $1,320 |
| German b. 1876 | | |
| ☐ **PINA, Alfredo** ................................... *sculpture* | | $2,420 |
| Italian 19th/20th cent. | | |
| ☐ **PINA, De la** .................................... *drawings* | $99 | $247 |
| Mexican 20th cent. | | |
| ☐ **PINCHART, Emile Auguste** ............... *paintings* | $770 | $9,900 |
| French 1842-after 1930 | | |
| ☐ **PINCHEVSKY, Leonid** ....................... *paintings* | | $209 |
| Russian 20th cent. | | |
| ☐ **PINCHINOT, Max** ............................ *paintings* | | $1,100 |
| Haitian | | |
| ☐ **PINCHON, Robert A.** ......................... *paintings* | $2,310 | $2,530 |
| ☐ **PINCON, Charles** .............................. *paintings* | | $330 |
| ☐ **PINE, Robert Edge** ........................... *paintings* | $110 | $1,540 |
| English 1730-1788 | | |
| ☐ **PINE, Theodore E.** ........................... *paintings* | $302 | $1,100 |
| American 1828-1905 | | |
| ☐ **PINEAUD-BAILLEU, F.L.** .................. *paintings* | | $302 |
| French 19th/20th cent. | | |
| ☐ **PINEDO, Emile** ................................ *sculpture* | | $1,320 |
| French 19th cent. | | |
| ☐ **PINEL DE GRANDCHAMP,** | | |
| **Louis Emile** ......................................... *paintings* | | $7,700 |
| French d. 1894 | | |
| ☐ **PINELLI, Bartolomeo** ......................... *drawings* | $357 | $22,000 |
| Italian 1781-1835 | | |

| | | Current Price Range | |
|---|---|---|---|
| | | *Low* | *High* |
| ☐ **PINGGERA, H.** ...................... *paintings* | | | **$4,400** |
| Italian 19th cent. | | | |
| ☐ **PINGRET, Edouard Henri Theophile** .... *paintings* | | | **$49,500** |
| French 1788-1875 | | | |
| ☐ **PINIO, Antonio** ...................... *paintings* | | | **$990** |
| Italian 19th cent. | | | |
| ☐ **PINKS, S.T.** ...................... *paintings* | | | **$522** |
| ☐ **PINNEY, Eunice** ...................... *drawings* | | | **$1,000** |
| American c. 1800 | | | |
| ☐ **PINTO, Silvio** ...................... *paintings* | | | **$275** |
| ☐ **PINTURICCHIO, Bernardino Betti** ....... *drawings* | | | **$19,800** |
| Italian 1454-1513 | | | |
| ☐ **PINXT, Plalo** ...................... *paintings* | | | **$850** |
| ☐ **PIOLA, Domenico** ...................... *drawings* | | **$605** | **$935** |
| ☐ **PIOLA, E.** ...................... *paintings* | | | **$330** |
| Italian 20th cent. | | | |
| ☐ **PIOLA, Paolo Girolamo** ...................... *drawings* | | | **$1,430** |
| Italian 1666-1724 | | | |
| ☐ **PIORKOWSKI** ...................... *drawings* | | **$137** | **$264** |
| Polish/American 20th cent. | | | |
| ☐ **PIOT, Etienne Adolphe** ...................... *paintings* | | **$192** | **$13,200** |
| French 1850-1910 | | | |
| ☐ **PIOT, Raphael** ...................... *paintings* | | | **$990** |
| ☐ **PIOT, Rene** ...................... *drawings* | | | **$357** |
| ☐ **PIOTROWSKI, Antoni** ...................... *paintings* | | **$7,700** | **$8,800** |
| Polish 1853-1924 | | | |
| ☐ **PIOTROWSKI, M.** ...................... *paintings* | | | **$220** |
| American 20th cent. | | | |
| ☐ **PIPER, John** ...................... *drawings* | | **$550** | **$825** |
| English b. 1903 | | | |
| ☐ **PIPO, Emanuel Ruiz** ...................... *paintings* | | | **$330** |
| Spanish b. 1928 | | | |
| ☐ **PIPPEL, Otto Eduard** ...................... *paintings* | | **$935** | **$8,525** |
| German b. 1878 | | | |
| ☐ **PIPPIN, Horace** ...................... *paintings* | | **$8,800** | **$57,750** |
| American 1888-1947 | | | |
| ☐ **PIRA, Gioachchino la** ...................... *drawings* | | | **$220** |
| Italian 18th/19th cent. | | | |
| ☐ **PIRCK, A.** ...................... *paintings* | | | **$385** |
| ☐ **PIRIE, George** ...................... *paintings* | | | **$605** |
| ☐ **PIRIGI, A.** ...................... *paintings* | | | **$220** |
| Italian 19th/20th cent. | | | |
| ☐ **PISA, Alberto** ...................... *paintings* | | | **$1,320** |
| Italian 1864-1931 | | | |
| ☐ **PISANI, Alberto** ...................... *paintings* | | | **$770** |
| Italian 1826-1899 | | | |
| ☐ **PISANI, Gustavo** ...................... *paintings* | | **$440** | **$1,210** |
| Italian b. 1877 | | | |

| | | Current Price Range | |
|---|---|---|---|
| | | *Low* | *High* |
| ☐ **PISANO, Eduardo** ............................. *paintings* | | | $440 |
| Spanish b. 1912 | | | |
| ☐ **PISARRO, Charles** ............................. *paintings* | | | $176 |
| French d. 1926 | | | |
| ☐ **PISEMSKY, Alexei A.** ...................... *paintings* | | | $550 |
| Russian 1859-1909 | | | |
| ☐ **PISIS, Filippo de** ............................. *paintings* | | $880 | $26,400 |
| Italian 1896-1956 ..................................... *drawings* | | $660 | $6,050 |
| ☐ **PISSALZZO, Felix** ............................ *paintings* | | | $220 |
| French 20th cent. | | | |
| ☐ **PISSARRO, Camille** ........................... *paintings* | | $27,500 | $935,000 |
| French 1830-1903 ..................................... *drawings* | | $440 | $132,000 |
| ☐ **PISSARRO, Lucien** ............................ *paintings* | | $5,500 | $20,900 |
| French 1863-1944 ..................................... *drawings* | | $330 | $605 |
| ☐ **PISSARRO, Paul Emile** ........................ *paintings* | | $330 | $4,400 |
| French 1884 ..................................... *drawings* | | $110 | $1,210 |
| ☐ **PISTOLETTO, Michelangelo** ............... *paintings* | | | $302 |
| Italian b. 1933 ......................................... *drawings* | | | $19,800 |
| ☐ **PISTOR, Hermann** ........................... *paintings* | | | $1,210 |
| German 19th cent. | | | |
| ☐ **PISTOR, O.V.** ................................. *paintings* | | | $330 |
| Continental 19th cent. | | | |
| ☐ **PITATI, Bonifazio de** | | | |
| **(called Bonifazio Veronese)** ...................... *paintings* | | | $3,850 |
| Italian 1487-1553 | | | |
| ☐ **PITCHFORTH, Vivian** ....................... *paintings* | | | $286 |
| English b. 1895 | | | |
| ☐ **PITKANEN, C.** ................................. *sculpture* | | | $247 |
| late 19th cent. | | | |
| ☐ **PITMAN, John** ................................. *paintings* | | | $7,700 |
| English ac. 1820-1832 | | | |
| ☐ **PITT, William** ................................. *paintings* | | $350 | $715 |
| English ac. 1849-1890 | | | |
| ☐ **PITTARA, Carlo** ............................... *paintings* | | $2,200 | $13,200 |
| Italian 1836-1890 | | | |
| ☐ **PITTMAN, Hobson** ........................... *paintings* | | $385 | $1,870 |
| American 1898/1900-1972 ........................... *drawings* | | $33 | $385 |
| ☐ **PITTO** ........................................... *paintings* | | | $450 |
| Italian 19th cent. | | | |
| ☐ **PITTONI, Giovanni Battista** ............... *paintings* | | $3,080 | $46,750 |
| Italian 1687-1767 | | | |
| ☐ **PITZ, Henry Clarence** ........................ *drawings* | | | $632 |
| American 1895-1976 | | | |
| ☐ **PITZNER, Max Joseph** ........................ *paintings* | | $2,310 | $12,100 |
| German 1855-1912 | | | |
| ☐ **PITZNER, S.** ................................... *paintings* | | | $1,100 |
| ☐ **PIZZELLA, Edmund** ........................... *drawings* | | | $605 |
| American 20th cent. | | | |
| ☐ **PIZZI, P.** ....................................... *paintings* | | | $440 |

| | | Current Price Range | |
|---|---|---|---|
| | | *Low* | *High* |
| ☐ **PLAGNET** ....................................... *sculpture* | | | $550 |
| ☐ **PLANELLA, Gabriel** ........................... *paintings* | | | $1,100 |
| Spanish 1780-1850 | | | |
| ☐ **PLANK, Josef** ................................... *paintings* | | $467 | $1,100 |
| Austrian 1815-1901 | | | |
| ☐ **PLANQUETTE, Felix** ........................ *paintings* | | $440 | $1,045 |
| French b. 1873 | | | |
| ☐ **PLANSON, Joseph Alphonse** ................ *paintings* | | | $1,430 |
| French b. 1799 | | | |
| ☐ **PLAS, Laurens** ................................ *paintings* | | $110 | $1,210 |
| Dutch 1828-1893 | | | |
| ☐ **PLASCHKE, Moriz** ........................... *paintings* | | $1,100 | $2,860 |
| German 1818-1888 | | | |
| ☐ **PLASSAN, Antoine Emile** ................... *paintings* | | $1,210 | $2,200 |
| French 1817-1903 | | | |
| ☐ **PLATE, Walter** ................................ *paintings* | | | $770 |
| ☐ **PLATEEL, Jean** ................................ *paintings* | | | $6,600 |
| ☐ **PLATHNER, Hermann** ....................... *paintings* | | | $4,620 |
| German 1831-1902 | | | |
| ☐ **PLATONOV, Chariton Platonovich** ....... *paintings* | | | $1,210 |
| Russian 1842-1907 | | | |
| ☐ **PLATT, Charles Adams** ...................... *paintings* | | $356 | $1,980 |
| American 1861-1933 | | | |
| ☐ **PLATT, J.C.** ................................... *paintings* | | | $1,100 |
| American d. 1882 | | | |
| ☐ **PLATTEEL, Jean** .............................. *paintings* | | $2,200 | $8,250 |
| Belgian 1839-1867 | | | |
| ☐ **PLATZER, Johann Georg** ................... *paintings* | | $14,300 | $14,300 |
| Austrian 1704-1761 | | | |
| ☐ **PLAZA, N.** ..................................... *sculpture* | | | $2,475 |
| ☐ **PLAZZOTTA, Enzo** ........................... *paintings* | | $2,420 | $3,080 |
| ☐ **PLE, Henri Honore** ......................... *sculpture* | | $990 | $1,870 |
| French 1853-1922 | | | |
| ☐ **PLEASONTON, Ruth** ......................... *paintings* | | $99 | $198 |
| American 20th cent. | | | |
| ☐ **PLEISSNER, Ogden M.** ...................... *paintings* | | $2,200 | $50,000 |
| American 1905-1983 .............................. *drawings* | | $550 | $30,800 |
| ☐ **PLETKA** ........................................ *paintings* | | | $200 |
| American 20th cent. .............................. *drawings* | | | $150 |
| ☐ **PLEYSIER, Ary** ............................... *paintings* | | | $715 |
| Dutch 1809-1879 | | | |
| ☐ **PLIMPTON, W. E.** ............................ *paintings* | | | $1,045 |
| English 19th cent. | | | |
| ☐ **PLOCK, K.** ..................................... *paintings* | | | $1,320 |
| ☐ **PLUMMER, William** ......................... *paintings* | | $2,530 | $3,500 |
| American 19th/20th cent. | | | |
| ☐ **PLUMOT, Andre** .............................. *paintings* | | $1,100 | $2,530 |
| Belgian 1829-1906 | | | |
| ☐ **PLUNKETT, Walter** ........................... *drawings* | | $1,540 | $2,200 |

| | | Current Price Range | |
|---|---|---|---|
| | | *Low* | *High* |
| ☐ **PLUVIOSE, Dieudonne** ........................ *paintings* | | $220 | $385 |
| ☐ **PLYASHNIKOV, Ivan** ......................... *paintings* | | | $3,300 |
| Russian 19th cent. | | | |
| ☐ **PLYMOUTH, Sibly (Captain)** ............... *paintings* | | | $357 |
| ☐ **PO, Giacomo del** .................................. *paintings* | | | $4,950 |
| Italian 1652-1726 | | | |
| ☐ **PO, Pietro del** ...................................... *paintings* | | | $2,750 |
| Italian 1610-1692 | | | |
| ☐ **POCOCK, Nicholas** ............................. *paintings* | | $7,150 | $18,700 |
| English 1740-1821 | | | |
| ☐ **PODCHERNIKOFF, Alexis** ................... *paintings* | | $77 | $1,650 |
| American b. 1912 | | | |
| ☐ **PODCHERNIKOFF, A. M.** ................. *paintings* | | $247 | $2,750 |
| Russian 1886-1931 | | | |
| ☐ **PODESTI, Vincenzo** ............................. *drawings* | | | $3,575 |
| Italian 1812-1897 | | | |
| ☐ **PODWIL, Jerry** .................................. *drawings* | | | $192 |
| American 20th cent. | | | |
| ☐ **POE, A.J.** ............................................ *paintings* | | | $330 |
| ☐ **POEHLMANN, Theo.** ......................... *paintings* | | | $192 |
| American early 20th cent. | | | |
| ☐ **POEL, Egbert van der** ......................... *paintings* | | $1,980 | $36,300 |
| Dutch 1621-1664 | | | |
| ☐ **POELENBURGH, Cornelis van** ............. *paintings* | | $880 | $25,300 |
| Dutch 1586-1667 | | | |
| ☐ **POERTZL, Professor Otto** ................... *sculpture* | | $660 | $9,900 |
| German b. 1876 | | | |
| ☐ **POEVIS(?), Paul** .................................. *paintings* | | | $467 |
| French 19th cent. | | | |
| ☐ **POGANY, William Andrew (or Willy)** .... *paintings* | | $247 | $356 |
| Hungarian/American 1882-1955 ...................... *drawings* | | $121 | $880 |
| ☐ **POGEDAIEFF, Georges De** ................. *drawings* | | $660 | $1,210 |
| ☐ **POGGI, P.** ........................................... *paintings* | | | $2,200 |
| Italian 19th cent. | | | |
| ☐ **POHE, G.** ............................................ *paintings* | | | $770 |
| ☐ **POHL, Edward H.** ............................... *paintings* | | $38 | $1,000 |
| American 19th/20th cent. | | | |
| ☐ **POHL, Hugo D.** ................................... *paintings* | | $137 | $440 |
| American b. 1878 | | | |
| ☐ **POHLE, Hermann** ............................... *paintings* | | $440 | $8,250 |
| German 1831-1901 ...................................... *drawings* | | | $11 |
| ☐ **POHLMEYER, Alana** ......................... *paintings* | | | $247 |
| American b. 1954 | | | |
| ☐ **POIDEVIN, F.** ..................................... *paintings* | | | $3,575 |
| French 19th cent. | | | |
| ☐ **POIDEVIN, P.J.** ................................. *paintings* | | $66 | $357 |
| Dutch 20th cent. | | | |
| ☐ **POILPOT, Theophile** ........................... *paintings* | | $3,025 | $33,000 |
| French 1848-1915 | | | |

| | | Current Price Range | |
|---|---|---|---|
| | | *Low* | *High* |
| ☐ **POINCY, Paul** .................... *paintings* | | **$1,100** | **$1,100** |
| American 1833-1909 | | | |
| ☐ **POINT, Armand** ............... *paintings* | | | **$30,800** |
| French 1860/61-1932 ..................... *drawings* | | **$132** | **$25,300** |
| ☐ **POIRSON, Maurice** ............ *paintings* | | | **$39,600** |
| French 1850-1882 | | | |
| ☐ **POISSON, Louverature** .......... *paintings* | | **$121** | **$5,500** |
| Haitian 1914-1985 | | | |
| ☐ **POITOU** .......................... *sculpture* | | | **$825** |
| ☐ **POKICT (?), E.** ................. *paintings* | | | **$385** |
| American 19th cent. | | | |
| ☐ **POKITONOV, Ivan** ............. *paintings* | | **$935** | **$4,180** |
| Russian 1851-c. 1924 | | | |
| ☐ **POKORNY, Richard** ............ *drawings* | | | **$385** |
| Austrian 20th cent. | | | |
| ☐ **POL, Christian van** ............. *paintings* | | **$5,500** | **$5,500** |
| Dutch 1752-1813 | | | |
| ☐ **POL, Louis van der** ............ *paintings* | | **$935** | **$1,980** |
| Dutch 1896-1982 | | | |
| ☐ **POLA, Hendrick** ............... *paintings* | | | **$1,100** |
| Dutch 1676-1748 | | | |
| ☐ **POLAEGEN, G.** ................. *paintings* | | | **$192** |
| American School late 19th cent. | | | |
| ☐ **POLELONEMA, Tyler** .......... *drawings* | | | **$880** |
| American (Hopi) | | | |
| ☐ **POLENBURGH, Cornelis van** .......... *paintings* | | | **$1,100** |
| Dutch 1586-1667 | | | |
| ☐ **POLEO, Hector** ................. *paintings* | | | **$44,000** |
| Venezuelan b. 1918 ..................... *drawings* | | | **$1,760** |
| ☐ **POLESELLO, Rogelio** .......... *paintings* | | **$1,870** | **$2,200** |
| b. Argentina 1939 | | | |
| ☐ **POLGARY, Geza** ............... *paintings* | | | **$1,760** |
| Hungarian b. 1862 | | | |
| ☐ **POLIAKOFF, Serge** ............ *paintings* | | **$4,400** | **$26,400** |
| French 1900-1969 ..................... *drawings* | | **$4,125** | **$5,500** |
| ☐ **POLIDORI, C.** .................. *paintings* | | | **$220** |
| Italian 19th/20th cent. ............... *drawings* | | **$360** | **$1,870** |
| ☐ **POLIDORI, Gian Carlo** .......... *paintings* | | | **$1,650** |
| ☐ **POLIEU, S.** ..................... *paintings* | | | **$467** |
| French 19th cent. | | | |
| ☐ **POLK, Charles Peale** .......... *paintings* | | **$2,750** | **$49,500** |
| American 1767-1822 | | | |
| ☐ **POLK, Frank** .................. *sculpture* | | **$1,000** | **$1,100** |
| American b. 1909 | | | |
| ☐ **POLLACK, Mark A.** ............ *paintings* | | **$88** | **$192** |
| American 20th cent. | | | |
| ☐ **POLLAK, August** ............... *paintings* | | | **$935** |
| Austrian b. 1838 | | | |

| | | Current Price Range | |
|---|---|---|---|
| | | Low | High |
| ☐ **POLLAK, James** .................................. *paintings* | | $4,180 | $29,700 |
| English 1797-1859/67 | | | |
| ☐ **POLLARD, Thane** ................................ *paintings* | | | $220 |
| English(?) 19th cent. | | | |
| ☐ **POLLENTINE, Alfred** .......................... *paintings* | | $330 | $1,760 |
| English ac. 1861-1880 | | | |
| ☐ **POLLET, Joseph Michel Ange** .............. *sculpture* | | | $4,620 |
| French 1814-1870 | | | |
| ☐ **POLLI, Felice** ...................................... *drawings* | | | $2,310 |
| 19th cent. | | | |
| ☐ **POLLOCK, Charles Cecil** ...................... *paintings* | | $165 | $2,200 |
| American b. 1902 | | | |
| ☐ **POLLOCK, Jackson** ............................. *paintings* | | $24,200 | $374,000 |
| American 1912-1956 ................................... *drawings* | | $4,400 | $165,000 |
| ................................................................ *sculpture* | | | $6,325 |
| ☐ **POLOWETSKY, C.E.** ............................ *paintings* | | | $300 |
| ☐ **POLYCARPE** ........................................ *paintings* | | | $357 |
| ☐ **POMERENKE, Heinrich** ....................... *paintings* | | | $4,400 |
| European 19th cent. | | | |
| ☐ **POMEY, Louis Edmond** ........................ *paintings* | | | $25,300 |
| French 1831-1891 | | | |
| ☐ **POMODORO, Arnaldo** ......................... *sculpture* | | $6,050 | $33,000 |
| Italian b. 1926 | | | |
| ☐ **POMODORO, Gio** ............................... *sculpture* | | $800 | $1,650 |
| Italian b. 1930 | | | |
| ☐ **POMPEUS, Carlo** ................................ *paintings* | | | $2,530 |
| ☐ **POMPIGNOLI, Luigi** ........................... *paintings* | | | $1,100 |
| Italian 19th cent. | | | |
| ☐ **POMPON, Francois** ............................. *sculpture* | | $1,760 | $5,500 |
| French 1855-1933 | | | |
| ☐ **PONCE DE LEON, A.** ......................... *paintings* | | | $275 |
| Spanish b. 1925 | | | |
| ☐ **PONCE DE LEON, Fidelio** .................. *paintings* | | $990 | $27,500 |
| Cuban 1895/1896-1957 ............................... *drawings* | | | $990 |
| ☐ **PONCET, Antoine** .............................. *sculpture* | | $1,430 | $3,025 |
| Swiss b. 1928 | | | |
| ☐ **PONCHON, A.** .................................... *paintings* | | | $1,100 |
| American 19th cent. | | | |
| ☐ **POND, Arthur** ................................... *paintings* | | | $660 |
| English 1705-1758 | | | |
| ☐ **POND, Dana** ...................................... *paintings* | | $137 | $770 |
| American 1880-1962 | | | |
| ☐ **PONDEL, Friedrich** ............................ *paintings* | | | $330 |
| German b. 1830 | | | |
| ☐ **PONGENIN, W.** ................................... *drawings* | | | $495 |
| ☐ **PONSEN, Tunis** ................................. *paintings* | | | $440 |
| American 20th cent. | | | |
| ☐ **PONSIN, Louis** .................................. *drawings* | | | $275 |
| ☐ **PONSON, Aime** .................................. *paintings* | | | $1,210 |

|  | | Current Price Range | |
|---|---|---|---|
|  | | Low | High |
| □ **PONTE, Francesco da** | | | |
| **(called Francesco BASSANO)** ............... *paintings* | | | $4,400 |
| □ **PONZIO, Paul** ................................. *paintings* | | | $880 |
| □ **POOKE, Marion L.** ........................... *paintings* | | | $7,700 |
| American 19th/20th cent. | | | |
| □ **POOLE, E.A.** ..................................... *paintings* | | $110 | $1,540 |
| American 1841-1912 | | | |
| □ **POOLE, James** .................................. *paintings* | | $440 | $2,090 |
| British 1804-1886 | | | |
| □ **POOLE, L.** ........................................ *paintings* | | | $52,800 |
| European 19th cent. | | | |
| □ **POOLE, Paul Falconer** ........................ *paintings* | | $412 | $797 |
| British 1807-1879 ..................................... *drawings* | | | $302 |
| □ **POOLEY, A.** ..................................... *drawings* | | | $302 |
| Canadian 19th cent. | | | |
| □ **POONS, Larry** .................................. *paintings* | | $1,430 | $22,000 |
| American b. 1937 ..................................... *drawings* | | | $770 |
| □ **POOR, Ann** ...................................... *paintings* | | | $521 |
| American 1887-1970 | | | |
| □ **POOR, Henry Varnum** ........................ *paintings* | | $110 | $2,200 |
| American 1888-1970 ................................. *drawings* | | $110 | $462 |
| □ **POORE, Harry** .................................. *paintings* | | | $605 |
| American 19th cent. | | | |
| □ **POORE, Henry Rankin** ........................ *paintings* | | $308 | $7,975 |
| American 1859-1940 ................................. *drawings* | | $137 | $385 |
| □ **POORTEN, Jacobus Johannes van** ........ *paintings* | | $385 | $825 |
| German 1841-1914 | | | |
| □ **POORTER, Willem de** ........................ *paintings* | | $3,025 | $7,700 |
| Dutch 1608-1648 | | | |
| □ **POOSCH, Max von** ........................... *paintings* | | $495 | $2,090 |
| Austrian b. 1872 | | | |
| □ **POOTER, J***de** ............................... *paintings* | | | $5,500 |
| Belgian 19th cent. | | | |
| □ **POPE, Alexander** ............................. *paintings* | | $220 | $187,000 |
| American 1849-1924 | | | |
| □ **POPE, David S.** ................................ *paintings* | | | $440 |
| English 19th cent. | | | |
| □ **POPE, John** ..................................... *paintings* | | $220 | $770 |
| American 1821-1881 | | | |
| □ **POPE, T.B.** ...................................... *paintings* | | | $330 |
| American late 19th cent. | | | |
| □ **POPEC, Duro** ................................... *paintings* | | | $1,540 |
| Yugoslavian b. 1943 | | | |
| □ **POPIEL, Thaddeus** ........................... *paintings* | | $3,300 | $6,875 |
| Polish 1832-1913 | | | |
| □ **POPOV, S.** ....................................... *paintings* | | | $220 |
| American 20th cent. | | | |
| □ **PORAY, Stan Pociecha** ........................ *paintings* | | $220 | $660 |
| Polish/American b. 1888 | | | |

| | | *Current Price Range* | |
|---|---|---|---|
| | | *Low* | *High* |
| ☐ **PORCELLIS, Jan** .............................. *paintings* | | $6,050 | $39,600 |
| Dutch c. 1584-1632 | | | |
| ☐ **PORIN, T.** ......................................... *paintings* | | | $385 |
| American 19th cent. | | | |
| ☐ **PORO, A.** .......................................... *paintings* | | | $1,430 |
| Cuban 19th cent. | | | |
| ☐ **PORPORA, Paolo** .............................. *paintings* | | $55,000 | $77,000 |
| Italian 1617-1673 | | | |
| ☐ **PORSCHE, Otto Maria** ........................ *paintings* | | | $330 |
| ☐ **PORT, A. Des** ..................................... *paintings* | | | $3,850 |
| 19th cent. | | | |
| ☐ **PORT, U.** .......................................... *paintings* | | | $247 |
| French 19th/20th cent. | | | |
| ☐ **PORTA, C.** ........................................ *paintings* | | | $660 |
| Italian 19th cent. | | | |
| ☐ **PORTA, Giuseppe (IL SALVIATI)** ......... *drawings* | | | $2,200 |
| Italian 1518/20-1585 | | | |
| ☐ **PORTAELS, Jean Francois** ................... *paintings* | | $385 | $2,530 |
| Belgian 1818-1895 | | | |
| ☐ **PORTE, H.A. de la** ............................. *paintings* | | | $264 |
| ☐ **PORTENGEN, Petrus** ........................... *paintings* | | | $8,800 |
| Dutch d. 1643 | | | |
| ☐ **PORTER, Alfred Thomas** ..................... *paintings* | | | $2,475 |
| British ac. 1882-1896 | | | |
| ☐ **PORTER, Bruce** .................................. *paintings* | | | $550 |
| ☐ **PORTER, David** .................................. *paintings* | | | $12,650 |
| American 1780-1843 | | | |
| ☐ **PORTER, Fairfield** .............................. *paintings* | | $5,500 | $154,000 |
| American 1907-1975 ................................. *drawings* | | $880 | $18,700 |
| ☐ **PORTER, Katherine** ............................ *paintings* | | | $6,050 |
| contemporary | | | |
| ☐ **PORTER, Mary King** ........................... *drawings* | | | $247 |
| American b. 1865 | | | |
| ☐ **PORTER, R.W.** ................................... *drawings* | | | $220 |
| American 19th/20th cent. | | | |
| ☐ **PORTER, Raymond Averill** .................. *sculpture* | | | $209 |
| American b. 1883 | | | |
| ☐ **PORTER, Rufus** ................................. *drawings* | | | $7,150 |
| American 1792-1884 | | | |
| ☐ **PORTER, S.R.** .................................... *paintings* | | $192 | $550 |
| 19th cent. | | | |
| ☐ **PORTER, V.F.** .................................... *paintings* | | $100 | $467 |
| American 20th cent. | | | |
| ☐ **PORTIELJE, Edward Antoon** ............... *paintings* | | $550 | $15,400 |
| Belgian 1861-1949 | | | |
| ☐ **PORTIELJE, Gerard** ............................ *paintings* | | $2,475 | $28,600 |
| Belgian 1856-1929 | | | |
| ☐ **PORTIELJE, Jon Frederik Pieter** .......... *paintings* | | $330 | $16,500 |
| Dutch 1829-1895 | | | |

**Cover Lot**

*A favorite subject of Fairfield Porter, the New York painter and art critic, was his childhood summer home. In 1979, this oil, "The Harbor — Great Spruce Head, 1974," was sold for $13,000 by Barridoff Galleries in Maine to a Connecticut collector.*

*The painting was subsequently selected to be the cover picture for the travelling exhibition "Fairfield Porter: Realist Painter in an Age of Abstraction" mounted in 1982 by Boston's Museum of Fine Arts. Consigned for sale by the owners in 1984, the work was again featured on a catalog cover, this time an auction catalog. At Barridoff Galleries, the lot sold for $154,000. (Fairfield Porter, "The Harbor — Great Spruce Head, 1974," oil on canvas, 20 x 36 in., Barridoff Galleries, September 22, 1984, $154,000.)*

|  |  | *Current Price Range* | |
|---|---|---|---|
|  |  | *Low* | *High* |
| ☐ **PORTIER** .................................... | *drawings* |  | **$550** |
| ☐ **PORTINARI, Candido** .................. | *paintings* | **$15,400** | **$49,500** |
| Brazilian 1903-1962 ....................... | *drawings* | **$1,100** | **$9,900** |
| ☐ **PORTMANN, Carl** .................... | *paintings* |  | **$3,300** |
| German 1837-1894 |  |  |  |
| ☐ **PORTOCARRERO, Rene** .............. | *paintings* | **$2,475** | **$12,100** |
| Cuban b. 1912 .............................. | *drawings* | **$550** | **$6,050** |
| ☐ **PORTTMANN, Wilhelm** ............ | *paintings* |  | **$1,980** |
| German 1819-1893 |  |  |  |
| ☐ **POSEN, Leonid** ...................... | *sculpture* |  | **$1,320** |
| Russian late 19th cent. |  |  |  |
| ☐ **POSEN, Stephen** .................... | *paintings* |  | **$22,000** |
| American b. 1939 |  |  |  |
| ☐ **POSSIN, Rudolph** .................. | *paintings* |  | **$412** |
| German b. 1862 |  |  |  |

|                                          |          | Current Price Range |           |
|------------------------------------------|----------|-----------|-----------|
|                                          |          | Low       | High      |
| ☐ **POSSNER, Hugo A.** ............................ *paintings* | | $140 | $176 |
| American 19th/20th cent. | | | |
| ☐ **POST, Edward C.** ............................. *paintings* | | | $6,325 |
| American ac. 1852-1858 | | | |
| ☐ **POST, Frans** ........................................ *paintings* | | $330,000 | $352,000 |
| Dutch c. 1612-1680 | | | |
| ☐ **POST, George** ..................................... *drawings* | | $10 | $357 |
| American b. 1906 | | | |
| ☐ **POST, W.** ............................................... *paintings* | | $55 | $275 |
| ☐ **POST, W.N.** .......................................... *paintings* | | | $330 |
| 19th cent. | | | |
| ☐ **POST, William Merritt** ....................... *paintings* | | $77 | $2,750 |
| American 1856-1935 ................................. *drawings* | | $137 | $330 |
| ☐ **POSTELLE, Germain** .......................... *paintings* | | $302 | $385 |
| ☐ **POSTIGLIONE, Luca** .......................... *paintings* | | $2,200 | $2,310 |
| Italian 1876-1936 | | | |
| ☐ **POSTIGLIONE, Luigi** ......................... *paintings* | | | $2,750 |
| Italian 1812-1881 | | | |
| ☐ **POSTIGLIONE, Salvatore** ................... *paintings* | | $1,100 | $3,850 |
| Italian 1861-1906 | | | |
| ☐ **POSTOLLE, Victor** ............................. *drawings* | | $1,430 | $4,400 |
| French b. 1836 | | | |
| ☐ **POT, Hendrick Gerritsz** ...................... *paintings* | | | $6,050 |
| Dutch c. 1585-1657 | | | |
| ☐ **POTEAU, Philip** ................................. *paintings* | | | $352 |
| ☐ **POTEMONT,** | | | |
| **Adolphe Theodore Jules Martial** ............ *paintings* | | | $2,090 |
| French 1828-1883 | | | |
| ☐ **POTEN, Guillame Maurice** .................. *paintings* | | | $330 |
| ☐ **POTHAST, Bernard** ............................ *paintings* | | $4,125 | $17,600 |
| Dutch 1882-1966 | | | |
| ☐ **POTHIER, Armand** ............................. *paintings* | | | $385 |
| ☐ **POTOCKA, Maria** ............................... *drawings* | | | $308 |
| ☐ **POTRONAT, L.** ................................... *paintings* | | $247 | $357 |
| French 20th cent. | | | |
| ☐ **POTT, Laslett John** ............................ *paintings* | | | $880 |
| British 1837-98 | | | |
| ☐ **POTTER, Edna** ................................... *paintings* | | | $302 |
| American 20th cent. | | | |
| ☐ **POTTER, Harry Spafford** ..................... *paintings* | | $110 | $198 |
| American b. 1870 | | | |
| ☐ **POTTER, Louis McClellan** ................... *sculpture* | | $330 | $14,300 |
| American 1873-1912 | | | |
| ☐ **POTTER, Pablo** ................................... *paintings* | | | $440 |
| Dutch | | | |
| ☐ **POTTER, Paulus** ............................... *paintings* | | $12,100 | $19,800 |
| Dutch 1625-1654 | | | |
| ☐ **POTTER, Pieter Symonsz** ..................... *paintings* | | $1,870 | $3,300 |
| Dutch c. 1597 or 1600-1652 | | | |

| | | *Current Price Range* | |
|---|---|---|---|
| | | Low | High |
| □ **POTTER, William J.** ............................ *paintings* | | $253 | $1,430 |
| American 1883-1964 | | | |
| □ **POTTHAST, Edward Henry** ................ *paintings* | | $1,320 | $176,000 |
| American 1857-1927 .................................... *drawings* | | $330 | $28,600 |
| □ **POTTS, William Sherman** ...................... *paintings* | | $22 | $440 |
| American b. 1876 | | | |
| □ **POUCETTE** ........................................ *drawings* | | | $220 |
| French 20th cent. | | | |
| □ **POUGHEON, Eugene Robert** ................ *paintings* | | $715 | $715 |
| French b. 1886 | | | |
| □ **POUGNY, Jean** .................................. *paintings* | | | $2,090 |
| French 1894-1956 | | | |
| □ **POUIS, Paul** ...................................... *paintings* | | | $522 |
| □ **POUJIULES, C.** .................................. *paintings* | | | $192 |
| American 20th cent. | | | |
| □ **POULAIN, Michel Marie** ...................... *paintings* | | $55 | $330 |
| French b. 1906 | | | |
| □ **POULSON, Charles A.** ........................ *drawings* | | | $385 |
| American 19th cent. | | | |
| □ **POULSON, M.B.** ................................ *paintings* | | | $2,750 |
| American 19th cent. | | | |
| □ **POULSON, N. Wm.** ............................ *paintings* | | $440 | $550 |
| □ **POULTON, James** ................................ *paintings* | | $1,045 | $1,540 |
| British ac. 1844-1859 | | | |
| □ **POUPELET, Jane** ................................ *sculpture* | | | $825 |
| □ **POURBUS, Frans (the younger)** ............ *paintings* | | $1,100 | $20,350 |
| Flemish 1569/70-1622 | | | |
| □ **POURBUS, Pieter** .............................. *paintings* | | | $5,500 |
| Flemish 1523-1584 | | | |
| □ **POURCELLY, J.B.** .............................. *drawings* | | | $330 |
| □ **POURTAU, Leon** ................................ *paintings* | | | $1,100 |
| □ **POUSETTE-DART, Richard** ................ *paintings* | | $8,800 | $50,600 |
| American b. 1916 ...................................... *drawings* | | $825 | $2,970 |
| □ **POUSSIN, G.** .................................... *paintings* | | | $650 |
| □ **POUSSIN, Pierre Charles** .................... *drawings* | | | $187 |
| French 1819-1904 | | | |
| □ **POVEDA Y JUAN, Vicente** .................. *paintings* | | | $3,300 |
| Spanish ? b. 1857; ac. 1895 ........................ *drawings* | | | $495 |
| □ **POWELL, Arthur James Emery** .......... *paintings* | | $330 | $880 |
| American 1864-1956 | | | |
| □ **POWELL, Asa L. (Ace)** ...................... *paintings* | | $880 | $4,400 |
| American 1912-1978 .................................. *drawings* | | $99 | $880 |
| .................................................................... *sculpture* | | $220 | $3,410 |
| □ **POWELL, Charles Marin** .................... *paintings* | | $2,090 | $6,600 |
| English d. 1824 | | | |
| □ **POWELL, Dave** ................................ *drawings* | | | $715 |
| American contemporary | | | |
| □ **POWELL, Jim** .................................... *drawings* | | | $550 |
| American | | | |

| | | Current Price Range | |
|---|---|---|---|
| | | Low | High |
| ☐ **POWELL, Joseph Rubens** ............... *paintings* | | | $2,200 |
| English ac. 1833-1871 | | | |
| ☐ **POWELL, Lucien Whiting** ............... *paintings* | | $198 | $3,740 |
| American 1846-1930 ............................ *drawings* | | $150 | $3,190 |
| ☐ **POWELL, W.E.** ................................. *drawings* | | | $192 |
| American 20th cent. | | | |
| ☐ **POWER, Harold Septimus** ............... *paintings* | | | $3,800 |
| ............................................................ *drawings* | | $352 | $462 |
| ☐ **POWER, James** ................................. *paintings* | | | $220 |
| American 19th cent. | | | |
| ☐ **POWERS, Asahel L.** ........................... *paintings* | | $13,200 | $15,950 |
| American 1813-1843 | | | |
| ☐ **POWERS, Harry W.** ............................ *paintings* | | | $1,430 |
| American 19th/20th cent. | | | |
| ☐ **POWERS, Hiram** .............................. *sculpture* | | $3,080 | $264,000 |
| American 1805-1873 | | | |
| ☐ **POWERS, Marion** ............................. *paintings* | | $220 | $264 |
| ☐ **POWIS, Paul** ..................................... *paintings* | | | $1,100 |
| ☐ **POWYS, Paul** ..................................... *paintings* | | | $1,980 |
| American 19th cent. | | | |
| ☐ **POYET, L.** ......................................... *paintings* | | | $550 |
| ☐ **POYLOS, F.N.** ................................... *paintings* | | | $412 |
| Greek 20th cent. | | | |
| ☐ **POYNTER, Sir Edward John** ............... *paintings* | | $4,125 | $66,000 |
| English 1836-1919 .................................... *drawings* | | $330 | $1,650 |
| ☐ **POZAHNDA(?), O.** ............................ *drawings* | | | $770 |
| Russian(?) 20th cent. | | | |
| ☐ **POZZATTI, Rudy** ............................... *paintings* | | | $192 |
| American 20th cent. | | | |
| ☐ **POZZI, Andrea** ................................. *paintings* | | | $19,800 |
| Italian 1778-1833 | | | |
| ☐ **PRADES, Alfred Frank de** ................... *paintings* | | $1,100 | $9,350 |
| British ac. 1862-1879 ............................. *drawings* | | $660 | $1,045 |
| ☐ **PRADIER, Jean Jacques** | | | |
| **(called James)** ..................................... *sculpture* | | $715 | $1,705 |
| French 1792-1852 | | | |
| ☐ **PRADILLA, C.** ................................... *paintings* | | | $440 |
| ☐ **PRADILLA Y ORTIZ, Francisco** .......... *paintings* | | | $2,860 |
| Spanish 1848-1921 | | | |
| ☐ **PRAMPOLINI, Enrico** ........................ *paintings* | | $6,600 | $6,875 |
| ☐ **PRANISHNIKOFF, Ivan P.** ................. *paintings* | | | $2,970 |
| Russian 19th cent. | | | |
| ☐ **PRATELLA, Attilio** ............................ *paintings* | | $110 | $8,250 |
| Italian 1856-1932 | | | |
| ☐ **PRATELLA, Fausto** ............................ *paintings* | | $220 | $1,100 |
| Italian 1888-1964 | | | |
| ☐ **PRATERE, Edmond Joseph de** .............. *paintings* | | $1,320 | $3,300 |
| Belgian 1826-1888 | | | |

| | | | *Current Price Range* | |
| --- | --- | --- | --- | --- |
| | | | *Low* | *High* |
| ☐ **PRATHER, William E.** | .............. | *paintings* | $231 | $385 |
| American 19th/20th cent. | | | | |
| ☐ **PRATI, Eugenio** | ........................ | *paintings* | | $1,100 |
| ☐ **PRATT, A.M.** | ........................ | *paintings* | | $935 |
| American 19th cent. | | | | |
| ☐ **PRATT, Elmar** | ........................ | *paintings* | | $264 |
| American School | | | | |
| ☐ **PRATT, Henry Cheeves** | ................ | *paintings* | $195 | $1,320 |
| American 1803-1880 | | | | |
| ☐ **PRATT, Matthew** | ........................ | *paintings* | $1,100 | $24,200 |
| American 1734-1805 | | | | |
| ☐ **PRATT, Robert M.** | ................ | *paintings* | $825 | $18,700 |
| American 1811-1888 | | | | |
| ☐ **PRATT, William** | ........................ | *paintings* | | $275 |
| ☐ **PRAX, Valentine** | ........................ | *paintings* | | $660 |
| ☐ **PRECHTEL, Don** | ........................ | *paintings* | | $550 |
| American | | | | |
| ☐ **PREISS, Ferdinand** | ................ | *sculpture* | $352 | $25,300 |
| German 1882-1943 | | | | |
| ☐ **PRELL, Walter** | ........................ | *paintings* | | $11,000 |
| French b. 1857 | | | | |
| ☐ **PRELLER** | ........................ | *paintings* | | $660 |
| ☐ **PREMAZZI, Luigi Ossipovich** | .............. | *drawings* | | $1,650 |
| Russian 1814-1891 | | | | |
| ☐ **PRENDERGAST, Charles E.** | ................ | *drawings* | | $27,500 |
| American 1868-1948 | | | | |
| ☐ **PRENDERGAST, Maurice Brazil** | .......... | *paintings* | $8,250 | $176,000 |
| American 1859-1924 | ........................ | *drawings* | $1,045 | $286,000 |
| ☐ **PRENTICE, J.R.** | ........................ | *drawings* | | $275 |
| ☐ **PRENTICE, Levi Wells** | ................ | *paintings* | $110 | $23,100 |
| American 1851-1935 | | | | |
| ☐ **PRENTICE, Michael** | ................ | *sculpture* | | $1,760 |
| American b. 1944 | | | | |
| ☐ **PRENTICE, Tim** | ........................ | *paintings* | | $275 |
| contemporary | ........................ | *drawings* | | $176 |
| ☐ **PRENTISS, Lillian** | ........................ | *paintings* | | $350 |
| American 20th cent. | | | | |
| ☐ **PRENTZEL, Hans** | ........................ | *paintings* | | $825 |
| German b. 1880 | | | | |
| ☐ **PRESCOTT, F.R.** | ........................ | *paintings* | | $220 |
| American 19th cent. | | | | |
| ☐ **PRESCOTT, Miles B.** | ................ | *paintings* | | $302 |
| American late 19th cent. | | | | |
| ☐ **PRESCOTT-DAVIES, Norman** | .............. | *paintings* | | $2,860 |
| ☐ **PRESSER, Henri** | ........................ | *paintings* | | $500 |
| French 19th cent. | | | | |
| ☐ **PRESSER, Josef** | ........................ | *paintings* | | $220 |
| Russian/American b. 1907 | ........................ | *drawings* | $165 | $198 |

| | | Current Price Range | |
|---|---|---|---|
| | | Low | High |
| ☐ **PRESSMANE, Joseph** ........................ *paintings* | | $60 | $880 |
| French 1904-1967 | | | |
| ☐ **PRESTON, James Moore** ..................... *paintings* | | | $1,430 |
| American 1874-1962 | | | |
| ☐ **PRESTON, May Wilson** ..................... *drawings* | | | $429 |
| American 1873-1949 | | | |
| ☐ **PRESTON, W.F.** ................................. *paintings* | | | $4,000 |
| American 19th/20th cent. | | | |
| ☐ **PRESTON, William H.** ...................... *drawings* | | | $770 |
| American 20th cent. | | | |
| ☐ **PRESTOPINO, Gregorio** ................... *paintings* | | $54 | $786 |
| American b. 1907 | | | |
| ☐ **PREUDHOMME, Jerome** .................... *drawings* | | | $550 |
| French 18th cent. | | | |
| ☐ **PREVAL, Christiane de** ..................... *paintings* | | | $4,730 |
| French b. 1876 | | | |
| ☐ **PREVAL, Jules** .................................. *paintings* | | | $385 |
| French 19th cent. | | | |
| ☐ **PREVOST, A.L. de** ............................ *paintings* | | | $12,100 |
| French | | | |
| ☐ **PREVOST, Jean Louis (the younger)** ...... *paintings* | | | $8,250 |
| ☐ **PREVOT-VALERI, A.** ......................... *paintings* | | | $1,210 |
| ☐ **PREY, Juan de'** ................................ *drawings* | | | $220 |
| American | | | |
| ☐ **PREYER, Emilie** ............................... *paintings* | | | $13,200 |
| German 1849-1930 | | | |
| ☐ **PREYER, Johann Wilhelm** .................. *paintings* | | $2,200 | $15,400 |
| German 1803-1889 | | | |
| ☐ **PREZIOSI, Count Amedeo** ................. *drawings* | | | $935 |
| ☐ **PREZZI, Wilma Maria** ...................... *paintings* | | $242 | $440 |
| American 1915-1965? | | | |
| ☐ **PRICE, C.S.** ..................................... *paintings* | | | $6,600 |
| American 1874-1950 | | | |
| ☐ **PRICE, Edward** ............................... *paintings* | | | $990 |
| British ac. 1823-1876 | | | |
| ☐ **PRICE, Garrett** ............................... *drawings* | | $176 | $550 |
| American b. 1896 | | | |
| ☐ **PRICE, Gary Lee** ............................. *sculpture* | | | $1,800 |
| American | | | |
| ☐ **PRICE, James** ................................. *drawings* | | | $302 |
| British ac. 1842-1876 | | | |
| ☐ **PRICE, Kenneth** .............................. *sculpture* | | $1,870 | $19,800 |
| American b. 1935 | | | |
| ☐ **PRICE, L.A.** .................................... *paintings* | | | $632 |
| American 19th/20th cent. | | | |
| ☐ **PRICE, Mary Elizabeth** .................... *paintings* | | $253 | $770 |
| American 20th cent. | | | |
| ☐ **PRICE, Norman Mills** ...................... *paintings* | | | $550 |
| American 1877-1951 ................................. *drawings* | | $220 | $1,760 |

|                                               |        | Current Price Range |
|-----------------------------------------------|--------|---------|
|                                               | Low    | High    |
| ☐ **PRICE, V.** .............................................. *paintings* |        | **$350** |
| ☐ **PRICE, William Henry** ....................... *paintings* | **$55** | **$1,100** |
| American 1864-1940                            |        |         |
| ☐ **PRICHARD, Ambrose** ......................... *paintings* |        | **$715** |
| American 1858-1905 ................................. *drawings* |        | **$121** |
| ☐ **PRICHART, Gordon Thompson** ........... *paintings* |        | **$2,750** |
| American 20th cent.                           |        |         |
| ☐ **PRIEBE, Karl** ...................................... *paintings* |        | **$209** |
| American b. 1914 ...................................... *drawings* | **$220** | **$1,265** |
| ☐ **PRIECHENFRIED, Alois Heinrich** ........ *paintings* | **$385** | **$8,250** |
| Austrian 1867-1953                            |        |         |
| ☐ **PRIECHENFRIED, G. Kalla** ................. *paintings* |        | **$1,320** |
| German 20th cent.                             |        |         |
| ☐ **PRIEG, R.** ............................................ *paintings* |        | **$385** |
| Austrian 19th cent.                           |        |         |
| ☐ **PRIESTER-MICHAELIS, Alice** ............ *drawings* | **$495** | **$550** |
| German b. 1875                                |        |         |
| ☐ **PRIESTLEY, Philip Collingwood** .......... *paintings* | **$2,090** | **$4,400** |
| English b. 1901                               |        |         |
| ☐ **PRIESTMAN, Bertram W.** .................... *paintings* | **$110** | **$770** |
| English 1868-1951                             |        |         |
| ☐ **PRIESTMAN, I.** .................................... *sculpture* |        | **$418** |
| American 19th cent.                           |        |         |
| ☐ **PRIESTMAN, James** ............................ *sculpture* |        | **$1,650** |
| American                                      |        |         |
| ☐ **PRIESTMAN, Joseph** ........................... *sculpture* |        | **$605** |
| American                                      |        |         |
| ☐ **PRIETO, Manuel Jimenez** ..................... *paintings* | **$990** | **$4,400** |
| Spanish 19th cent.                            |        |         |
| ☐ **PRIETO, Manuel Tommaso** ................. *paintings* |        | **$9,900** |
| Spanish 19th cent.                            |        |         |
| ☐ **PRIKING, Frantz** ................................. *paintings* | **$110** | **$660** |
| German b. 1927                                |        |         |
| ☐ **PRINCE, Leonado (?) de** ...................... *paintings* |        | **$1,430** |
| French 18th/19th cent.                        |        |         |
| ☐ **PRINCE, William Meade** ...................... *paintings* | **$250** | **$1,650** |
| American 1893-1951                            |        |         |
| ☐ **PRINET, Rene Francois Xavier** ............. *paintings* |        | **$440** |
| French 1861-1946                             |        |         |
| ☐ **PRINGLE, James Fulton** ...................... *paintings* |        | **$9,900** |
| American 1788-1847                            |        |         |
| ☐ **PRINGLE, William** ............................. *paintings* | **$935** | **$7,975** |
| British ac. 1840-1858                         |        |         |
| ☐ **PRINS, Johannes Huibert** ..................... *paintings* |        | **$5,500** |
| Dutch 1757-1806                              |        |         |
| ☐ **PRINS, Pierre** ..................................... *drawings* |        | **$990** |
| ☐ **PRINSEP, Valentine Cameron** .............. *paintings* |        | **$1,320** |
| English 1836-1904                            |        |         |

| | | *Current Price Range* | |
|---|---|---|---|
| | | *Low* | *High* |
| ☐ **PRINZ, A. Emil** ..................... *paintings* | | **$440** | **$825** |
| German 19th/20th cent. | | | |
| ☐ **PRINZ, Karl Ludwig** ............ *paintings* | | **$495** | **$900** |
| Austrian 1875-1944 | | | |
| ☐ **PRIOLD** ....................... *paintings* | | | **$1,980** |
| ☐ **PRIOR, William Matthew** ............ *paintings* | | **$220** | **$41,800** |
| American 1806-1873 | | | |
| ☐ **PRIOU, Gaston** ..................... *paintings* | | | **$2,750** |
| ☐ **PRITCHARD, Ambrose S.** ............ *drawings* | | | **$264** |
| American | | | |
| ☐ **PRITCHARD, C. Thompson** ............ *paintings* | | | **$280** |
| ☐ **PRITCHARD, E. Thompson** ............ *paintings* | | | **$550** |
| ☐ **PRITCHARD, George Thompson** .......... *paintings* | | **$605** | **$935** |
| American b. 1878 | | | |
| ☐ **PRITCHARD, H.** ..................... *paintings* | | | **$521** |
| English 19th/20th cent. | | | |
| ☐ **PRITCHARD, J. Ambrose** ............ *drawings* | | | **$330** |
| American 1858-1905 | | | |
| ☐ **PRITCHETT, Edward** ............ *paintings* | | **$522** | **$7,975** |
| British ac. 1828-1864 ............ *drawings* | | **$880** | **$2,750** |
| ☐ **PRIWIKOWA, B.** ..................... *paintings* | | | **$412** |
| ☐ **PRIX, Jean Louis** ............ *paintings* | | | **$660** |
| French 20th cent. | | | |
| ☐ **PROBST, Carl** ..................... *paintings* | | **$1,210** | **$9,900** |
| Austrian 1854-1924 | | | |
| ☐ **PROBST, Joachim** ............ *paintings* | | **$110** | **$220** |
| American b. 1913 | | | |
| ☐ **PROBST, Thorwald A.** ............ *paintings* | | **$110** | **$660** |
| American 1886-1948? | | | |
| ☐ **PROCACCINI, Camillo** ............ *drawings* | | **$1,540** | **$1,650** |
| Italian 1546-1629 | | | |
| ☐ **PROCACCINI, Ercole (the younger)** ...... *paintings* | | | **$1,980** |
| Italian 1515-1595 | | | |
| ☐ **PROCACCINI, Guilio Cesare** ............ *drawings* | | | **$24,200** |
| Italian 1570-1625 | | | |
| ☐ **PROCHAZKA, Joseph** ............ *paintings* | | **$275** | **$450** |
| American 20th cent. | | | |
| ☐ **PROCOPIO, Joseph** ............ *paintings* | | **$110** | **$319** |
| American contemporary | | | |
| ☐ **PROCTER, Dod** ..................... *paintings* | | | **$1,045** |
| British 1892-1972 | | | |
| ☐ **PROCTOR, Alexander Phimister** .......... *drawings* | | **$220** | **$1,980** |
| American 1862-1950 ............ *sculpture* | | **$500** | **$175,000** |
| ☐ **PROCTOR, Burt** ..................... *paintings* | | | **$1,320** |
| ☐ **PROHASKA, Raymond** ............ *paintings* | | **$550** | **$660** |
| American b. 1901 | | | |
| ☐ **PROHASKA, Roy** ............ *paintings* | | | **$220** |
| American | | | |
| ☐ **PROHASZKA, Jozsef** ............ *paintings* | | | **$302** |

| | | Current Price Range | |
|---|---|---|---|
| | | Low | High |
| ☐ **PRONK, Cornelis** .............. *drawings* | | $192 | $220 |
| Dutch 1691-1759 | | | |
| ☐ **PROOM, Al** ....................... *paintings* | | $137 | $550 |
| American b. 1933 | | | |
| ☐ **PROOYEN, Albert Jurardus van** .......... *paintings* | | | $2,090 |
| Dutch 1834-1898 | | | |
| ☐ **PROSDOCINI, Alberto** ............... *drawings* | | $137 | $1,100 |
| Italian b. 1852 | | | |
| ☐ **PROSPERINO** ...................... *paintings* | | | $2,640 |
| Italian 19th/20th cent. | | | |
| ☐ **PROST, Maurice** ................... *sculpture* | | | $935 |
| French b. 1894 | | | |
| ☐ **PROSTEJOWSKI, A. Rud** .............. *paintings* | | | $715 |
| ☐ **PROTAIS, Alexandre** .............. *paintings* | | | $1,100 |
| French 1826-1890 | | | |
| ☐ **PROTEAU** ....................... *drawings* | | | $330 |
| ☐ **PROUHO, Paul** ................... *paintings* | | | $4,180 |
| French 1849-1931 | | | |
| ☐ **PROUST, M.** ..................... *drawings* | | | $990 |
| ☐ **PROUT, John Skinner** .............. *drawings* | | | $440 |
| British 1806-1876 | | | |
| ☐ **PROUT, Samuel** ................... *paintings* | | $45 | $2,200 |
| English 1783-1852 | | | |
| ☐ **PROVIS, Alfred** .................. *paintings* | | $1,500 | $2,200 |
| British ac. 1843-1886 | | | |
| ☐ **PROVOST, Jan** ................... *paintings* | | | $154,000 |
| Flemish 1462/65-1529 | | | |
| ☐ **PROWETT, James C.** .............. *paintings* | | | $600 |
| British 19th cent. | | | |
| ☐ **PRUCHA, Gustav** ................. *paintings* | | $495 | $4,125 |
| Austrian b. 1875 | | | |
| ☐ **PRUD'HON, Pierre Paul** ............ *paintings* | | $2,200 | $99,000 |
| French 1758-1823 ..................... *drawings* | | | $1,320 |
| ☐ **PRUETT** ....................... *paintings* | | | $396 |
| ☐ **PRUNA O'CERANS, Pedro** ......... *paintings* | | $286 | $9,350 |
| Spanish b. 1904 ..................... *drawings* | | | $302 |
| ☐ **PRUNIER, Bernard** .............. *paintings* | | | $192 |
| French 20th cent. | | | |
| ☐ **PRUNIER, Gaston** ............... *drawings* | | | $275 |
| ☐ **PRUSHECK, Harvey Gregory** .......... *paintings* | | | $308 |
| American | | | |
| ☐ **PRYCE, G. Willis** .............. *paintings* | | $210 | $450 |
| English 19th cent. | | | |
| ☐ **PSEUDO AMBROGIO DI BALDESE** .... *paintings* | | | $4,800 |
| Italian first half 14th cent. | | | |
| ☐ **PSEUDO-PIER FRANCESCO** | | | |
| **FIORENTINO** ................... *paintings* | | | $28,600 |
| Italian ac. 1470-1500 | | | |
| ☐ **PSULMAR, E.** ................... *paintings* | | | $412 |

|                                              |            | Current Price Range |          |
|----------------------------------------------|------------|--------|----------|
|                                              |            | Low    | High     |
| ☐ **PU RU** .............................................. *drawings* | | $1,210 | $4,180 |
| 1896-1963 | | | |
| ☐ **PUBLICO, R.B.** .................................... *sculpture* | | | $880 |
| ☐ **PUCCINELLI, Antonio** ......................... *paintings* | | | $2,090 |
| Italian 1822-97 | | | |
| ☐ **PUCCINI, Biagio** ............................... *paintings* | | | $1,870 |
| Italian 1675-1721 | | | |
| ☐ **PUCCIO DI SIMONE** ........................... *paintings* | | | $34,100 |
| Italian ac. 1320-1358 | | | |
| ☐ **PUDENI, P.** ...................................... *paintings* | | | $2,200 |
| ☐ **PUECH (?)** ......................................... *paintings* | | | $192 |
| French 18th cent. | | | |
| ☐ **PUGARRI** ......................................... *paintings* | | | $1,650 |
| Italian 19th cent. | | | |
| ☐ **PUGI** ................................................. *sculpture* | | $1,100 | $1,485 |
| French early 20th cent. | | | |
| ☐ **PUIGAUDEAU, Fernand de** ................. *paintings* | | $770 | $5,500 |
| French 1864 or 1866-1930 | | | |
| ☐ **PUJA, Florica** .................................... *paintings* | | | $440 |
| Yugoslavian b. 1920 | | | |
| ☐ **PUJOL DE GUASTAVINO, Clement** ..... *paintings* | | $1,540 | $36,300 |
| French 19th cent. | | | |
| ☐ **PULESTON, Dennis** ........................... *drawings* | | | $330 |
| American 20th cent. | | | |
| ☐ **PULIGO, Domenico** ........................... *paintings* | | | $6,050 |
| Italian 1492-1527 | | | |
| ☐ **PULINCKX, Louis** .............................. *paintings* | | | $4,400 |
| Belgian b. 1843 | | | |
| ☐ **PULLER, John Anthony** ....................... *paintings* | | | $2,420 |
| British 19th cent. | | | |
| ☐ **PULUSO** ............................................. *paintings* | | | $770 |
| ☐ **PUMMILL, Robert** .............................. *paintings* | | $8,000 | $50,000 |
| American contemporary ................................. *sculpture* | | | $3,750 |
| ☐ **PUPINI, Biagio (called Della Lame)** ........ *drawings* | | $1,210 | $11,000 |
| Italian ac. 1530-1540 | | | |
| ☐ **PURCHAS, Thomas J.** ........................... *paintings* | | | $770 |
| British ac. 1880-1894 | | | |
| ☐ **PURDY, Donald Ray** ........................... *paintings* | | $55 | $576 |
| American b. 1924 ....................................... *drawings* | | | $220 |
| ☐ **PURDY, Robert** .................................... *paintings* | | | $275 |
| American 20th cent. | | | |
| ☐ **PURRMANN, Hans** ............................. *paintings* | | $10,450 | $17,600 |
| German 1880-1966 | | | |
| ☐ **PURSALS** ........................................... *paintings* | | | $605 |
| Continental School 19th cent. | | | |
| ☐ **PUSHMAN, Hovsep T.** ......................... *paintings* | | $3,850 | $20,000 |
| American 1877-1966 | | | |

## Photomechanical Prints

Hovsep Pushman, an Armenian emigre to America, achieved his reputation as a painter of academic still life compositions. Early in his career he studied in Paris at the Académie Julian, and then, like many of his contemporaries, travelled to the Orient. He subsequently produced a number of still lifes of oriental subjects, including fans, screens, bowls, and porcelain.

While he spent most of his life in America, Pushman continued to exhibit occasionally at the Paris Salon. Toward the end of his career, he supervised the production of limited editions of photomechanical prints of his paintings which he signed. These works frequently appear at auction where they are sold for a fraction of the price of an oil, providing an affordable alternative for a collector. (Hovsep Pushman, "The Young Prince," oil on canvas, 6³/₁₆ × 7⅛ in., Hanzel, November 14, 1982, $20,000.)

| | | Current Price Range | |
|---|---|---|---|
| | | *Low* | *High* |
| ☐ **PUTEANI,** | | | |
| **Emil Maximilian Joseph von** ............... *paintings* | | | **$467** |
| German 1805-1856 | | | |
| ☐ **PUTHUFF, Hanson Duvall** ................... *paintings* | | **$308** | **$4,675** |
| American 1875-1972 ................................. *drawings* | | | **$357** |
| ☐ **PUTMAN, Donald** .............................. *paintings* | | **$2,750** | **$3,500** |
| American b. 1927 ..................................... *drawings* | | **$2,100** | **$4,100** |
| ☐ **PUTNAM, Arthur** ............................. *paintings* | | | **$220** |
| American 1873-1930 ................................. *sculpture* | | **$825** | **$1,100** |
| ☐ **PUTTNER, J.C.B.** ............................. *paintings* | | | **$990** |
| ☐ **PUTTNER, M.** ................................... *paintings* | | | **$3,080** |
| ☐ **PUTZEYS, G.** .................................... *paintings* | | | **$3,630** |
| Belgian 19th cent. | | | |
| ☐ **PUVIS DE CHAVANNES, Pierre** ......... *paintings* | | **$550** | **$38,500** |
| French 1824-1898 .................................... *drawings* | | **$55** | **$2,200** |
| ☐ **PUY, Jean** ....................................... *paintings* | | **$1,430** | **$19,800** |
| French b. 1876 | | | |
| ☐ **PYLE, Howard** ................................. *paintings* | | **$3,850** | **$14,300** |
| American 1853-1911 ................................. *drawings* | | **$1,760** | **$7,700** |

| | | Current Price Range | |
|---|---|---|---|
| | | Low | High |
| □ **PYNACKER, Adam** ............... *paintings* | | | $3,080 |
| Dutch 1622-1673 | | | |
| □ **PYNAS, Jacob** ............... *paintings* | | | $4,400 |
| Dutch 1585-1648 | | | |
| □ **PYNAS, Jan** ............... *paintings* | | $3,300 | $5,060 |
| Dutch 1583/84-1631 | | | |
| □ **PYNE, George** ............... *drawings* | | | $1,100 |
| British 1800-1884 | | | |
| □ **PYNE, J.B.** ............... *paintings* | | | $1,100 |
| □ **PYNE, James Baker** ............... *paintings* | | $412 | $880 |
| British 1800-1870 ............... *drawings* | | $1,100 | $1,320 |
| □ **PYNE, Thomas** ............... *drawings* | | $137 | $550 |
| English 1843-1935 | | | |
| □ **PYNSON** ............... *paintings* | | | $935 |
| British 19th cent. | | | |
| □ **QUA, Sun** ............... *paintings* | | | $5,000 |
| Chinese 19th cent. | | | |
| □ **QUADAL, Martin Ferdinand** ............... *paintings* | | | $1,980 |
| □ **QUADRAS, Vidal** ............... *paintings* | | | $467 |
| American 20th cent. | | | |
| □ **QUAEDVLIEG,** | | | |
| **Carel Max Gerlach Anton** ............... *paintings* | | | $12,100 |
| Dutch 1823-1874 | | | |
| □ **QUAGLIO, Franz** ............... *paintings* | | $1,210 | $12,100 |
| German 1844-1920 | | | |
| □ **QUANTIN, Henri** ............... *paintings* | | | $418 |
| □ **QUARTER, A.** ............... *paintings* | | | $825 |
| □ **QUARTLEY, Arthur** ............... *paintings* | | $137 | $3,850 |
| American 1839-1886 ............... *drawings* | | $246 | $1,200 |
| □ **QUAST, Pieter Jansz** ............... *paintings* | | $2,970 | $3,300 |
| Dutch 1605/06-1647 ............... *drawings* | | | $770 |
| □ **QUELLINUS, Jan Erasmus** ............... *drawings* | | | $495 |
| Flemish 1634-1715 | | | |
| □ **QUENARD, Armand** ............... *sculpture* | | | $1,430 |
| French b. 1865 | | | |
| □ **QUERCI, Dario** ............... *paintings* | | $440 | $880 |
| Italian b. 1831 | | | |
| □ **QUERENA, Luigi** ............... *paintings* | | | $1,430 |
| Italian 1860-1890 | | | |
| □ **QUERFURT, August** ............... *paintings* | | | $6,875 |
| German 1696-1761 | | | |
| □ **QUESNE, Fernand le** ............... *paintings* | | $1,100 | $8,800 |
| French 19th cent. | | | |
| □ **QUESNEO, A.** ............... *paintings* | | | $850 |
| □ **QUESNET,** | | | |
| **Jean-Baptiste Balthazar Eugene** ............... *paintings* | | | $1,045 |
| □ **QUESTA, Francesco della** ............... *paintings* | | | $7,700 |
| Italian 1652-1723 | | | |

| | Current Price Range | |
|---|---|---|
| | Low | High |
| ☐ **QUIGG, J.** ............................ *paintings* <br> c. 1870 | | $22,000 |
| ☐ **QUIGLEY, W.** ......................... *paintings* | | $825 |
| ☐ **QUIGNON, Fernand Just** ............ *paintings* <br> French b. 1854 | | $1,100 |
| ☐ **QUIJADA, Robert** .................... *drawings* <br> contemporary | | $1,760 |
| ☐ **QUINCY, Edmund** ................... *paintings* <br> American b. 1903 | $302 | $990 |
| ☐ **QUINLAN, Will J.** .................. *paintings* <br> American 1877-after 1934 | $60 | $550 |
| ☐ **QUINN, Edmond T.** ................ *paintings* <br> American 20th cent. | $660 | $825 |
| ☐ **QUINONES, Jose Luis** ............. *paintings* <br> contemporary | | $4,180 |
| ☐ **QUINQUELA MARTIN, Benito** ........ *paintings* <br> Argentinian 1870-1977 | $4,400 | $25,300 |
| ☐ **QUINTANILLA, Luis** ............... *paintings* <br> Spanish 20th cent. ..................... *drawings* | | $275 <br> $198 |
| ☐ **QUIREGA** ........................... *paintings* | | $275 |
| ☐ **QUIROS, Antonio** ................. *paintings* | | $330 |
| ☐ **QUIROS, Cesareo Bernaldo de** ......... *paintings* <br> Argentinian 1881-1968 | | $1,650 |
| ☐ **QUIRT, Walter W.** .................. *paintings* <br> American 1902-1968 | $495 | $1,320 |
| ☐ **QUISPEL, Matthys** ................ *paintings* <br> Dutch 1805-1858 | $1,100 | $1,320 |
| ☐ **QUITTON, Edouard** ............... *paintings* <br> Belgian b. 1842 | $1,000 | $2,090 |
| ☐ **QUIZET, Alphonse Leon** ............ *paintings* <br> French 1885-1955 ..................... *drawings* | $220 | $2,200 <br> $1,650 |
| ☐ **QUZAIRMOFF** ...................... *drawings* <br> French 19th cent. | $2,475 | $2,475 |
| ☐ **RAADSIG, Peter** ................... *paintings* <br> Danish 1806-1882 | | $1,650 |
| ☐ **RAANAN, Yoram** ................. *paintings* <br> 20th cent. | | $770 |
| ☐ **RAAPHORST, Cornelis** ............ *paintings* <br> Dutch 1875-1974 | $1,760 | $2,860 |
| ☐ **RABE, Edmund Friedrich Theodor** ....... *paintings* <br> German 1815-1902 | | $4,950 |
| ☐ **RABE, J.** ........................... *paintings* | | $495 |
| ☐ **RABINE, Oscar** .................... *paintings* <br> Russian 20th cent. | | $275 |
| ☐ **RABKIN, Leo** ...................... *paintings* | | $330 |
| ☐ **RABL, S.S.** ........................ *paintings* <br> 20th cent. | | $440 |
| ☐ **RABORG, Benjamin** ............... *paintings* <br> American 1871-1918 | | $220 |

|                                      |            | Current Price Range |           |
|--------------------------------------|------------|---------------------|-----------|
|                                      |            | Low                 | High      |
| ☐ **RACHEN, Henry** .................... | *paintings* |                    | $412      |
| ☐ **RACHMIEL, Jean** ................... | *paintings* |                    | $880      |
| American 19th/20th cent.             |            |                     |           |
| ☐ **RACK, K.** ......................... | *paintings* |                    | $352      |
| ☐ **RACKHAM, Arthur** ................. | *paintings* |                    | $13,200   |
| English 1867-1939 ..................... | *drawings* | $302                | $30,800   |
| ☐ **RACKOW, Leo** .................... | *drawings* |                    | $1,100    |
| American b. 1901                     |            |                     |           |
| ☐ **RACKWITZ, Piet** .................. | *paintings* |                    | $300      |
| Dutch 19th cent.                     |            |                     |           |
| ☐ **RADFORD, Edward** .............. | *drawings* |                    | $275      |
| British 1831-1920                    |            |                     |           |
| ☐ **RADITTI (?), A.** .................. | *paintings* |                    | $330      |
| Italian 19th/20th cent.              |            |                     |           |
| ☐ **RADITZ, Lazar** ................... | *paintings* | $99                | $577      |
| Russian/American b. 1887             |            |                     |           |
| ☐ **RADZIEJOWSKI, Stanislaw** ....... | *paintings* |                    | $650      |
| Polish 19th cent.                    |            |                     |           |
| ☐ **RAE, John** ....................... | *drawings* |                    | $440      |
| American 1882-1963                   |            |                     |           |
| ☐ **RAEBURN, Sir Henry** .......... | *paintings* | $1,210             | $148,500  |
| Scottish 1756-1823                   |            |                     |           |
| ☐ **RAEMAEKERS, Louis** ........... | *paintings* |                    | $1,980    |
| Dutch 1869-1956                      |            |                     |           |
| ☐ **RAFAEL, B.** ...................... | *paintings* | $77                | $605      |
| ☐ **RAFAELLI, F.** .................... | *drawings* |                    | $180      |
| French early 20th cent.              |            |                     |           |
| ☐ **RAFFAEL, Joseph** ............... | *paintings* | $1,320             | $29,700   |
| American b. 1933 ..................... | *drawings* | $330                | $7,975    |
| ☐ **RAFFAELLI, Jean Francois** ....... | *paintings* | $850               | $38,500   |
| French 1850-1924 ..................... | *drawings* | $1,100              | $3,300    |
| ☐ **RAFFAELO, M.** .................. | *paintings* |                    | $440      |
| 19th cent.                           |            |                     |           |
| ☐ **RAFFET, Auguste** ............... | *drawings* |                    | $1,100    |
| French 1804-1860                     |            |                     |           |
| ☐ **RAFFY LE PERSAN** ............. | *paintings* |                    | $330      |
| French b. 1919                       |            |                     |           |
| ☐ **RAGAN, Leslie** .................. | *drawings* |                    | $990      |
| American b. 1897                     |            |                     |           |
| ☐ **RAGGI, G.** ....................... | *drawings* |                    | $1,430    |
| Italian 19th cent.                   |            |                     |           |
| ☐ **RAGONEAU** ...................... | *sculpture* |                   | $1,320    |
| ☐ **RAHN, A. D.** ..................... | *paintings* |                   | $247      |
| American 19th/20th cent.             |            |                     |           |
| ☐ **RAIMONDI, R.** .................. | *drawings* |                    | $1,100    |
| Italian 19th cent.                   |            |                     |           |
| ☐ **RAIN, Charles Wheedon** ......... | *paintings* | $137               | $550      |
| American b. 1911                     |            |                     |           |

| | | *Current Price Range* | |
|---|---|---|---|
| | | Low | High |
| ☐ **RAINBIRD, Walter Nobel** ............... *drawings* | | | $220 |
| French 19th/20th cent. | | | |
| ☐ **RAINE, Thomas Surtees** ............. *paintings* | | | $990 |
| British 19th cent. | | | |
| ☐ **RAINER, Johann Joseph** ............. *paintings* | | | $7,700 |
| Austrian 19th cent. | | | |
| ☐ **RAJON, P.** .................................. *drawings* | | | $412 |
| ☐ **RALEIGH, Charles Sidney** ......... *paintings* | | $4,750 | $10,450 |
| American 1831-1925 | | | |
| ☐ **RALEIGH, Henry Patrick** ........... *paintings* | | | $357 |
| American 1880-1945 ......................... *drawings* | | $99 | $1,430 |
| ☐ **RALL, Wilfrid** ............................. *drawings* | | | $187 |
| English (?) 19th/20th cent. | | | |
| ☐ **RALLI, Theodore** ....................... *paintings* | | | $825 |
| Italian 1852-1909 | | | |
| ☐ **RAME, Achille Alexis** ................ *paintings* | | $440 | $1,650 |
| French 19th cent. | | | |
| ☐ **RAMENGHI, Bartolomeo** | | | |
| **(IL BAGNACAVALLO)** ............... *paintings* | | | $3,080 |
| ☐ **RAMENGHI, Giovanni Battista** | | | |
| **(the younger)** ............................... *paintings* | | | $7,700 |
| ☐ **RAMIREZ, Dan** ........................... *drawings* | | | $440 |
| ☐ **RAMIREZ, Saturnino** .................. *paintings* | | | $4,125 |
| Colombian b. 1946 ........................... *drawings* | | $550 | $2,750 |
| ☐ **RAMIREZ IBANEZ, Manuel** ....... *paintings* | | | $2,750 |
| Spanish 1856-1925 | | | |
| ☐ **RAMM, J.M.** ................................ *paintings* | | | $275 |
| American 20th cent. | | | |
| ☐ **RAMME, H.** ................................ *paintings* | | | $385 |
| American early 20th cent. | | | |
| ☐ **RAMON, Jose** ............................. *paintings* | | | $466 |
| ☐ **RAMOS, Domingo** ....................... *paintings* | | | $17,600 |
| Cuban | | | |
| ☐ **RAMOS, Garcin J.** ...................... *paintings* | | | $600 |
| Spanish 19th cent. | | | |
| ☐ **RAMOS, Mel** .............................. *paintings* | | $2,090 | $18,700 |
| American b. 1935 ............................. *drawings* | | | $770 |
| ☐ **RAMOS CATALAN, B.** ................ *paintings* | | $660 | $1,100 |
| Chilean 20th cent. | | | |
| ☐ **RAMOS PRIDA, Fernando** .......... *paintings* | | $660 | $2,530 |
| Mexican b. 1937 | | | |
| ☐ **RAMOS-MARTINEZ, Alfredo** ...... *paintings* | | $11,000 | $31,900 |
| ................................................ *drawings* | | | $1,650 |
| ☐ **RAMPOLLO, J.** ........................... *paintings* | | | $825 |
| Italian 19th cent. | | | |
| ☐ **RAMSAY, Allan** .......................... *paintings* | | $495 | $8,250 |
| English 1713-1784 | | | |
| ☐ **RAMSAY, Milne** ......................... *paintings* | | $770 | $23,100 |
| American 1847-1915 ......................... *drawings* | | $220 | $1,045 |

|  | | Current Price Range | |
|---|---|---|---|
|  | | Low | High |
| ☐ **RAMSDELL, Fred Winthrop** ............... *paintings* | | **$110** | **$467** |
| American 1865-1915 | | | |
| ☐ **RAMSEY, C.** ..................................... *paintings* | | **$165** | **$275** |
| English 19th cent. | | | |
| ☐ **RAMUS, A.** ....................................... *drawings* | | **$300** | **$357** |
| British 19th/20th cent. | | | |
| ☐ **RANCOULET, Ernest** ......................... *sculpture* | | | **$850** |
| French ac. c. 1870-1915 | | | |
| ☐ **RAND, Henry Asbury** .......................... *paintings* | | | **$1,320** |
| American b. 1886 | | | |
| ☐ **RANDALL, George** ............................ *drawings* | | **$88** | **$247** |
| 20th cent. | | | |
| ☐ **RANDANINI, Carlo** ............................ *drawings* | | | **$1,540** |
| Italian ac. 1881, d. 1884 | | | |
| ☐ **RANDOLPH, John T.** .......................... *paintings* | | **$357** | **$660** |
| American 19th/20th cent. | | | |
| ☐ **RANDOLPH, Lee P.** ............................ *paintings* | | | **$605** |
| b. 1880 | | | |
| ☐ **RANGER, Henry Ward** ........................ *paintings* | | **$192** | **$19,800** |
| American 1858-1916 ................................... *drawings* | | **$246** | **$5,775** |
| ☐ **RANGIUS** ......................................... *paintings* | | | **$2,500** |
| ☐ **RANKEN, William Bruce Ellis** .............. *paintings* | | | **$660** |
| British 1881-1941 ...................................... *drawings* | | | **$1,100** |
| ☐ **RANN, Vollian Burr** ............................ *paintings* | | | **$880** |
| American 1897-1956 | | | |
| ☐ **RANNEY, William Tylee** ....................... *paintings* | | **$192,500** | **$748,000** |
| American 1813-1857 ................................... *drawings* | | | **$3,850** |
| ☐ **RANSOM, Alexander** .......................... *paintings* | | | **$2,640** |
| American ac. 1840s-1865 | | | |
| ☐ **RANSON, Caroline L. Ormes** .............. *paintings* | | | **$605** |
| American 1838-1910 | | | |
| ☐ **RANSON, Paul** ..................................... *paintings* | | | **$990** |
| French 1864-1909 | | | |
| ☐ **RANZONI, Gustav** ............................. *paintings* | | **$1,650** | **$1,760** |
| Austrian 1826-1900 | | | |
| ☐ **RANZONI, Hans** ................................. *paintings* | | | **$352** |
| ☐ **RAOUX, Jean** ..................................... *paintings* | | **$12,000** | **$12,100** |
| French 1677-1734 | | | |
| ☐ **RAPHAEL, Joseph** ............................. *paintings* | | **$1,650** | **$19,800** |
| American 1872-1950 ................................... *drawings* | | **$302** | **$880** |
| ☐ **RAPHAEL, Mary F.** ............................ *paintings* | | | **$5,225** |
| English 19th cent. | | | |
| ☐ **RAPHAELY, Svi** ................................. *paintings* | | **$660** | **$1,760** |
| ☐ **RAPHANEL** ....................................... *sculpture* | | | **$770** |
| French late 19th cent. | | | |
| ☐ **RAPISARDI, Michele** .......................... *paintings* | | | **$2,750** |
| Italian 1822-1886 | | | |
| ☐ **RAPKE** ............................................... *drawings* | | **$220** | **$605** |

| | | Current Price Range | |
|---|---|---|---|
| | | *Low* | *High* |
| ☐ **RAPP, J.** ............ *paintings* <br> 19th/20th cent. | | | $715 |
| ☐ **RASCH, Heinrich** ............ *paintings* <br> German 1840-1913 | | $198 | $2,860 |
| ☐ **RASCHEN, Henry** ............ *paintings* <br> American 1856/57-1937/38 | | $880 | $55,000 |
| ☐ **RASER, J. Heyl** ............ *paintings* <br> American 19th cent. | | $330 | $550 |
| ☐ **RASKIN, Joseph** ............ *paintings* | | | $250 |
| ☐ **RASKIN, Saul** ............ *paintings* | | | $750 |
| ............ *drawings* | | $350 | $1,000 |
| ☐ **RASKO, M.A.** ............ *paintings* <br> American 20th cent. | | | $275 |
| ☐ **RASMUSSEN, Georg Anton** ............ *paintings* <br> Norwegian 1842-1914 | | $1,980 | $5,225 |
| ☐ **RASMUSSEN, John** ............ *paintings* <br> American 1828-1895 | | | $41,800 |
| ☐ **RATHBONE, John** ............ *paintings* <br> English 1750-1807 | | $352 | $3,300 |
| ☐ **RATTNER, Abraham** ............ *paintings* <br> American 1895-1978 ............ *drawings* | | $165 <br> $275 | $13,200 <br> $605 |
| ☐ **RAU, Emil Karl** ............ *paintings* <br> German b. 1858 | | $3,300 | $10,450 |
| ☐ **RAU, William** ............ *paintings* <br> American b. 1874 ............ *drawings* | | $550 | $1,430 <br> $66 |
| ☐ **RAU, Woldemar Heinrich** ............ *paintings* <br> German ac. 1827-1889 | | | $330 |
| ☐ **RAUCH, Christian Daniel** ............ *sculpture* <br> German 1777-1857 | | | $18,150 |
| ☐ **RAUDNITZ, Alert** ............ *paintings* | | | $4,180 |
| ☐ **RAUMANN** ............ *paintings* | | | $462 |
| ☐ **RAUPP, Carl** ............ *paintings* <br> German 1837-1918 | | | $13,200 |
| ☐ **RAUSCHENBERG, Robert** ............ *paintings* <br> American b. 1925 ............ *drawings* <br> ............ *sculpture* | | $17,050 <br> $1,870 | $462,000 <br> $35,200 <br> $4,400 |
| ☐ **RAUSCHNABEL, William F.** ............ *paintings* <br> American 20th cent. | | $440 | $825 |
| ☐ **RAUX, Marchand des** ............ *paintings* | | $55 | $385 |
| ☐ **RAVEN, Samuel** ............ *paintings* <br> English | | $1,650 | $1,980 |
| ☐ **RAVENSCROFT, F.W.** ............ *paintings* <br> American 19th cent. | | | $412 |
| ☐ **RAVENSTEIN, Paul van** ............ *paintings* | | | $825 |
| ☐ **RAVENSTEYN, Nicholas van** ............ *paintings* | | | $440 |
| ☐ **RAVENSWAY, A. V. von** ............ *paintings* | | | $2,420 |
| ☐ **RAVENZWAAY,** <br> **Hendrikje Adriana van** ............ *drawings* <br> Dutch 1816-1872 | | | $660 |

| | Current Price Range | |
|---|---|---|
| | *Low* | *High* |
| ☐ **RAVESTEYN, Hubert van** .................... *paintings* | **$990** | **$165,000** |
| Dutch d. 1670 | | |
| ☐ **RAVESTEYN, Jan Anthonisz van** ......... *paintings* | **$3,410** | **$10,450** |
| Dutch c. 1570-1657 | | |
| ☐ **RAVET, V.** ......................................... *paintings* | | **$1,100** |
| French 19th cent. | | |
| ☐ **RAWSON, Albert Leighton** ................... *paintings* | | **$2,750** |
| American 1829-1902 | | |
| ☐ **RAWSON, Carl W.** ............................ *paintings* | **$275** | **$715** |
| American 1884-1970 | | |
| ☐ **RAY, A.** ............................................. *paintings* | | **$192** |
| French 19th cent. | | |
| ☐ **RAY, Man** ....................................... *paintings* | **$880** | **$319,000** |
| American 1890-1976 ................................ *drawings* | **$825** | **$57,750** |
| ............................................................. *sculpture* | **$185** | **$9,900** |
| ☐ **RAY, Ruth** ....................................... *paintings* | | **$220** |
| American 20th cent. | | |
| ☐ **RAYBET, F.** ...................................... *paintings* | | **$715** |
| ☐ **RAYMAL-AMOUROUX, Blanche** ......... *paintings* | | **$605** |
| French 19th cent. | | |
| ☐ **RAYMOND, H.** ................................... *paintings* | | **$1,045** |
| ☐ **RAYNAL** ........................................... *paintings* | | **$275** |
| ☐ **RAYNAUD, Auguste** ........................... *paintings* | **$2,750** | **$4,400** |
| French 19th cent. | | |
| ☐ **RAYNAUD, R.A.** ............................... *paintings* | **$250** | |
| French 20th cent. | | |
| ☐ **RAYNER, Louise J.** ........................... *drawings* | **$880** | **$5,500** |
| English 1829-1924 | | |
| ☐ **RAYO, Omar** ..................................... *paintings* | **$880** | **$2,750** |
| South American 20th cent. ........................... *drawings* | **$605** | **$880** |
| ☐ **RAZZIER, G.** ..................................... *paintings* | **$247** | **$522** |
| French 19th cent. | | |
| ☐ **RE, Vincenzo dal** ............................... *drawings* | | **$1,430** |
| Italian d. 1762 | | |
| ☐ **REA, Louis E.** ................................... *paintings* | **$275** | **$1,430** |
| American b. 1868 | | |
| ☐ **READ, B.** ......................................... *paintings* | | **$1,045** |
| 19th cent. | | |
| ☐ **READ, Samuel** ................................... *drawings* | **$352** | |
| ☐ **READ, Thomas Buchanan** ................... *paintings* | **$577** | **$3,520** |
| American 1822-1878 | | |
| ☐ **REALFONSO, Tommaso** | | |
| **(called Masillo)** .................................... *paintings* | | **$4,000** |
| Italian 1st half 18th cent. | | |
| ☐ **REAM, Carducius Plantagenet** ............. *paintings* | **$550** | **$5,280** |
| American 1837-1917 | | |
| ☐ **REAM, Morston Constantine** ................ *paintings* | **$605** | **$9,350** |
| American 1840-1898 | | |
| ☐ **REARSON, James** ............................... *paintings* | | **$440** |

| | | | Current Price Range | |
|---|---|---|---|---|
| | | | Low | High |
| ☐ REASER, Wilbur Aaron | ..................... | *drawings* | $165 | $550 |
| American b. 1860 | | | | |
| ☐ REATTU, Jacques | ............................. | *paintings* | | $4,620 |
| French 1760-1833 | | | | |
| ☐ REBELL, Joseph | ............................. | *paintings* | $7,150 | $18,700 |
| Austrian 1787-1828 | .................................. | *drawings* | | $990 |
| ☐ REBOLLAR, S. | .................................. | *paintings* | | $770 |
| ☐ REBULL, Santiago | ............................. | *paintings* | | $82,500 |
| Mexican 1829-1902 | | | | |
| ☐ RECCO, Giuseppe | ............................. | *paintings* | | $8,250 |
| Italian 1634-1695 | | | | |
| ☐ RECCO, Nicola | ............................. | *paintings* | | $2,750 |
| Italian 18th cent. | | | | |
| ☐ RECKHARD, Gardner Arnold | .............. | *paintings* | $412 | $660 |
| American 1858-1908 | | | | |
| ☐ RECKNAGEL, John | ........................ | *drawings* | $660 | $880 |
| German 19th/20th cent. | | | | |
| ☐ RECKNAGEL, Theodore | ...................... | *paintings* | | $550 |
| ☐ RECKNAGL, Thomas | .......................... | *paintings* | | $396 |
| ☐ REDBIRD, Robert | ............................. | *drawings* | | $286 |
| American (Kiowa) | | | | |
| ☐ REDCORN, Jimmy | ............................. | *paintings* | | $825 |
| American (Osage) | | | | |
| ☐ REDELIUS, F.H. | ............................. | *paintings* | $522 | $935 |
| American 20th cent. | | | | |
| ☐ REDER, Bernard | ................................ | *sculpture* | | $1,300 |
| Rumanian/American 1897-1963 | | | | |
| ☐ REDER, Heinrich Richard | ................... | *paintings* | $605 | $880 |
| German 1862-1942 | | | | |
| ☐ REDFERN, Helen L. | .......................... | *paintings* | | $264 |
| American | | | | |
| ☐ REDFIELD, Edward Willis | ................. | *paintings* | $968 | $52,800 |
| American 1869-1965 | .................................. | *drawings* | $99 | $412 |
| ☐ REDGRAVE, Alice | ............................. | *paintings* | | $462 |
| ☐ REDGRAVE, Richard | .......................... | *paintings* | | $1,320 |
| English 1804-1888 | | | | |
| ☐ REDICK, C.E.D. | ............................. | *paintings* | | $440 |
| ☐ REDMAN, B. | ....................................... | *paintings* | | $2,310 |
| American 19th/20th cent. | | | | |
| ☐ REDMOND, Granville | ...................... | *paintings* | $330 | $4,125 |
| American 1871-1935 | .................................. | *drawings* | | $467 |
| ☐ REDMORE, E.K. | ............................. | *paintings* | | $825 |
| English c. 1860-1939 | | | | |
| ☐ REDMORE, Henry | ............................. | *paintings* | $1,760 | $3,080 |
| English 1820-1887 | | | | |
| ☐ REDON, Odilon | ................................. | *paintings* | $27,500 | $462,000 |
| French 1840-1916 | ....................................... | *drawings* | $250 | $330,000 |
| ☐ REDOUTE, Pierre Joseph | .................... | *drawings* | $5,060 | $18,400 |
| French 1759-1840 | | | | |

| | | Current Price Range | |
|---|---|---|---|
| | | Low | High |
| ☐ **REDWOOD, Allen C.** ............... *drawings* | | $825 | $1,760 |
| American 1844-1922 | | | |
| ☐ **REE, Anita** ............... *paintings* | | | $1,870 |
| German 1885-1933 ............... *drawings* | | | $770 |
| ☐ **REECE, Maynard** ............... *paintings* | | | $15,000 |
| American b. 1920 | | | |
| ☐ **REED, Billie Lucille** ............... *paintings* | | $77 | $220 |
| American 20th cent. | | | |
| ☐ **REED, Ethel** ............... *drawings* | | | $660 |
| ☐ **REED, Fred** ............... *paintings* | | | $825 |
| ☐ **REED, Marjorie** ............... *paintings* | | $165 | $330 |
| American b. 1915 | | | |
| ☐ **REED, R.H.** ............... *paintings* | | | $550 |
| English 19th cent. | | | |
| ☐ **REEDY, Leonard Howard** ............... *paintings* | | $650 | $2,200 |
| American 1899-1956 ............... *drawings* | | $137 | $880 |
| ☐ **REEKERS, Hendrik** ............... *paintings* | | | $14,300 |
| Dutch 1815-1854 | | | |
| ☐ **REES, M.** ............... *paintings* | | | $1,870 |
| ☐ **REESBROECK, Jacob van** ............... *paintings* | | $1,100 | $2,200 |
| ☐ **REESE, Bernard (Jr.)** ............... *paintings* | | | $605 |
| ☐ **REEVE** ............... *paintings* | | | $880 |
| ☐ **REEVES, Richard Stones** ............... *paintings* | | | $9,350 |
| ☐ **REEVES, Walter** ............... *paintings* | | | $176 |
| British 19th cent. | | | |
| ☐ **REGGIANINI, Vittorio** ............... *paintings* | | $1,650 | $20,900 |
| Italian b. 1858 | | | |
| ☐ **REGNAULT,** | | | |
| **Henri Alexandre Georges** ............... *paintings* | | $1,760 | $4,950 |
| French 1843-1871 ............... *drawings* | | | $330 |
| ☐ **REGNAULT, Jean Baptiste** ............... *paintings* | | $2,200 | $2,200 |
| French | | | |
| ☐ **REGNIER** ............... *paintings* | | | $660 |
| French 18th/19th cent. | | | |
| ☐ **REGTERS, Tiebout** ............... *paintings* | | | $11,000 |
| Dutch 1710-1768 | | | |
| ☐ **REGULESCO** ............... *drawings* | | | $466 |
| ☐ **REHDER, Julius Christian** ............... *paintings* | | | $1,870 |
| German b. 1861 | | | |
| ☐ **REHN, Frank Knox Morton** ............... *paintings* | | $50 | $4,950 |
| American 1848-1914 ............... *drawings* | | $110 | $1,100 |
| ☐ **REHS, Theodore** ............... *paintings* | | | $880 |
| Belgian 19th cent. | | | |
| ☐ **REICH, Albert** ............... *paintings* | | | $6,875 |
| German b. 1881 | | | |
| ☐ **REICH-STAFFILSTEIN, A.** ............... *paintings* | | | $467 |
| European 19th cent. | | | |
| ☐ **REICHARDT, T.** ............... *paintings* | | | $2,310 |
| American 19th cent. | | | |

| | Current Price Range | |
|---|---|---|
| | Low | High |
| ☐ **REICHERD, A.** ..................................... *paintings* | | $385 |
| European 19th/20th cent. | | |
| ☐ **REICHERT, Karl** ................................ *paintings* | $935 | $4,180 |
| Austrian 1836-1918 | | |
| ☐ **REICHHARDT, Franz Heinrich** ............ *paintings* | | $400 |
| Austrian 19th cent. | | |
| ☐ **REICHMANN, Josephine Lemos** ........... *paintings* | $110 | $192 |
| American 1864-1939 | | |
| ☐ **REID, Flora MacDonald** ........................ *paintings* | | $1,760 |
| English 19th/20th cent. | | |
| ☐ **REID, George** ..................................... *paintings* | | $522 |
| Scottish 1841-1913 | | |
| ☐ **REID, George Ogilvy** ........................... *paintings* | | $1,650 |
| British 1851-1928 | | |
| ☐ **REID, Jean Arnot** ................................ *paintings* | | $330 |
| ☐ **REID, John Robertson** ......................... *paintings* | $495 | $990 |
| Scottish 1851-1926 | | |
| ☐ **REID, John T.** ..................................... *paintings* | | $770 |
| American 19th cent. | | |
| ☐ **REID, Robert** ...................................... *paintings* | $1,045 | $115,500 |
| American 1862-1929 .................................... *drawings* | $55 | $35,200 |
| ☐ **REID, Robert Payton** ......................... *paintings* | $660 | $660 |
| British b. 1859 | | |
| ☐ **REIFFEL, Charles** ............................... *paintings* | $1,650 | $2,640 |
| American 1862-1942 .................................... *drawings* | | $385 |
| ☐ **REIGEAULT** ...................................... *sculpture* | | $550 |
| ☐ **REIGER, Shay** .................................... *sculpture* | | $357 |
| ☐ **REIGNIER, Jean Marie** ....................... *paintings* | | $7,975 |
| French 1815-86 | | |
| ☐ **REINAGLE, Philip** .............................. *paintings* | $990 | $115,500 |
| English 1749-1833 | | |
| ☐ **REINAGLE, Ramsay Richard** ............... *paintings* | $660 | $22,000 |
| English 1775-1862 ...................................... *drawings* | | $1,100 |
| ☐ **REINDEL, William George** ................... *paintings* | | $247 |
| American 1871-1948 .................................... *drawings* | $60 | $71 |
| ☐ **REINER** ............................................ *paintings* | | $495 |
| ☐ **REINFUSS** ......................................... *paintings* | | $467 |
| German (?) 19th cent. | | |
| ☐ **REINHARDT, Ad** ............................... *paintings* | $3,960 | $143,000 |
| American 1913-1967 .................................... *drawings* | $2,310 | $14,300 |
| ☐ **REINHARDT, J.** ................................. *paintings* | | $308 |
| ☐ **REINHARDT, Ludwig** ......................... *paintings* | $1,210 | $495 |
| German d. 1870 | | |
| ☐ **REINHARDT, Siegfried** ........................ *paintings* | $797 | $3,850 |
| American 1925-1984 .................................... *drawings* | | $467 |
| ☐ **REINHART, Benjamin Franklin** ........... *paintings* | $7,150 | $14,300 |
| American 1829-1885 | | |
| ☐ **REINHART, Charles Stanley** ................ *paintings* | $220 | $467 |
| American 1844-1896 | | |

| | Current Price Range | |
|---|---|---|
| | *Low* | *High* |
| ☐ **REINHART, Steuart** ............... *paintings* | | $550 |
| American 20th cent. | | |
| ☐ **REINHERT, F.** ..................... *paintings* | | $522 |
| German 19th cent. | | |
| ☐ **REINICKE, Rene** ............... *paintings* | | $3,520 |
| .................................. *drawings* | | $440 |
| ☐ **REINIKE, Charles** ............... *drawings* | $247 | $330 |
| American b. 1907 | | |
| ☐ **REINIKE, Vera A.** ............... *drawings* | | $242 |
| American 20th cent. | | |
| ☐ **REINMANN, Paul** ............... *paintings* | $110 | $440 |
| ☐ **REISENBERG, Sidney** ............ *paintings* | | $2,200 |
| ☐ **REISMAN, Philip** ............... *paintings* | | $275 |
| American 20th cent. ............... *drawings* | | $220 |
| ☐ **REISS, Fritz Winold** ............ *paintings* | $660 | $7,700 |
| German/American 1886-1953 .......... *drawings* | $132 | $17,050 |
| ☐ **REISS, H.** ...................... *paintings* | | $330 |
| ☐ **REISS, Lionel S.** ............... *drawings* | | $192 |
| b. 1894 | | |
| ☐ **REISSNER, Martin Andreas** .......... *paintings* | | $126,500 |
| American | | |
| ☐ **REISZ, Hermann** ............... *paintings* | | $2,860 |
| ☐ **REKOWSKY, F.** ............... *paintings* | | $550 |
| ☐ **REKSHAM, K.** ............... *drawings* | $27 | $750 |
| ☐ **RELAVERO** ...................... *paintings* | | $187 |
| 19th/20th cent. | | |
| ☐ **RELYEA, Charles M.** ............ *paintings* | $220 | $990 |
| American b. 1863 | | |
| ☐ **REM, L\*\*\*** ...................... *paintings* | | $2,310 |
| ☐ **REMBRANDT,** | | |
| (Rembrandt Harmensz van RIJN) .......... *paintings* | $52,500 | $990,000 |
| Dutch 1606-1669 | | |
| ☐ **REMEGELLE, Paul** ............ *drawings* | | $440 |
| French 20th cent. | | |
| ☐ **REMENICK, Seymour** ............ *paintings* | $209 | $247 |
| American 20th cent. ............... *drawings* | | $99 |
| ☐ **REMINGTON, Frederic Sackrider** ........ *paintings* | $16,500 | $627,000 |
| American 1861-1909 ............... *drawings* | $1,320 | $150,000 |
| .................................. *sculpture* | $13,200 | $715,000 |
| ☐ **REMINGTON, S.J.** ............ *paintings* | $330 | $1,925 |
| American 19th cent. | | |
| ☐ **REMISOFF, Nicolai** ............ *paintings* | | $1,760 |
| Russian/American 20th cent. .......... *drawings* | $25 | $550 |
| ☐ **REMNICK, Seymour** ............ *paintings* | | $200 |
| American 20th cent. | | |
| ☐ **REMUR** ...................... *paintings* | | $900 |
| ☐ **REMY, Louis Jean Marie** ............ *paintings* | | $247 |
| French 1792-1869 | | |

## Remington Bronzes

*Frederic Sackrider Remington was one of America's best-known Western artists. A prolific painter, sculptor, and author, he lived to be only forty-eight years old. "Bronco Buster" is one of Remington's most famous bronze sculptures and it exists in many variations.*

*From 1900 on, Remington had all his bronzes cast at the Roman Bronze Works Foundry in Brooklyn, New York. Each bronze was numbered, then incised with the sculptor's signature, date of cast, and copyright. Each cast after #1 differed further in detail as Remington experimented, changing the angle of a hand or the position of a horse's tail.*

*During his lifetime, Remington authorized 163 casts of "Bronco Buster." After his death, his widow authorized another 144. After her death in 1919, an enormous number of "surmoulages" (casts made without the artist's authorization from*

*another bronze, rather than from the artist's wax or clay model) were produced. More recently, once the copyright expired, there have been restrikes – smaller, less detailed casts. Casts made in the years since Remington's death in 1909 vary widely in size, quality, and price.*

*For many years, the whereabouts of cast #1 of "Bronco Buster" had been unknown. It surfaced in 1984 after remaining for many years in the possession of a family that was unaware of its value. The bronze sold for $630,000, while smaller, later casts of the same figure sold the same season for $50,000 to $60,000. (Frederic Sackrider Remington, "The Bronco Buster," cast #1, bronze, height, 32¼ in., Christie's, June 1, 1984, $630,000.)*

|  |  | Current Price Range | |
|---|---|---|---|
|  |  | *Low* | *High* |
| ☐ **REMY, R.** ............................... *paintings* |  |  | **$2,310** |
| Haitian |  |  |  |
| ☐ **REN, Chuck** ............................... *paintings* |  | **$5,500** | **$10,000** |
| American contemporary |  |  |  |
| ☐ **RENA** ............................... *sculpture* |  |  | **$308** |
| ☐ **RENALDI, Francesco** ......................... *paintings* |  |  | **$5,500** |
| ☐ **RENARD, Fernand** ........................... *paintings* |  | **$330** | **$4,400** |
| contemporary |  |  |  |

| | | Current Price Range | |
|---|---|---|---|
| | | Low | High |
| ☐ **RENARD, H.** ..................................... *paintings* | | | $715 |
| French 20th cent. | | | |
| ☐ **RENARD, Jean Augustin** ...................... *drawings* | | | $1,760 |
| French 1744-1807 | | | |
| ☐ **RENARD, Marius** ............................ *paintings* | | $77 | $247 |
| Belgian b. 1869 | | | |
| ☐ **RENAUD, Adrien** ............................ *paintings* | | | $220 |
| French 19th cent. | | | |
| ☐ **RENAUD, E.** ..................................... *paintings* | | | $990 |
| ☐ **RENAUD, F.** ..................................... *paintings* | | | $411 |
| ☐ **RENAUDIN, Alfred** ........................... *paintings* | | $2,970 | $4,675 |
| French b. 1866 | | | |
| ☐ **RENAULI, L.M.** ............................... *paintings* | | $2,530 | $2,860 |
| French ac. 1870 | | | |
| ☐ **RENAULT, Lewis** ............................ *drawings* | | | $1,870 |
| American | | | |
| ☐ **RENAULT, Lex de** ............................ *paintings* | | | $2,200 |
| French 19th cent. | | | |
| ☐ **RENAULT, M.** .................................... *paintings* | | | $1,210 |
| American mid 19th cent. | | | |
| ☐ **RENAULT, Y.** .................................... *paintings* | | | $935 |
| ☐ **RENAULT-DES-GRAVIERS,** | | | |
| **Victor J.** ............................................... *paintings* | | | $3,520 |
| French d. 1905 | | | |
| ☐ **RENAVO** ........................................... *paintings* | | | $1,045 |
| Italian 19th cent. | | | |
| ☐ **RENE** ............................................... *sculpture* | | $660 | $2,420 |
| ☐ **RENE-HIS, E.** ................................... *paintings* | | | $550 |
| French 19th cent. | | | |
| ☐ **RENESSE, Constantijn A.** ................... *drawings* | | | $3,630 |
| Dutch 1626-1680 | | | |
| ☐ **RENGER, Herman** ............................. *paintings* | | | $301 |
| ☐ **RENI, Guido** ..................................... *paintings* | | | $660,000 |
| Italian 1575-1642 | | | |
| ☐ **RENIE, Nicolas** ................................. *paintings* | | | $1,100 |
| ☐ **RENO, Jim** ........................................ *sculpture* | | $17,000 | $27,000 |
| American contemporary | | | |
| ☐ **RENOIR, Pierre Auguste** ...................... *paintings* | | $2,860 | $2,750,000 |
| French 1841-1919 ..................................... *drawings* | | $2,860 | $687,500 |
| .......................................................... *sculpture* | | $2,750 | $154,000 |
| ☐ **RENOUARD** ...................................... *paintings* | | | $418 |
| American | | | |
| ☐ **RENOUARD, Charles Paul** ................... *drawings* | | | $357 |
| French 1845-1924 | | | |
| ☐ **RENOUARD, George** ........................... *paintings* | | $88 | $850 |
| American 19th cent. | | | |
| ☐ **RENOUF, Edda** ................................. *drawings* | | | $880 |
| Mexican/American b. 1943 | | | |

| | | Current Price Range | |
|---|---|---|---|
| | | Low | High |
| ☐ **RENOUF, Emile** .................. *paintings* | | | $660 |
| French 1845-1894 | | | |
| ☐ **RENOUX, Jules Ernest** ........... *paintings* | | | $1,540 |
| French 1863-1932 | | | |
| ☐ **RENSHAW, Alice** ................ *drawings* | | $93 | $231 |
| American 19th cent. | | | |
| ☐ **RENSHAW, T.** ................... *paintings* | | | $330 |
| ☐ **REPIN, Ilya Yefimovich** ........ *paintings* | | $3,025 | $3,410 |
| Russian 1844-1930 ................. *drawings* | | $231 | $3,740 |
| ☐ **RESCALLI, Don Angelo** .......... *paintings* | | | $462 |
| ☐ **RESCH, Ernst** .................. *paintings* | | | $550 |
| German 1807-64 | | | |
| ☐ **RESCH, Willi** .................. *paintings* | | | $2,000 |
| ☐ **RESCHI, Pandolfo** .............. *paintings* | | | $4,180 |
| Polish 1634 or 1643-1699 | | | |
| ☐ **RESCHULZ** ..................... *paintings* | | | $300 |
| ☐ **RESIO, R.** ..................... *drawings* | | | $200 |
| Italian 19th cent. | | | |
| ☐ **RESNICK, Milton** ............... *paintings* | | $660 | $12,100 |
| American b. 1917 .................. *drawings* | | | $33 |
| ☐ **RESTOUT, Jean (younger)** ....... *paintings* | | $3,850 | $1,100 |
| French 1692-1768 .................. *drawings* | | | $28,600 |
| ☐ **RESTOUT, Jean Bernard** ......... *paintings* | | | $1,760 |
| French 1732-1797 | | | |
| ☐ **RESZO, Burghardt** .............. *paintings* | | | $990 |
| Hungarian 1884-1968 | | | |
| ☐ **RET, Etienne** .................. *paintings* | | | $55 |
| French/American b. 1900 ........... *drawings* | | $33 | $330 |
| ☐ **RETH, Alfred** .................. *paintings* | | $7,150 | $13,200 |
| Hungarian/French 1884-1966 ........ *drawings* | | | $1,650 |
| ☐ **RETTIG, Heinrich** .............. *paintings* | | | $13,200 |
| German 1859-1921 | | | |
| ☐ **RETTIG, John** .................. *paintings* | | | $220 |
| American 1860-1932 | | | |
| ☐ **REUNAI, G.** .................... *paintings* | | | $220 |
| 19th/20th cent. | | | |
| ☐ **REUSSWIG, William** ............. *paintings* | | $1,100 | $2,200 |
| American 1902-1978 ................ *drawings* | | $880 | $990 |
| ☐ **REUTER, Wilhelm** ............... *paintings* | | | $330 |
| German b. 1859 | | | |
| ☐ **REUTER, William** ............... *paintings* | | | $63,250 |
| ☐ **REUTERDAHL, Henry** ............. *paintings* | | | $3,520 |
| American 1871-1925 ................ *drawings* | | $500 | $2,860 |
| ☐ **REUX, John Henry le** ........... *drawings* | | | $356 |
| British 1812-1896 | | | |
| ☐ **REVERON, Armando** .............. *drawings* | | $23,100 | $74,250 |
| Venezuelan 1889/90-1954 | | | |
| ☐ **REVESZ, Imre Emerich** .......... *paintings* | | | $3,080 |
| Hungarian 1859-1945 | | | |

| | | Current Price Range | |
|---|---|---|---|
| | | Low | High |
| ☐ **REVILL, H.W.** .................................. *paintings* | | $250 | $495 |
| ☐ **REVUELTAS, Fermin** ......................... *paintings* | | | $7,700 |
| Mexican b. 1903 | | | |
| ☐ **REX, Julian** ...................................... *paintings* | | | $423 |
| ☐ **REYERSON, L.L.** ............................... *paintings* | | | $1,050 |
| American 19th cent. | | | |
| ☐ **REYES, Emma** .................................. *drawings* | | | $1,100 |
| Colombian | | | |
| ☐ **REYNA, Antonio** ............................... *paintings* | | $990 | $14,300 |
| Spanish 19th/20th cent. | | | |
| ☐ **REYNARD, Grant** .............................. *drawings* | | $187 | $605 |
| 1887-1968 | | | |
| ☐ **REYNAUD, Francois** ........................... *paintings* | | | $275 |
| French 1825-1909 | | | |
| ☐ **REYNE, Charles** ............................... *paintings* | | | $715 |
| French School 19th cent. | | | |
| ☐ **REYNOLDS, Alan** .............................. *paintings* | | | $935 |
| English contemporary | | | |
| ☐ **REYNOLDS, G.W.** ............................. *paintings* | | | $528 |
| ☐ **REYNOLDS, James** ............................ *paintings* | | $10,000 | $50,000 |
| American b. 1926 | | | |
| ☐ **REYNOLDS, R.D.** .............................. *paintings* | | | $1,980 |
| ☐ **REYNOLDS, Sir Joshua** ....................... *paintings* | | $1,485 | $79,200 |
| English 1723-1792 | | | |
| ☐ **REYNOLDS, W*S*** ............................. *paintings* | | | $2,600 |
| American 19th/20th cent. | | | |
| ☐ **REYNOLDS, Wellington Jared** ............. *paintings* | | | $1,100 |
| American b. 1866 | | | |
| ☐ **REYNTJENS, Henrich Engelbert** .......... *paintings* | | | $1,650 |
| Dutch 1817-1859 | | | |
| ☐ **REZIA, F.J.** ...................................... *paintings* | | | $1,540 |
| ☐ **RHEAD, F.A.** .................................... *drawings* | | | $275 |
| American 20th cent. | | | |
| ☐ **RHEAD, Louis John** ........................... *paintings* | | $1,320 | $1,760 |
| American 1857-1926 ................................. *drawings* | | $110 | $1,320 |
| ☐ **RHEAN, Henry Meynell** ...................... *drawings* | | | $660 |
| ☐ **RHEINHOLD, Hugo Wolfgang** ............. *sculpture* | | | $1,320 |
| German 19th cent. | | | |
| ☐ **RHIND, John Massey** ......................... *sculpture* | | $4,000 | $4,400 |
| Scottish/American 1860-1936 | | | |
| ☐ **RHODES, Ida F.** ............................... *paintings* | | | $550 |
| American 19th cent. | | | |
| ☐ **RHODES, John** ................................. *paintings* | | $770 | $935 |
| ☐ **RHODES, Joseph** .............................. *paintings* | | $935 | $3,080 |
| British 1782-1854 | | | |
| ☐ **RHODES, W.B.** ................................. *paintings* | | | $192 |
| English 19th cent. | | | |
| ☐ **RHOMBERG, Hanno** ........................... *paintings* | | $1,550 | $8,800 |
| German 1820-1869 | | | |

| | | Current Price Range | |
|---|---|---|---|
| | | Low | High |
| ☐ **RHYNEN, J. van** ................................ *paintings* | | | **$467** |
| Dutch 19th cent. | | | |
| ☐ **RHYS, Oliver** ...................................... *paintings* | | | **$3,025** |
| German 19th cent. | | | |
| ☐ **RIANCHO Y MORA, Agustin** .............. *paintings* | | | **$715** |
| ☐ **RIBA, Paul** ........................................ *paintings* | **$495** | | **$1,485** |
| American 20th cent. | | | |
| ☐ **RIBAK, Louis** .................................... *paintings* | **$3,750** | | **$5,775** |
| American 1902/03-1980 | | | |
| ☐ **RIBARD, Jules** .................................... *paintings* | | | **$660** |
| ☐ **RIBCOWSKY, Dey de** .......................... *paintings* | **$137** | | **$852** |
| American 1880-1935 | | | |
| ☐ **RIBERA, Jusepe de** | | | |
| **(called LO SPAGNOLETTO)** ................. *paintings* | **$2,035** | | **$374,000** |
| Spanish 1588/90-1652/56 | | | |
| ☐ **RIBERA, Pierre** ................................... *paintings* | | | **$2,475** |
| French b. 1867 | | | |
| ☐ **RIBERA, Roman** ................................. *paintings* | | | **$29,700** |
| Spanish b. 1848 | | | |
| ☐ **RIBONI, Giacinto** .............................. *paintings* | | | **$880** |
| Italian/American d. 1838 | | | |
| ☐ **RIBOT, Germain Theodore** ................. *paintings* | **$220** | | **$2,475** |
| French d. 1893 | | | |
| ☐ **RIBOT, L.** ........................................... *paintings* | | | **$550** |
| ☐ **RIBOT, Theodule Augustin** .................. *paintings* | **$550** | | **$35,200** |
| French 1823-1891 ..................................... *drawings* | **$220** | | **$1,760** |
| ☐ **RICARD, G.** ....................................... *paintings* | | | **$357** |
| ☐ **RICARD, Rene** ................................... *paintings* | **$200** | | **$440** |
| French b. 1889 | | | |
| ☐ **RICARD, S.** ........................................ *paintings* | | | **$440** |
| ☐ **RICARDI** ........................................... *paintings* | | | **$220** |
| French (?) 19th cent. | | | |
| ☐ **RICARDO, M.** ..................................... *paintings* | | | **$440** |
| Spanish b. 1876 | | | |
| ☐ **RICCARD, C.** ..................................... *paintings* | | | **$467** |
| Italian 19th/20th cent. | | | |
| ☐ **RICCI, Alfredo** ................................. *paintings* | | | **$2,500** |
| Italian 1864-1889 | | | |
| ☐ **RICCI, Arturo** ................................... *paintings* | **$770** | | **$19,800** |
| Italian b. 1854 | | | |
| ☐ **RICCI, Danti** .................................... *drawings* | | | **$550** |
| Italian b. 1879 | | | |
| ☐ **RICCI, F.** .......................................... *paintings* | **$220** | | **$301** |
| Italian 19th cent. | | | |
| ☐ **RICCI, Francesco** ............................... *paintings* | | | **$4,400** |
| Italian ac. 1770 | | | |
| ☐ **RICCI, Gian Pietro** ............................ *paintings* | | | **$11,000** |
| Italian 16th cent. | | | |

| | | | *Current Price Range* | |
|---|---|---|---|---|
| | | | *Low* | *High* |
| ☐ **RICCI, Marco** .................. *paintings* | | | $4,400 | $28,600 |
| Italian 1676-1729 | | | | |
| ☐ **RICCI, Pio** ........................... *paintings* | | | $2,200 | $7,425 |
| Italian d. 1919 | | | | |
| ☐ **RICCI, Sebastiano** .............. *paintings* | | | $44,000 | $90,750 |
| Italian 1659-1734 | | | | |
| ☐ **RICCI, Ulysses A.** ................ *paintings* | | | | $275 |
| 20th cent. | | | | |
| ☐ **RICCIARDI, C.** .................. *paintings* | | | $27 | $330 |
| American 20th cent. | | | | |
| ☐ **RICCIARDI, Cesare** ........................ *paintings* | | | | $220 |
| American 20th cent. | | | | |
| ☐ **RICCIARDI, Oscar** ............ *paintings* | | | $440 | $2,200 |
| Italian 1864-1935 | | | | |
| ☐ **RICE, G.S.** ..................... *paintings* | | | $330 | $357 |
| Canadian/American ac.1859 | | | | |
| ☐ **RICE, Marion** ..................... *paintings* | | | $220 | $300 |
| 20th cent. | | | | |
| ☐ **RICE, W.J.** ..................... *drawings* | | | | $660 |
| 20th cent. | | | | |
| ☐ **RICE, William Clarke** ......................... *paintings* | | | | $605 |
| American 1875-1928 | | | | |
| ☐ **RICE, William Morton Jackson** ............ *paintings* | | | | $467 |
| American 1854-1922 | | | | |
| ☐ **RICE-PEREIRA, Irene** ....................... *paintings* | | | $190 | $3,300 |
| American 1901/07-1971 ............................. *drawings* | | | $110 | $4,400 |
| ☐ **RICH, Alfred William** ......................... *drawings* | | | $50 | $247 |
| English 1856-1921 | | | | |
| ☐ **RICH, E.L.** ..................... *paintings* | | | | $385 |
| contemporary | | | | |
| ☐ **RICH, James Rogers** ......................... *paintings* | | | | $600 |
| American early 20th cent. | | | | |
| ☐ **RICH, John Hubbard** ......................... *paintings* | | | $550 | $30,800 |
| American 1876-1955? | | | | |
| ☐ **RICH, R.** ..................... *paintings* | | | | $264 |
| ☐ **RICHARD, Alfred** ............... *sculpture* | | | | $660 |
| French 19th cent. | | | | |
| ☐ **RICHARD, W.** ..................... *paintings* | | | | $357 |
| American 19th cent. | | | | |
| ☐ **RICHARD-PUTZ, Michel** ................... *paintings* | | | | $1,210 |
| French b. 1868 | | | | |
| ☐ **RICHARDS** ..................... *paintings* | | | | $450 |
| American 19th/20th cent. | | | | |
| ☐ **RICHARDS, Ceri** ............... *paintings* | | | | $2,750 |
| British b. 1903 | | | | |
| ☐ **RICHARDS, Ella E.** ............ *paintings* | | | | $550 |
| American 19th/20th cent. | | | | |
| ☐ **RICHARDS, Frederick de Bourg** ........... *paintings* | | | $1,320 | $6,050 |
| American 1822-1903 ................................. *drawings* | | | | $550 |

| | Current Price Range | |
|---|---|---|
| | Low | High |
| ☐ **RICHARDS, John** ............................ *paintings* | | **$412** |
| ☐ **RICHARDS, L.** ................................ *paintings* | | **$880** |
| British 19th cent. | | |
| ☐ **RICHARDS, Lucy Currier** .................... *sculpture* | | **$1,210** |
| American | | |
| ☐ **RICHARDS, Richard Peter** .................. *drawings* | **$250** | **$440** |
| English, d. Italy 1839/40-1877 | | |
| ☐ **RICHARDS, Ridgway** ........................... *paintings* | | **$462** |
| ☐ **RICHARDS, Thomas Addison** ............... *paintings* | **$418** | **$19,800** |
| Anglo/American 1820-1900 ........................... *drawings* | | **$247** |
| ☐ **RICHARDS, William Trost** ................. *paintings* | **$110** | **$187,000** |
| American 1833-1905 ................................ *drawings* | **$82** | **$38,500** |
| ☐ **RICHARDSON** ................................ *paintings* | | **$4,620** |
| 19th cent. | | |
| ☐ **RICHARDSON, Allan** ........................ *paintings* | | **$2,860** |
| American 20th cent. | | |
| ☐ **RICHARDSON, Charles** ....................... *paintings* | **$143** | **$770** |
| English 19th cent. | | |
| ☐ **RICHARDSON, Edward** ....................... *drawings* | | **$660** |
| ☐ **RICHARDSON, F. Stuart** .................... *drawings* | | **$440** |
| ☐ **RICHARDSON, Francis Henry** ............. *paintings* | **$165** | **$3,740** |
| American 1859-1934 | | |
| ☐ **RICHARDSON, George** ........................ *paintings* | | **$330** |
| English 19th cent. | | |
| ☐ **RICHARDSON, John** .......................... *paintings* | | **$770** |
| European | | |
| ☐ **RICHARDSON, Margaret Foster** .......... *paintings* | | **$6,600** |
| American b. 1881 | | |
| ☐ **RICHARDSON, Mary Curtis** ............... *paintings* | **$825** | **$6,600** |
| American 1848-1931 | | |
| ☐ **RICHARDSON, Mary Neal** ................... *paintings* | **$55** | **$385** |
| American b. 1859 | | |
| ☐ **RICHARDSON, Theodore** .................... *drawings* | **$220** | **$550** |
| American 1855-1914 | | |
| ☐ **RICHARDSON, Thomas Miles (Jr.)** ....... *drawings* | **$290** | **$1,870** |
| English 1813-1890 | | |
| ☐ **RICHARDSON, Thomas Miles (Sr.)** ....... *drawings* | **$137** | **$2,860** |
| English 1784-1848 | | |
| ☐ **RICHARDSON, Volney Allen** ............... *drawings* | | **$220** |
| American b. 1880 | | |
| ☐ **RICHARDT, Ferdinand Joachim** .......... *paintings* | **$467** | **$6,600** |
| Danish/American 1819-1895 .......................... *drawings* | | **$192** |
| ☐ **RICHE, Louis** ................................. *sculpture* | | **$550** |
| ☐ **RICHENBERG, Robert** ....................... *paintings* | | **$385** |
| contemporary | | |
| ☐ **RICHER, Paul** ................................... *sculpture* | | **$220** |
| French 1849-1933 | | |
| ☐ **RICHERT, Charles Henry** ................... *paintings* | **$100** | **$250** |
| American b. 1880 ...................................... *drawings* | **$40** | **$440** |

| | | *Current Price Range* | |
|---|---|---|---|
| | | *Low* | *High* |
| ☐ **RICHES, Wm. J.** .............................. *paintings* | | | $220 |
| American School late 19th cent. | | | |
| ☐ **RICHET, Leon** ................................. *paintings* | | $220 | $11,000 |
| French 1847-1907 | | | |
| ☐ **RICHIER, Germaine** ........................... *sculpture* | | $3,300 | $19,800 |
| French 1904-1959 | | | |
| ☐ **RICHIR, Herman Jean** ........................ *paintings* | | | $8,800 |
| Belgian b. 1866 | | | |
| ☐ **RICHMAN, Julie** ................................ *paintings* | | | $522 |
| ☐ **RICHMOND, Agnes M.** ........................ *paintings* | | $220 | $14,300 |
| American c. 1870-1964 | | | |
| ☐ **RICHMOND, Leonard** ......................... *paintings* | | | $400 |
| British d. 1965 | | | |
| ☐ **RICHOMME, Jules** ............................. *paintings* | | | $1,430 |
| French 1818-1903 | | | |
| ☐ **RICHTER, Adrian Ludwig** ................... *paintings* | | | $2,200 |
| German 1803-1884 ..................................... *drawings* | | | $100 |
| ☐ **RICHTER, Bruno** ............................. *drawings* | | | $440 |
| German b. 1872 | | | |
| ☐ **RICHTER, Edouard Frederic Wilhelm** .. *paintings* | | $2,200 | $7,920 |
| French 1844-1913 | | | |
| ☐ **RICHTER, Hans** ................................ *drawings* | | $440 | $990 |
| German ac. 1597 | | | |
| ☐ **RICHTER, Henry L.** ............................ *paintings* | | $275 | $302 |
| American b. 1870 ...................................... *drawings* | | | $220 |
| ☐ **RICHTER, Herbert Davis** ..................... *paintings* | | $302 | $935 |
| English 1874-1955 | | | |
| ☐ **RICHTER, Hermann** ........................... *paintings* | | | $550 |
| American 20th cent. | | | |
| ☐ **RICHTER, Johann Heinrich** ................. *paintings* | | $450 | $1,210 |
| German 1803-1845 | | | |
| ☐ **RICHTER, Julius** ............................. *paintings* | | $110 | $225 |
| American 20th cent. | | | |
| ☐ **RICHTER, Luisa** ............................. *drawings* | | | $880 |
| contemporary | | | |
| ☐ **RICHTER, M.J.** ................................ *paintings* | | $2,200 | $6,600 |
| German b. 1860 | | | |
| ☐ **RICHTER, Oswald** ............................. *paintings* | | | $220 |
| German 19th cent. | | | |
| ☐ **RICHTER, Otto** ................................. *sculpture* | | | $880 |
| German early 20th cent. | | | |
| ☐ **RICHTER, P.** ................................... *paintings* | | | $550 |
| ☐ **RICHTER, Wilhelm M.** ........................ *paintings* | | | $2,475 |
| Austrian 1824-1892 | | | |
| ☐ **RICHTSCHEL, William P.** ................... *drawings* | | | $242 |
| American | | | |
| ☐ **RICIARDI** ........................................ *paintings* | | | $209 |
| Italian early 20th cent. | | | |

|  | | Current Price Range | |
|---|---|---|---|
|  | | *Low* | *High* |
| ☐ **RICKARD, O.** ...................................... *paintings* | | | **$357** |
| Continental 18th cent. | | | |
| ☐ **RICKARDS, F.** ..................................... *paintings* | | | **$1,320** |
| 19th cent. | | | |
| ☐ **RICKETSON, Louise D.** ...................... *paintings* | | | **$301** |
| ☐ **RICKEY, George** ............................... *sculpture* | | **$770** | **$27,500** |
| American b. 1907 | | | |
| ☐ **RICKMAN, Philip** ............................ *drawings* | | | **$1,650** |
| English b. 1891, exhib. 1936 | | | |
| ☐ **RICKS, Douglas** ................................. *paintings* | | **$3,500** | **$6,000** |
| American contemporary | | | |
| ☐ **RICKS, James** ................................... *paintings* | | **$880** | **$2,200** |
| English 19th cent. | | | |
| ☐ **RICO Y CEJUDO, Jose** ........................ *paintings* | | **$385** | **$4,125** |
| Spanish b. 1864 | | | |
| ☐ **RICO Y ORTEGA, Martin** ................... *paintings* | | **$1,100** | **$28,600** |
| Spanish 1833-1908 ..................................... *drawings* | | **$1,320** | **$4,675** |
| ☐ **RICOIS, Jean** ................................... *paintings* | | | **$302** |
| European 19th/20th cent. | | | |
| ☐ **RICQUIER, Louis** ............................. *paintings* | | | **$660** |
| ☐ **RIDDEL, James** ................................. *paintings* | | **$302** | **$412** |
| Scottish 1857-1928 | | | |
| ☐ **RIDDLES, Leonard** ........................... *drawings* | | | **$3,520** |
| American(Comanche) b. 1910 | | | |
| ☐ **RIDE, G.F.** ...................................... *paintings* | | | **$1,760** |
| British 19th cent. | | | |
| ☐ **RIDENHOUR, William** ......................... *paintings* | | | **$3,025** |
| ☐ **RIDEON, Charles H.** ........................... *paintings* | | | **$224** |
| English 19th cent. | | | |
| ☐ **RIDEOUT, John G.** ............................ *drawings* | | | **$374** |
| ☐ **RIDEOUT, Philip H.** ........................... *paintings* | | | **$3,300** |
| British 20th cent. | | | |
| ☐ **RIDER, Arthur G.** ............................ *paintings* | | **$209** | **$770** |
| American 20th cent. | | | |
| ☐ **RIDER, Henry Orne** ......................... *paintings* | | **$110** | **$495** |
| American b. 1860 | | | |
| ☐ **RIECHARD, B.C.** ............................... *paintings* | | | **$660** |
| Austrian 19th cent. | | | |
| ☐ **RIECK, E.** ...................................... *paintings* | | | **$990** |
| ☐ **RIECKE, George** ................................. *paintings* | | **$264** | **$330** |
| American 19th cent. | | | |
| ☐ **RIECKE, Johann George Lodewyk** ........ *paintings* | | **$275** | **$1,980** |
| Dutch/American 1817-1898 | | | |
| ☐ **RIEDEL, August** ................................. *paintings* | | **$770** | **$4,620** |
| German 1799-1883 | | | |
| ☐ **RIEDEL, H.** ...................................... *paintings* | | | **$1,980** |
| German 19th cent. | | | |
| ☐ **RIEDER, C.** ...................................... *paintings* | | | **$286** |
| German 19th cent. | | | |

|                                                   |            | Current Price Range | |
|---------------------------------------------------|------------|---------|---------|
|                                                   |            | *Low*   | *High*  |
| ☐ **RIEDER, Marcel** ............................ *paintings* | | $495 | $6,325 |
| French b. 1852 | | | |
| ☐ **RIEFSTAHL,** | | | |
| **Wilhelm Ludwig Friedrich** ................... *paintings* | | | $1,760 |
| German 1827-1888 | | | |
| ☐ **RIEGEN, Nicolaas** ............................ *paintings* | | $2,750 | $8,525 |
| Dutch 1827-1889 | | | |
| ☐ **RIEGER, Albert** ................................ *paintings* | | $110 | $1,320 |
| Austrian b. 1834 | | | |
| ☐ **RIEPER, August** ............................... *paintings* | | $950 | $1,430 |
| German b. 1865 | | | |
| ☐ **RIES, Wilhelm** ................................. *paintings* | | | $467 |
| German 19th cent. | | | |
| ☐ **RIESEN, A.V.** ................................... *paintings* | | | $1,045 |
| ☐ **RIESENBERG, Sidney** ........................ *paintings* | | $495 | $660 |
| American b. 1885 | | | |
| ☐ **RIESENER, Louis Antoine Leon** ........... *drawings* | | | $198 |
| French 1808-1878 | | | |
| ☐ **RIET, Willem van** .............................. *paintings* | | $264 | $605 |
| Belgian 19th/20th cent. | | | |
| ☐ **RIETSCHOOF, Jan Claes** ..................... *paintings* | | | $4,950 |
| Dutch 1652-1719 | | | |
| ☐ **RIGAUD, Emile** ................................. *paintings* | | | $825 |
| ☐ **RIGAUD, Hyacinthe** ........................... *paintings* | | | $7,700 |
| French 1659-1743 | | | |
| ☐ **RIGAUD, Pierre Gaston** ....................... *paintings* | | $121 | $715 |
| French b. 1874 | | | |
| ☐ **RIGAULT, G.** ..................................... *sculpture* | | | $1,430 |
| ☐ **RIGBY, E.M.** ..................................... *paintings* | | | $198 |
| English early 20th cent. | | | |
| ☐ **RIGG, Arthur M.** ............................... *paintings* | | | $412 |
| English 19th cent. | | | |
| ☐ **RIGG, Ernest Higgins** ......................... *paintings* | | | $495 |
| British 19th/20th cent. | | | |
| ☐ **RIGGS, Robert** .................................. *paintings* | | $3,520 | $4,675 |
| American 1896-1970 ............................... *drawings* | | $110 | $550 |
| ☐ **RIGI** .............................................. *drawings* | | | $220 |
| American (?) 19th cent. | | | |
| ☐ **RIGNANO, V.** .................................... *paintings* | | $770 | $935 |
| Italian 19th cent. | | | |
| ☐ **RIGOLOT, Albert Gabriel** .................... *paintings* | | $93 | $3,300 |
| French 1862-1932 | | | |
| ☐ **RIGOT** ............................................. *sculpture* | | | $935 |
| ☐ **RIJSBRUCK, G.** ................................. *paintings* | | | $3,850 |
| European 19th cent. | | | |
| ☐ **RIJSDIJK, C. van** ............................... *paintings* | | | $412 |
| Dutch 20th cent. | | | |
| ☐ **RIKI, Laura Richiello** .......................... *paintings* | | $88 | $192 |
| Italian b. 1929 | | | |

| | | Current Price Range | |
|---|---|---|---|
| | | *Low* | *High* |
| ☐ **RILEY, Bridget** .................... *drawings*<br>English b. 1931 | | $1,540 | $1,870 |
| ☐ **RILEY, E.** ........................... *paintings*<br>English 20th cent. | | | $319 |
| ☐ **RILEY, John** ..................... *paintings*<br>English 1646-1691 | | $1,375 | $2,310 |
| ☐ **RILEY, Kenneth** ................ *paintings*<br>American b. 1919 | | $700 | $25,000 |
| ☐ **RILEY, Mary G.** ................ *paintings*<br>American 1883-1939 | | | $275 |
| ☐ **RILEY, Nicholas F.** ............ *drawings*<br>1900-1944 | | | $275 |
| ☐ **RILEY, Thomas** ................. *paintings*<br>English ac. 1880-1892 | | $1,540 | $1,650 |
| ☐ **RIMBOECK, Max** .............. *paintings*<br>German b. 1890 | | | $605 |
| ☐ **RIMMER, G.** ...................... *drawings*<br>English 20th cent. | | | $200 |
| ☐ **RIMMER, William P.** .......... *paintings*<br>American 1816-1879 | | $3,850 | $57,750 |
| ☐ **RINALDİ, Claudio** ............. *paintings*<br>Italian 19th/20th cent. | | $357 | $4,950 |
| ☐ **RINCK, Adolph D.** ............. *paintings*<br>American c. 1815 | | $220 | $440 |
| ☐ **RINEHART, William Henry** ............ *sculpture*<br>American 1825-1874 | | $12,100 | $55,000 |
| ☐ **RING, Alice Blair** .............. *paintings*<br>American b. 1869 | | | $6,600 |
| ☐ **RING, Pieter de** ............... *paintings*<br>Dutch 1615-1660 | | | $24,200 |
| ☐ **RINGI, H. Serenson** .......... *sculpture* | | | $1,045 |
| ☐ **RINGIUS, Carl** .................. *paintings*<br>American b. 1879 | | | $275 |
| ☐ **RIOPELLE, Jean Paul** ........ *paintings*<br>Canadian b. 1923 ............... *drawings* | | $4,950<br>$660 | $143,000<br>$4,950 |
| ☐ **RIORDAN, Eric** ................ *paintings*<br>Canadian 1906-1948 | | $495 | $440 |
| ☐ **RIOS, Del** ........................ *paintings* | | | $825 |
| ☐ **RIOS, L. da** ..................... *drawings*<br>Italian 19th cent. | | | $1,045 |
| ☐ **RIP, Willem Cornelis** .......... *paintings*<br>Dutch 1856-1922 ............... *drawings* | | $137 | $825<br>$1,100 |
| ☐ **RIPAMONTE, Carlos** ......... *paintings*<br>Argentinian 19th cent. | | | $412 |
| ☐ **RIPARI, Virgilio** ............... *paintings*<br>Italian 1843/46-1902 | | $550 | $1,155 |
| ☐ **RIPLEY, Aiden Lassell** ......... *paintings*<br>American 1896-1969 .............. *drawings* | | $302<br>$110 | $17,600<br>$4,400 |

| | | Current Price Range | |
|---|---|---|---|
| | | Low | High |
| ☐ **RIPLEY, Helen** ............................ *paintings* | | | $650 |
| American 19th cent. | | | |
| ☐ **RIPPEL, Morris** ........................... *paintings* | | $10,500 | $18,000 |
| American b. 1930 ................................. *drawings* | | | $10,560 |
| ☐ **RIPPS, Rodney** ............................ *sculpture* | | $770 | $8,250 |
| American 20th cent. | | | |
| ☐ **RISNER** ...................................... *paintings* | | | $192 |
| Belgian 20th cent. | | | |
| ☐ **RISPOLI, G.** ................................ *paintings* | | $80 | $192 |
| Italian 20th cent. | | | |
| ☐ **RISSON, Charles** ......................... *paintings* | | | $412 |
| French 19th cent. | | | |
| ☐ **RITCHIE, Alexander Haye** .......... *paintings* | | | $330 |
| American 1822-1895 | | | |
| ☐ **RITCHIE, John** ............................ *paintings* | | | $5,500 |
| English | | | |
| ☐ **RITSCHARD, L.** ........................... *paintings* | | | $935 |
| Swiss (?) 19th cent. | | | |
| ☐ **RITSCHARD, R.** ........................... *paintings* | | | $308 |
| ☐ **RITSCHEL, William P.** ................. *paintings* | | $302 | $3,575 |
| German/American 1864-1949 ................. *drawings* | | $209 | $1,000 |
| ☐ **RITSCHER, Moritz** ...................... *paintings* | | | $1,650 |
| German 1827-75 | | | |
| ☐ **RITSCHL, Otto** ........................... *paintings* | | | $1,650 |
| German 20th cent. | | | |
| ☐ **RITSCHOL, W.** ............................ *paintings* | | | $550 |
| ☐ **RITTENBERG, Henry R.** ............... *paintings* | | $330 | $2,090 |
| Russian/American 1879-1969 ................. *drawings* | | | $660 |
| ☐ **RITTER, C. H.** ............................ *paintings* | | | $209 |
| American 20th cent. | | | |
| ☐ **RITTER, Eduard** ......................... *paintings* | | | $2,750 |
| German 1820-1892 | | | |
| ☐ **RITTER, Louis** ........................... *paintings* | | $3,300 | $4,180 |
| American 1854-1892 | | | |
| ☐ **RITTER, Paul** ............................. *paintings* | | $1,540 | $1,980 |
| American 19th cent. | | | |
| ☐ **RITZBERGER, Albert** ................... *paintings* | | | $4,950 |
| Austrian 1853-1915 | | | |
| ☐ **RITZENHOFER, Hubert** ................ *paintings* | | | $1,320 |
| German b. 1879 | | | |
| ☐ **RIVARA, Jorge** ........................... *paintings* | | $440 | $1,430 |
| ☐ **RIVAS, Antonio** .......................... *paintings* | | $385 | $3,300 |
| Spanish b. 1840 ................................. *drawings* | | | $192 |
| ☐ **RIVAS, Barbaro** .......................... *drawings* | | | $2,200 |
| ☐ **RIVERA, Diego** ........................... *paintings* | | $3,410 | $429,000 |
| Mexican 1886-1957 ............................. *drawings* | | $770 | $162,250 |
| ☐ **RIVERA, Jose de** ........................ *sculpture* | | $4,510 | $20,900 |
| American b. 1904 | | | |
| ☐ **RIVERAIN, A.** ............................. *paintings* | | | $275 |

| | | Current Price Range | |
|---|---|---|---|
| | | Low | High |
| ☐ **RIVERON, Enrique** ............... *drawings* | | $275 | $990 |
| Cuban b. 1902 | | | |
| ☐ **RIVERS, D.** ........................ *paintings* | | | $770 |
| ☐ **RIVERS, Larry** ................... *paintings* | | $385 | $61,600 |
| American b. 1923 ..................... *drawings* | | $275 | $46,200 |
| ................................ *sculpture* | | $4,400 | $5,720 |
| ☐ **RIVERS, Leopold** ............... *paintings* | | $935 | $1,265 |
| English 1850/52-1905 ............ *drawings* | | $286 | $495 |
| ☐ **RIVIER, J.** ....................... *paintings* | | | $1,100 |
| ☐ **RIVIERE, Henri** ............... *paintings* | | | $8,525 |
| French 1864-1951 | | | |
| ☐ **RIVIERE, Henry Parsons** ........ *drawings* | | | $440 |
| English 1811-1888 | | | |
| ☐ **RIVIERE, Maurice Guiraud** ....... *sculpture* | | $550 | $4,180 |
| French early 20th cent. | | | |
| ☐ **RIVIERE, Theodore** ........... *sculpture* | | $1,760 | $1,760 |
| French early 20th cent. | | | |
| ☐ **RIVOIRE, Francois** ........... *drawings* | | $250 | $1,430 |
| French 1842-1919 | | | |
| ☐ **RIVOIRE, L.** .................... *paintings* | | $220 | $330 |
| French 19th cent. | | | |
| ☐ **RIVOIRE, Raymond Leon** ....... *drawings* | | | $990 |
| French b. 1884 ..................... *sculpture* | | $1,980 | $3,080 |
| ☐ **RIVOLI, Mario** ............... *drawings* | | | $385 |
| ☐ **RIX, Julian Walbridge** ....... *paintings* | | $220 | $4,950 |
| American 1851-1903 ............... *drawings* | | $165 | $330 |
| ☐ **RIXENS, Jean Andre** ........... *paintings* | | $1,760 | $33,000 |
| French 1846-1924 | | | |
| ☐ **RIZZO, Eduardo** ............... *paintings* | | | $412 |
| Italian 1881-1952 | | | |
| ☐ **ROBART, Leopold** ........... *paintings* | | | $522 |
| ☐ **ROBB, Samuel A.** ............... *sculpture* | | | $44,000 |
| American 1851-1928 | | | |
| ☐ **ROBBA, G.** .................... *paintings* | | | $396 |
| ☐ **ROBBE, Henri** ............... *paintings* | | $3,850 | $15,950 |
| Belgian 1807-1899 | | | |
| ☐ **ROBBE, Louis** ............... *paintings* | | $1,045 | $3,300 |
| Belgian 1806-1887 | | | |
| ☐ **ROBBINS, Ellen** ............... *paintings* | | $220 | $880 |
| American 1828-1905 ............... *drawings* | | $330 | $1,540 |
| ☐ **ROBBINS, Horace Walcott** ...... *paintings* | | $385 | $13,750 |
| American 1842-1904 | | | |
| ☐ **ROBBINS, Lee** ............... *paintings* | | | $330 |
| ☐ **ROBELLAZ, Emile** ............... *paintings* | | | $1,540 |
| Swiss 1844-1882 | | | |
| ☐ **ROBERT, Hubert** ............... *paintings* | | $385 | $286,000 |
| French 1733-1808 ................... *drawings* | | $462 | $38,500 |
| ☐ **ROBERT, Leopold Louis** ....... *paintings* | | | $3,300 |
| French 1794-1835 | | | |

| | Current Price Range | |
|---|---|---|
| | Low | High |
| ☐ **ROBERT, Louis Valentin Elias** .............. *sculpture* | | **$1,430** |
| French 19th cent. | | |
| ☐ **ROBERT, Marius Hubert** ..................... *paintings* | **$242** | **$522** |
| French 19th/20th cent. | | |
| ☐ **ROBERT, Theophile Paul** ..................... *paintings* | | **$4,400** |
| Swiss 1879-1954 | | |
| ☐ **ROBERT-FLEURY, Tony** ..................... *paintings* | | **$4,620** |
| French 1838-1912 | | |
| ☐ **ROBERTI, Antonio de** ......................... *paintings* | | **$352** |
| ☐ **ROBERTI, M.** ................................... *drawings* | **$70** | **$467** |
| Italian 19th cent. | | |
| ☐ **ROBERTIN, Sibylle (Schweiter)** ............ *paintings* | | **$302** |
| Austrian b. 1898 | | |
| ☐ **ROBERTO, E.** ................................... *drawings* | | **$374** |
| Italian late 19th cent. | | |
| ☐ **ROBERTS, David** ............................... *paintings* | **$550** | **$11,000** |
| Scottish, d.London 1864 ............................ *drawings* | **$440** | **$12,100** |
| ☐ **ROBERTS, Edwin Thomas** ................. *paintings* | **$605** | **$7,150** |
| English 1840-1917 | | |
| ☐ **ROBERTS, G.** ................................... *paintings* | | **$715** |
| English 19th cent. | | |
| ☐ **ROBERTS, Henry Benjamin** ................ *paintings* | | **$1,870** |
| British 1831-1915 | | |
| ☐ **ROBERTS, L.** .................................... *paintings* | | **$528** |
| ☐ **ROBERTS, Morton** ............................ *paintings* | | **$12,650** |
| American 1927-1964 | | |
| ☐ **ROBERTS, Robert** .............................. *paintings* | | **$550** |
| ☐ **ROBERTS, Thomas Sautell** ................... *paintings* | | **$5,500** |
| Irish c. 1760-1826 | | |
| ☐ **ROBERTS, W.** .................................. *paintings* | | **$605** |
| American 19th cent. | | |
| ☐ **ROBERTS, W.P.** ................................ *sculpture* | | **$220** |
| British | | |
| ☐ **ROBERTSON, Anne L.** ........................ *paintings* | **$770** | **$900** |
| American 1844-1933 | | |
| ☐ **ROBERTSON, C. Kay** .......................... *paintings* | | **$302** |
| ☐ **ROBERTSON, George Edward** ............. *paintings* | **$121** | **$660** |
| British b. 1864 | | |
| ☐ **ROBERTSON, Robert** .......................... *paintings* | | **$550** |
| American 20th cent. | | |
| ☐ **ROBERTY, Andre Felix** ....................... *drawings* | **$165** | **$1,320** |
| French b. 1877 | | |
| ☐ **ROBICHON, Jules Paul Victor** ............. *paintings* | | **$8,800** |
| French 19th/20th cent. | | |
| ☐ **ROBIE, Jean Baptiste** ......................... *paintings* | **$302** | **$24,200** |
| Belgian 1821-1910 | | |
| ☐ **ROBIN, Georges** ................................ *paintings* | | **$715** |
| Belgian d. after 1590 | | |

| | | Current Price Range | |
|---|---|---|---|
| | | Low | High |
| ☐ **ROBIN, Red** .............................. *drawings* | | $220 | $231 |
| American b. 1910 | | | |
| ☐ **ROBINET, Paul** ................................ *paintings* | | | $3,520 |
| ☐ **ROBINS, A.** ........................................ *paintings* | | $357 | $495 |
| British 19th cent. | | | |
| ☐ **ROBINS, H.** ........................................ *paintings* | | | $1,320 |
| English 19th cent. | | | |
| ☐ **ROBINS, Thomas Sewell** ........................ *paintings* | | | $660 |
| English 1814-1880 ...................................... *drawings* | | | $825 |
| ☐ **ROBINSON, Alexander Charles** ............ *drawings* | | $99 | $1,430 |
| American 1867-1940 | | | |
| ☐ **ROBINSON, Boardman** ........................ *paintings* | | | $440 |
| American 1876-1952 ................................ *drawings* | | $11 | $176 |
| ☐ **ROBINSON, Charles Dorman** .............. *paintings* | | $220 | $2,475 |
| American 1847-1933 .................................. *drawings* | | | $220 |
| ☐ **ROBINSON, David** ................................ *drawings* | | $550 | $550 |
| ☐ **ROBINSON, Florence Vincent** ............... *paintings* | | | $357 |
| American 1874-1937 ................................... *drawings* | | $77 | $302 |
| ☐ **ROBINSON, Frederic Cayley** ............... *drawings* | | | $385 |
| English 1862-1927 | | | |
| ☐ **ROBINSON, Hal** .............................. *paintings* | | $137 | $3,300 |
| American 1875-1933 .................................. *drawings* | | | $220 |
| ☐ **ROBINSON, Mrs. A.K.** ........................ *paintings* | | | $650 |
| American 19th cent. | | | |
| ☐ **ROBINSON, R.B.** .............................. *paintings* | | | $424 |
| ☐ **ROBINSON, Robert** ............................ *paintings* | | | $352 |
| American | | | |
| ☐ **ROBINSON, Sarah** ................................ *paintings* | | | $1,650 |
| ☐ **ROBINSON, Theodore** ........................ *paintings* | | $1,980 | $258,500 |
| American 1852-1896 .................................. *drawings* | | $495 | $3,300 |
| ☐ **ROBINSON, Thomas** ............................ *paintings* | | $220 | $1,100 |
| American 1835-1888 | | | |
| ☐ **ROBINSON, V.** .................................. *drawings* | | | $880 |
| British (?) 19th cent. | | | |
| ☐ **ROBINSON, William Heath** ................. *drawings* | | $110 | $2,310 |
| British 1872-1944 | | | |
| ☐ **ROBINSON, William S.** ........................ *paintings* | | $247 | $1,650 |
| American 1861-1945 | | | |
| ☐ **ROBINSON, William T.** ........................ *paintings* | | $192 | $550 |
| American 1852-1934 | | | |
| ☐ **ROBSON, Forster** ............................ *drawings* | | | $2,310 |
| English 19th/20th cent. | | | |
| ☐ **ROBUS, Hugo** .............................. *sculpture* | | $1,320 | $4,400 |
| American 1885-1964 | | | |
| ☐ **ROCCA, J. Della** ................................ *paintings* | | | $825 |
| Italian 19th cent. | | | |
| ☐ **ROCCO, Giovanni Luigi** ...................... *paintings* | | $8,250 | $8,800 |
| Italian first half 18th cent. | | | |

| | | Current Price Range | |
|---|---|---|---|
| | | *Low* | *High* |
| ☐ **ROCHARD, Rene** ............................ *sculpture* | | $198 | $440 |
| French 20th cent. | | | |
| ☐ **ROCHE, C.A. la** ............................ *paintings* | | | $825 |
| French 19th cent. | | | |
| ☐ **ROCHE, Odilon** ............................ *drawings* | | $220 | $660 |
| French 1868-1947 | | | |
| ☐ **ROCHEGROSSE, Georges Antoine** ....... *paintings* | | $1,540 | $9,900 |
| French 1859-1938 ............................ *drawings* | | | $715 |
| ☐ **ROCHENOIRE, Pierre** ................... *paintings* | | | $275 |
| French 20th cent. | | | |
| ☐ **ROCHER, Camy** ............................ *paintings* | | | $935 |
| ☐ **ROCHER, Charles** ....................... *drawings* | | | $550 |
| French 1890-1962 | | | |
| ☐ **ROCHUSSEN, Charles** .................. *drawings* | | $220 | $440 |
| Dutch 1814-1894 | | | |
| ☐ **ROCKBURNE, Dorothea** ............... *drawings* | | $2,200 | $16,500 |
| Canadian ac. 1970-1974 | | | |
| ☐ **ROCKWELL, Augustus** ................ *paintings* | | $50 | $2,860 |
| American ac. 1855-after 1860 | | | |
| ☐ **ROCKWELL, Cleveland** ............... *paintings* | | | $495 |
| American 1837-1907 ......................... *drawings* | | $550 | $3,850 |
| ☐ **ROCKWELL, Norman** .................. *paintings* | | $2,750 | $253,000 |
| American 1894-1978 ......................... *drawings* | | $1,000 | $19,250 |
| ☐ **ROCKWELL, Robert H.** ............... *sculpture* | | $385 | $880 |
| American b. 1885 | | | |
| ☐ **RODA, G. Puig** ........................... *paintings* | | | $28,600 |
| Italian 19th cent. ............................. *drawings* | | | $7,425 |
| ☐ **RODCHENKO, Alexander** ............ *drawings* | | | $30,800 |
| Russian 1891-1956 | | | |
| ☐ **RODE, Edmund Adler** .................. *paintings* | | $1,760 | $5,500 |
| ☐ **RODECK, H.** ............................... *paintings* | | | $231 |
| Austrian (?) 19th cent. | | | |
| ☐ **RODEN, W.T.** ............................. *paintings* | | | $412 |
| American 19th cent. | | | |
| ☐ **RODETTI, A.** .............................. *paintings* | | | $330 |
| Italian c. 1900 | | | |
| ☐ **RODIN, Auguste** ......................... *drawings* | | $220 | $13,200 |
| French 1840-1917 ............................ *sculpture* | | $1,650 | $385,000 |
| ☐ **RODNEY, Charles** ....................... *paintings* | | | $209 |
| English 19th cent. | | | |
| ☐ **RODNEY, H.C.** ............................ *paintings* | | | $2,200 |
| American | | | |
| ☐ **RODNEY, Herbert** ....................... *paintings* | | | $825 |
| American 19th/20th cent. | | | |
| ☐ **RODRIGUES, Hugo** ...................... *sculpture* | | | $1,650 |
| Latin American | | | |
| ☐ **RODRIGUEZ, A.C.** ....................... *paintings* | | | $330 |
| American 19th cent. | | | |

## An All-American Artist

*For more than half a century, Norman Rockwell helped America create a vision of itself. His paintings portrayed an idealized view of American society, depicting the modest triumphs and disappointments of everyday life. Primarily an illustration artist, Rockwell reached a vast audience through "The Saturday Evening Post" for which he created 300 covers in forty years. The magazine's subscribers were charmed by his humor and captivated by the warmth of his work, which today evokes nostalgic memories of a bygone time.*

*"All American Boy" was painted in 1922 as a cover for "Country Gentleman" magazine. The work was actually the winner's prize in the magazine's "Beautiful Boy Contest," which attracted 500,000 entries from all parts of the country in an effort to find America's most appealing child. Working from the winning photographs, Rockwell fashioned a portrait which was later presented to the child's family. The painting stayed with the "Most Beautiful Boy" until, at age seventy-three, he decided to sell it as he began to settle his estate. Auctioned in upstate New York in 1983, it brought $37,500. (Norman Rockwell, "All American Boy," oil on canvas, Mapes Auctioneers, April 30, 1983, $37,500.)*

|  |  | *Current Price Range* | |
|---|---|---|---|
|  |  | *Low* | *High* |
| ☐ **RODRIGUEZ, Alirio** ............................ *paintings* |  |  | **$3,300** |
| Latin American contemporary |  |  |  |
| ☐ **RODRIGUEZ, Mariano** ......................... *drawings* |  |  | **$1,210** |
| Latin American |  |  |  |
| ☐ **RODRIGUEZ DE GUZMAN, Manuel** ... *paintings* |  | **$2,090** | **$2,530** |
| Spanish 1818-1867 |  |  |  |
| ☐ **RODRIQUEZ JUAREZ, Nicolas** ............ *paintings* |  |  | **$11,000** |
| Mexican 1667-1734 |  |  |  |
| ☐ **RODSZUC, Anthony** ............................ *paintings* |  |  | **$440** |
| European 20th cent. |  |  |  |
| ☐ **RODWELL, Dianne T.** ......................... *paintings* |  |  | **$800** |
| American |  |  |  |
| ☐ **ROE, Clarence** ...................................... *paintings* |  | **$247** | **$742** |
| English ac. 1870; d. 1909 |  |  |  |

| | Current Price Range | |
|---|---|---|
| | Low | High |
| ☐ **ROE, Fred** ............................ *drawings* | | $247 |
| English 19th/20th cent. | | |
| ☐ **ROE, Robert Ernest** ........................... *paintings* | $770 | $1,045 |
| British 19th cent. | | |
| ☐ **ROE, Robert Henry** ......................... *paintings* | | $1,100 |
| ☐ **ROEDER, Max** ............................ *paintings* | | $2,475 |
| German 1866-1947 | | |
| ☐ **ROEGGE, Wilhelm** ........................... *paintings* | $2,090 | $3,520 |
| German 19th cent. | | |
| ☐ **ROEKENS, Paulette van** ...................... *paintings* | $297 | $330 |
| American/French b. 1898 | | |
| ☐ **ROELANDS, Willem** ......................... *paintings* | | $440 |
| Dutch 19th cent. | | |
| ☐ **ROELANT, E.** ............................. *paintings* | | $550 |
| French 19th cent. | | |
| ☐ **ROELOFS, Albert** ............................ *paintings* | $1,320 | $2,420 |
| Belgian 1877-1920 | | |
| ☐ **ROELOFS, Willem** ........................... *paintings* | $1,210 | $23,100 |
| Dutch 1822-1897 | | |
| ☐ **ROELOFS, Willem Eliza** ...................... *paintings* | $330 | $650 |
| Dutch 1874-1940 | | |
| ☐ **ROEPEL, Coenraet** ........................... *paintings* | | $7,150 |
| Dutch 1678-1748 | | |
| ☐ **ROERICH, Nikolai** ........................... *paintings* | | $412 |
| Russian 1874-1947 ...................................... *drawings* | | $2,200 |
| ☐ **ROESCH, Robert** ............................. *paintings* | | $935 |
| ☐ **ROESELER, August** ........................... *paintings* | $275 | $850 |
| German 1866-1934 | | |
| ☐ **ROESEN, Severin** ............................ *paintings* | $550 | $57,750 |
| German/American d. 1871 ........................... *drawings* | | $880 |
| ☐ **ROESLER FRANZ, Ettore** ................... *drawings* | $220 | $2,860 |
| Italian 1845-1907 | | |
| ☐ **ROESSLER, Georg** ........................... *paintings* | | $330 |
| German 1861-1925 | | |
| ☐ **ROESSLER, Walter R.** ........................ *paintings* | $300 | $990 |
| Russian 19th/20th cent. | | |
| ☐ **ROESTEL, A.** ............................... *paintings* | | $1,540 |
| contemporary | | |
| ☐ **ROESTRATEN, Pieter Gerritsz van** ...... *paintings* | $1,000 | $19,800 |
| Dutch c. 1630-1700 | | |
| ☐ **ROETER, L.A. de Koningh-de** .............. *paintings* | | $250 |
| Belgian 19th/20th cent. | | |
| ☐ **ROETING, Julius** ............................. *paintings* | | $462 |
| ☐ **ROFFIAEN, Jean Francois Xavier** ......... *paintings* | | $3,300 |
| Belgian 1820-1898 | | |
| ☐ **ROGAN, R. A.** ............................... *paintings* | | $825 |
| ☐ **ROGER, Charles A.** ........................... *paintings* | $220 | $770 |
| American 1866-1907 | | |

| | | | Current Price Range | |
|---|---|---|---|---|
| | | | Low | High |
| ☐ ROGERS, C.P. | paintings | | | $302 |
| American 20th cent. | | | | |
| ☐ ROGERS, F.K. | drawings | | $210 | $300 |
| ☐ ROGERS, Franklin Whiting | paintings | | $192 | $220 |
| American b. 1854 | | | | |
| ☐ ROGERS, G. | paintings | | | $2,420 |
| British 19th cent. | | | | |
| ☐ ROGERS, Gretchen W. | paintings | | | $2,750 |
| American b. 1881 | | | | |
| ☐ ROGERS, John | sculpture | | $55 | $8,800 |
| American 1829-1904 | | | | |
| ☐ ROGERS, Lilli | paintings | | | $192 |
| American 20th cent. | | | | |
| ☐ ROGERS, Margaret O. | paintings | | | $357 |
| American 20th cent. | | | | |
| ☐ ROGERS, Randolph | sculpture | | $880 | $7,700 |
| American 1825-1892 | | | | |
| ☐ ROGERS, W.G. | paintings | | | $935 |
| ☐ ROGERS, William Allen | paintings | | $66 | $660 |
| American 1854-1931 | | | | |
| ☐ ROGET, John L. | drawings | | | $176 |
| American 19th cent. | | | | |
| ☐ ROGHMAN, Roelandt | paintings | | | $104,500 |
| Dutch 1597-1680 | drawings | | $357 | $3,080 |
| ☐ ROGNE, R.D. | sculpture | | | $850 |
| American | | | | |
| ☐ ROHDE, Frederik Niels Martin | paintings | | $330 | $525 |
| Danish 1816-1886 | | | | |
| ☐ ROHDE, H. | paintings | | $357 | $467 |
| American 20th cent. | | | | |
| ☐ ROHLAND, Paul | paintings | | $220 | $242 |
| American | | | | |
| ☐ ROHLFS, Christian | paintings | | $990 | $27,500 |
| German 1849-1938 | drawings | | $4,675 | $14,300 |
| ☐ ROHLING, Carl | paintings | | | $990 |
| German 1849-1922 | sculpture | | | $286 |
| ☐ ROHNER, Georges | paintings | | $302 | $412 |
| French b. 1913 | | | | |
| ☐ ROHR, Frans Friederich | paintings | | | $550 |
| ☐ ROHRBACH, G.C. | paintings | | | $660 |
| ☐ ROHRHIRSCH, Richard | paintings | | | $715 |
| Austrian 1833-1892 | | | | |
| ☐ ROJAS, Carlos | paintings | | | $1,650 |
| Latin American 20th cent. | | | | |
| ☐ ROJAS, Elmar | paintings | | $1,320 | $4,675 |
| Guatemalan b. 1938 | | | | |
| ☐ ROJAS, Santiago | paintings | | | $357 |
| ☐ ROLAND, E. | paintings | | | $330 |

|  | | *Current Price Range* | |
| --- | --- | --- | --- |
|  | | Low | High |
| ☐ **ROLFE, A.F.** ................................... *paintings* | | | $13,200 |
| English ac. 1866 | | | |
| ☐ **ROLFE, Alexander T.** ........................... *paintings* | | | $770 |
| British 19th cent. | | | |
| ☐ **ROLFE, Henry Leonidas** ...................... *paintings* | | $1,100 | $2,420 |
| British fl. 1847-1881 | | | |
| ☐ **ROLL** ........................................ *paintings* | | | $330 |
| ☐ **ROLLE, August H.O.** ........................... *paintings* | | $495 | $1,650 |
| American 1875-1941 ................................. *drawings* | | $330 | $605 |
| ☐ **ROLLIG, E.** ................................... *paintings* | | | $825 |
| Austrian 19th cent. | | | |
| ☐ **ROLLIN, J. Plank** .............................. *paintings* | | | $1,100 |
| French (?) 19th cent. | | | |
| ☐ **ROLLINS, J.** ................................... *paintings* | | | $935 |
| American 19th cent. | | | |
| ☐ **ROLLINS, Warren E.** ........................... *paintings* | | $550 | $5,500 |
| American 1861-1962 ................................. *drawings* | | | $247 |
| ☐ **ROLSHOVEN, Julius** ........................... *paintings* | | $165 | $3,300 |
| American 1858-1930 ................................. *drawings* | | $137 | $522 |
| ☐ **ROLYAT, V.** ................................... *paintings* | | | $770 |
| British 19th cent. | | | |
| ☐ **ROM, J. H.** ................................... *paintings* | | | $825 |
| ☐ **ROMA, Emilia Janni** ........................... *drawings* | | | $209 |
| Italian 19th cent. | | | |
| ☐ **ROMACKO, A.** ................................. *paintings* | | | $1,045 |
| ☐ **ROMAGNOLI, Angiolo** ........................ *paintings* | | | $800 |
| Italian 2nd half 19th cent. | | | |
| ☐ **ROMAGNOLI, Giovanni** ...................... *paintings* | | | $715 |
| Italian b. 1883 | | | |
| ☐ **ROMAINE, H.** ................................. *paintings* | | | $990 |
| ☐ **ROMAKO, Anton** .............................. *paintings* | | $550 | $3,300 |
| Austrian 1832-1889 | | | |
| ☐ **ROMANACH, Leopoldo** ....................... *paintings* | | $1,980 | $14,300 |
| a. Cuban 1862-1951 | | | |
| ☐ **ROMANELLI** ................................... *sculpture* | | $2,750 | $8,800 |
| Italian 19th/20th cent. | | | |
| ☐ **ROMANELLI, Galli** ........................... *sculpture* | | $715 | $750 |
| ☐ **ROMANELLI, Giovanni Francesco** ....... *paintings* | | | $9,350 |
| Italian 1610-1662 | | | |
| ☐ **ROMANELLI, Pasquale** ....................... *sculpture* | | $660 | $9,900 |
| Italian 1812-1887 | | | |
| ☐ **ROMANELLI, Raffaelo** ....................... *sculpture* | | $605 | $4,400 |
| Italian early 20th cent. | | | |
| ☐ **ROMANINO, Girolamo di Romano** ....... *paintings* | | | $6,050 |
| Italian c. 1484/87-1562 ? | | | |
| ☐ **ROMANO, G.** ................................... *paintings* | | | $302 |
| Italian 19th cent. | | | |

| | Current Price Range | |
|---|---|---|
| | *Low* | *High* |

☐ **ROMANO, Giulio**
(**Giulio di Pietro de Gianuzzi PIPPI**) ........ *drawings* $4,125 | $7,700
Italian 1499-1546

☐ **ROMANO, Umberto** ............................ *paintings* $176 | $356
American b. 1905 ........................................ *drawings* $44 | $440

☐ **ROMANOVSKY, Dimitri** ...................... *paintings* $110 | $880
American 20th cent.

☐ **ROMARE, J.L.** .................................... *paintings* | $357
Continental 19th cent.

☐ **ROMBOUTS, Gillis Aegidius** ............... *paintings* $1,100 | $2,310
Dutch 1630-1678

☐ **ROMBOUTS, Salomon** ......................... *paintings* $4,125 | $33,000
Dutch ac. c. 1652; d. c. 1702

☐ **ROMEK, Arpad** .................................. *paintings* | $550

☐ **ROMERO DE TORRES, Julio** ............. *paintings* | $4,675
Spanish 1880-1930

☐ **ROMES, A.** ........................................ *paintings* | $330
Italian 19th cent.

☐ **ROMEYN, Willem** .............................. *paintings* | $3,300
Dutch c. 1624-1694

☐ **ROMHOFF, O.** .................................... *drawings* | $467
German 19th/20th cent.

☐ **ROMITI, Gino** .................................... *paintings* $165 | $385
Italian b. 1881

☐ **ROMNEY, George** .............................. *paintings* $825 | $28,600
English 1734-1802 ..................................... *drawings* $110 | $2,860

☐ **ROMOLINI, D.** .................................... *paintings* | $330
Italian 19th cent.

☐ **ROMRHIRSCH, K.** .............................. *paintings* | $440

☐ **RONAI, Jozsef Rippl** .......................... *drawings* | $440

☐ **RONALD, William** .............................. *paintings* | $320

☐ **RONAY, J.L.** ...................................... *paintings* $275 | $440
East Europe School 19th cent.

☐ **RONCALLI, Cristofano**
(**called IL POMARANCIO**) .................... *drawings* | $1,540

☐ **RONCARD, P.** .................................... *paintings* | $550
French 19th/20th cent.

☐ **RONDE, M.** ........................................ *paintings* | $330
European 19th cent.

☐ **RONDEL, Frederick** ............................ *paintings* $247 | $5,500
American 1826-1892 ................................. *drawings* $137 | $467

☐ **RONDEL, Henri** .................................. *paintings* $605 | $1,210
French 1857-1919

☐ **RONDEL, S.** ...................................... *paintings* | $880
American 19th cent.

☐ **RONGIER, Jeanne** .............................. *paintings* | $4,400
French ac. 1869-1900

☐ **RONIGE, M.** ...................................... *paintings* | $440
Italian 19th cent.

|                                                              |          | Current Price Range |          |
|--------------------------------------------------------------|----------|---------|----------|
|                                                              |          | *Low*   | *High*   |
| ☐ **RONNER-KNIP, Henriette** .................. *paintings*  |          | **$660**| **$25,300** |
| Dutch 1821-1909                                              |          |         |          |
| ☐ **RONTINI, Alessandro** ......................... *paintings* |       |         | **$9,350** |
| Italian b. 1854                                              |          |         |          |
| ☐ **ROOK, Edward F.** ............................. *paintings* |       |         | **$880** |
| 1870-1960                                                    |          |         |          |
| ☐ **ROOKE, F.J.** ..................................... *paintings* |    |         | **$260** |
| ☐ **ROOKE, Thomas Matthews** ................. *paintings*   |          | **$632**| **$5,775** |
| English 1842-1942 ..................................... *drawings* |    |         | **$450** |
| ☐ **ROOKER, Michael Angelo** .................... *paintings* |        |         | **$4,950** |
| English 1743-1801                                           |          |         |          |
| ☐ **ROOS, J.G.H.** ................................... *paintings* |     |         | **$605** |
| ☐ **ROOS, Jan (called Giovanni Rosa)** ......... *drawings*  |          |         | **$880** |
| ☐ **ROOS, Johann Heinrich** ...................... *paintings* |        |         | **$1,430** |
| German 1631-1685                                            |          |         |          |
| ☐ **ROOS, Peter** ................................... *paintings* |       | **$247**| **$1,210** |
| American b. 1850 ..................................... *drawings* |      |         | **$220** |
| ☐ **ROOS, Philipp Peter**                                    |          |         |          |
| **(called Rosa da Tivoli)** ........................ *paintings* |       | **$1,045** | **$5,500** |
| German 1657-1706                                            |          |         |          |
| ☐ **ROOSDORP, Frederik** ....................... *paintings* |          |         | **$1,100** |
| Dutch 1839-1865                                             |          |         |          |
| ☐ **ROOSENBOOM, Albert** ...................... *paintings*  |          | **$1,155** | **$18,700** |
| Belgian 1845-1875                                           |          |         |          |
| ☐ **ROOSENBOOM, Margarete** ................. *paintings*    |          |         | **$2,750** |
| Dutch 1843-1896 ..................................... *drawings* |      | **$165**| **$187** |
| ☐ **ROOSENBOOM, Nicolaas Johannes** ...... *paintings*      |          | **$1,760** | **$4,620** |
| Dutch 1805/08-1880                                         |          |         |          |
| ☐ **ROOSEVELT, S. Montgomery** .............. *drawings*     |          |         | **$275** |
| American 1863-1929                                         |          |         |          |
| ☐ **ROOT, Robert Marshall** ...................... *paintings* |        |         | **$55**  |
| b. 1863 ................................................. *drawings* |   |         | **$275** |
| ☐ **ROOTIUS, Jan Albertsz** ...................... *paintings* |        |         | **$11,000** |
| Dutch c. 1615-1674                                         |          |         |          |
| ☐ **ROOZEE, H.** ..................................... *paintings* |      |         | **$330** |
| ☐ **ROPER, E.** ...................................... *paintings* |       |         | **$495** |
| ☐ **ROPES, Joseph** ............................... *paintings* |         | **$660**| **$6,050** |
| American 1812-1885                                         |          |         |          |
| ☐ **ROPP, Hubert** ................................... *paintings* |      |         | **$715** |
| American b. 1894                                           |          |         |          |
| ☐ **ROPS, Felicien Joseph Victor** .............. *paintings* |         |         | **$4,400** |
| Belgian 1833-1898 .................................... *drawings* |      | **$192**| **$1,870** |
| ☐ **ROQUEPLAN,**                                             |          |         |          |
| **Camille Joseph Etienne** ...................... *paintings* |          | **$686**| **$880** |
| French 1803-1855 .................................... *drawings* |       |         | **$440** |
| ☐ **RORKE, E.A.** .................................... *paintings* |       |         | **$660** |
| ☐ **ROS, Van** ............................................. *paintings* | | **$110**| **$275** |

| | | Current Price Range | |
|---|---|---|---|
| | | *Low* | *High* |
| ☐ **ROSA, Francesco de** | | | |
| **(called Pacecco de ROSA)** ...... *paintings* | | **$4,950** | **$7,700** |
| Italian c. 1600-1654 | | | |
| ☐ **ROSA, Luigi** ...... *paintings* | | **$165** | **$220** |
| Italian 1850-1919 | | | |
| ☐ **ROSA, Salvator** ...... *paintings* | | | **$24,200** |
| Italian 1615-1673 ...... *drawings* | | **$1,265** | **$5,060** |
| ☐ **ROSAI, Ottone** ...... *paintings* | | **$1,430** | **$7,500** |
| Italian 1895-1957 | | | |
| ☐ **ROSATI, Giulio** ...... *paintings* | | **$550** | **$3,080** |
| Italian 1858-1917 ...... *drawings* | | **$2,090** | **$20,900** |
| ☐ **ROSATI, Guilio** ...... *drawings* | | | **$1,500** |
| Italian 1675-1757 | | | |
| ☐ **ROSATI, James** ...... *drawings* | | | **$418** |
| ☐ **ROSCH, L.** ...... *drawings* | | **$990** | **$1,100** |
| ☐ **ROSE, Alexandre Auguste** ...... *paintings* | | | **$14,300** |
| French ac. 1866-1878 | | | |
| ☐ **ROSE, Anthony Lewis de** ...... *paintings* | | **$418** | **$660** |
| American 1803-1886 | | | |
| ☐ **ROSE, Edward** ...... *drawings* | | | **$192** |
| American 19th/20th cent. | | | |
| ☐ **ROSE, Giovanni Luigi** ...... *paintings* | | | **$2,585** |
| Italian 19th cent. | | | |
| ☐ **ROSE, Guy** ...... *paintings* | | **$1,430** | **$18,150** |
| American 1867-1925 | | | |
| ☐ **ROSE, Herman** ...... *paintings* | | **$1,320** | **$1,540** |
| American b. 1909 | | | |
| ☐ **ROSE, Horace L.** ...... *paintings* | | | **$660** |
| American 20th cent. | | | |
| ☐ **ROSE, Iver** ...... *paintings* | | **$176** | **$495** |
| American 20th cent. | | | |
| ☐ **ROSE, Julius** ...... *paintings* | | **$605** | **$7,700** |
| German 1828-1911 | | | |
| ☐ **ROSE, Paul** ...... *paintings* | | | **$3,300** |
| South African | | | |
| ☐ **ROSE, Sir Richard** ...... *paintings* | | | **$220** |
| British 20th cent. | | | |
| ☐ **ROSE, W.** ...... *paintings* | | | **$650** |
| American d. 1938 | | | |
| ☐ **ROSE, William S.** ...... *paintings* | | | **$3,300** |
| English 1810-1873 | | | |
| ☐ **ROSEBOOM** ...... *paintings* | | | **$192** |
| German 19th cent. | | | |
| ☐ **ROSELAND, Harry** ...... *paintings* | | **$275** | **$24,200** |
| American 1868-1950 ...... *drawings* | | | **$4,125** |
| ☐ **ROSELL, A.** ...... *paintings* | | | **$660** |
| ☐ **ROSELL, H.** ...... *paintings* | | | **$880** |
| 19th cent. | | | |

| | | *Current Price Range* | |
|---|---|---|---|
| | | Low | High |
| ☐ **ROSELLI, C.** ............................... *paintings* | | | **$660** |
| Italian 19th/20th cent. | | | |
| ☐ **ROSELLI, Matteo** ............................ *drawings* | | | **$3,960** |
| Italian 1578-1650 | | | |
| ☐ **ROSELY, H.** ................................. *paintings* | | | **$495** |
| American | | | |
| ☐ **ROSEN, Charles** ........................... *paintings* | **$440** | **$5,775** |
| American 1878-1950 .......................... *drawings* | | | **$99** |
| ☐ **ROSEN, Louis** ............................. *paintings* | **$75** | **$250** |
| ☐ **ROSENBERG, B.** ............................ *drawings* | | | **$440** |
| American early 20th cent. | | | |
| ☐ **ROSENBERG, Henry M.** ................. *paintings* | **$247** | **$495** |
| Canadian 1858-1947 | | | |
| ☐ **ROSENBERG, James N.** ................. *paintings* | **$110** | **$176** |
| American b. 1874 | | | |
| ☐ **ROSENBOOM, A.** .......................... *paintings* | | | **$1,100** |
| ☐ **ROSENBOOM, Nicholas Johannes** ........ *paintings* | | | **$9,900** |
| Dutch 19th cent. | | | |
| ☐ **ROSENFELD, Edward** ..................... *paintings* | **$66** | **$220** |
| American 20th cent. | | | |
| ☐ **ROSENKRANZ, Clarence C.** ............. *paintings* | **$120** | **$660** |
| American 19th/20th cent. | | | |
| ☐ **ROSENMEYER, B.J.** ....................... *drawings* | | | **$220** |
| American | | | |
| ☐ **ROSENQUIST, James** ...................... *paintings* | **$1,760** | **$66,000** |
| American b. 1933 .............................. *drawings* | **$1,650** | **$12,100** |
| ............................................. *sculpture* | | | **$3,080** |
| ☐ **ROSENSTOCK, Isidor** ..................... *drawings* | | | **$385** |
| French b. 1880 | | | |
| ☐ **ROSENTHAL, Albert** ...................... *paintings* | **$180** | **$3,190** |
| American 1863-1939 | | | |
| ☐ **ROSENTHAL, Bernard** .................... *sculpture* | **$165** | **$2,475** |
| ☐ **ROSENTHAL, Doris** ....................... *paintings* | **$88** | **$825** |
| American 1895-1971 .......................... *drawings* | **$66** | **$190** |
| ☐ **ROSENTHAL, Max** ........................ *paintings* | | | **$990** |
| American late 19th cent. | | | |
| ☐ **ROSENTHAL, Toby Edward** ............. *paintings* | **$770** | **$19,800** |
| American 1848-1917 | | | |
| ☐ **ROSIER, Amedee** ......................... *paintings* | | | **$1,100** |
| French b. 1831 | | | |
| ☐ **ROSIER, Jean Guillaume** ................ *paintings* | | | **$1,650** |
| Belgian 1858-1931 | | | |
| ☐ **ROSIERSE, Johannes** ..................... *paintings* | **$550** | **$4,180** |
| Dutch 1818-1901 | | | |
| ☐ **ROSIMI, R.** ............................... *paintings* | **$110** | **$191** |
| Italian 20th cent. | | | |
| ☐ **ROSIN, Harry** ............................ *paintings* | | | **$253** |
| American 20th cent. | | | |
| ☐ **ROSKER, Furmin** ......................... *drawings* | | | **$275** |

| | Current Price Range | |
|---|---|---|
| | *Low* | *High* |
| ☐ **ROSLIN, Alexander** ............................ *paintings* | | **$3,300** |
| Swedish 1718-1793 | | |
| ☐ **ROSNER, Charles** ............................... *paintings* | | **$220** |
| German/American 1894-after 1975 ................ *drawings* | **$400** | **$900** |
| ☐ **ROSOFSKY** ...................................... *drawings* | | **$600** |
| ☐ **ROSS, Alex** ..................................... *paintings* | **$330** | **$495** |
| b. 1908 ............................................. *drawings* | | **$660** |
| ☐ **ROSS, Alvin** .................................... *paintings* | **$165** | **$275** |
| American | | |
| ☐ **ROSS, D.A.** ..................................... *paintings* | | **$275** |
| American 19th cent. | | |
| ☐ **ROSS, Gordon** ................................. *drawings* | **$247** | **$275** |
| American 20th cent. | | |
| ☐ **ROSS, H.** ....................................... *paintings* | | **$522** |
| American late 19th cent. | | |
| ☐ **ROSS, James** ................................... *paintings* | | **$13,200** |
| British ac. 1745-1821 | | |
| ☐ **ROSS, John** ..................................... *paintings* | | **$330** |
| English 19th/20th cent. | | |
| ☐ **ROSS, Karl (Charles)** ......................... *paintings* | | **$935** |
| German 1816-1858 | | |
| ☐ **ROSS, Mary Herrick** .......................... *paintings* | | **$385** |
| American 20th cent. | | |
| ☐ **ROSS, Olivier** .................................. *paintings* | | **$330** |
| French b. 1920 | | |
| ☐ **ROSS, Robert Thorburn** ...................... *paintings* | | **$2,420** |
| British 1816-1876 | | |
| ☐ **ROSS, Sanford** ................................. *drawings* | **$27** | **$209** |
| American 20th cent. | | |
| ☐ **ROSS, Thomas** .................................. *paintings* | | **$7,700** |
| ☐ **ROSSANO, Frederico** .......................... *paintings* | | **$1,320** |
| Italian 1835-1912 | | |
| ☐ **ROSSANT, James A.** ........................... *drawings* | | **$330** |
| ☐ **ROSSE, F.** ...................................... *sculpture* | | **$550** |
| ☐ **ROSSEAU, Percival Leonard** ............... *paintings* | **$418** | **$22,000** |
| American 1859/69-1937 .............................. *drawings* | **$605** | **$715** |
| ☐ **ROSSEELS, Jacob Cornelis** ................. *paintings* | | **$3,300** |
| Belgian 1828-1912 | | |
| ☐ **ROSSETTI, Dante Gabriel** .................... *paintings* | | **$99,000** |
| English 1828-1882 ................................... *drawings* | **$13,200** | **$20,900** |
| ☐ **ROSSI, Alberto** ................................. *paintings* | | **$990** |
| Italian 1858-1936 ................................... *drawings* | | **$385** |
| ☐ **ROSSI, Alec** .................................... *paintings* | | **$550** |
| ☐ **ROSSI, Alexander M.** .......................... *paintings* | | **$275** |
| English ac. 1870-1903 | | |
| ☐ **ROSSI, Gino** .................................... *paintings* | | **$440** |
| Italian 1884-1947 | | |
| ☐ **ROSSI, Giovanni Battista** ..................... *paintings* | | **$1,320** |
| Italian | | |

|                                                      |           | Current Price Range |          |
|------------------------------------------------------|-----------|---------|----------|
|                                                      |           | Low     | High     |
| ☐ **ROSSI, Guiseppe** ............... *paintings*<br>Italian 19th cent. |  |         | $302     |
| ☐ **ROSSI, Lucius** ............... *paintings*<br>French 1846-1913 |  | $3,300  | $6,600   |
| ☐ **ROSSI, Luigi** ............... *paintings*<br>Swiss 1853-1923 |  |         | $4,400   |
| ☐ **ROSSI, Pasquale** ............... *drawings*<br>Italian b. 1861 |  |         | $440     |
| ☐ **ROSSITER, Thomas Pritchard** ......... *paintings*<br>American 1818-1871 |  | $990 | $5,170 |
| ☐ **ROSSLER, Georg** ............... *paintings*<br>German b. 1861 |  |         | $467     |
| ☐ **ROSSNER, Charles** ............... *drawings*<br>American 20th cent. |  |         | $247     |
| ☐ **ROSSO, Medardo** ............... *sculpture*<br>Italian 1858-1928 |  | $2,750 | $3,520  |
| ☐ **ROSSUM DU CHATTEL,**<br>**Fredericus Jacobus van** ......... *drawings*<br>Dutch 1856-1917 |  |         | $715     |
| ☐ **ROSTEL, Agathe** ............... *paintings*<br>German ac. 1871-1893 |  |         | $5,225   |
| ☐ **ROSTOCK MASTER** ............... *paintings* |  |         | $30,800  |
| ☐ **ROSZAK, Theodore** ............... *drawings*<br>American b. 1907 |  | $264 | $825 |
| ☐ **ROSZEZEWSKI, H.D.** ............... *paintings* |  |         | $1,100   |
| ☐ **ROTA, G.** ............... *paintings* |  |         | $850     |
| ☐ **ROTARI, Pietro Antonio** ............... *paintings*<br>Italian 1707-1762 ............... *drawings* |  | $880 | $30,800<br>$20,900 |
| ☐ **ROTCH, Benjamin Smith** ............... *paintings*<br>American 1817-1882 |  |         | $1,100   |
| ☐ **ROTELLA, Mimo** ............... *drawings*<br>Italian 1760 |  | $880 | $1,760 |
| ☐ **ROTENBERG, Harold** ............... *paintings*<br>American 20th cent. |  |         | $220     |
| ☐ **ROTERS, Carl** ............... *drawings*<br>American 20th cent. |  |         | $220     |
| ☐ **ROTH, Andreas** ............... *paintings*<br>American 20th cent. |  | $71 | $550 |
| ☐ **ROTH, C.** ............... *drawings*<br>French 19th cent. |  |         | $1,210   |
| ☐ **ROTH, Ernest David** ............... *paintings*<br>American 1879-1964 |  | $99 | $1,430 |
| ☐ **ROTH, Frank** ............... *paintings*<br>American b. 1936 ............... *drawings* |  | $66 | $418<br>$220 |
| ☐ **ROTH, Frederick George Richard** ......... *sculpture*<br>American 1872-1944 |  |         | $1,320   |
| ☐ **ROTH, Peter** ............... *paintings*<br>Dutch 20th cent. |  |         | $385     |

| | | | Current Price Range | |
| --- | --- | --- | --- | --- |
| | | | *Low* | *High* |
| ☐ **ROTH, Philipp** | .............................. | *paintings* | $1,650 | $17,600 |
| German 1841-1921 | | | | |
| ☐ **ROTH, Richard** | ............................... | *paintings* | | $990 |
| ☐ **ROTH, Wolfgang** | ............................... | *drawings* | | $247 |
| American | | | | |
| ☐ **ROTHAUG, Leopold** | .......................... | *paintings* | | $2,310 |
| Austrian b. 1868 | | | | |
| ☐ **ROTHBORT, Samuel** | ......................... | *paintings* | $1,650 | $3,850 |
| American b. 1882 | | | | |
| ☐ **ROTHENBERG, Susan** | ........................ | *paintings* | | $35,200 |
| American b. 1945 | | | | |
| ☐ **ROTHENSTEIN, Sir William** | ............... | *paintings* | | $990 |
| English 1872-1945 | .................................... | *drawings* | $231 | $467 |
| ☐ **ROTHKO, Mark** | ................................ | *paintings* | $4,950 | $1,815,000 |
| Russian/American 1903-1970 | .................... | *drawings* | $1,870 | $28,600 |
| ☐ **ROTHKOWITZ, Mark** | ......................... | *paintings* | | $3,850 |
| ☐ **ROTHMEL, Peter Frederick** | ................ | *paintings* | $495 | $2,640 |
| American 1817-1895 | | | | |
| ☐ **ROTHSTEIN, E.** | ................................. | *paintings* | $165 | $440 |
| German 19th/20th cent. | | | | |
| ☐ **ROTIG, Georges Frederic** | ..................... | *paintings* | $990 | $3,850 |
| French 1873-1961 | | | | |
| ☐ **ROTTENHAMMER, Johann** | ............... | *paintings* | $5,500 | $9,900 |
| German 1564-1625 | | | | |
| ☐ **ROTTERDAM, Paul Z.** | ....................... | *paintings* | $3,300 | $5,775 |
| Austrian/American b. 1939 | ........................ | *drawings* | | $1,210 |
| ☐ **ROTTMAN, George** | ........................... | *sculpture* | $302 | $385 |
| ☐ **ROTTMANN, Carl** | ............................. | *drawings* | | $700 |
| ☐ **ROTTMANN, Mozart** | ......................... | *paintings* | $550 | $21,450 |
| Austrian b. 1874 | | | | |
| ☐ **ROTTOMARA, F.A.** | .......................... | *drawings* | | $385 |
| ☐ **ROUAULT, Georges** | ........................... | *paintings* | $7,150 | $110,000 |
| French 1871-1958 | .................................... | *drawings* | $2,090 | $46,750 |
| ☐ **ROUBAUD, Francois Felix (the elder)** | ..... | *sculpture* | | $632 |
| French 1825-1876 | | | | |
| ☐ **ROUBAUD, Franz** | ............................. | *paintings* | $2,200 | $25,300 |
| Russian 1856-1928 | | | | |
| ☐ **ROUBY, A.** | ...................................... | *paintings* | | $1,430 |
| ☐ **ROUCH, V. de** | ................................. | *paintings* | | $825 |
| Belgian (?) 19th cent. | | | | |
| ☐ **ROUFF, Emile** | ................................. | *sculpture* | | $495 |
| ☐ **ROUFFET, Jules** | ............................... | *paintings* | | $1,870 |
| French 1862-1931 | | | | |
| ☐ **ROUGERON, Jules** | ............................ | *paintings* | | $3,575 |
| French 1841-1880 | | | | |
| ☐ **ROULAND, Orlando** | ........................... | *paintings* | | $907 |
| American 1871-1945 | | | | |
| ☐ **ROUMEGOUS, Auguste Francois** | ......... | *paintings* | $1,045 | $1,540 |
| French 19th cent. | | | | |

| | | | Current Price Range | |
|---|---|---|---|---|
| | | | Low | High |
| ☐ ROUNTREE, Herman | drawings | | | $330 |
| English 1878-1950 | | | | |
| ☐ ROUSE, H.L. | paintings | | | $2,090 |
| British 19th cent. | | | | |
| ☐ ROUSEL, Pierre | paintings | | | $495 |
| French 20th cent. | | | | |
| ☐ ROUSSE, C. | drawings | | | $275 |
| English 19th cent. | | | | |
| ☐ ROUSSEAU | sculpture | | | $411 |
| ☐ ROUSSEAU | paintings | | | $3,575 |
| British 19th cent. | | | | |
| ☐ ROUSSEAU, G. | paintings | | $247 | $300 |
| 19th cent. | | | | |
| ☐ ROUSSEAU, Henri (called LE DOUANIER) | paintings | | $28,600 | $264,000 |
| French 1844-1910 | | | | |
| ☐ ROUSSEAU, Henri Emilien | paintings | | $1,100 | $10,450 |
| French 1875-1933 | | | | |
| ☐ ROUSSEAU, Maurice | paintings | | $400 | $715 |
| French 19th cent. | | | | |
| ☐ ROUSSEAU, N. | paintings | | | $440 |
| ☐ ROUSSEAU, Philippe | paintings | | $1,100 | $1,870 |
| French 1816-1887 | | | | |
| ☐ ROUSSEAU, T.T. | drawings | | | $2,090 |
| French 18th/19th cent. | | | | |
| ☐ ROUSSEAU, Theodore Etienne Pierre | paintings | | $2,420 | $28,600 |
| French 1812-1867 | drawings | | $467 | $11,000 |
| ☐ ROUSSEAU, Victor | sculpture | | | $440 |
| ☐ ROUSSEFF, W. Vladimar | paintings | | | $302 |
| American 1890-1934 | | | | |
| ☐ ROUSSEL, Ker Xavier | paintings | | $5,000 | $15,400 |
| French 1867-1944 | drawings | | $82 | $3,080 |
| ☐ ROUSSEL, Paul | sculpture | | | $412 |
| French 1867-1928 | | | | |
| ☐ ROUSSEL, Paul Marie | paintings | | | $198 |
| French 1804-1877 | | | | |
| ☐ ROUSSEL, Pierre | paintings | | $467 | $2,420 |
| French b. 1927 | | | | |
| ☐ ROUSSET, Pierre-Noel | drawings | | | $4,180 |
| ☐ ROUSSLEY, G.J. | paintings | | | $550 |
| Swiss late 19th cent. | | | | |
| ☐ ROUVIERE | paintings | | | $330 |
| ☐ ROUX, Antoine | drawings | | | $3,850 |
| French 1799-1872 | | | | |
| ☐ ROUX, Antoine | drawings | | $1,600 | $5,500 |
| French 1765-1835 | | | | |
| ☐ ROUX, Carl | paintings | | $550 | $1,000 |
| German 1826-1894 | | | | |
| ☐ ROUX, Constant | sculpture | | | $302 |

| | | Current Price Range | |
|---|---|---|---|
| | | Low | High |
| ☐ **ROUX, Hector le** ............... *paintings* | | | $990 |
| ☐ **ROUX, Hippolyte** ................. *paintings* | | | $192 |
| French b. 1852 | | | |
| ☐ **ROUX, Louis** ................. *drawings* | | | $3,000 |
| French 1817-1903 | | | |
| ☐ **ROUZEE, M.** ................. *paintings* | | $275 | $357 |
| French 19th cent. | | | |
| ☐ **ROUZEE, W.** ................. *paintings* | | $60 | $410 |
| American 19th cent. | | | |
| ☐ **ROVATKAY** ................. *paintings* | | | $176 |
| Hungarian contemporary | | | |
| ☐ **ROVERE, Giovanni Mauro Delle** .......... *paintings* | | | $1,320 |
| ☐ **ROVLLO, Y.** ................. *paintings* | | | $275 |
| ☐ **ROWBOTHAM, Charles** ................. *drawings* | | $154 | $2,200 |
| English ac. 1877-1913 | | | |
| ☐ **ROWBOTHAM, Claude H.** ................. *drawings* | | $165 | $357 |
| British late 19th cent. | | | |
| ☐ **ROWBOTHAM, Thomas Leeson** .......... *paintings* | | $110 | $275 |
| English 1823-1875 ................. *drawings* | | $247 | $715 |
| ☐ **ROWBURY, Guy** ................. *drawings* | | | $700 |
| American | | | |
| ☐ **ROWDEN, Thomas** ................. *paintings* | | | $242 |
| British 1842-1926 | | | |
| ☐ **ROWE, Charles** ................. *paintings* | | | $800 |
| American | | | |
| ☐ **ROWE, E.** ................. *paintings* | | | $275 |
| ☐ **ROWE, Sidney Grant** ................. *paintings* | | | $1,650 |
| English 1861-1928 | | | |
| ☐ **ROWLAND, William** ................. *paintings* | | | $522 |
| British 20th cent. | | | |
| ☐ **ROWLANDSON, George Derville** ......... *paintings* | | $600 | $5,280 |
| British b. 1861 ................. *drawings* | | | $7,975 |
| ☐ **ROWLANDSON, Thomas** ................. *drawings* | | $330 | $37,400 |
| English 1756-1827 | | | |
| ☐ **ROWLES, Stanley Charles** ................. *paintings* | | | $2,310 |
| British b. 1887 | | | |
| ☐ **ROY, F.** ................. *paintings* | | $143 | $770 |
| French 19th cent. | | | |
| ☐ **ROY, Jean Baptiste de** ................. *paintings* | | | $2,750 |
| Belgian 1759-1839 | | | |
| ☐ **ROY, Marius** ................. *paintings* | | $1,650 | $2,090 |
| French b. 1833 | | | |
| ☐ **ROY, Pierre** ................. *paintings* | | $13,750 | $14,300 |
| ................. *drawings* | | | $165 |
| ☐ **ROYAL, Thomas** ................. *paintings* | | | $467 |
| English 18th cent. | | | |
| ☐ **ROYBAL, Alfonso** ................. *drawings* | | | $770 |
| ☐ **ROYBET, Ferdinand** ................. *paintings* | | $242 | $16,500 |
| French 1840-1920 ................. *drawings* | | $66 | $605 |

| | Current Price Range | |
|---|---|---|
| | *Low* | *High* |
| ☐ **ROYER, Charles** .................................. *paintings* | | **$1,540** |
| French 19th cent. | | |
| ☐ **ROYLE, Herbert** .................................. *paintings* | | **$550** |
| British 19th/20th cent. | | |
| ☐ **ROYLE, Stanley** .................................. *paintings* | | **$2,475** |
| British/Canadian 1888-1962 | | |
| ☐ **ROZEN, Jerome** .................................. *paintings* | | **$440** |
| ☐ **ROZET, Fanny** .................................. *sculpture* | | **$1,430** |
| French b. 1881 | | |
| ☐ **ROZIER, Dominique** .......................... *paintings* | **$1,100** | **$1,100** |
| French 1840-1901 | | |
| ☐ **ROZIER, Jules Charles** ........................ *paintings* | **$286** | **$4,950** |
| French 1821-1882 | | |
| ☐ **ROZIER, Prosper Roch** ........................ *paintings* | | **$1,540** |
| French 19th cent. | | |
| ☐ **ROZMAINSKY, Vladimir** .................... *paintings* | | **$521** |
| Russian 1885-1943 | | |
| ☐ **RUBELLI, Ludwig de** .......................... *paintings* | | **$1,760** |
| Austrian 1841-1905 | | |
| ☐ **RUBEN, Franz Leo** ............................ *paintings* | **$990** | **$2,860** |
| Austrian/Czech 1842/43-1920 ......................... *drawings* | | **$110** |
| ☐ **RUBEN, Richard** .................................. *drawings* | | **$231** |
| American b. 1925 | | |
| ☐ **RUBENS, Franz** .................................. *paintings* | | **$742** |
| Czechoslovakian b. 1843 | | |
| ☐ **RUBENS, Sir Peter Paul** ...................... *paintings* | **$33,000** | **$352,000** |
| Flemish 1577-1640 | | |
| ☐ **RUBIN** .................................. *paintings* | | **$1,100** |
| ☐ **RUBIN, Reuven** .................................. *paintings* | **$5,500** | **$41,800** |
| Israeli 1893-1974 ......................... *drawings* | **$220** | **$7,425** |
| ☐ **RUBINGI, Lajos Kubanyi von** .............. *paintings* | | **$522** |
| Hungarian 1855-1912 | | |
| ☐ **RUBIO, Louis** .................................. *paintings* | | **$990** |
| Italian 18th/19th cent. | | |
| ☐ **RUBIO, Nicolas** .................................. *paintings* | | **$880** |
| ☐ **RUBOVICZ, M.** .................................. *paintings* | | **$275** |
| ☐ **RUCKER, Robert** .................................. *paintings* | **$440** | **$797** |
| American 20th cent. | | |
| ☐ **RUDA, Edwin** .................................. *paintings* | | **$330** |
| ☐ **RUDD, N.** .................................. *paintings* | | **$1,760** |
| ☐ **RUDECK, P.H.** .................................. *paintings* | | **$627** |
| German 19th/20th cent. | | |
| ☐ **RUDELL, Peter Edward** ........................ *paintings* | **$220** | **$1,210** |
| American 1854-1899 | | |
| ☐ **RUDISUHLI, Hermann** ........................ *paintings* | **$1,430** | **$1,540** |
| Swiss 1864-1945 | | |
| ☐ **RUDOLPH, Ernest** .................................. *paintings* | | **$1,650** |
| American | | |

| | | | Current Price Range | |
| --- | --- | --- | --- | --- |
| | | | Low | High |
| ☐ **RUDOLPH, Harold** | ............................ | *paintings* | | $1,320 |
| American 1850-1884 | | | | |
| ☐ **RUDOLPHI, Johannes** | .......................... | *paintings* | | $1,100 |
| German b. 1877 | | | | |
| ☐ **RUE, Louis Felix de la** | ......................... | *drawings* | | $440 |
| ☐ **RUE, Maurice la** | ................................ | *paintings* | | $440 |
| French 1861-1935 | | | | |
| ☐ **RUEDA, E.** | .......................................... | *paintings* | | $302 |
| American 19th/20th cent. | | | | |
| ☐ **RUEFF (?), E.A.** | ................................. | *paintings* | | $715 |
| German 19th cent. | | | | |
| ☐ **RUFF, Beatrice** | ................................... | *paintings* | | $440 |
| American 20th cent. | | | | |
| ☐ **RUGE, Carl** | ........................................ | *drawings* | | $330 |
| American 20th cent. | | | | |
| ☐ **RUGENDAS, Johann Moritz** | ................ | *paintings* | $11,000 | $53,900 |
| German 1802-1858 | ..................................... | *drawings* | $3,300 | $12,100 |
| ☐ **RUGGERILLO** | ................................... | *paintings* | | $550 |
| 19th cent. | | | | |
| ☐ **RUGGIERO, P.** | ................................... | *paintings* | | $1,045 |
| Italian 19th cent. | | | | |
| ☐ **RUGGLES, Eliza E.** | ............................ | *drawings* | | $220 |
| American 19th cent. | | | | |
| ☐ **RUGIERE, N.** | ..................................... | *paintings* | | $264 |
| ☐ **RUISDAEL, Jacob van** | ........................ | *drawings* | $8,800 | $470,000 |
| Dutch 1828/29-1882 | | | | |
| ☐ **RUISDAEL, Salomon van** | ..................... | *paintings* | | $55,000 |
| Dutch c. 1600-1670 | | | | |
| ☐ **RUITH, Horace van** | ........................... | *drawings* | | $357 |
| British 1872-1947 | | | | |
| ☐ **RUIZ, B.G.** | ......................................... | *paintings* | | $660 |
| American 19th cent. | | | | |
| ☐ **RUIZ, B.L.** | ......................................... | *paintings* | | $440 |
| American 1872-1920 | | | | |
| ☐ **RUIZ, B.Y.** | ......................................... | *paintings* | $110 | $605 |
| American 20th cent. | | | | |
| ☐ **RUIZ, Enrique Martinez Cubells** | ........... | *paintings* | | $715 |
| ☐ **RUIZ, Juan** | ........................................ | *paintings* | | $7,150 |
| Spanish 16th cent. | | | | |
| ☐ **RUIZ, Luis Mora** | ............................... | *paintings* | | $440 |
| Spanish 19th cent. | | | | |
| ☐ **RUIZ, Tommaso** | ................................. | *paintings* | $2,860 | $9,900 |
| Italian 17th cent. | | | | |
| ☐ **RUMMELHOFF, John** | ......................... | *paintings* | $110 | $1,100 |
| American b. 1942 | ..................................... | *drawings* | $60 | $275 |
| ☐ **RUMMELL, Richard** | ........................... | *drawings* | $522 | $3,410 |
| American 1848-1924 | | | | |
| ☐ **RUMMELSPACHER, Joseph** | ................ | *paintings* | | $715 |
| German 1852-1921 | | | | |

| | | Current Price Range | |
|---|---|---|---|
| | | *Low* | *High* |
| ☐ **RUMONATO, E.** .................... *paintings* | | | $825 |
| Spanish 19th cent. | | | |
| ☐ **RUMPF, Philipp** .................... *paintings* | | | $2,600 |
| German 1821-1896 .................... *drawings* | | | $500 |
| ☐ **RUMSEY, Charles Cary** .................... *sculpture* | | | $352 |
| American | | | |
| ☐ **RUNDLE, J.S.** .................... *drawings* | | | $330 |
| American | | | |
| ☐ **RUNDT, Hans Hinrich** .................... *paintings* | | | $3,850 |
| ☐ **RUNGE, Julius** .................... *paintings* | | | $412 |
| German 1843-1922 | | | |
| ☐ **RUNGIUS, C.R.** .................... *sculpture* | | | $10,250 |
| ☐ **RUNGIUS, Carl** .................... *paintings* | | $330 | $77,000 |
| American 1869-1959 .................... *drawings* | | $605 | $12,100 |
| ☐ **RUNZE, Wilhelm** .................... *paintings* | | $165 | $247 |
| German b. 1887 | | | |
| ☐ **RUOPPOLO, Giovanni Battista** .................... *paintings* | | $16,500 | $24,200 |
| Italian 1629-1693 | | | |
| ☐ **RUPPERT, Otto von** .................... *paintings* | | | $11,000 |
| German b. 1841 | | | |
| ☐ **RUPPRECHT, H.** .................... *paintings* | | $136 | $302 |
| ☐ **RUPPRECHT, Tini** .................... *drawings* | | | $2,530 |
| German b. 1868 | | | |
| ☐ **RUPPRECHT, W.** .................... *paintings* | | | $550 |
| ☐ **RUPRECHT, Adele** .................... *paintings* | | | $6,325 |
| Austrian ac. 1839-1845 | | | |
| ☐ **RURZWELL, T.** .................... *paintings* | | | $1,100 |
| ☐ **RUSALL, J.L.** .................... *paintings* | | | $182 |
| American 19th cent. | | | |
| ☐ **RUSCHA, Edward** .................... *paintings* | | $2,475 | $137,500 |
| American b. 1937 .................... *drawings* | | $605 | $5,500 |
| ☐ **RUSCHI, Francesco** .................... *paintings* | | | $16,500 |
| Italian ac. 1643-1656 | | | |
| ☐ **RUSCONI, Camillo** .................... *sculpture* | | | $14,850 |
| Italian 1658-1728 | | | |
| ☐ **RUSH, A.** .................... *paintings* | | | $1,760 |
| ☐ **RUSH, H.R.B.** .................... *drawings* | | | $495 |
| American 19th cent. | | | |
| ☐ **RUSH, Olive** .................... *drawings* | | | $302 |
| American 20th cent. | | | |
| ☐ **RUSH, William** .................... *sculpture* | | $1,650 | $275,000 |
| American 1754-1833 | | | |
| ☐ **RUSHELBERGER, A.** .................... *sculpture* | | | $1,650 |
| German 19th/20th cent. | | | |
| ☐ **RUSHMER, W.** .................... *paintings* | | | $275 |
| ☐ **RUSHTON, George** .................... *drawings* | | | $385 |
| English 19th cent. | | | |
| ☐ **RUSINYAK, Greg** .................... *sculpture* | | | $2,800 |
| American contemporary | | | |

| | | Current Price Range | |
|---|---|---|---|
| | | Low | High |
| ☐ **RUSKIN, John** ............................ *drawings* | | $247 | $990 |
| English 1819-1900 | | | |
| ☐ **RUSS, C.B.** ............................ *paintings* | | $165 | $825 |
| American 19th/20th cent. | | | |
| ☐ **RUSS, Franz** ............................ *paintings* | | | $1,430 |
| Austrian 1844-1906 ............................ *drawings* | | | $192 |
| ☐ **RUSS, Robert** ............................ *paintings* | | | $3,080 |
| Austrian 1847-1922 ............................ *drawings* | | | $3,300 |
| ☐ **RUSS, S.B.** ............................ *paintings* | | | $247 |
| American 19th cent. | | | |
| ☐ **RUSSART, M.** ............................ *paintings* | | | $522 |
| French 19th cent. | | | |
| ☐ **RUSSELL, Benjamin** ............................ *drawings* | | $1,200 | $6,250 |
| American 1804-1885 | | | |
| ☐ **RUSSELL, Charles** ............................ *paintings* | | | $4,125 |
| British 1852-1910 | | | |
| ☐ **RUSSELL, Charles Marion** ............... *paintings* | | $104,500 | $110,000 |
| American 1864-1926 ............................ *drawings* | | $605 | $165,000 |
| ............................ *sculpture* | | $550 | $45,000 |
| ☐ **RUSSELL, Donn** ............................ *sculpture* | | | $264 |
| ☐ **RUSSELL, Edward John** ............... *paintings* | | | $300 |
| Canadian 1832-1906 ............................ *drawings* | | $1,430 | $2,600 |
| ☐ **RUSSELL, George William** ............... *paintings* | | $440 | $880 |
| Irish 1867-1935 | | | |
| ☐ **RUSSELL, Gyrth** ............................ *paintings* | | $150 | $260 |
| Canadian b. 1892 | | | |
| ☐ **RUSSELL, J.B.** ............................ *paintings* | | | $357 |
| English 19th/20th cent. | | | |
| ☐ **RUSSELL, John** ............................ *paintings* | | $385 | $1,650 |
| British 1745-1806 ............................ *drawings* | | $247 | $4,510 |
| ☐ **RUSSELL, M.B.** ............................ *paintings* | | | $880 |
| 19th cent. | | | |
| ☐ **RUSSELL, Morgan** ............................ *paintings* | | $550 | $4,950 |
| American 1886-1953 | | | |
| ☐ **RUSSELL, Moses B.** ............................ *paintings* | | | $330 |
| American 1810-1884 | | | |
| ☐ **RUSSELL, Shirley** ............................ *paintings* | | | $385 |
| American b. 1886 | | | |
| ☐ **RUSSELL, William George** ............... *paintings* | | | $450 |
| American b. 1860 ............................ *drawings* | | $66 | $220 |
| ☐ **RUSSELLE, E.N.** ............................ *paintings* | | | $275 |
| ☐ **RUSSEN, Lester** ............................ *paintings* | | $110 | $200 |
| American contemporary | | | |
| ☐ **RUSSMAN, Felix** ............................ *paintings* | | $242 | $1,100 |
| American 1888-1962 | | | |
| ☐ **RUST, Johan Adolph** ............................ *paintings* | | | $7,150 |
| Dutch 1828-1915 | | | |
| ☐ **RUSTON, C.** ............................ *paintings* | | | $522 |
| French late 19th cent. | | | |

| | Current Price Range | |
|---|---|---|
| | *Low* | *High* |

☐ **RUTGERS, Abraham** .......................... *drawings*      **$7,425**
  Dutch ac. c. 1660-1690

☐ **RUTGERS, Johanna Judith** .................. *paintings*      **$301**
  Dutch 1851-1919

☐ **RUTH, Jan de** ..................................... *paintings*      **$175**
  American b. 1922

☐ **RUTH, Jan de** ..................................... *paintings*    **$220**    **$660**
  German 1825-1905 ..................................... *drawings*      **$140**

☐ **RUTHERFORD, C.W.** ......................... *paintings*      **$220**
  American 19th/20th cent.

☐ **RUTI, J.** ............................................. *paintings*    **$110**    **$400**

☐ **RUTLEDGE, June** .............................. *paintings*      **$385**

☐ **RUTS, F.** ............................................. *paintings*      **$1,100**
  German 19th cent.

☐ **RUTTEN, Anne** .................................. *drawings*      **$522**
  Continental 20th cent.

☐ **RUYENT, F.H.** .................................... *paintings*      **$1,045**
  Continental School 19th cent.

☐ **RUYL, Louis** ...................................... *drawings*    **$275**    **$286**
  American 19th/20th cent.

☐ **RUYS, D.R.** ........................................ *paintings*      **$1,320**
  Dutch School 19th cent.

☐ **RUYS, Theodore van** .......................... *paintings*      **$2,200**
  Dutch 18th cent.

☐ **RUYSCH, Rachel** ................................ *paintings*    **$23,100**    **$77,000**
  Dutch 1664-1750

☐ **RUYSDAEL, Jacob Salomonsz van** ........ *paintings*      **$27,500**
  Dutch 1628/30-1681/82

☐ **RUYSDAEL, Salomon van** .................... *paintings*    **$28,600**    **$418,000**
  Dutch c. 1600-1670

☐ **RUYTEN, Jan Michael** ......................... *paintings*    **$2,530**    **$7,150**
  Belgian 1813-1881

☐ **RUZ, G. Dela** ..................................... *paintings*      **$467**
  Spanish 19th cent.

☐ **RYALL, Harry Thomas** ......................... *paintings*      **$880**
  British 1811-1867

☐ **RYAN, Anne** ...................................... *paintings*    **$2,420**    **$6,050**
  contemporary

☐ **RYAN, Tom** ....................................... *paintings*    **$220**    **$43,000**
  American b. 1922 ..................................... *drawings*    **$330**    **$37,500**

☐ **RYBACK, Issachar** .............................. *paintings*      **$3,300**
  Russian b. 1897

☐ **RYBKOVSKI, Thadeusz** ....................... *paintings*      **$2,420**
  Polish 1848-1926 ..................................... *drawings*      **$110**

☐ **RYCK, Jacob van** ................................ *paintings*      **$1,210**
  Continental 19th/20th cent.

☐ **RYCKAERT, David** .............................. *paintings*    **$4,400**    **$8,250**
  Flemish

| | | | Current Price Range | |
|---|---|---|---|---|
| | | | Low | High |
| ☐ **RYCKAERT, Martin** .......................... *paintings* | | | $12,100 | $15,400 |
| Flemish 1587/91-1631/38 | | | | |
| ☐ **RYDEN, Henning** ............................... *paintings* | | | $715 | $1,980 |
| American b. 1869 | | | | |
| ☐ **RYDER, Chauncey Foster** .................... *paintings* | | | $220 | $35,200 |
| American 1868-1949 ................................. *drawings* | | | $99 | $1,870 |
| ☐ **RYDER, Henning** ............................... *paintings* | | | | $275 |
| ☐ **RYDER, Henry Orne** .......................... *paintings* | | | $49 | $4,675 |
| American b. 1860 ...................................... *drawings* | | | | $132 |
| ☐ **RYDER, J.S.** ....................................... *paintings* | | | | $400 |
| American early 20th cent. | | | | |
| ☐ **RYDER, Jack van** .............................. *paintings* | | | | $440 |
| American | | | | |
| ☐ **RYDER, Plath Powell** .......................... *paintings* | | | $1,430 | $11,000 |
| American 1821-1896 | | | | |
| ☐ **RYDER, Worth** .................................. *drawings* | | | | $274 |
| ☐ **RYLAND, Henry** ................................. *drawings* | | | $1,210 | $1,650 |
| English 1856/59-1924 | | | | |
| ☐ **RYLAND, Robert Knight** ....................... *paintings* | | | $110 | $1,980 |
| American 1873-1951 | | | | |
| ☐ **RYLOV, Arkadij Aleksandrovich** .......... *paintings* | | | | $990 |
| ☐ **RYLSKI, A.** ....................................... *paintings* | | | | $352 |
| ☐ **RYMAN, Herbert** ............................... *paintings* | | | | $550 |
| American 20th cent. | | | | |
| ☐ **RYMAN, Robert** ............................... *paintings* | | | $3,300 | $38,500 |
| American b. 1930 | | | | |
| ☐ **RYNDEN, Nikolas** ............................... *drawings* | | | | $264 |
| ☐ **RYSBRACK, Peter Andreas** ................. *paintings* | | | | $4,400 |
| Flemish 1690-1748 | | | | |
| ☐ **RYSBRAECK, Lodovicsus** .................... *paintings* | | | | $4,950 |
| Flemish 18th cent. | | | | |
| ☐ **RYSER** ............................................. *paintings* | | | | $1,980 |
| ☐ **RYSSELBERGHE, Theo van** ................. *paintings* | | | $770 | $198,000 |
| Belgian 1862-1926 ..................................... *drawings* | | | $209 | $20,900 |
| ☐ **RZEPINSKI, Czeslav** ........................... *paintings* | | | $834 | $935 |
| Polish b. 1905 | | | | |
| ☐ **SAAL, Georg Eduard Otto** .................... *paintings* | | | $330 | $3,850 |
| German 1818-1870 | | | | |
| ☐ **SAALMANN, E.** ................................. *sculpture* | | | | $302 |
| early 20th cent. | | | | |
| ☐ **SAARI, Omni** .................................... *drawings* | | | | $462 |
| ☐ **SABA, H.** ......................................... *paintings* | | | | $1,100 |
| ☐ **SABATELLI, Luigi** ............................. *drawings* | | | | $209 |
| Italian | | | | |
| ☐ **SABATI, V.** ....................................... *paintings* | | | $1,320 | $1,650 |
| 19th cent. | | | | |
| ☐ **SABATINI, I.** ..................................... *paintings* | | | | $1,650 |

| | | Current Price Range | |
|---|---|---|---|
| | | Low | High |
| ☐ **SABBATINI, Andrea** | | | |
| **(called Andrea de SALERNO)** ............... *paintings* | | **$1,100** | **$35,200** |
| Italian 1487-1530 | | | |
| ☐ **SABBATINI, Lorenzo** ........................... *paintings* | | | **$1,000** |
| Italian 1530-1576 ....................................... *drawings* | | | **$4,400** |
| ☐ **SABELLIERI, A.** .............................. *sculpture* | | | **$440** |
| ☐ **SABINOLI, A.** ...................................... *paintings* | | | **$220** |
| Italian 19th/20th cent. | | | |
| ☐ **SABO, Ladis W.** ............................... *paintings* | | | **$330** |
| ☐ **SABOGAL, Jose** ................................. *paintings* | | **$192** | **$1,980** |
| Peruvian 1888-1935 | | | |
| ☐ **SABOLINI, A.** ..................................... *paintings* | | | **$275** |
| Italian 19th/20th cent. | | | |
| ☐ **SABOURAUD, Emile** ........................... *paintings* | | | **$990** |
| French b. 1900 | | | |
| ☐ **SACCHETTI, Lorenzo** ........................ *drawings* | | | **$660** |
| Italian ac. 1490 | | | |
| ☐ **SACCO, Luca** ...................................... *paintings* | | **$176** | **$2,970** |
| American 1858-1912 | | | |
| ☐ **SACHS, Balthasar** ............................. *paintings* | | | **$770** |
| ☐ **SACKS, Walter T.** .............................. *drawings* | | | **$475** |
| American b. 1895 | | | |
| ☐ **SADEE,** | | | |
| **Philip Lodowyck Jacob Frederik** ............ *paintings* | | **$1,320** | **$23,100** |
| Dutch 1837-1904 | | | |
| ☐ **SADKOWSKI** ....:................................. *paintings* | | | **$3,850** |
| Austrian 19th/20th cent. | | | |
| ☐ **SADLER, George** ................................. *paintings* | | | **$1,320** |
| British ac. 1878-1883 | | | |
| ☐ **SADLER, Walter Dendy** ....................... *paintings* | | **$1,100** | **$18,700** |
| English 1854-1923 | | | |
| ☐ **SADOLETTI, Alfredo** ........................... *paintings* | | | **$990** |
| Italian b. 1866 | | | |
| ☐ **SAENZ Y SAENZ, Pedro** ..................... *paintings* | | **$935** | **$2,200** |
| Spanish c. 1860 | | | |
| ☐ **SAEYS, Jakob Ferdinand** ..................... *paintings* | | **$2,200** | **$4,400** |
| Flemish 1658-1725 | | | |
| ☐ **SAFFORD, Ruth Appleton Perkins** ........ *drawings* | | **$55** | **$330** |
| American 1897-1979 | | | |
| ☐ **SAFREY, Augusto** ............................... *paintings* | | | **$300** |
| ☐ **SAFTLEVEN, Cornelis** ........................ *drawings* | | | **$3,410** |
| Dutch 1607-1681 | | | |
| ☐ **SAFTLEVEN, Herman (II)** ..................... *paintings* | | | **$8,800** |
| Dutch c. 1609-1685 ..................................... *drawings* | | | **$1,760** |
| ☐ **SAGE, Kay** ......................................... *paintings* | | **$1,320** | **$1,650** |
| American 1898-1961 ................................... *drawings* | | | **$1,045** |
| ☐ **SAGER, Xavier** ................................... *paintings* | | | **$247** |
| French 20th cent. | | | |

| | | Current Price Range | |
|---|---|---|---|
| | | *Low* | *High* |
| ☐ **SAGRADO, Luigi** ............... *paintings* | | | $990 |
| Italian 19th cent. | | | |
| ☐ **SAHULA-DYCKE, Ignatz** .............. *paintings* | | | $935 |
| Czechoslovakian b. 1900 | | | |
| ☐ **SAIN, Edouard Alexandre** .............. *paintings* | | | $10,450 |
| French 1830-1910 | | | |
| ☐ **SAIN, Paul Jean Marie** .............. *paintings* | | | $1,870 |
| French 1853-1908 | | | |
| ☐ **SAINT BRICE, Robert** .............. *paintings* | | $550 | $2,640 |
| ☐ **SAINT JAQUES, R.** .............. *paintings* | | | $660 |
| French 18th/19th cent. | | | |
| ☐ **SAINT JOHN, David** .............. *paintings* | | $495 | $1,650 |
| American 19th cent. | | | |
| ☐ **SAINT JOHN, J. Allen** .............. *paintings* | | $1,045 | $3,575 |
| American b. 1872 | | | |
| ☐ **SAINT LOU** .............. *paintings* | | | $286 |
| ☐ **SAINT PHALLE, Niki de** .............. *drawings* | | $385 | $9,900 |
| French b. 1930 .............. *sculpture* | | $1,000 | $10,450 |
| ☐ **SAINT VIL, Murat** .............. *paintings* | | | $880 |
| ☐ **SAINT-AUBIN, Augustin de** .............. *drawings* | | | $275 |
| French 1736-1807 | | | |
| ☐ **SAINT-DELIS, Henri Rene de la** .............. *paintings* | | | $467 |
| French 1879-1949 | | | |
| ☐ **SAINT-GAUDENS, Augustus** .............. *sculpture* | | $220 | $120,000 |
| American 1848-1907 | | | |
| ☐ **SAINT-JEAN, George** .............. *sculpture* | | | $990 |
| ☐ **SAINT-MARCEL-CABIN,** | | | |
| **Charles Edme** .............. *drawings* | | | $660 |
| ☐ **SAINT-MEMIN,** | | | |
| **Charles Balthazar Julien Fevret de** .............. *paintings* | | | $4,400 |
| French/American 1770-1852 .............. *drawings* | | $715 | $8,800 |
| ☐ **SAINT-NON,** | | | |
| **Jean Claude Richard, abbe de** .............. *drawings* | | $550 | $605 |
| French 1727-1791 | | | |
| ☐ **SAINT-PIERRE, Gaston Casimir** .............. *paintings* | | $3,850 | $5,500 |
| French 1833-1916 | | | |
| ☐ **SAINTIN, Jules Emile** .............. *paintings* | | $495 | $8,250 |
| French 1829-1894 | | | |
| ☐ **SAINTON, Charles Prosper** .............. *drawings* | | | $330 |
| ☐ **SAKEVA, Al** .............. *drawings* | | | $880 |
| American (Hopi) | | | |
| ☐ **SALA, F.** .............. *drawings* | | | $220 |
| Italian 19th cent. | | | |
| ☐ **SALA, Paolo** .............. *paintings* | | | $2,310 |
| Italian 1859-1924 .............. *drawings* | | | $1,100 |
| ☐ **SALA Y FRANCES, Emilio** .............. *paintings* | | | $9,900 |
| Spanish 1850-1910 | | | |
| ☐ **SALAMON, G.** .............. *paintings* | | | $400 |
| 20th cent. | | | |

|  | | *Current Price Range* | |
|---|---|---|---|
|  | | Low | High |
| ☐ **SALAZAR, A.** .................................... *paintings* | | | **$1,320** |
| ☐ **SALAZAR, Rosendo** ............................ *paintings* | | **$2,090** | **$2,750** |
| ☐ **SALDANA, Mateo** ............................... *paintings* | | | **$4,400** |
| ☐ **SALEMME, Attilio** .............................. *paintings* | | **$3,410** | **$5,500** |
| American 1911-1955 ................................. *drawings* | | **$330** | **$550** |
| ☐ **SALENTIN, Hubert** ............................ *paintings* | | **$5,500** | **$30,800** |
| German 1822-1910 | | | |
| ☐ **SALENTIN, K.** .................................... *paintings* | | | **$770** |
| Italian 19th cent. | | | |
| ☐ **SALES, Francesco** .............................. *paintings* | | | **$495** |
| ☐ **SALIGER, Ivo** .................................... *paintings* | | | **$357** |
| Austrian b. 1894 | | | |
| ☐ **SALINAS, A.** ...................................... *paintings* | | | **$300** |
| ☐ **SALINAS, Juan Pablo** ......................... *paintings* | | **$990** | **$28,600** |
| Spanish 1871-1946 | | | |
| ☐ **SALINAS, Porfirio** .............................. *paintings* | | **$1,320** | **$22,000** |
| American 1910-1972 | | | |
| ☐ **SALINAS Y TERUEL, Augustin** ........... *paintings* | | **$880** | **$2,640** |
| Spanish b. 1862 | | | |
| ☐ **SALING, Paul E.** ................................. *paintings* | | **$330** | **$1,540** |
| American 1876-1936 | | | |
| ☐ **SALLAERT, Anthonis** .......................... *drawings* | | | **$495** |
| ☐ **SALLE, David** ..................................... *paintings* | | **$4,400** | **$33,000** |
| American b. 1952 ..................................... *drawings* | | **$2,420** | **$6,875** |
| ☐ **SALLES, De** ....................................... *paintings* | | **$550** | **$825** |
| ☐ **SALLES WAGNER, Jules** ..................... *paintings* | | | **$600** |
| French 1814-1898 | | | |
| ☐ **SALM, A.** .......................................... *drawings* | | | **$1,870** |
| ☐ **SALMEGGIA, Enea (Enea TALPINO)** ... *paintings* | | | **$2,200** |
| Italian 1558-1626 | | | |
| ☐ **SALMON, John Francis** ........................ *drawings* | | | **$302** |
| ☐ **SALMON, Robert** ............................... *paintings* | | **$4,250** | **$101,750** |
| Anglo/American 1775-c. 1842/44 | | | |
| ☐ **SALMORES, Victor** ............................. *sculpture* | | | **$825** |
| ☐ **SALMSON, Hugo** ............................... *paintings* | | **$6,600** | **$8,250** |
| Swedish 1844-1894 | | | |
| ☐ **SALMSON, Jean Jules** ......................... *sculpture* | | **$198** | **$1,430** |
| French 19th cent. | | | |
| ☐ **SALOME** .......................................... *drawings* | | | **$9,900** |
| contemporary | | | |
| ☐ **SALOME, Emile** ................................. *paintings* | | **$522** | **$2,750** |
| French 1833-1881 | | | |
| ☐ **SALOMON, Jacques** ............................ *paintings* | | | **$467** |
| .............................................................. *drawings* | | | **$247** |
| ☐ **SALT, James** ..................................... *paintings* | | | **$550** |
| ☐ **SALT, John** ....................................... *paintings* | | **$8,250** | **$18,700** |
| English b. 1937 | | | |
| ☐ **SALTER, John Falconer** ...................... *paintings* | | | **$825** |

| | Current Price Range | |
|---|---|---|
| | *Low* | *High* |
| ☐ **SALTINI, Pietro** ............... *paintings* | $467 | $20,900 |
| Italian 1839-1908 | | |
| ☐ **SALTMER, Florence A.** ......... *paintings* | | $3,850 |
| English ac. 1882-1908 | | |
| ☐ **SALTOFT, Edvard Anders Christian** ..... *drawings* | $550 | $550 |
| ☐ **SALTZMANN, Carl** ........... *paintings* | | $6,600 |
| German 1847-1923 | | |
| ☐ **SALVAT, Francois** ........... *paintings* | $330 | $550 |
| French 1892-1976 | | |
| ☐ **SALVATI** ............... *paintings* | | $385 |
| ☐ **SALVETTI, Antonio** ........... *paintings* | $165 | $330 |
| Italian 1854-1931 | | |
| ☐ **SALVI, Giovanni Battista** | | |
| **(called IL SASSOFERRATO)** ........ *paintings* | $5,500 | $28,600 |
| Italian 1609-1685 | | |
| ☐ **SALVIATI, Antonio** ........... *drawings* | | $247 |
| Italian 1816-1890 | | |
| ☐ **SALVIN, M. de** ............... *paintings* | | $3,300 |
| French 19th/20th cent. | | |
| ☐ **SALZMANN, E.** ............... *paintings* | | $550 |
| American 19th cent. | | |
| ☐ **SAMARAN, U.M.** ........... *paintings* | $2,750 | $7,150 |
| French 19th cent. | | |
| ☐ **SAMARAS, Lucas** ........... *drawings* | $770 | $5,280 |
| Greek/American b. 1936 ........... *sculpture* | $4,950 | $63,800 |
| ☐ **SAMARCO, E.** ............... *paintings* | | $308 |
| ☐ **SAMBACH, Franz** ........... *paintings* | | $1,430 |
| German 1715-1795 | | |
| ☐ **SAMBROOK, Russell** ........... *paintings* | | $660 |
| ☐ **SAMILA, David** ............... *paintings* | | $462 |
| ☐ **SAMMAN, Detlef** ........... *paintings* | | $550 |
| American 20th cent. | | |
| ☐ **SAMMONS, Carl** ........... *paintings* | $88 | $1,045 |
| American ............... *drawings* | $275 | $301 |
| ☐ **SAMOKICH, Nicolai Semionovitch** ..... *paintings* | $880 | $6,050 |
| Russian b. 1860 ............... *drawings* | $770 | $1,650 |
| ☐ **SAMOLAR** ............... *sculpture* | $660 | $1,100 |
| ☐ **SAMPLE, Paul Starrett** ......... *paintings* | $165 | $9,625 |
| American 1896-1974 ............... *drawings* | $275 | $825 |
| ☐ **SAMPSON, A.** ............... *paintings* | | $1,400 |
| European 19th cent. | | |
| ☐ **SAMSTAG, Gordon** ........... *paintings* | | $187 |
| American | | |
| ☐ **SANBORN, Percy** ............... *paintings* | | $495 |
| American 19th/20th cent. ........... *drawings* | | $27 |
| ☐ **SANCHEZ, Emilio** ........... *paintings* | $1,210 | $10,725 |
| Cuban b. 1921 ............... *drawings* | $715 | $2,310 |
| ☐ **SANCHEZ COTAN, Juan** ......... *paintings* | | $22,000 |
| Spanish 1560/61-1627 | | |

|  | | Current Price Range | |
|---|---|---|---|
|  | | Low | High |
| ☐ **SANCHEZ-PERRIER, Emilio** .............. *paintings* | | **$1,320** | **$19,800** |
| Spanish 1855-1907 ...................................... *drawings* | | **$880** | **$1,980** |
| ☐ **SAND, Percy Tsisete** ............................ *drawings* | | | **$301** |
| American Indian b. 1918 | | | |
| ☐ **SANDBY, Paul** ................................... *drawings* | | **$824** | **$4,400** |
| English 1725-1809 | | | |
| ☐ **SANDER, Ludwig** ............................... *paintings* | | **$770** | **$7,700** |
| American 1906-1975 | | | |
| ☐ **SANDER, Sherry** ............................... *sculpture* | | **$800** | **$2,400** |
| American | | | |
| ☐ **SANDER, Tom** ................................... *paintings* | | **$1,500** | **$2,500** |
| American contemporary ............................... *drawings* | | | **$165** |
| ☐ **SANDERS, Christopher** ..................... *paintings* | | | **$770** |
| British b. 1905 | | | |
| ☐ **SANDERS, David** ............................... *drawings* | | | **$5,000** |
| American contemporary | | | |
| ☐ **SANDERS, Hercules** ........................... *paintings* | | | **$3,300** |
| Dutch 1606-1663 | | | |
| ☐ **SANDERS, Sherry** ............................. *sculpture* | | | **$1,300** |
| American | | | |
| ☐ **SANDERS, T. Hale** ............................ *paintings* | | | **$1,300** |
| British 19th cent. | | | |
| ☐ **SANDERSON-WELLS, John** .............. *paintings* | | | **$1,320** |
| British 20th cent. | | | |
| ☐ **SANDHAM, Henry** ............................ *drawings* | | **$200** | **$247** |
| Canadian-American 1842-1912 | | | |
| ☐ **SANDO, Donn** ................................... *sculpture* | | | **$330** |
| American 20th cent. | | | |
| ☐ **SANDONA, Matteo** ............................ *paintings* | | | **$1,210** |
| Italian/American b. 1883 | | | |
| ☐ **SANDORHAZE, W.B.** ......................... *paintings* | | | **$770** |
| Hungarian 20th cent. | | | |
| ☐ **SANDOZ, Edouard Marcel** ............... *sculpture* | | **$154** | **$4,400** |
| Swiss 1881-1971 | | | |
| ☐ **SANDRART, Johann Jakob von** ........... *drawings* | | | **$1,155** |
| German 1655-1698 | | | |
| ☐ **SANDRINI, A.** ................................... *paintings* | | | **$605** |
| Italian 19th cent. | | | |
| ☐ **SANDRUCCI, Giovanni** ....................... *paintings* | | **$1,980** | **$2,750** |
| ☐ **SANDS, W.L.** ................................... *paintings* | | | **$411** |
| ☐ **SANDUCCI, G.** ................................. *paintings* | | **$935** | **$1,760** |
| ☐ **SANDY, Percy** ................................... *drawings* | | | **$374** |
| American (Zuni) b. 1918 | | | |
| ☐ **SANDYS, Emma** ............................... *paintings* | | | **$880** |
| British fl. 1868-74 | | | |
| ☐ **SANDYS,** | | | |
| **Frederick Anthony Augustus** ............... *paintings* | | | **$990** |
| British 1832-1904 | | | |

| | | Current Price Range | |
|---|---|---|---|
| | | Low | High |
| ☐ SANDZEN, Birger ............... *paintings* | | | $1,595 |
| American 1871-1954 | | | |
| ☐ SANFORD, Edward Field (Jr.) ............... *sculpture* | | | $3,080 |
| American b. 1887 | | | |
| ☐ SANFORD, George T. ............... *drawings* | | $1,430 | $3,850 |
| American ac. 1843-1846 | | | |
| ☐ SANFORD, Margaret ............... *sculpture* | | | $2,310 |
| American ac. 1920-40 | | | |
| ☐ SANGLOIS, Eustache N. ............... *drawings* | | | $1,540 |
| French 19th cent. | | | |
| ☐ SANGUINO, Louis ............... *sculpture* | | $160 | $550 |
| American 20th cent. | | | |
| ☐ SANI, Alessandro ............... *paintings* | | $385 | $4,400 |
| Italian 19th cent. | | | |
| ☐ SANI, David ............... *paintings* | | | $1,650 |
| Italian 19th cent. | | | |
| ☐ SANI, Gioconda ............... *paintings* | | | $825 |
| ☐ SANIDZIN, Birger ............... *drawings* | | | $275 |
| ☐ SANO DI PIETRO ............... *paintings* | | $8,800 | $82,500 |
| Italian 1406-1481 | | | |
| ☐ SANT, James ............... *paintings* | | $825 | $3,300 |
| English 1820-1916 | | | |
| ☐ SANTA, Serra ............... *paintings* | | $137 | $357 |
| Continental 20th cent. | | | |
| ☐ SANTA MARIA, Andres de ............... *paintings* | | | $1,760 |
| Colombian 1869-1945 | | | |
| ☐ SANTERNE, Robert ............... *paintings* | | $121 | $770 |
| French b. 1903 | | | |
| ☐ SANTERRE, Jean Baptiste ............... *paintings* | | | $13,750 |
| French 1651/58-1771 | | | |
| ☐ SANTI, Giovanni ............... *paintings* | | | $5,280 |
| Italian | | | |
| ☐ SANTIAGO, Filemon ............... *drawings* | | | $715 |
| Mexican b. 1958 | | | |
| ☐ SANTINI, Antelma ............... *paintings* | | | $2,090 |
| Italian b. 1896 | | | |
| ☐ SANTINI, Giuseppe ............... *drawings* | | | $550 |
| ☐ SANTIS, S.T. ............... *paintings* | | | $301 |
| ☐ SANTLIO, N. ............... *paintings* | | | $687 |
| European 19th cent. | | | |
| ☐ SANTORA, Antonio ............... *paintings* | | | $198 |
| 17th cent. | | | |
| ☐ SANTORI, J.J. ............... *paintings* | | | $275 |
| American 20th cent. | | | |
| ☐ SANTORO, Francesco Raffaello ............... *paintings* | | | $1,650 |
| Italian b. 1844 ............... *drawings* | | | $247 |
| ☐ SANTORO, Rubens ............... *paintings* | | $1,540 | $23,100 |
| Italian 1843/59-1942 | | | |

| | | Current Price Range | |
|---|---|---|---|
| | | Low | High |
| ☐ **SANTRY, Daniel** .............................. *paintings* | | $77 | $1,540 |
| American 1867-1951 | | | |
| ☐ **SANTVOORT, Dirck van** ..................... *paintings* | | $3,500 | $19,800 |
| Dutch 1610-1680 | | | |
| ☐ **SANZINI** ............................................. *paintings* | | | $385 |
| contemporary | | | |
| ☐ **SARACENI** ......................................... *paintings* | | | $466 |
| Italian 18th cent. | | | |
| ☐ **SARAZIN, Jean Philippe** ...................... *drawings* | | | $495 |
| French d. 1795 | | | |
| ☐ **SARCENI, Carlo** | | | |
| **(called VENEZIANO)** ............................. *paintings* | | | $30,000 |
| ac. 1580-1585 | | | |
| ☐ **SARDI** ................................................ *paintings* | | | $577 |
| European 19th/20th cent. | | | |
| ☐ **SARET, Alan** ..................................... *drawings* | | $1,870 | $2,860 |
| American b. 1944 | | | |
| ☐ **SARG, Tony** ....................................... *drawings* | | $209 | $577 |
| 1882-1942 | | | |
| ☐ **SARGENT, Frederick** ........................... *paintings* | | | $770 |
| ☐ **SARGENT, Geneve Rixford** ................... *paintings* | | | $440 |
| American b. 1868 | | | |
| ☐ **SARGENT, John Singer** ........................ *paintings* | | $3,850 | $605,000 |
| American 1856-1925 ................................ *drawings* | | $990 | $41,800 |
| ............................................................ *sculpture* | | | $825 |
| ☐ **SARGENT, Paul T.** ............................. *paintings* | | | $605 |
| b. 1880 | | | |
| ☐ **SARGENT, Walter** ............................. *paintings* | | | $440 |
| American 20th cent. | | | |
| ☐ **SARIAN, Martiros Segueevitch** ............. *drawings* | | | $550 |
| Russian b. 1880 | | | |
| ☐ **SARKISIAN, Sarkis** ............................. *paintings* | | $165 | $1,650 |
| American 1909-1977 ................................ *drawings* | | $150 | $660 |
| ☐ **SARLUIS, Leonard** ............................. *paintings* | | | $880 |
| French 1874-1949 | | | |
| ☐ **SARNO, Matteo** ................................. *paintings* | | | $286 |
| ☐ **SARNOFF, Arthur** ............................. *paintings* | | $357 | $522 |
| American 20th cent. ................................ *drawings* | | $220 | $715 |
| ☐ **SARONY** ........................................... *drawings* | | $66 | $300 |
| ☐ **SARRASIN** ........................................ *paintings* | | | $495 |
| English 19th cent. | | | |
| ☐ **SARRAZIN, Louise** ............................. *drawings* | | $246 | $356 |
| American 20th cent. | | | |
| ☐ **SARRY** ............................................. *sculpture* | | | $1,000 |
| French 19th cent. | | | |
| ☐ **SARSONY, Robert** ............................. *paintings* | | $330 | $330 |
| American b. 1938 | | | |
| ☐ **SARTAIN, Harriet** ............................. *paintings* | | | $247 |
| American 19th/20th cent. | | | |

| | | | Current Price Range | |
|---|---|---|---|---|
| | | | Low | High |
| ☐ **SARTAIN, William** | .............................. | *paintings* | $66 | $1,320 |
| American 1843-1924 | | | | |
| ☐ **SARTELLE, Herbert** | ........................... | *paintings* | $192 | $385 |
| American 20th cent. | | | | |
| ☐ **SARTERNE, Robert** | ........................... | *paintings* | | $330 |
| ☐ **SARTHOU, Maurice E.** | ....................... | *paintings* | | $550 |
| ☐ **SARTNER, R.** | .................................... | *paintings* | | $330 |
| ☐ **SARTORIO, Aristide** | .......................... | *paintings* | $385 | $1,650 |
| Italian 1860-1932 | ....................................... | *drawings* | $55 | $275 |
| ☐ **SARTORIUS, Francis** | ......................... | *paintings* | $2,200 | $44,000 |
| English 1734-1804 | | | | |
| ☐ **SARTORIUS, John Francis** | ................. | *paintings* | $2,420 | $9,900 |
| English c. 1775-1831 | | | | |
| ☐ **SARTORIUS, John N.** | ......................... | *paintings* | $660 | $24,200 |
| English 1759-1828 | | | | |
| ☐ **SARTORIUS, W.** | ............................... | *paintings* | $825 | $3,850 |
| 18th cent. | | | | |
| ☐ **SASELL** | ............................................... | *paintings* | | $550 |
| ☐ **SASHI, Sylwerjusz** | ............................ | *paintings* | | $1,540 |
| Polish School 19th cent. | | | | |
| ☐ **SASLOW, Herbert** | ............................. | *paintings* | | $467 |
| ☐ **SASSO, A.** | ....................................... | *paintings* | | $770 |
| Italian 19th cent. | | | | |
| ☐ **SASSON, L.** | ..................................... | *sculpture* | $550 | $660 |
| ☐ **SASSONE, Marco** | ............................. | *paintings* | | $2,310 |
| Italian 20th cent. | ...................................... | *drawings* | | $385 |
| ☐ **SATA, F.** | ......................................... | *paintings* | | $385 |
| ☐ **SATTERLEE, Walter** | .......................... | *paintings* | $330 | $1,980 |
| American 1844-1908 | ................................... | *drawings* | $71 | $100 |
| ☐ **SATTLER, Hubert** | ............................. | *paintings* | $9,020 | $13,200 |
| Austrian 1817-1904 | | | | |
| ☐ **SAUBER, Robert** | ............................... | *paintings* | | $990 |
| British b. 1868 | | | | |
| ☐ **SAUBERT, Tom** | ................................. | *drawings* | | $1,200 |
| contemporary | | | | |
| ☐ **SAUERFELT, Leonard** | ........................ | *paintings* | | $1,320 |
| French 19th cent. | | | | |
| ☐ **SAUERWEIN, Frank P.** | ...................... | *paintings* | | $9,900 |
| American 1871-1910 | ................................... | *drawings* | $880 | $935 |
| ☐ **SAUL, Charles** | ................................. | *paintings* | | $275 |
| ☐ **SAUL, Peter** | .................................... | *paintings* | | $15,400 |
| American b. 1934 | ...................................... | *drawings* | $3,850 | $4,180 |
| ☐ **SAULES, Deg** | ................................... | *paintings* | | $275 |
| ☐ **SAUNDERS, J.** | .................................. | *paintings* | | $247 |
| British 19th cent. | | | | |
| ☐ **SAUNDERS, Norman** | .......................... | *paintings* | $550 | $770 |
| b. 1907 | | | | |
| ☐ **SAUNIER, Noel** | ................................ | *paintings* | | $4,125 |
| French 1847-1890 | | | | |

| | | | Current Price Range |
|---|---|---|---|
| | | Low | High |
| ☐ **SAURA, Antonio** .................... *paintings* | | | $2,310 |
| Spanish b. 1930 ...................... *drawings* | | | $1,540 |
| ☐ **SAUREZ, Arturo** .................... *paintings* | | | $880 |
| Spanish b. 1923 | | | |
| ☐ **SAURFELT, Leonard** .......................... *paintings* | | $935 | $6,050 |
| French 19th cent. | | | |
| ☐ **SAUTER, Rudolph** ............................ *drawings* | | | $440 |
| ☐ **SAUTNER, G.** ................................ *paintings* | | | $6,600 |
| ☐ **SAUVAGE, A.** ................................ *paintings* | | | $660 |
| ☐ **SAUVAGE, Philippe Francois** ............... *paintings* | | $825 | $4,950 |
| French b. 19th cent. | | | |
| ☐ **SAUVAGE, Piat Joseph** .......... *paintings* | | $3,740 | $11,000 |
| Flemish c. 1744-1818 | | | |
| ☐ **SAUVAN, H. de** .................. *paintings* | | | $308 |
| ☐ **SAUZAY, Adrien Jacques** .................. *paintings* | | | $8,800 |
| French 1841-1928 | | | |
| ☐ **SAVAGE, Eugene Francis** ............... *paintings* | | | $247 |
| American b. 1883 | | | |
| ☐ **SAVAGE, R.A.** .................................. *paintings* | | $650 | $1,045 |
| American 19th cent. | | | |
| ☐ **SAVAIN, Petion** .................................. *paintings* | | $357 | $3,520 |
| Haitian 20th cent. | | | |
| ☐ **SAVERY, H.P.** ................................ *paintings* | | $550 | $2,200 |
| ☐ **SAVERY, Jacob (the elder)** .................... *paintings* | | | $137,500 |
| Dutch 1545-1602 | | | |
| ☐ **SAVERY, Roeland** .............................. *paintings* | | $43,000 | $60,500 |
| Flemish 1576-1639 | | | |
| ☐ **SAVERYS, Albert** .............................. *paintings* | | | $2,860 |
| Belgian 1886-1964 | | | |
| ☐ **SAVINI, Alfonso** .......................... *paintings* | | $770 | $935 |
| Italian 1836-1908 | | | |
| ☐ **SAVITZ, Frieda** .......................... *paintings* | | | $11 |
| American 20th cent. .......................... *drawings* | | | $616 |
| ☐ **SAVRASOV, Aleksei Kondratievitch** ..... *paintings* | | | $1,760 |
| Russian 1830-1897 | | | |
| ☐ **SAVRY, Hendrick** .............................. *paintings* | | $467 | $4,730 |
| Dutch 1823-1907 | | | |
| ☐ **SAVRY, Henrik** ............................ *paintings* | | | $825 |
| ☐ **SAWIN, Josef** .............................. *paintings* | | | $1,320 |
| ☐ **SAWTELLE, Elizabeth A.** ................... *paintings* | | | $220 |
| American 20th cent. | | | |
| ☐ **SAWTELLE, Mary Berkeley** ................. *paintings* | | $2,310 | $4,180 |
| American b. 1872 | | | |
| ☐ **SAWYER, Helen Alton** ......................... *paintings* | | $121 | $385 |
| American b. 1900 | | | |
| ☐ **SAWYER, Moses** .............................. *paintings* | | | $726 |
| ☐ **SAWYER, Paul** .............................. *paintings* | | $165 | $770 |
| ☐ **SAWYER, W.B.** .............................. *paintings* | | | $467 |
| American 20th cent. | | | |

|                                                        |            | Current Price Range | |
|--------------------------------------------------------|------------|---------|----------|
|                                                        |            | Low     | High     |
| ☐ **SAWYER, Wells M.** ........................ *paintings* | | $176 | $247 |
| American 1863-1961 | | | |
| ☐ **SAY, Frederick Richard** ...................... *paintings* | | | $7,700 |
| English 1827-1860 | | | |
| ☐ **SAY, William** .................................. *paintings* | | | $1,430 |
| English 1768-1834 | | | |
| ☐ **SAYER, Raymond** ............................. *paintings* | | | $330 |
| American 19th/20th cent. ........................... *drawings* | | | $84 |
| ☐ **SAYERS, Reuben** ............................ *paintings* | | | $880 |
| British 1814-1888 | | | |
| ☐ **SAYRE, Fred Grayson** ...................... *paintings* | | $165 | $1,870 |
| American 1879-1938/39 ............................. *drawings* | | $467 | $825 |
| ☐ **SAYRES, S.T.** .................................. *paintings* | | | $385 |
| American 19th cent. | | | |
| ☐ **SCACCIATI, Andrea (the elder)** ........... *paintings* | | | $11,000 |
| Italian 1642-1704 | | | |
| ☐ **SCAFER, H.** .................................... *drawings* | | | $412 |
| Dutch late 19th cent. | | | |
| ☐ **SCAFFAI, Luigi** ............................... *paintings* | | $1,100 | $3,200 |
| Italian b. 1837 | | | |
| ☐ **SCALBERGE, Pierre** .......................... *paintings* | | $5,280 | $8,800 |
| French 1592-1640 | | | |
| ☐ **SCALBERT, Jules** ............................. *paintings* | | | $11,000 |
| French b. 1851, ac 1876-1891 | | | |
| ☐ **SCANDRETT, Thomas** ...................... *drawings* | | | $935 |
| English 1797-1870 | | | |
| ☐ **SCARAMUCCIA, Giovanni Antonio** ...... *drawings* | | | $6,820 |
| Italian 1580-1633 | | | |
| ☐ **SCARAVAGLIONE, Concetta** ............. *sculpture* | | | $880 |
| American 1900-1975 | | | |
| ☐ **SCARBINA, F.** ................................. *paintings* | | | $1,100 |
| ☐ **SCARI, A.** ..................................... *paintings* | | | $950 |
| ☐ **SCARLETT, Rolph** ........................... *drawings* | | | $1,320 |
| American contemporary | | | |
| ☐ **SCARNICCI, Emanuele** ....................... *sculpture* | | $200 | $200 |
| Italian b. 1916 | | | |
| ☐ **SCARSELLA, Ippolito** | | | |
| **(called LO SCARSELLINO)** ................... *paintings* | | $1,980 | $11,550 |
| Italian 1551-1620 | | | |
| ☐ **SCHAAN, Paul** ................................ *paintings* | | $3,300 | $3,960 |
| French 19th/20th cent. | | | |
| ☐ **SCHAAP, Ch.** .................................. *paintings* | | | $330 |
| Dutch 19th/20th cent. | | | |
| ☐ **SCHAARE, Harry** ............................ *paintings* | | $5,000 | $5,000 |
| American contemporary | | | |
| ☐ **SCHABELITZ, Rudolph Frederick** ........ *paintings* | | $1,210 | $1,980 |
| American b. 1884 ................................... *drawings* | | | $176 |
| ☐ **SCHACHINGER, Gabriel** .................... *paintings* | | $700 | $6,875 |
| German 1850-1912 ................................. *drawings* | | | $4,400 |

| | Current Price Range | |
|---|---|---|
| | *Low* | *High* |
| ☐ **SCHACHT, Rudolph** ............................ *paintings* | | $880 |
| German School 20th cent. | | |
| ☐ **SCHADE, Karl Martin** ...................... *paintings* | $99 | $2,090 |
| Austrian 1862-1954 | | |
| ☐ **SCHADE, R.** ....................................... *paintings* | | $850 |
| American 19th/20th cent. | | |
| ☐ **SCHAEFELS, Hendrik Frans** ................ *paintings* | $1,320 | $33,000 |
| Belgian 1827-1904 | | |
| ☐ **SCHAEFELS, Lucas** ............................ *paintings* | $660 | $11,000 |
| Belgian 1824-1885 | | |
| ☐ **SCHAEFER, Henry Thomas** ................ *paintings* | $400 | $3,025 |
| British ac. 1873-1915 ................................ *drawings* | | $250 |
| ☐ **SCHAEFER, Johannes** ........................ *paintings* | | $1,100 |
| American 20th cent. | | |
| ☐ **SCHAEFER, Maximilian** ...................... *drawings* | | $715 |
| German 1851-1916 | | |
| ☐ **SCHAEFFER, August** ........................... *paintings* | | $1,870 |
| Austrian 1833-1916 | | |
| ☐ **SCHAEFFER, J.** ................................... *paintings* | | $209 |
| contemporary | | |
| ☐ **SCHAEFFER, Mead** ........................... *paintings* | $550 | $3,850 |
| American 1898-1980 | | |
| ☐ **SCHAEP, Henri Adolphe** ...................... *paintings* | | $1,870 |
| Dutch 1826-70 | | |
| ☐ **SCHAETTE** ........................................ *paintings* | $770 | $770 |
| French School 19th cent. | | |
| ☐ **SCHAFER, Frederick Ferdinand** ........... *paintings* | $165 | $4,125 |
| German/American 1841-1917 ......................... *drawings* | | $605 |
| ☐ **SCHAFER, Heinrich (or Hermann)** ........ *paintings* | $357 | $5,500 |
| German 19th cent. ...................................... *drawings* | $137 | $2,200 |
| ☐ **SCHAFER, Laurenz** ............................. *paintings* | | $825 |
| German 1840-1904 | | |
| ☐ **SCHAFFENKER, C. E.** ...................... *drawings* | | $275 |
| 19th/20th cent. | | |
| ☐ **SCHAFFER, Adalbert** ........................... *paintings* | $440 | $2,530 |
| Hungarian 1815-71 | | |
| ☐ **SCHAFFER, Fritz** ............................... *paintings* | | $1,430 |
| German 19th cent. | | |
| ☐ **SCHAFFER, Ludwig** ........................... *paintings* | | $220 |
| German 19th cent. | | |
| ☐ **SCHAFFER, Mead** ............................. *paintings* | | $2,000 |
| American b. 1898 | | |
| ☐ **SCHAIK, W. von** ............................... *paintings* | | $750 |
| ☐ **SCHALCKEN, Godfried** ...................... *paintings* | $6,380 | $13,200 |
| Dutch 1643-1706 | | |
| ☐ **SCHALDACH, William J.** .................... *drawings* | $154 | $220 |
| American b. 1890 | | |
| ☐ **SCHALL, Jean Frederic** ...................... *paintings* | $385 | $6,600 |
| French 1752-1825 | | |

| | | Current Price Range | |
|---|---|---|---|
| | | Low | High |
| ☐ **SCHAMPHELEER, Edmund de** ............ *paintings* | | | $4,125 |
| Belgian 1824-1899 | | | |
| ☐ **SCHANKER, Louis** ............................ *paintings* | | $880 | $3,630 |
| American b. 1903 ..................................... *drawings* | | $495 | $1,320 |
| ................................................................ *sculpture* | | $1,430 | $1,870 |
| ☐ **SCHANS, S.V.D.** ................................ *paintings* | | | $20,900 |
| 19th cent. | | | |
| ☐ **SCHAPIRO, Miriam** ........................... *paintings* | | | $2,420 |
| ................................................................ *drawings* | | | $495 |
| ☐ **SCHARER, \*\*\*** .................................... *paintings* | | | $7,700 |
| German 19th cent. | | | |
| ☐ **SCHARF, Kenny** ............................... *paintings* | | | $2,640 |
| contemporary | | | |
| ☐ **SCHARF, Viktor** ............................... *paintings* | | | $500 |
| Austrian b. 1872 | | | |
| ☐ **SCHARL, Josef** ................................ *paintings* | | | $15,400 |
| German/American 1896-1954 | | | |
| ☐ **SCHARY, Susan** ................................ *paintings* | | | $198 |
| American 20th cent. | | | |
| ☐ **SCHATEL, J.C.G.** .............................. *paintings* | | | $467 |
| ☐ **SCHATER, F.** ..................................... *paintings* | | | $3,575 |
| American 19th cent. | | | |
| ☐ **SCHATTENSTEIN, Nikol** ..................... *paintings* | | $550 | $3,080 |
| Russian/American 1877-1954 | | | |
| ☐ **SCHATZ, Manford** ............................ *paintings* | | | $1,430 |
| ☐ **SCHEBEK, Ferdinand** ......................... *paintings* | | | $2,530 |
| Austrian 1875-1949 | | | |
| ☐ **SCHECHTER, Emanuel** ....................... *paintings* | | | $605 |
| American | | | |
| ☐ **SCHECK, M.** ..................................... *paintings* | | | $330 |
| European 20th cent. | | | |
| ☐ **SCHEENLOOP, C.P.** ........................... *paintings* | | | $275 |
| ☐ **SCHEFFER, Ary** ................................ *paintings* | | | $2,475 |
| French 1795-1858 ..................................... *drawings* | | | $2,860 |
| ☐ **SCHEFFER, Henri** ............................. *paintings* | | | $1,650 |
| French 1798-1862 | | | |
| ☐ **SCHEIBER, Hugo** ............................. *paintings* | | $550 | $5,225 |
| Hungarian 1873-1950 ................................. *drawings* | | $174 | $4,180 |
| ☐ **SCHEIDEL, Franz Anton von** .............. *drawings* | | $110 | $11,000 |
| Austrian 1731-1801 | | | |
| ☐ **SCHELFHOUT, Andreas** ...................... *paintings* | | $1,980 | $20,900 |
| Dutch 1787-1870 ...................................... *drawings* | | $274 | $330 |
| ☐ **SCHELL, Frederick B.** ........................ *drawings* | | $495 | $605 |
| American | | | |
| ☐ **SCHELLING, George Luther** ................ *drawings* | | | $467 |
| 20th cent. | | | |
| ☐ **SCHELVER, V.** ................................... *paintings* | | $220 | $302 |
| European 19th cent. | | | |

| | Current Price Range | |
|---|---|---|
| | *Low* | *High* |
| ☐ **SCHENCK, August Friedrich Albrecht** .. *paintings* | $550 | $4,400 |
| Danish 1828-1901 | | |
| ☐ **SCHENCK, Bill** ..................................... *paintings* | $302 | $1,540 |
| American 20th cent. | | |
| ☐ **SCHENCK, M.** ..................................... *paintings* | | $275 |
| Continental School 19th cent. | | |
| ☐ **SCHENCK, William** ............................ *paintings* | $1,760 | $5,500 |
| ☐ **SCHENDEL, Bernardus van** ................ *paintings* | | $2,200 |
| Dutch 1649-1709 | | |
| ☐ **SCHENDEL, Petrus van** ....................... *paintings* | $165 | $39,600 |
| Belgian 1806-1870 | | |
| ☐ **SCHEPERS, Maria** ............................. *drawings* | | $22,000 |
| ☐ **SCHEPPELIN, Jakob Andreas** .............. *paintings* | | $324 |
| Swiss ac. 1760 | | |
| ☐ **SCHERMER, Cornelis** .......................... *paintings* | | $1,430 |
| Dutch 1824-1915 | | |
| ☐ **SCHERREWITZ, Johan** ....................... *paintings* | $467 | $7,700 |
| Dutch 1868-1951 | | |
| ☐ **SCHEUERER, Julius** ........................... *paintings* | $1,430 | $9,900 |
| German 1859-1913 | | |
| ☐ **SCHEUERER, Otto** ............................. *paintings* | | $1,760 |
| German 1862-1934 | | |
| ☐ **SCHEUERLE, Joe** .............................. *drawings* | | $1,149 |
| American 1873-1948 | | |
| ☐ **SCHEUREN,** | | |
| **Caspar Johann Nepomuk** ...................... *drawings* | | $880 |
| German 1810-1887 | | |
| ☐ **SCHEUREN, K.** ................................ *paintings* | | $1,100 |
| ☐ **SCHEURENBERG, Joseph** ................... *paintings* | | $2,530 |
| German 1846-1914 | | |
| ☐ **SCHGOER, Julius** ............................. *paintings* | | $1,650 |
| German 1847-1885 | | |
| ☐ **SCHIANSKI, M.** ................................ *drawings* | | $385 |
| ☐ **SCHIAVON, Vittorio** .......................... *paintings* | | $770 |
| ☐ **SCHICK, Rudolf** .............................. *paintings* | | $247 |
| German 1840-1887 | | |
| ☐ **SCHIEDGES, Peter Paul** ...................... *paintings* | $247 | $4,180 |
| Dutch 1812-1876 ................................... *drawings* | | $660 |
| ☐ **SCHIEFER, Johannes** ......................... *paintings* | $22 | $275 |
| French 20th cent. | | |
| ☐ **SCHIELE, Egon** .............................. *paintings* | $2,430,000 | $2,530,000 |
| German 1890-1918 ................................... *drawings* | $935 | $220,000 |
| ☐ **SCHIERTZ, Franz Wilhelm** ................. *paintings* | | $9,350 |
| German 1813-1887 | | |
| ☐ **SCHIESS, Traugott** ........................... *paintings* | | $605 |
| Swiss 1834-1869 | | |
| ☐ **SCHIFFE, R. (?)** ............................... *drawings* | | $330 |
| Austrian 19th/20th cent. | | |

## German Expressionism

Although Austrian born, Egon Schiele is considered a member of the German Expressionist movement of the 1900s. His intensity is considered unique in a movement marked by a consistent overriding of the boundaries of proportion in realist painting. Schiele lived only to the age of thirty-eight, but he produced more than 300 paintings, over half of which are considered important examples of his work.

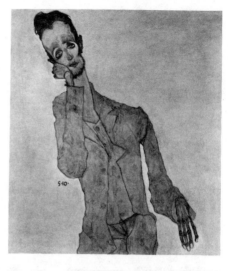

Because nearly all of Schiele's major canvases are in permanent collections, there was considerable excitement when "Portrat Des Malers Karl Zakovsek" was offered at auction in 1983. The work had been purchased for $5,000 in 1959 at a charity benefit. The buyer, a New York doctor, was unaware of the painting's value and hung it in his waiting room. Twenty-four years later, it sold for $2,420,000 at Sotheby's. (Egon Schiele, "Portrat Des Malers Karl Zakovsek," oil on canvas, 39⅜ x 35½ in., Sotheby's, November 16, 1983, $2,420,000.)

| | | *Current Price Range* | |
| --- | --- | --- | --- |
| | | *Low* | *High* |
| □ **SCHIFFER, Anton** ............................ *paintings* | | | **$1,650** |
| Austrian 1811-1876 | | | |
| □ **SCHIIFER, H.** .................................... *drawings* | | | **$247** |
| German 19th cent. | | | |
| □ **SCHILDER, Andrei Nicoloivich** ........... *paintings* | | | **$4,125** |
| Russian b. 1861 | | | |
| □ **SCHILDT, Gary** ................................... *drawings* | | | **$192** |
| American 20th cent. ..................................... *sculpture* | **$450** | | **$3,200** |
| □ **SCHILL, Adriaan** ................................ *paintings* | **$137** | | **$1,650** |
| Dutch 1849-1902 | | | |
| □ **SCHILLE, Alice** .................................... *paintings* | | | **$440** |
| American 1869-1955 | | | |
| □ **SCHIMMEL, Wilhelm** ......................... *sculpture* | **$5,500** | | **$9,900** |
| American 1865-1890 | | | |
| □ **SCHINDLER, A. Zeno** ........................ *paintings* | | | **$495** |
| American 1813-c. 1880 ................................ *drawings* | | | **$3,960** |
| □ **SCHINDLER, Emile Jacob** ................... *drawings* | | | **$495** |
| Austrian 1842-1892 | | | |

| | | Current Price Range | |
|---|---|---|---|
| | | Low | High |
| ☐ **SCHIOETTZ-JENSEN, Niels Frederik** ... *paintings* | | | $935 |
| Danish 1855-1941 | | | |
| ☐ **SCHIPPERS, Charles Joseph** ............... *drawings* | | | $192 |
| Belgian 1813-1874 | | | |
| ☐ **SCHIPPERS, Joseph** ........................... *paintings* | | | $330 |
| d. 1917 | | | |
| ☐ **SCHIPPERUS, Pieter Adrianus** ............. *drawings* | | | $247 |
| Dutch 1840-1929 | | | |
| ☐ **SCHIRFEN, Johannes** .......................... *paintings* | | | $880 |
| European 19th cent. | | | |
| ☐ **SCHIRMER, Johann Wilhelm** .............. *paintings* | | | $2,090 |
| German 1807-63 | | | |
| ☐ **SCHISCHKIN, Ivan Ivanovitch** ............ *drawings* | | $660 | $935 |
| Russian 1831-1898 | | | |
| ☐ **SCHISSLER, Janeen A.** ........................ *drawings* | | | $1,150 |
| American | | | |
| ☐ **SCHIVERT, Viktor** ............................ *paintings* | | | $1,540 |
| Romanian b. 1863 | | | |
| ☐ **SCHLAGETER, Karl** ........................... *paintings* | | | $192 |
| Swiss b. 1894 | | | |
| ☐ **SCHLAIKJER, Jes William** ................. *paintings* | | $550 | $1,650 |
| American b. 1897 | | | |
| ☐ **SCHLATTER, A.** ................................ *paintings* | | | $880 |
| Swiss 19th cent. | | | |
| ☐ **SCHLEETER, Howard Behling** ............. *paintings* | | | $246 |
| American b. 1903 | | | |
| ☐ **SCHLEGEL, Fridolin** .......................... *paintings* | | | $715 |
| American 19th cent. | | | |
| ☐ **SCHLEH, Anna** ................................. *paintings* | | | $1,320 |
| German 1833-1879 | | | |
| ☐ **SCHLEICH, Eduard (the elder)** ............. *paintings* | | | $25,300 |
| German 1812-1874 | | | |
| ☐ **SCHLEICH, Eduard (the younger)** ......... *paintings* | | | $6,875 |
| German 1853-1893 | | | |
| ☐ **SCHLEICH, Robert** ............................ *paintings* | | $2,420 | $13,200 |
| German 1845-1934 ................................. *drawings* | | $330 | $1,760 |
| ☐ **SCHLEICHER, Carl** ............................ *paintings* | | $550 | $3,850 |
| Austrian ac. 1859-1871 | | | |
| ☐ **SCHLEICHON, J.** ............................... *paintings* | | | $880 |
| Eastern European 19th cent. | | | |
| ☐ **SCHLEINIGER, Adolf** ......................... *paintings* | | $247 | $440 |
| German 19th cent. | | | |
| ☐ **SCHLEMM, Ed** ................................. *paintings* | | | $4,620 |
| ☐ **SCHLEMMER, Oskar** ......................... *drawings* | | $16,500 | $110,000 |
| ☐ **SCHLENIER, T.M.** ............................. *paintings* | | | $825 |
| American 19th cent. | | | |
| ☐ **SCHLESINGER, Felix** ......................... *paintings* | | $5,750 | $41,250 |
| German 1833-1910 | | | |

| | Current Price Range | |
|---|---|---|
| | *Low* | *High* |
| ☐ **SCHLESINGER, Karl** .......................... *paintings* | $770 | $5,280 |
| Swiss 1825/26-1893 | | |
| ☐ **SCHLESSING, C.** ............................. *paintings* | | $220 |
| German 19th cent. | | |
| ☐ **SCHLIECKER, August** ................... *paintings* | | $900 |
| ☐ **SCHLIER, Michael** ......................... *paintings* | | $1,100 |
| German 1744-1807 | | |
| ☐ **SCHLINGER, C.** ............................. *paintings* | | $412 |
| ☐ **SCHLIP, E.** ....................................... *sculpture* | | $440 |
| German 19th cent. | | |
| ☐ **SCHLITZER, M.** ............................. *paintings* | | $935 |
| ☐ **SCHLOESSER, Carl Bernhard** ............ *paintings* | $1,980 | $5,775 |
| German 1832-1914 | | |
| ☐ **SCHLOESSER, G.** ............................. *paintings* | | $1,430 |
| German 19th cent. | | |
| ☐ **SCHLOGL, Josef Von** ..................... *paintings* | | $1,650 |
| Austrian b. 1851 | | |
| ☐ **SCHLOMER, Richard** ........................ *paintings* | | $900 |
| German b. 1921 | | |
| ☐ **SCHLOSSER, \*\*\*** ............................... *drawings* | | $1,980 |
| Continental 20th cent. | | |
| ☐ **SCHLUTTER** ....................................... *paintings* | | $605 |
| ☐ **SCHMAEDEL, Max von** ....................... *paintings* | | $990 |
| German b. 1856 | | |
| ☐ **SCHMANNS** ....................................... *paintings* | | $330 |
| ☐ **SCHMARLING, Felix** ......................... *paintings* | | $577 |
| Austrian 19th cent. | | |
| ☐ **SCHMAUSS, C. F.** ............................. *paintings* | | $330 |
| German 19th cent. | | |
| ☐ **SCHMID, J.** ....................................... *paintings* | | $1,045 |
| German or Austrian 19th cent. | | |
| ☐ **SCHMID, R.** ....................................... *sculpture* | | $2,860 |
| ☐ **SCHMID, Richard Allan** ....................... *paintings* | $275 | $825 |
| American b. 1934 | | |
| ☐ **SCHMID-BREITENBACH, Franz** ......... *paintings* | | $1,980 |
| German 1857-1927 | | |
| ☐ **SCHMIDT, Adolphe** ........................... *paintings* | | $7,700 |
| German 19th cent. | | |
| ☐ **SCHMIDT, Eduard Allan** ................... *paintings* | $4,400 | $7,150 |
| German b. 1809 | | |
| ☐ **SCHMIDT, Frederic Albert** ................. *paintings* | $1,650 | $1,980 |
| French 1846-1916 | | |
| ☐ **SCHMIDT, Fritz** ............................. *sculpture* | | $352 |
| European 20th cent. | | |
| ☐ **SCHMIDT, Hans** ............................. *paintings* | | $1,100 |
| German b. 1877 | | |
| ☐ **SCHMIDT, Harold von** ....................... *paintings* | $275 | $46,200 |
| American 1893-1982 ................................. *drawings* | | $825 |

| | Current Price Range | |
|---|---|---|
| | Low | High |
| ☐ **SCHMIDT, Jay** ................................. *paintings* | | **$660** |
| American b. 1929 | | |
| ☐ **SCHMIDT, John W.** ............................ *paintings* | **$400** | **$2,100** |
| American 20th cent. | | |
| ☐ **SCHMIDT, Marius** ............................. *paintings* | | **$467** |
| American 20th cent. ................................. *drawings* | | **$220** |
| ☐ **SCHMIDT, T.** ................................... *paintings* | | **$352** |
| ☐ **SCHMIDT-BREITENBACH,** | | |
| **Franz Xavier** ..................................... *paintings* | | **$1,540** |
| ☐ **SCHMIDT-CASSEL, Gustav** ................ *sculpture* | **$330** | **$3,190** |
| German b. 1867 | | |
| ☐ **SCHMIDT-FELLING** .......................... *sculpture* | **$286** | **$440** |
| German ac. 1895-1930 | | |
| ☐ **SCHMIDT-HAMBURG, R.** ................... *paintings* | | **$550** |
| German 20th cent. | | |
| ☐ **SCHMIDT-ROTTLUFF, Karl** ............... *paintings* | **$74,800** | **$77,000** |
| German b. 1884 ..................................... *drawings* | **$1,980** | **$27,500** |
| ☐ **SCHMITT, Albert Felix** ........................ *paintings* | | **$1,100** |
| American b. 1873 | | |
| ☐ **SCHMITT, Carl** .................................. *paintings* | **$137** | **$275** |
| American | | |
| ☐ **SCHMITT, Guido** .............................. *paintings* | | **$2,640** |
| German 1834-1922 | | |
| ☐ **SCHMITT, Paul A.** ............................ *paintings* | | **$660** |
| American b. 1893 | | |
| ☐ **SCHMITZ, Ernst** ............................... *paintings* | **$2,200** | **$3,410** |
| German 1859-1917 | | |
| ☐ **SCHMITZBERGER, Josef** ................... *paintings* | **$1,210** | **$6,050** |
| German b. 1851 | | |
| ☐ **SCHMUTZER, Ferdinand** .................... *paintings* | | **$3,080** |
| Austrian 1870-1928 | | |
| ☐ **SCHMUTZLER, Leopold** ...................... *paintings* | | **$1,980** |
| Bohemian 1864-1941 | | |
| ☐ **SCHNABEL, Julian** ............................ *paintings* | **$10,450** | **$93,500** |
| American b. 1951 .................................... *drawings* | **$1,430** | **$4,950** |
| ☐ **SCHNAKENBERG, Henry Ernest** ......... *paintings* | **$412** | **$4,950** |
| American 1892-1970 ................................. *drawings* | **$192** | **$605** |
| ☐ **SCHNEE, Herman** ............................. *paintings* | **$385** | **$1,980** |
| German 1840-1926 | | |
| ☐ **SCHNEIDER, Arthur** .......................... *paintings* | | **$302** |
| American 20th cent. | | |
| ☐ **SCHNEIDER, Felicie Fournier** ............. *paintings* | | **$880** |
| French 1831-1888 | | |
| ☐ **SCHNEIDER, Frank** ........................... *paintings* | **$192** | **$605** |
| American b. 1935 | | |
| ☐ **SCHNEIDER, Georg** ........................... *paintings* | | **$550** |
| German 1759-1842 | | |
| ☐ **SCHNEIDER, George** .......................... *paintings* | | **$4,125** |
| German 19th cent. | | |

| | Current Price Range | |
|---|---|---|
| | Low | High |

☐ **SCHNEIDER, Gerard Ernest** ............... *paintings* $880 | $3,300
French 1896-1948

☐ **SCHNEIDER, H.** ..................... *paintings* $1,320 | $2,310
German 19th cent.

☐ **SCHNEIDER, Max** ........................... *paintings* | $2,200
20th cent.

☐ **SCHNEIDER, P.** ................................. *paintings* | $770

☐ **SCHNEIDER, Susan Hayward** ............. *paintings* $82 | $209
American b. 1876

☐ **SCHNEIDER, Theophile** ...................... *paintings* $121 | $200
American b. 1872

☐ **SCHNORR, Franz** ............................. *paintings* | $3,080
German 1794-1859

☐ **SCHODL, Max** ................................. *paintings* $440 | $5,775
Austrian 1834-1921

☐ **SCHOEFER, H.** ................................. *paintings* | $687
German late 19th cent.

☐ **SCHOEFF, Johannes** .......................... *paintings* $17,050 | $22,000
Dutch 1608-1666

☐ **SCHOEN, Celeste** ............................... *paintings* | $187
American 20th cent.

☐ **SCHOEN, Eugen** ................................ *paintings* | $350
German 1863-1908

☐ **SCHOEN, Eugene** .............................. *paintings* $440 | $880
American 1880-1957

☐ **SCHOENBECK, Richard** ...................... *sculpture* | $825
German

☐ **SCHOENEWERK** ............................... *sculpture* $330 | $357

☐ **SCHOENLOOP, C.D.** .......................... *paintings* | $440

☐ **SCHOEVAERDTS, Mathys** ................... *paintings* $605 | $30,800
Flemish b. 1665

☐ **SCHOFIELD, Walter Elmer** ............... *paintings* $495 | $23,100
American 1867-1944 ................................. *drawings* $66 | $275

☐ **SCHOFREN, H.J.** .............................. *paintings* | $3,960
German b. 1817

☐ **SCHOLDER, Fritz** ............................. *paintings* $2,750 | $9,075
American b. 1937

☐ **SCHOLTEN, Hendrik Jacobus** ............. *paintings* $1,650 | $4,180
Dutch 1824-1907

☐ **SCHOLTEN, L.** ................................. *paintings* | $466
Dutch 19th cent.

☐ **SCHOLZ, Max** ................................. *paintings* $660 | $4,400
German b. 1855

☐ **SCHOLZ, Werner** ............................. *paintings* | $418

☐ **SCHOMMER, Francois** ........................ *paintings* | $741
French 19th cent.

☐ **SCHONBERG, G.** .............................. *paintings* | $1,045

☐ **SCHONBRUNNER, Ignaz** ................... *paintings* $418 | $715
Austrian b. 1835

| | *Current Price Range* | |
|---|---|---|
| | *Low* | *High* |

| | | Low | High |
|---|---|---|---|
| ☐ **SCHONFELD, Ignatius** .......................... *paintings* | | | $605 |
| German 19th/20th cent. | | | |
| ☐ **SCHONFIELD, J.** ............................ *paintings* | | | $275 |
| Scandinavian 19th cent. | | | |
| ☐ **SCHONGRI, A.** ................................ *paintings* | | | $1,100 |
| German 19th cent.(?) | | | |
| ☐ **SCHONIAN, Alfred** ............................ *paintings* | $605 | | $2,200 |
| German b. 1856 | | | |
| ☐ **SCHONLEBER, Gustav** ........................ *paintings* | $605 | | $3,080 |
| German 1851-1917 | | | |
| ☐ **SCHONN, Alois** ................................ *paintings* | $825 | | $22,000 |
| Austrian 1826-1897 | | | |
| ☐ **SCHONZEIT, Ben** ............................ *paintings* | $1,650 | | $16,500 |
| American b. 1942 | | | |
| ☐ **SCHOONOVER, Frank Earle** ............... *paintings* | $132 | | $15,400 |
| American 1877-1972 ................................. *drawings* | $110 | | $1,210 |
| ☐ **SCHOOTEN, Floris Gerritsz van** .......... *paintings* | $38,500 | | $52,250 |
| Dutch ac. 1605-1655 | | | |
| ☐ **SCHORM, F.** ..................................... *paintings* | | | $1,210 |
| ☐ **SCHOTEL, Jan Christianus** ................. *paintings* | | | $12,100 |
| Dutch 1787-1838 | | | |
| ☐ **SCHOTH, A.** ..................................... *paintings* | $715 | | $880 |
| ☐ **SCHOTTLE, Mark** ............................. *paintings* | | | $357 |
| American 20th cent. | | | |
| ☐ **SCHOU, Peter Alfred** .......................... *paintings* | | | $385 |
| Danish 1844-1914 | | | |
| ☐ **SCHOUBROECK, Pieter** ...................... *paintings* | | | $53,900 |
| Flemish 1570-1607 | | | |
| ☐ **SCHOUMAN, Aert** ............................ *paintings* | | | $2,860 |
| Dutch 1710-1792 | | | |
| ☐ **SCHOUTEN, Henry** ............................ *paintings* | $330 | | $1,540 |
| Dutch 1864-1927 | | | |
| ☐ **SCHOUTEN, Hubert Pieter** ................. *drawings* | | | $660 |
| Dutch 1747-1822 | | | |
| ☐ **SCHOUTEN, P.H.** ............................ *paintings* | | | $412 |
| ☐ **SCHOYERER, Josef** ............................ *paintings* | $715 | | $3,025 |
| German 1844-1923 | | | |
| ☐ **SCHRADER, R.** ................................ *paintings* | | | $330 |
| German 19th cent. | | | |
| ☐ **SCHRADY, Henry Merwin** ................. *sculpture* | | | $7,150 |
| American 1871-1922 | | | |
| ☐ **SCHRAG, Karl** ................................. *drawings* | $385 | | $2,090 |
| American b. 1912 | | | |
| ☐ **SCHRAM, Alois Hans** ........................ *paintings* | $990 | | $8,800 |
| Austrian 1864-1919 | | | |
| ☐ **SCHRANZ, Anton** ............................ *paintings* | | | $500 |
| ☐ **SCHREIBER** ..................................... *drawings* | | | $1,320 |
| German 19th cent. | | | |

| | | Current Price Range | |
|---|---|---|---|
| | | Low | High |
| ☐ **SCHREIBER, Charles Baptiste** ............ *paintings* | | $770 | $2,860 |
| French d. 1903 | | | |
| ☐ **SCHREIBER, Georges** .................... *paintings* | | $1,210 | $2,300 |
| American 1904-1977 ................................ *drawings* | | $88 | $1,980 |
| ☐ **SCHREINER, Phoebe C.** .................... *paintings* | | | $176 |
| American 19th/20th cent. | | | |
| ☐ **SCHRENK, Joseph** ............................ *paintings* | | | $2,970 |
| Austrian 19th cent. | | | |
| ☐ **SCHREYER, Adolf** .............................. *paintings* | | $495 | $104,500 |
| German 1828-1899 .................................... *drawings* | | $4,620 | $8,800 |
| ☐ **SCHREYER, C.W.** ............................ *paintings* | | $192 | $577 |
| American 19th/20th cent. | | | |
| ☐ **SCHREYER, Franz** ............................ *paintings* | | | $880 |
| German b. 1858 | | | |
| ☐ **SCHREYVOGEL, Charles** .................... *paintings* | | $3,740 | $198,000 |
| American 1861-1912 ................................ *drawings* | | | $2,090 |
| .................................................. *sculpture* | | $5,250 | $42,500 |
| ☐ **SCHRIBER, George** ............................ *paintings* | | | $440 |
| ☐ **SCHRICK, J.E.** ................................ *paintings* | | | $1,045 |
| German 20th cent. | | | |
| ☐ **SCHRIMPF, Georg** ............................ *paintings* | | | $37,400 |
| German 1889-1938 | | | |
| ☐ **SCHRODER, Albert Friedrich** ............ *paintings* | | $550 | $4,950 |
| German b. 1854 | | | |
| ☐ **SCHRODER, Justin** ............................ *paintings* | | | $3,520 |
| German 19th/20th cent. | | | |
| ☐ **SCHRODER, Thom** ............................ *paintings* | | | $5,500 |
| ☐ **SCHROEDER, W.** ............................ *paintings* | | | $302 |
| German(?) 19th cent. | | | |
| ☐ **SCHROETER, Alex** ............................ *paintings* | | $220 | $330 |
| German 19th cent. | | | |
| ☐ **SCHROTTER, Alfred von** .................... *paintings* | | | $1,760 |
| Austrian 1856-1935 | | | |
| ☐ **SCHRYVER, Louis Marie de** ............ *paintings* | | | $3,630 |
| 1863-1942 .................................................... *drawings* | | | $1,210 |
| ☐ **SCHUBACK, Emil Gottlieb** ................ *paintings* | | $7,150 | $8,525 |
| German 1820-1902 | | | |
| ☐ **SCHUBAKOFF, Sergey** ...................... *drawings* | | | $220 |
| Russian/American 20th cent. | | | |
| ☐ **SCHUBERTH, Carolus** ........................ *drawings* | | | $495 |
| ☐ **SCHUCHARDT, Ferdinand (Jr.)** ............ *paintings* | | $800 | $935 |
| 1855-after 1887 | | | |
| ☐ **SCHUCKER, James W.** ........................ *paintings* | | | $357 |
| b. 1903 | | | |
| ☐ **SCHUELER, Jon** .............................. *paintings* | | $220 | $550 |
| American b. 1916 | | | |
| ☐ **SCHUESSELE, Christian** .................... *paintings* | | | $7,700 |
| American 1824-1879 ................................ *drawings* | | | $1,210 |

| | Current Price Range | |
|---|---|---|
| | Low | High |

☐ **SCHUESSLER, Mary** ........................ *paintings* | | $246
American 20th cent.

☐ **SCHUFFENECKER, Claude Emile** ....... *paintings* | $418 | $7,700
French 1851-1934 ...................................... *drawings* | $275 | $1,980

☐ **SCHUFRIED, Dominik** ......................... *paintings* | | $1,650
Austrian b. 1810

☐ **SCHUIZ, Christian Georg** ..................... *paintings* | $1,760 | $16,500
German 1718-1791

☐ **SCHULDT, Fritiof** ............................... *paintings* | | $1,650
Swedish b. 1891

☐ **SCHULER, Heinrich** ............................ *paintings* | | $935
German 1857-1885

☐ **SCHULER, Remington** ......................... *paintings* | | $715
American b. 1887

☐ **SCHULHEIM, Heinrich** ........................ *paintings* | | $1,320

☐ **SCHULMAN, David** ............................ *paintings* | | $484
Dutch 1881-1966

☐ **SCHULMAN, Gian L.** ......................... *paintings* | $308 | $385

☐ **SCHULTEN, Arnold** ............................ *paintings* | | $8,800
German 1809-1874

☐ **SCHULTHEISS, Carl** ........................... *paintings* | | $4,125
German b. 1852

☐ **SCHULTHEISS, Natalie** ....................... *paintings* | | $1,650
Austrian 1865-1932

☐ **SCHULTZ, Carl** ................................. *drawings* | | $1,870
American 19th cent.

☐ **SCHULTZ, George F.** .......................... *paintings* | $175 | $3,250
American b. 1869 ...................................... *drawings* | $55 | $242

☐ **SCHULTZ, Robert E.** .......................... *paintings* | | $1,870
1928-1978

☐ **SCHULTZ, Stanley** ............................. *paintings* | $110 | $247
American 20th cent.

☐ **SCHULTZ-STRADTMANN, Otto** ......... *paintings* | | $990
German early 20th cent.

☐ **SCHULTZBERG, Anshelm** ................... *paintings* | $1,760 | $30,800
Swedish 1862-1945

☐ **SCHULTZE, Carl** ............................... *paintings* | $550 | $1,760
German b. 1856

☐ **SCHULTZE, Jean** ............................... *paintings* | | $990
Russian 19th/20th cent.

☐ **SCHULTZE, Robert** ............................ *paintings* | | $474
Swedish 1862-1945

☐ **SCHULTZE, Robert** ............................ *paintings* | $275 | $605
German b. 1828

☐ **SCHULZ, Adrien** ............................... *paintings* | | $550

☐ **SCHULZ, Charles** .............................. *drawings* | $110 | $770
American b. 1922

☐ **SCHULZ, Ella** .................................. *paintings* | | $2,420

☐ **SCHULZ, Max** .................................. *paintings* | | $2,860

| | | Current Price Range | |
|---|---|---|---|
| | | *Low* | *High* |
| ☐ **SCHULZ, Robert** .............................. *paintings* | | **$6,600** | **$6,710** |
| American 1928-1978 | | | |
| ☐ **SCHULZ, Toni** ............................... *paintings* | | | **$412** |
| German/American 19th cent. | | | |
| ☐ **SCHULZE** ......................................... *paintings* | | | **$302** |
| American 19th/20th cent. | | | |
| ☐ **SCHUMACHER** ................................. *sculpture* | | | **$660** |
| ☐ **SCHUMACHER, C.J.** ........................ *paintings* | | | **$1,075** |
| 19th cent. | | | |
| ☐ **SCHUMACHER, Emil** ......................... *paintings* | | **$4,675** | **$14,300** |
| German b. 1912 ..................................... *drawings* | | | **$4,675** |
| ☐ **SCHUMACHER, Willem** ...................... *paintings* | | | **$300** |
| Dutch b. 1891 | | | |
| ☐ **SCHUMACHER, William E.** ............... *paintings* | | **$150** | **$275** |
| American 1870-1931 | | | |
| ☐ **SCHUMAKER** ................................... *paintings* | | | **$308** |
| ☐ **SCHUMANN, Ludwig** ......................... *paintings* | | | **$660** |
| German 19th/20th cent. | | | |
| ☐ **SCHUPPEN, Jakob van** ...................... *paintings* | | | **$6,600** |
| German 1670-1751 | | | |
| ☐ **SCHUR, I.** ........................................ *paintings* | | | **$715** |
| ................................................ *drawings* | | | **$462** |
| ☐ **SCHURR, Claude** ............................. *paintings* | | **$132** | **$330** |
| ☐ **SCHUSSELE, Christian** ....................... *paintings* | | | **$6,000** |
| French/American 1824/26-1879 ...................... *drawings* | | | **$1,320** |
| ☐ **SCHUSTER, Donna N.** ....................... *paintings* | | **$247** | **$412** |
| American 20th cent. .................................. *drawings* | | **$220** | **$247** |
| ☐ **SCHUSTER, Heinrich Rudolf** ............... *paintings* | | | **$5,775** |
| German 1848-1902 | | | |
| ☐ **SCHUSTER, Ludwig** ......................... *paintings* | | | **$1,210** |
| Austrian 1820-1873 | | | |
| ☐ **SCHUT, Cornelis** ................................. *paintings* | | | **$1,870** |
| Flemish | | | |
| ☐ **SCHUTSMANS, T.** ........................... *paintings* | | | **$1,870** |
| Dutch 19th cent. | | | |
| ☐ **SCHUTZ, E.** ...................................... *drawings* | | | **$324** |
| 19th cent. | | | |
| ☐ **SCHUTZ, Jan Frederick** ...................... *paintings* | | | **$330** |
| Dutch 1817-1888 | | | |
| ☐ **SCHUTZ, Johann Georg** ...................... *paintings* | | | **$6,000** |
| German 1755-1813 | | | |
| ☐ **SCHUTZ, Wilhelm J.** ......................... *drawings* | | | **$274** |
| German 19th/20th cent. | | | |
| ☐ **SCHUTZE, Wilhelm** ............................ *paintings* | | **$16,500** | **$26,400** |
| German 1840-1898 | | | |
| ☐ **SCHUTZENBERG, Louis Frederic** ........ *paintings* | | **$4,400** | **$4,620** |
| French 1825-1903 | | | |
| ☐ **SCHUYLER, Remington** ...................... *paintings* | | **$250** | **$2,310** |
| American 1884/87-1955 | | | |

|  | | Current Price Range | |
| --- | --- | --- | --- |
|  | | Low | High |
| ☐ **SCHVIERMANN, J.** ............................ *paintings* | | | $330 |
| Dutch 20th cent. | | | |
| ☐ **SCHWABE, Carlos** ............................. *paintings* | | | $16,500 |
| Swiss 1866-1926 ....................................... *drawings* | | | $1,650 |
| ☐ **SCHWANENFLUGAL, H.V.** ................ *paintings* | | $132 | $220 |
| American 19th/20th cent. | | | |
| ☐ **SCHWANFELDER, Henry** ................... *paintings* | | | $4,800 |
| English 1773/74-1837 | | | |
| ☐ **SCHWAR, Wilhelm** ............................. *paintings* | | | $4,125 |
| German b. 1860 | | | |
| ☐ **SCHWARTZ, Andrew T.** ....................... *paintings* | | | $302 |
| American | | | |
| ☐ **SCHWARTZ, Daniel** ........................... *paintings* | | | $495 |
| ☐ **SCHWARTZ, Davis Francis** .................. *paintings* | | $38 | $990 |
| American 1879-1969 ................................. *drawings* | | $66 | $467 |
| ☐ **SCHWARTZ, William S.** ...................... *paintings* | | $550 | $5,500 |
| Russian/American 1896-after 1934, d. 1977? ...... *drawings* | | | $1,100 |
| ☐ **SCHWARZ, A.W.** ............................... *paintings* | | | $192 |
| American 20th cent. | | | |
| ☐ **SCHWARZ, Christoph** ......................... *paintings* | | | $33,000 |
| German c. 1545-1592 | | | |
| ☐ **SCHWARZ, H.K.** ............................... *paintings* | | | $990 |
| ☐ **SCHWARZENFELD,** | | | |
| **Adolph Franz Christian Schreitter von** ... *paintings* | | | $1,100 |
| Bohemian b. 1854 | | | |
| ☐ **SCHWARZMAYR, Carl** ....................... *paintings* | | | $192 |
| 20th cent. | | | |
| ☐ **SCHWEGLER, Xavier** ......................... *paintings* | | | $1,500 |
| Swiss 1832-1902 ...................................... *drawings* | | | $165 |
| ☐ **SCHWEICH, Carl** ............................... *paintings* | | | $2,090 |
| German 1823-1898 | | | |
| ☐ **SCHWEICKARDT, Hendrik Willem** ..... *paintings* | | $1,100 | $4,400 |
| German 1746-1797 | | | |
| ☐ **SCHWEICKHARDT, Johan** ................. *paintings* | | | $330 |
| ☐ **SCHWEIDER, Arthur** .......................... *paintings* | | | $330 |
| American 20th cent. | | | |
| ☐ **SCHWEITZER, Adolf Gustav** .............. *paintings* | | $2,090 | $3,740 |
| German 1847-1914 | | | |
| ☐ **SCHWEITZER, Gertrude** ..................... *paintings* | | | $825 |
| American | | | |
| ☐ **SCHWEITZER, R.** .............................. *paintings* | | | $3,025 |
| German 19th/20th cent. | | | |
| ☐ **SCHWENDER, Hanns Paulus** .............. *drawings* | | | $1,320 |
| ☐ **SCHWENINGER, Carl (the elder)** .......... *paintings* | | | $2,200 |
| Austrian 1818-1887 | | | |
| ☐ **SCHWENINGER, Karl (the elder)** ......... *paintings* | | $1,540 | $2,475 |
| Austrian 1854-1903 | | | |
| ☐ **SCHWERIN, Amelie von** ..................... *paintings* | | | $660 |
| Swedish 1819-1897 | | | |

| | Current Price Range | |
|---|---|---|
| | *Low* | *High* |
| ☐ **SCHWICHTENBERG, Martel** ............. *paintings* | **$1,650** | **$1,980** |
| ☐ **SCHWIERING, Conrad** ....................... *paintings* | | **$440** |
| American | | |
| ☐ **SCHWIMMER, J.** ................................ *paintings* | | **$495** |
| German 19th cent. | | |
| ☐ **SCHWIND, Moritz** ............................ *paintings* | | **$165** |
| Austrian 1804-1871 ................................... *drawings* | | **$2,200** |
| ☐ **SCHWING, \*\*\*** ................................ *paintings* | | **$3,300** |
| German 19th cent. | | |
| ☐ **SCHWITTERS, Kurt** ........................... *paintings* | **$3,300** | **$33,000** |
| German 1887-1948 ................................. *drawings* | **$2,420** | **$22,000** |
| ☐ **SCHWORMSTADT, Felix** ................... *drawings* | | **$440** |
| German b. 1870 | | |
| ☐ **SCHWOTENBERG, S.** ........................ *sculpture* | | **$302** |
| ☐ **SCIOCCHETTI, L.** ............................. *paintings* | | **$220** |
| American 20th cent. | | |
| ☐ **SCIVER, Pearl Aiman van** ................. *paintings* | **$132** | **$247** |
| b. 1896 | | |
| ☐ **SCKELL, Ludwig** ............................... *paintings* | | **$3,190** |
| German 1842-1905 | | |
| ☐ **SCOPPA, Raimondo** ........................... *paintings* | | **$3,300** |
| Italian b. 1820 | | |
| ☐ **SCOPPAX, Giuseppe** ......................... *drawings* | | **$330** |
| ☐ **SCOPPETTA, Pietro** .......................... *paintings* | | **$1,430** |
| Italian 1863-1920 | | |
| ☐ **SCORRANO, Luigi** ............................ *paintings* | | **$357** |
| ☐ **SCOT, Horatio McCulloch** .................. *paintings* | | **$440** |
| 1805-1867 | | |
| ☐ **SCOTT, A.E.** ..................................... *paintings* | | **$330** |
| English 19th cent. | | |
| ☐ **SCOTT, Campbell** ............................. *paintings* | **$385** | **$385** |
| Scottish 19th/20th cent. | | |
| ☐ **SCOTT, Charles** ................................. *drawings* | | **$1,210** |
| American | | |
| ☐ **SCOTT, Colin A.** ............................... *paintings* | | **$577** |
| Canadian 20th cent. | | |
| ☐ **SCOTT, Frank Edwin** ......................... *paintings* | | **$660** |
| American 1863-1929 | | |
| ☐ **SCOTT, Harold W.** ............................ *paintings* | | **$200** |
| American c. 1934 | | |
| ☐ **SCOTT, Henry** ................................... *paintings* | | **$770** |
| ☐ **SCOTT, Howard** ................................ *paintings* | **$632** | **$825** |
| b. 1902 | | |
| ☐ **SCOTT, James R.** .............................. *paintings* | **$550** | **$2,860** |
| British ac. 1850-73 | | |
| ☐ **SCOTT, James V.** .............................. *paintings* | | **$192** |
| Scottish ac. 1877-1889 | | |
| ☐ **SCOTT, John** ..................................... *paintings* | **$8,000** | **$20,000** |
| American contemporary | | |

| | | Current Price Range | |
|---|---|---|---|
| | | Low | High |
| ☐ SCOTT, John W.A. .............................. *paintings* | | $352 | $4,675 |
| American 1815-1907 | | | |
| ☐ SCOTT, Julian .................................... *paintings* | | $550 | $33,000 |
| American 1846-1901 | | | |
| ☐ SCOTT, Samuel ................................. *paintings* | | | $16,500 |
| English 1703-1772 | | | |
| ☐ SCOTT, Sir Peter ............................... *paintings* | | $2,640 | $6,050 |
| English b. 1909 | | | |
| ☐ SCOTT, Thomas J. ............................ *paintings* | | | $550 |
| American 19th cent. | | | |
| ☐ SCOTT, W.E. .................................... *paintings* | | | $192 |
| American b. 1884 | | | |
| ☐ SCOTT, William ................................ *paintings* | | | $4,400 |
| b. 1956 | | | |
| ☐ SCOTT, William J. ............................ *paintings* | | | $474 |
| American 20th cent. .................................... *drawings* | | $385 | $715 |
| ☐ SCOUEZEC, Maurice Le ..................... *drawings* | | | $880 |
| ☐ SCPOCSOME, J.L. ............................. *paintings* | | | $440 |
| ☐ SCRAGGS, James ............................... *paintings* | | | $2,970 |
| English 19th cent. | | | |
| ☐ SCRIVER, Bob ................................... *sculpture* | | $825 | $20,000 |
| American b. 1914 | | | |
| ☐ SCUDDER, James Long ........................ *paintings* | | | $577 |
| American 1836-1881 | | | |
| ☐ SCUDDER, Janet ................................. *sculpture* | | $2,640 | $4,950 |
| American 1875-1940 | | | |
| ☐ SCULL, Nina W. ................................ *paintings* | | $132 | $280 |
| American b. 1902 | | | |
| ☐ SCULLY, Sean ................................... *paintings* | | $1,320 | $8,800 |
| English b. 1946 | | | |
| ☐ SCULTHORPE, Peter ........................ *drawings* | | $4,675 | $7,700 |
| American b. 1948 | | | |
| ☐ SEAGO, Edward Brian ........................ *paintings* | | $1,430 | $11,550 |
| English 1910-1974 | | | |
| ☐ SEALY, Allen Culpepper ..................... *paintings* | | | $522 |
| ☐ SEAMAN, Percival ............................. *drawings* | | | $1,320 |
| ☐ SEARBY, Willis ................................. *paintings* | | $800 | $825 |
| ☐ SEARLE, Alice T. .............................. *paintings* | | | $1,100 |
| American b. 1869 | | | |
| ☐ SEARLE, Helen R. ............................. *paintings* | | | $18,700 |
| American 1830-1889 | | | |
| ☐ SEARS, Taber .................................... *drawings* | | | $192 |
| American d. 1870 | | | |
| ☐ SEAVEY, E. Leone ............................. *paintings* | | | $1,100 |
| American 19th cent. | | | |
| ☐ SEAVEY, George W. ........................... *paintings* | | $165 | $1,800 |
| American 1841-1916 | | | |
| ☐ SEBEN, Henri van .............................. *paintings* | | $1,540 | $5,060 |
| Belgian 1825-1913 | | | |

|                                                      |         | Current Price Range |           |
|------------------------------------------------------|---------|--------------------|-----------|
|                                                      |         | Low                | High      |
| ☐ **SEBIEZ, S.R.** .................................. *paintings* |         | **$495**  |
| ☐ **SEBIRE, Gaston** .................................. *paintings* | **$165** | **$2,090** |
| French b. c. 1920/25                                 |         |                    |           |
| ☐ **SECATERO, Johnny** ........................... *paintings* |  | **$1,045** |
| American (Navajo)                                    |         |                    |           |
| ☐ **SECKENDORF, Gotz von** ..................... *paintings* |  | **$1,650** |
| German 19th cent.                                    |         |                    |           |
| ☐ **SECOLA, A.** ....................................... *paintings* | **$1,870** | **$3,300** |
| ☐ **SEDDON, Thomas** .............................. *paintings* | **$30,250** | **$41,250** |
| British 1821-1856                                    |         |                    |           |
| ☐ **SEDLACEK, Stephen** ........................ *paintings* |  | **$3,080** |
| German 19th/20th cent.                               |         |                    |           |
| ☐ **SEDLINER, Stephan** ......................... *paintings* |  | **$2,310** |
| European 19th cent.                                  |         |                    |           |
| ☐ **SEDLMEIER, J.** ................................. *paintings* | **$82** | **$286** |
| ☐ **SEEBACH,**                                       |         |                    |           |
| **Lothar Hans Emmanuel von** ................. *paintings* |  | **$770** |
| German 1853-1930                                     |         |                    |           |
| ☐ **SEEBOLD, M.M.** ............................... *paintings* |  | **$660** |
| American 19th cent.                                  |         |                    |           |
| ☐ **SEEGHERS, Hub.** ............................. *paintings* |  | **$1,210** |
| ☐ **SEEKATZ, Gunther** ........................... *paintings* |  | **$350** |
| German/Austrian b. 1928                              |         |                    |           |
| ☐ **SEEL, Adolf** ...................................... *paintings* |  | **$8,800** |
| German 1829-1907                                     |         |                    |           |
| ☐ **SEEL, William R.** .............................. *paintings* |  | **$850** |
| 19th/20th cent.                                      |         |                    |           |
| ☐ **SEEMAN, Enoch** .............................. *paintings* | **$495** | **$880** |
| ☐ **SEEREY-LESTER, John** ...................... *drawings* | **$192** | **$220** |
| American 19th cent.                                  |         |                    |           |
| ☐ **SEERY, John** .................................... *paintings* | **$286** | **$3,300** |
| American b. 1914                                     |         |                    |           |
| ☐ **SEGAL, George** ................................. *drawings* | **$1,045** | **$1,540** |
| American b. 1924 ................................. *sculpture* | **$14,300** | **$88,000** |
| ☐ **SEGALMAN, Richard** ........................ *drawings* |  | **$220** |
| American 20th cent.                                  |         |                    |           |
| ☐ **SEGANTINI, Gottardo** ........................ *paintings* |  | **$2,860** |
| Italian b. 1882                                      |         |                    |           |
| ☐ **SEGARD** .......................................... *paintings* |  | **$550** |
| ☐ **SEGE, Alexander** .............................. *paintings* |  | **$357** |
| ☐ **SEGHERS, Daniel** ............................. *paintings* | **$24,200** | **$37,400** |
| Flemish 1590-1661                                    |         |                    |           |
| ☐ **SEGMOLEY, R.** ................................. *paintings* |  | **$357** |
| Dutch 20th cent.                                     |         |                    |           |
| ☐ **SEGNA, Niccolo Di** ........................... *paintings* |  | **$126,500** |
| ☐ **SEGOVIA, Andres** ........................... *paintings* | **$55** | **$770** |
| Spanish b. 1929                                      |         |                    |           |
| ☐ **SEGUI, Antonio** ................................ *paintings* | **$1,100** | **$13,200** |
| Argentinian b. 1934 ................................ *drawings* | **$880** | **$7,425** |

| | | Current Price Range | |
|---|---|---|---|
| | | Low | High |
| ☐ **SEGUI, Jose** ......................................... *paintings* | | $935 | $4,950 |
| 19th cent. | | | |
| ☐ **SEHRING, A.** ...................................... *paintings* | | | $374 |
| ☐ **SEIBERBERGER, S.** ........................... *paintings* | | | $700 |
| ☐ **SEIBERT, J.O.** ................................... *paintings* | | | $247 |
| American (?) 19th/20th cent. | | | |
| ☐ **SEIDEL, August** ................................. *paintings* | | | $2,640 |
| ☐ **SEIDEL, Emory P.** ............................. *sculpture* | | $2,200 | $3,520 |
| American ac. c. 1925-1935 | | | |
| ☐ **SEIDL, Ernst** ...................................... *paintings* | | | $330 |
| ☐ **SEIFERT, Alfred** ................................ *paintings* | | $411 | $33,000 |
| Czechoslovakian 1850-1901 | | | |
| ☐ **SEIFERT, Paul** ................................... *paintings* | | | $8,800 |
| American 1840-1921 | | | |
| ☐ **SEIFERT, Victor Heinrich** ................. *sculpture* | | $165 | $1,870 |
| German 1870-1953 | | | |
| ☐ **SEIFERT, W.** ...................................... *sculpture* | | | $2,178 |
| ☐ **SEIFFERT, F.** ..................................... *sculpture* | | | $440 |
| ☐ **SEIGER, Aug** ..................................... *paintings* | | | $385 |
| Italian 19th cent. | | | |
| ☐ **SEIGERSCHMLEDT, A. Sattler** ........... *paintings* | | | $440 |
| ☐ **SEIGNAC, Guillaume** .......................... *paintings* | | $550 | $40,700 |
| French ac. c. 1903 | | | |
| ☐ **SEIGNAC, Paul** ................................... *paintings* | | $1,760 | $27,500 |
| French 1826-1904 | | | |
| ☐ **SEIKOKU, (of Takoaka)** ....................... *sculpture* | | $2,420 | $2,750 |
| ☐ **SEILER, Carl Wilhelm Anton** ............... *paintings* | | $797 | $12,100 |
| German 1846-1921 | | | |
| ☐ **SEILER, E.** ......................................... *paintings* | | | $2,800 |
| ☐ **SEILLIER** ........................................... *paintings* | | | $418 |
| ☐ **SEISENEGGER, Jakob** ........................ *paintings* | | | $36,300 |
| Austrian 1505-1567 | | | |
| ☐ **SEITZ, Anton** ..................................... *paintings* | | $1,430 | $7,975 |
| German 1829-1900 ..................................... *sculpture* | | | $275 |
| ☐ **SEITZ, G.** ......................................... *sculpture* | | | $275 |
| ☐ **SEITZ, Georg** ..................................... *paintings* | | $1,320 | $2,200 |
| German 1810-1870 | | | |
| ☐ **SEITZ, Otto** ...................................... *paintings* | | | $990 |
| German 1846-1912 | | | |
| ☐ **SELBY, J.** .......................................... *drawings* | | | $412 |
| American 19th cent. | | | |
| ☐ **SELDEN, Dixie** ................................... *paintings* | | | $800 |
| American 20th cent. | | | |
| ☐ **SELEY, Jason** ..................................... *sculpture* | | $242 | $352 |
| ☐ **SELIGMAN, Adalbert Franz** ................. *paintings* | | $1,650 | $2,200 |
| German 1862-1945 | | | |
| ☐ **SELIGMANN, Kurt** ............................. *paintings* | | $330 | $5,500 |
| Swiss 1900-1962 ..................................... *drawings* | | $132 | $2,090 |

| | | *Current Price Range* | |
|---|---|---|---|
| | | Low | High |
| ☐ **SELINGER, Jean Paul** .......................... *paintings* | | $176 | $1,540 |
| American 1850-1909 | | | |
| ☐ **SELL, Christian** .................................. *paintings* | | $660 | $3,080 |
| German 1831-1883 | | | |
| ☐ **SELLAER, Vincent** | | | |
| **(called GELDERSMANN)** ...................... *paintings* | | $4,125 | $5,000 |
| Flemish b. 1539 | | | |
| ☐ **SELLAIO, Jacopo del** .......................... *paintings* | | $15,500 | $28,000 |
| Italian 1441/42-1493 | | | |
| ☐ **SELLERS, Anna** ................................. *paintings* | | | $1,650 |
| American 1824-1905 | | | |
| ☐ **SELLSTEDT, Lars Gustav** ................... *paintings* | | | $275 |
| American 1819-1911 | | | |
| ☐ **SELMY, Eugene Benjamin** ................... *paintings* | | $220 | $660 |
| French b. 1874 | | | |
| ☐ **SELMYHR, Conrad** ........................... *paintings* | | $770 | $1,300 |
| Scandinavian 19th cent. | | | |
| ☐ **SELTZER, Olaf Carl** ........................... *paintings* | | $1,045 | $75,000 |
| American 1877-1957 ................................... *drawings* | | $715 | $34,100 |
| ☐ **SELTZER, W. Steve** ........................... *paintings* | | | $2,900 |
| American contemporary | | | |
| ☐ **SELUM, J.B.** ..................................... *paintings* | | | $190 |
| American late 19th cent. | | | |
| ☐ **SELVA, R. De La** ............................... *paintings* | | | $825 |
| ☐ **SELVE, W.** ....................................... *paintings* | | | $522 |
| ☐ **SELZER, F.** ...................................... *paintings* | | $577 | $1,320 |
| ☐ **SEMENOWSKY, Eisman** ..................... *paintings* | | $660 | $6,050 |
| French 19th cent. | | | |
| ☐ **SEMERAND, G.** ................................. *paintings* | | | $357 |
| Haitian | | | |
| ☐ **SEMIATIN, Jacob** ............................. *paintings* | | | $715 |
| ☐ **SEMINO, Andrea** | | | |
| **(called Semino il Vecchio)** ...................... *drawings* | | | $420 |
| Italian c. 1525-1595 | | | |
| ☐ **SEMPLE, J.** ....................................... *paintings* | | $1,045 | $3,200 |
| American 19th cent. | | | |
| ☐ **SENAT, Prosper Louis** ......................... *paintings* | | $110 | $1,980 |
| American 1852-1925 ................................... *drawings* | | $90 | $660 |
| ☐ **SENATUS, Jean-Louis** ......................... *paintings* | | $770 | $990 |
| ☐ **SENAVE, Jacques Albert** ..................... *paintings* | | | $2,640 |
| Belgian 1758-1829 | | | |
| ☐ **SENET, Rafael Perez** ......................... *paintings* | | $330 | $10,450 |
| Spanish b. 1856 ...................................... *drawings* | | | $1,045 |
| ☐ **SENEZCOURT, Charlotte de** ................ *paintings* | | | $495 |
| ☐ **SENNO, Pietro** ................................. *paintings* | | | $302 |
| Italian 1831-1904 | | | |
| ☐ **SENSEMAN, Raphael** ......................... *paintings* | | | $187 |
| American 1870-1965 ................................... *drawings* | | $77 | $231 |
| ☐ **SENTIERI** ........................................ *drawings* | | $1,320 | $1,320 |

| | | Current Price Range | |
|---|---|---|---|
| | | Low | High |
| ☐ **SEPESHY, Zoltan L.** ..................... *paintings* | | $220 | $935 |
| Hungarian/American 1898-after 1934 ........... *drawings* | | | $258 |
| ☐ **SEPHTON, George Harcourt** ............. *paintings* | | | $880 |
| British 19th cent. | | | |
| ☐ **SEQUEIRA, Julio** .......................... *paintings* | | $1,210 | $2,750 |
| Latin American | | | |
| ☐ **SEREBRIAKOVA, Catherine** ............. *paintings* | | | $220 |
| 20th cent. | | | |
| ☐ **SERGENT, Lucien Pierre** ................. *paintings* | | | $880 |
| French 1849-1904 | | | |
| ☐ **SERGENT, Rene** ........................... *paintings* | | | $605 |
| ☐ **SERGER, Frederick B.** ..................... *paintings* | | $11 | $748 |
| Czech/American 1889-1965 | | | |
| ☐ **SERIEZ, Auguste** .......................... *paintings* | | | $660 |
| French 19th cent. | | | |
| ☐ **SERIO, Giovanni** .......................... *paintings* | | | $330 |
| Italian b. 1872 | | | |
| ☐ **SERIO, V.** .................................. *paintings* | | | $302 |
| ☐ **SERISAWA, Sueo** ......................... *paintings* | | $192 | $1,760 |
| Japanese/American b. 1910 | | | |
| ☐ **SERNICOLI, N.G.** ......................... *paintings* | | | $1,045 |
| Italian 19th cent. | | | |
| ☐ **SEROLI, Domenico** ....................... *drawings* | | | $2,420 |
| ☐ **SERRA, Richard** .......................... *paintings* | | $2,090 | $16,500 |
| American b. 1939 | | | |
| ☐ **SERRA Y AUGUE, Enrique** .............. *paintings* | | $550 | $880 |
| Spanish 1859-1918 | | | |
| ☐ **SERRA Y PORSON, Jose** ................. *paintings* | | $1,100 | $1,430 |
| Spanish 1824-1910 | | | |
| ☐ **SERRA-BADUE, Daniel** ................... *paintings* | | $1,100 | $1,650 |
| Cuban/American b. 1914 | | | |
| ☐ **SERRALUNGA, Luigi** ..................... *paintings* | | $6,600 | $12,100 |
| Italian b. 1880 | | | |
| ☐ **SERRES, Antony** .......................... *paintings* | | $522 | $660 |
| French 1828-1898 | | | |
| ☐ **SERRES, Dominic** ......................... *paintings* | | $7,700 | $60,000 |
| English | | | |
| ☐ **SERRES, Dominic (the elder)** ............. *paintings* | | $7,700 | $60,000 |
| English 1722-1793 | | | |
| ☐ **SERRES, John Thomas** ................... *paintings* | | $10,450 | $13,200 |
| English 1759-1825 | | | |
| ☐ **SERRI, Alfredo** ........................... *paintings* | | $2,200 | $6,600 |
| Italian 1897-1972 | | | |
| ☐ **SERRURE, Auguste** ....................... *paintings* | | $4,070 | $8,800 |
| Flemish 1825-1903 | | | |
| ☐ **SERRUTTI, F.** .............................. *paintings* | | $137 | $462 |
| ☐ **SERSHALL, G.J.** ........................... *paintings* | | | $715 |
| ☐ **SERT Y BADIA, Jose Maria** ............. *paintings* | | $2,420 | $4,950 |
| Spanish 1874/76-1945 | | | |

| | | | *Current Price Range* | |
|---|---|---|---|---|
| | | | *Low* | *High* |
| ☐ **SERUSIER, Louis Paul Henri** | .............. | *paintings* | **$3,000** | **$41,250** |
| French 1863-1927 | .................................... | *drawings* | | **$3,410** |
| ☐ **SERVAES, Albert** | ............... | *paintings* | | **$16,000** |
| Belgian 1883-1966 | | | | |
| ☐ **SERVEAU, Clement** | ............................ | *paintings* | **$550** | **$880** |
| French 1886-1972 | | | | |
| ☐ **SESLIC** | ........................................ | *paintings* | | **$440** |
| ☐ **SESSIONS, James** | ............................ | *paintings* | **$275** | **$2,310** |
| American | | | | |
| ☐ **SETHER, Gulbrand** | ........................... | *paintings* | **$50** | **$357** |
| 19th/20th cent. | | | | |
| ☐ **SETTANNI, Luigi** | ............................ | *paintings* | | **$467** |
| Italian/American 20th cent. | | | | |
| ☐ **SEURAT, Georges** | ............................ | *paintings* | **$110,000** | **$275,000** |
| French 1859-1891 | .................................... | *drawings* | **$6,050** | **$77,000** |
| ☐ **SEURRE, Charles Emile Marie** | ............ | *sculpture* | | **$242** |
| French 19th cent. | | | | |
| ☐ **SEVERAC, V.** | ................................... | *paintings* | | **$330** |
| French 19th cent. | | | | |
| ☐ **SEVERDONCK, A. van** | ....................... | *paintings* | | **$385** |
| ☐ **SEVERDONCK, Franz van** | ................... | *paintings* | **$550** | **$8,800** |
| Belgian 1809-1889 | | | | |
| ☐ **SEVERDONCK, Joseph van** | ................. | *paintings* | | **$1,980** |
| Belgian 1819-1905 | | | | |
| ☐ **SEVERE, Jean Claude** | ........................ | *paintings* | **$165** | **$715** |
| ☐ **SEVERINI, Gino** | ............................... | *paintings* | **$15,950** | **$71,500** |
| Italian 1883-1966 | ...................................... | *drawings* | **$467** | **$93,500** |
| | ........................................................ | *sculpture* | | **$7,700** |
| ☐ **SEVERINO DA CINGOLI,** | | | | |
| **Messer Ulisse** | ................................ | *drawings* | | **$1,980** |
| ☐ **SEVERN, Arthur** | ............................... | *drawings* | **$165** | **$418** |
| English 1842/48-1931 | | | | |
| ☐ **SEVESTRE, Jules Marie** | ..................... | *paintings* | | **$1,980** |
| French 1834-1901 | | | | |
| ☐ **SEVILLE, Juan de** | .............................. | *paintings* | | **$3,500** |
| ☐ **SEWELL, Amos** | .................................. | *paintings* | **$55** | **$715** |
| American b. 1901 | ...................................... | *drawings* | **$110** | **$198** |
| ☐ **SEWELL, Lydia Amanda Brewster** | ....... | *paintings* | | **$411** |
| American 1859-1926 | | | | |
| ☐ **SEWELL, Robert van Vorst** | ................. | *paintings* | **$220** | **$4,125** |
| American 1860-1924 | | | | |
| ☐ **SEWOHL, Waldemar** | ......................... | *paintings* | | **$550** |
| German b. 1887 | | | | |
| ☐ **SEXTIE, William A.** | ........................... | *paintings* | | **$24,200** |
| ☐ **SEXTON, Frederick Lester** | ................. | *paintings* | **$110** | **$1,320** |
| American b. 1889 | | | | |
| ☐ **SEXTON, S. H.** | .................................. | *paintings* | | **$198** |
| American 19th cent. | | | | |

| | Current Price Range | |
|---|---|---|
| | Low | High |

☐ **SEYDEL, Edward Gustav** ..................... *paintings* | | $1,760
Luxembourgian 1822-1881

☐ **SEYFFERT, Leopold** ........................... *paintings* | | $467
American 1887-1956

☐ **SEYMOUR, H.V.S.** ............................ *paintings* | | $198
English 19th cent.

☐ **SEYMOUR, James** ........................... *paintings* | $15,400 | $24,200
English 1702-1752

☐ **SEYMOUR, Tom** ............................ *paintings* | $192 | $1,760

☐ **SEYMOUR HADEN, Francis** ............... *drawings* | | $250

☐ **SEYPPEL, Carl Maria** ........................ *paintings* | | $660
German 1847-1913

☐ **SEYSSES, Auguste** ............................. *sculpture* | $440 | $990
French b. 1862

☐ **SHACKENBERG, Henry E.** .................. *paintings* | | $660
American

☐ **SHADE, F.** ..................................... *drawings* | | $357
British 19th cent.

☐ **SHADE, William Auguste** .................... *paintings* | $1,430 | $2,750
American 1848-1890

☐ **SHAFER, L.A.** .................................. *drawings* | | $220
American b. 1866

☐ **SHAFER, Mrs. Simon P. (Ella M.)** ......... *paintings* | $55 | $412
American ac. 1885-1897

☐ **SHAHN, Ben** ................................... *paintings* | | $7,150
American 1898-1969 ................................ *drawings* | $165 | $10,450

☐ **SHAIELTON, Mart.** ............................ *paintings* | | $242
English 19th cent.

☐ **SHALDERS, George** .......................... *paintings* | $660 | $3,850
English 1826-1873 ................................... *drawings* | | $2,860

☐ **SHALOM OF SAFED,**
**(Shalom MOSKOVITZ)** ..................... *drawings* | $2,640 | $3,300
Israeli b.c. 1892

☐ **SHAMBER** ......................................... *paintings* | | $357
Dutch 19th cent.

☐ **SHANKER, Louis** ............................... *drawings* | | $550
American

☐ **SHANKS, John Alec** ........................... *drawings* | | $385
French 19th cent.

☐ **SHANKS, William Somersville** .............. *paintings* | | $330
English 1864-1951

☐ **SHANNON, Charles Haslewood** ............ *paintings* | | $412
English 1863-1937 ................................... *drawings* | | $120

☐ **SHAPIRO, Joel Elias** ........................... *drawings* | $286 | $3,520
American b. 1941 .................................... *sculpture* | $10,450 | $24,200

☐ **SHAPIRO, Miriam** .............................. *paintings* | | $330

☐ **SHAPLEIGH, Frank Henry** .................. *paintings* | $200 | $4,125
American 1842-1906 ................................ *drawings* | | $99

| | Current Price Range | |
|---|---|---|
| | Low | High |

| | | Low | High |
|---|---|---|---|
| ☐ **SHARE, Harry Pruitt** ............................ *paintings* | | | $330 |
| Canadian 1853-1935 | | | |
| ☐ **SHARKEY, Bert** ................................ *drawings* | | | $550 |
| 20th cent. | | | |
| ☐ **SHARP, J.H.** ...................................... *paintings* | | | $330 |
| ☐ **SHARP, James C.** ................................ *paintings* | | | $29,700 |
| American 1818-1897 | | | |
| ☐ **SHARP, Joseph Henry** .......................... *paintings* | | $825 | $110,000 |
| American 1859-1953 | | | |
| ☐ **SHARP, Louis Hovey** ............................ *paintings* | | $275 | $1,540 |
| American 1875-1946 | | | |
| ☐ **SHARP, William** ................................ *paintings* | | | $7,700 |
| American ac. c. 1839-1885 | | | |
| ☐ **SHARPLES, I.** ...................................... *paintings* | | $137 | $192 |
| American 20th cent. | | | |
| ☐ **SHARPLES, James (the elder)** ............... *drawings* | | $852 | $6,600 |
| Anglo/American 1751-1811 | | | |
| ☐ **SHATTUCK, Aaron Draper** ................... *paintings* | | $66 | $4,950 |
| American 1832-1928 ................................ *drawings* | | $110 | $550 |
| ☐ **SHAW, Arthur William** ........................ *paintings* | | | $220 |
| contemporary | | | |
| ☐ **SHAW, Charles Green** .......................... *paintings* | | $121 | $5,775 |
| American 1892-1974 | | | |
| ☐ **SHAW, Elsa V.** .................................... *paintings* | | | $3,960 |
| American b. 1891 | | | |
| ☐ **SHAW, Ernest** .................................... *sculpture* | | | $1,700 |
| American b.1942 | | | |
| ☐ **SHAW, G.** ........................................ *paintings* | | | $3,300 |
| American 19th cent. | | | |
| ☐ **SHAW, Joshua (called Shaw of Bath)** ...... *paintings* | | $3,750 | $44,000 |
| Anglo/American 1776-1860 | | | |
| ☐ **SHAW, Sidney Dale** ............................ *drawings* | | $198 | $300 |
| American 1879-1915 | | | |
| ☐ **SHAW, Walter** .................................... *paintings* | | | $605 |
| ☐ **SHAWZIN, Stella** ................................ *sculpture* | | | $247 |
| contemporary | | | |
| ☐ **SHAYEN, F.** ...................................... *paintings* | | | $1,430 |
| ☐ **SHAYER** .......................................... *drawings* | | | $192 |
| British/American 1776-1860 | | | |
| ☐ **SHAYER, C.** ...................................... *paintings* | | | $330 |
| English 19th cent. | | | |
| ☐ **SHAYER, J. (Sr.)** ................................ *paintings* | | $715 | $935 |
| ☐ **SHAYER, William (Jr.)** ........................ *paintings* | | $1,430 | $12,100 |
| English 1811-1892 | | | |
| ☐ **SHAYER, William (Sr.)** ........................ *paintings* | | $550 | $34,100 |
| English 1788-1879 | | | |
| ☐ **SHAYLOR, H.W.** ................................ *paintings* | | | $302 |
| American 19th cent. .................................. *drawings* | | $55 | $605 |

| | | Current Price Range | |
|---|---|---|---|
| | | Low | High |
| ☐ **SHEAN, Charles M.** ............................ *paintings* | | | $605 |
| American d. 1925 | | | |
| ☐ **SHEARBORN, Andrew** ....................... *paintings* | | $1,100 | $3,080 |
| British 19th cent. | | | |
| ☐ **SHEARER, Charles** ............................ *paintings* | | $220 | $357 |
| ☐ **SHEARER, Christopher H.** ................... *paintings* | | $90 | $3,300 |
| American 1840-1926 | | | |
| ☐ **SHECTER, Laura** ............................. *paintings* | | | $286 |
| ☐ **SHED, Charles D.** ............................. *paintings* | | | $715 |
| American 1818-1893 | | | |
| ☐ **SHEE, Sir Martin Archer** ................... *paintings* | | $880 | $16,500 |
| Irish 1769-1850 | | | |
| ☐ **SHEELER, Charles** ............................ *paintings* | | $6,325 | $1,870,000 |
| American 1883-1965 .................................. *drawings* | | $550 | $209,000 |
| ☐ **SHEERBOOM, Andries** ........................ *paintings* | | $1,320 | $3,025 |
| Dutch 1832-1880 | | | |
| ☐ **SHEERBORN, Andrew** ........................ *paintings* | | | $550 |
| English 19th cent. | | | |
| ☐ **SHEETS, Millard** ............................... *paintings* | | | $3,300 |
| American b. 1907 ...................................... *drawings* | | $330 | $3,300 |
| ☐ **SHEFFER, Glen C.** ............................ *paintings* | | $350 | $495 |
| American b. 1881 | | | |
| ☐ **SHEFFERS, Peter W.** .......................... *paintings* | | | $880 |
| American 1894-1949 | | | |
| ☐ **SHEFFIELD, Isaac** .............................. *paintings* | | | $13,200 |
| American 1798-1845 | | | |
| ☐ **SHELDON, Charles Gates** ................... *drawings* | | $55 | $825 |
| d. 1961 | | | |
| ☐ **SHELDON, Charles Mills** ................... *drawings* | | $44 | $242 |
| American 1866-1928 | | | |
| ☐ **SHELDON, F.S.** ................................. *paintings* | | | $412 |
| English fl. 1885-1886 | | | |
| ☐ **SHELDON, J.** ..................................... *paintings* | | | $1,100 |
| ☐ **SHELDRAKE, A.M.** ........................... *paintings* | | | $275 |
| 19th cent. | | | |
| ☐ **SHEPARD, Ernest Howard** .................. *drawings* | | $935 | $3,850 |
| British b. 1870 | | | |
| ☐ **SHEPARD, F. Newton** ........................ *drawings* | | | $440 |
| ☐ **SHEPHERD, David** ............................ *paintings* | | $1,100 | $19,800 |
| ☐ **SHEPHERD, George** .......................... *drawings* | | | $880 |
| British c. 1782-c. 1830 | | | |
| ☐ **SHEPHERD, J. Clinton** ....................... *paintings* | | $200 | $1,430 |
| American b. 1888 | | | |
| ☐ **SHEPHERD, Thomas Hosmer** ............... *drawings* | | | $330 |
| British 1792-1864 | | | |
| ☐ **SHEPPARD, Joseph Sherly** .................. *paintings* | | $385 | $660 |
| American b. 1930 | | | |
| ☐ **SHEPPARD, Warren** ........................... *paintings* | | $110 | $12,100 |
| American 1858-1937 ................................... *drawings* | | $88 | $352 |

| | | Current Price Range | |
| | | Low | High |
|---|---|---|---|
| ☐ **SHEPPARD, William Ludlow** ............... *drawings* | | | $1,980 |
| American 1833-1912 | | | |
| ☐ **SHERBELL, Rhoda** ............................ *sculpture* | | | $357 |
| ☐ **SHERER, F.** ........................................ *drawings* | | | $302 |
| ☐ **SHERIFF, William Craig** ...................... *paintings* | | | $231 |
| English 1786-1805 | | | |
| ☐ **SHERLINGH, Michael** ......................... *paintings* | | $412 | $495 |
| American 19th cent. | | | |
| ☐ **SHERLOCK, W. P.** ............................. *paintings* | | $357 | $715 |
| English b. 1780 | | | |
| ☐ **SHERRIN, Daniel** .............................. *paintings* | | $330 | $3,080 |
| British ac. 1895-1915 ............................. *drawings* | | $66 | $1,210 |
| ☐ **SHERRIN, David** ............................... *paintings* | | $357 | $550 |
| English b. 1868 | | | |
| ☐ **SHERRIN, John** ................................. *drawings* | | $220 | $308 |
| English 1819-1896 | | | |
| ☐ **SHERVASHIDZE, Alexandre** ............... *drawings* | | | $440 |
| ☐ **SHERWOOD, Mary Clare** ................... *paintings* | | | $6,050 |
| American 1868-1943 | | | |
| ☐ **SHERWOOD, William A.** ..................... *paintings* | | $385 | $880 |
| Canadian/American 1875-1951 | | | |
| ☐ **SHEYS, William P.** ............................ *paintings* | | | $2,310 |
| American ac. c. 1813-1821 | | | |
| ☐ **SHIELDS, Alan** ................................. *paintings* | | | $6,000 |
| American b. 1944 ...................................... *drawings* | | $550 | $1,760 |
| ..................................................... *sculpture* | | | $605 |
| ☐ **SHIELDS, Thomas W.** ......................... *paintings* | | | $8,000 |
| American 1849/50-1920 ............................... *drawings* | | | $121 |
| ☐ **SHIELDS, W.** ..................................... *paintings* | | | $1,100 |
| ☐ **SHIELS, William** ................................ *paintings* | | | $7,700 |
| British 1785-1857 | | | |
| ☐ **SHIERE, W.** ....................................... *paintings* | | | $825 |
| European 19th cent. | | | |
| ☐ **SHIFRIN, Ray** ..................................... *sculpture* | | | $660 |
| ☐ **SHIKLER, Aaron** ............................... *drawings* | | $176 | $3,575 |
| American b. 1922 | | | |
| ☐ **SHILLING, Alexander** .......................... *paintings* | | $209 | $247 |
| American b. 1859 | | | |
| ☐ **SHINN, Everett** ................................. *paintings* | | $350 | $95,000 |
| American 1876-1953 ................................... *drawings* | | $99 | $66,000 |
| ☐ **SHINN, Florence Searle** ...................... *drawings* | | | $330 |
| American | | | |
| ☐ **SHIPPIU, Joseph** ............................... *paintings* | | | $330 |
| ☐ **SHIRK, Jeanette C.** ............................. *drawings* | | | $220 |
| American 19th/20th cent. | | | |
| ☐ **SHIRLAW, Walter** ............................... *paintings* | | $55 | $16,500 |
| Scottish/American 1838-1909 ....................... *drawings* | | $55 | $440 |

## "The Eight"

*In the late 19th century, artist-illustrators William Glackens, George Luks, Everett Shinn, and John Sloan ("The Philadelphia Four") became friends and associates. Seeking a teacher, they turned to Robert Henri, who had just returned from Paris and had a considerable reputation as a painter. Together, they began to paint the drab squalor of urban life. By the turn of the century, they were all painting in or around New York, the center of activity in American art. Their realistic works were consistently rejected by the National Academy, which refused to show them.*

*Led by Henri, "The Philadelphia Four," together with three New York artists —Arthur B. Davies, Maurice Prendergast, and Ernest Lawson — secured a private gallery in 1907 for two weeks in order to bring their work before the public. The show was a dramatic success. By the time it ended, over 7,000 people had seen the new paintings of "The Eight," and the artists had established the concept of independent exhibitions. Led by Henri, "The Eight," also known as "The Ashcan School," continued to organize exhibits unsanctioned by the Academy for several more years. (Everett Shinn, "Chinese Restaurant," gouache, Freeman Galleries, April 22, 1985, $15,400.)*

|                                              |            | *Current Price Range* | |
|----------------------------------------------|------------|-----------|-----------|
|                                              |            | *Low*     | *High*    |
| ☐ **SHISHKIN, Ivan Ivanovich** ............ | *paintings* | **$1,650** | **$10,450** |
| Russian 1821/31-1898/99 ................. | *drawings*  | **$77**    | **$220**    |
| ☐ **SHITE, Julia** ......................... | *drawings*  |           | **$605**    |
| American 20th cent.                          |            |           |           |
| ☐ **SHIVELY, Douglas** .................... | *paintings* |           | **$220**    |
| American b. 1896                             |            |           |           |
| ☐ **SHOENBERG, Sheldon** ............... | *drawings*  |           | **$440**    |
| American 20th cent.                          |            |           |           |
| ☐ **SHONNEY, H.** ......................... | *paintings* |           | **$352**    |

| | | Current Price Range | |
|---|---|---|---|
| | | Low | High |
| ☐ SHOPE, Irwin "Shorty" ........................ *paintings* | | $330 | $6,000 |
| American b. 1900 ...................................... *drawings* | | | $165 |
| ☐ SHORE, H.O. ................................ *paintings* | | | $605 |
| ☐ SHORT, Frederick Golden ................... *paintings* | | $275 | $412 |
| British 19th cent. | | | |
| ☐ SHORT, Jessie Francis ...................... *drawings* | | $137 | $247 |
| American 20th cent. | | | |
| ☐ SHORT, Richard ............................. *paintings* | | | $440 |
| English 1841-1916 ..................................... *drawings* | | | $90 |
| ☐ SHOTWELL, Helen H. ....................... *paintings* | | | $1,210 |
| American b. 1908 | | | |
| ☐ SHOUKHAIEFF, Vassily Ivanovitch ...... *drawings* | | | $1,650 |
| ☐ SHRADY, Henry Merwin ................... *sculpture* | | $1,980 | $17,600 |
| American 1871-1922 | | | |
| ☐ SHRAPNIL, Edward Scope .................. *paintings* | | | $6,000 |
| Canadian 19th/20th cent. | | | |
| ☐ SHRIVER ........................................... *paintings* | | | $467 |
| 19th cent. | | | |
| ☐ SHUCKER, James W. .......................... *paintings* | | | $176 |
| American 19th/20th cent. | | | |
| ☐ SHUKAYEV, Stephan Grigorievich ....... *paintings* | | | $2,420 |
| Russian 1830-1888 | | | |
| ☐ SHUKHAEV, Vasilii Ivanovich ............. *paintings* | | | $1,870 |
| Russian 1887-1972 | | | |
| ☐ SHULZ, Adolph Robert ....................... *paintings* | | $55 | $550 |
| American b. 1869 | | | |
| ☐ SHUNNEY, Andrew ........................... *paintings* | | $55 | $302 |
| American b. 1921 | | | |
| ☐ SHURTLEFF, Roswell Morse ............... *paintings* | | $110 | $1,650 |
| American 1838-1915 | | | |
| ☐ SHURTZMAN, S. (of Safed) .................. *drawings* | | | $2,000 |
| Israeli | | | |
| ☐ SHUSTER, Joe .................................... *drawings* | | | $935 |
| b. 1914 | | | |
| ☐ SHUSTER, William Howard ................ *paintings* | | $1,100 | $1,320 |
| American b. 1893 | | | |
| ☐ SHYE, Velino (Ma Pi Wi) ..................... *paintings* | | | $742 |
| ☐ SIBAN, H.V. ..................................... *paintings* | | | $385 |
| ☐ SIBERDT, Eugene .............................. *paintings* | | | $1,100 |
| Belgian 1851-1931 | | | |
| ☐ SIBERECHTS, Jan .............................. *paintings* | | $4,620 | $16,500 |
| Flemish 1627-c. 1703 | | | |
| ☐ SIBEUD ............................................. *sculpture* | | | $1,650 |
| French early 20th cent. | | | |
| ☐ SIBLEY, Charles ................................ *paintings* | | | $192 |
| American b. 1921 | | | |
| ☐ SIBURNEY, Alex ................................ *paintings* | | | $715 |
| ........................................................... *drawings* | | | $302 |
| ☐ SICARD, Francois .............................. *sculpture* | | | $1,210 |

| | | Current Price Range | |
|---|---|---|---|
| | | *Low* | *High* |
| ☐ **SICARD, Pierre** ................................ *paintings* | | | $1,045 |
| French b. 1900 | | | |
| ☐ **SICCIOLANTE, Gerolamo** | | | |
| **(called IL SERMONETA)** ...................... *drawings* | | | $3,850 |
| Italian 1521-1580 | | | |
| ☐ **SICHEL, Nathaniel** ............................. *paintings* | | | $1,980 |
| German 1843-1907 | | | |
| ☐ **SICKELS, Noel** ................................. *paintings* | $5,000 | $6,000 |
| American b. 1910 | | | |
| ☐ **SICKERT, Walter Richard** ................... *paintings* | $1,650 | $13,200 |
| English 1860-1942 ..................................... *drawings* | $440 | $880 |
| ☐ **SICRE, Juan Jose** ............................... *sculpture* | | | $3,300 |
| contemporary | | | |
| ☐ **SIEBEL, Fred** ..................................... *drawings* | | | $440 |
| 20th cent. | | | |
| ☐ **SIEBENTHAL, M.M.** ........................... *paintings* | | | $440 |
| American 20th cent. | | | |
| ☐ **SIEBER, Edward** ................................ *paintings* | | | $385 |
| ☐ **SIEBERT, Edward Selmar** ................... *paintings* | $302 | $374 |
| American 1856-1938 ................................... *drawings* | | | $225 |
| ☐ **SIEBERT, Johanns** ............................. *paintings* | | | $220 |
| Dutch 20th cent. | | | |
| ☐ **SIEFERT, Arthur** ............................... *paintings* | | | $1,210 |
| ☐ **SIEFFERT, Paul** ................................ *paintings* | $2,090 | $4,675 |
| French b. 1874 | | | |
| ☐ **SIEGEN, Auguste** .............................. *paintings* | $1,430 | $2,750 |
| European 19th cent. | | | |
| ☐ **SIEGEN, J. van de** ............................. *paintings* | | | $1,430 |
| Austrian 19th cent. | | | |
| ☐ **SIEGER, August** ............................... *paintings* | | | $550 |
| Austrian ac. 1900 | | | |
| ☐ **SIEGER, Victor** ................................. *paintings* | | | $1,650 |
| German 1843-1905 | | | |
| ☐ **SIEGERT, August** .............................. *paintings* | $900 | $3,850 |
| German 1786-1869 | | | |
| ☐ **SIEGERT, August Friedrich** ................ *paintings* | $1,870 | $3,740 |
| German 1820-1883 | | | |
| ☐ **SIEGRIEST, Lundy** ............................ *drawings* | | | $385 |
| American 20th cent. | | | |
| ☐ **SIENKIEWICZ, Casimire A.** ............... *paintings* | $88 | $220 |
| American 1890-1974 | | | |
| ☐ **SIES, Walter** ................................... *paintings* | | | $935 |
| American 19th cent. | | | |
| ☐ **SIEVERS, Gregory** ............................ *paintings* | | | $1,700 |
| American | | | |
| ☐ **SIGLER, Hollis** ............................... *paintings* | | | $4,950 |
| American contemporary ............................... *drawings* | | | $5,280 |
| ☐ **SIGLING, George Adam** ...................... *paintings* | | | $1,320 |

| | Current Price Range | |
|---|---|---|
| | Low | High |
| ☐ **SIGMUND, Benjamin J.** ........................ *drawings* | $330 | $330 |
| German 19th/20th cent. | | |
| ☐ **SIGNAC, Paul** ................................... *paintings* | $57,200 | $396,000 |
| French 1863-1935 ..................................... *drawings* | $825 | $24,200 |
| ☐ **SIGNORELLI, Francesco** ..................... *paintings* | | $4,180 |
| Italian d. 1559 | | |
| ☐ **SIGNORET, Charles Louis** ................. *paintings* | $302 | $1,870 |
| French 1867-1932 | | |
| ☐ **SIGNORI, Sergio Carlo** ..................... *sculpture* | $357 | $770 |
| ☐ **SIGNORINI, Giovanni** ........................ *paintings* | $1,210 | $3,300 |
| Italian 1808-1858 | | |
| ☐ **SIGNORINI, Giuseppe** ........................ *drawings* | $330 | $6,600 |
| Italian 1857-1932 | | |
| ☐ **SIGNORINI, Telemaco** ........................ *paintings* | $7,700 | $165,000 |
| Italian 1835-1901 | | |
| ☐ **SIGRISTE, Guido** ............................... *paintings* | | $440 |
| Swiss 1864-1915 | | |
| ☐ **SIGWALT, O.** ..................................... *paintings* | | $495 |
| ☐ **SIL, J. van** ....................................... *paintings* | | $577 |
| Dutch 19th cent. | | |
| ☐ **SILAS, L.** .......................................... *paintings* | | $605 |
| ☐ **SILBERT, Max** ................................... *paintings* | $247 | $528 |
| French b. 1871 | | |
| ☐ **SILENNE** .......................................... *paintings* | | $275 |
| contemporary | | |
| ☐ **SILO, Adam** ..................................... *paintings* | | $3,000 |
| ☐ **SILVA, C.** ......................................... *paintings* | | $357 |
| European 19th cent. | | |
| ☐ **SILVA, Francis Augustus** ..................... *paintings* | $2,750 | $143,000 |
| American 1835-1886 ................................... *drawings* | $411 | $27,500 |
| ☐ **SILVA, Gerald** ................................... *drawings* | | $275 |
| American contemporary | | |
| ☐ **SILVA, William Posey** ........................ *paintings* | $137 | $1,980 |
| American 1859-1948 ................................... *drawings* | | $247 |
| ☐ **SILVA-BRUHNS, Ivan** ........................ *drawings* | | $1,045 |
| French d. 1980 | | |
| ☐ **SILVAY, Van** ..................................... *drawings* | | $220 |
| American 19th/20th cent. | | |
| ☐ **SILVERMAN, Bernardine** ..................... *sculpture* | | $175 |
| American contemporary | | |
| ☐ **SILVERMAN, Mel** ............................... *drawings* | | $246 |
| 20th cent. | | |
| ☐ **SILVESTRE, Albert** ........................... *paintings* | | $1,760 |
| Swiss b. 1869 | | |
| ☐ **SILVESTRE, G.** ................................... *paintings* | | $1,100 |
| ☐ **SILVESTRE, Louis de** ........................ *paintings* | | $5,225 |
| French 1675-1760 ..................................... *drawings* | | $1,870 |
| ☐ **SILVESTRE, Nicolas Charles de** ........... *drawings* | | $1,540 |
| French 1699-1767 | | |

| | | | Current Price Range | |
|---|---|---|---|---|
| | | | Low | High |
| ☐ SILVESTRE, Paul | sculpture | | $1,100 | $1,540 |
| French early 20th cent. | | | | |
| ☐ SIMANETTI, F. | drawings | | | $301 |
| ☐ SIMBARI, Nicola | paintings | | $330 | $10,450 |
| Italian b. 1927 | drawings | | $440 | $3,080 |
| ☐ SIMIL, Emilcar | paintings | | | $1,980 |
| ☐ SIMKHOVITCH, Simka | paintings | | $4,180 | $7,150 |
| American | | | | |
| ☐ SIMKINS, Henry | drawings | | | $385 |
| ☐ SIMM, E. | paintings | | | $275 |
| German 19th cent. | | | | |
| ☐ SIMMENS, Corday | paintings | | | $660 |
| American 20th cent. | | | | |
| ☐ SIMMONDS, Charles Frederick | sculpture | | | $20,900 |
| American b. 1945 | | | | |
| ☐ SIMMONDS, Julius | paintings | | | $2,970 |
| German 1843-1924 | | | | |
| ☐ SIMMONS, Edward Emerson | paintings | | $880 | $11,000 |
| American 1852-1931 | | | | |
| ☐ SIMON, Bernard | sculpture | | | $825 |
| ☐ SIMON, Herman | paintings | | $220 | $522 |
| American b. 1846 | | | | |
| ☐ SIMON, Lucien | paintings | | $1,100 | $2,310 |
| French 1861-1945 | | | | |
| ☐ SIMON, Maria | sculpture | | | $1,980 |
| b. Argentina | | | | |
| ☐ SIMONE, De | paintings | | | $412 |
| French 19th cent. | drawings | | | $330 |
| ☐ SIMONE, Tommaso de | paintings | | $2,200 | $10,450 |
| Italian ac. 1852-1857 | drawings | | $900 | $1,100 |
| ☐ SIMONETI | drawings | | | $220 |
| Italian 19th/20th cent. | | | | |
| ☐ SIMONETTI, Amedeo | drawings | | $2,299 | $2,310 |
| Italian 1874-1922 | | | | |
| ☐ SIMONETTI, Attilio | paintings | | | $330 |
| Italian 1843-1925 | drawings | | $220 | $4,070 |
| ☐ SIMONETTI, Ettore | paintings | | $1,980 | $8,250 |
| Italian 19th cent. | drawings | | $231 | $15,400 |
| ☐ SIMONETTI, H. | paintings | | | $330 |
| ☐ SIMONI | drawings | | | $907 |
| Italian 19th cent. | | | | |
| ☐ SIMONI, Alfredo de | paintings | | $632 | $4,125 |
| Italian 19th cent. | | | | |
| ☐ SIMONI, Gustavo | paintings | | $715 | $14,300 |
| Italian b. 1846 | drawings | | $220 | $11,000 |
| ☐ SIMONI, Sapione | drawings | | | $1,320 |
| Italian 19th cent. | | | | |
| ☐ SIMONINI, Francesco | paintings | | | $4,675 |
| Italian 1686-1753 | drawings | | | $550 |

| | | Current Price Range | |
|---|---|---|---|
| | | Low | High |
| ☐ **SIMONS, D.** .................................. *paintings* | | | $1,430 |
| ☐ **SIMONS, Frans** .................................. *paintings* | | | $1,210 |
| Belgian 1855-1919 | | | |
| ☐ **SIMONS, Michiel** .................................. *paintings* | | $10,450 | $19,800 |
| Dutch d. 1673 | | | |
| ☐ **SIMPSON, A.B.** .................................. *paintings* | | | $1,100 |
| British exhib. 1904-31 | | | |
| ☐ **SIMPSON, Adam M.** .................................. *paintings* | | | $8,360 |
| ☐ **SIMPSON, Charles** .................................. *paintings* | | $302 | $2,800 |
| American 19th cent. .................................. *drawings* | | | $9,900 |
| ☐ **SIMPSON, William** .................................. *paintings* | | | $2,200 |
| British 1823-1899 | | | |
| ☐ **SIMS, Charles** .................................. *paintings* | | $605 | $11,000 |
| British 1873-1928 | | | |
| ☐ **SIMS, F.** .................................. *paintings* | | | $357 |
| American 19th cent. | | | |
| ☐ **SIMSON, G.** .................................. *paintings* | | | $275 |
| ☐ **SINCLAIR, A.** .................................. *paintings* | | | $605 |
| American 19th cent. | | | |
| ☐ **SINCLAIR, Alfredo** .................................. *paintings* | | | $3,960 |
| b. Panama 1915 | | | |
| ☐ **SINCLAIR, Duncan** .................................. *paintings* | | | $302 |
| ☐ **SINCLAIR, G.** .................................. *paintings* | | | $1,760 |
| European 19th cent. | | | |
| ☐ **SINCLAIR, Gerrit V.** .................................. *paintings* | | $302 | $715 |
| American 1890-1955 | | | |
| ☐ **SINCLAIR, Irving** .................................. *paintings* | | $137 | $1,650 |
| American 20th cent. | | | |
| ☐ **SINCLAIR, John** .................................. *paintings* | | $660 | $20,000 |
| English ac. 1872-1890 | | | |
| ☐ **SINCLAIR, Max** .................................. *paintings* | | $187 | $3,850 |
| British 19th cent. | | | |
| ☐ **SINDALL, H.S.** .................................. *paintings* | | | $1,650 |
| American 19th cent. | | | |
| ☐ **SINDBERG, Adamine** .................................. *paintings* | | $231 | $495 |
| 19th cent. | | | |
| ☐ **SINDING, Otto** .................................. *paintings* | | $308 | $935 |
| Norwegian 1842-1909 | | | |
| ☐ **SINDING, Stephen Abel** .................................. *sculpture* | | | $1,430 |
| Norwegian 1846-1922 | | | |
| ☐ **SINGER, Clyde** .................................. *paintings* | | $192 | $2,310 |
| American b. 1908 | | | |
| ☐ **SINGER, William H. (Jr.)** .................................. *paintings* | | $880 | $2,750 |
| American 1868-1943 .................................. *drawings* | | | $7,150 |
| ☐ **SINGLETON, Gib** .................................. *sculpture* | | | $1,430 |
| American contemporary | | | |
| ☐ **SINGLETON, Henry** .................................. *paintings* | | | $4,400 |
| English 1766-1839 | | | |

|  |  | *Current Price Range* | |
|---|---|---|---|
|  |  | *Low* | *High* |
| ☐ **SINIBALDI, G.** .................................... *paintings* | | | $220 |
| Italian 20th cent. | | | |
| ☐ **SINIBALDI, Jean Paul** ........................ *paintings* | | $2,255 | $7,700 |
| French 1857-1909 | | | |
| ☐ **SINIDO, Emile** .................................... *paintings* | | | $286 |
| French 19th cent. | | | |
| ☐ **SINKO, A.** ........................................... *sculpture* | | | $600 |
| ☐ **SINNOT, J.** .......................................... *paintings* | | | $715 |
| French 19th cent. | | | |
| ☐ **SINTENIS, Renee** ................................ *sculpture* | | $1,045 | $18,700 |
| German 1888-1965 | | | |
| ☐ **SIPORIN, Mitchell** ............................... *drawings* | | $302 | $308 |
| ☐ **SIQUEIROS, David Alfaro** ................... *paintings* | | $2,475 | $55,000 |
| Mexican 1896/98-1974 ............................... *drawings* | | $440 | $46,200 |
| ☐ **SIRANI, Barbara** ................................. *paintings* | | | $495 |
| ☐ **SIRANI, Elisabetta** .............................. *paintings* | | $3,300 | $15,000 |
| Italian 1638-1665 ....................................... *drawings* | | | $990 |
| ☐ **SIRANI, Giovanni Andrea** .................... *paintings* | | | $1,000 |
| Italian 1610-1670 | | | |
| ☐ **SIRONI, Mario** .................................... *paintings* | | $2,090 | $17,600 |
| Italian 1885-1961 ....................................... *drawings* | | $550 | $3,080 |
| ☐ **SIRVENT** ............................................. *paintings* | | | $1,760 |
| ☐ **SISAY, Juan** ........................................ *paintings* | | | $522 |
| ☐ **SISLEY, Alfred** .................................... *paintings* | | $5,500 | $495,000 |
| French 1839-1899 ....................................... *drawings* | | $495 | $28,600 |
| ☐ **SISSON, Laurence P.** .......................... *drawings* | | $440 | $1,210 |
| American b. 1928 | | | |
| ☐ **SISTI, Anthony** ................................... *drawings* | | | $220 |
| American b. 1901 | | | |
| ☐ **SITZMAN, Edward R.** ......................... *paintings* | | $110 | $550 |
| American b. 1874 | | | |
| ☐ **SIVEL** .................................................. *paintings* | | | $192 |
| Dutch 20th cent. | | | |
| ☐ **SIX, Micheal** ....................................... *sculpture* | | | $286 |
| ☐ **SJAMAAR, Pieter Geerard** ................... *paintings* | | $495 | $1,980 |
| Dutch 1819-1876 | | | |
| ☐ **SKANECTELES (?), John** .................... *paintings* | | | $275 |
| American (?) 19th cent. | | | |
| ☐ **SKARBINA, Franz** ............................... *paintings* | | $3,300 | $6,050 |
| German 1849-1910 | | | |
| ☐ **SKEAPING, John** ................................. *paintings* | | $3,740 | $4,675 |
| English b. 1901 | | | |
| ☐ **SKEELE, Hannah Brown** ...................... *paintings* | | | $650 |
| American 1829-1901 | | | |
| ☐ **SKEELE, Katherine** ............................. *paintings* | | | $950 |
| American 1896-1963 | | | |
| ☐ **SKELTON, Leslie James** ...................... *paintings* | | $550 | $2,420 |
| Canadian 1848-1929 | | | |

| | | Current Price Range | |
| --- | --- | --- | --- |
| | | *Low* | *High* |
| ☐ **SKELTON, Percival** .............. *drawings* | | | $495 |
| British b.c. 1781 | | | |
| ☐ **SKIDMORE, Thornton** ........... *paintings* | | | $2,090 |
| American b. 1884 | | | |
| ☐ **SKILLING, William** ............... *paintings* | | $2,200 | $2,200 |
| Scottish/American 20th cent. | | | |
| ☐ **SKIRMUNT, Szymon** ............ *paintings* | | | $2,200 |
| Polish 1835-1902 | | | |
| ☐ **SKOU, Sigurd** ..................... *paintings* | | $165 | $1,540 |
| Norwegian/American d. 1929 | | | |
| ☐ **SKRAMLICK, Jan** ............... *paintings* | | | $2,750 |
| Czechoslovakian b. 1860 | | | |
| ☐ **SLADE, Caleb Arnold** ......... *paintings* | | $330 | $2,200 |
| American 1882-1961 | | | |
| ☐ **SLADE, Sydney** ................... *paintings* | | | $605 |
| British 20th cent. | | | |
| ☐ **SLADER, Samuel M.** ............ *paintings* | | | $2,640 |
| British b. 1861 | | | |
| ☐ **SLATER, Charles H.** ............ *drawings* | | $247 | $357 |
| British ac. 1860-1870 | | | |
| ☐ **SLATER, Harry** ................... *drawings* | | | $770 |
| ☐ **SLATER, John Falconer** ........ *paintings* | | | $880 |
| British 1857-1937 | | | |
| ☐ **SLAUGHTER, Stephen** .......... *paintings* | | | $3,190 |
| ☐ **SLAYTON, M.E.** ................. *paintings* | | | $2,860 |
| American b. 1901 | | | |
| ☐ **SLEETH, L. Mac D.** ............. *paintings* | | | $467 |
| American 20th cent. | | | |
| ☐ **SLEICHER, Robert S.** ........... *paintings* | | | $385 |
| ☐ **SLEVOGT, Max** .................. *paintings* | | | $1,650 |
| German 1868-1932 | | | |
| ☐ **SLINGENEYER, Ernest** ......... *paintings* | | | $1,320 |
| Belgian 1820-1894 | | | |
| ☐ **SLOAN, Frank van** .............. *paintings* | | | $250 |
| ☐ **SLOAN, John** ..................... *paintings* | | $880 | $93,500 |
| American 1871-1951 ................... *drawings* | | $110 | $5,500 |
| ☐ **SLOAN, R.** ......................... *paintings* | | | $605 |
| ☐ **SLOAN, Samuel** .................. *paintings* | | | $850 |
| American 1815-1884 .................... *drawings* | | $935 | $2,420 |
| ☐ **SLOANE, Eric** ..................... *paintings* | | $550 | $7,150 |
| American 1905/1910-1985 ............ *drawings* | | $165 | $825 |
| ☐ **SLOANE, George** ................. *paintings* | | $4,950 | $7,700 |
| American b. 1864 | | | |
| ☐ **SLOANE, Marian P.** ............. *paintings* | | $130 | $1,430 |
| American 20th cent. | | | |
| ☐ **SLOCOMBE, Frederick Albert** ............. *drawings* | | $165 | $4,950 |
| English 1847-1920 | | | |
| ☐ **SLOMAN, Joseph** ................ *paintings* | | $174 | $605 |
| American b. 1883 | | | |

| | | *Current Price Range* | |
|---|---|---|---|
| | | Low | High |
| ☐ **SLOTH, W.R.** ..................................... *paintings* | | | $550 |
| British 19th cent. | | | |
| ☐ **SLOUN, Frank van** ............................. *paintings* | | | $1,650 |
| American 1879-1938 ................................. *drawings* | | $55 | $825 |
| ☐ **SLUIS, George van der** ....................... *paintings* | | | $420 |
| ☐ **SLUITER, Willy** ................................. *paintings* | | $192 | $1,210 |
| Dutch b. 1873 ......................................... *drawings* | | | $2,310 |
| ☐ **SLUKERS, H.** ..................................... *paintings* | | | $247 |
| German 20th cent. | | | |
| ☐ **SLUYS, Theo van** ............................. *paintings* | | $1,650 | $4,290 |
| Belgian 19th cent. | | | |
| ☐ **SLUYTERS, Jan** ................................. *paintings* | | | $2,090 |
| Dutch 1881-1957 | | | |
| ☐ **SLYKERMAN** ..................................... *paintings* | | | $577 |
| Dutch 19th cent. | | | |
| ☐ **SMALL, Arthur** ................................. *paintings* | | | $3,700 |
| American 20th cent. | | | |
| ☐ **SMALL, D.** ........................................ *drawings* | | | $192 |
| English 19th/20th cent. | | | |
| ☐ **SMALL, Frank O.** ............................. *paintings* | | | $247 |
| American b. 1860 | | | |
| ☐ **SMART, Edmund Hodgson** .................. *paintings* | | | $8,250 |
| English b. 1873 | | | |
| ☐ **SMART, John (IV)** ............................. *paintings* | | $110 | $1,320 |
| British 1838-1899 | | | |
| ☐ **SMART, R. Bruce** ............................. *paintings* | | | $990 |
| British 20th cent. | | | |
| ☐ **SMEDLEY, Will Larymore** .................. *paintings* | | $176 | $330 |
| American 1871-1958 | | | |
| ☐ **SMEDLEY, William Thomas** ............... *paintings* | | $165 | $550 |
| American 1858-1920 ................................. *drawings* | | $154 | $247 |
| ☐ **SMEERDIJK, Anton** ......................... *paintings* | | | $330 |
| Dutch 1885-1965 | | | |
| ☐ **SMEERS, Franz** ................................. *paintings* | | | $1,760 |
| Belgian 1873-1960 | | | |
| ☐ **SMETHAM, James** ............................. *paintings* | | $1,980 | $5,500 |
| British 1821-89 | | | |
| ☐ **SMIBERT, John** ................................. *paintings* | | | $5,225 |
| American 1688-1751 | | | |
| ☐ **SMILLIE, George Henry** ...................... *paintings* | | $330 | $12,100 |
| American 1840-1921 ................................. *drawings* | | $110 | $1,980 |
| ☐ **SMILLIE, Helen Sheldon Jacobs** .......... *paintings* | | | $1,430 |
| American 1854-1926 | | | |
| ☐ **SMILLIE, James** ................................. *drawings* | | | $1,650 |
| American 1807-1885 | | | |
| ☐ **SMILLIE, James David** ...................... *paintings* | | $550 | $6,050 |
| American 1833-1909 ................................. *drawings* | | $165 | $7,500 |
| ☐ **SMILLIE, James H.** ........................... *paintings* | | | $17,600 |
| American Western | | | |

| | Current Price Range | |
|---|---|---|
| | Low | High |

| | | Low | High |
|---|---|---|---|
| ☐ **SMINZO, Y.** ........................ *paintings* | | | $424 |
| European 19th/20th cent. | | | |
| ☐ **SMIRKE, Robert** ........................ *paintings* | | | $7,150 |
| English 1752-1845 | | | |
| ☐ **SMISSEN, L. van der** ........................ *paintings* | | | $880 |
| Dutch 19th/20th cent. | | | |
| ☐ **SMITH, Alan** ........................ *paintings* | | $220 | $440 |
| ☐ **SMITH, Albert Delmont** ........................ *paintings* | | | $220 |
| American 1886-1962 | | | |
| ☐ **SMITH, Alfred E.** ........................ *paintings* | | $192 | $825 |
| American 1863-1955 | | | |
| ☐ **SMITH, Archibald Carey** ........................ *paintings* | | $246 | $990 |
| American 1837-1911 | | | |
| ☐ **SMITH, Bartholomew** ........................ *paintings* | | | $1,760 |
| British 19th cent. | | | |
| ☐ **SMITH, Calvin Rae** ........................ *paintings* | | $1,100 | $1,980 |
| American 1850-1918 | | | |
| ☐ **SMITH, Carl Frithjof** ........................ *paintings* | | | $16,500 |
| Norwegian 1859-1917 | | | |
| ☐ **SMITH, Carlton Alfred** ........................ *paintings* | | $660 | $852 |
| English b. 1853 ........................ *drawings* | | | $1,870 |
| ☐ **SMITH, Charles L.A.** ........................ *paintings* | | $275 | $880 |
| American b. 1871 ........................ *drawings* | | $220 | $385 |
| ☐ **SMITH, Dan W.** ........................ *drawings* | | $467 | $825 |
| English early 20th cent. | | | |
| ☐ **SMITH, David** ........................ *paintings* | | $3,080 | $18,700 |
| American 1906-1965 ........................ *drawings* | | | $10,450 |
| ........................ *sculpture* | | $9,900 | $572,000 |
| ☐ **SMITH, De Cost** ........................ *drawings* | | | $880 |
| American 1864-1939 | | | |
| ☐ **SMITH, Denzler** ........................ *paintings* | | | $302 |
| ☐ **SMITH, Elmer Boyd** ........................ *paintings* | | $110 | $770 |
| American 1860-1943 ........................ *drawings* | | | $220 |
| ☐ **SMITH, F. Hollin** ........................ *paintings* | | | $2,000 |
| English 19th cent. | | | |
| ☐ **SMITH, Francis Hopkinson** ........................ *drawings* | | $110 | $6,050 |
| American 1838-1915 | | | |
| ☐ **SMITH, Frank Hill** ........................ *paintings* | | $110 | $1,540 |
| American 1841-1904 | | | |
| ☐ **SMITH, Frank Vining** ........................ *paintings* | | $385 | $4,125 |
| American 1879-1967 ........................ *drawings* | | $44 | $1,600 |
| ☐ **SMITH, Fred Thomas** ........................ *paintings* | | | $550 |
| British 19th cent. | | | |
| ☐ **SMITH, Frederick Carl** ........................ *paintings* | | $165 | $467 |
| American 1868-1955 | | | |
| ☐ **SMITH, Frederick Ford** ........................ *paintings* | | | $440 |
| British 19th cent. | | | |
| ☐ **SMITH, Gean** ........................ *paintings* | | $99 | $990 |
| American 1851-1928 ........................ *drawings* | | | $800 |

| | | Current Price Range | |
|---|---|---|---|
| | | Low | High |
| ☐ **SMITH, George (of Chichester)** .............. *paintings* <br> English 1714-1776 | | **$1,100** | **$11,000** |
| ☐ **SMITH, George Armfield** ..................... *paintings* <br> British fl. 1840-1875 | | | **$935** |
| ☐ **SMITH, George Dee** ........................... *paintings* | | | **$4,015** |
| ☐ **SMITH, Gertrude R.** ........................... *paintings* <br> American b. 1869 | | | **$275** |
| ☐ **SMITH, Graham** ............................... *drawings* | | | **$4,400** |
| ☐ **SMITH, Harry Knox** ........................... *paintings* <br> American 1879-1934 ................................. *drawings* | | **$220** <br> **$110** | **$385** <br> **$550** |
| ☐ **SMITH, Harvey K.** ............................. *paintings* | | | **$550** |
| ☐ **SMITH, Hassel** ................................ *paintings* <br> American b. 1915 | | **$660** | **$2,475** |
| ☐ **SMITH, Henry Pember** ......................... *paintings* <br> American 1854-1907 ............................... *drawings* | | **$330** <br> **$220** | **$6,050** <br> **$1,760** |
| ☐ **SMITH, Herbert Luther** ....................... *paintings* <br> British 1811-1870 | | | **$1,760** |
| ☐ **SMITH, Hope** ................................. *paintings* <br> American b. 1879 | | **$550** | **$742** |
| ☐ **SMITH, Houghton Cranford** ................. *paintings* <br> American 19th/20th cent. | | | **$275** |
| ☐ **SMITH, Howard Everett** ...................... *paintings* <br> American b. 1885 ..................................... *drawings* | | **$385** | **$2,750** <br> **$385** |
| ☐ **SMITH, J. Raphael** ............................ *drawings* | | | **$495** |
| ☐ **SMITH, J. Wells** ............................... *paintings* <br> English ac. 1870-1875 | | | **$1,300** |
| ☐ **SMITH, Jack Wilkinson** ....................... *paintings* <br> American 1873-1949 | | **$275** | **$7,700** |
| ☐ **SMITH, James Burrell** ........................ *paintings* <br> English 1822-1897 | | **$600** | **$1,320** |
| ☐ **SMITH, James Whittet** ........................ *drawings* | | **$330** | **$770** |
| ☐ **SMITH, Jerome Howard** ....................... *paintings* <br> American 1861-1941 | | | **$550** |
| ☐ **SMITH, Jessie Willcox** ........................ *paintings* <br> American d. 1935 ................................... *drawings* | | **$2,200** <br> **$275** | **$2,530** <br> **$1,430** |
| ☐ **SMITH, John Brandon** ........................ *paintings* <br> British 1848-84 | | | **$2,970** |
| ☐ **SMITH, John Henry** ........................... *paintings* <br> British ac. 1852-93 | | | **$1,320** |
| ☐ **SMITH, John Warwick** ....................... *drawings* | | **$385** | **$770** |
| ☐ **SMITH, Joseph Lindon** ....................... *paintings* <br> American 1863-1950 ................................. *drawings* | | **$137** <br> **$45** | **$715** <br> **$880** |
| ☐ **SMITH, Leon Polk** ............................ *paintings* <br> American b. 1906 ..................................... *drawings* | | **$385** <br> **$275** | **$9,350** <br> **$1,870** |
| ☐ **SMITH, Letta Crapo** .......................... *paintings* <br> American 1862-1921 | | | **$330** |
| ☐ **SMITH, Lillian Gertrude** ...................... *drawings* <br> American 19th/20th cent. | | | **$600** |

|  | | | Current Price Range | |
|---|---|---|---|---|
|  | | | Low | High |
| ☐ SMITH, Lowell Ellsworth | ...... | *drawings* | $3,250 | $17,000 |
| American b. 1924 | | | | |
| ☐ SMITH, Mary | ...... | *paintings* | $1,650 | $11,000 |
| American 1842-1878 | | | | |
| ☐ SMITH, Maryan | ...... | *drawings* | | $16,500 |
| American ac. c. 1854 | | | | |
| ☐ SMITH, Moore | ...... | *paintings* | | $220 |
| American | | | | |
| ☐ SMITH, Mortimer L. | ...... | *paintings* | $440 | $1,430 |
| American 19th cent. | | | | |
| ☐ SMITH, Oliver Phelps | ...... | *paintings* | | $220 |
| American b. 1867 | | | | |
| ☐ SMITH, Paul Williamson | ...... | *paintings* | $290 | $474 |
| American d. 1949 | | | | |
| ☐ SMITH, Rancliff | ...... | *paintings* | | $275 |
| ☐ SMITH, Reginald | ...... | *drawings* | $330 | $660 |
| English c. 1870-1925 | | | | |
| ☐ SMITH, Richard | ...... | *paintings* | | $3,850 |
| British 19th cent. | | | | |
| ☐ SMITH, Richard | ...... | *drawings* | | $165 |
| English b. 1931 | ...... | *sculpture* | | $1,320 |
| ☐ SMITH, Robert Sidney | ...... | *drawings* | $60 | $220 |
| 1877-1935 | | | | |
| ☐ SMITH, Rosamond Lombard | ...... | *paintings* | | $1,300 |
| American 20th cent. | | | | |
| ☐ SMITH, Royall Brewster | ...... | *paintings* | | $8,800 |
| American 1801-1849 | | | | |
| ☐ SMITH, Rufus W. | ...... | *paintings* | | $660 |
| American 19th cent. | | | | |
| ☐ SMITH, Russell | ...... | *paintings* | $330 | $3,520 |
| American 1812-1896 | ...... | *drawings* | | $165 |
| ☐ SMITH, Tony | ...... | *sculpture* | $17,600 | $19,800 |
| American b. 1912 | | | | |
| ☐ SMITH, Vernon | ...... | *paintings* | | $500 |
| English 20th cent. | ...... | *drawings* | | $412 |
| ☐ SMITH, Wallace H. | ...... | *paintings* | $253 | $550 |
| American contemporary | | | | |
| ☐ SMITH, William Collingwood | ...... | *drawings* | | $3,575 |
| British 1815-1887 | | | | |
| ☐ SMITH, Xanthus | ...... | *paintings* | $400 | $35,200 |
| American 1838/39-1929 | | | | |
| ☐ SMITH-HALD, Frithjof | ...... | *paintings* | $797 | $25,000 |
| Norwegian 1846-1903 | | | | |
| ☐ SMITHSON, Robert | ...... | *paintings* | | $550 |
| American 1938-1972/73 | ...... | *drawings* | $770 | $1,100 |
| | ...... | *sculpture* | | $7,975 |
| ☐ SMITS, Jasper | ...... | *paintings* | | $17,600 |
| ☐ SMOL, Bernard | ...... | *paintings* | | $209 |
| French 20th cent. | | | | |

| | | | Current Price Range | |
|---|---|---|---|---|
| | | | Low | High |
| ☐ SMOLOGES, D. | .............................. | *paintings* | | $1,320 |
| ☐ SMUTNY, Joseph | .............................. | *paintings* | $220 | $825 |
| American 1855-1903 | | | | |
| ☐ SMYTH, Admiral | ................................ | *paintings* | | $550 |
| Scottish 19th cent. | | | | |
| ☐ SMYTH, Ed | ......................................... | *sculpture* | | $5,500 |
| American b. 1916 | | | | |
| ☐ SMYTH, Emily R. | ................................ | *paintings* | | $300 |
| English 19th cent. | | | | |
| ☐ SMYTH, Eugene Leslie | ......................... | *paintings* | $110 | $650 |
| American 1857-1932 | | | | |
| ☐ SMYTH, H. | ........................................ | *paintings* | | $825 |
| ☐ SMYTHE, C.R. | .................................. | *paintings* | | $440 |
| ☐ SMYTHE, Edward Robert | ..................... | *paintings* | $357 | $2,200 |
| English 1810-1899 | | | | |
| ☐ SMYTHE, Leslie E.B. | ........................... | *paintings* | | $385 |
| British 19th cent. | | | | |
| ☐ SMYTHE, Thomas | ............................. | *paintings* | $3,190 | $7,150 |
| English 1825-1906/07 | | | | |
| ☐ SNAYERS, Pieter | .............................. | *paintings* | $4,400 | $9,350 |
| Flemish 1592-1667 | | | | |
| ☐ SNELL, Henry Bayley | .......................... | *paintings* | $225 | $1,320 |
| American 1858-1943 | ................................ | *drawings* | $220 | $990 |
| ☐ SNELL, Ida | ...................................... | *paintings* | | $500 |
| American 19th cent. | | | | |
| ☐ SNELL, James Herbert | ......................... | *paintings* | $198 | $330 |
| English 1861-1935 | | | | |
| ☐ SNELLINCK, Geeraert | ......................... | *paintings* | | $1,100 |
| Flemish b. 1577 | | | | |
| ☐ SNELSON, Kenneth | ............................ | *sculpture* | $2,860 | $4,675 |
| American b. 1927 | | | | |
| ☐ SNIDOW, Gordon | ............................... | *paintings* | $17,000 | $50,000 |
| American b. 1936 | ................................... | *drawings* | $2,500 | $41,000 |
| | ................................ | *sculpture* | | $9,000 |
| ☐ SNOECK, Jacques | .............................. | *paintings* | $935 | $1,320 |
| Dutch 1881-1921 | | | | |
| ☐ SNOW, Gordon | .................................. | *drawings* | | $9,000 |
| American contemporary | | | | |
| ☐ SNOW, James Wray | ........................... | *paintings* | | $2,640 |
| English ac. 1832 | | | | |
| ☐ SNOW, P. | ......................................... | *paintings* | $302 | $400 |
| ☐ SNOW, W.P. | ..................................... | *paintings* | | $770 |
| Canadian 19th cent. | | | | |
| ☐ SNOWDON | ....................................... | *paintings* | | $440 |
| ☐ SNOWE, Frank | .................................. | *paintings* | $264 | $357 |
| American 19th/20th cent. | | | | |
| ☐ SNOWMAN, Isaac | ............................... | *paintings* | $650 | $880 |
| Israeli b. 1874 | | | | |

| | Current Price Range | |
|---|---|---|
| | Low | High |
| ☐ **SNYDER, Bladen Tasker** .............. *paintings* | | **$192** |
| American 1864-1923 | | |
| ☐ **SNYDER, Joan** .................... *drawings* | **$660** | **$6,875** |
| American b. 1940 | | |
| ☐ **SNYDER, William Henry** ............ *paintings* | **$715** | **$2,750** |
| American 1829-1910 | | |
| ☐ **SNYDERS, C.** ........................ *paintings* | | **$330** |
| ☐ **SNYDERS, Frans** .................... *paintings* | **$6,600** | **$57,200** |
| Flemish 1579-1657 | | |
| ☐ **SNYERS, Pieter** .................... *paintings* | | **$15,400** |
| Flemish 1681-1752 | | |
| ☐ **SOBLE, John Jacob** ................ *paintings* | | **$3,850** |
| Russian/American b. 1893 | | |
| ☐ **SODERSTEN, Yerm** ............ *paintings* | | **$1,100** |
| 20th cent. | | |
| ☐ **SODERSTON, Leon** ............ *paintings* | | **$275** |
| American 20th cent. | | |
| ☐ **SODOMA, IL,** | | |
| **(Giovanni Antonio BAZZI)** ........ *drawings* | | **$22,000** |
| Italian 1477-1549 | | |
| ☐ **SOEST, Gerard van** ............ *paintings* | | **$1,100** |
| English c. 1600 or 1637-1681 | | |
| ☐ **SOEST, Louis Willem van** ........ *paintings* | **$275** | **$770** |
| Dutch b. 1867 | | |
| ☐ **SOEUR, S.** ........................ *paintings* | | **$600** |
| French 19th cent. | | |
| ☐ **SOGLOW, Otto** .................... *drawings* | **$165** | **$302** |
| American b. 1900 | | |
| ☐ **SOGOR, William** ................ *sculpture* | | **$385** |
| contemporary | | |
| ☐ **SOHN, Carl (Jr.)** ................ *paintings* | **$2,090** | **$9,350** |
| German 1845-1908 | | |
| ☐ **SOHNGER, L.** ........................ *drawings* | | **$175** |
| German 19th cent. | | |
| ☐ **SOIMIE** ............................ *sculpture* | | **$466** |
| French late 19th cent. | | |
| ☐ **SOKOLOV, Piotr Petrovich** ........ *paintings* | **$1,650** | **$2,090** |
| Russian 1821-1899 | | |
| ☐ **SOKOLOVSKY, Sigmond** ........ *paintings* | | **$440** |
| Polish 1859-1888 | | |
| ☐ **SOKOLOWSKY, Suliamith** ........ *paintings* | | **$385** |
| ☐ **SOL, H.** ............................ *paintings* | | **$275** |
| ☐ **SOLARI, Achille** ................ *paintings* | | **$192** |
| Italian 1835-? | | |
| ☐ **SOLAROLI** ........................ *sculpture* | | **$275** |
| ☐ **SOLDI, Andrea** ................ *paintings* | | **$4,400** |
| Italian 1682-1766 | | |
| ☐ **SOLDI, Raul** ........................ *paintings* | | **$1,650** |
| Argentinian b. 1905 | | |

|  | | *Current Price Range* | |
| --- | --- | --- | --- |
|  | | Low | High |
| ☐ **SOLER Y LOPIS, L. Eduardo** ............. *paintings* | | | $330 |
| ☐ **SOLGER** ..................................... *paintings* | | | $495 |
| ☐ **SOLIDAY, Tim** ................................ *paintings* | | | $500 |
| ☐ **SOLIMENA, Francesco** ......................... *paintings* | | | $9,350 |
| Italian 1657-1747 | | | |
| ☐ **SOLIN, Suzanne Daynes Grassot** ........... *paintings* | | | $1,980 |
| French b. 1884 | | | |
| ☐ **SOLLIER, H.** ...................................... *paintings* | | | $605 |
| French 20th cent. | | | |
| ☐ **SOLMAN, Joseph** ................................ *paintings* | | | $4,070 |
| American b. 1909 | | | |
| ☐ **SOLOMON, Abraham** .......................... *paintings* | | | $132,000 |
| English 1823/24-1862 | | | |
| ☐ **SOLOMON, Rebekka** ........................... *paintings* | | | $2,200 |
| ☐ **SOLOMON, Simeon** ............................. *paintings* | | | $49,500 |
| British 1840-1905 ....................... *drawings* | | $192 | $1,870 |
| ☐ **SOLOMON, Syd** ................................. *paintings* | | $154 | $3,850 |
| American b. 1917 | | | |
| ☐ **SOMER, Hendrick van** ........................ *paintings* | | | $23,100 |
| Dutch 1615-c. 1684/85 | | | |
| ☐ **SOMER, Paulus van** .......................... *paintings* | | | $880 |
| Dutch 1570-1621 | | | |
| ☐ **SOMER, R. C.** .................................... *paintings* | | | $467 |
| English 19th/20th cent. | | | |
| ☐ **SOMERBY, Lorenzo** .......................... *paintings* | | $3,300 | $3,850 |
| American | | | |
| ☐ **SOMERS, H.** ..................................... *paintings* | | | $850 |
| Alsatian b. 1922 | | | |
| ☐ **SOMERSCALES, Thomas** .................... *paintings* | | $440 | $24,200 |
| English 1842-1927 | | | |
| ☐ **SOMERSET, Chedder** ......................... *paintings* | | | $605 |
| European 19th cent. | | | |
| ☐ **SOMERSET, Richard Gay** .................... *paintings* | | | $660 |
| ☐ **SOMERVILLE, Howard** ........................ *paintings* | | | $2,530 |
| English b. 1873 | | | |
| ☐ **SOMM, Henri** ................................... *drawings* | | $484 | $1,650 |
| French 1810-1889 | | | |
| ☐ **SOMM, Henry** ................................... *drawings* | | $44 | $770 |
| French 1844-1907 | | | |
| ☐ **SOMMER, Charles A.** ......................... *paintings* | | | $1,320 |
| American 19th cent. | | | |
| ☐ **SOMMER, F.** ..................................... *paintings* | | | $605 |
| ☐ **SOMMER, G.E.** ................................. *sculpture* | | $550 | $550 |
| Italian | | | |
| ☐ **SOMMER, Georg** .............................. *paintings* | | | $990 |
| German 19th cent. | | | |
| ☐ **SOMMER, Otto** ............................... *paintings* | | $1,100 | $4,070 |
| German 19th cent. | | | |

| | | | Current Price Range | |
|---|---|---|---|---|
| | | | *Low* | *High* |
| SOMMER, Richard ......................... *paintings* | | | $2,750 | $5,500 |
| German 19th cent. | | | | |
| SOMMER, William ......................... *paintings* | | | $1,925 | $2,860 |
| American 1867-1949 ......................... *drawings* | | | $88 | $902 |
| SOMMERS, Ivan ......................... *paintings* | | | | $275 |
| American 20th cent. | | | | |
| SOMMERS, O. ......................... *paintings* | | | | $550 |
| German/American 19th cent. | | | | |
| SOMN, David S. ......................... *paintings* | | | | $935 |
| British 19th cent. | | | | |
| SOMOV, Constantin Andreievich .......... *paintings* | | | | $2,750 |
| Russian b. 1869 ......................... *drawings* | | | | $850 |
| SONDERBORG, Kurt ......................... *paintings* | | | | $990 |
| SONDERLAND, Fritz ......................... *paintings* | | | $4,400 | $20,900 |
| German 1836-1896 | | | | |
| SONIER, J. ......................... *paintings* | | | $825 | $1,430 |
| French 19th cent. | | | | |
| SONJE, Jan ......................... *paintings* | | | | $2,420 |
| Dutch d. 1691 | | | | |
| SONJE, Jan Gabrielsz ......................... *paintings* | | | $770 | $1,100 |
| Dutch 1625-1707 | | | | |
| SONKANECK, E. ......................... *sculpture* | | | | $300 |
| SONN, Albert H. ......................... *drawings* | | | | $440 |
| American b. 1869 | | | | |
| SONNENSON, Carl ......................... *sculpture* | | | | $440 |
| SONNTAG, W.H. ......................... *paintings* | | | | $1,760 |
| American | | | | |
| SONNTAG, William Louis (Jr.) ............. *paintings* | | | | $240 |
| American b. 1870 ......................... *drawings* | | | $400 | $1,870 |
| SONNTAG, William Louis (Sr.) ............. *paintings* | | | $440 | $13,200 |
| American 1822-1900 ......................... *drawings* | | | $242 | $2,420 |
| SONREL, Elizabeth ......................... *paintings* | | | | $550 |
| French b. 1874 | | | | |
| SOOLMAKER, Jan Frans ................... *paintings* | | | $1,650 | $5,775 |
| Flemish 1635-1685 | | | | |
| SOPATAK, Laszlo Pataky von ............. *paintings* | | | | $440 |
| Hungarian 1857-1912 | | | | |
| SORBI, Raffaelo ......................... *paintings* | | | $3,000 | $39,600 |
| Italian 1844-1931 | | | | |
| SOREE, L. ......................... *paintings* | | | | $852 |
| English 19th cent. | | | | |
| SOREN, John Johnston ......................... *paintings* | | | | $660 |
| American mid 19th cent. | | | | |
| SORENSEN, Carl Fredrick ................... *paintings* | | | $2,090 | $2,750 |
| Danish 1818-1879 | | | | |
| SOREZ, E. ......................... *paintings* | | | | $2,200 |
| SORGH, Hendrick Maartensz Rokes ..... *paintings* | | | $440 | $29,700 |
| Dutch c. 1611-1670 | | | | |

| | Current Price Range | |
|---|---|---|
| | Low | High |
| ☐ **SORIANO, Juan** .................... *paintings* | **$1,320** | **$1,760** |
| Mexican b. 1919/20 | | |
| ☐ **SORIANO, Rafael** ............................. *paintings* | | **$2,310** |
| ☐ **SORKAU, Albert** ............................. *paintings* | | **$450** |
| French b. 1874 | | |
| ☐ **SOROLLA Y BASTIDA, Joaquin** ......... *paintings* | **$1,650** | **$264,000** |
| Spanish 1863-1923 ...................................... *drawings* | **$1,430** | **$27,500** |
| ☐ **SOROTANEFF, Boris** .......................... *drawings* | | **$330** |
| Russian 20th cent. | | |
| ☐ **SOSSON, Louis** ............................. *sculpture* | | **$990** |
| ☐ **SOTHERN, E.H. (Jr.)** .......................... *paintings* | | **$275** |
| ☐ **SOTO, Carlos** .................................... *paintings* | | **$2,090** |
| Italian 19th cent. | | |
| ☐ **SOTO, Jesus Rafael** ............................ *sculpture* | **$1,100** | **$30,800** |
| Venezuelan b. 1923 | | |
| ☐ **SOTO, Roberto** .................................. *paintings* | **$1,100** | **$1,980** |
| ☐ **SOTTA** ................................................ *paintings* | | **$770** |
| ☐ **SOTTLIEB, M.** ..................................... *paintings* | | **$660** |
| ☐ **SOTTOCORNOLA, Giovanni** .............. *paintings* | | **$7,700** |
| Italian 1855-1917 | | |
| ☐ **SOUBRIN, Jean de** ............................. *paintings* | | **$660** |
| French 19th cent. | | |
| ☐ **SOUDEIKINE, Sergei** .......................... *paintings* | **$132** | **$3,850** |
| Russian/American 1883/86-1946 .................... *drawings* | **$66** | **$6,600** |
| ☐ **SOUKANCICH** .................................... *sculpture* | | **$385** |
| ☐ **SOUKOP, W.** ...................................... *sculpture* | | **$286** |
| ☐ **SOULACROIX, Charles** | | |
| **(or Joseph Frederic Charles)** .................. *paintings* | **$1,870** | **$26,400** |
| French b. 1825 | | |
| ☐ **SOULAGES, Pierre** ............................. *paintings* | **$7,700** | **$27,500** |
| French b. 1919 | | |
| ☐ **SOULEN, Henry James** ........................ *paintings* | **$528** | **$2,530** |
| American 1888-1965 | | |
| ☐ **SOULES, Ettienne Edward** ................... *drawings* | **$165** | **$192** |
| French 19th cent. | | |
| ☐ **SOULES, Eugene Edouard** .................. *drawings* | | **$8,250** |
| French d. 1876 | | |
| ☐ **SOUSA, Pedro Correa de** ................... *drawings* | | **$770** |
| ☐ **SOUTER, John B.** ............................. *paintings* | | **$1,100** |
| American 19th/20th cent. | | |
| ☐ **SOUTHERDEN, E. Thompson** .............. *paintings* | | **$1,100** |
| ☐ **SOUTINE, Chaim** .............................. *paintings* | **$330** | **$220,000** |
| Russian 1894-1943 | | |
| ☐ **SOUVERBIE, Jean** ............................. *paintings* | **$550** | **$4,400** |
| French b. 1891 | | |
| ☐ **SOWER, F.D.** ...................................... *paintings* | | **$440** |
| American 19th cent. | | |
| ☐ **SOYER, Issac** ...................................... *paintings* | | **$324** |

| | | | *Current Price Range* | |
| :--- | :--- | :--- | ---: | ---: |
| | | | Low | High |
| ☐ **SOYER, Moses** | ................................. | *paintings* | $132 | $13,200 |
| Russian/American 1898/99-1974 | ..................... | *drawings* | $77 | $1,430 |
| ☐ **SOYER, Paul** | ..................................... | *paintings* | $1,800 | $3,080 |
| French 1823-1903 | | | | |
| ☐ **SOYER, Raphael** | ............................... | *paintings* | $275 | $49,500 |
| American b. 1899 | ..................................... | *drawings* | $82 | $1,870 |
| ☐ **SOYER, Will** | ..................................... | *paintings* | | $2,750 |
| ☐ **SPADA, Lionello** | ............................... | *paintings* | | $23,100 |
| Italian 1576-1622 | | | | |
| ☐ **SPADARO, Peter** | ............................... | *paintings* | | $192 |
| American early 20th cent. | | | | |
| ☐ **SPADER, William Edgar** | ..................... | *paintings* | | $275 |
| American b. 1875 | | | | |
| ☐ **SPAENDONCK, Cornelis van** | ............... | *paintings* | | $29,700 |
| French 1756-1840 | | | | |
| ☐ **SPAHR, John** | ..................................... | *paintings* | | $176 |
| American 20th cent. | | | | |
| ☐ **SPALATINO, J.D.** | ............................... | *paintings* | | $319 |
| ☐ **SPALDING, C.B.** | ............................... | *paintings* | | $1,870 |
| English 19th cent. | | | | |
| ☐ **SPALDING, P.H.** | ............................... | *paintings* | | $660 |
| ☐ **SPALTHOFF, Jan Philip** | ..................... | *paintings* | | $3,300 |
| Flemish ac. 1705 | | | | |
| ☐ **SPAMPINATO, Clemente** | ............... | *sculpture* | $1,650 | $2,640 |
| American b. 1912 | | | | |
| ☐ **SPANGE** | ..................................... | *paintings* | | $220 |
| American 19th cent. | | | | |
| ☐ **SPANGENBERG, Paul** | ........................ | *paintings* | | $1,870 |
| German 1843-1918 | | | | |
| ☐ **SPANISH FORGER** | ............................... | *paintings* | $385 | $1,650 |
| ac. 1890-1920 | | | | |
| ☐ **SPARKS, Arthur Watson** | ..................... | *paintings* | $424 | $750 |
| American 1870-1919 | ............................... | *drawings* | | $77 |
| ☐ **SPARKS, H. Blande** | ........................... | *paintings* | | $825 |
| English 19th cent. | | | | |
| ☐ **SPARKS, Will** | ..................................... | *paintings* | $165 | $2,200 |
| American 1862-1937 | | | | |
| ☐ **SPAT, Gabriel** | ..................................... | *paintings* | $66 | $2,860 |
| French 19th/20th cent. | ..................................... | *drawings* | $55 | $495 |
| ☐ **SPAULDING, Henry Plympton** | ............. | *paintings* | $165 | $600 |
| American b. 1868 | ..................................... | *drawings* | $55 | $375 |
| ☐ **SPEAR, Arthur P.** | ............................... | *drawings* | $121 | $935 |
| American b. 1879 | | | | |
| ☐ **SPEAR, Thomas Truman** | ..................... | *paintings* | $715 | $715 |
| American 1803-c. 1882 | | | | |
| ☐ **SPEARS, Harry** | ............................... | *drawings* | | $220 |
| American | | | | |
| ☐ **SPECHT, E.** | ..................................... | *paintings* | | $220 |
| German 19th cent. | | | | |

| | | Current Price Range | |
|---|---|---|---|
| | | *Low* | *High* |
| ☐ **SPECHT, Friedrich** ............................ *drawings* | | $330 | $330 |
| ☐ **SPEED, Harold** ................................. *paintings* | | | $20,350 |
| British 1872-1957 | | | |
| ☐ **SPEED, U. Grant** ................................ *sculpture* | | $2,500 | $25,000 |
| American b.1930 | | | |
| ☐ **SPEER, Michael J.** ............................. *paintings* | | | $9,350 |
| ☐ **SPEICHER, Eugene Edward** ................. *paintings* | | $274 | $8,250 |
| American 1883-1962 ................................. *drawings* | | $33 | $990 |
| ☐ **SPEIGHT, Francis** ............................. *paintings* | | | $467 |
| American 20th cent. | | | |
| ☐ **SPENCE, Harry** ................................. *paintings* | | $352 | $1,155 |
| English 1860-1928 | | | |
| ☐ **SPENCE, Thomas Ralph** ...................... *paintings* | | | $1,100 |
| British b. 1855 | | | |
| ☐ **SPENCELAYH, Charles** ...................... *paintings* | | $2,420 | $6,050 |
| British 1865-1958 | | | |
| ☐ **SPENCER, Frederick R.** ...................... *paintings* | | $385 | $1,980 |
| American 1806-1875 | | | |
| ☐ **SPENCER, J.A.** ................................. *paintings* | | | $1,650 |
| British 19th cent. | | | |
| ☐ **SPENCER, John C.** ............................ *paintings* | | $33 | $2,200 |
| American 19th/20th cent. | | | |
| ☐ **SPENCER, Lillie Martin** ...................... *paintings* | | $1,980 | $99,000 |
| American 1822/27-1902 ............................ *drawings* | | $330 | $495 |
| ☐ **SPENCER, Margaret Fulton** ................. *paintings* | | $220 | $880 |
| American b. 1882 | | | |
| ☐ **SPENCER, Niles** ............................... *paintings* | | $110 | $8,250 |
| American 1893-1952 | | | |
| ☐ **SPENCER, R.B.** ................................ *paintings* | | $825 | $3,300 |
| British ac. 1805-1870 | | | |
| ☐ **SPENCER, Robert** ............................. *paintings* | | $220 | $12,000 |
| American 1879-1931 | | | |
| ☐ **SPENCER, Thomas** ........................... *paintings* | | | $16,500 |
| British ac. 1700-1767 | | | |
| ☐ **SPERL, Johann** ................................ *paintings* | | $35,200 | $68,750 |
| German 1840-1914 | | | |
| ☐ **SPERLICH, J.** ................................. *paintings* | | | $2,640 |
| ☐ **SPERLICH, Sophie** ............................ *paintings* | | $770 | $1,320 |
| German 19th cent. | | | |
| ☐ **SPERLING, Heinrich** .......................... *paintings* | | | $1,100 |
| German 1844-1924 | | | |
| ☐ **SPEYER, Christian Georg** .................... *paintings* | | | $18,700 |
| German 1855-1929 ................................. *drawings* | | | $550 |
| ☐ **SPEYER, Nora** ................................. *paintings* | | | $275 |
| American | | | |
| ☐ **SPICER, Clayton** ............................. *paintings* | | | $302 |
| American 20th cent. | | | |
| ☐ **SPICJZZA (?), F.S.** ............................ *paintings* | | | $198 |
| American 20th cent. | | | |

|  | | *Current Price Range* | |
| | | Low | High |
| --- | --- | --- | --- |
| ☐ **SPICUZZA, Francesco J.** ..................... *paintings* | | $25 | $770 |
| Italian/American 1883-1962? ......................... *drawings* | | $121 | $522 |
| ☐ **SPIEGAL, A\*** ..................................... *paintings* | | | $500 |
| American 20th cent. | | | |
| ☐ **SPIELTER, Carl Johann** ................... *paintings* | | | $6,600 |
| German 1851-1922 | | | |
| ☐ **SPIERS, Benjamin Walter** .................... *drawings* | | | $4,180 |
| English ac. 1875-1893 | | | |
| ☐ **SPIERS, Harry** ...................................... *paintings* | | $137 | $550 |
| English/American 1869-after 1934 ................... *drawings* | | $88 | $275 |
| ☐ **SPILIMBERGO, Lino Eneas** ................. *paintings* | | | $19,800 |
| Argentinian 1896-1964 | | | |
| ☐ **SPILLIAERT, Leon** .............................. *paintings* | | | $1,760 |
| Belgian 1881-1948 | | | |
| ☐ **SPINETTI, Mario** ................................. *paintings* | | | $9,350 |
| Italian 19th/20th cent. .................................. *drawings* | | $247 | $770 |
| ☐ **SPINKS, Thomas** .................................. *paintings* | | $220 | $1,320 |
| British ac. 1872-1907 | | | |
| ☐ **SPINNER, L. P.** .................................. *paintings* | | | $330 |
| American 19th cent. | | | |
| ☐ **SPIRIDON, Ignace** .............................. *paintings* | | $770 | $9,350 |
| Italian ac. 1889-1900 | | | |
| ☐ **SPIRO, Eugene** ................................. *paintings* | | | $1,320 |
| German/American 1874-1972 | | | |
| ☐ **SPIRO, Georges** ................................. *paintings* | | $660 | $1,100 |
| French b. 1909 | | | |
| ☐ **SPISANELLI, Vincenzo** ....................... *paintings* | | | $1,210 |
| ☐ **SPITZER, Emanuel** ............................. *paintings* | | | $3,960 |
| German 1844-1919 | | | |
| ☐ **SPITZER, Joseph** ............................... *paintings* | | | $302 |
| ☐ **SPITZER, Walter** ............................... *paintings* | | $247 | $522 |
| German b. 1927 | | | |
| ☐ **SPITZWEG, Carl** ............................... *paintings* | | $33,000 | $72,600 |
| German 1808-1885 ..................................... *drawings* | | $495 | $1,540 |
| ☐ **SPIZZIRI, Luigi** .................................. *paintings* | | | $726 |
| Philadelphian b. 1894 | | | |
| ☐ **SPLITGERBER, August Karl Martin** .... *paintings* | | $1,210 | $2,200 |
| German 1844-1918 | | | |
| ☐ **SPODE, John** ................................... *paintings* | | | $4,675 |
| British 19th cent. | | | |
| ☐ **SPODE, Samuel** ................................. *paintings* | | $935 | $5,500 |
| British 19th cent. | | | |
| ☐ **SPOHLER, Jacob Jan Coenraad** .......... *paintings* | | $550 | $23,100 |
| Dutch 1837-1923 | | | |
| ☐ **SPOHLER, Jan Jacob** .......................... *paintings* | | $1,045 | $33,000 |
| Dutch 1811-1879 | | | |
| ☐ **SPOHLER, Johannes Franciscus** .......... *paintings* | | $880 | $5,500 |
| Dutch 1853-1894 | | | |

| | | | *Current Price Range* | |
|---|---|---|---|---|
| | | | *Low* | *High* |
| ☐ **SPOHLER, Johannes Franciscus** ........... *paintings* | | | $550 | $4,950 |
| Dutch 1811-1879 | | | | |
| ☐ **SPOLANDER, F.** ................................ *paintings* | | | | $440 |
| ☐ **SPOLVERINI, Ilario** | | | | |
| **(called IL MERCANTI)** ...................... *drawings* | | | | $550 |
| ☐ **SPRAGUE, Al** ................................. *paintings* | | | | $2,310 |
| ☐ **SPREAD, Henry Fenton** ........................ *paintings* | | | | $715 |
| Italian b. 1844 | | | | |
| ☐ **SPREUWEN, Jacob van** ................. *paintings* | | | | $1,320 |
| Dutch b. 1611 | | | | |
| ☐ **SPRINCHORN, Carl** ........................... *paintings* | | | $400 | $1,870 |
| American 1887-1971 ............................... *drawings* | | | $100 | $15,400 |
| ☐ **SPRING, Alfons** ............................. *paintings* | | | $1,320 | $11,000 |
| German 1843-1908 | | | | |
| ☐ **SPRINGER, Carl** ............................. *paintings* | | | | $260 |
| ☐ **SPRINGER, Charles Henry** ................. *paintings* | | | | $330 |
| American 1857-1920 | | | | |
| ☐ **SPRINGER, Cornelis** ........................... *paintings* | | | $10,450 | $37,400 |
| Dutch 1817-1891 ..................................... *drawings* | | | $385 | $1,760 |
| ☐ **SPRINGER, L.** ..................................... *paintings* | | | | $3,850 |
| Dutch School | | | | |
| ☐ **SPRINKMANN, C.** ............................. *paintings* | | | | $550 |
| German 19th cent. | | | | |
| ☐ **SPRUANCE, Benton Murdoch** ............. *paintings* | | | $143 | $660 |
| American 1904-1967 ................................. *drawings* | | | $308 | $1,760 |
| ☐ **SQUINT-EYE** ..................................... *drawings* | | | | $1,980 |
| American Indian ac. 1887 | | | | |
| ☐ **SQUIRE, E.P.** ..................................... *paintings* | | | | $2,530 |
| American 19th cent. | | | | |
| ☐ **SQUIRE, Maud Hunt** .......................... *drawings* | | | | $192 |
| American 1853-1930 | | | | |
| ☐ **SQUIRES, C. Clyde** ........................... *paintings* | | | $550 | $880 |
| 1883-1970 | | | | |
| ☐ **SRAC, J.** ............................................. *sculpture* | | | | $1,540 |
| ☐ **ST. CZAJKOWSKI** ............................. *paintings* | | | | $264 |
| ☐ **ST. MARTIN, Alexandre Pau de** ........... *paintings* | | | | $264 |
| ☐ **STAAKMAN** ....................................... *paintings* | | | | $2,200 |
| ☐ **STAAL, Gustave Pierre Eugene** ............. *paintings* | | | | $1,980 |
| French 1817-1882 ..................................... *drawings* | | | | $55 |
| ☐ **STAATEN, Louis van** .......................... *drawings* | | | $121 | $660 |
| Dutch 19th/20th cent. | | | | |
| ☐ **STABLER** ........................................... *paintings* | | | | $275 |
| American 19th cent. | | | | |
| ☐ **STACEY, Anna Lee** ........................... *paintings* | | | $356 | $1,430 |
| American d. 1943 | | | | |
| ☐ **STACEY, John F.** ............................... *paintings* | | | $180 | $750 |
| ☐ **STACEY, L.** ....................................... *paintings* | | | | $825 |
| ☐ **STACHOWSKI, Vladislav** ................... *paintings* | | | | $330 |
| Polish 1852-1932 | | | | |

| | | Current Price Range | |
|---|---|---|---|
| | | Low | High |
| ☐ **STACQUET, Henry** ............................ *drawings* | | $220 | $1,100 |
| Belgian 1838-1907 | | | |
| ☐ **STACY, Max** ..................................... *paintings* | | | $302 |
| American 19th cent. | | | |
| ☐ **STADELMANN, Hans** ........................ *paintings* | | | $1,650 |
| German b. 1876 | | | |
| ☐ **STADEMANN, Adolf** ......................... *paintings* | | $550 | $29,700 |
| German 1824-1895 | | | |
| ☐ **STADLER, Toni (or Anton van)** ............. *paintings* | | $1,430 | $1,540 |
| German b. 1850 | | | |
| ☐ **STAEHL, Albert** ................................. *drawings* | | | $1,320 |
| ☐ **STAEL, Nicolas de** ............................ *paintings* | | $19,800 | $159,500 |
| French 1913-1955 ..................................... *drawings* | | $1,540 | $8,800 |
| ☐ **STAETS, Hendrik** .............................. *paintings* | | | $2,200 |
| ☐ **STAFFORD, Burgess** .......................... *drawings* | | | $660 |
| ☐ **STAGER, B.** ..................................... *paintings* | | | $220 |
| American | | | |
| ☐ **STAGGS, Sari** ................................... *drawings* | | $1,540 | $2,400 |
| American | | | |
| ☐ **STAHL, Benjamin Albert** ..................... *paintings* | | $99 | $660 |
| American b. 1910 | | | |
| ☐ **STAHL, Friedrich** .............................. *drawings* | | | $462 |
| ☐ **STAHLY, Francois** ............................. *sculpture* | | | $1,650 |
| French b. 1911 | | | |
| ☐ **STAHR, Paul** .................................... *paintings* | | $660 | $4,400 |
| American 1883-1953 ................................. *drawings* | | $110 | $247 |
| ☐ **STAIGER, Paul** ................................. *paintings* | | | $2,200 |
| ☐ **STAINER** ........................................ *sculpture* | | | $715 |
| European 19th cent. | | | |
| ☐ **STAINFORTH, Martin** ......................... *drawings* | | | $330 |
| American 20th cent. | | | |
| ☐ **STAINTON, George** ........................... *paintings* | | | $825 |
| late 19th cent. ......................................... *drawings* | | | $220 |
| ☐ **STAMMEL, Eberhard** ......................... *paintings* | | $357 | $7,150 |
| German 1832/33-1906 | | | |
| ☐ **STAMOS, Theodoros** .......................... *paintings* | | $1,430 | $90,750 |
| American b. 1922 ..................................... *drawings* | | $440 | $16,500 |
| ☐ **STANCZAK, Julian** ............................ *paintings* | | $605 | $880 |
| ☐ **STANDING, H.W.** .............................. *drawings* | | $242 | $1,760 |
| English 19th/20th cent. | | | |
| ☐ **STANEK, Emmanuel** ........................... *paintings* | | | $2,200 |
| Austrian 1862-1920 | | | |
| ☐ **STANESBY, Alexander** ......................... *drawings* | | | $1,980 |
| English ac. 1845-1854 | | | |
| ☐ **STANFIELD, George Clarkson** ............. *paintings* | | $1,100 | $1,815 |
| English 1828-1878 | | | |
| ☐ **STANFIELD, William Clarkson** ............. *paintings* | | $286 | $2,200 |
| English 1793-1867 ..................................... *drawings* | | $357 | $2,090 |

| | | Current Price Range | |
|---|---|---|---|
| | | Low | High |
| ☐ **STANGE, Emile** .............................. *paintings* | | | $302 |
| American 1863-1943 | | | |
| ☐ **STANIEK, A.** ..................................... *paintings* | | | $385 |
| ☐ **STANKIEWICZ, Richard** ..................... *sculpture* | | $1,760 | $14,300 |
| American b. 1922 | | | |
| ☐ **STANLAWS, Penhryn** ......................... *paintings* | | | $577 |
| American 1877-1957 .............................. *drawings* | | $55 | $1,650 |
| ☐ **STANLEY, Charles St. George** ............. *drawings* | | | $330 |
| American ac. 1870-1880 | | | |
| ☐ **STANLEY, Frederic** ............................ *paintings* | | | $605 |
| American | | | |
| ☐ **STANLEY, John Mix** .......................... *paintings* | | $1,760 | $8,250 |
| American 1814-1872 .............................. *drawings* | | | $132 |
| ☐ **STANNARD, Eloise Harriet** ................. *paintings* | | $660 | $5,775 |
| English 1828/29-1915 | | | |
| ☐ **STANNARD, Emily** ............................. *paintings* | | $3,520 | $4,675 |
| English 1803-1885 | | | |
| ☐ **STANNARD, Henry** ............................ *drawings* | | | $192 |
| English 1844-1920 | | | |
| ☐ **STANNARD, Henry Sylvester** ............... *drawings* | | $274 | $880 |
| English 1870-1951 | | | |
| ☐ **STANNARD, Lillian** ........................... *drawings* | | | $550 |
| ☐ **STANNUS, Anthony Carey** .................. *paintings* | | $302 | $715 |
| English 1862-1903 | | | |
| ☐ **STANTON, B.** .................................... *drawings* | | | $275 |
| ☐ **STANTON, George** ............................. *paintings* | | | $302 |
| American 19th/20th cent. | | | |
| ☐ **STANTON, J.A.** .................................. *paintings* | | | $522 |
| American 19th/20th cent. | | | |
| ☐ **STANWOOD, Franklin** ........................ *paintings* | | $385 | $1,540 |
| American 1856-1888 | | | |
| ☐ **STANZIONE, Massimo** | | | |
| (called Cavalierre Massimo) .................... *paintings* | | $1,650 | $11,000 |
| Italian 1585-1656 | | | |
| ☐ **STAPLES, Robert Ponsonby** ................ *paintings* | | $99 | $242 |
| Irish 1853-1943 | | | |
| ☐ **STARCKE, J.** .................................... *sculpture* | | | $308 |
| ☐ **STARGARDT, J.** ................................ *paintings* | | | $385 |
| ☐ **STARK, F.** ........................................ *paintings* | | | $385 |
| ☐ **STARK, Jack Gage** ............................. *paintings* | | | $308 |
| American 1882-1950 | | | |
| ☐ **STARK, James** ................................... *paintings* | | $770 | $880 |
| British 1794-1859 .................................. *drawings* | | | $192 |
| ☐ **STARK, Otto** ................................... *paintings* | | | $2,200 |
| 1859-1926 | | | |
| ☐ **STARKENBORGH,** | | | |
| **Jacobus Nicolas baron Tjarda van** ......... *paintings* | | $1,320 | $3,630 |
| Dutch 1822-1895 | | | |

| | | Current Price Range | |
|---|---|---|---|
| | | *Low* | *High* |
| ☐ **STARKENBORGH STACHOUWER,** | | | |
| **Willem Tjarda van** ............................. *paintings* | | **$1,045** | **$1,210** |
| Dutch 1823-1885 | | | |
| ☐ **STARKWEATHER,** | | | |
| **William Edward Bloomfield** ................... *paintings* | | **$110** | **$522** |
| American 1879-1969 | | | |
| ☐ **STAVERDEN, Jacob van** ...................... *paintings* | | | **$4,400** |
| Dutch 17th cent. | | | |
| ☐ **STAVROWSKY, Oleg** ......................... *paintings* | | **$300** | **$28,500** |
| American b. 1927 | | | |
| ☐ **STAZEWSKI, Henryck** ...................... *paintings* | | | **$220** |
| Polish 20th cent. | | | |
| ☐ **STEADMAN, J.T.** .............................. *paintings* | | | **$990** |
| British ac. 1887-91 | | | |
| ☐ **STEARNS, Junius Brutus** ..................... *paintings* | | **$550** | **$27,500** |
| American 1810-1885 | | | |
| ☐ **STEAVER, George** ............................ *paintings* | | | **$495** |
| ☐ **STEEL, A.** .................................... *paintings* | | | **$324** |
| ☐ **STEEL, David George** ......................... *paintings* | | | **$330** |
| English 1856-1930 | | | |
| ☐ **STEELE, A.R.** ................................. *drawings* | | | **$385** |
| ☐ **STEELE, Edwin** ............................... *paintings* | | **$220** | **$990** |
| British 19th cent. | | | |
| ☐ **STEELE, F.M.** ................................. *paintings* | | | **$330** |
| ☐ **STEELE, Theodore Clement** ................. *paintings* | | | **$3,960** |
| American 1847-1926 | | | |
| ☐ **STEELE, Thomas Sedgwick** ................. *paintings* | | **$352** | **$2,750** |
| American 1845-1903 | | | |
| ☐ **STEELE, William S.** ........................... *paintings* | | | **$200** |
| American 19th cent. | | | |
| ☐ **STEELE, Zulma (Mrs. Parker)** ............. *paintings* | | **$192** | **$220** |
| American b. 1881 | | | |
| ☐ **STEELINK, Willem** ............................ *paintings* | | | **$715** |
| Dutch 1826-1913 | | | |
| ☐ **STEELINK, Willem (the younger)** .......... *paintings* | | **$495** | **$1,430** |
| Dutch 1856-1928 ..................................... *drawings* | | | **$257** |
| ☐ **STEELL, David George** ....................... *drawings* | | **$77** | **$192** |
| British 1856-1930 | | | |
| ☐ **STEELL, Gourlay** ............................. *paintings* | | **$1,870** | **$5,225** |
| British 1814-1894 | | | |
| ☐ **STEEN, D.** .................................... *paintings* | | | **$264** |
| ☐ **STEEN, Jan Havicksz** .......................... *paintings* | | **$7,425** | **$74,250** |
| Dutch 1626-1679 | | | |
| ☐ **STEEN, Philip Wilson** ......................... *drawings* | | | **$330** |
| ☐ **STEENE, William** .............................. *paintings* | | **$440** | **$2,200** |
| American 1888-1965 | | | |
| ☐ **STEENKS, Guy L.** .............................. *paintings* | | | **$1,540** |
| American late 19th cent. | | | |

|  | | *Current Price Range* | |
|--|--|--------|--------|
|  | | *Low* | *High* |
| ☐ **STEENWYCK, Hendrick van** | | | |
| **(the younger)** .................... *paintings* | | $5,775 | $14,300 |
| Flemish c. 1580-1649 | | | |
| ☐ **STEENWYCK, Hendrik van** | | | |
| **(the elder)** ..................... *paintings* | | $2,750 | $11,000 |
| Dutch c. 1550-1603 | | | |
| ☐ **STEEPLE, John** ................... *paintings* | | | $2,640 |
| English ac. 1846-1852, d. 1887 | | | |
| ☐ **STEFAN, Ross** ................... *paintings* | | $2,500 | $3,500 |
| American b. 1934 | | | |
| ☐ **STEFANELLI, Joseph** .......... *paintings* | | | $660 |
| American b. 1921 | | | |
| ☐ **STEFANORI, Attillio** .......... *paintings* | | | $990 |
| Italian 1860-1941 | | | |
| ☐ **STEFFECK,** | | | |
| **Carl Constantine Heinrich** ...... *paintings* | | | $82,500 |
| German 1818-1890 | | | |
| ☐ **STEFFELAAR, Cornelis (?)** ........ *paintings* | | | $1,320 |
| Dutch 1795-1861 | | | |
| ☐ **STEGLICH, A.** .................. *paintings* | | | $302 |
| American 19th cent. | | | |
| ☐ **STEIB, J.** ..................... *paintings* | | | $352 |
| ☐ **STEICHEN, Edward J.** ......... *paintings* | | $2,750 | $28,600 |
| American 1879-1973 | | | |
| ☐ **STEIGER, I. De** ............... *paintings* | | | $880 |
| German 19th cent. | | | |
| ☐ **STEIN, Georges** ............... *paintings* | | $440 | $19,800 |
| French 20th cent. ................ *drawings* | | $1,650 | $1,760 |
| ☐ **STEIN, Leo** .................. *paintings* | | | $330 |
| ☐ **STEINACH, Anton Victor Alexander** ..... *paintings* | | | $1,320 |
| Swiss 1819-1891 | | | |
| ☐ **STEINACKER, Alfred** .......... *paintings* | | | $2,310 |
| Austrian b. 1838 | | | |
| ☐ **STEINBERG, Karl** ............. *paintings* | | | $385 |
| ☐ **STEINBERG, Saul** ............. *paintings* | | $605 | $154,000 |
| Rumanian/American b. 1914 | | | |
| ☐ **STEINER, Agnes** .............. *paintings* | | | $715 |
| German 1845-1925 | | | |
| ☐ **STEINER, Anton** .............. *paintings* | | | $7,700 |
| German 19th cent. | | | |
| ☐ **STEINER, Clement Leopold** ......... *sculpture* | | | $3,300 |
| French 1853-1899 | | | |
| ☐ **STEINER, Josef** .............. *paintings* | | $1,045 | $1,200 |
| Austrian b. 1898 | | | |
| ☐ **STEINER, Michael** ............ *sculpture* | | $1,045 | $3,300 |
| Austrian c. 1684-1764 | | | |
| ☐ **STEINHARDT** .................. *paintings* | | | $522 |
| Israeli 20th cent. | | | |

| | Current Price Range | |
|---|---|---|
| | Low | High |
| ☐ **STEINHARDT, Friedrich Karl** .............. *paintings*<br>German b. 1844 | | $2,750 |
| ☐ **STEINHARDT, Jacob** .......................... *drawings* | | $495 |
| ☐ **STEINHEIL, Carl Friedrich** .................. *paintings*<br>German 1860-1917 | | $1,100 |
| ☐ **STEINHILBER, Walter** ........................ *drawings*<br>American 20th cent. | $76 | $440 |
| ☐ **STEINKE, Bettina** .............................. *paintings* | | $12,000 |
| American b. 1913 ...................................... *drawings* | | $301 |
| ☐ **STEINLE, Johann Edward Von** ............ *drawings*<br>Austrian 1810-1886 | | $4,400 |
| ☐ **STEINLEN, Theophile Alexandre** .......... *paintings* | $1,155 | $1,650 |
| Swiss/French 1859-1923 .............................. *drawings* | $110 | $13,200 |
| ☐ **STEINMETZ-NORIS, Fritz** .................. *paintings* | | $550 |
| ☐ **STEINMULLER, G.F.** ......................... *paintings*<br>German 19th cent. | | $412 |
| ☐ **STEINTHAL, Traute Tomine** .............. *paintings*<br>German 1868-1906 | | $770 |
| ☐ **STEIR, Pat** ...................................... *paintings* | | $3,300 |
| American b. 1938 ...................................... *drawings* | $1,100 | $8,250 |
| ☐ **STELE(?), W.P.** ................................ *paintings*<br>Italian 19th cent. | | $412 |
| ☐ **STELLA, Etienne Alexandre** ................ *sculpture*<br>French ac. 1878-1892 | | $2,250 |
| ☐ **STELLA, Frank** ................................ *paintings* | $15,400 | $462,000 |
| American b. 1936 ...................................... *drawings* | $2,860 | $40,700 |
| .............................................. *sculpture* | $22,000 | $319,000 |
| ☐ **STELLA, Ignaz Stern**<br>**(called Ignaz STERN)** ........................... *paintings*<br>German 1680-1748 | $7,700 | $33,000 |
| ☐ **STELLA, Jacques** .............................. *paintings*<br>French 1596-1657 | $3,000 | $3,575 |
| ☐ **STELLA, Joseph** .............................. *paintings* | $1,210 | $10,450 |
| American, b. Italy 1880-1946 ........................ *drawings* | $165 | $14,300 |
| ☐ **STEMKOWSKI, Gerard** ....................... *paintings*<br>American 20th cent. | | $275 |
| ☐ **STENBERG, Georgiy** ......................... *drawings* | | $4,675 |
| ☐ **STENGEL, G.J.** ................................ *paintings*<br>American 1872-1937 | $357 | $385 |
| ☐ **STENGEL, Hans** .............................. *drawings*<br>American 1894-1928 | | $605 |
| ☐ **STENLEY, W.** .................................. *paintings* | | $440 |
| ☐ **STEPANOV, Aleksei Stepanovich** .......... *paintings*<br>Russian 1858-1923 | | $302 |
| ☐ **STEPHAN, A.** .................................. *paintings*<br>Austrian b. 1882 | | $302 |
| ☐ **STEPHAN, Gary** .............................. *paintings* | $3,000 | $13,200 |
| American b. 1942 ...................................... *drawings* | $440 | $1,320 |

|  | | *Current Price Range* | |
|---|---|---|---|
|  | | *Low* | *High* |
| ☐ **STEPHANE, Micius** .............................. *paintings* | | $495 | $9,900 |
| Haitian b. 1912 | | | |
| ☐ **STEPHANOFF, James** .......................... *drawings* | | $247 | $302 |
| ☐ **STEPHENS, Alice Barber** ..................... *drawings* | | $192 | $2,090 |
| American 1858-1932 | | | |
| ☐ **STEPHENS, Charles H.** ........................ *paintings* | | | $495 |
| ☐ **STEPHENS, Henry Louis** ..................... *drawings* | | | $330 |
| ☐ **STEPHENS, Owen** .............................. *paintings* | | | $286 |
| American | | | |
| ☐ **STEPHENSON, Lionel McDonald** ......... *paintings* | | $715 | $1,100 |
| Canadian 1854-1907 ..................................... *drawings* | | | $192 |
| ☐ **STEPHENSON, W.** ............................. *drawings* | | $412 | $825 |
| English 19th/20th cent. | | | |
| ☐ **STERKENBURG, Pieter** ........................ *paintings* | | $407 | $550 |
| Dutch 19th/20th cent. | | | |
| ☐ **STERLING, Lindsey Morris** ................. *sculpture* | | $715 | $1,320 |
| American 1876-1931 | | | |
| ☐ **STERN, J.** .......................................... *paintings* | | | $440 |
| American 19th cent. | | | |
| ☐ **STERN, Max** ....................................... *paintings* | | | $1,045 |
| German 1872-1943 | | | |
| ☐ **STERNE, Hedda** ................................. *paintings* | | $88 | $3,850 |
| Rumanian/American b. 1916 | | | |
| ☐ **STERNE, Maurice** ............................... *paintings* | | | $1,960 |
| American 1877-1957 ................................... *drawings* | | $55 | $1,100 |
| ☐ **STERNE, Sidney C.** ............................. *paintings* | | $220 | $1,760 |
| British 19th cent. | | | |
| ☐ **STERNER, Albert Edward** ................... *paintings* | | $110 | $4,000 |
| American 1863-1946 ................................... *drawings* | | $22 | $3,190 |
| ☐ **STERRER, Karl** ................................... *sculpture* | | | $466 |
| Austrian 1844-1918 | | | |
| ☐ **STERRER, Louis** ................................. *drawings* | | | $275 |
| ☐ **STETSON, Charles Walter** ................... *paintings* | | $55 | $1,430 |
| American 1858-1911 | | | |
| ☐ **STEVENS, Agapit** .............................. *paintings* | | $2,750 | $4,400 |
| Belgian 19th cent. | | | |
| ☐ **STEVENS, Alfred** .............................. *paintings* | | $935 | $115,500 |
| Belgian 1823-1906 | | | |
| ☐ **STEVENS, Beatrice** ............................. *drawings* | | | $440 |
| 19th/20th cent. | | | |
| ☐ **STEVENS, D.W.** ................................. *sculpture* | | | $440 |
| Scottish 19th cent. | | | |
| ☐ **STEVENS, John Calvin** ........................ *paintings* | | | $660 |
| American b. 1855 | | | |
| ☐ **STEVENS, Joseph D.** .......................... *paintings* | | | $2,750 |
| ☐ **STEVENS, Joseph Edouard** ................. *paintings* | | | $467 |
| Belgian 1819-1892 | | | |
| ☐ **STEVENS, William Charles** ................. *paintings* | | $110 | $275 |
| American 1854-1917 | | | |

| | | Current Price Range | |
| --- | --- | --- | --- |
| | | *Low* | *High* |
| ☐ **STEVENS, William Lester** .................. *paintings* | | **$110** | **$3,410** |
| American 1888-1969 ................................. *drawings* | | **$110** | **$990** |
| ☐ **STEVENSON, Harold** .......................... *drawings* | | | **$192** |
| American 20th cent. | | | |
| ☐ **STEVENSON, Marie** ........................... *sculpture* | | | **$800** |
| American | | | |
| ☐ **STEVENSON, R. Macaulay** ................. *paintings* | | | **$330** |
| ☐ **STEVENSON, Ruth Rolston** ................ *paintings* | | | **$286** |
| American b. 1897 | | | |
| ☐ **STEVER, Jorg** .................................... *paintings* | | **$1,320** | **$1,320** |
| German b. 1940 | | | |
| ☐ **STEVER, Josephine** ........................... *paintings* | | | **$605** |
| American | | | |
| ☐ **STEWARD, Joseph** ............................. *paintings* | | | **$30,800** |
| 1753-1822 | | | |
| ☐ **STEWARD, Seth W.** ........................... *paintings* | | **$77** | **$3,850** |
| American 19th/20th cent. | | | |
| ☐ **STEWART, Arthur** ............................. *drawings* | | **$800** | **$3,300** |
| American b. 1915 | | | |
| ☐ **STEWART, Bill** ................................. *sculpture* | | | **$320** |
| ☐ **STEWART, Charles Edward** ................ *paintings* | | **$1,980** | **$3,410** |
| English ac. 1890-1930 | | | |
| ☐ **STEWART, Frank Algernon** ................ *drawings* | | **$1,045** | **$2,090** |
| British 1877-1945 | | | |
| ☐ **STEWART, James** ............................... *paintings* | | | **$247** |
| British 19th cent. | | | |
| ☐ **STEWART, Jeannette A.** ...................... *paintings* | | | **$330** |
| American b. 1867 | | | |
| ☐ **STEWART, Julius L.** .......................... *paintings* | | **$880** | **$170,500** |
| American 1855-1919 ................................. *drawings* | | **$935** | **$15,400** |
| ☐ **STEWART, M.** .................................... *paintings* | | **$192** | **$220** |
| English 19th/20th cent. | | | |
| ☐ **STEWART, Robert W.** ......................... *paintings* | | **$308** | **$550** |
| American | | | |
| ☐ **STEWART, Seth** ................................. *paintings* | | | **$495** |
| American 19th cent. | | | |
| ☐ **STICK, Frank** ................................... *paintings* | | | **$1,210** |
| American 1884-1966 | | | |
| ☐ **STICKNEY, H.A.** ............................... *paintings* | | | **$3,080** |
| American 19th cent. | | | |
| ☐ **STICKS, George Blackie** ...................... *paintings* | | **$440** | **$880** |
| British 1843-1938 ...................................... *drawings* | | | **$88** |
| ☐ **STICKS, Harry** .................................... *paintings* | | **$385** | **$770** |
| English ac. 1894-1911 | | | |
| ☐ **STIELER, Joseph Karl** ........................ *drawings* | | | **$1,210** |
| German 1781-1858 | | | |
| ☐ **STIELER, R.** ..................................... *paintings* | | | **$440** |
| German 1847-1908 | | | |

| | | | Current Price Range | |
|---|---|---|---|---|
| | | | *Low* | *High* |
| ☐ **STIEPEVICH, Vincent G.** | *paintings* | | $660 | $34,100 |
| Russian 1841-1910 | *drawings* | | $440 | $528 |
| ☐ **STIFTER, Moritz** | *paintings* | | $220 | $1,320 |
| Austrian 1857-1905 | | | | |
| ☐ **STILL, Clyfford** | *paintings* | | $14,300 | $797,500 |
| American b. 1904 | | | | |
| ☐ **STILLERICH, Johann** | *paintings* | | | $900 |
| Austrian 1802-1843 | | | | |
| ☐ **STILLMANN, Maria Spartali** | *drawings* | | $1,650 | $12,650 |
| British 1844-1927 | | | | |
| ☐ **STIMSON, John Ward** | *paintings* | | | $265 |
| American 1850-1930 | | | | |
| ☐ **STINSKI, Gerald Paul** | *paintings* | | $715 | $1,045 |
| American b. 1929 | | | | |
| ☐ **STIRLING, Dave** | *paintings* | | $124 | $495 |
| American b. 1889 | | | | |
| ☐ **STISTED, Major** | *paintings* | | | $330 |
| ☐ **STITES, John R.** | *paintings* | | | $357 |
| ☐ **STIVERS, Don** | *paintings* | | | $15,000 |
| American contemporary | | | | |
| ☐ **STOBART, John** | *paintings* | | $16,000 | $65,000 |
| American contemporary | | | | |
| ☐ **STOCK, Joseph Whiting** | *paintings* | | $1,650 | $30,800 |
| American 1815-1855 | | | | |
| ☐ **STOCKLER, Emmanuel** | *drawings* | | | $990 |
| Austrian 1819-1893 | | | | |
| ☐ **STOCKMANN, Anton** | *paintings* | | | $1,430 |
| Swiss b. 1868 | | | | |
| ☐ **STODDARD, Alice Kent** | *paintings* | | $27 | $4,400 |
| American 1885/93-1976 | | | | |
| ☐ **STODDARD, Frederick Lincoln** | *paintings* | | $495 | $1,210 |
| American 1861-1940 | | | | |
| ☐ **STOFFE, Jan Jacobsz van der** | *paintings* | | $1,045 | $3,080 |
| Dutch 1611-1682 | | | | |
| ☐ **STOILOFF-BAUMGARTNER,** **Constantin** | *paintings* | | $1,100 | $4,125 |
| Russian/Austrian 1850-1924 | | | | |
| ☐ **STOITZNER, Josef** | *paintings* | | $1,760 | $3,300 |
| Austrian b. 1884 | | | | |
| ☐ **STOITZNER, Konstantin** | *paintings* | | $330 | $1,320 |
| Austrian 1863-1934 | | | | |
| ☐ **STOITZNER, Rudolf** | *paintings* | | | $715 |
| Austrian 1873-1933 | | | | |
| ☐ **STOITZNER, Walter** | *paintings* | | $1,320 | $2,640 |
| Austrian 1890-1921 | | | | |
| ☐ **STOJANOW, Constantine** | *paintings* | | $1,320 | $4,400 |
| Russian 19th cent. | | | | |
| ☐ **STOKELD, James** | *drawings* | | $495 | $605 |
| British 1827-1877 | | | | |

| | | | Current Price Range | |
| --- | --- | --- | --- | --- |
| | | | *Low* | *High* |
| ☐ **STOKES, Adrian** ............... *paintings* | | | | $880 |
| British 1854-1935 | | | | |
| ☐ **STOKES, Frank Wilbert** ......... *paintings* | | | | $1,045 |
| American b. 1858 | | | | |
| ☐ **STOL, Dominicus Van** ......... *paintings* | | | | $1,320 |
| Dutch 1635-1676 | | | | |
| ☐ **STOLL, John Theodore** ......... *paintings* | | | | $385 |
| American b. 1889 ................. *drawings* | | | | $110 |
| ☐ **STOLL, Leopold** ............... *drawings* | | $1,540 | | $1,760 |
| German d. 1869 | | | | |
| ☐ **STOLL, Rolf** ............... *paintings* | | | | $357 |
| American b. 1892 | | | | |
| ☐ **STOLTENBERG, Hans J.** ......... *paintings* | | | | $192 |
| American 20th cent. | | | | |
| ☐ **STOLTENBERG, Otto** ......... *drawings* | | $176 | | $880 |
| ☐ **STOLTING, C.** ............... *paintings* | | | | $632 |
| American 19th cent. | | | | |
| ☐ **STOMER, Mathaus** ............... *paintings* | | | | $198,000 |
| Flemish | | | | |
| ☐ **STOMME, Jan Jansz de** ......... *paintings* | | | | $1,760 |
| Dutch ac. 1643-1657 | | | | |
| ☐ **STONE, Aston** ............... *paintings* | | $110 | | $2,200 |
| ............... *drawings* | | | | $41 |
| ☐ **STONE, C.E.** ............... *paintings* | | | | $176 |
| American late 19th cent. | | | | |
| ☐ **STONE, Don** ............... *drawings* | | | | $330 |
| 20th cent. | | | | |
| ☐ **STONE, Edward Durrell** ......... *drawings* | | | | $550 |
| American 1902-1978 | | | | |
| ☐ **STONE, Marcus** ............... *paintings* | | $10,450 | | $15,400 |
| British 1840-1921 | | | | |
| ☐ **STONE, Robert** ............... *paintings* | | $1,430 | | $6,600 |
| Australian 20th cent. | | | | |
| ☐ **STONE, Rudolf** ............... *paintings* | | | | $495 |
| ☐ **STONE, Tom** ............... *paintings* | | | | $900 |
| Canadian 1897-1978 | | | | |
| ☐ **STONE, Walter King** ......... *paintings* | | | | $165 |
| American b. 1875 ............... *drawings* | | $75 | | $247 |
| ☐ **STONE, William (Jr.)** ......... *paintings* | | | | $1,980 |
| English 19th cent. | | | | |
| ☐ **STONE-DELATTRE, Viviane** ......... *paintings* | | | | $660 |
| French 20th cent. | | | | |
| ☐ **STONELAKE, Frank** ......... *paintings* | | | | $302 |
| English ac. 1900 | | | | |
| ☐ **STOOP, Dirk** ............... *paintings* | | $2,200 | | $2,750 |
| Dutch 1610/18-1681/86 | | | | |
| ☐ **STOOPENDAEL, F.** ......... *paintings* | | | | $1,100 |
| ☐ **STOOPS, Herbert Morton** ......... *paintings* | | $550 | | $27,500 |
| American 1888-1948 ............... *drawings* | | $88 | | $660 |

|  | | | *Current Price Range* | |
|---|---|---|---|---|
|  | | | Low | High |
| ☐ **STOPPOLONI, Augusto** | ........................ | *paintings* | $467 | $1,485 |
| Italian b. 1855 | | | | |
| ☐ **STORCK, Abraham** | ............................ | *paintings* | $4,400 | $14,300 |
| Dutch c. 1635-c. 1710 | | | | |
| ☐ **STORCK, Jacobus** | ............................ | *paintings* | $12,100 | $22,000 |
| Dutch ac. 1610-1686 | | | | |
| ☐ **STORCK, Johannes** | ............................ | *paintings* | | $5,720 |
| ☐ **STORER, Charles** | ............................ | *paintings* | | $1,650 |
| American 1817-1907 | | | | |
| ☐ **STOREY, F.** | ........................ | *paintings* | | $330 |
| ☐ **STOREY, George Adolphus** | ................. | *paintings* | $1,310 | $6,050 |
| English 1834-1919 | | | | |
| ☐ **STORK, Frank** | ............................ | *sculpture* | $192 | $412 |
| ☐ **STORK, T.** | ............................ | *paintings* | | $220 |
| American (?) 19th cent. | | | | |
| ☐ **STORM, George** | ............................ | *paintings* | | $440 |
| American 1830-1913 | | | | |
| ☐ **STORRS, John** | ............................ | *drawings* | | $770 |
| American 1885-1956 | .................................. | *sculpture* | $521 | $30,800 |
| ☐ **STORRS, John Bradley** | ........................ | *paintings* | | $7,425 |
| American 1887-1966 | | | | |
| ☐ **STORTENBEKER, Pieter** | ................. | *paintings* | | $1,870 |
| Dutch 1828-1898 | .................................. | *drawings* | | $742 |
| ☐ **STORY, F.** | ............................ | *paintings* | | $274 |
| American 19th/20th cent. | | | | |
| ☐ **STORY, George Henry** | ........................ | *paintings* | $1,870 | $15,400 |
| American 1835-1923 | | | | |
| ☐ **STORY, Julian Russel** | ........................ | *paintings* | $495 | $6,600 |
| American 1850-1919 | | | | |
| ☐ **STORY, Waldo** | .................................. | *sculpture* | $1,210 | $2,420 |
| American 19th/20th cent. | | | | |
| ☐ **STOTHARD, Thomas** | ........................ | *paintings* | $242 | $3,850 |
| English 1755-1834 | .................................. | *drawings* | | $352 |
| ☐ **STOTT, Edward William** | ................. | *drawings* | | $2,200 |
| English 1859-1918 | | | | |
| ☐ **STOUF, Jean Baptiste** | ............................ | *paintings* | | $880 |
| French 19th cent. | | | | |
| ☐ **STOUT, E.** | ............................ | *paintings* | | $440 |
| American 20th cent. | | | | |
| ☐ **STOVER, Allan James** | ........................ | *paintings* | | $357 |
| American b. 1887 | | | | |
| ☐ **STRAATEN, B. van** | ............................ | *paintings* | | $550 |
| ☐ **STRACHAN, Arthur Claude** | ................. | *drawings* | $275 | $1,760 |
| Scottish b. 1865, exhib. until 1929 | | | | |
| ☐ **STRACHEY, Henry** | ............................ | *paintings* | $1,100 | $4,950 |
| British b. 1863 | | | | |
| ☐ **STRACKE, Johannes Paulus Leo** | .......... | *drawings* | | $385 |
| ☐ **STRAETEN, Georges van der** | ................. | *sculpture* | $165 | $275 |
| Belgian b. 1856 | | | | |

| | | Current Price Range | |
|---|---|---|---|
| | | Low | High |
| ☐ **STRAIN, John Paul** .......................... *paintings* | | $605 | $715 |
| ☐ **STRALEN, Anthony Van** ..................... *paintings* | | | $1,870 |
| Dutch 1594-1641 | | | |
| ☐ **STRALSER, A.** ................................. *sculpture* | | | $2,200 |
| European 19th/20th cent. | | | |
| ☐ **STRANG, Ray C.** .............................. *paintings* | | $700 | $1,100 |
| American 1893-1954/57 | | | |
| ☐ **STRANG, William** ............................ *drawings* | | $220 | $935 |
| Scottish 1859-1921 | | | |
| ☐ **STRANOVER, Tobias** ........................ *paintings* | | | $7,700 |
| Czechoslovakian c. 1684- after 1724 | | | |
| ☐ **STRASSER, Arthur** ........................... *sculpture* | | | $1,540 |
| Austrian 1854-1927 | | | |
| ☐ **STRATAMEYER** .............................. *paintings* | | | $385 |
| ☐ **STRATVDENVEL** ............................ *paintings* | | | $275 |
| ☐ **STRAUCH, Lorenz** ........................... *paintings* | | | $770 |
| German 1643-1677 | | | |
| ☐ **STRAUS, Meyer** .............................. *paintings* | | $124 | $2,200 |
| American 1831-1905 ................................ *drawings* | | | $220 |
| ☐ **STRAW, M.E.** ................................. *paintings* | | | $209 |
| American c. 1881 | | | |
| ☐ **STRAYER, Paul** ............................... *paintings* | | $412 | $1,375 |
| American b. 1885 | | | |
| ☐ **STREATOR, Harold A.** ........................ *paintings* | | | $1,210 |
| American 1861-1926 | | | |
| ☐ **STRECH, Aov.** ................................ *paintings* | | | $275 |
| German 19th cent. | | | |
| ☐ **STRECKENBACH, Max T.** .................... *paintings* | | $121 | $550 |
| German 1865-1936 | | | |
| ☐ **STREECK, Hendrik Juriaensz. van** ....... *paintings* | | | $44,000 |
| Dutch | | | |
| ☐ **STREEP, Christian van** ........................ *paintings* | | | $3,850 |
| ☐ **STREET, Frank** ................................ *paintings* | | $770 | $825 |
| American 1893-1944 | | | |
| ☐ **STREET, Robert** ............................... *paintings* | | $825 | $26,400 |
| American 1796-1865 | | | |
| ☐ **STREITT, Franciszek** ......................... *paintings* | | | $4,620 |
| Polish 1839-1890 | | | |
| ☐ **STREMPEL, R. von** ........................... *paintings* | | | $247 |
| German 19th/20th cent. | | | |
| ☐ **STREUTZEL, Otto** ............................ *paintings* | | | $550 |
| German 19th/20th cent. | | | |
| ☐ **STREVENS, John** | | | |
| **(called Frederick John Lloyd)** ................ *paintings* | | | $880 |
| English b. 1902 | | | |
| ☐ **STRIAKA, Josef** ............................... *paintings* | | | $550 |
| ☐ **STRIGELLY, Ernesto** ......................... *paintings* | | | $3,850 |
| ☐ **STRIJ, Abraham van** ......................... *paintings* | | | $1,870 |
| German 1753-1826 ................................. *drawings* | | | $440 |

| | | Current Price Range | |
|---|---|---|---|
| | | Low | High |
| ☐ **STRINDBERG, Tore** ............................ *sculpture* | | **$11,000** | **$11,000** |
| Swedish b. 1882 | | | |
| ☐ **STRISIK, Paul** ..................................... *paintings* | | **$440** | **$10,500** |
| American b. 1918 | | | |
| ☐ **STROBEL, Oscar** ................................ *paintings* | | | **$385** |
| American 20th cent. | | | |
| ☐ **STROEBEL,** | | | |
| **Johann Anthonie Balthasar** .................... *paintings* | | **$385** | **$4,620** |
| Dutch 1821-1905 | | | |
| ☐ **STROMEYER, Helene Marie** ................ *paintings* | | | **$9,350** |
| German 1834-1924 | | | |
| ☐ **STRONG, Elizabeth** ............................ *paintings* | | **$88** | **$1,870** |
| American 1855-1941 | | | |
| ☐ **STRONG, Joseph D.** ............................ *paintings* | | **$770** | **$1,100** |
| American 1852-1900 | | | |
| ☐ **STROOBANT, Francois** ....................... *paintings* | | **$715** | **$3,300** |
| Belgian 1819-1916 | | | |
| ☐ **STROUD, Ida Wells** ............................ *drawings* | | | **$1,155** |
| American b. 1869 | | | |
| ☐ **STROZZI, Bernardo** ............................ *paintings* | | **$1,320** | **$13,200** |
| Italian 1581-1644 | | | |
| ☐ **STRUCK, Herman** ............................... *paintings* | | **$357** | **$1,430** |
| American 20th cent. | | | |
| ☐ **STRUCK, Hugo** ................................... *paintings* | | | **$192** |
| German b. 1860 | | | |
| ☐ **STRUTT, Alfred William** ...................... *paintings* | | **$330** | **$990** |
| English 1856-1924 .................................... *drawings* | | | **$55** |
| ☐ **STRUTT, Arthur John** ......................... *paintings* | | | **$6,050** |
| British 1819-1888 | | | |
| ☐ **STRUTT, William** ............................... *paintings* | | **$1,320** | **$2,860** |
| British 1825-1915 | | | |
| ☐ **STRUTZEL, Leopold Otto** .................... *paintings* | | | **$7,150** |
| German 1855-1930 | | | |
| ☐ **STRY, Abraham van** ........................... *drawings* | | | **$880** |
| ☐ **STRY, Jacob van** ................................ *paintings* | | | **$440** |
| Dutch 1756-1815 .................................... *drawings* | | **$1,155** | **$1,650** |
| ☐ **STRYDONK, Guillaume van** ................ *paintings* | | | **$4,675** |
| Belgian 1861-1937 | | | |
| ☐ **STUART, Charles** ............................... *paintings* | | **$137** | **$605** |
| English ac. 1880-1904 | | | |
| ☐ **STUART, Frederick T.** ......................... *paintings* | | | **$357** |
| ☐ **STUART, Gilbert** ............................... *paintings* | | **$3,300** | **$41,800** |
| American 1755-1828 | | | |
| ☐ **STUART, James Everett** ...................... *paintings* | | **$33** | **$4,125** |
| American 1852-1941 ................................ *drawings* | | | **$187** |
| ☐ **STUART, Jane** ................................... *paintings* | | **$247** | **$4,620** |
| American c. 1816-1888 | | | |
| ☐ **STUART, L.** ....................................... *paintings* | | | **$880** |

|  | | Current Price Range | |
|---|---|---|---|
|  | | Low | High |
| ☐ **STUART, R.T.** ...................................... *paintings* | | | $187 |
| English 19th cent. | | | |
| ☐ **STUART, W.** ...................................... *paintings* | | | $4,070 |
| English 19th cent. | | | |
| ☐ **STUBBS, George** .................................. *paintings* | | $6,056 | $605,000 |
| English 1724-1806 | | | |
| ☐ **STUBBS, William Pierce** ....................... *paintings* | | $330 | $8,030 |
| American 1842-1909 | | | |
| ☐ **STUBER, Dedrick B.** ........................... *paintings* | | $330 | $1,540 |
| American 1878-1954 | | | |
| ☐ **STUBNER, Robert** ............................. *paintings* | | $522 | $4,400 |
| German 1874-1931 | | | |
| ☐ **STUCK, Franz von** ............................. *paintings* | | $220 | $13,750 |
| German 1863-1928 ....................................... *drawings* | | $825 | $2,640 |
| ................................................................. *sculpture* | | $3,740 | $6,600 |
| ☐ **STUECKMANN, Frederick C.** .............. *paintings* | | | $825 |
| American 20th cent. | | | |
| ☐ **STUEMPFIG, Walter** ........................... *paintings* | | $275 | $6,875 |
| American 1914-1970 | | | |
| ☐ **STUHLMULLER, Karl** ....................... *paintings* | | $3,575 | $28,600 |
| French 1858-1930 | | | |
| ☐ **STUHR, Johann Georg** ....................... *paintings* | | | $8,800 |
| German 1640-1721 | | | |
| ☐ **STULL, Henry** ...................................... *paintings* | | $1,100 | $77,000 |
| American 1851-1913 | | | |
| ☐ **STURGESS, John** ................................. *paintings* | | $2,420 | $8,250 |
| British ac. 1875-1884 | | | |
| ☐ **STURGESS, W.** ...................................... *paintings* | | | $8,800 |
| ☐ **STURM, E.** ...................................... *paintings* | | | $2,475 |
| ☐ **STURM, Fritz Ludwig Christian** ........... *paintings* | | | $550 |
| German 1834-1906 | | | |
| ☐ **STURTEVANT, Helen** ......................... *paintings* | | | $356 |
| American b. 1926 | | | |
| ☐ **STYKA, Adam** ...................................... *paintings* | | $1,100 | $6,050 |
| French 1890-1959 | | | |
| ☐ **STYKA, Jan** ...................................... *paintings* | | $1,650 | $4,400 |
| Polish/French 1858-1925 | | | |
| ☐ **STYKA, Tade** ...................................... *paintings* | | | $770 |
| American b. 1889 | | | |
| ☐ **SUAA, Joseph** ...................................... *paintings* | | | $440 |
| ☐ **SUAREZ, Alfredo Galvez** ...................... *paintings* | | $440 | $3,300 |
| Guatemalen contemporary ............................ *drawings* | | | $187 |
| ☐ **SUAREZ, Antonio** ............................. *paintings* | | | $385 |
| ☐ **SUAREZ, Librado** ............................. *paintings* | | | $2,790 |
| ☐ **SUBA, Miklos** ...................................... *drawings* | | | $1,320 |
| Hungarian/American 1880-1944 | | | |
| ☐ **SUBIRACHS** ...................................... *sculpture* | | | $275 |
| ☐ **SUBOWSKY, B.** ...................................... *paintings* | | | $935 |
| Russian 19th cent. | | | |

| | | | Current Price Range | |
| | | | Low | High |
|---|---|---|---|---|
| ☐ SUCCA, August De | ............................. | *paintings* | $11,000 | $11,000 |
| ☐ SUCHINI, A. | ................................... | *sculpture* | | $330 |
| ☐ SUDONI, F. | ....................................... | *paintings* | | $715 |
| ☐ SUETIN, Nicolai | ................................. | *sculpture* | | $6,050 |
| Russian 1897-1954 | | | | |
| ☐ SUGAI, Kumi | .................................. | *paintings* | $715 | $4,950 |
| Japanese b. 1919 | ................................. | *drawings* | | $165 |
| ☐ SUGERTH, F. | ..................................... | *sculpture* | | $440 |
| Austrian c. 1908 | | | | |
| ☐ SUGLIEMI, George | ............................. | *paintings* | | $770 |
| ☐ SUHRLANDT, Carl | ............................. | *paintings* | | $2,750 |
| German 1828-1919 | | | | |
| ☐ SUHS, Joseph | .................................. | *paintings* | $715 | $935 |
| ☐ SUISSE, Gaston | ................................. | *sculpture* | $4,675 | $8,800 |
| ☐ SUITZENICH, Eugene | ......................... | *drawings* | | $715 |
| American 19th cent. | | | | |
| ☐ SULLIVAN, Denis | ............................... | *drawings* | | $286 |
| American 19th cent. | | | | |
| ☐ SULLIVAN, Patrick J. | ......................... | *paintings* | | $1,320 |
| American 1894-1967 | | | | |
| ☐ SULLIVAN, William Holmes | ................ | *paintings* | | $440 |
| British d. 1908 | | | | |
| ☐ SULLIVANT, Thomas S. | ...................... | *drawings* | $33 | $275 |
| American b. 1854-after 1926 | | | | |
| ☐ SULLY, Alfred | .................................... | *paintings* | | $3,025 |
| American 1820-1879 | | | | |
| ☐ SULLY, Jane Cooper | ........................... | *paintings* | | $935 |
| American 1807-1877 | | | | |
| ☐ SULLY, Thomas | ................................. | *paintings* | $770 | $24,200 |
| American 1783-1872 | ................................. | *drawings* | $1,870 | $15,400 |
| ☐ SULLY, Thomas (Jr.) | ........................... | *paintings* | | $3,300 |
| American 1811-1847 | | | | |
| ☐ SULTAN, Donald | ............................... | *drawings* | | $60,500 |
| American b. 1951 | ..................................... | *sculpture* | $20,900 | $49,500 |
| ☐ SULTZER, Fletcher | ............................. | *paintings* | | $330 |
| ☐ SUMMERS, Robert | ............................. | *paintings* | $9,500 | $18,500 |
| American b. 1940 | ..................................... | *sculpture* | $2,000 | $3,500 |
| ☐ SUNDBLOM, Haddon | ......................... | *paintings* | $550 | $13,200 |
| American b. 1899 | ..................................... | *drawings* | $412 | $825 |
| ☐ SUNOL, Alvar | ................................... | *paintings* | | $528 |
| Spanish b. 1935 | ..................................... | *drawings* | | $2,500 |
| ☐ SUNYER, Joaquin S. Y Myro | .............. | *drawings* | $660 | $2,420 |
| Spanish b. 1875 | | | | |
| ☐ SUPPANTSCHITSCH, Max | .................. | *paintings* | $1,760 | $2,750 |
| Austrian 1865-1954? | | | | |
| ☐ SUPPLEE, Sarah | ................................. | *paintings* | | $4,400 |
| American contemporary | | | | |
| ☐ SUQUET (?), E.T. | .............................. | *drawings* | | $385 |

| | | Current Price Range | |
|---|---|---|---|
| | | Low | High |
| ☐ **SURBER, Paul** .................... *drawings* | | $302 | $950 |
| American | | | |
| ☐ **SURDI, Luigi** ...................... *paintings* | | | $715 |
| Italian 1897-1959 | | | |
| ☐ **SUREAU, J.** ........................ *paintings* | | $385 | $440 |
| French 19th cent. | | | |
| ☐ **SUREDA, Andre** ................... *drawings* | | | $3,300 |
| French 1872-1930 | | | |
| ☐ **SURIGNY, T.** ...................... *paintings* | | | $330 |
| English (?) 19th cent. | | | |
| ☐ **SURIN, R.** ......................... *paintings* | | | $935 |
| ☐ **SURTEES, R.** ...................... *paintings* | | | $412 |
| English 19th cent. | | | |
| ☐ **SURVAGE, Leopold** ................. *paintings* | | $660 | $2,200 |
| French 1879-1968 ...................... *drawings* | | $121 | $3,520 |
| ☐ **SUS, Gustav Konrad** ............... *paintings* | | $522 | $2,200 |
| German 1823-1881 ...................... *drawings* | | | $330 |
| ☐ **SUSS, Josef** ....................... *paintings* | | | $1,980 |
| ☐ **SUSSE** ............................. *sculpture* | | | $605 |
| ☐ **SUSSE, Carl** ...................... *paintings* | | | $825 |
| ☐ **SUTCLIFFE, Harriette** ........... *paintings* | | | $1,320 |
| English ac. 1881-1907 | | | |
| ☐ **SUTHERLAND, Graham** ............. *paintings* | | | $24,200 |
| English b. 1903 ...................... *drawings* | | $825 | $1,980 |
| ☐ **SUTIL, Francisca** ............... *drawings* | | $1,320 | $4,125 |
| b. Chile 1952 | | | |
| ☐ **SUTTER, David** ................... *paintings* | | $165 | $385 |
| French 1811-1880 | | | |
| ☐ **SUTTER, Joseph (II)** ............ *drawings* | | | $770 |
| Austrian 1781-1866 | | | |
| ☐ **SUTTER, Samuel** ................. *paintings* | | $77 | $440 |
| American 20th cent. | | | |
| ☐ **SUTTERLIN, C.** .................. *paintings* | | | $247 |
| American 20th cent. | | | |
| ☐ **SUTTON, Frederick** ............. *paintings* | | $150 | $880 |
| ☐ **SUTTON, G.B.** ................... *paintings* | | | $440 |
| American | | | |
| ☐ **SUTTON, Harry (Jr.)** ........... *paintings* | | $220 | $330 |
| American b. 1897 | | | |
| ☐ **SUTTON, N.C.** ................... *paintings* | | | $187 |
| American early 20th cent. | | | |
| ☐ **SUTZ, Robert** .................... *paintings* | | $1,870 | $8,800 |
| American contemporary | | | |
| ☐ **SUURBIER (?), A. V.** ............ *paintings* | | | $825 |
| ☐ **SUYDAM, James Augustus** ........ *paintings* | | | $6,600 |
| American 1819-1865 ................... *drawings* | | $132 | $356 |
| ☐ **SUYKENS, Henri** ................. *paintings* | | | $385 |

|  | | Current Price Range | |
|  | | Low | High |
|---|---|---|---|
| ☐ **SUZOR-COTI, Aurele** ........................ *paintings* | | | $13,200 |
| Canadian 19th cent. ..................................... *drawings* | | | $1,100 |
| .............................................................. *sculpture* | | | $1,210 |
| ☐ **SUZUKI, James** .................................. *paintings* | | $99 | $275 |
| American b. 1933 ..................................... *drawings* | | $192 | $192 |
| ☐ **SVENDSEN, Charles C.** ...................... *paintings* | | | $605 |
| ☐ **SVENDSON, Svend** ............................ *paintings* | | $100 | $2,310 |
| Norwegian/American b. 1864 | | | |
| ☐ **SVENSON, Gunner** ............................ *paintings* | | | $440 |
| Swedish b. 1892 | | | |
| ☐ **SVOBODA, Vincent A.** ....................... *drawings* | | | $440 |
| Czechoslovakian/American 1877-1961 | | | |
| ☐ **SWABUCH, E.** ..................................... *paintings* | | | $1,210 |
| ☐ **SWAIN, C.** ......................................... *drawings* | | | $302 |
| American | | | |
| ☐ **SWAN, Christiana Keadie** ..................... *paintings* | | | $880 |
| American early 19th cent. | | | |
| ☐ **SWAN, Cuthbert Edmund** .................... *paintings* | | $440 | $1,870 |
| Irish 1870/73-1931 | | | |
| ☐ **SWAN, Emma Levina** .......................... *paintings* | | $77 | $220 |
| American 1853-1927 | | | |
| ☐ **SWANEVELT, Herman van** ................. *paintings* | | | $5,225 |
| Dutch 1600-1665 | | | |
| ☐ **SWANN, Valetta** ................................. *paintings* | | | $330 |
| ☐ **SWANSON, Gary** ................................ *paintings* | | | $18,000 |
| American contemporary | | | |
| ☐ **SWANSON, Gloria** ............................. *paintings* | | $136 | $1,210 |
| American c. 1899-1983 ............................. *sculpture* | | $385 | $1,430 |
| ☐ **SWANSON, Jack** ................................. *paintings* | | | $3,100 |
| American b. 1927 | | | |
| ☐ **SWANSON, Jonathan M.** ..................... *drawings* | | | $466 |
| American b. 1888 | | | |
| ☐ **SWANSON, Mark** ............................... *paintings* | | $665 | $7,500 |
| American contemporary | | | |
| ☐ **SWANSON, Ray** ................................. *paintings* | | $8,000 | $25,000 |
| American b. 1937 ..................................... *drawings* | | | $4,000 |
| ☐ **SWART, Albert Gerrits** ...................... *paintings* | | | $1,100 |
| d. 1833 | | | |
| ☐ **SWARTZ, Beth Ann** ............................ *paintings* | | | $2,860 |
| ☐ **SWEBACH, Edouard Bernard** .............. *paintings* | | | $1,870 |
| French 1800-1870 | | | |
| ☐ **SWEBACH DESFONTAINES,** | | | |
| **Jacques Francois** ................................ *drawings* | | | $2,860 |
| ☐ **SWEERTS, Jeronimus** ........................ *paintings* | | | $13,750 |
| Dutch 1603-1636 | | | |
| ☐ **SWEERTS, Michael** ............................ *paintings* | | $11,000 | $93,500 |
| Dutch 1624-1664 | | | |
| ☐ **SWEET, Charles A.** ............................ *paintings* | | | $935 |
| American 20th cent. | | | |

|                                                      | | Current Price Range | |
|------------------------------------------------------|------------|---------|---------|
|                                                      |            | *Low* | *High* |
| ☐ **SWEET, F.H.** ..................................... *paintings* |            |         | $275 |
| American ac. 1880-1890                               |            |         |      |
| ☐ **SWEET (?), W.H.** .............................. *drawings* |            |         | $225 |
| British School 19th cent.                            |            |         |      |
| ☐ **SWENSON, E.S.** ................................ *paintings* |            |         | $495 |
| ☐ **SWENSSON, Christian Fredrik** ............ *paintings* |            |         | $550 |
| Swedish 1834-1909                                    |            |         |      |
| ☐ **SWERINGEN, Ron van** ........................ *paintings* | $300 |         | $440 |
| American contemporary                                |            |         |      |
| ☐ **SWERTIKOFF** ..................................... *paintings* |            |         | $1,540 |
| ☐ **SWETT, William Otis (Jr.)** .................... *paintings* | $27 |         | $300 |
| American b. 1859                                     |            |         |      |
| ☐ **SWIESZEWSKI, Alexander** ................. *paintings* | $3,190 |     | $5,225 |
| Polish 1839-1895                                     |            |         |      |
| ☐ **SWIFT, Clement N.** ............................ *paintings* | $400 |     | $2,800 |
| American 19th cent.                                  |            |         |      |
| ☐ **SWIFT, Ivan** ..................................... *paintings* |            |         | $330 |
| American b. 1873                                     |            |         |      |
| ☐ **SWINBURNE, Edward** ........................ *drawings* |            |         | $660 |
| English 1765-c. 1829                                 |            |         |      |
| ☐ **SWINNERTON, James Guilford** .......... *paintings* | $174 |     | $9,350 |
| American 1875-1974 ................................. *drawings* | $165 |     | $242 |
| ☐ **SWINSON, I.** ..................................... *paintings* |            |         | $550 |
| ☐ **SWOBODA, Rudolf** ............................ *paintings* |            |         | $27,500 |
| Austrian 1859-1914                                   |            |         |      |
| ☐ **SWOPE, David** ................................... *drawings* |            |         | $1,980 |
| American 18th cent.                                  |            |         |      |
| ☐ **SWORD, James Brade** ......................... *paintings* | $275 |     | $10,780 |
| American 1839-1915 ................................. *drawings* | $275 |     | $660 |
| ☐ **SWORDS, Cramer** .............................. *paintings* | $198 |     | $495 |
| American 20th cent.                                  |            |         |      |
| ☐ **SWYNNERTON, Joseph William** .......... *paintings* |            |         | $1,650 |
| British 1848-1910                                    |            |         |      |
| ☐ **SYARTO, Ron** ................................... *paintings* |            |         | $495 |
| American 20th cent.                                  |            |         |      |
| ☐ **SYER, John** ..................................... *paintings* | $935 |     | $15,400 |
| English 1815-1885 ................................... *drawings* |            |         | $385 |
| ☐ **SYKES, Annie G.** .............................. *drawings* |            |         | $220 |
| American 20th cent.                                  |            |         |      |
| ☐ **SYKES, Charles** ............................... *sculpture* |            |         | $6,000 |
| 20th cent.                                           |            |         |      |
| ☐ **SYLVA, Emile Van Damme** ................. *paintings* |            |         | $2,090 |
| ☐ **SYLVESTER, Frederick Oakes** ............ *paintings* | $356 |     | $1,320 |
| American 1869-1915 ................................. *drawings* |            |         | $99 |
| ☐ **SYLVESTER, H.M.** ............................ *paintings* |            |         | $247 |
| American 19th/20th cent.                             |            |         |      |
| ☐ **SYLVESTRE, Jules N.** ........................ *paintings* |            |         | $2,200 |
| French 19th cent. ................................... *drawings* |            |         | $1,650 |

| | | *Current Price Range* | |
|---|---|---|---|
| | | Low | High |
| ☐ **SYLVIA, Louis** .................................... *paintings* | | | $325 |
| American b. 1911 ..................................... *drawings* | | $50 | $100 |
| ☐ **SYMONDS, E.T.** .................................. *paintings* | | | $220 |
| English early 20th cent. | | | |
| ☐ **SYMONDS, William Robert** .................. *paintings* | | | $3,300 |
| English 1851-1934 | | | |
| ☐ **SYMONS, George Gardner** .................. *paintings* | | $209 | $22,000 |
| American 1863-1930 ................................. *drawings* | | | $605 |
| ☐ **SZANKOWSKI, Boleslaw von** .............. *paintings* | | | $605 |
| Polish b. 1873 | | | |
| ☐ **SZANTHO, Maria** ............................. *paintings* | | $302 | $605 |
| Hungarian b. 1898 | | | |
| ☐ **SZANTO, A. Karoly L.** ........................ *drawings* | | | $990 |
| American 20th cent. | | | |
| ☐ **SZCWERINO (?), K.** ........................... *paintings* | | $165 | $192 |
| Polish 20th cent. | | | |
| ☐ **SZCZEBLEWSKI, V.** .......................... *sculpture* | | | $742 |
| ☐ **SZEMERI, Bela M.** ............................ *paintings* | | | $275 |
| Hungarian 20th cent. | | | |
| ☐ **SZENDY, H.** ..................................... *paintings* | | | $220 |
| Hungarian 20th cent. | | | |
| ☐ **SZENTES** ........................................ *paintings* | | | $1,600 |
| ☐ **SZERNER, Vladyslav (Jr.)** ..................... *paintings* | | | $605 |
| Polish 1870-1936 | | | |
| ☐ **SZEWCZENKO, K.** ............................ *paintings* | | $55 | $330 |
| Polish b. 1891 | | | |
| ☐ **SZIBIRIA** ........................................ *paintings* | | | $330 |
| Russian 20th cent. | | | |
| ☐ **SZIRMAI, Antal** ................................. *paintings* | | | $1,760 |
| ☐ **SZOZEBLEWSKI, V.** .......................... *sculpture* | | $330 | $2,310 |
| Continental 19th cent. | | | |
| ☐ **SZULE, Peter** ................................... *paintings* | | | $440 |
| Hungarian 1886-1944 | | | |
| ☐ **SZYK, Arthur** ................................... *drawings* | | $192 | $11,000 |
| Polish/American 1894-1951 | | | |
| ☐ **SZYSZLO, Fernando de** ....................... *paintings* | | $1,100 | $18,700 |
| Peruvian b. 1925 ..................................... *drawings* | | | $2,640 |
| ☐ **TAANMAN, Jacob** ............................ *paintings* | | | $825 |
| Dutch 1836-1923 | | | |
| ☐ **TABARA, Enrique** ............................ *drawings* | | | $1,100 |
| Latin American | | | |
| ☐ **TACK, Augustus Vincent** ..................... *paintings* | | $308 | $2,750* |
| American 1870-1949 | | | |
| ☐ **TADASKY, Kuwayama** ........................ *paintings* | | | $1,100 |
| contemporary | | | |
| ☐ **TAFFS, C. H.** ................................... *paintings* | | $242 | $550 |
| American | | | |
| ☐ **TAFT, Lorado** .................................. *sculpture* | | | $550 |
| American b. 1860 | | | |

| | | | Current Price Range | |
|---|---|---|---|---|
| | | | Low | High |
| ☐ **TAFURI, Clemente** | .............................. | *paintings* | $495 | $3,850 |
| Italian 1903-1971 | | | | |
| ☐ **TAFURI, Raffaele** | .............................. | *paintings* | | $2,640 |
| Italian 1857-1929 | | | | |
| ☐ **TAGGART, John G.** | ........................... | *paintings* | | $825 |
| American ac. 1846-1864 | | | | |
| ☐ **TAGLINI, V.** | ...................................... | *paintings* | | $715 |
| Italian 19th cent. | | | | |
| ☐ **TAHOMA, Quincy** | ............................ | *drawings* | $528 | $3,080 |
| American (Navajo) 1921-1956 | | | | |
| ☐ **TAILLASSON, Jean Joseph** | ................... | *drawings* | | $220 |
| French 1745-1809 | | | | |
| ☐ **TAILLE, Edouard de** | ........................... | *drawings* | | $935 |
| French 1848-1912 | | | | |
| ☐ **TAINGUE, F.** | ...................................... | *sculpture* | | $495 |
| ☐ **TAIT, Arthur Fitzwilliam** | ..................... | *paintings* | $302 | $275,000 |
| American 1819-1905 | .................................. | *drawings* | | $3,800 |
| ☐ **TAIT, John** | ........................................ | *paintings* | | $715 |
| ☐ **TAIT, Joseph** | .................................,.... | *paintings* | | $990 |
| English | | | | |
| ☐ **TAJIRI, Shinkichi** | ............................ | *sculpture* | | $385 |
| ☐ **TAKACH VON GYONGYOSHALASZ,** | | | | |
| **Bela** | ................................................. | *paintings* | | $330 |
| Hungarian b. 1874 | | | | |
| ☐ **TAKIS, Nicholas** | ............................... | *paintings* | $66 | $302 |
| American 1903-1965 | ................................. | *sculpture* | $2,420 | $4,620 |
| ☐ **TAL COAT, Pierre** | ............................. | *paintings* | | $1,155 |
| French b. 1905 | ....................................... | *drawings* | $38 | $308 |
| ☐ **TAL-ADAM** | ....................................... | *paintings* | | $825 |
| ☐ **TALBOT, Grace Helen** | ........................ | *sculpture* | | $1,650 |
| American b. 1901 | | | | |
| ☐ **TALBOT, Henry S.** | ............................ | *drawings* | | $200 |
| American 19th cent. | | | | |
| ☐ **TALBOT, Jesse** | ................................... | *paintings* | $770 | $9,900 |
| American 1806-1879 | | | | |
| ☐ **TALBOYS, Agnes Augusta** | .................. | *paintings* | | $1,100 |
| English 19th cent. | | | | |
| ☐ **TALLANT, Richard H.** | ........................ | *paintings* | $99 | $3,025 |
| American 1853-1934 | | | | |
| ☐ **TALLBACKEN (?), Einar Soderval** | ....... | *paintings* | | $330 |
| Swedish 20th cent. | | | | |
| ☐ **TALLONE, Cesare** | ............................. | *paintings* | $110 | $220 |
| Italian 1853-1919 | | | | |
| ☐ **TAM, Reuben** | .................................... | *paintings* | | $825 |
| American b. 1916 | | | | |
| ☐ **TAMARIZ, Eduardo** | ........................... | *paintings* | $825 | $990 |
| b. Mexico 1945 | | | | |
| ☐ **TAMASURE, E.** | ................................... | *drawings* | | $242 |
| 19th cent. | | | | |

|                                                              | Current Price Range |          |
|                                                              | Low      | High     |
|--------------------------------------------------------------|----------|----------|
| ☐ **TAMAYO, Rufino** ............................ *paintings* | **$22,000** | **$275,000** |
| Mexican b. 1899 ....................................... *drawings* | **$1,100** | **$28,600** |
| ☐ **TAMBOIS, M.** ................................. *sculpture* |          | **$467** |
| ☐ **TAMBURINI, Arnaldo** ..................... *paintings* | **$440** | **$4,400** |
| Italian b. 1843 .......................................... *drawings* |          | **$49** |
| ☐ **TAMBURINI, Aronne** ..................... *paintings* | **$1,430** | **$1,650** |
| Italian 20th cent.                                           |          |          |
| ☐ **TAMBURINI, Jose Maria** ................... *paintings* |          | **$467** |
| Spanish 19th cent.                                           |          |          |
| ☐ **TAMLIN, John** ............................... *paintings* |          | **$2,530** |
| British 19th cent.                                           |          |          |
| ☐ **TANAKA, Akira** ............................. *paintings* |          | **$715** |
| ☐ **TANAKA, Toshio** ........................... *paintings* |          | **$424** |
| ☐ **TANCREDI, Parmeggiani** ................. *paintings* |          | **$5,500** |
| Italian b. 1927                                              |          |          |
| ☐ **TANDI, James** ............................... *sculpture* | **$495** | **$550** |
| African 20th cent.                                           |          |          |
| ☐ **TANEY, S.** ..................................... *paintings* |          | **$275** |
| French 19th cent.                                            |          |          |
| ☐ **TANGER, Susanna** ........................... *paintings* |          | **$3,300** |
| American b. 1942                                             |          |          |
| ☐ **TANGO, Giuseppe** ........................... *paintings* |          | **$550** |
| English 19th cent.                                           |          |          |
| ☐ **TANGUY, Yves** ............................... *paintings* | **$60,500** | **$203,500** |
| French/American 1900-1955 ..................... *drawings* | **$1,100** | **$47,300** |
| ☐ **TANKEREN, H. von** ....................... *paintings* |          | **$357** |
| Dutch 20th cent.                                             |          |          |
| ☐ **TANNER, C. (of Dublin)** ................... *paintings* |          | **$6,050** |
| ☐ **TANNER, Henry Ossawa** ................... *paintings* | **$2,400** | **$275,000** |
| American 1859-1937                                           |          |          |
| ☐ **TANNING, Dorothea** ........................ *paintings* | **$14,300** | **$16,500** |
| American b. 1912                                             |          |          |
| ☐ **TANOUX, Adrien Henri** ................... *paintings* | **$550** | **$2,420** |
| French 1865-1923                                             |          |          |
| ☐ **TANSZKY, D. Anthony** ..................... *paintings* |          | **$550** |
| ☐ **TANZI, Leon Louis Antoine** ............... *paintings* |          | **$302** |
| French 1846-1913                                             |          |          |
| ☐ **TANZIO DA VARALLO,** <br> **Antonio d'Enrico (called Il Tanzio)** ......... *paintings* |          | **$49,500** |
| Italian 1574/75-1635/44                                      |          |          |
| ☐ **TAPIES, Antoni** ............................... *paintings* | **$3,850** | **$33,000** |
| Spanish b. 1923 ...................................... *drawings* | **$1,650** | **$46,200** |
| ☐ **TAPIRO Y BARO, Jose** ..................... *drawings* | **$198** | **$350** |
| Spanish 1830-1930                                            |          |          |
| ☐ **TAPPERT, Georg** ........................... *paintings* | **$12,100** | **$187,000** |
| German 1880-1957                                             |          |          |
| ☐ **TARBELL, Edmund Charles** ............... *paintings* | **$6,325** | **$203,500** |
| American 1862-1938 ............................... *drawings* | **$275** | **$5,500** |

**Early Black Artists**

*Henry Ossawa Tanner was one of the best known of 19th-century black artists. Raised in a religious family, he specialized in Biblical subjects. For two years during the 1880s, Tanner studied at the Pennsylvania Academy of Fine Arts under Thomas Eakins. With the backing of an affluent patron, Tanner left for Paris in 1891 where he studied under Constant and Laurens at the Académie Julian. He exhibited regularly and, in 1897, won a prize for "The Raising of Lazarus," which was purchased by the French government and hung in the Luxembourg Museum. In 1927 he became the first black artist to be elected to the National Academy in the United States. Tanner's work is now in the Louvre, the Chicago Art Institute, and the Metropolitan Museum in New York.*

*This work was deaccessioned by the Pennsylvania School for the Deaf and sold at Sotheby's in 1981. It is owned by Bill Cosby and on loan to a travelling exhibition of early black artists, which will tour the United States during 1986 to 1988. (Henry Ossawa Tanner, "The Thankful Poor," oil on canvas, 35½ x 44¼ in., Sotheby's, December 10, 1981, $275,000.)*

|  |  | *Current Price Range* | |
| --- | --- | --- | --- |
|  |  | *Low* | *High* |
| ☐ **TARDONI, T.** .................................... *drawings* |  |  | **$176** |
| Italian 19th cent. |  |  |  |
| ☐ **TARENGHI, Enrico** ............................ *paintings* |  |  | **$605** |
| Italian b. 1848 .......................................... *drawings* |  | **$110** | **$11,000** |
| ☐ **TARRYL, C.** ..................................... *paintings* |  |  | **$275** |
| European 19th cent. |  |  |  |

| | | *Current Price Range* | |
|---|---|---|---|
| | | Low | High |
| ☐ **TARTAGLIA, Marian** ........................ *paintings* | | $60 | $187 |
| Yugoslavian b. 1904 | | | |
| ☐ **TARTARAT,** | | | |
| **George Emmanuel Oscar** ..................... *paintings* | | | $660 |
| French 19th cent. | | | |
| ☐ **TASKER, William** ............................. *paintings* | | | $2,200 |
| English 1808-1852 | | | |
| ☐ **TASSAERT, Octave** ........................... *paintings* | | $715 | $4,675 |
| French 1800-1874 | | | |
| ☐ **TASSI, Agostino (BUONAMICO)** .......... *paintings* | | $3,850 | $8,250 |
| Italian 1565-1644 ....................................... *drawings* | | | $1,870 |
| ☐ **TASSO, T.** .................................... *sculpture* | | | $1,320 |
| ☐ **TATE, John R.** ............................... *paintings* | | | $198 |
| American 1834-1909 | | | |
| ☐ **TATTEGRAIN, Francis** ....................... *paintings* | | | $352 |
| ☐ **TAUBERT, Bertoldo** .......................... *paintings* | | $136 | $500 |
| French b. 1915 | | | |
| ☐ **TAUBES, Frederick** ........................... *paintings* | | $385 | $2,420 |
| American 1900-1981 | | | |
| ☐ **TAUNAY, Nicolas Antoine** ................... *paintings* | | $4,400 | $39,600 |
| French 1755-1830 | | | |
| ☐ **TAUPIN, Jules Charles Clement** ........... *paintings* | | | $880 |
| French 1863-1932 | | | |
| ☐ **TAURATI** ......................................... *paintings* | | | $467 |
| French 20th cent. | | | |
| ☐ **TAUSS, Herb** ..................................... *paintings* | | $577 | $825 |
| b. 1929 | | | |
| ☐ **TAUSZKY, David Anthony** ................... *paintings* | | $110 | $825 |
| American b. 1878 | | | |
| ☐ **TAVARONE, Lazzaro** .......................... *drawings* | | $495 | $825 |
| ☐ **TAVELLA, Carlo Antonio** | | | |
| **(called IL SOLTAROLA)** ....................... *drawings* | | | $2,090 |
| Italian 1668-1738 | | | |
| ☐ **TAVERNIER, Jules** ............................ *paintings* | | $800 | $17,600 |
| French/American 1844-1889/99 ..................... *drawings* | | | $192 |
| ☐ **TAVERNIER, Paul** ............................. *paintings* | | | $9,350 |
| French b. 1852 | | | |
| ☐ **TAYLER, John Frederick** ..................... *drawings* | | $1,100 | $1,320 |
| ☐ **TAYLOR, Alfred Henry** ....................... *paintings* | | | $302 |
| British 19th cent. | | | |
| ☐ **TAYLOR, Anna Heyward** ...................... *drawings* | | | $247 |
| American b. 1879 | | | |
| ☐ **TAYLOR, Bertha Fanning** ..................... *drawings* | | | $247 |
| American b. 1883 | | | |
| ☐ **TAYLOR, Charles Jay** .......................... *paintings* | | $165 | $385 |
| American 1855-1929 | | | |
| ☐ **TAYLOR, Edgar J.** ............................. *drawings* | | $220 | $400 |
| American b. 1862 | | | |

| | | Current Price Range | |
|---|---|---|---|
| | | Low | High |
| ☐ **TAYLOR, Eliza Ann** ............ *paintings* | | | $935 |
| American mid 19th cent. | | | |
| ☐ **TAYLOR, Frank H.** ............ *drawings* | | $77 | $1,540 |
| American 19th/20th cent. | | | |
| ☐ **TAYLOR, Frank Walter** ............ *paintings* | | $55 | $1,045 |
| American 1874-1921 ............ *drawings* | | | $110 |
| ☐ **TAYLOR, Frederick B.** ............ *paintings* | | | $192 |
| British 1875-1963 | | | |
| ☐ **TAYLOR, Helen Campbell** ............ *paintings* | | | $412 |
| ☐ **TAYLOR, J.C.** ............ *paintings* | | $60 | $440 |
| American 19th/20th cent. | | | |
| ☐ **TAYLOR, L. Campbell** ............ *paintings* | | | $990 |
| British b. 1874 | | | |
| ☐ **TAYLOR, Loretta** ............ *paintings* | | $3,800 | $4,500 |
| American contemporary ............ *drawings* | | | $300 |
| ☐ **TAYLOR, M.A.** ............ *paintings* | | | $851 |
| American 19th cent. | | | |
| ☐ **TAYLOR, Maria Spilsbury** ............ *paintings* | | $450 | $577 |
| British early 19th cent. | | | |
| ☐ **TAYLOR, Newton** ............ *paintings* | | | $1,100 |
| ☐ **TAYLOR, Richard** ............ *drawings* | | | $275 |
| ☐ **TAYLOR, Stephen** ............ *paintings* | | | $8,250 |
| English ac. 1817-1849 | | | |
| ☐ **TAYLOR, Walter** ............ *drawings* | | $247 | $385 |
| American 20th cent. | | | |
| ☐ **TAYLOR, William Francis** ............ *paintings* | | $825 | $825 |
| American 1883-1934 | | | |
| ☐ **TAYLOR, William Ladd** ............ *drawings* | | $220 | $605 |
| American 1854-1926 | | | |
| ☐ **TAYMANS, Louis** ............ *paintings* | | | $1,650 |
| Belgian 19th cent. | | | |
| ☐ **TCHELITCHEV, Pavel** ............ *paintings* | | $4,950 | $14,300 |
| Russian 1898-1957 ............ *drawings* | | $137 | $18,700 |
| ☐ **TCHERIKOVA, Ludmilla** ............ *drawings* | | | $330 |
| ☐ **TCHERPINE, Alexander** ............ *paintings* | | | $3,300 |
| Russian 19th cent. | | | |
| ☐ **TCHISTOVSKY, L.** ............ *paintings* | | | $192 |
| Russian 20th cent. | | | |
| ☐ **TEAGUE, Donald** ............ *paintings* | | | $16,500 |
| American b. 1897 ............ *drawings* | | $770 | $35,000 |
| ☐ **TEATER, Archie B.** ............ *paintings* | | | $495 |
| American 20th cent. | | | |
| ☐ **TEBO** ............ *drawings* | | | $440 |
| ☐ **TEED, Douglas Arthur** ............ *paintings* | | $136 | $3,630 |
| American 1864-1929 ............ *drawings* | | | $165 |
| ☐ **TEICHMAN, Sabina** ............ *paintings* | | $522 | $1,980 |
| American b. 1905 | | | |
| ☐ **TEJEIRO, C.** ............ *drawings* | | $990 | $990 |
| Cuban 19th cent. | | | |

| | | Current Price Range | |
|---|---|---|---|
| | | *Low* | *High* |
| ☐ **TELEKE, V.** ........................................ *drawings* | | | $495 |
| 19th cent. | | | |
| ☐ **TELEKI, Ralph** .................................... *paintings* | | | $550 |
| ☐ **TELICHER, V.** ..................................... *drawings* | | | $264 |
| ☐ **TELLANDER, Frederick** ...................... *paintings* | | | $500 |
| ☐ **TELLES, Sergio Barcellos** ..................... *paintings* | | $1,650 | $2,420 |
| Portuguese b. 1936 | | | |
| ☐ **TELSER, A.** ......................................... *paintings* | | $1,980 | $6,710 |
| German(?) 19th cent. | | | |
| ☐ **TEMLINSEN, M.E.** ........................... *paintings* | | | $200 |
| English early 20th cent. | | | |
| ☐ **TEMPEL, Gustav** ............................... *paintings* | | | $2,000 |
| 19th cent. | | | |
| ☐ **TEMPEST, Cyrel** ................................ *paintings* | | | $467 |
| English 1865-1942 | | | |
| ☐ **TEMPESTA, Antonio** .......................... *drawings* | | $1,100 | $2,090 |
| ☐ **TEMPLE, Hans** ................................... *paintings* | | | $1,100 |
| Austrian 1857-1931 | | | |
| ☐ **TEN CATE, Jan Hendrik** ...................... *paintings* | | | $192 |
| Dutch 1867-1955 | | | |
| ☐ **TEN CATE, Siebe Johannes** ................. *paintings* | | | $577 |
| Dutch 1858-1908 | | | |
| ☐ **TEN KATE, Herman Frederik Carel** ..... *paintings* | | $3,300 | $6,050 |
| Dutch 1822-1891 ...................................... *drawings* | | $990 | $2,640 |
| ☐ **TEN KATE, Johan Mari Henri** ............. *paintings* | | $411 | $23,100 |
| Dutch 1831-1910 ...................................... *drawings* | | $352 | $2,250 |
| ☐ **TEN KATE, Johannes Marinus** ............. *drawings* | | $1,000 | $2,200 |
| Dutch 1859-1896 | | | |
| ☐ **TEN KOMPE, Jan** ............................... *paintings* | | | $24,200 |
| Dutch 1713-1761 | | | |
| ☐ **TENDA, Fr---** ..................................... *paintings* | | | $715 |
| Dutch (?) 19th cent. | | | |
| ☐ **TENIERS, Abraham** ............................ *paintings* | | | $3,000 |
| Flemish baptized 1629, d. 1670 | | | |
| ☐ **TENIERS, David (the younger)** ............. *paintings* | | $3,000 | $154,000 |
| Flemish 1610-1690 | | | |
| ☐ **TENKATE, Jan Jacob Lodewijk** .......... *paintings* | | | $1,980 |
| Dutch 1850-1929 | | | |
| ☐ **TENNANT, John F.** ............................. *paintings* | | $935 | $1,100 |
| 1796-1872 | | | |
| ☐ **TENRE, Henry** ................................... *paintings* | | $660 | $3,080 |
| French 1864-1926 ...................................... *drawings* | | | $880 |
| ☐ **TEPA, Franz** ...................................... *paintings* | | | $1,650 |
| Polish 1828-1889 | | | |
| ☐ **TEPPER, Saul** ................................... *paintings* | | $1,980 | $7,150 |
| American b. 1899 ...................................... *drawings* | | $880 | $1,210 |
| ☐ **TER BORCH, Gerard** ......................... *paintings* | | $3,300 | $52,250 |
| Dutch | | | |

| | | Current Price Range | |
|---|---|---|---|
| | | *Low* | *High* |
| ☐ **TER MEULEN, Frans Pieter** ................. *paintings* | | $880 | $4,510 |
| Dutch 1843-1927 ........................................ *drawings* | | | $550 |
| ☐ **TER VERDOENK, A.** .......................... *paintings* | | | $192 |
| Dutch b. 1906 | | | |
| ☐ **TER-ARUTUNIAN, Rouben** ................. *drawings* | | | $385 |
| ☐ **TERECHKOVITCH,** | | | |
| **Konstantin (Kostia)** ............................ *paintings* | | $605 | $11,000 |
| Russian/Fremch 1902-1978 .......................... *drawings* | | $275 | $3,300 |
| ☐ **TERELAK, John** ................................ *paintings* | | | $2,860 |
| American | | | |
| ☐ **TERESZCUK, Paul** ............................ *sculpture* | | | $467 |
| ☐ **TERESZCZUK, P.** ............................. *sculpture* | | $132 | $1,210 |
| ac. 1895-1925 | | | |
| ☐ **TERIGAL, Arthur** ............................ *paintings* | | | $330 |
| ☐ **TERNI, A.L.** ..................................... *paintings* | | | $350 |
| ☐ **TERPNING, Howard** .......................... *paintings* | | $25,000 | $105,000 |
| American b. 1927 ....................................... *drawings* | | | $15,000 |
| ☐ **TERRINI** ........................................... *paintings* | | $300 | $935 |
| Italian 20th cent. | | | |
| ☐ **TERRIT** ............................................. *drawings* | | | $1,100 |
| ☐ **TERSCHELLING, W.R.** ...................... *drawings* | | | $275 |
| English 19th cent. | | | |
| ☐ **TERWESTEN, Matthaus** ..................... *paintings* | | $1,320 | $5,225 |
| Dutch 1670-1757 | | | |
| ☐ **TESI, Mauro** ................................... *drawings* | | | $550 |
| ☐ **TESSARI, Vittorio** ............................ *drawings* | | $220 | $302 |
| Italian b. 1860 | | | |
| ☐ **TESSARI, Vittrio** ............................. *drawings* | | | $341 |
| French b. 1938 | | | |
| ☐ **TESSON, Louis** ................................. *paintings* | | $1,100 | $4,950 |
| French b. 19th cent. | | | |
| ☐ **TESTA, Pietro** .................................. *drawings* | | | $4,400 |
| ☐ **TESTELIN, Louis** .............................. *paintings* | | | $3,300 |
| ☐ **TETAR VAN ELVEN,** | | | |
| **Pierre Henri Theodore** ...................... *paintings* | | $1,320 | $14,300 |
| Dutch 1831-1908 ....................................... *drawings* | | $715 | $1,870 |
| ☐ **TETAR VON ELVEN, Jan Baptist** ........ *paintings* | | | $1,430 |
| Dutch 1805-1879 | | | |
| ☐ **TETMAYER, Wlodzimierz** ................. *paintings* | | | $5,282 |
| Polish 1862-1923 | | | |
| ☐ **TEUPKEN, D.A.** ............................... *drawings* | | | $1,760 |
| ☐ **TEUTTER, M.K.** .............................. *paintings* | | | $2,530 |
| ☐ **TEYE, (Teresa CUELLAR)** ................. *drawings* | | | $9,350 |
| Colombian | | | |
| ☐ **TEYRAL, John** .................................. *paintings* | | | $385 |
| American | | | |
| ☐ **THABARD, Adolphe Martial** ............... *sculpture* | | | $1,210 |
| French | | | |

|                                        |           | Current Price Range |           |
|----------------------------------------|-----------|:-------------------:|-----------|
|                                        |           | Low                 | High      |
| ☐ THADDEUS, M.J. ............................. *paintings* |   |                     | $715      |
| ☐ THAL, Sam ........................................ *drawings* |   |                 | $275      |
| American 20th cent.                    |           |                     |           |
| ☐ THALINGER, E. Oscar ........................ *paintings* |   | $99                 | $385      |
| American b. 1885                       |           |                     |           |
| ☐ THAREL ............................................. *sculpture* |   |             | $1,320    |
| ☐ THAULOW, Fritz ............................... *paintings* |   | $3,850              | $63,250   |
| Norwegian 1847-1906 .................................. *drawings* |   |             | $5,000    |
| ☐ THAXTER, Edward R. ........................ *sculpture* |   |                 | $2,750    |
| American d. 1881                       |           |                     |           |
| ☐ THAYER, Abbott Handerson ............... *paintings* |   | $120                | $9,900    |
| American 1849-1921 ................................... *drawings* |   |             | $1,320    |
| ☐ THAYER, Albert R. ............................ *paintings* |   |             | $950      |
| American 19th/20th cent.               |           |                     |           |
| ☐ THAYER, Karen ................................. *paintings* |   |                 | $1,150    |
| American                               |           |                     |           |
| ☐ THENN, C. ........................................ *sculpture* |   |             | $330      |
| ☐ THEOBALD, Samuel (Jr.) ..................... *paintings* |   | $1,100              | $5,720    |
| American 19th/20th cent.               |           |                     |           |
| ☐ THERIAT, Charles James ................... *paintings* |   |                 | $5,225    |
| American b. 1860                       |           |                     |           |
| ☐ THERON, Pierre ................................ *paintings* |   |             | $275      |
| European                               |           |                     |           |
| ☐ THERY, Madeleine ............................. *drawings* |   |                 | $1,210    |
| French 20th cent.                      |           |                     |           |
| ☐ THEVENET, L. .................................... *paintings* |   |             | $660      |
| Belgian 20th cent.                     |           |                     |           |
| ☐ THIBAULT, Jean Thomas .................... *paintings* |   |                 | $8,800    |
| French 1757-1826                       |           |                     |           |
| ☐ THIEBAUD, Wayne ........................... *paintings* |   | $6,600              | $143,000  |
| American b. 1920 ..................................... *drawings* |   | $605            | $23,100   |
| ☐ THIELEMANN, Alfred Rudolph ........... *paintings* |   |                 | $2,640    |
| Danish 1851-1927                       |           |                     |           |
| ☐ THIELEN, Jan van ............................. *paintings* |   |                 | $20,900   |
| ☐ THIEM, Paul ..................................... *paintings* |   |             | $962      |
| American                               |           |                     |           |
| ☐ THIEMANN, Hans ............................. *paintings* |   |                 | $825      |
| German b. 1910                         |           |                     |           |
| ☐ THIEME, Anthony .............................. *paintings* |   | $137                | $6,600    |
| Dutch/American 1888-1954 ......................... *drawings* |   | $110             | $687      |
| ☐ THIERSCH, Ludwig ........................... *paintings* |   |                 | $6,050    |
| German 1825-1909                       |           |                     |           |
| ☐ THIERY DE SAINTE-COLOMBE,            |           |                     |           |
| Luc Vincent .................................... *drawings* |   |                 | $440      |
| French 1734-1811                       |           |                     |           |
| ☐ THIMOTHEE, C. ............................... *paintings* |   |             | $385      |
| ☐ THIREL, V. ....................................... *paintings* |   |             | $1,100    |
| ☐ THIRION, Charles Victor .................... *paintings* |   |                 | $13,200   |
| French 1833-1878                       |           |                     |           |

| | | Current Price Range | |
|---|---|---|---|
| | | Low | High |
| ☐ **THIVET, Antoine August** ...................... *paintings* French | | | $11,000 |
| ☐ **THOL, Hendrick Otto von** ................... *paintings* Dutch 1859-1902 | | | $825 |
| ☐ **THOLEN, Willem Bastiaan** ................... *paintings* | | | $600 |
| Dutch 1860-1931 ...................................... *drawings* | | | $770 |
| ☐ **THOLER, Raymond** ............................. *paintings* French b. 1859 | | | $2,300 |
| ☐ **THOM, James Crawford** ...................... *paintings* | | $110 | $4,620 |
| American 1838/42-1898 ............................... *drawings* | | | $418 |
| ☐ **THOMA, Hans** .................................. *paintings* German 1839-1924 | | $2,420 | $19,800 |
| ☐ **THOMA, Josef** ................................. *paintings* Austrian 1828-1899 | | $605 | $4,180 |
| ☐ **THOMAS, Albert** ............................... *paintings* British School 19th cent. | | | $495 |
| ☐ **THOMAS, Alice Blair** .......................... *paintings* American d. 1939 | | $357 | $522 |
| ☐ **THOMAS, Charles H.** .......................... *drawings* American ac. 1839 | | | $6,050 |
| ☐ **THOMAS, Grosvenor** ........................... *paintings* English 1856-1923 | | $99 | $192 |
| ☐ **THOMAS, Mathilde** ............................. *sculpture* French ac. 1879-1914 | | | $1,760 |
| ☐ **THOMAS, Paul** ................................. *paintings* French b. 1859 | | | $1,089 |
| ☐ **THOMAS, Peter** ................................ *drawings* English b. 1927 | | $121 | $275 |
| ☐ **THOMAS, Reynolds** ............................ *drawings* American 20th cent. | | | $302 |
| ☐ **THOMAS, Richard D.** .......................... *paintings* American 20th cent. | | | $715 |
| ☐ **THOMAS, Richard Strickland** .............. *paintings* British 1787-1853 | | | $6,600 |
| ☐ **THOMAS, Stephen Seymour** ................. *paintings* | | $88 | $1,760 |
| American 1868-1956 ................................... *drawings* | | | $44 |
| ☐ **THOMAS, W.** .................................... *paintings* American 20th cent. | | | $412 |
| ☐ **THOMAS, W.A.** ................................. *paintings* American 19th cent. | | | $825 |
| ☐ **THOMAS, Wilfred** .............................. *paintings* | | | $600 |
| ☐ **THOMASCH** ..................................... *sculpture* | | | $418 |
| ☐ **THOMASIN, S.** .................................. *paintings* | | | $1,540 |
| ☐ **THOMASON, R.S.** .............................. *paintings* American 19th/20th cent. | | | $330 |
| ☐ **THOMASSIN, Desire** ........................... *paintings* German 1858-1933 | | $1,650 | $11,000 |
| ☐ **THOMASSIN, Louis** ............................ *paintings* French 18th cent. | | | $26,400 |

|  | | *Current Price Range* | |
|--|--|--|--|
|  | | Low | High |
| ☐ **THOMBURY, W.** ............................ *paintings* | | | $302 |
| late 19th cent. | | | |
| ☐ **THOMPKINS, Frank Hector** ............... *paintings* | | | $550 |
| American 1847-1922 | | | |
| ☐ **THOMPSON, A. Wordsworth** ............. *paintings* | | $247 | $25,300 |
| American 1840-1896 ................................. *drawings* | | $192 | $200 |
| ☐ **THOMPSON, Albert** .......................... *paintings* | | | $990 |
| American b. 1853 | | | |
| ☐ **THOMPSON, Bob** .............................. *paintings* | | $1,980 | $3,850 |
| American 1937-1966 | | | |
| ☐ **THOMPSON, Cephas** ......................... *paintings* | | $600 | $1,100 |
| American 1775-1856 | | | |
| ☐ **THOMPSON, Cephas Giovanni** ............. *paintings* | | $110 | $2,860 |
| American 1809-1888 | | | |
| ☐ **THOMPSON, Charles A.** ...................... *paintings* | | | $330 |
| American ac. 1852-1855 | | | |
| ☐ **THOMPSON, Edward H.** ..................... *paintings* | | | $220 |
| English 19th/20th cent. | | | |
| ☐ **THOMPSON, Elise** .............................. *paintings* | | | $247 |
| American 19th cent. | | | |
| ☐ **THOMPSON, Frederic Louis** ............... *paintings* | | $124 | $1,500 |
| American b. 1868 | | | |
| ☐ **THOMPSON, George Albert** ................ *paintings* | | $660 | $2,500 |
| American 1868-1938 .................................. *drawings* | | | $275 |
| ☐ **THOMPSON, Harry** ........................... *paintings* | | | $1,540 |
| British d. 1901 | | | |
| ☐ **THOMPSON, Harry Ives** ...................... *paintings* | | $550 | $3,080 |
| American 1840-1906 | | | |
| ☐ **THOMPSON, J. Harry** ......................... *paintings* | | | $350 |
| American 19th/20th cent. | | | |
| ☐ **THOMPSON, J.C.** .............................. *paintings* | | | $198 |
| English 19th cent. | | | |
| ☐ **THOMPSON, Jacob** ............................ *paintings* | | | $495 |
| ☐ **THOMPSON, Jerome B.** ....................... *paintings* | | $2,090 | $60,500 |
| American 1814-1886 .................................. *drawings* | | | $550 |
| ☐ **THOMPSON, Launt** ........................... *sculpture* | | $220 | $605 |
| American 1833-1894 | | | |
| ☐ **THOMPSON, Leslie Prince** ................. *paintings* | | $1,540 | $13,200 |
| American 1880-1963 .................................. *drawings* | | | $2,090 |
| ☐ **THOMPSON, Robert** ........................... *paintings* | | $770 | $4,400 |
| ☐ **THOMPSON, Walter W.** ...................... *paintings* | | $385 | $1,100 |
| American 1881/82-1948 | | | |
| ☐ **THOMPSON, Wordsworth** ................... *paintings* | | $550 | $12,100 |
| American 1840-1896 | | | |
| ☐ **THOMPSON-PRITCHARD, E.** ............. *paintings* | | | $880 |
| American 20th cent. | | | |
| ☐ **THOMSON, Arthur** ............................ *paintings* | | | $350 |
| 19th cent. | | | |

| | Current Price Range | |
|---|---|---|
| | Low | High |

| | | Low | High |
|---|---|---|---|
| ☐ **THOMSON, Clifton** ............................ *paintings* | | | **$2,200** |
| British 1775-1843 | | | |
| ☐ **THOMSON,** | | | |
| **Frances Ingram Dalrymple** .................... *paintings* | | | **$968** |
| English d. 1845 | | | |
| ☐ **THOMSON, Hugh** ............................ *drawings* | | **$825** | **$2,420** |
| British 1860-1920 | | | |
| ☐ **THON, William** .................................. *paintings* | | | **$357** |
| American b. 1906 ...................................... *drawings* | | | **$440** |
| ☐ **THONE, Franz** .................................. *paintings* | | | **$1,650** |
| German 1851-1906 | | | |
| ☐ **THORBURN, Archibald** ...................... *drawings* | | | **$6,600** |
| Scottish 1860-1935 | | | |
| ☐ **THOREN, Otto von** ............................ *paintings* | | **$1,045** | **$7,700** |
| Austrian 1828-1889 | | | |
| ☐ **THORN, James Crawford** .................... *paintings* | | | **$550** |
| American 1835-1898 | | | |
| ☐ **THORNE, Alfred** ............................... *paintings* | | | **$880** |
| ☐ **THORNE, Diana** ............................... *paintings* | | **$385** | **$880** |
| American b. 1895 ...................................... *drawings* | | | **$165** |
| ☐ **THORNE, Joan** .................................. *paintings* | | | **$4,180** |
| contemporary | | | |
| ☐ **THORNE, S.A.** .................................... *drawings* | | | **$1,320** |
| American | | | |
| ☐ **THORNE, Thomas Elston** .................... *paintings* | | | **$550** |
| American 1909-1976 | | | |
| ☐ **THORNE, William** ............................ *paintings* | | **$308** | **$385** |
| ☐ **THORNLEY, J.** .................................. *paintings* | | | **$577** |
| British 19th cent. | | | |
| ☐ **THORNLEY, L.** .................................. *paintings* | | | **$286** |
| British (?) 19th cent. | | | |
| ☐ **THORNLEY, William** | | | |
| **(or Georges William)** ............................ *paintings* | | **$935** | **$1,925** |
| French b. 1857 | | | |
| ☐ **THORNLEY, William A.** ...................... *paintings* | | | **$1,650** |
| British 19th/20th cent. .................................. *drawings* | | | **$990** |
| ☐ **THORNTON, Herbert** ........................ *paintings* | | **$8,525** | **$10,450** |
| British 19th cent. | | | |
| ☐ **THORNYCROFT, Thomas** .................... *sculpture* | | | **$2,860** |
| English mid 19th cent. | | | |
| ☐ **THORPE** ............................................ *paintings* | | | **$220** |
| 19th cent. ................................................ *drawings* | | | **$466** |
| ☐ **THORS, Joseph** .................................. *paintings* | | **$302** | **$3,520** |
| English ac. 1883-1898 | | | |
| ☐ **THORTON, Charles H.** ........................ *paintings* | | | **$330** |
| American 19th cent. | | | |
| ☐ **THRASHER, Leslie** ............................ *paintings* | | **$880** | **$880** |
| American 1889-1936 | | | |
| ☐ **THUILLER, Pierre** ............................ *drawings* | | | **$638** |

| | Current Price Range | |
|---|---|---|
| | Low | High |
| ☐ **THULDEN, Theodoor van** ............... *drawings* | | **$1,540** |
| Flemish 1606-1669 | | |
| ☐ **THURBER, C.** ............... *paintings* | | **$962** |
| American 19th cent. | | |
| ☐ **THURBER, James** ............... *drawings* | **$495** | **$880** |
| American 1894-1961 | | |
| ☐ **THURNER, Gabriel Edouard** ............... *paintings* | | **$550** |
| French 1840-1907 | | |
| ☐ **THURSTON, J.K.** ............... *drawings* | **$99** | **$385** |
| American late 19th cent. | | |
| ☐ **THURSTON, John R.** ............... *drawings* | | **$385** |
| American | | |
| ☐ **THYSEBARET, Emile** ............... *paintings* | | **$330** |
| ☐ **THYSEN, C.J.** ............... *drawings* | | **$577** |
| ☐ **TIBBERSTON, A.F.** ............... *drawings* | | **$192** |
| English 19th cent. | | |
| ☐ **TIBBITS, J.** ............... *paintings* | **$385** | **$715** |
| ☐ **TIBBLE, Geoffrey Arthur** ............... *paintings* | **$385** | **$1,100** |
| English 1909-1952 | | |
| ☐ **TIBMANN, Albin** ............... *paintings* | | **$191** |
| Belgian 19th cent. | | |
| ☐ **TICCINO, E.** ............... *paintings* | | **$385** |
| ☐ **TICE, Charles Winfield** ............... *paintings* | **$2,200** | **$3,500** |
| American 1810-1870 | | |
| ☐ **TIDEMAND, Adolphe** ............... *paintings* | | **$1,870** |
| Norwegian 1814-1876 | | |
| ☐ **TIDEY, Alfred** ............... *paintings* | **$3,850** | **$7,700** |
| British 1808-1892 | | |
| ☐ **TIELEMANNS, Lodewyk** ............... *paintings* | **$8,800** | **$17,600** |
| Belgian 1826-1856 | | |
| ☐ **TIEPOLO, Giovanni Battista** ............... *paintings* | | **$39,600** |
| Italian 1696-1770 ............... *drawings* | **$4,620** | **$7,700** |
| ☐ **TIEPOLO, Giovanni Domenico** ............... *drawings* | **$3,300** | **$85,250** |
| Italian 1727-1804 | | |
| ☐ **TIEPOLO, Lorenzo** ............... *drawings* | | **$2,420** |
| Italian 1736-1776 | | |
| ☐ **TIETJENS, M.H.** ............... *paintings* | | **$550** |
| American 20th cent. | | |
| ☐ **TIFFANY, Louis Comfort** ............... *paintings* | **$990** | **$7,700** |
| American 1848-1933 ............... *drawings* | **$935** | **$7,150** |
| ☐ **TIFFIN, Henry** ............... *paintings* | | **$440** |
| French 19th cent. | | |
| ☐ **TILBORG, Gillis van (or TILBORCH)** ... *paintings* | | **$24,200** |
| Flemish 1625-1678 | | |
| ☐ **TILBURN, E.O.** ............... *paintings* | | **$462** |
| American | | |
| ☐ **TILDEN, Douglas** ............... *sculpture* | | **$79,200** |
| American 1860-1935 | | |

|  | | | Current Price Range | |
|--|--|--|--------|------|
|  | | | Low | High |
| ☐ **TILDEN, George S.** ............................ *paintings*<br>American 19th/20th cent. | | | $66 | $220 |
| ☐ **TILGNER, F.** ..................................... *paintings* | | | | $660 |
| ☐ **TILIMAN** ........................................ *paintings* | | | | $352 |
| ☐ **TILL, Leopold** ................................. *paintings*<br>Austrian 1830-1893 | | | | $1,320 |
| ☐ **TILL, Walter** .................................. *drawings* | | | | $1,650 |
| ☐ **TILLBERG, Harald** ........................... *paintings*<br>German b. 1877 | | | | $275 |
| ☐ **TILTON, John Rollin** ......................... *paintings*<br>American 1833-1888 ................................... *drawings* | | | $1,045 | $1,100<br>$132 |
| ☐ **TILYARD, Philip Thomas** .................... *paintings*<br>American 1785-1830 | | | | $935 |
| ☐ **TIMMERMANS, Henri** ........................ *paintings* | | | | $440 |
| ☐ **TIMMERMANS, Louis Etienne** ............. *paintings*<br>French 1846-1910 ..................................... *drawings* | | | $1,045 | $3,630<br>$352 |
| ☐ **TIMMERS, Adriaan** ........................... *paintings* | | | | $330 |
| ☐ **TIMMINS, Harry** .............................. *paintings*<br>American b. 1887 | | | | $220 |
| ☐ **TIMMONS, Edward J. Finley** .............. *paintings*<br>American b. 1882 | | | $27 | $440 |
| ☐ **TING, Walasse** ................................. *paintings*<br>American 20th cent. ................................... *drawings* | | | $330 | $825<br>$1,650 |
| ☐ **TINGLEY, Frank Foster** ....................... *drawings* | | | | $715 |
| ☐ **TINGUELY, Jean** ............................... *drawings*<br>Swiss b. 1925 ......................................... *sculpture* | | | $110<br>$6,875 | $1,980<br>$15,400 |
| ☐ **TINKHAM, Sarah Emily** ..................... *paintings*<br>c. 1820 | | | | $600 |
| ☐ **TINSLEY, F.** ..................................... *paintings*<br>American 19th/20th cent. | | | | $250 |
| ☐ **TINTORE, Simone del** ........................ *paintings*<br>Italian 2nd half 17th cent. | | | | $242,000 |
| ☐ **TINTORETTO, Domenico Robusti**<br>**(called IL)** ...................................... *paintings*<br>Italian 1560-1635 | | | $1,980 | $13,200 |
| ☐ **TINTORETTO, Jacopo Robusti**<br>**(IL FURIOSO)** ................................ *paintings*<br>Italian 1518/19-1594 | | | $15,400 | $82,500 |
| ☐ **TIPPET, Wolfgang Von** ........................ *paintings* | | | | $412 |
| ☐ **TIRATELLI, Aurelio** ........................... *paintings*<br>Italian 1842-1900 | | | | $6,050 |
| ☐ **TIRATELLI, Cesare** ............................ *paintings*<br>Italian b. 1864 | | | | $8,800 |
| ☐ **TIRELUTH** ....................................... *paintings*<br>American 20th cent. | | | | $825 |
| ☐ **TIRILLO** ......................................... *paintings* | | | | $358 |
| ☐ **TIRONI, Francesco** ............................ *paintings*<br>Italian 18th/19th cent. | | | $10,000 | $26,000 |

|  | | Current Price Range | |
|---|---|---|---|
|  | | Low | High |
| ☐ **TIRRELL, G.** ........................ *paintings* | | $4,675 | $7,425 |
| American 19th cent. | | | |
| ☐ **TISCHBEIN, Johann Heinrich** ............. *paintings* | | | $550 |
| German 1722-1789 | | | |
| ☐ **TISCHLER, V.** ........................ *paintings* | | | $605 |
| ☐ **TISCHLER, Victor** ..................... *paintings* | | | $330 |
| Austrian/American 1890-1951 | | | |
| ☐ **TISSOT, James Jacques Joseph** ............ *paintings* | | $6,875 | $407,000 |
| French 1836-1902 ........................ *drawings* | | $660 | $16,500 |
| ☐ **TITCOMB, Mary Bradish** .................. *paintings* | | $5,225 | $9,900 |
| American 1856-1927 ...................... *drawings* | | | $330 |
| ☐ **TITCOMB, William Holt Yates** ............ *paintings* | | | $15,400 |
| English 1858-1930 | | | |
| ☐ **TITO, Ettore** ........................ *paintings* | | | $19,800 |
| Italian 1859-1941 | | | |
| ☐ **TITO, Santi di** ...................... *paintings* | | $8,250 | $121,000 |
| Italian 1536-1603 ....................... *drawings* | | | $5,940 |
| ☐ **TITTLE, Walter Ernest** ................. *paintings* | | $66 | $77 |
| American 1880/83-1960 .................... *drawings* | | $500 | $550 |
| ☐ **TITZE** ............................. *sculpture* | | | $440 |
| ☐ **TIVOLI, P.** .......................... *drawings* | | | $1,320 |
| Italian 19th cent. | | | |
| ☐ **TIVOLI, Serafino De** ................... *paintings* | | | $2,420 |
| Italian 1826-92 | | | |
| ☐ **TOBALDI, Sergio** ..................... *paintings* | | | $605 |
| ☐ **TOBER, K.** .......................... *paintings* | | | $1,650 |
| German 19th cent. | | | |
| ☐ **TOBEY, Mark** ........................ *paintings* | | $715 | $45,100 |
| American 1890-1976 ...................... *drawings* | | $286 | $2,860 |
| ☐ **TOBIASSE, Theo** ...................... *paintings* | | $1,760 | $4,180 |
| Israeli/French b. 1927 ................... *drawings* | | $1,320 | $1,540 |
| ☐ **TOBIE** ............................. *paintings* | | | $300 |
| 19th cent. | | | |
| ☐ **TOBIN, George T.** .................... *paintings* | | | $450 |
| American b. 1864 | | | |
| ☐ **TOCQUE, Louis** ...................... *paintings* | | $28,600 | $46,200 |
| French 1696-1772 ....................... *drawings* | | | $2,310 |
| ☐ **TODAHL, J.O.** ....................... *paintings* | | | $440 |
| American 20th cent. | | | |
| ☐ **TODARO, V.** ......................... *paintings* | | | $1,760 |
| Italian 19th cent. | | | |
| ☐ **TODD, Charles Stewart** ................ *paintings* | | | $467 |
| American b. 1885 | | | |
| ☐ **TODD, Henry George** .................. *paintings* | | $660 | $770 |
| British 1847-1898 ....................... *drawings* | | | $770 |
| ☐ **TODD, Henry Stanley** ................. *paintings* | | | $522 |
| American b. 1871 | | | |
| ☐ **TODDY, Jimmy (Beatien Yazz)** ............ *paintings* | | | $605 |
| American (Navajo) b. 1928 ................ *drawings* | | $286 | $990 |

| | | | Current Price Range | |
|---|---|---|---|---|
| | | | *Low* | *High* |
| ☐ **TODHUNTER, Francis** .................... *drawings* | | | $77 | $275 |
| American 1884-1962 | | | | |
| ☐ **TODT, Max** .................... *paintings* | | | $550 | $3,520 |
| German 1847-1890 | | | | |
| ☐ **TOESCHI, G.** .................... *paintings* | | | $1,650 | $4,810 |
| Italian 19th cent. | | | | |
| ☐ **TOFANO, Edouard** .................... *paintings* | | | | $6,050 |
| Italian 1838-1920 | | | | |
| ☐ **TOFF, P.** .................... *drawings* | | | | $1,045 |
| contemporary | | | | |
| ☐ **TOFT, P.** .................... *drawings* | | | | $500 |
| American 19th cent. | | | | |
| ☐ **TOJETTI, D.** .................... *paintings* | | | | $192 |
| American 19th/20th cent. | | | | |
| ☐ **TOJETTI, Eduardo** .................... *paintings* | | | $165 | $440 |
| Italian/American 1852-1930 | | | | |
| ☐ **TOJETTI, Virgilio** .................... *paintings* | | | $192 | $8,250 |
| Italian/American 1849-1901 | | | | |
| ☐ **TOL, Dominicus van** .................... *paintings* | | | $4,400 | $17,600 |
| Dutch 1635-1676 | | | | |
| ☐ **TOLDT, A.** .................... *paintings* | | | | $935 |
| European 19th/20th cent. | | | | |
| ☐ **TOLDY, M.** .................... *paintings* | | | $165 | $187 |
| Hungarian b. 1911 | | | | |
| ☐ **TOLEDO, Francisco** .................... *paintings* | | | $2,200 | $33,000 |
| Mexican b. 1940 .................... *drawings* | | | $220 | $17,600 |
| .................... *sculpture* | | | $2,750 | $7,700 |
| ☐ **TOLEGIAN, Manuel** .................... *paintings* | | | $357 | $1,045 |
| American 20th cent. | | | | |
| ☐ **TOLLEY, Edward** .................... *paintings* | | | | $2,500 |
| ☐ **TOLLINI, E.** .................... *paintings* | | | | $550 |
| Italian 19th cent. | | | | |
| ☐ **TOLMAN, Stacy** .................... *paintings* | | | $82 | $825 |
| American 1860-1935 .................... *drawings* | | | | $44 |
| ☐ **TOM, Jan Bedys** .................... *paintings* | | | $900 | $3,300 |
| Dutch 1813-1894 | | | | |
| ☐ **TOMANEK, Joseph** .................... *paintings* | | | $187 | $880 |
| Czech/American b. 1899 | | | | |
| ☐ **TOMAO** .................... *paintings* | | | | $600 |
| ☐ **TOMASSI, Publio de** .................... *drawings* | | | | $4,950 |
| ☐ **TOMBA, Aldini Casimiro** .................... *drawings* | | | | $770 |
| Italian 1857-1929 | | | | |
| ☐ **TOMINZ, Alfredo** .................... *paintings* | | | | $2,200 |
| Austrian 1854-1936 | | | | |
| ☐ **TOMLIN, Bradley Walker** .................... *paintings* | | | $110 | $71,500 |
| American 1899-1953 .................... *drawings* | | | $550 | $13,750 |
| ☐ **TOMMASI, Adolfo** .................... *paintings* | | | $330 | $4,400 |
| Italian 1851-1933 | | | | |
| ☐ **TOMMASO** .................... *paintings* | | | | $24,200 |

| | | Current Price Range | |
|---|---|---|---|
| | | Low | High |
| ☐ **TOMPKINS, Frank Hector** .................. *paintings* | | $770 | $1,870 |
| American 1847-1922 .................................. *drawings* | | $96 | $825 |
| ☐ **TOMSON, Clifton** .............................. *paintings* | | $770 | $20,000 |
| English 1775-1835 | | | |
| ☐ **TOMSON, J.** ........................................ *paintings* | | | $450 |
| British 19th cent. | | | |
| ☐ **TONAY, J.L.** ........................................ *paintings* | | | $385 |
| European 19th cent. | | | |
| ☐ **TONEAU, Henry** ............................... *paintings* | | | $385 |
| ☐ **TONEE, D. Paul** ............................... *paintings* | | | $275 |
| American 20th cent. | | | |
| ☐ **TONEY, Anthony** ............................... *paintings* | | $82 | $600 |
| American 20th cent. | | | |
| ☐ **TONGA, L.** ........................................ *paintings* | | | $247 |
| Italian 20th cent. | | | |
| ☐ **TONGE, Louis Lammert Leire van de** ... *paintings* | | $825 | $3,190 |
| Dutch 1871-1937 | | | |
| ☐ **TONGE, Robert** .................................... *paintings* | | $176 | $3,300 |
| ☐ **TONK, Ernest** ..................................... *paintings* | | $3,575 | $5,775 |
| American b. 1889 ...................................... *drawings* | | $1,650 | $1,870 |
| ☐ **TONNEAU, Joseph** ............................... *paintings* | | | $770 |
| ☐ **TONNER, Ferdinand** ............................ *paintings* | | | $302 |
| German b. 1859 | | | |
| ☐ **TONNERY, John** ................................. *paintings* | | | $302 |
| ☐ **TONNETS, F.M.L.** ............................ *sculpture* | | | $440 |
| ☐ **TOOBY, Charles Richard** .................... *paintings* | | | $715 |
| ☐ **TOOKER, George** ............................... *paintings* | | $22,000 | $70,000 |
| American b. 1920 ...................................... *drawings* | | $4,400 | $6,600 |
| ☐ **TOORENVLICT, Jacob** ........................ *paintings* | | | $1,320 |
| ☐ **TOOROP, Charley** ............................... *paintings* | | | $246 |
| Dutch 1881-1955 | | | |
| ☐ **TOOROP, Jan** ..................................... *paintings* | | | $2,200 |
| Dutch 1858-1928 | | | |
| ☐ **TOPCHEVSKY, Marrie** ........................ *paintings* | | | $302 |
| ☐ **TOPCHEVSKY, Morris** ........................ *paintings* | | $880 | $935 |
| American 1899-1947 | | | |
| ☐ **TOPHAM, Francis William** .................... *paintings* | | | $440 |
| English 1808-1877 | | | |
| ☐ **TOPHAM, Frank William Warwick** ...... *paintings* | | $330 | $1,650 |
| British 1838-1929 | | | |
| ☐ **TOPOLSKI, Feliks** ............................... *drawings* | | $165 | $412 |
| Polish b. 1907 | | | |
| ☐ **TOPPAN, Charles** ............................... *paintings* | | | $440 |
| American 1796-1874 | | | |
| ☐ **TOPPING, James** ............................... *paintings* | | $198 | $4,125 |
| American 1879-1949 | | | |
| ☐ **TORAL, Mario** ..................................... *paintings* | | $1,650 | $1,650 |
| b. Chile 1934 | | | |
| ☐ **TORDINI** ............................................. *paintings* | | | $715 |

| | Current Price Range | |
|---|---|---|
| | Low | High |
| ☐ **TORERRI, G.** ................................. *paintings* | | **$467** |
| ☐ **TORIES, Morgan** ............................... *paintings* | | **$467** |
| British 19th cent. | | |
| ☐ **TORNAI, Gyula** ............................... *paintings* | **$1,100** | **$8,800** |
| Hungarian 1861-1928 | | |
| ☐ **TORNOE, Wenzel Ulrik** ...................... *paintings* | | **$30,800** |
| Danish 1844-1907 | | |
| ☐ **TORO, A.** ......................................... *paintings* | | **$330** |
| ☐ **TORR, Brian** ..................................... *paintings* | | **$275** |
| ☐ **TORRE, Giulio del** ............................. *paintings* | | **$3,520** |
| ☐ **TORREANO, John Francis** .................. *paintings* | **$5,280** | **$6,875** |
| American b. 1941 | | |
| ☐ **TORRES, Antonio** ............................... *paintings* | **$110** | **$880** |
| Spanish b. 1851 | | |
| ☐ **TORRES, Julio Romero de** .................. *paintings* | | **$4,400** |
| Spanish 1879-1930 | | |
| ☐ **TORRES-GARCIA, Joaquin** ................ *paintings* | **$2,310** | **$110,000** |
| Uruguayan 1874-1949 ................................ *drawings* | **$770** | **$3,630** |
| ☐ **TORREY, Elliot Bouton** ...................... *paintings* | **$220** | **$880** |
| American 1867-1949 | | |
| ☐ **TORREY, George B.** ........................... *paintings* | | **$246** |
| American b. 1863 | | |
| ☐ **TORRIGLIA, Giovanni Battista** .......... *paintings* | **$4,125** | **$40,700** |
| Italian 1858-1937 | | |
| ☐ **TORRINI, E.** ..................................... *paintings* | **$301** | **$20,900** |
| Italian 19th cent. | | |
| ☐ **TORRINI, F.** ..................................... *paintings* | | **$330** |
| Italian 19th cent. | | |
| ☐ **TORTEZ, Victor** ................................. *paintings* | | **$1,980** |
| French d. 1890 | | |
| ☐ **TOSSEY, Verne** ................................. *paintings* | **$880** | **$880** |
| ☐ **TOTIN, V.** ......................................... *paintings* | **$412** | **$495** |
| European late 19th cent. | | |
| ☐ **TOUDOUZE, Edouard** ........................ *paintings* | | **$6,600** |
| French 1848-1907 | | |
| ☐ **TOUISSAINT, Pierre Joseph** ................ *paintings* | | **$1,760** |
| ☐ **TOULMOUCHE, Auguste** .................... *paintings* | **$275** | **$20,350** |
| French 1829-1890 | | |
| ☐ **TOULOUSE-LAUTREC, Henri de** ........ *paintings* | **$30,800** | **$5,280,000** |
| French 1864-1901 ...................................... *drawings* | **$1,045** | **$407,000** |
| ☐ **TOUR-DONAS, Marthe** ....................... *paintings* | **$2,420** | **$6,600** |
| Belgian 1885-1967 | | |
| ☐ **TOURGUENEFF, Pierre Nicolas** ........... *sculpture* | **$275** | **$423** |
| French 1854-1912 | | |
| ☐ **TOURNAY, H.** .................................... *paintings* | **$143** | **$412** |
| Swiss b. 1890 | | |
| ☐ **TOURNEMINE, Charles** ...................... *paintings* | **$1,100** | **$1,980** |
| French 1812-1872 | | |

|  | | Current Price Range | |
|---|---|---|---|
|  | | Low | High |
| ☐ **TOURNIER, Nicolas** ............................ *paintings* | | | **$33,000** |
| French 1590-1657 | | | |
| ☐ **TOURNIER (?), T. le** ........................... *drawings* | | | **$302** |
| French 20th cent. | | | |
| ☐ **TOURNIERES, Robert** ........................ *paintings* | | | **$1,100** |
| ☐ **TOUSSAINT, Auguste** ........................ *paintings* | **$1,100** | **$8,800** |
| Haitian 20th cent. | | | |
| ☐ **TOUSSAINT, Fernand** ......................... *paintings* | **$550** | **$3,300** |
| Belgian 1873-1956 | | | |
| ☐ **TOUSSAINT, Louis** ............................ *paintings* | | | **$8,250** |
| European 19th cent. | | | |
| ☐ **TOUSSAINT, Pierre** ............................ *paintings* | **$3,080** | **$5,225** |
| French 19th cent. | | | |
| ☐ **TOUSSAINT, Pierre Joseph** .................. *paintings* | | | **$3,000** |
| Belgian 1822-1888 | | | |
| ☐ **TOVAR, Ivan** ..................................... *paintings* | **$880** | **$3,300** |
| Czechoslovakian 20th cent. | | | |
| ☐ **TOVAR Y TOVAR, Martin** .................. *paintings* | | | **$20,900** |
| Venezuelan 1827-1902 | | | |
| ☐ **TOVISH, Harold** ............................... *sculpture* | | | **$1,650** |
| American b. 1921 | | | |
| ☐ **TOWERS, S.** ..................................... *drawings* | | | **$275** |
| English 19th/20th cent. | | | |
| ☐ **TOWNE, Charles** ............................... *paintings* | **$770** | **$66,000** |
| English 18th/19th cent. | | | |
| ☐ **TOWNE, Charles (of Liverpool)** ............. *paintings* | **$797** | **$1,210** |
| English 1763-1840 | | | |
| ☐ **TOWNE, Charles (of London)** ................ *paintings* | **$660** | **$2,530** |
| English 1781-1854 | | | |
| ☐ **TOWNE, Francis** ............................... *drawings* | **$1,320** | **$1,760** |
| British 1739/40-1816 | | | |
| ☐ **TOWNSEND, Ernest** ......................... *paintings* | **$385** | **$4,675** |
| 1893-1945 | | | |
| ☐ **TOWNSEND, H.R.** ........................... *paintings* | **$165** | **$800** |
| American 19th/20th cent. | | | |
| ☐ **TOWNSEND, Harry** ......................... *paintings* | **$247** | **$522** |
| American 1879-1941 | | | |
| ☐ **TOWNSEND, J.** ............................... *paintings* | | | **$247** |
| late 18th cent. | | | |
| ☐ **TOWNSHEND, Arthur Louis** .............. *paintings* | **$330** | **$385** |
| British 19th/20th cent. | | | |
| ☐ **TOWNSHEND, James** ........................ *paintings* | | | **$605** |
| ☐ **TOZZI, Mario** ................................... *drawings* | | | **$6,875** |
| Italian b. 1895 | | | |
| ☐ **TRACHE, Rudolph** ........................... *paintings* | | | **$825** |
| European | | | |
| ☐ **TRACY, John Michael** ........................ *paintings* | **$825** | **$50,600** |
| ☐ **TRAIES, William** ............................... *paintings* | | | **$6,875** |
| English 1789-1872 | | | |

| | | *Current Price Range* | |
|---|---|---|---|
| | | Low | High |
| ☐ **TRAIN, Edward** .................... *paintings* <br> English 19th cent. | | | $357 |
| ☐ **TRAMANEO, Gianni** ........... *paintings* <br> Italian 19th/20th cent. | | | $1,650 |
| ☐ **TRAPPES, Francis M.** .......... *paintings* <br> British ac. 1868-1885 | | | $3,410 |
| ☐ **TRATMAN, Robert** ............ *paintings* <br> American 20th cent. | | | $412 |
| ☐ **TRAUTMANN, Johann** ........ *paintings* <br> German 1713-1769 | | 1,540 | $2,750 |
| ☐ **TRAVAUX, Pierre** ............ *sculpture* <br> French 19th cent. | | | $352 |
| ☐ **TRAVER, George A.** .......... *paintings* <br> American b. 1864 ................ *drawings* | | $132 | $412 <br> $275 |
| ☐ **TRAVER, Marion Gray** ........ *paintings* <br> American 1896-after 1934 | | $198 | $264 |
| ☐ **TRAVERSI, Gaspare** .......... *paintings* <br> Italian d. 1769 | | | $6,600 |
| ☐ **TRAVI, Antonio** .................. *paintings* | | | $5,500 |
| ☐ **TRAVIS, Paul Bough** ........... *paintings* <br> American b. 1891 ................ *drawings* | | $174 | $495 <br> $302 |
| ☐ **TRAYER, Jean Baptiste Jules** ...... *paintings* <br> French 1824-1908/09 | | $1,870 | $15,400 |
| ☐ **TREAT, Asa** ..................... *paintings* <br> 19th cent. | | | $1,100 |
| ☐ **TREBILCOCK, Paul** ........... *paintings* <br> American b. 1902 | | $110 | $1,980 |
| ☐ **TREBLE, William** ............ *paintings* | | | $250 |
| ☐ **TREDUPP, Charles** ............ *paintings* <br> American 19th/20th cent. | | $220 | $715 |
| ☐ **TREMBELLI, C.** ................. *paintings* | | | $825 |
| ☐ **TREMOLIERES, Pierre Charles** .......... *paintings* | | | $8,800 |
| ☐ **TRENHOLM, William Carpenter** ......... *paintings* <br> American 1856-1931 | | | $3,300 |
| ☐ **TRENT, Victor Pedretti** ......... *paintings* <br> American b. 1891 | | $275 | $550 |
| ☐ **TRENTANOVE, Raimondo** ............ *sculpture* <br> Italian 1792-1832 | | | $1,870 |
| ☐ **TREPOLO, Giovanni Domenico** ........... *drawings* <br> Italian 1727-1804 | | | $1,650 |
| ☐ **TREPORT,** <br> **Camille Victor Louis Muller du** ........... *paintings* | | | $770 |
| ☐ **TRETCHIKOFF, Vladimir** ................ *paintings* <br> Russian 20th cent. | | | $220 |
| ☐ **TREVASON, A.** ................. *drawings* <br> Continental 19th cent. | | $357 | $412 |
| ☐ **TREVILLE, De** .................. *paintings* <br> American 19th/20th cent. | | $77 | $302 |

| | | Current Price Range | |
|---|---|---|---|
| | | Low | High |
| ☐ TREVISAN, A. ...................................... *paintings* | | | $242 |
| Italian 20th cent. | | | |
| ☐ TREVISANI, Francesco ......................... *paintings* | | $851 | $3,080 |
| Italian 1656-1746 | | | |
| ☐ TREVISO, Girolamo da (the elder) ......... *paintings* | | | $3,300 |
| ☐ TREVOR, Helen Mabel ......................... *paintings* | | | $467 |
| ☐ TREZZINI, B. ...................................... *paintings* | | | $412 |
| Italian 19th cent. | | | |
| ☐ TRIBOUT, George O. ........................... *paintings* | | $220 | $495 |
| ☐ TRIESTE, Joansovich ........................... *paintings* | | | $1,430 |
| 19th cent. | | | |
| ☐ TRIGEN ............................................... *paintings* | | | $2,860 |
| ☐ TRIGERIOS, R. ................................... *paintings* | | $220 | $330 |
| European 19th/20th cent. | | | |
| ☐ TRIGUEROS, Ramiro ........................... *drawings* | | | $550 |
| Spanish 1860-1939 | | | |
| ☐ TRIMONT ........................................... *paintings* | | | $6,875 |
| French(?) 19th cent. | | | |
| ☐ TRINQUESSE, Louis Rolland ............... *paintings* | | $31,900 | $31,900 |
| French 1746-c. 1800 ................................. *drawings* | | | $247 |
| ☐ TRIONFI, Emanuele ........................... *paintings* | | | $742 |
| Italian 1832-1900 | | | |
| ☐ TRIOSON, Girodet De Roucy ............... *paintings* | | | $900 |
| French 18th cent. | | | |
| ☐ TRIPET, Alfred ................................... *paintings* | | | $2,750 |
| French ac. 1861-1882 | | | |
| ☐ TRIPLER, Charles Eastman ................. *paintings* | | | $3,080 |
| ☐ TRIPP, T. ........................................... *drawings* | | | $1,650 |
| ☐ TRIPP, W.H. ....................................... *drawings* | | | $650 |
| ☐ TRIPPE, Frederick Kenyon ................. *paintings* | | $200 | $385 |
| 19th/20th cent. | | | |
| ☐ TRIPPEL, Albert Ludwia ..................... *paintings* | | | $1,760 |
| German 1813-54 | | | |
| ☐ TRIRUM (?), J.W.V. ........................... *paintings* | | | $385 |
| ☐ TRISCOTT, Samuel Peter Rolt ............. *drawings* | | $50 | $1,540 |
| American 1846-1925 | | | |
| ☐ TRIST, Martha Jefferson ..................... *drawings* | | | $440 |
| ☐ TROENBLE, Hugo ............................... *paintings* | | | $440 |
| ☐ TROGER, Paul ................................... *paintings* | | | $7,700 |
| Austrian 1698-1762 | | | |
| ☐ TROIANI, Don ..................................... *paintings* | | | $4,000 |
| American contemporary .............................. *drawings* | | | $220 |
| ☐ TROKES, Heinz ................................... *paintings* | | $247 | $880 |
| ☐ TROMP, Jan Zoetelief ......................... *paintings* | | $2,475 | $7,700 |
| Dutch b. 1872 | | | |
| ☐ TRONDER (?), M. ............................... *drawings* | | | $302 |

| | | | Current Price Range | |
|---|---|---|---|---|
| | | | Low | High |
| ☐ **TROOD, William Henry Hamilton** ........ | *paintings* | | $1,980 | $5,225 |
| English 1848/60-1899 | | | | |
| ☐ **TROOST, Cornelis** ............................ | *drawings* | | | $9,350 |
| Dutch 1697-1750 | | | | |
| ☐ **TROTTER, Newbold Hough** ................ | *paintings* | | $275 | $17,050 |
| American 1827-1898 | | | | |
| ☐ **TROUBETZKOY, Pierre** ...................... | *paintings* | | | $605 |
| ☐ **TROUBETZKOY, Prince Paul** ............. | *paintings* | | $330 | $3,850 |
| Russian/American 1866-1933/38 .................... | *sculpture* | | $770 | $15,400 |
| ☐ **TROUILLEBERT, E.** .......................... | *drawings* | | | $440 |
| ☐ **TROUILLEBERT, Paul Desire** ............. | *paintings* | | $192 | $16,500 |
| French 1829-1900 ...................................... | *drawings* | | $1,100 | $2,090 |
| ☐ **TROUSSER, L.** ................................ | *drawings* | | | $5,280 |
| American | | | | |
| ☐ **TROUSSET, L.** ................................ | *paintings* | | | $12,650 |
| ☐ **TROUTOVSKY,** | | | | |
| **Konstantin Alexandrovitch** ................... | *paintings* | | $1,650 | $2,530 |
| Russian 1826-1893 | | | | |
| ☐ **TROVA, Ernest** ............................... | *paintings* | | $1,045 | $7,150 |
| American b. 1927 ...................................... | *drawings* | | | $990 |
| .................................................. | *sculpture* | | $1,430 | $13,200 |
| ☐ **TROY, Francois de** ........................... | *paintings* | | $200 | $7,700 |
| French 1645-1730 | | | | |
| ☐ **TROY, Hugh** .................................. | *paintings* | | | $935 |
| ☐ **TROY, Jean Francois de** ..................... | *paintings* | | | $6,600 |
| French 1697-1752 | | | | |
| ☐ **TROYE, Edward** ............................... | *paintings* | | $19,800 | $55,000 |
| American 1808-1874 | | | | |
| ☐ **TROYON, Constant** ........................... | *paintings* | | $550 | $39,600 |
| French 1810-1865 ...................................... | *drawings* | | $220 | $6,600 |
| ☐ **TRUBNER, Wilhelm** .......................... | *paintings* | | | $2,310 |
| German 1851-1917 ...................................... | *drawings* | | | $165 |
| ☐ **TRUDY, Milne** ................................ | *paintings* | | | $605 |
| French 1842-1900 | | | | |
| ☐ **TRUE, David** .................................. | *paintings* | | | $3,025 |
| American b. 1942 ...................................... | *drawings* | | $990 | $2,640 |
| ☐ **TRUELSEN, Mathias Jacob Theodore** ... | *drawings* | | | $3,080 |
| ☐ **TRUESDELL, Gaylord Sangston** .......... | *paintings* | | $302 | $2,750 |
| American 1850-1899 | | | | |
| ☐ **TRUEX, Van Day** .............................. | *drawings* | | $110 | $220 |
| American 20th cent. | | | | |
| ☐ **TRUGER, Ed** .................................. | *paintings* | | | $2,860 |
| ☐ **TRUITT, Anne** ................................ | *paintings* | | | $605 |
| ☐ **TRUJILLO, Guillermo** ......................... | *paintings* | | $1,650 | $4,125 |
| Panamanian b. 1927 | | | | |
| ☐ **TRUMBULL, Edward** .......................... | *drawings* | | | $440 |
| American | | | | |
| ☐ **TRUMBULL, John** ............................. | *paintings* | | $2,750 | $41,250 |
| American 1756-1843 | | | | |

|  | | Current Price Range | |
| | | Low | High |
| --- | --- | --- | --- |
| ☐ **TRUPHEME, Auguste Joseph** ............... *paintings* | | | **$1,320** |
| French 1836-1898 | | | |
| ☐ **TRUPHEMUS, Jacques** ........................ *paintings* | | **$176** | **$330** |
| French b. 1922 | | | |
| ☐ **TRUPPE, Karl** ........................................ *paintings* | | | **$1,210** |
| ☐ **TRYON, Dwight William** ..................... *paintings* | | **$440** | **$30,000** |
| American 1849-1925 ................................. *drawings* | | **$330** | **$550** |
| ☐ **TSATOKE, Monroe** ............................... *paintings* | | | **$1,430** |
| American (Kiowa) 1904-1937 | | | |
| ☐ **TSCHACBASOV, Nahum** ...................... *paintings* | | **$77** | **$356** |
| American b. 1899 ..................................... *drawings* | | | **$66** |
| ☐ **TSCHEGGENY, Charles** ...................... *paintings* | | **$605** | **$1,210** |
| Belgian 1815-1894 | | | |
| ☐ **TSCHELAN, Hans** ............................... *paintings* | | | **$850** |
| Viennese b. 1873 | | | |
| ☐ **TSCHUDI, Rudolf** ............................... *paintings* | | **$220** | **$660** |
| American 1855-1923 | | | |
| ☐ **TSCHUDY, Herbert Bolivar** ................. *paintings* | | **$192** | **$660** |
| American 1874-1946 | | | |
| ☐ **TUBBECKE, Paul W.** ........................... *paintings* | | **$2,200** | **$2,200** |
| German 1848-1924 | | | |
| ☐ **TUBBY, J.T.** ....................................... *drawings* | | **$247** | **$280** |
| American 20th cent. | | | |
| ☐ **TUCCI, Guiseppe** ................................ *paintings* | | | **$275** |
| ☐ **TUCKER, Allen** .................................. *paintings* | | **$550** | **$10,450** |
| American 1866-1939 ................................. *drawings* | | **$110** | **$880** |
| ☐ **TUCKER, E. (of Exeter)** ....................... *paintings* | | | **$605** |
| British 19th cent. | | | |
| ☐ **TUCKER, Mary B.** ............................... *drawings* | | | **$3,575** |
| American 19th cent. | | | |
| ☐ **TUCKER, Virginia** .............................. *paintings* | | | **$325** |
| American 19th cent. | | | |
| ☐ **TUCKERMAN, Stephen Salisbury** ......... *paintings* | | **$825** | **$1,320** |
| American 1830-1904 | | | |
| ☐ **TUCTUC A., Santiago** ......................... *paintings* | | **$110** | **$767** |
| ☐ **TUKE, Henry Scott** ............................. *paintings* | | | **$220** |
| English 1858-1929 | | | |
| ☐ **TUMA, K.** .......................................... *paintings* | | | **$1,540** |
| ☐ **TUNISON** ........................................... *drawings* | | **$330** | **$1,100** |
| American 20th cent. | | | |
| ☐ **TUNKEL, V.** ....................................... *drawings* | | **$770** | **$1,540** |
| ☐ **TUNNARD, John** ................................ *paintings* | | **$825** | **$1,980** |
| English b. 1900 | | | |
| ☐ **TURCHI, Alessandro** ........................... *paintings* | | | **$19,800** |
| ☐ **TURENNE, Fr.** .................................... *paintings* | | | **$412** |
| ☐ **TURINA, Carlo** .................................. *paintings* | | | **$1,430** |
| Italian b. 1885 | | | |
| ☐ **TURINA Y AREAL, Joaquin** ................ *paintings* | | | **$3,080** |
| ☐ **TURJANSKY, Leonid Viktorovich** ........ *paintings* | | **$302** | **$550** |

| | | | Current Price Range | |
|---|---|---|---|---|
| | | | *Low* | *High* |
| ☐ **TURK, Francis H.** .............................. *paintings* | | | | $352 |
| American 19th cent. | | | | |
| ☐ **TURNBULL, Grace** ........................... *paintings* | | | $220 | $907 |
| American 1880-1976 | | | | |
| ☐ **TURNBULL, James B.** ........................ *paintings* | | | | $2,600 |
| American 1909-1976 | | | | |
| ☐ **TURNEAUX, E.F.** .............................. *paintings* | | | | $220 |
| 19th cent. | | | | |
| ☐ **TURNER, A.L.** .................................. *paintings* | | | | $385 |
| American 19th cent. | | | | |
| ☐ **TURNER, Alan** .................................. *paintings* | | | | $990 |
| contemporary | | | | |
| ☐ **TURNER, Alfred M.** .......................... *drawings* | | | | $1,320 |
| British 1852-1932 | | | | |
| ☐ **TURNER, C.H.** .................................. *paintings* | | | | $495 |
| American early 20th cent. | | | | |
| ☐ **TURNER, Charles L.** ......................... *paintings* | | | | $935 |
| ac. 1902-1918 | | | | |
| ☐ **TURNER, Charles Yardley** .................. *paintings* | | | $110 | $8,800 |
| American 1850-1919 ............................. *drawings* | | | | $220 |
| ☐ **TURNER, Daniel** ............................... *paintings* | | | $605 | $2,475 |
| English 18th cent. | | | | |
| ☐ **TURNER, Edward Dewey** ................... *paintings* | | | | $440 |
| American b. 1920 | | | | |
| ☐ **TURNER, Francis Calcraft** .................. *paintings* | | | $1,100 | $22,000 |
| British 1795-1846 | | | | |
| ☐ **TURNER, George** .............................. *paintings* | | | $3,400 | $4,125 |
| British 19th cent. | | | | |
| ☐ **TURNER, George (Jr.)** ........................ *paintings* | | | $1,320 | $1,870 |
| English 19th cent. | | | | |
| ☐ **TURNER, Helen M.** ............................ *paintings* | | | $2,200 | $7,425 |
| American 1858-1943/58 | | | | |
| ☐ **TURNER, Henry** ............................... *paintings* | | | | $935 |
| ☐ **TURNER, James Alfred** ....................... *paintings* | | | | $12,100 |
| European | | | | |
| ☐ **TURNER, Joseph Mallord William** ........ *paintings* | | | $1,320 | $275,000 |
| English 1775-1851 | | | | |
| ☐ **TURNER, L.** .................................... *paintings* | | | | $880 |
| English 19th cent. | | | | |
| ☐ **TURNER, Major C.E.** .......................... *paintings* | | | $302 | $330 |
| ☐ **TURNER, Ross Sterling** ...................... *paintings* | | | | $605 |
| American 1847-1915 ............................. *drawings* | | | $88 | $880 |
| ☐ **TURNER, William Eddowes** ................. *paintings* | | | $440 | $990 |
| British 19th cent. | | | | |
| ☐ **TURNER, William H.** .......................... *paintings* | | | $1,500 | $3,575 |
| British ac. 1840-1887 | | | | |
| ☐ **TURNER, William L.** .......................... *paintings* | | | $165 | $990 |
| British 1867-1936 | | | | |

| | | Current Price Range | |
|---|---|---|---|
| | | Low | High |
| ☐ **TURNEY, Winthrop** ............................ *paintings* | | | **$522** |
| American b. 1884 | | | |
| ☐ **TURNOCK, Jaine** ............................... *paintings* | | | **$1,320** |
| Continental School 19th/20th cent. | | | |
| ☐ **TURSHANSKY, Leonid Viktorovich** ...... *paintings* | | | **$2,090** |
| Russian 1875-1945 | | | |
| ☐ **TURTER, William** ............................... *paintings* | | **$192** | **$440** |
| ☐ **TUSHAUS, Fritz** ............................... *paintings* | | | **$6,160** |
| German 1832-1885 | | | |
| ☐ **TUSQUETS Y MAIGNON, Ramon** ....... *paintings* | | **$1,600** | **$2,600** |
| Italian d. 1904 | | | |
| ☐ **TUTTLE, Franklin** ............................... *paintings* | | | **$495** |
| American | | | |
| ☐ **TUTTLE, J.H.** ................................... *paintings* | | **$165** | **$880** |
| American 19th cent. | | | |
| ☐ **TUTTLE, Macowin** ............................ *paintings* | | | **$495** |
| American 1861-1935 | | | |
| ☐ **TUTTLE, Richard** ............................... *paintings* | | | **$7,150** |
| American 20th cent. ................................. *drawings* | | **$605** | **$660** |
| ☐ **TUTUNDJIAN, Leon Arthur** ............... *paintings* | | | **$3,850** |
| French 1906-1968 ................................. *drawings* | | **$770** | **$2,200** |
| ☐ **TWACHTMAN, John Henry** ................ *paintings* | | **$1,089** | **$143,000** |
| American 1853-1902 ............................... *drawings* | | **$110** | **$10,450** |
| ☐ **TWEED, W.** ..................................... *sculpture* | | | **$550** |
| ☐ **TWEEDLE, John** ............................... *paintings* | | | **$6,050** |
| ☐ **TWOMBLY, Cy** .................................. *paintings* | | **$5,500** | **$198,000** |
| American b. 1929 ................................. *drawings* | | **$2,640** | **$24,200** |
| ☐ **TWORKOV, Jack** ............................... *paintings* | | **$2,860** | **$52,800** |
| Polish/American b. 1900 ............................ *drawings* | | **$550** | **$6,380** |
| ☐ **TYCK, Edward** .................................. *paintings* | | | **$424** |
| Belgium b. 1847 | | | |
| ☐ **TYLER, Alice de Wolf Kellogg** .............. *paintings* | | | **$385** |
| American c. 1866-1900 | | | |
| ☐ **TYLER, Bayard Henry** ......................... *paintings* | | **$165** | **$2,750** |
| American 1855-1931 | | | |
| ☐ **TYLER, Hattie** .................................. *paintings* | | | **$231** |
| American 20th cent. | | | |
| ☐ **TYLER, James Gale** ............................ *paintings* | | **$110** | **$35,750** |
| American 1855-1931 ............................... *drawings* | | | **$550** |
| ☐ **TYLER, Stella Eakins** .......................... *sculpture* | | **$302** | **$550** |
| American 19th/20th cent. | | | |
| ☐ **TYLER, William R.** ............................ *paintings* | | **$330** | **$1,430** |
| American 19th cent. | | | |
| ☐ **TYLOR, Bayard H.** ............................. *paintings* | | | **$300** |
| American 1855-1931 | | | |
| ☐ **TYNDALE, Thomas Nicholson** .............. *paintings* | | **$192** | **$247** |
| British 19th/20th cent. | | | |
| ☐ **TYNG, Griswold** ............................... *paintings* | | **$165** | **$605** |
| American b. 1883 | | | |

|  | | Current Price Range | |
|---|---|---|---|
|  | | Low | High |
| ☐ TYRRELL, Brinsley .......................... *paintings* | | $220 | $260 |
| ☐ TYSON, Carroll Sargent ....................... *paintings* | | $302 | $4,400 |
| American 1878-1956 ............................... *drawings* | | | $253 |
| ☐ TYTGAT, Medard .......................... *paintings* | | | $22,000 |
| Belgian b. 1871 | | | |
| ☐ UBAC, Raoul ..................................... *drawings* | | $136 | $330 |
| ☐ UBEDA, Augustin .......................... *paintings* | | $99 | $825 |
| ☐ UDEN, Lucas van .......................... *paintings* | | $7,700 | $24,200 |
| Flemish 1595-1672/1673 | | | |
| ☐ UDVARY, Gyula .......................... *paintings* | | | $275 |
| ☐ UECKER, Gunther ............................. *drawings* | | | $467 |
| German b. 1930 ..................................... *sculpture* | | | $770 |
| ☐ UFER, Walter ..................................... *paintings* | | $495 | $374,000 |
| American 1876-1936 ............................... *drawings* | | $137 | $1,000 |
| ☐ UHDE, Friedrich Karl Hermann von | | | |
| (or Fritz) ................................................. *paintings* | | $4,620 | $30,800 |
| German 1848-1911 | | | |
| ☐ UHL, S. Jerome ..................................... *paintings* | | $110 | $1,815 |
| American 1842-1916 | | | |
| ☐ UHLE, Bernard .......................... *paintings* | | $50 | $797 |
| American 1847-1930 | | | |
| ☐ UHLMAN, R. C. ..................................... *paintings* | | | $528 |
| ☐ UJVARY, Farenc .......................... *paintings* | | | $357 |
| Hungarian b. 1898 | | | |
| ☐ ULFSTEN, Nicolay .......................... *paintings* | | | $880 |
| Dutch b. 1855 | | | |
| ☐ ULFT, Jacob van der .......................... *paintings* | | | $26,400 |
| Dutch 1627-1689 | | | |
| ☐ ULLMAN, R. A. ..................................... *paintings* | | | $467 |
| ☐ ULLMAN, Th. ..................................... *sculpture* | | $191 | $275 |
| German ac. c. 1920-1930 | | | |
| ☐ ULMANN, Ch. ..................................... *paintings* | | | $880 |
| German or Swedish 19th cent. | | | |
| ☐ ULMANN, Jans .......................... *paintings* | | | $1,045 |
| German 20th cent. | | | |
| ☐ ULREICH, Eduard Buk .......................... *paintings* | | | $550 |
| American 20th cent. | | | |
| ☐ ULRICH, Charles Frederic ................... *paintings* | | $29,700 | $31,900 |
| American 1858-1908 | | | |
| ☐ ULRICH, Johann Jakob Hans .............. *paintings* | | | $2,860 |
| Swiss 1798-1877 | | | |
| ☐ ULRICH, L. W. ..................................... *paintings* | | | $220 |
| American 19th/20th cent. | | | |
| ☐ ULRICH, T. .......................... *sculpture* | | | $660 |
| ☐ UMLAUF, Charles .......................... *sculpture* | | | $467 |
| ☐ UNDERHILL, Frederick Charles .......... *paintings* | | $1,980 | $4,125 |
| English ac. 1851-1875 | | | |
| ☐ UNDERHILL, William .......................... *paintings* | | | $4,675 |
| British ac. 1848-1870 | | | |

| | | | Current Price Range | |
|---|---|---|---|---|
| | | | Low | High |
| ☐ UNDERWOOD, Clarence F. | ............... | *drawings* | $247 | $715 |
| American 1871-1929 | | | | |
| ☐ UNDIN | ................... | *paintings* | | $935 |
| ☐ UNGER, E. | ................... | *paintings* | | $577 |
| ☐ UNGER, Hans | ................... | *paintings* | | $550 |
| ☐ UNGER, Hella | ................... | *sculpture* | | $440 |
| ☐ UNGER, Th. | ................... | *paintings* | | $246 |
| Dutch 20th cent. | | | | |
| ☐ UNGEWITTER, Hugo | ................... | *paintings* | $4,400 | $11,000 |
| German b. 1869 | | | | |
| ☐ UNKER, Carl Henrik | ................... | *paintings* | $715 | $1,375 |
| Swedish 1828-1866 | | | | |
| ☐ UNOLD, Max | ................... | *paintings* | | $550 |
| German b. 1885 | | | | |
| ☐ UNTERBERGER, Franz Richard | .......... | *paintings* | $1,100 | $39,600 |
| Belgian 1838-1902 | | | | |
| ☐ UPELNIEKS | ................... | *paintings* | $400 | $550 |
| Dutch contemporary | | | | |
| ☐ UPHAM, William Hervey | ................... | *drawings* | | $231 |
| American early 20th cent. | | | | |
| ☐ URBAIN, T. | ................... | *paintings* | | $467 |
| ☐ URBAN, Hermann | ................... | *paintings* | $330 | $357 |
| German 1866-1946 | | | | |
| ☐ URBAN, Joseph | ................... | *paintings* | $275 | $302 |
| American 1872-1933 | ................... | *drawings* | $192 | $1,650 |
| ☐ URBAN, K. | ................... | *paintings* | | $796 |
| ☐ URBANEK, Jacqueline Gord | ................... | *paintings* | | $330 |
| ☐ URIANO | ................... | *sculpture* | | $330 |
| ☐ URIBURU, Nicholas Garcia | ................... | *paintings* | | $3,080 |
| Argentinian b. 1937 | | | | |
| ☐ URILLIOT, P. | ................... | *paintings* | $1,650 | $1,870 |
| Belgian 19th cent. | | | | |
| ☐ URLASS, Louis | ................... | *paintings* | $770 | $935 |
| French b. 1804 | | | | |
| ☐ URY, A. Muller | ................... | *paintings* | | $220 |
| German 19th cent. | | | | |
| ☐ USSEL | ................... | *paintings* | | $2,750 |
| European 19th cent. | | | | |
| ☐ USSHER, A. | ................... | *paintings* | | $412 |
| ☐ USSI, Stefano | ................... | *paintings* | | $14,850 |
| Italian 1822-1901 | | | | |
| ☐ USUI, Bumpei | ................... | *paintings* | | $1,430 |
| American 20th cent. | | | | |
| ☐ UTRILLO, Maurice | ................... | *paintings* | $9,350 | $137,500 |
| French 1883-1955 | ................... | *drawings* | $3,300 | $44,000 |
| ☐ UTTER, Andre | ................... | *paintings* | $330 | $440 |
| ☐ UTTER, Janene Grende | ................... | *drawings* | | $650 |
| American | | | | |

## Montmartre

*Aspiring artists all over the world yearn to travel to France and study in Paris. Perhaps no other artists' quarter of any city is so celebrated as Montmartre, famous for its studios and galleries, and Pére-Lachaise, the final resting place of some of the most noted figures in all the arts.*

*In many paintings, Maurice Utrillo, a prolific French painter of the early 20th century, celebrated Montmartre. Utrillo's best-known pictures are from his White Period (1908-1910), which depict the deserted streets of this bohemian corner of Paris. They are among the artist's best work. Some scholars hold that subsequent to Utrillo's marriage in 1935, while his production increased, the quality of individual works diminished. (Maurice Utrillo, "Sannois," oil on panel, 21 x 28 in., Doyle, May 17, 1984, $68,750.)*

|  | | *Current Price Range* | |
|---|---|---|---|
|  | | *Low* | *High* |
| ☐ **UTZ, Thornton** ....................................... *paintings* | | **$137** | **$2,000** |
| b. 1915 | | | |
| ☐ **UWINS, Thomas** ................................. *paintings* | | | **$2,200** |
| ☐ **UYTEWAEL, Joachim** ........................ *paintings* | | **$1,100** | **$16,500** |
| Dutch 1566-1638 ...................................... *drawings* | | | **$7,700** |
| ☐ **UYTTENBROECK, Moses van** ............ *paintings* | | | **$49,500** |
| ☐ **VAARBERG, H.** ................................. *paintings* | | | **$1,980** |
| American ac. 1860 | | | |
| ☐ **VAARBERG, Johannes Christoffel** ........ *paintings* | | **$1,650** | **$2,200** |
| Dutch 1825-1871 | | | |

## Regional Artist

*Sandor Vago was a Hungarian immigrant who settled in Cleveland and achieved considerable local fame as a portrait painter.*

*Born in Hungary in 1887, Vago studied at the Royal Academy in Budapest and the Royal Academy of Munich. He also studied in Trieste and in Florence, and he exhibited widely in Hungary. He served in the first World War as a lieutenant in the Austro-Hungarian army, was captured by the Russians, and spent two years in a prisoner-of-war camp. The paintings he completed there were all destroyed by his captors.*

*Emigrating to the United States in 1921, he settled in the midwest and worked as an artist, painting portraits, still lifes, landscapes, and seascapes. In addition, he taught at the Akron Art Institute and the Art Institute of Cleveland. (Sandor Vago, "Village Scene," oil on artist's board, 19 x 24 in., Wolf's, April 19, 1985, $302.)*

|  |  | *Current Price Range* | |
|---|---|---|---|
|  |  | *Low* | *High* |
| ☐ **VACCA, Alessandro** ............................ *paintings* |  |  | **$1,100** |
| Italian b. 1836 |  |  |  |
| ☐ **VACCARO, Andrea** ........................... *paintings* |  | **$1,430** | **$3,300** |
| Italian 1598(?)-1670 |  |  |  |
| ☐ **VACCARO, Nicola** ............................ *paintings* |  |  | **$7,700** |
| Italian 1634?-1709 |  |  |  |
| ☐ **VACHER, Charles** ............................. *drawings* |  |  | **$770** |
| British 1818-1883 |  |  |  |
| ☐ **VACIN, Gerard** ................................. *paintings* |  |  | **$66** |
| Haitian b. 1923 ..................................... *drawings* |  |  | **$770** |
| ☐ **VADDER, Lodewyk de** ........................ *paintings* |  | **$1,320** | **$1,650** |
| Flemish 1605-1655 |  |  |  |
| ☐ **VAGH, Albert** ................................... *paintings* |  |  | **$6,600** |
| French b. 1831 |  |  |  |
| ☐ **VAGNETTI, Gianni** ........................... *paintings* |  |  | **$1,320** |
| Italian b. 1898 |  |  |  |
| ☐ **VAGO, Paul** ...................................... *paintings* |  |  | **$1,210** |
| Hungarian 1853-1928 |  |  |  |
| ☐ **VAGO, Sandor** .................................. *paintings* |  | **$82** | **$2,090** |
| Hungarian/American b. 1887 |  |  |  |
| ☐ **VAIL, Eugene Laurent** ....................... *paintings* |  | **$412** | **$8,250** |
| American 1857-1934 |  |  |  |
| ☐ **VAILLANT, Pierre Henri** ................... *paintings* |  |  | **$1,540** |
| French 1878-1939 |  |  |  |

| | | Current Price Range | |
|---|---|---|---|
| | | *Low* | *High* |

| | | Low | High |
|---|---|---|---|
| ☐ **VAILLANT, Wallerant** .............. *paintings* | | | $26,400 |
| Dutch 1623-1677 ...................... *drawings* | | | $1,540 |
| ☐ **VAIZATA, P.** .............. *paintings* | | | $528 |
| ☐ **VALADE, Jean** ................ *paintings* | | | $27,500 |
| French 1709-1787 | | | |
| ☐ **VALADON, Suzanne** ........... *paintings* | | $6,875 | $24,200 |
| French 1865-1938 ...................... *drawings* | | $385 | $2,860 |
| ☐ **VALCIN, Gerard** ............... *paintings* | | $302 | $5,500 |
| Haitian b. 1923 | | | |
| ☐ **VALDA, J.H.** .............. *paintings* | | | $275 |
| Continental School 20th cent. | | | |
| ☐ **VALDIVIESO, Raul** ............ *sculpture* | | | $1,210 |
| Chilean b. 1931 | | | |
| ☐ **VALE, J.** .............. *paintings* | | | $330 |
| ☐ **VALENCIA, Manuel** ............ *paintings* | | $165 | $2,200 |
| American 1856-1935/36 | | | |
| ☐ **VALENCIA, Ramona** ........... *paintings* | | $302 | $440 |
| American 20th cent. | | | |
| ☐ **VALENCIENNES, Pierre Henri de** ........ *paintings* | | | $2,750 |
| French 1750-1819 ...................... *drawings* | | | $880 |
| ☐ **VALENKAMPH,** | | | |
| **Theodore Victor Carl** ............ *paintings* | | $143 | $1,980 |
| American 1868-1924 | | | |
| ☐ **VALENSI, Henry** ................ *paintings* | | $528 | $715 |
| French 1883-1960 ...................... *drawings* | | | $220 |
| ☐ **VALENTA, Ludwig** ............ *paintings* | | | $1,650 |
| ☐ **VALENTI, P.** .............. *paintings* | | | $330 |
| ☐ **VALENTINE, Albert R.** ...................... *paintings* | | $93 | $264 |
| American 1856-1925 | | | |
| ☐ **VALENTINE, De Wain** ........... *sculpture* | | | $1,210 |
| American b. 1936 | | | |
| ☐ **VALENTINE, Edward Virginius** .......... *sculpture* | | | $2,860 |
| American 1838-1930 | | | |
| ☐ **VALENTINE, J.** ............... *paintings* | | | $1,870 |
| ☐ **VALENTINE, R.** ............... *paintings* | | | $330 |
| ☐ **VALENTINI, Gottardo** ............ *paintings* | | | $660 |
| Italian 1820-1884 | | | |
| ☐ **VALENTINI, Valentino** ...................... *paintings* | | | $1,320 |
| Italian b. 1858 | | | |
| ☐ **VALERI, Silvestro** ............... *drawings* | | $302 | $550 |
| Italian 1814-1902 | | | |
| ☐ **VALERIANI, Giuseppe** ...................... *drawings* | | | $302 |
| ☐ **VALERIO, Silvio B.** ............ *paintings* | | | $500 |
| American b. 1897 | | | |
| ☐ **VALERO, D.C.** .............. *paintings* | | | $1,540 |
| Italian 19th/20th cent. | | | |
| ☐ **VALERO, J. Pio** ................ *paintings* | | | $4,125 |
| Spanish 1830-1911 | | | |
| ☐ **VALERO, R.** ...................... *paintings* | | | $880 |

| | | Current Price Range | |
|---|---|---|---|
| | | *Low* | *High* |
| ☐ **VALERY, Paul** .................. *drawings* | | | **$440** |
| French 1871-1945 | | | |
| ☐ **VALETTA** .......................... *paintings* | | | **$500** |
| ☐ **VALEUR, Cecil** ................. *paintings* | | | **$325** |
| ☐ **VALK, Hendrik de** ............. *paintings* | | | **$6,325** |
| Dutch 17th cent. | | | |
| ☐ **VALKENBORCH, Gillis van** ........ *paintings* | | | **$13,200** |
| Flemish 1570-1622 | | | |
| ☐ **VALKENBORCH, Lucas van** ........ *paintings* | | | **$61,600** |
| Flemish c. 1530/35-1597 | | | |
| ☐ **VALKENBURG, Dirk** ............ *paintings* | **$11,000** | **$22,000** |
| Dutch 1675-1727 | | | |
| ☐ **VALKENBURG, Hendrik** .......... *paintings* | **$192** | **$8,800** |
| Dutch 1826-1896 .................. *drawings* | **$110** | **$660** |
| ☐ **VALLARDI** ......................... *paintings* | | | **$1,100** |
| ☐ **VALLAYER-MOUTET, Pauline** ......... *paintings* | | | **$3,850** |
| French 19th cent. | | | |
| ☐ **VALLEE, Etienne Maxime** ........ *paintings* | **$880** | **$3,850** |
| French ac. 1873-1881 | | | |
| ☐ **VALLEJO, Antonio** ............. *paintings* | | | **$2,200** |
| ☐ **VALLES, Lorenzo** ............... *paintings* | | | **$13,200** |
| Spanish 1830-1910 | | | |
| ☐ **VALLET, Emile** .................. *paintings* | | | **$1,980** |
| French d. 1899 | | | |
| ☐ **VALLETTE-FALGORES, Jean** | | | |
| **(called PENOT)** .............. *paintings* | | | **$35,200** |
| French 1710-1777 | | | |
| ☐ **VALLI, A.** .......................... *paintings* | | | **$330** |
| Italian School late 19th cent. | | | |
| ☐ **VALLOIS, Paul Felix** ............ *paintings* | **$1,320** | **$1,430** |
| French ac. 1876-1882 | | | |
| ☐ **VALLOTTON, Felix** ............. *drawings* | **$82** | **$176** |
| Swiss 1865-1925 | | | |
| ☐ **VALMIER, Georges** ............. *paintings* | | | **$19,800** |
| French 1885-1937 .................. *drawings* | **$2,200** | **$6,050** |
| ☐ **VALORE-UTRILLO, Lucie** .......... *paintings* | | | **$1,210** |
| French 19th/20th cent. | | | |
| ☐ **VALTAT, Louis** .................. *paintings* | **$550** | **$41,800** |
| French 1869-1952 .................. *drawings* | **$143** | **$3,300** |
| ☐ **VALTON, Charles** ............... *sculpture* | **$198** | **$1,650** |
| French 1851-1918 | | | |
| ☐ **VAN DER LEY** .................... *paintings* | | | **$4,675** |
| ☐ **VAN LOON, A.S.** ................ *paintings* | | | **$385** |
| ☐ **VAN SOELEN, Theodore** ........ *paintings* | | | **$5,500** |
| American 1890-1964 .................. *drawings* | | | **$275** |
| ☐ **VAN ZANDT, William Taylor** ......... *paintings* | | | **$935** |
| ac. 1844-1860 | | | |
| ☐ **VAN-GANA** ....................... *drawings* | | | **$192** |
| Dutch (?) 19th/20th cent. | | | |

| | | Current Price Range | |
|---|---|---|---|
| | | Low | High |
| □ **VANDERBANK, John** .......... *paintings* | | $1,540 | $2,750 |
| English c. 1694-1739 .......... *drawings* | | | $77 |
| □ **VANDERBILT** .......... *paintings* | | | $467 |
| Flemish or Dutch 19th cent. | | | |
| □ **VANDERBILT, Gloria** .......... *drawings* | | | $192 |
| American contemporary | | | |
| □ **VANDERCOOK, M.** .......... *sculpture* | | | $385 |
| □ **VANDERLYN, John (Jr.)** .......... *paintings* | | | $286 |
| American 1805-1876 | | | |
| □ **VANDERLYN, Pieter** | | | |
| **(The GANSEVOORT LIMNER)** .......... *paintings* | | | $126,500 |
| American c. 1687-1778 | | | |
| □ **VANDERMAN, E.** .......... *paintings* | | | $1,430 |
| Dutch 18th/19th cent. | | | |
| □ **VANDERMULEN** .......... *paintings* | | | $357 |
| □ **VANDERSTRATEN, Georges** .......... *sculpture* | | | $220 |
| late 19th cent. | | | |
| □ **VANDERVEIGH** .......... *paintings* | | | $2,420 |
| □ **VANDETTI, F.** .......... *paintings* | | | $1,870 |
| □ **VANDEVERDONCK, F.** .......... *paintings* | | $1,400 | $3,250 |
| Belgian 19th cent. | | | |
| □ **VANETTI** .......... *sculpture* | | | $275 |
| □ **VANLAER, Alexander T.** .......... *drawings* | | | $220 |
| American b. 1857 | | | |
| □ **VANLIER, B.** .......... *paintings* | | | $1,540 |
| Dutch 19th cent. | | | |
| □ **VANMEBLAERT, \*G.** .......... *paintings* | | | $1,100 |
| Dutch 19th cent. | | | |
| □ **VANMOUR, Jean Baptiste** .......... *paintings* | | | $2,090 |
| Flemish 1671-1737 | | | |
| □ **VANNES, A. du** .......... *paintings* | | | $605 |
| □ **VANOLY** .......... *paintings* | | | $1,870 |
| Eastern European 19th cent. | | | |
| □ **VANSCIVER, Paul A.** .......... *paintings* | | | $412 |
| American 20th cent. | | | |
| □ **VANSTAATEN, L.** .......... *drawings* | | $160 | $495 |
| □ **VANTHIER, Moreau** .......... *sculpture* | | | $3,630 |
| □ **VANTONGERLOO, Georges** .......... *paintings* | | | $27,500 |
| Belgian 1886-1965 | | | |
| □ **VANVITELLI, Luigi** .......... *drawings* | | | $1,100 |
| □ **VARDI, E.** .......... *drawings* | | | $605 |
| Italian 19th/20th cent. | | | |
| □ **VARENBERGH (?), J.** .......... *paintings* | | | $825 |
| German (?) ac. 1871 | | | |
| □ **VARGA, F.R.** .......... *sculpture* | | $248 | $385 |
| □ **VARI, Sophia** .......... *paintings* | | | $1,430 |
| contemporary | | | |
| □ **VARIAN, George E.** .......... *paintings* | | $352 | $880 |
| American 1865-1923 .......... *drawings* | | | $132 |

## Op Art

*Op Art uses geometric shapes and interacting colors to create an illusion of movement. Completely nonrepresentational, it is an exploration of the possibilities of the interplay of sharp-edged circles, squares, dots, triangles, stripes, or lines. It was quickly adopted by textile designers and decorative artists.*

*Victor Vasarely, Yaacov Gipstein, Gene Davis, and Bridget Riley are several of the dominant names in Op Art. Vasarely was born in Hungary, studied in Budapest, and went to Paris in 1930. He worked initially as a commercial artist, but had a one-man show in 1940. His early work especially shows the influence of The Bauhaus. (Victor Vasarely, "Orion-Or," gouache on board, 33 x 31½ in., Christie's, November 2, 1984, $4,840.)*

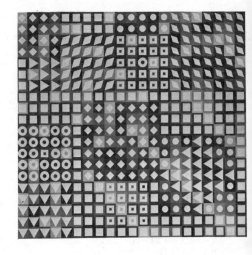

|  |  | Current Price Range | |
|---|---|---|---|
|  |  | *Low* | *High* |
| ☐ **VARLEY, John (I)** .............................. *drawings* | | **$605** | **$2,090** |
| English 1778-1842 | | | |
| ☐ **VARLEY, John (II)** ............................. *paintings* | | **$1,650** | **$18,700** |
| English ac. 1870-1896; d. c. 1899 ................... *drawings* | | **$191** | **$935** |
| ☐ **VARLORE, J.** ..................................... *sculpture* | | | **$550** |
| ☐ **VARO, Remedios** .............................. *paintings* | | **$25,300** | **$52,250** |
| Spanish 1900-1963 ..................................... *sculpture* | | | **$16,500** |
| ☐ **VARRELON** ....................................... *paintings* | | | **$770** |
| French 19th cent. | | | |
| ☐ **VASARELY, Victor** ............................ *paintings* | | **$880** | **$30,800** |
| French b. 1908 ......................................... *drawings* | | **$660** | **$4,840** |
| ☐ **VASARI, Giorgio** .............................. *drawings* | | | **$6,600** |
| Italian | | | |
| ☐ **VASARRI, Emilio** ............................. *paintings* | | | **$6,600** |
| Italian 19th cent. | | | |
| ☐ **VASILIEFF, Nicholas** ......................... *paintings* | | **$192** | **$1,760** |
| American 1892-1970 | | | |
| ☐ **VASNETSNOV, Victor Mikailovich** ....... *paintings* | | | **$1,210** |
| Russian 1848-1919 | | | |
| ☐ **VASSALLO, Anton Maria** .................... *paintings* | | | **$550** |
| ☐ **VASSE, Louis Claude** .......................... *drawings* | | | **$1,980** |
| French 1716-1772 | | | |

| | | *Current Price Range* | |
|---|---|---|---|
| | | *Low* | *High* |
| ☐ **VASSELON, Marius** ............................ *paintings* | | | $550 |
| ☐ **VASSILIEFF, Marie** ............................ *paintings* | | $385 | $2,640 |
| Russian 1884-1957 | | | |
| ☐ **VASSONY, Charles le** ......................... *paintings* | | | $247 |
| French 19th cent. | | | |
| ☐ **VASTAGH, Geza** ................................. *paintings* | | | $4,125 |
| Hungarian 1866-1919 | | | |
| ☐ **VAUGHAN, Keith** ............................... *paintings* | | | $550 |
| English b. 1912 | | | |
| ☐ **VAULIER, J.C.** ................................... *paintings* | | | $1,870 |
| French 19th cent. | | | |
| ☐ **VAUTHIER, Pierre Louis Leger** ........... *paintings* | | | $2,200 |
| French 1845-1916 | | | |
| ☐ **VAUTIER, Marc Louis Benjamin** | | | |
| **(the elder)** ............................................. *paintings* | | $8,580 | $19,800 |
| German 1829-1898 .................................. *drawings* | | $110 | $220 |
| ☐ **VAWTER, John William** ...................... *paintings* | | | $330 |
| American b. 1871 | | | |
| ☐ **VAYSSE, Leonce** ................................ *paintings* | | | $275 |
| French b. 1844 | | | |
| ☐ **VAZQUEZ, M. Tito** ............................. *paintings* | | | $357 |
| ☐ **VEAL, George** ................................... *paintings* | | | $8,800 |
| English 19th cent. | | | |
| ☐ **VEBER, Jean** .................................... *paintings* | | $1,210 | $1,540 |
| ☐ **VECSEY, Kalman** .............................. *paintings* | | | $246 |
| Hungarian b. 1925 | | | |
| ☐ **VEDDER, Elihu** ................................. *paintings* | | $440 | $33,000 |
| American 1836-1923 ................................ *drawings* | | $220 | $3,300 |
| ............................................................... *sculpture* | | $2,860 | $9,900 |
| ☐ **VEDER, Eugene Louis** ........................ *drawings* | | | $302 |
| French b. 1876 | | | |
| ☐ **VEEN, Pieter van** ............................... *paintings* | | $247 | $6,325 |
| Dutch 1563-1629 | | | |
| ☐ **VEEN, Pieter van** ............................... *paintings* | | | $1,375 |
| American 1875-1961 | | | |
| ☐ **VEENTLIET, Robert** ........................... *drawings* | | | $302 |
| French 20th cent. | | | |
| ☐ **VEENTLIET, Robert** ........................... *drawings* | | | $495 |
| American late 19th cent. | | | |
| ☐ **VEER, J.P. de** .................................. *paintings* | | | $440 |
| ☐ **VEER, Mary van der** ........................... *drawings* | | $110 | $467 |
| American b. 1865 | | | |
| ☐ **VEERENDAEL, Nicolaes van** ............... *paintings* | | $41,800 | $88,000 |
| Flemish 1640-1691 | | | |
| ☐ **VEERKAMP, L.** .................................. *paintings* | | | $187 |
| Dutch 19th cent. | | | |
| ☐ **VEGA, A. de** ..................................... *paintings* | | | $2,750 |
| ☐ **VEGA, F\*\*\*** ....................................... *paintings* | | $44 | $1,045 |

|  | | *Current Price Range* | |
| --- | --- | --- | --- |
| | | *Low* | *High* |
| ☐ **VEGA, Jorge de la** ............................. *paintings* | | | $16,500 |
| Argentinian b. 1930 | | | |
| ☐ **VEGA, Jose de la** ............................. *paintings* | | | $550 |
| 19th cent. | | | |
| ☐ **VEGAS Y MUNOZ, Pedro de** .............. *paintings* | | | $1,650 |
| Spanish 19th cent. | | | |
| ☐ **VEGER, H.J.** ....................................... *paintings* | | | $192 |
| Dutch | | | |
| ☐ **VEIT, Philipp** ..................................... *drawings* | | | $1,650 |
| German 1793-1877 | | | |
| ☐ **VEITH, Edouard** ................................. *paintings* | | | $1,100 |
| Austrian 1856-1925 | | | |
| ☐ **VEITHI, Michel** ................................. *paintings* | | | $440 |
| Austrian 1799-1846 | | | |
| ☐ **VELA, Vincenzo** ................................. *sculpture* | | | $22,000 |
| Italian 1820-1891 | | | |
| ☐ **VELANKAMPH, V.C.** ......................... *paintings* | | | $418 |
| ☐ **VELARDE, Pablita** ............................. *paintings* | | $198 | $1,100 |
| American b. 1918 | | | |
| ☐ **VELASCO, Jose Maria** ......................... *paintings* | | $99,000 | $137,500 |
| Mexican 1840-1912 ..................................... *drawings* | | $1,100 | $6,600 |
| ☐ **VELASCO, Leandro** ............................. *paintings* | | | $1,540 |
| Colombian b. 1933 | | | |
| ☐ **VELASQUEZ, Jose Antonio** .................. *paintings* | | $715 | $23,100 |
| Honduran b. 1906 | | | |
| ☐ **VELASQUEZ, Juan Ramon** .................. *paintings* | | | $1,210 |
| Puerto Rican b. 1950 ..................................... *drawings* | | $550 | $1,430 |
| ☐ **VELDE, Adriaen van de** ....................... *paintings* | | $2,860 | $28,600 |
| Dutch 1636-1672 | | | |
| ☐ **VELDE, Cornelis van de** ....................... *paintings* | | $2,640 | $3,520 |
| English ac. 1710-1729 | | | |
| ☐ **VELDE, Esaias van de (the elder)** .......... *paintings* | | $880 | $79,750 |
| Dutch 1590/91-1630 | | | |
| ☐ **VELDE, Geer van** ............................... *paintings* | | $990 | $4,950 |
| Dutch b. 1898 ......................................... *drawings* | | $154 | $1,210 |
| ☐ **VELDE, Pieter van de** ......................... *paintings* | | | $1,650 |
| Flemish 1634-1687 | | | |
| ☐ **VELDE, Willem van de (the elder)** .......... *paintings* | | $16,500 | $16,500 |
| 1611-1693 ......................................... *drawings* | | $440 | $2,200 |
| ☐ **VELDE, Willem van de (the younger)** ..... *drawings* | | | $1,320 |
| 1633-1707 | | | |
| ☐ **VELDEN, Petrus van der** ....................... *drawings* | | | $1,210 |
| Dutch 1837-1915 | | | |
| ☐ **VELDHUYZEN, Johannes Hendrik** ....... *paintings* | | | $385 |
| ☐ **VELTEN, Wilhelm** ............................. *paintings* | | $330 | $13,750 |
| Russian 1847-1929 | | | |
| ☐ **VELTER, W.** ....................................... *paintings* | | | $935 |
| ☐ **VELZEN, Gerard van** ........................... *paintings* | | | $825 |
| Dutch 19th cent. | | | |

|                                                          | Current Price Range |          |
|----------------------------------------------------------|:-------------------:|:--------:|
|                                                          |         Low         |   High   |
| ☐ **VENANT, Francois** ............... *paintings*<br>Dutch c. 1592-1636 |                     | $2,000   |
| ☐ **VENARD, Claude** ............... *paintings*<br>French b. 1913 |       $165           | $2,200   |
| ☐ **VENETO, Bartolomeo** ............... *paintings*<br>Italian ac. 1502-1555 |                     | $13,200  |
| ☐ **VENNE, Adolf van der** ............... *paintings*<br>Austrian 1828-1911 |     $1,760           | $3,410   |
| ☐ **VENNE, Adriaen van de** ............... *paintings*<br>Dutch 1589-1662 |     $4,400           | $8,800   |
| ☐ **VENNE, Fritz van der** ............... *paintings*<br>German b. 1900 |       $650           | $6,600   |
| ☐ **VENNE, Johanne van de** ............... *paintings* |                     | $352     |
| ☐ **VENNE, Pseudo van der** ............... *paintings* |                     | $550     |
| ☐ **VENNEMAN, Camille** ............... *paintings* |                     | $385     |
| ☐ **VENNEMAN, Charles Ferdinand** ............... *paintings*<br>Flemish 1802-1875 |       $357           | $14,300  |
| ☐ **VENNEMAN, Rosa** ............... *paintings*<br>Belgian 19th cent. |                     | $990     |
| ☐ **VENTNOR, Arthur** ............... *paintings*<br>English 1896-1926 |                     | $308     |
| ☐ **VENTURI, Roberto** ............... *paintings*<br>Italian 1846-1883 |                     | $1,540   |
| ☐ **VENUSTI, Marcello** ............... *paintings*<br>Italian 1512/15-1579 |                     | $4,400   |
| ☐ **VERBECK, Frank** ............... *drawings*<br>b. 1858 |       $302           | $935     |
| ☐ **VERBEECK, Francois Xavier Henri** ...... *paintings* |     $1,870           | $4,675   |
| ☐ **VERBEET, Gigsberta** ............... *paintings*<br>Dutch 1838-1916 |     $7,700           | $13,200  |
| ☐ **VERBOECKHOVEN, Charles Louis** ..... *paintings*<br>Belgian 1802-1889 |     $1,100           | $16,500  |
| ☐ **VERBOECKHOVEN, Eugene Joseph** .... *paintings*<br>Belgian 1798/99-1881 ............... *drawings* |  $550<br>$110  | $74,250<br>$1,100 |
| ☐ **VERBOOM, Adriaen Frans** ............... *paintings*<br>Dutch |     $4,950           | $7,150   |
| ☐ **VERBRUGGE, Emile** ............... *paintings*<br>Flemish b. 1856 |                     | $1,100   |
| ☐ **VERBRUGGEN, Gaspar Peeter**<br>**(the Elder)** ............... *paintings*<br>Flemish 1635-1687 |                     | $30,000  |
| ☐ **VERBRUGGEN, Gasper Pieter**<br>**(the Younger)** ............... *paintings*<br>Flemish 1664-1730 |       $577           | $12,100  |
| ☐ **VERBRUGGHE, Charles** ............... *paintings* |                     | $550     |
| ☐ **VERBRUGGHE, Charles** ............... *paintings*<br>Dutch b. 1877 |                     | $906     |
| ☐ **VERBURG, Mepard** ............... *paintings* |                     | $275     |
| ☐ **VERBURGH, D.** ............... *paintings* |                     | $770     |

| | | Current Price Range | |
|---|---|---|---|
| | | *Low* | *High* |
| ☐ **VERBURGH, Dionys** ............................ *paintings* | | | $2,200 |
| Dutch ac. 1708 | | | |
| ☐ **VERBURGH, Medard** ........................ *paintings* | | | $220 |
| Belgian 1886-1957 | | | |
| ☐ **VERDIER, Francois** ............................ *paintings* | | | $605 |
| French 1651-1730 ........................................ *drawings* | | $120 | $880 |
| ☐ **VERDIER, Jules Victor** ......................... *paintings* | | | $2,200 |
| French b. 1862 | | | |
| ☐ **VERELST, Maria** ............................... *paintings* | | | $2,310 |
| Dutch 1680-1744 | | | |
| ☐ **VERELST, Pieter Harmensz** ................. *paintings* | | | $15,400 |
| Dutch c. 1618-after 1668 | | | |
| ☐ **VERESMITH, Daniel Albert** ................. *paintings* | | | $495 |
| German b. 1861 | | | |
| ☐ **VEREY, Arthur** .................................... *paintings* | | | $1,540 |
| English 19th cent. | | | |
| ☐ **VERGANI, R.** .......................................... *paintings* | | | $1,650 |
| ☐ **VERGE-SARRAT, Henri** ...................... *drawings* | | $55 | $247 |
| French 1880-1966 | | | |
| ☐ **VERGIN, Denis** ...................................... *paintings* | | | $44,000 |
| Haitian | | | |
| ☐ **VERHAEREN, Alfred** ......................... *paintings* | | | $192 |
| Belgian b. 1849 | | | |
| ☐ **VERHAERT, Pieter** | | | |
| **(called Piet VERHAERT)** ...................... *paintings* | | $550 | $1,100 |
| Flemish 1852-1908 | | | |
| ☐ **VERHAGAN, Pierre Jan Joseph** .......... *paintings* | | | $660 |
| ☐ **VERHAS, Frans** .................................... *paintings* | | | $3,410 |
| Belgian 1827-1897 | | | |
| ☐ **VERHAS, Theodor** ............................... *drawings* | | | $1,540 |
| German 1811-1872 | | | |
| ☐ **VERHEYDEN, Francois** ...................... *paintings* | | $880 | $3,630 |
| Belgian 1806-1890(?) | | | |
| ☐ **VERHEYDEN, Isidoor** ......................... *paintings* | | | $2,970 |
| Belgian 1846-1905 | | | |
| ☐ **VERHEYEN, Jan Hendrik** .................... *paintings* | | | $12,650 |
| Dutch 1778-1846 | | | |
| ☐ **VERHOESEN, Albertus** ....................... *paintings* | | $577 | $3,080 |
| Dutch 1806-1881 | | | |
| ☐ **VERHOEVEN-BALL, Adrien Joseph** .... *paintings* | | $3,300 | $7,700 |
| Belgian 1824-1882 | | | |
| ☐ **VERK, J.** .............................................. *paintings* | | | $770 |
| ☐ **VERKOLJE, Nicholaas** ......................... *paintings* | | | $550 |
| Dutch 1673-1746 | | | |
| ☐ **VERLAT, Charles Michel Maria** .......... *paintings* | | | $990 |
| Belgian 1824-1890 | | | |
| ☐ **VERLINDE, Pierre Antoine Augustin** .... *paintings* | | $715 | $1,650 |
| Belgian 1801-1877 | | | |

| | | Current Price Range | |
|---|---|---|---|
| | | Low | High |
| ☐ **VERMEER,** | | | |
| **(Jan VERMEER de Haarlem)** .............. *paintings* | | $7,500 | $24,200 |
| Dutch 1628-1691 | | | |
| ☐ **VERMEIR, Alfons** ............................ *paintings* | | | $880 |
| Belgian 20th cent. ..................................... *drawings* | | | $176 |
| ☐ **VERMERMAN, C.** ............................ *paintings* | | | $330 |
| ☐ **VERMERSCH, Ambros** ...................... *drawings* | | | $2,530 |
| Flemish 1810-1852/54 | | | |
| ☐ **VERMEULEN, Andreas Franciscus** ....... *paintings* | | | $4,070 |
| Belgian 1821-1884 | | | |
| ☐ **VERMEULEN, Andries** ...................... *paintings* | | $935 | $14,300 |
| Dutch 1763-1814 | | | |
| ☐ **VERMEYEN, Jan Cornelisz** | | | |
| **(called Juan de Mayo)** ......................... *paintings* | | $14,300 | $25,000 |
| Dutch c. 1500-1559 | | | |
| ☐ **VERMOLEN, Hans** ............................ *paintings* | | | $247 |
| Dutch late 19th cent. | | | |
| ☐ **VERNER, Frederick Arthur** ................ *paintings* | | $715 | $4,125 |
| Canadian 1836-1928 ................................. *drawings* | | $825 | $7,700 |
| ☐ **VERNET, Antoine Charles Horace** | | | |
| **(called Charlot or Carle)** ........................ *paintings* | | | $10,450 |
| French 1758-1836 .................................... *drawings* | | $1,540 | $1,980 |
| ☐ **VERNET, Claude Joseph** ................... *paintings* | | $13,200 | $165,000 |
| French 1712/14-1789 ................................. *drawings* | | $605 | $750 |
| ☐ **VERNET, Emile Jean Horace** | | | |
| **(called Horace)** ................................... *paintings* | | $2,750 | $41,250 |
| French 1789-1863 ..................................... *drawings* | | $165 | $4,400 |
| ☐ **VERNET, J.** ................................... *paintings* | | | $1,210 |
| ☐ **VERNIER** ....................................... *paintings* | | | $550 |
| ☐ **VERNIER, Emile Louis** ...................... *paintings* | | $550 | $2,750 |
| French 1829-1887 | | | |
| ☐ **VERNON, Arthur Longley** ................... *paintings* | | $3,520 | $7,700 |
| British ac. 1871-1922 | | | |
| ☐ **VERNON, Emile** ............................... *paintings* | | $1,540 | $16,500 |
| British 19th cent. | | | |
| ☐ **VERNON, Paul** ................................ *paintings* | | $770 | $2,750 |
| French 19th cent. | | | |
| ☐ **VERNON, William H.** ........................ *paintings* | | | $1,210 |
| English b. 1820 | | | |
| ☐ **VEROLI, C. de** ................................. *sculpture* | | | $275 |
| ☐ **VERON, A.L.** .................................. *paintings* | | | $3,410 |
| French 19th cent. | | | |
| ☐ **VERON, Alexandre Rene** .................... *paintings* | | $495 | $3,850 |
| French 1826-1897 | | | |
| ☐ **VERON, Jules** ................................ *paintings* | | $495 | $3,850 |
| French School 19th cent. | | | |
| ☐ **VERON-FARE, Jules Henri** ................ *paintings* | | $825 | $3,300 |
| French ac. 1836-1870 | | | |

| | | Current Price Range | |
|---|---|---|---|
| | | Low | High |
| ☐ **VERONELLI** .................................... *drawings* | | | $330 |
| Italian 18th cent. | | | |
| ☐ **VERONESE, Bonifazio** ......................... *paintings* | | | $28,600 |
| Italian b.c. 1487-1533 | | | |
| ☐ **VERRE, Antony** ............................... *paintings* | | | $385 |
| ☐ **VERRIER, Max le** ............................. *sculpture* | | $308 | $3,080 |
| French early 20th cent. | | | |
| ☐ **VERSAILLE, E.** ................................ *paintings* | | | $715 |
| French 19th cent. | | | |
| ☐ **VERSCHNEIDER, Jean** ....................... *sculpture* | | | $1,320 |
| French | | | |
| ☐ **VERSCHUUR, Cornelis (or Carel)** ......... *paintings* | | | $990 |
| ☐ **VERSCHUUR, Cornelis Bouter** ............. *paintings* | | | $880 |
| ☐ **VERSCHUUR, Wouterus** ...................... *paintings* | | $950 | $48,400 |
| Dutch 1812-1874 | | | |
| ☐ **VERSTRAETE, Theodore** ...................... *paintings* | | | $412 |
| Belgian 1850-1907 | | | |
| ☐ **VERTANGEN, Daniel** .......................... *paintings* | | | $2,750 |
| Dutch c. 1598-before 1684 | | | |
| ☐ **VERTES, Marcel** ............................... *paintings* | | $88 | $5,500 |
| French 1895-1961 ..................................... *drawings* | | $55 | $2,420 |
| ☐ **VERTIN, Pieter Gerardus** .................... *paintings* | | $220 | $5,500 |
| Dutch 1819-1893 ..................................... *drawings* | | | $550 |
| ☐ **VERTUNNI, Achille** ........................... *paintings* | | $440 | $550 |
| European | | | |
| ☐ **VERVEER, Elanchon** .......................... *paintings* | | $2,200 | $3,300 |
| Dutch 1826-1900 | | | |
| ☐ **VERVEER, Salomon Leonardus** ............ *paintings* | | | $11,000 |
| Dutch 1813-1876 | | | |
| ☐ **VERVOORT, Michael** ......................... *paintings* | | | $6,600 |
| Dutch 19th cent. | | | |
| ☐ **VERWEE, Louis Charles** ..................... *paintings* | | | $660 |
| Belgian d. 1882 | | | |
| ☐ **VERWEE, Louis Pierre** ....................... *paintings* | | $2,200 | $10,450 |
| Belgian 1807-1877 | | | |
| ☐ **VERWER, Justus de** .......................... *paintings* | | | $11,000 |
| Dutch c.1626-c.1688 | | | |
| ☐ **VERWILT, Francois** .......................... *paintings* | | | $2,640 |
| Dutch 1629-1691 | | | |
| ☐ **VESCOVI, Avis** ................................ *paintings* | | | $330 |
| Italian early 20th cent. | | | |
| ☐ **VESIN, Jaroslav Fr. Julius** ................... *paintings* | | $4,125 | $17,600 |
| Bulgarian d. 1915 | | | |
| ☐ **VESPIGNANI, Renzo** .......................... *paintings* | | | $3,300 |
| Italian b. 1924 | | | |
| ☐ **VESTER, Willem** ............................... *paintings* | | $1,045 | $7,700 |
| Dutch 1824-1871 | | | |
| ☐ **VESTIER, Antoine** ............................ *paintings* | | | $6,050 |
| French 1740-1824 ..................................... *drawings* | | | $440 |

| | Current Price Range | |
|---|---|---|
| | *Low* | *High* |
| ☐ **VETTER, Charles Friedrich Alfred** ....... *paintings* <br> German b. 1858 | | **$3,850** |
| ☐ **VETTER, Cornelia Cowles** .................... *paintings* <br> American b. 1881 | **$27** | **$220** |
| ☐ **VEYEZ, P. de** ........................................... *paintings* | | **$825** |
| ☐ **VEYRASSART, Auguste** ...................... *drawings* | | **$275** |
| ☐ **VEYRASSAT, Jules Jacques** ................ *paintings* <br> French 1828-1893 ....................................... *drawings* | **$522** <br> **$110** | **$13,200** <br> **$385** |
| ☐ **VEZIEN, V.** ............................................... *paintings* <br> French 19th cent. | | **$286** |
| ☐ **VEZIN, Charles** ...................................... *paintings* <br> American 1858-1942 | **$495** | **$3,960** |
| ☐ **VEZIN, Frederick** .................................. *paintings* <br> American b. 1859 | | **$357** |
| ☐ **VEZIN, Yaroslav** .................................... *paintings* | | **$1,650** |
| ☐ **VIAES, H.** ................................................ *paintings* | | **$440** |
| ☐ **VIANDEN, Henry** ................................... *paintings* <br> American 1814-1899 | **$330** | **$715** |
| ☐ **VIANELLI, Achille** ................................ *drawings* <br> Italian 1803-1894 | | **$1,210** |
| ☐ **VIANELLO, Giovanni** ........................... *paintings* | | **$715** |
| ☐ **VIANI, Alberto** ..................................... *sculpture* <br> Italian b. 1906 | | **$5,500** |
| ☐ **VIANILLI** .............................................. *drawings* | | **$352** |
| ☐ **VIAVANT, George L.** ............................ *paintings* <br> American 1872-1925 .................................. *drawings* | **$495** | **$2,640** <br> **$3,630** |
| ☐ **VIBERT, Jean Georges** .......................... *paintings* <br> French 1840-1902 ...................................... *drawings* | **$550** <br> **$385** | **$33,000** <br> **$2,420** |
| ☐ **VICARI, C.** ............................................. *sculpture* <br> early 20th cent. | | **$385** |
| ☐ **VICENRIA, C.** ........................................ *paintings* | — | **$2,750** |
| ☐ **VICENTE, Esteban** ................................ *paintings* <br> Spanish/American b. 1904/06 ......................... *drawings* | **$605** | **$8,525** <br> **$880** |
| ☐ **VICHI, Prof. Ferd.** ................................ *sculpture* | **$187** | **$250** |
| ☐ **VICK, L.L.** .............................................. *paintings* | | **$750** |
| ☐ **VICKERS, Alfred** ................................... *paintings* <br> British 1786-1868 | **$550** | **$5,225** |
| ☐ **VICKERS, Alfred H.** ............................... *paintings* <br> British ac. 1853-1907 | **$350** | **$2,860** |
| ☐ **VICKERS, Henry Harold** ...................... *paintings* <br> Canadian 1851-1918 | | **$935** |
| ☐ **VICKERS, Russ** ..................................... *paintings* <br> American contemporary | **$3,750** | **$6,500** |
| ☐ **VICKREY, Robert** ................................. *paintings* <br> American b. 1926 ....................................... *drawings* | **$2,860** <br> **$22** | **$14,850** <br> **$2,640** |
| ☐ **VICTOR** ................................................ *sculpture* <br> Dutch 1620-1676 | | **$797** |
| ☐ **VICTORS, Jan** ....................................... *paintings* <br> Dutch 1620-1676 | **$6,050** | **$13,200** |

| | | Current Price Range |  |
| --- | --- | --- | --- |
| | | Low | High |
| ☐ **VICTORYNS, Anthoni** ...................... *paintings* | | | $6,050 |
| Dutch 1620?-1656? | | | |
| ☐ **VIDAL, Eugene** ..................... *drawings* | | | $528 |
| ☐ **VIDAL, Margarita Hahn** ...................... *paintings* | | $220 | $231 |
| American 20th cent. | | | |
| ☐ **VIDAL, Miguel Angel** ...................... *paintings* | | | $770 |
| b. Argentina 1928 | | | |
| ☐ **VIDAL-QUADRAS, A.** ..................... *paintings* | | | $605 |
| ☐ **VIE, B. la** ...................... *paintings* | | | $302 |
| French b. 1923 | | | |
| ☐ **VIEILLARD, Robert** ........................... *paintings* | | | $220 |
| French 19th cent. | | | |
| ☐ **VIEIRA DA SILVA, Maria Elena** ......... *paintings* | | $8,800 | $30,800 |
| French b. 1908 ..................... *drawings* | | $2,090 | $11,000 |
| ☐ **VIELLARD, Robert** ........................... *paintings* | | | $880 |
| French 19th cent. | | | |
| ☐ **VIELLEVOYE, Josef Bartholomeus** ...... *paintings* | | | $1,320 |
| Belgian 1788-1855 | | | |
| ☐ **VIEN, Joseph Marie** ........................... *drawings* | | $1,980 | $20,350 |
| French 1716-1809 | | | |
| ☐ **VIETTER, A. de** ............................... *paintings* | | | $300 |
| ☐ **VIGAS, Oswaldo** ............................... *drawings* | | | $2,420 |
| Venezuelan b. 1926 | | | |
| ☐ **VIGAS, R.** ........................................ *paintings* | | | $330 |
| Italian 19th cent. | | | |
| ☐ **VIGEE, Louis** ...................................... *drawings* | | | $24,200 |
| French 1715 or 1720/27-1767 | | | |
| ☐ **VIGIL, Frank** ...................................... *drawings* | | | $880 |
| American (Apache) | | | |
| ☐ **VIGIL, Romando** ............................... *drawings* | | $880 | $1,760 |
| American (San Ild.) | | | |
| ☐ **VIGIL, Veloy** ........................................ *paintings* | | $770 | $2,200 |
| American 20th cent. | | | |
| ☐ **VIGNAL, Pierre** ............................... *drawings* | | | $275 |
| ☐ **VIGNARI, John T.** ............................... *paintings* | | | $275 |
| American 20th cent. | | | |
| ☐ **VIGNE, Edouard de** ........................... *paintings* | | | $4,950 |
| Belgian 1808-1866 | | | |
| ☐ **VIGNE, Theodore de** ........................... *paintings* | | | $1,155 |
| ☐ **VIGNERON, Pierre Roch** ...................... *drawings* | | $165 | $330 |
| ☐ **VIGNOLES, Andre** ............................... *paintings* | | $220 | $715 |
| ☐ **VIGNON, Claude** ............................... *paintings* | | $3,080 | $7,700 |
| French | | | |
| ☐ **VIGNON, Victor** ................................... *paintings* | | $2,970 | $13,200 |
| French 1847-1909 | | | |
| ☐ **VIGNY, Silvain** ................................... *paintings* | | $82 | $357 |
| French 1902-1970 ..................... *drawings* | | | $110 |
| ☐ **VIGO, Flamma** ................................... *paintings* | | | $440 |
| 20th cent. | | | |

| | | Current Price Range | |
|---|---|---|---|
| | | Low | High |
| ☐ **VIGOVA, V.** ..................................... *paintings* | | | $352 |
| ☐ **VIKOS, K.** ......................................... *paintings* | | $495 | $650 |
| ☐ **VILA, C.** ............................................ *paintings* | | | $1,210 |
| ☐ **VILLA, Emile** ................................... *paintings* | | | $10,450 |
| French 19th cent. | | | |
| ☐ **VILLA, Hernando Gonzallo** ................. *paintings* | | $247 | $2,750 |
| American 1881-1952 ................................ *drawings* | | $137 | $330 |
| ☐ **VILLA, Theodore B.** .......................... *drawings* | | $1,650 | $4,500 |
| American | | | |
| ☐ **VILLAAMIL Y LUCAS, Eugenio** ......... *paintings* | | | $247 |
| Spanish late 19th cent. | | | |
| ☐ **VILLACRES, Cesar A.** ........................ *paintings* | | $165 | $4,675 |
| Ecuadorian b. 1880 | | | |
| ☐ **VILLAGRAN, Flavio** ........................... *paintings* | | | $550 |
| ☐ **VILLAMI** ......................................... *sculpture* | | | $2,090 |
| ☐ **VILLAMIL, Perez** ............................. *paintings* | | | $650 |
| ☐ **VILLANIS, Emmanuel** ........................ *sculpture* | | $99 | $2,255 |
| Italian 19th/20th cent. | | | |
| ☐ **VILLARD, Antoine** ............................. *paintings* | | | $825 |
| French 1867-1934 | | | |
| ☐ **VILLARSS, C.** .................................... *paintings* | | | $308 |
| ☐ **VILLEGAS, Armando** .......................... *paintings* | | $660 | $1,100 |
| Latin American | | | |
| ☐ **VILLEGAS Y CORDERO, Jose** ............ *paintings* | | $1,320 | $96,250 |
| Spanish 1848-1922 | | | |
| ☐ **VILLEGAS Y CORDERO, Ricardo** ....... *paintings* | | | $4,620 |
| Spanish b. 1852 | | | |
| ☐ **VILLEMSENS, Jean Blaise** ................... *paintings* | | | $5,720 |
| French 1806-1859 | | | |
| ☐ **VILLEON, Emmanuel de la** ................. *paintings* | | $1,650 | $2,420 |
| French 1858-1944 | | | |
| ☐ **VILLEROY, Eugene** ............................ *drawings* | | | $770 |
| ☐ **VILLIEW** .......................................... *sculpture* | | | $500 |
| ☐ **VILLON, A.** ...................................... *paintings* | | | $935 |
| ☐ **VILLON, Jacques** ............................... *paintings* | | $1,320 | $34,100 |
| French 1875-1963 ................................... *drawings* | | $209 | $48,400 |
| ☐ **VILLORESI, D.** .................................. *paintings* | | | $770 |
| ☐ **VILLORSS, C.** .................................... *paintings* | | | $308 |
| ☐ **VIN, Francois Saint Bon** ................... *paintings* | | | $385 |
| ☐ **VIN, Paul van der** ............................. *paintings* | | $1,100 | $3,850 |
| Belgian 1823-1887 | | | |
| ☐ **VINAY, Jean** ..................................... *paintings* | | $88 | $330 |
| French b. 1907 | | | |
| ☐ **VINCENT, Alexander** .......................... *paintings* | | | $2,200 |
| ☐ **VINCENT, August** .............................. *paintings* | | | $330 |
| 19th cent. | | | |
| ☐ **VINCENT, B.C.** ................................. *paintings* | | | $374 |

| | Current Price Range | |
|---|---|---|
| | Low | High |
| ☐ **VINCENT, Francois Andre** .................... *drawings*<br>French 1746-1816 | $8,800 | $9,350 |
| ☐ **VINCENT, Harry Aiken** ...................... *paintings*<br>American 1864-1931 ................................. *drawings* | $110 | $2,300<br>$550 |
| ☐ **VINCENT, John** .................................. *paintings*<br>American 19th/20th cent. | $110 | $187 |
| ☐ **VINCENT, Rene** .................................. *paintings*<br>French 1879-1936 | | $6,050 |
| ☐ **VINCIATA** ........................................... *paintings* | | $380 |
| ☐ **VINCIATO** .......................................... *paintings* | | $550 |
| ☐ **VINCK, Franz** ..................................... *paintings*<br>Belgian 1827-1903 | $770 | $1,210 |
| ☐ **VINCK, Joseph** ................................... *paintings* | | $880 |
| ☐ **VINCKBOONS, David** .......................... *paintings*<br>Flemish 1576-1629 | | $52,800 |
| ☐ **VINCZE, Paul** ..................................... *sculpture*<br>American 20th cent. | | $330 |
| ☐ **VINE, John** ........................................ *paintings* | | $1,100 |
| ☐ **VINEA, Francesco** .............................. *paintings*<br>Italian 1845/46-1902/04 | $341 | $8,800 |
| ☐ **VINES, H.** ........................................... *paintings* | | $275 |
| ☐ **VINEZE, Paul** ..................................... *sculpture* | | $1,045 |
| ☐ **VINGOE, Frank** .................................. *paintings*<br>American 19th cent. | | $330 |
| ☐ **VINNE, Vincent Jans van der** ................ *paintings*<br>Dutch 1736-1811 | | $3,960 |
| ☐ **VINNE, Vincent Laurensz van der** ......... *paintings*<br>Dutch 1629-1702 | | $33,000 |
| ☐ **VINOGRADOFF, M.** ............................ *paintings*<br>Russian 19th cent. | | $880 |
| ☐ **VINOGRADOV, Sergei Arssenievich** ..... *paintings*<br>Russian b. 1869 | | $495 |
| ☐ **VINTON, Frederick Porter** ................... *paintings*<br>American 1846-1911 | $495 | $4,125 |
| ☐ **VINTON, J.R.** ...................................... *paintings* | | $6,200 |
| ☐ **VIOLLET-LE-DUC,**<br>**Eugene Emmanuel** ............................. *drawings*<br>French 1814-1879 | | $880 |
| ☐ **VIOLLET-LE-DUC, Victor** ................... *paintings*<br>French 1848-1901 | $825 | $3,300 |
| ☐ **VIORE MASTER** ................................. *paintings* | | $5,500 |
| ☐ **VIORENTINO, E.** ................................ *drawings*<br>late 19th cent. | | $200 |
| ☐ **VIORSKY, L.** ....................................... *paintings* | | $1,100 |
| ☐ **VIRANO, A.J.** ..................................... *paintings*<br>Italian 19th cent. | | $1,430 |
| ☐ **VIRULY, Willem** ................................. *paintings* | | $2,200 |
| ☐ **VIRY, Paul Alphonse** ........................... *paintings*<br>French 1861-1881 | $1,210 | $38,500 |

|  | | | Current Price Range | |
|--|--|--|--------------------|--|
|  | | | *Low* | *High* |

| | | | Low | High |
|--|--|--|--|--|
| ☐ **VISCHER, August** .............................. *paintings*<br>German 1821-1898 | | | | $2,750 |
| ☐ **VISCONTI, F.** ..................................... *paintings*<br>Italian 19th cent. | | | | $2,750 |
| ☐ **VISKI, Janos** ...................................... *paintings*<br>Hungarian b. 1891 | | | $330 | $990 |
| ☐ **VISO, Andrea** ................................... *paintings*<br>Italian 1658-1740 | | | | $1,870 |
| ☐ **VISSOTSKY, Konstantin** ...................... *paintings*<br>Russian 20th cent. | | | | $3,300 |
| ☐ **VITAL, Diecilus** ................................. *paintings* | | | | $412 |
| ☐ **VITAL, Maurice** ................................. *paintings* | | | | $385 |
| ☐ **VITAL, Pauleus** ................................. *paintings* | | | | $660 |
| ☐ **VITATI, Ettore** .................................. *paintings* | | | | $264 |
| ☐ **VITERBO, Antonio da** ........................ *paintings* | | | | $8,800 |
| ☐ **VITERI, Alicia** ................................... *paintings* | | | | $1,100 |
| ☐ **VITO, L.** .............................................. *paintings*<br>European 19th/20th cent. | | | | $302 |
| ☐ **VITOLLO** ............................................ *paintings* | | | $220 | $418 |
| ☐ **VITTORI, F.** ....................................... *paintings*<br>Italian 19th cent. | | | $1,100 | $1,870 |
| ☐ **VITULLO, Sesostris** ........................... *paintings*<br>Argentinian 1899-1953 | | | | $220 |
| ☐ **VIVANCOS, Miguel Garcia** ................. *paintings*<br>Spanish 1895-1972 | | | $880 | $1,100 |
| ☐ **VIVAR, Juan Correa de** ...................... *paintings* | | | | $1,980 |
| ☐ **VIVARINI, Bartolommeo** ...................... *paintings*<br>Italian 1432-1499 | | | | $29,700 |
| ☐ **VIVIAN, George** ................................. *paintings*<br>British 1798-1873 | | | | $700 |
| ☐ **VIVIAN, Giuseppi** ............................. *drawings* | | | $192 | $330 |
| ☐ **VIVIAN, Joseph** ............................... *paintings*<br>British 19th cent. | | | $605 | $1,320 |
| ☐ **VIVIANI, J.** ....................................... *paintings*<br>Italian 19th cent. | | | | $412 |
| ☐ **VIVIEN, Narcisse** ............................. *paintings*<br>French 19th cent. | | | | $3,850 |
| ☐ **VIVIN, Louis** ................................... *paintings*<br>French 1861-1936 | | | $3,850 | $4,400 |
| ☐ **VIVO, Pio** ......................................... *paintings* | | | | $385 |
| ☐ **VIZZOTTO-ALBERTI, Giuseppe** .......... *drawings*<br>Italian 1862-1931 | | | $467 | $605 |
| ☐ **VLAMINCK, Maurice de** ..................... *paintings*<br>French 1876-1958 ..................................... *drawings* | | | $1,100<br>$495 | $154,000<br>$26,400 |
| ☐ **VLETTER, Samuel de** ........................ *paintings*<br>Dutch 1816-1844 | | | | $6,600 |
| ☐ **VLIEGER, Simon de** ........................... *paintings*<br>Dutch b.c. 1600, buried 1653 | | | | $12,100 |

| | | | Current Price Range | |
| | | | Low | High |
|---|---|---|---|---|
| ☐ **VLIET, Hendrick Cornelisz van der** | ...... | *paintings* | $15,400 | $24,200 |
| Dutch c. 1611-1675 | ...... | *drawings* | | $8,800 |
| ☐ **VLLSICK, Max Vogt** | ...... | *paintings* | | $175 |
| Austrian contemporary | | | | |
| ☐ **VOELCKER, Rudolph A.** | ...... | *paintings* | | $330 |
| ☐ **VOERGEN, C.** | ...... | *paintings* | | $3,850 |
| ☐ **VOERMAN, Jan** | ...... | *paintings* | $440 | $990 |
| Dutch b. 1857 | | | | |
| ☐ **VOERMAN, Jan (Jr.)** | ...... | *paintings* | $137 | $660 |
| b. 1890 | | | | |
| ☐ **VOERMAN, N.M.** | ...... | *paintings* | | $192 |
| Dutch 20th cent. | | | | |
| ☐ **VOESCHER, Leopold Heinrich** | ...... | *paintings* | | $3,080 |
| Austrian 1830-1877 | | | | |
| ☐ **VOET, Ferdinand** | ...... | *paintings* | | $2,860 |
| Flemish 17th cent. | | | | |
| ☐ **VOGEL, Cornelis Johann de** | ...... | *paintings* | $2,200 | $2,860 |
| Flemish 1824-1879 | | | | |
| ☐ **VOGEL, Johannes Gijsbert** | ...... | *drawings* | $136 | $352 |
| Dutch 1828-1915 | | | | |
| ☐ **VOGEL, Ludwig** | ...... | *drawings* | | $467 |
| Swiss 1788-1879 | | | | |
| ☐ **VOGEL, Valentine** | ...... | *paintings* | | $990 |
| American 1906-1965 | | | | |
| ☐ **VOGELAER, Karel van** | | | | |
| **(called Carlo Dei Fiori)** | ...... | *paintings* | | $11,000 |
| Dutch 1653-1695 | | | | |
| ☐ **VOGH, S.** | ...... | *paintings* | | $440 |
| ☐ **VOGLER, Paul** | ...... | *paintings* | $550 | $4,620 |
| French 1852-1904 | | | | |
| ☐ **VOGT, Adolf** | ...... | *paintings* | | $990 |
| American 1843-1871 | | | | |
| ☐ **VOGT, Fritz G.** | ...... | *paintings* | | $2,970 |
| American 1842-1900 | ...... | *drawings* | $110 | $8,800 |
| ☐ **VOGT, Gundo** | ...... | *paintings* | | $880 |
| German 1852-1939 | | | | |
| ☐ **VOGT, Louis Charles** | ...... | *paintings* | | $308 |
| American b. 1864 | ...... | *drawings* | | $77 |
| ☐ **VOGT, V.** | ...... | *paintings* | | $198 |
| American 20th cent. | | | | |
| ☐ **VOHBURGE, H.** | ...... | *sculpture* | | $275 |
| ☐ **VOIGHT, Charles A.** | ...... | *drawings* | | $220 |
| 1887-1947 | | | | |
| ☐ **VOIGT, August** | ...... | *paintings* | | $990 |
| German 19th cent. | | | | |
| ☐ **VOILLEMOT, Andre Charles** | ...... | *paintings* | $825 | $3,300 |
| French 1823-1893 | | | | |

## Art Research

Many older public libraries maintain files of ephemera: newspaper clippings, exhibition notes, and magazine articles about individual artists. Copies may be made for a nominal fee. If you are doing research on an individual artist, you may find a wealth of information in the library of his hometown or the town in which he lived.

Valentine Vogel is listed in most standard reference works as a St. Louis artist, born in 1906. "The American Art Annual" and "Who Was Who" provide her address in 1934 and information on some of the prizes she won. Phone calls to the Missouri Historical Society and the St. Louis Art Library revealed the existence of an ephemera file on Vogel. For a $4 fee, librarians photocopied the clippings and mailed them out.

Information in the file provided a more complete picture. Vogel studied in Paris in the 1920s, where she had her first exhibition. Her work was first shown in St. Louis in 1932, but she had already aroused a furor in Chicago in 1930 with

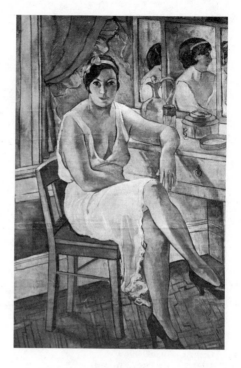

"Aprés," a nude painting of Adam and Eve. Working for the WPA during the same period, she created additional controversy with "Leda and the Swan."

Vogel married in 1940 and ran an art school in her home. She worked and exhibited actively almost to the time of her death in 1965. Her paintings ranged from portraits to abstracts, landscapes, still lifes, and animals. (Valentine Vogel, "Portrait of a Woman Seated at a Vanity Table," oil on canvas, 60 x 40 in., Selkirk Galleries, April 29, 1985, $990.)

|  | | *Current Price Range* | |
|---|---|---|---|
|  | | *Low* | *High* |
| ☐ **VOINIER, Antoine** ............................. *drawings* | | | **$23,100** |
| French ac. 1795-1810 | | | |
| ☐ **VOIS, Arie de** ................................... *paintings* | | | **$3,300** |
| Flemish c. 1631-1680 | | | |
| ☐ **VOJNITS** ........................................... *paintings* | | | **$1,000** |
| Dutch(?) 20th cent. | | | |
| ☐ **VOKERS, A.** ...................................... *paintings* | | | **$385** |
| Dutch School 19th cent. | | | |

| | | Current Price Range | |
|---|---|---|---|
| | | Low | High |
| ☐ **VOLAIRE, Jacques Antoine** (or Pierre Jacques) ................... *paintings* French 1729-1802 | | $4,950 | $17,600 |
| ☐ **VOLANCK, R.** ........................... *paintings* German 19th/20th cent. | | $275 | $286 |
| ☐ **VOLCKER, Robert** ........................ *paintings* German 1854-1924 | | $825 | $2,750 |
| ☐ **VOLFER, S.** ........................... *paintings* | | | $605 |
| ☐ **VOLK, Douglas** ........................ *paintings* American 1856-1935 | | $242 | $3,520 |
| ☐ **VOLK, Leonard Wells** ................... *sculpture* American 1828-1895 | | $412 | $5,500 |
| ☐ **VOLKER, G.** ........................... *paintings* German 19th cent. | | | $797 |
| ☐ **VOLKERS, Emil** ........................ *paintings* German 1831-1905 | | $770 | $3,080 |
| ☐ **VOLKERT, Edward Charles** ............. *paintings* American 1871-1935 ..................... *drawings* | | $900 | $4,400 $440 |
| ☐ **VOLKHART, Max** ....................... *paintings* German 1848-1924 | | $240 | $12,100 |
| ☐ **VOLKMAR, Charles** .................... *paintings* American 1841-1914 | | $302 | $330 |
| ☐ **VOLKONSKY, P.** ....................... *paintings* | | | $495 |
| ☐ **VOLKOV, E.** ........................... *paintings* Russian 19th cent. | | | $550 |
| ☐ **VOLLERDT, Jan Christian** ............. *paintings* German 1708/09-1769 | | $880 | $23,100 |
| ☐ **VOLLMERING, Joseph** .................. *paintings* American 1810-1887 | | | $14,300 |
| ☐ **VOLLON, Alexis** ....................... *paintings* French b. 1865 | | $800 | $19,800 |
| ☐ **VOLLON, Antoine** ...................... *paintings* French 1833-1900 | | $495 | $29,700 |
| ☐ **VOLLWEIDER, August** .................. *paintings* German b. 1835; ac. 1867 | | | $3,520 |
| ☐ **VOLLWEIDER, Johann Jacob** ............ *paintings* German 1834-1891 | | $990 | $1,870 |
| ☐ **VOLPINI, J.R.** ........................ *paintings* | | | $1,045 |
| ☐ **VOLTERRA, C.** ........................ *paintings* 20th cent. | | | $990 |
| ☐ **VOLTINI, G. A.** ....................... *paintings* | | | $1,650 |
| ☐ **VOLTNER, R.** ......................... *paintings* | | | $605 |
| ☐ **VOLTZ, Friedrich Johann** .............. *paintings* German 1817-1886 ...................... *drawings* | | $2,200 $22 | $55,000 $1,320 |
| ☐ **VOLTZ, Ludwig** ....................... *paintings* German 1825-1911 | | $220 | $990 |
| ☐ **VOLZ, W.** ............................. *paintings* German 19th/20th cent. | | | $319 |

|  | | *Current Price Range* | |
| --- | --- | --- | --- |
|  | | Low | High |
| ☐ **VONCK, Elias** .............................. *paintings* | | | $11,000 |
| Dutch c. 1605-1652 | | | |
| ☐ **VONDROUS, J. C.** ............................ *paintings* | | | $187 |
| b. 1884 | | | |
| ☐ **VONNOH, Bessie Onahotema Potter** ..... *sculpture* | | $1,815 | $10,450 |
| American 1872-1955 | | | |
| ☐ **VONNOH, R.W.** .................................. *paintings* | | | $357 |
| ☐ **VONNOH, Robert William** .................. *paintings* | | $880 | $28,600 |
| American 1858-1933 | | | |
| ☐ **VOO, A.V.D.** ..................................... *paintings* | | | $385 |
| Dutch 19th cent. | | | |
| ☐ **VOORDEN, August Willem van** ........... *paintings* | | $420 | $605 |
| Dutch 1881-1921 | | | |
| ☐ **VOORHEES, Clark** ........................... *paintings* | | | $1,100 |
| American 1871-1933 | | | |
| ☐ **VOORST** ....................................... *paintings* | | | $330 |
| ☐ **VORDEMBERGE-GILDEWART,** | | | |
| **Friedrich** ........................................ *drawings* | | | $13,200 |
| German/Dutch 1899-1963 | | | |
| ☐ **VOROS, Bela** ..................................... *drawings* | | $275 | $385 |
| Hungarian 20th cent. .............................. *sculpture* | | $1,100 | $3,960 |
| ☐ **VORPICCHIO, A.** ............................. *paintings* | | | $1,430 |
| ☐ **VOS, Cornelis de** ............................. *paintings* | | $2,420 | $6,050 |
| Flemish 1585-1651 | | | |
| ☐ **VOS, Harry** ..................................... *paintings* | | $220 | $356 |
| Dutch 20th cent. | | | |
| ☐ **VOS, Hubert** .................................... *paintings* | | $187 | $2,750 |
| Dutch/American 1855-1935 ......................... *drawings* | | $200 | $1,430 |
| ☐ **VOS, Isaak de** .................................. *paintings* | | | $330 |
| American 19th/20th cent. | | | |
| ☐ **VOS, J.C.J. de** ................................. *paintings* | | $660 | $880 |
| Dutch 19th/20th cent. | | | |
| ☐ **VOS, Leon de** .................................. *paintings* | | | $1,100 |
| Belgian 20th cent. | | | |
| ☐ **VOS, Martin de** ................................. *paintings* | | $1,760 | $4,180 |
| Flemish 1532-1603 | | | |
| ☐ **VOS, Paul de** .................................... *paintings* | | $3,080 | $7,150 |
| Flemish 1596-1678 | | | |
| ☐ **VOS, Simon de** ................................. *paintings* | | $3,300 | $9,900 |
| Flemish 1603-1676 | | | |
| ☐ **VOS, Vincent de** ............................... *paintings* | | $440 | $935 |
| Belgian 1829-1875 | | | |
| ☐ **VOSS, Carl Leopold** ........................... *paintings* | | | $1,870 |
| German 1856-1921 | | | |
| ☐ **VOSS, Franklin Brooke** ....................... *paintings* | | | $7,150 |
| American 20th cent. | | | |
| ☐ **VOSS, H.G.** ....................................... *paintings* | | | $176 |
| American 19th/20th cent. | | | |

| | | *Current Price Range* | |
| --- | --- | --- | --- |
| | | *Low* | *High* |
| ☐ **VOTER (?), Phillip** ............................ *sculpture* | | | $247 |
| contemporary | | | |
| ☐ **VOULKOS, Peter** ........................ *sculpture* | | $2,200 | $14,300 |
| American b. 1924 | | | |
| ☐ **VOUTIER, J.C.** ................................ *paintings* | | $1,320 | $1,760 |
| French 19th cent. | | | |
| ☐ **VOYET, Jacques** ............................... *paintings* | | | $275 |
| French b. 1927 | | | |
| ☐ **VOYEZ, Emile** ................................. *sculpture* | | $1,650 | $2,178 |
| French ac. 1873-1892, d. 1895 | | | |
| ☐ **VRANCX, Sebastian** ......................... *paintings* | | $11,000 | $44,000 |
| Flemish 1573/78-1647 | | | |
| ☐ **VREEDENBURGH, Cornelis** .............. *paintings* | | $2,090 | $5,225 |
| Dutch 1880-1946 ........................................ *drawings* | | $82 | $209 |
| ☐ **VREELAND, Anderson** ....................... *paintings* | | $1,430 | $1,540 |
| American 19th cent. | | | |
| ☐ **VREELAND, F. van** ............................ *paintings* | | $247 | $375 |
| Dutch 19th cent. ..................................... *drawings* | | $27 | $660 |
| ☐ **VRERBERT** ....................................... *paintings* | | | $700 |
| ☐ **VREY, Tom** ....................................... *paintings* | | | $220 |
| American 19th cent. | | | |
| ☐ **VRIENDT, Juliaan de** ......................... *paintings* | | $1,540 | $1,760 |
| Belgian 1842-1935 | | | |
| ☐ **VRIES, Anthoni de** ............................ *paintings* | | | $1,980 |
| Dutch 1841-1872 | | | |
| ☐ **VRIES, Corstiaan de** ........................... *drawings* | | $77 | $220 |
| Dutch 20th cent. | | | |
| ☐ **VRIES, Jogh. de** .................................. *paintings* | | | $8,500 |
| Dutch 18th cent. | | | |
| ☐ **VRIES, Roelof Jansz de** .................... *paintings* | | $22,000 | $20,900 |
| Dutch c. 1631-1681 | | | |
| ☐ **VROLYK, Adrianus Jacobus** ............... *paintings* | | $2,475 | $5,225 |
| Dutch 1834-1862 | | | |
| ☐ **VROLYK, Jan Martinus** ....................... *paintings* | | $1,430 | $1,760 |
| Dutch 1845-1894 ....................................... *drawings* | | $275 | $412 |
| ☐ **VROOM, Hendrik Cornelisz** ............... *paintings* | | | $660 |
| Dutch 1566-1640 ...................................... *drawings* | | | $5,720 |
| ☐ **VU CAO DAM** .................................... *paintings* | | $302 | $990 |
| b. 1908 | | | |
| ☐ **VUCHT, Gerrit van** ............................ *paintings* | | | $12,100 |
| Dutch c. 1610-1697 | | | |
| ☐ **VUCHT, Jan van** ............................... *paintings* | | $7,700 | $9,075 |
| ☐ **VUILLARD, Edouard** ......................... *paintings* | | $6,700 | $341,000 |
| French 1868-1940 ..................................... *drawings* | | $1,100 | $297,000 |
| ☐ **VUKOVIC, Marko** ............................ *paintings* | | $137 | $715 |
| American 20th cent. | | | |
| ☐ **VUTINI** ............................................ *paintings* | | | $300 |
| ☐ **VUUREN, Jan van** .............................. *paintings* | | | $385 |

| | | | Low | High |
|---|---|---|---|---|
| ☐ **VUYST, Jan de** | ...................................... | *paintings* | | $192 |
| Belgian 19th cent. | | | | |
| ☐ **VYARET, August** | ................................... | *paintings* | | $770 |
| ☐ **VYLDER, C. de** | .................................... | *paintings* | | $1,540 |
| ☐ **VYTLACIL, Vaclav** | ............................. | *paintings* | $27 | $2,090 |
| American b. 1893 | ...................................... | *drawings* | $121 | $1,210 |
| ☐ **VYUSQUAIZ** | ........................................ | *paintings* | | $412 |
| Continental 19th cent. | | | | |
| ☐ **WAAGEN** | .......................................... | *sculpture* | $12,100 | $16,500 |
| German 19th cent. | | | | |
| ☐ **WAAY, Nicholas van der** | ..................... | *paintings* | | $5,390 |
| Dutch 1855-1936 | ...................................... | *drawings* | | $302 |
| ☐ **WABEL, C.** | ....................................... | *paintings* | | $522 |
| American 19th cent. | | | | |
| ☐ **WACH, Aloys (or WACHLMAYR)** | ........ | *drawings* | $385 | $715 |
| Austrian 1892-1940 | | | | |
| ☐ **WACHEN, E.R.** | .................................... | *sculpture* | | $308 |
| ☐ **WACHTEL, Elmer** | ................................ | *paintings* | $715 | $4,180 |
| American 1864-1929 | ................................... | *drawings* | | $880 |
| ☐ **WACHTEL, Marion Kavanaugh** | ........... | *drawings* | $440 | $1,800 |
| American 1875-1954 | | | | |
| ☐ **WADE, C.T.** | ...................................... | *paintings* | | $522 |
| ☐ **WADHAM, W. Joseph** | ........................ | *drawings* | | $330 |
| American 20th cent. | | | | |
| ☐ **WADSWORTH, Edward** | ..................... | *paintings* | | $2,310 |
| English b. 1889 | | | | |
| ☐ **WADSWORTH, Frank R.** | .................... | *paintings* | | $1,210 |
| American 1874-1905 | | | | |
| ☐ **WAEL, Cornelis de** | ............................ | *paintings* | $1,760 | $14,300 |
| Flemish 1592-1667 | | | | |
| ☐ **WAERHERD, Arthur de** | ..................... | *paintings* | | $330 |
| ☐ **WAGEMAN, Thomas Charles** | .............. | *drawings* | | $220 |
| British 1787-1863 | | | | |
| ☐ **WAGEMANS, P.J.A.** | .......................... | *paintings* | | $935 |
| Dutch 1879-1955 | | | | |
| ☐ **WAGNER, Alexander von** | ..................... | *paintings* | | $1,430 |
| Hungarian 1838-1919 | | | | |
| ☐ **WAGNER, Alois** | ................................. | *drawings* | | $275 |
| Austrian 1765-1841 | | | | |
| ☐ **WAGNER, C.** | ..................................... | *paintings* | | $660 |
| German (?) 19th/20th cent. | | | | |
| ☐ **WAGNER, Elyse Puyroche** | ................. | *paintings* | | $935 |
| German 1828-1895 | | | | |
| ☐ **WAGNER, Ernest** | ............................. | *sculpture* | | $467 |
| ☐ **WAGNER, Fred** | ................................. | *paintings* | $198 | $5,280 |
| American 1864-1940 | ................................... | *drawings* | $110 | $495 |
| ☐ **WAGNER, Fritz** | ................................. | *paintings* | $770 | $770 |
| Swiss b. 1872 | | | | |
| ☐ **WAGNER, Hans** | ................................. | *paintings* | $66 | $550 |

| | | Current Price Range | |
|---|---|---|---|
| | | *Low* | *High* |
| ☐ **WAGNER, Jacob** ............................ *paintings* | | $385 | $660 |
| American 1852-1898 | | | |
| ☐ **WAGNER, Joseph** ............................ *paintings* | | | $935 |
| 19th cent. | | | |
| ☐ **WAGNER, Karl** ............................... *paintings* | | $880 | $1,760 |
| Austrian/German late 19th/early 20th cent. | | | |
| ☐ **WAGNER, L.** ................................... *paintings* | | | $176 |
| American 19th/20th cent. | | | |
| ☐ **WAGNER, Paul** ............................... *paintings* | | $2,860 | $4,950 |
| German ac. 1889 | | | |
| ☐ **WAGNER, V. G.** .............................. *paintings* | | | $825 |
| ☐ **WAGNER, Wolfgang** ........................ *paintings* | | | $660 |
| German 19th cent. | | | |
| ☐ **WAGNER-HOHENBERG, Josef** .......... *paintings* | | $4,400 | $8,800 |
| German b. 1870 | | | |
| ☐ **WAGONER, Harry B.** ....................... *paintings* | | $412 | $2,475 |
| American 1889-1950 | | | |
| ☐ **WAGREZ, Jacques Clement** ............... *paintings* | | $8,800 | $13,750 |
| French 1846/50-1908 | | | |
| ☐ **WAGUE, J.R.** .................................. *paintings* | | | $175 |
| American 19th cent. | | | |
| ☐ **WAHLBERG, Alfred** .......................... *paintings* | | $1,430 | $2,860 |
| Swedish 1834-1906 | | | |
| ☐ **WAINEWRIGHT, Thomas Francis** ....... *drawings* | | $99 | $385 |
| English 19th cent. | | | |
| ☐ **WAINWRIGHT, John** ........................ *paintings* | | $5,225 | $44,000 |
| British ac. 1859-1869 | | | |
| ☐ **WAINWRIGHT, William John** ............. *drawings* | | | $715 |
| British 1855-1931 | | | |
| ☐ **WAISS, J.** ...................................... *paintings* | | | $770 |
| ☐ **WAITE, A. A.** .................................. *paintings* | | | $660 |
| 19th cent. | | | |
| ☐ **WAITE, Edward W.** ........................... *paintings* | | | $1,375 |
| English 19th/20th cent. | | | |
| ☐ **WAITE, Robert Thorne** ...................... *drawings* | | | $412 |
| British 1842-1935 | | | |
| ☐ **WAITT, Marion Martha Parkhurst** ....... *paintings* | | | $495 |
| ☐ **WAKE, C.** ...................................... *paintings* | | | $1,870 |
| Continental 19th cent. | | | |
| ☐ **WAKEFIELD, Manville B.** ................... *paintings* | | $330 | $440 |
| American 20th cent. | | | |
| ☐ **WALBOURN, Ernest** .......................... *paintings* | | $275 | $3,300 |
| British ac. 1895-1920 | | | |
| ☐ **WALCH, Charles** .............................. *paintings* | | $550 | $4,180 |
| French 1898-1948 | | | |
| ☐ **WALCKIERS, Gustave** ....................... *paintings* | | | $5,775 |
| Belgian 1831-91 | | | |
| ☐ **WALCOT, William** ............................ *drawings* | | $275 | $500 |
| English 1874-1943 | | | |

**English Country Scenes**

*There were many attractive, sweet, and decorative pictures painted to grace the front parlors of proper Victorian homes. These paintings, often garden scenes, retain their appeal.*

*Ernest Walbourn was a Victorian landscape painter in the tradition of Helen Allingham, who was the acknowledged master of this genre. Walbourn's landscape is reminiscent of the paintings of cottage gardens which were very popular during the 19th century. (Ernest Walbourn, "Goose Girl on a Bridge," oil on canvas, 16 x 24¼ in., Christie's East, May 22, 1985, $3,300.)*

| | | Current Price Range | |
| --- | --- | --- | --- |
| | | *Low* | *High* |
| ☐ **WALCUTT, William** .......................... *sculpture* | | | **$8,800** |
| American 1819-1895 | | | |
| ☐ **WALDAU, Grete** ................................ *paintings* | | | **$275** |
| ☐ **WALDE, Alfons** ................................ *paintings* | | | **$6,875** |
| Austrian b. 1891 | | | |
| ☐ **WALDECK, Nina** .............................. *paintings* | | | **$247** |
| b. 1868 | | | |
| ☐ **WALDEGG, F.** .................................. *paintings* | | | **$1,320** |
| German 19th cent. | | | |
| ☐ **WALDEGG, T.** .................................. *paintings* | | | **$550** |
| American early 20th cent. | | | |
| ☐ **WALDMAN, Paul** .............................. *paintings* | | | **$770** |
| ☐ **WALDMANN, L.** ................................ *paintings* | | | **$275** |
| German 19th cent. | | | |

## Genre Scenes of Plantation Life

Many art historians consider the paintings of William Aiken Walker a chronicle of black life after the Civil War. Born in South Carolina, Walker was an itinerant artist with little formal training. He travelled throughout the South, stopping everywhere to paint. His typical choices of subjects included blacks in front of cabins, in wagons, or working in cotton fields. The paintings vary in size — some of the smaller, simpler oils were actually sold on the streets of New Orleans as postcard-like souvenirs. Following the 1972 publication of a lavishly illustrated monograph on Walker, prices of his work escalated sharply. (William Aiken Walker, "Cabin Scene With Cotton Pickers," oil on artist's board, 6⅛ x 12¼ in., Bourne, August 9, 1983, $8,250.)

| | | Current Price Range | |
|---|---|---|---|
| | | *Low* | *High* |
| ☐ **WALDMANN, Oscar** ............................ *sculpture* | | | $286 |
| Swiss b. 1856 | | | |
| ☐ **WALDO, Samuel Lovett** ...................... *paintings* | | $330 | $4,675 |
| American 1783-1861 | | | |
| ☐ **WALDORP, Antoine** ........................... *paintings* | | | $1,760 |
| Dutch 1803-1866 | | | |
| ☐ **WALE, Samuel** ................................. *paintings* | | | $495 |
| English 1721-1786 | | | |
| ☐ **WALES, J.** ....................................... *paintings* | | | $660 |
| American 19th cent. | | | |
| ☐ **WALES, Orlando G.** .......................... *paintings* | | | $275 |
| ☐ **WALES, Susan Makepiece Larkin** ......... *drawings* | | $50 | $286 |
| American 1839-1927 | | | |
| ☐ **WALKER, Ada H.** ............................. *drawings* | | | $49 |
| British 19th/20th cent. ............................... *sculpture* | | $4,750 | $40,000 |
| ☐ **WALKER, Barvo** .............................. *sculpture* | | $4,750 | $40,000 |
| American contemporary | | | |
| ☐ **WALKER, Charles Alvah** ..................... *paintings* | | $350 | $1,320 |
| American 1848-1920 ................................. *drawings* | | | $495 |

| | | Current Price Range | |
|---|---|---|---|
| | | *Low* | *High* |

☐ **WALKER, D.L.** ..................... *paintings* | | $412
American

☐ **WALKER, Faten** ..................... *paintings* | | $297
☐ **WALKER, Frederick** ..................... *paintings* | | $4,675
British 1840-1875

☐ **WALKER, Harold** ..................... *paintings* | | $412
American b. 1890

☐ **WALKER, Henry Oliver** ..................... *paintings* | $275 | $2,035
American 1843-1929 ..................... *drawings* | | $660

☐ **WALKER, Horatio** ..................... *paintings* | $660 | $5,720
Canadian 1858-1938 ..................... *drawings* | $224 | $1,100

☐ **WALKER, J.F.** ..................... *paintings* | | $20,000
☐ **WALKER, Jesse A.** ..................... *drawings* | | $192
American ac. 1898

☐ **WALKER, John** ..................... *paintings* | $935 | $22,000
English b. 1939

☐ **WALKER, R. Hollands** ..................... *paintings* | $1,100 | $1,430
British ac. 1892-1920

☐ **WALKER, Robert** ..................... *paintings* | | $1,760
English 1607-1658

☐ **WALKER, Samuel** ..................... *paintings* | | $1,100
American ac. 1853-1855

☐ **WALKER, William Aiken** ..................... *paintings* | $660 | $34,100
American c. 1838-1921 ..................... *drawings* | $715 | $4,070

☐ **WALKER, William Henry** ..................... *drawings* | $110 | $330
American b. 1871

☐ **WALKLEY, David Birdsley** ..................... *paintings* | $192 | $7,425
American 1849-1934

☐ **WALKOWITZ, Abraham** ..................... *paintings* | $242 | $3,850
American 1880-1965 ..................... *drawings* | $44 | $1,760

☐ **WALKY, M.** ..................... *paintings* | | $1,430
Swiss (?) 19th cent.

☐ **WALL, A. Bryan** ..................... *paintings* | $467 | $1,100
American 1872-1937

☐ **WALL, Alfred S.** ..................... *paintings* | $81 | $13,475
American 1825-1896

☐ **WALL, Bernard** ..................... *paintings* | $55 | $192
American 20th cent.

☐ **WALL, Herman C.** ..................... *paintings* | $1,100 | $1,980
American b. 1875

☐ **WALL, J.** ..................... *paintings* | | $357
☐ **WALL, William A** ..................... *drawings* | | $330
American 1801-1885

☐ **WALL, William Archibald** ..................... *paintings* | $286 | $1,375
British 1828-1875

☐ **WALL, William Guy** ..................... *drawings* | $385 | $770
American 1792-after 1864

☐ **WALLACE, Donald** ..................... *paintings* | | $577
British 20th cent.

| | | | Current Price Range | |
|---|---|---|---|---|
| | | | Low | High |
| ☐ **WALLACE, George** | ........................... | *paintings* | | $247 |
| Irish/Canadian b. 1920 | | | | |
| ☐ **WALLACE, Harry** | ............................. | *paintings* | | $935 |
| British ac. 1886 | | | | |
| ☐ **WALLACE, James** | ............................. | *paintings* | | $660 |
| British d. 1911 | | | | |
| ☐ **WALLACE, John** | ................................ | *paintings* | | $462 |
| ☐ **WALLACE, William** | ........................... | *sculpture* | | $474 |
| ☐ **WALLANS, A.R.** | ................................ | *drawings* | | $440 |
| ☐ **WALLBURG, Egon** | ............................. | *drawings* | | $385 |
| ☐ **WALLER, Frank** | ............................... | *paintings* | $121 | $4,400 |
| American 1842-1923 | | | | |
| ☐ **WALLER, Johannes** | ........................... | *paintings* | | $467 |
| German d. 1945 | | | | |
| ☐ **WALLER, Margaret Mary** | ................... | *paintings* | | $175 |
| English 20th cent. | | | | |
| ☐ **WALLER, Samuel Edmund** | ................. | *paintings* | $660 | $8,250 |
| British 1850-1903 | | | | |
| ☐ **WALLERN** | ....................................... | *paintings* | | $200 |
| American contemporary | | | | |
| ☐ **WALLIS, Alfred** | ............................... | *paintings* | | $467 |
| English 1855-1924 | | | | |
| ☐ **WALLIS, Frank** | ............................... | *paintings* | | $550 |
| American d. 1934 | | | | |
| ☐ **WALLIS, Henry** | ............................... | *paintings* | $605 | $1,430 |
| British 1830-1916 | | | | |
| ☐ **WALLNER, Th.** | ................................ | *paintings* | | $605 |
| European 19th/20th cent. | | | | |
| ☐ **WALLS, W.H.** | .................................. | *paintings* | | $192 |
| English 19th cent. | | | | |
| ☐ **WALMSLEY, Thomas** | ........................ | *drawings* | | $467 |
| Irish 1763-1805 | | | | |
| ☐ **WALRAVEN, Jan** | .............................. | *paintings* | $742 | $6,600 |
| Dutch 1827-after 1874 | | | | |
| ☐ **WALSH, Nellie T.** | ............................. | *paintings* | $150 | $660 |
| American 19th cent. | | | | |
| ☐ **WALSH, T.** | ...................................... | *drawings* | | $715 |
| ☐ **WALT DISNEY PRODUCTIONS** | .......... | *paintings* | $55 | $1,320 |
| | .................................................... | *drawings* | $110 | $20,900 |
| ☐ **WALTENSPERGER, Charles E.** | .......... | *paintings* | $115 | $550 |
| American 1871-1931 | | | | |
| ☐ **WALTER, A.** | ..................................... | *paintings* | | $825 |
| ☐ **WALTER, Charles** | ............................. | *paintings* | | $275 |
| American 19th/20th cent. | | | | |
| ☐ **WALTER, Christian J.** | ........................ | *paintings* | $330 | $4,125 |
| American 1872-1938 | | | | |
| ☐ **WALTER, F.** | ..................................... | *paintings* | | $412 |
| English 19th cent. | | | | |

## Animation Art

Animation cels, backgrounds, drawings, and model sheets have begun to capture the public collecting interest as evidenced by the popularity of recent exhibits at the Museum of Modern Art and the Whitney Museum. The most sought-after and desirable art is that actually used in classic short and feature-length films.

Collecting animation art was the inspiration of Guthrey Courvoisier who, in 1937, became the first licensee to offer Disney animation art for sale. The powerful impetus of potential sales and immense public acceptance of "Snow White and the Seven Dwarfs" prompted Disney to set up a special department of twenty artists to prepare the art for sale. Many of the objects being sold today feature the original Courvoisier label.

Prices vary widely for animation art depending on age, condition, pose, and completeness. Some art from recent films can be purchased for as little as $35. This cel "setup" of Mickey Mouse, estimated by Christie's East at $2,500, sold for $20,900 in December 1984. The lot was especially desirable because the cel was accompanied by the original matching background and its condition excellent. Rumors circulated after the sale that the intense bidding was the result of a rivalry between movie makers George Lucas and Steven Spielberg. (Walt Disney Studios, "Brave Little Tailor, 1938," celluloid, 8⅛ x 10⅝ in., Christie's East, December 8, 1984, $20,900.)

| | | Current Price Range | |
|---|---|---|---|
| | | Low | High |
| ☐ **WALTER, Henry** .................... drawings | | | **$2,200** |
| English 1786-1849 | | | |
| ☐ **WALTER, J.** ...................... paintings | | | **$440** |
| ☐ **WALTER, L.** ...................... paintings | | | **$1,320** |
| American 19th cent. | | | |
| ☐ **WALTER, Martha** ............... paintings | | **$3,300** | **$11,000** |
| American 1875-1976 .................. drawings | | | **$1,100** |
| ☐ **WALTER, W.J.** ................... paintings | | | **$385** |
| Dutch 1818-1894 | | | |
| ☐ **WALTERS, Emile** ............... paintings | | **$110** | **$1,540** |
| American b. 1893 | | | |
| ☐ **WALTERS, George Stanfield** ....... paintings | | | **$3,300** |
| British 1838-1924 ...................... drawings | | **$150** | **$1,050** |

| | Current Price Range | |
|---|---|---|
| | Low | High |

☐ **WALTERS, H.** ..................................... *paintings* | | $907
American 19th cent.

☐ **WALTERS, J.** ..................................... *paintings* | | $375
English 19th cent.

☐ **WALTERS, Samuel** ............................. *paintings* | $286 | $19,800
British 1811-1882

☐ **WALTHER, Charles H.** ........................ *paintings* | | $192
American 1879-1938

☐ **WALTHER, Emmi** ............................. *paintings* | $550 | $1,320

☐ **WALTMAN, Harry Franklin** ................ *paintings* | | $400
American 1871-1951

☐ **WALTON, Cecile** ............................... *paintings* | | $3,000
British 1891-1956

☐ **WALTON, Edward Arthur** ................... *paintings* | $1,650 | $7,000
British 1860-1922 ..................................... *drawings* | | $385

☐ **WALTON, F.** ..................................... *paintings* | | $220
German 19th cent.

☐ **WALTON, Henry** ............................... *paintings* | | $786

☐ **WALTON, M.** ..................................... *paintings* | | $220
English

☐ **WALTON, William** ........................... *paintings* | | $935
1843-1915

☐ **WALYN** ............................................... *paintings* | | $250
2Oth cent.

☐ **WANE, Harold** ................................... *drawings* | | $176
English 1879-1900

☐ **WANE, Richard** ................................... *paintings* | | $660

☐ **WANING, Cornelis van** ........................ *paintings* | $220 | $280
Dutch 1861-1929

☐ **WANING, Martin van** ........................ *paintings* | | $467

☐ **WANKOWSKI** ..................................... *paintings* | | $2,310
Polish 19th cent.

☐ **WAPPERS, Baron de Gustave** ............... *paintings* | $3,025 | $4,950
Belgian 1803-1874

☐ **WARD, A.R.** ..................................... *paintings* | | $440
American 19th cent.

☐ **WARD, Camille** ............................... *paintings* | | $715
English 19th cent.

☐ **WARD, Charles Caleb** ........................ *drawings* | $880 | $1,430
American c. 1831-1896

☐ **WARD, Charles D.** ............................. *paintings* | $440 | $521

☐ **WARD, Edgar Melville** ........................ *paintings* | $99 | $6,300
American 1839-1915

☐ **WARD, Edmund F.** ............................. *paintings* | $330 | $4,125
American b. 1892

☐ **WARD, Edwin Arthur** ........................ *paintings* | | $550
British 19th cent.

☐ **WARD, Enoch** ..................................... *paintings* | $66 | $220
British 1859-1922 ..................................... *drawings* | $137 | $220

| | | Current Price Range | |
|---|---|---|---|
| | | *Low* | *High* |
| ☐ **WARD, Everett** ............................ *paintings* | | | **$330** |
| ☐ **WARD, James** ............................ *paintings* | | **$660** | **$60,500** |
| British 1769-1859 ............................ *drawings* | | | **$495** |
| ☐ **WARD, James Charles** ..................... *paintings* | | | **$1,250** |
| English ac. 1830-1875 | | | |
| ☐ **WARD, John Quincy Adams** ............... *sculpture* | | **$660** | **$28,600** |
| American 1830-1910 | | | |
| ☐ **WARD, Kenneth** ............................ *paintings* | | | **$2,640** |
| ☐ **WARD, Lynd** ............................ *sculpture* | | | **$1,320** |
| English early 20th cent. | | | |
| ☐ **WARD, Martin Theodore** .................. *paintings* | | **$1,870** | **$4,800** |
| English 1799-1874 | | | |
| ☐ **WARD, Matthew Edward** .................. *paintings* | | **$385** | **$550** |
| British 1816-1879 | | | |
| ☐ **WARD, Myron** ............................ *paintings* | | | **$385** |
| English 19th cent. | | | |
| ☐ **WARD, William (Jr.)** ...................... *paintings* | | **$440** | **$440** |
| ☐ **WARD, William H.** ........................ *paintings* | | | **$1,045** |
| ☐ **WARDE, J.C.** ............................ *paintings* | | | **$270** |
| ☐ **WARDLE, Arthur** ........................ *paintings* | | **$1,700** | **$9,350** |
| English 1864-1949 ............................ *drawings* | | **$220** | **$247** |
| ☐ **WARDLEWORTH, J.L.** .................... *paintings* | | **$1,100** | **$2,090** |
| British 19th cent. | | | |
| ☐ **WARE, Charles M.** ........................ *drawings* | | | **$330** |
| Dutch 20th cent. | | | |
| ☐ **WARE, Tomas** ............................ *paintings* | | | **$2,200** |
| American 19th cent. | | | |
| ☐ **WARHAM, W.** ............................ *paintings* | | | **$330** |
| ☐ **WARHOL, Andy** ............................ *paintings* | | **$176** | **$148,500** |
| American b. 1930 ............................ *drawings* | | **$286** | **$10,450** |
| ............................ *sculpture* | | **$3,850** | **$3,850** |
| ☐ **WARLE, Arthor** ............................ *drawings* | | | **$275** |
| English 1864-1947 | | | |
| ☐ **WARNER, Everett Longley** ............... *paintings* | | **$88** | **$2,970** |
| American 1877-1963 ............................ *drawings* | | | **$418** |
| ☐ **WARNER, J.** ............................ *paintings* | | | **$770** |
| American 19th cent. | | | |
| ☐ **WARNER, Nell Walker** .................... *paintings* | | | **$330** |
| American 1891-1970 | | | |
| ☐ **WARREN, Andrew W.** ...................... *paintings* | | **$1,045** | **$9,000** |
| American d. 1873 | | | |
| ☐ **WARREN, C.W.** ............................ *sculpture* | | | **$4,675** |
| American | | | |
| ☐ **WARREN, Constance Whitney** ............ *drawings* | | | **$330** |
| American 1888-1948 | | | |
| ☐ **WARREN, Edmund George** ................. *paintings* | | | **$1,430** |
| English d. 1900 | | | |
| ☐ **WARREN, Ferdinand** ...................... *paintings* | | **$44** | **$357** |
| American | | | |

| | | *Current Price Range* | |
|---|---|---|---|
| | | *Low* | *High* |
| ☐ **WARREN, Harold Broadfield** .............. *drawings* | | $66 | $302 |
| American 1859-1934 | | | |
| ☐ **WARREN, Henry** ................................ *paintings* | | | $770 |
| British 1794-1879 | | | |
| ☐ **WARREN, Joseph** ............................ *paintings* | | $990 | $1,430 |
| British 19th/20th cent. | | | |
| ☐ **WARREN, Knighton** ........................... *paintings* | | | $528 |
| ☐ **WARREN, Melvin Charles** ................... *paintings* | | $20,000 | $140,000 |
| American b. 1920 ..................................... *drawings* | | $8,500 | $19,000 |
| ............................................................ *sculpture* | | $1,000 | $21,000 |
| ☐ **WARREN, Russ** ................................ *paintings* | | | $1,650 |
| contemporary | | | |
| ☐ **WARREN, Wesley** ............................ *paintings* | | | $330 |
| ☐ **WARSHAWSKY, Abel George** ........... *paintings* | | $220 | $4,125 |
| American 1883-1962 | | | |
| ☐ **WARTHEN, Lee R.** ............................ *paintings* | | $302 | $330 |
| American 20th cent. | | | |
| ☐ **WARWICK** ........................................ *paintings* | | | $220 |
| American 20th cent. | | | |
| ☐ **WARWICK, Ethel H.** .......................... *paintings* | | | $247 |
| American 20th cent. | | | |
| ☐ **WARWICK, J.** ................................... *paintings* | | | $4,675 |
| American 19th cent. | | | |
| ☐ **WASHBURN, Cadwallader** .................. *paintings* | | $242 | $3,400 |
| American 20th cent. | | | |
| ☐ **WASHBURN, Jessie M.** ....................... *paintings* | | | $440 |
| American 20th cent. | | | |
| ☐ **WASHES, J.** ...................................... *drawings* | | $275 | $302 |
| American 19th/20th cent. | | | |
| ☐ **WASHINGTON, Elizabeth Fisher** ......... *paintings* | | $176 | $2,860 |
| American 20th cent. | | | |
| ☐ **WASHINGTON, Georges** ..................... *paintings* | | $2,475 | $30,800 |
| French 1827-1910 ..................................... *drawings* | | $1,100 | $1,430 |
| ☐ **WASHINGTON, H. Elizabeth** .............. *paintings* | | | $220 |
| American 19th/20th cent. | | | |
| ☐ **WASHINGTON, Th. Wust** .................. *drawings* | | | $495 |
| ☐ **WASMUTH, Ernst** ............................. *paintings* | | | $770 |
| ☐ **WASSE, Arthur** ................................ *paintings* | | | $3,520 |
| ☐ **WASSERBURGER, Nathan** .................. *paintings* | | $88 | $440 |
| ☐ **WASSNETZOFF,** | | | |
| **Apolinarii Michailovitch** ........................ *paintings* | | | $275 |
| Russian 1858-1933 | | | |
| ☐ **WASSON, George Savary** ..................... *paintings* | | $130 | $176 |
| American b. 1855 | | | |
| ☐ **WATCHATAKER, George S.** .............. *drawings* | | | $550 |
| American(Comanche) b. 1916 | | | |
| ☐ **WATCHELL, Elmer** ............................. *paintings* | | | $880 |
| American b. 1864 | | | |

| | | Current Price Range | |
|---|---|---|---|
| | | *Low* | *High* |
| ☐ **WATELET, Charles Joseph** ............... *paintings* | | $880 | $8,250 |
| Belgian 1867-1954 | | | |
| ☐ **WATELET, Louis Etienne** ............... *paintings* | | $2,420 | $3,850 |
| French 1780-1866 ..................................... *drawings* | | $350 | $715 |
| ☐ **WATELIN, J.E.** ............... *paintings* | | | $357 |
| Continental School late 19th cent. | | | |
| ☐ **WATELIN, Louis Francois Victor** ......... *paintings* | | $715 | $1,540 |
| French 1838-1907 | | | |
| ☐ **WATERHOUSE, Alfred** ....................... *drawings* | | | $3,080 |
| English 1830-1905 | | | |
| ☐ **WATERHOUSE, John William** ............. *paintings* | | $1,980 | $264,000 |
| British 1849-1917 | | | |
| ☐ **WATERHOUSE, M.S.** ........................ *paintings* | | | $357 |
| American late 19th cent. | | | |
| ☐ **WATERHOUSE, W.** ........................... *paintings* | | | $770 |
| British 19th cent. | | | |
| ☐ **WATERLOO, Anthonie** ....................... *drawings* | | $1,650 | $7,150 |
| Flemish 1610-1690 | | | |
| ☐ **WATERLOO, Dennis** ......................... *paintings* | | | $4,950 |
| ☐ **WATERMAN, M.S.** ........................... *paintings* | | | $440 |
| American | | | |
| ☐ **WATERMAN, Marcus** ........................ *paintings* | | $165 | $2,750 |
| American 1834-1914 | | | |
| ☐ **WATERS, A.** ..................................... *drawings* | | $132 | $247 |
| English 19th cent. | | | |
| ☐ **WATERS, George W.** ......................... *paintings* | | $137 | $2,200 |
| American 1832-1912 | | | |
| ☐ **WATERS, Susan C.** ........................... *paintings* | | $715 | $92,950 |
| American 1823-1900 | | | |
| ☐ **WATKINS, B. Colles** ......................... *paintings* | | | $412 |
| Irish 1833-1891 | | | |
| ☐ **WATKINS, Franklin Chenault** ............. *paintings* | | $264 | $3,080 |
| American 1894-1972 ................................. *drawings* | | $286 | $660 |
| ☐ **WATKINS, Susan** ............................. *paintings* | | $165 | $1,540 |
| American 1875-1913 | | | |
| ☐ **WATRIN, E.** ....................................... *sculpture* | | | $1,100 |
| ☐ **WATRIN, Etienne** ............................... *sculpture* | | | $1,320 |
| ☐ **WATROUS, Harry Willson** .................. *paintings* | | $220 | $40,700 |
| American 1857-1940 | | | |
| ☐ **WATSON, C.D.** ................................. *paintings* | | | $302 |
| ☐ **WATSON, C.T.** ................................. *paintings* | | | $550 |
| American 20th cent. | | | |
| ☐ **WATSON, Cari E.** ............................. *paintings* | | | $605 |
| British 20th cent. | | | |
| ☐ **WATSON, Charles A.** ......................... *paintings* | | $275 | $2,310 |
| American 1857-1923 | | | |
| ☐ **WATSON, Charles Edward** .................. *paintings* | | | $1,650 |
| British 19th cent. | | | |

**Itinerant Artist**

In her lifetime, Susan Waters was best known as a Victorian painter of still-lifes of fruit and barnyard scenes, which she produced between 1863 and her death in 1900. These sentimental genre paintings now sell in the $5,000 to $15,000 range. More highly prized (and priced) today are the works she produced between 1843 to 1845, though she was not known for them in her lifetime. In order to support her ailing husband, she spent two years as an itinerant portrait painter in southern New York and Pennsylvania.

In the fall of 1981, an upstate New York family consigned an unsigned portrait of three girls to the Mapes Auctioneers. Owner David Mapes recognized the characteristic elements which identify the work of Susan Waters — the small brown and white dog in the corner, the stemmed plum in the girl's hand, and the flowers in pots. This was most likely a very expensive painting in its day. Itinerant artists charged more for detail work and for the numbers of persons depicted. It was also an expensive painting in 1981. Estimated at $50,000 to $60,000, the work sold to a dealer for $92,950 and now hangs in the Museum of Fine Arts in Boston. (Susan C. Waters, "Dr. Lincoln's Daughters," oil on canvas, 45 x 50 in., Mapes Auctioneers, September 19, 1981, $92,950.)

| | Current Price Range | |
|---|---|---|
| | Low | High |

| | | Low | High |
|---|---|---|---|
| ☐ **WATSON, Charles J.** ............ *drawings* | | | $412 |
| early 20th cent. | | | |
| ☐ **WATSON, Elizabeth Vila Taylor** .......... *paintings* | | $191 | $220 |
| American d. 1934 | | | |
| ☐ **WATSON, George** ............... *paintings* | | | $550 |
| 1817-1892 | | | |
| ☐ **WATSON, Hamlin** ............... *paintings* | | | $715 |
| British 20th cent. | | | |
| ☐ **WATSON, Harry** ............... *paintings* | | | $605 |
| British 1871-1936 | | | |
| ☐ **WATSON, Homer Ransford** ............... *paintings* | | | $2,750 |
| Canadian 1855-1936 ............... *drawings* | | $121 | $550 |
| ☐ **WATSON, Hy S.** ............... *paintings* | | $715 | $935 |
| 1868-1933 | | | |
| ☐ **WATSON, John Dawson** ............... *paintings* | | $495 | $935 |
| British 1832-1892 | | | |
| ☐ **WATSON, Robert** ............... *paintings* | | $33 | $2,750 |
| British 19th/20th cent. | | | |
| ☐ **WATSON, Robert** ............... *paintings* | | $220 | $247 |
| American 20th cent. | | | |
| ☐ **WATSON, Syd** ............... *paintings* | | | $231 |
| British 19th/20th cent. | | | |
| ☐ **WATSON, William (Jr.)** ............... *paintings* | | $935 | $6,600 |
| British d. 1921 | | | |
| ☐ **WATSON, William R.** ............... *paintings* | | | $220 |
| American 19th/20th cent. | | | |
| ☐ **WATT, Linnie** ............... *paintings* | | | $880 |
| English 19th/20th cent. | | | |
| ☐ **WATTEAU, Jean Antoine** ............... *paintings* | | | $77,000 |
| French 1684-1721 ............... *drawings* | | $165,000 | $165,000 |
| ☐ **WATTEAU, Louis Joseph** | | | |
| **(called WATTEAU de Lille)** ............... *paintings* | | | $11,000 |
| ☐ **WATTENHOFER, Ray** ............... *sculpture* | | | $660 |
| American contemporary | | | |
| ☐ **WATTER, Joseph** ............... *paintings* | | $900 | $4,400 |
| German 1838-1913 | | | |
| ☐ **WATTERSON, Alice** ............... *paintings* | | | $522 |
| 20th cent. | | | |
| ☐ **WATTS, Frederick Waters** ............... *paintings* | | $198 | $57,200 |
| English 1800-1862 | | | |
| ☐ **WATTS, George Frederick** ............... *paintings* | | $3,300 | $26,400 |
| British 1817-1904 ............... *drawings* | | $302 | $440 |
| ☐ **WATTS, James T.** ............... *drawings* | | | $385 |
| ☐ **WATTS, Jean** ............... *paintings* | | | $247 |
| American contemporary | | | |
| ☐ **WATTS, William Clothier** ............... *paintings* | | | $660 |
| American 19th/20th cent. ............... *drawings* | | $158 | $440 |
| ☐ **WATTS-DUNTON, Walter Theodore** .... *paintings* | | | $200 |
| British 1832-1914 | | | |

|  | | *Current Price Range* | |
|---|---|---|---|
|  | | *Low* | *High* |
| ☐ **WAUD, Alfred** .......................... *drawings* | | | $302 |
| American 1828-1891 | | | |
| ☐ **WAUGH, Coulton** ......................... *paintings* | | $200 | $396 |
| American 1896-1973 ................................ *drawings* | | $66 | $110 |
| ☐ **WAUGH, Frederick Judd** .............. *paintings* | | $357 | $40,700 |
| American 1861-1940 ................................ *drawings* | | $143 | $880 |
| ☐ **WAUGH, Henry W.** ....................... *drawings* | | | $660 |
| ☐ **WAUGH, Ida** ............................... *paintings* | | $165 | $660 |
| American d. 1919 | | | |
| ☐ **WAUGH, Samuel Bell** ................... *paintings* | | $247 | $2,200 |
| American 1814-1885 | | | |
| ☐ **WAULWYK(?), J.** ......................... *paintings* | | | $302 |
| ☐ **WAY, Andrew John Henry** ............ *paintings* | | $356 | $1,430 |
| American 1826-1888 ................................ *drawings* | | | $88 |
| ☐ **WAY, Charles Jones** ..................... *drawings* | | | $440 |
| British 1834-1919 | | | |
| ☐ **WAY, E.W.** .................................. *drawings* | | | $660 |
| ☐ **WAY, George Brevitt** .................... *paintings* | | | $440 |
| ☐ **WAY, J.C.** ................................... *drawings* | | | $275 |
| American 19th cent. | | | |
| ☐ **WAYLAND** .................................. *paintings* | | | $412 |
| English School 19th cent. | | | |
| ☐ **WEATHERSTONE, Alfred C.** .......... *paintings* | | | $3,850 |
| English ac. 1888-1903 | | | |
| ☐ **WEAVER, Arthur** .......................... *paintings* | | | $350 |
| .......................................................... *drawings* | | | $165 |
| ☐ **WEAVER, Clay** ............................. *paintings* | | | $275 |
| ☐ **WEAVER, Thomas** ......................... *paintings* | | $2,750 | $24,200 |
| English 1774-1844 | | | |
| ☐ **WEBB, A.C.** ................................. *paintings* | | $605 | $1,760 |
| American b. 1888 | | | |
| ☐ **WEBB, Byron** .............................. *paintings* | | $1,320 | $8,800 |
| ac. 1846-1866 | | | |
| ☐ **WEBB, Charles Meer** ..................... *paintings* | | $2,750 | $9,075 |
| British 1830-1895 | | | |
| ☐ **WEBB, James** .............................. *paintings* | | $412 | $13,200 |
| English 1825-1895 | | | |
| ☐ **WEBB, S. Carroll** ......................... *paintings* | | | $440 |
| ☐ **WEBB, Shirley Anne** ...................... *paintings* | | | $275 |
| British | | | |
| ☐ **WEBB, Tom** ................................. *paintings* | | | $1,430 |
| American | | | |
| ☐ **WEBB, William Edward** ................. *paintings* | | $935 | $2,200 |
| British ac. 1881-d. 1903 | | | |
| ☐ **WEBBER, Alfred Charles** ............... *paintings* | | | $4,950 |
| French 1862-1922 | | | |
| ☐ **WEBBER, Carl** .............................. *paintings* | | | $1,100 |
| ☐ **WEBBER, Charles T.** ..................... *paintings* | | | $880 |
| American 1825-1911 | | | |

| | Current Price Range | |
|---|---|---|
| | *Low* | *High* |
| ☐ **WEBBER, Elbridge Wesley** ................... *paintings* <br> American 1839-1914 | $1,000 | $3,250 |
| ☐ **WEBBER, Wesley** ............................. *paintings* <br> American 1841-1914 ................................ *drawings* | $247 | $3,850 <br> $132 |
| ☐ **WEBER, Alfred Charles** ...................... *paintings* <br> French 1862-1922 ................................ *drawings* | $632 | $3,300 <br> $330 |
| ☐ **WEBER, Anton** ................................. *drawings* <br> German 1833-1909 | | $264 |
| ☐ **WEBER, C. Philip** ............................. *paintings* <br> American ............................................. *drawings* | $352 <br> $55 | $3,086 <br> $165 |
| ☐ **WEBER, C. Rob.** ............................... *paintings* | | $605 |
| ☐ **WEBER, Carl** ................................... *paintings* <br> American 1850-1921 ............................... *drawings* | $198 <br> $121 | $4,620 <br> $2,860 |
| ☐ **WEBER, E.R.** ................................... *paintings* <br> American 20th cent. | | $192 |
| ☐ **WEBER, F. William** ........................... *paintings* <br> American 19th/20th cent. | $80 | $495 |
| ☐ **WEBER, Frederick Theodore** ............... *paintings* <br> American 1883-1906 | $80 | $500 |
| ☐ **WEBER, Gottlieb Daniel Paul** .............. *paintings* <br> German 1823-1916 | $300 | $13,750 |
| ☐ **WEBER, Heinrich** ............................. *paintings* <br> German 1843-1913 | | $4,400 |
| ☐ **WEBER, Marie Philips** ........................ *paintings* <br> German 19th cent. | | $1,650 |
| ☐ **WEBER, Max** .................................. *paintings* <br> American 1881-1961 ............................... *drawings* | $1,320 <br> $275 | $47,300 <br> $12,100 |
| ☐ **WEBER, Otis S.** ................................ *paintings* <br> American late 19th cent. | $124 | $990 |
| ☐ **WEBER, Otto** .................................. *paintings* <br> German 1832-1888 | $3,575 | $9,350 |
| ☐ **WEBER, Philip** ................................. *paintings* <br> American b. 1849 | | $363 |
| ☐ **WEBER, Rudolf** ................................ *paintings* <br> Austrian b. 1872 | | $1,028 |
| ☐ **WEBER, Theodore** ............................. *paintings* <br> French 1838-1907 ................................ *drawings* | $165 | $8,525 <br> $385 |
| ☐ **WEBERN, Carl** ................................. *paintings* <br> Continental School 19th cent. | | $577 |
| ☐ **WEBSTER, E. Ambrose** ....................... *paintings* | | $462 |
| ☐ **WEBSTER, Harold T.** ......................... *drawings* <br> 1885-1953 | | $660 |
| ☐ **WEBSTER, Herman Armour** ................. *paintings* <br> American b. 1878 | | $880 |
| ☐ **WEBSTER, J.** ................................... *paintings* <br> British 19th/20th cent. | | $247 |
| ☐ **WEBSTER, Thomas** ............................ *paintings* <br> British 1800-1886 | $495 | $4,675 |

|  | | *Current Price Range* | |
|---|---|---|---|
|  | | Low | High |
| ☐ **WEDEPOHL, Theodor** .......................... *paintings* | | | $110 |
| American 1863-1923 ................................... *drawings* | | | $275 |
| ☐ **WEEDON, Augustus Walford** .............. *paintings* | | | $1,760 |
| British 1838-1908 ..................................... *drawings* | | | $332 |
| ☐ **WEEDON, J.** ........................................ *drawings* | | | $275 |
| British 19th/20th cent. | | | |
| ☐ **WEEGEWIJS, H.** ................................. *paintings* | | | $275 |
| ☐ **WEEKES, A.** ....................................... *paintings* | | | $770 |
| American late 19th cent. | | | |
| ☐ **WEEKES, Henry** .................................. *paintings* | | | $4,950 |
| British ac. 1851-1888 | | | |
| ☐ **WEEKES, Herbert William** .................. *paintings* | | $1,210 | $2,860 |
| British 1864-1904 | | | |
| ☐ **WEEKS, Edwin Lord** .......................... *paintings* | | $330 | $77,000 |
| American 1849-1903 ................................... *drawings* | | $275 | $440 |
| ☐ **WEEKS, James (Darrell Northrup)** ....... *paintings* | | $9,350 | $13,200 |
| American b. 1922 ..................................... *drawings* | | | $1,210 |
| ☐ **WEEKS, L.E.** ...................................... *paintings* | | | $220 |
| American 19th cent. | | | |
| ☐ **WEELE, Herman Johannes van der** ...... *paintings* | | $650 | $1,760 |
| Dutch 1852-1930 ...................................... *drawings* | | $330 | $550 |
| ☐ **WEENIX, Jan (the Younger)** ................. *paintings* | | $1,430 | $2,200 |
| Dutch 1640-1719 | | | |
| ☐ **WEENIX, Jan Baptist (the Elder)** ........... *paintings* | | $3,575 | $88,000 |
| Dutch 1621-before 1663 | | | |
| ☐ **WEERTS, Jean Joseph** .......................... *paintings* | | | $605 |
| French 1847-1927 | | | |
| ☐ **WEGENER, Gerda** ............................... *drawings* | | | $495 |
| ☐ **WEGENER,** | | | |
| **Johann Friedrich Wilhelm** ..................... *drawings* | | | $275 |
| German 1812-1879 | | | |
| ☐ **WEGLE, A. Palmer** ............................. *paintings* | | | $650 |
| ☐ **WEGMAN, Bertha** ............................... *paintings* | | | $4,620 |
| Danish 1847-1926 | | | |
| ☐ **WEHRLIN, Schmidt** ............................ *paintings* | | | $880 |
| German 19th cent. | | | |
| ☐ **WEICHBERGER, Eduard** ..................... *paintings* | | | $770 |
| German 1843-1913 | | | |
| ☐ **WEIDENBACH, Augustus** ..................... *drawings* | | | $550 |
| ☐ **WEIDENBUSH, Henrietta** ..................... *paintings* | | | $880 |
| ☐ **WEIDNER, Carl** ................................... *paintings* | | | $308 |
| American | | | |
| ☐ **WEIFS, M.** .......................................... *paintings* | | | $440 |
| German late 19th cent. | | | |
| ☐ **WEIL, Fernand** ................................... *paintings* | | $55 | $363 |
| ☐ **WEIL, Van der** ................................... *paintings* | | | $275 |
| contemporary | | | |
| ☐ **WEILAND, Johannes** ............................ *paintings* | | $660 | $2,750 |
| Dutch 1856-1909 ...................................... *drawings* | | $220 | $660 |

| | | Current Price Range | |
|---|---|---|---|
| | | Low | High |

| | | Low | High |
|---|---|---|---|
| ☐ **WEILER, Max C.** .............................. *drawings* <br> Austrian b. 1910 | | | $522 |
| ☐ **WEILER, Milton C.** ........................... *drawings* <br> American 20th cent. | | | $302 |
| ☐ **WEILUC** ............................................. *drawings* <br> French 19th cent. | | | $440 |
| ☐ **WEIMANN** ....................................... *paintings* <br> German 19th cent. | | | $412 |
| ☐ **WEIMAR, Erwin Braune** .................... *paintings* <br> German | | | $253 |
| ☐ **WEIN, Kong** ................................... *paintings* <br> Chinese 19th cent. | | | $3,000 |
| ☐ **WEINBERG, Elbert** ........................... *sculpture* <br> American b. 1928 | | | $440 |
| ☐ **WEINBERG, Emilie Sievert** ................ *paintings* <br> American ac. 1934 | | | $264 |
| ☐ **WEINBERGER, Anton** ......................... *paintings* | | | $605 |
| ☐ **WEINER, W.** ..................................... *paintings* | | | $275 |
| ☐ **WEINGART, Joseph** ........................... *paintings* | | | $286 |
| ☐ **WEINGOTT, Victor Marcus** ................ *paintings* | | | $330 |
| ☐ **WEINMAN, Adolph Alexander** ............. *sculpture* <br> German/American 1870-1952 | | $770 | $35,200 |
| ☐ **WEINMANN, Elemer** .......................... *paintings* | | | $264 |
| ☐ **WEINRICH, Agnes** ............................. *paintings* <br> American 1873-1946 | | $247 | $660 |
| ☐ **WEIR, John Ferguson** ........................ *paintings* <br> American 1841-1926 | | $700 | $6,600 |
| ☐ **WEIR, Julian Alden** .......................... *paintings* <br> American 1852-1919 .................................. *drawings* | | $484 <br> $660 | $66,000 <br> $15,400 |
| ☐ **WEIR, Robert Walter** ......................... *paintings* <br> American 1803-1889 .................................. *drawings* | | $440 | $66,000 <br> $550 |
| ☐ **WEIR, William** ................................. *paintings* <br> English d. 1865 ....................................... *drawings* | | | $907 <br> $143 |
| ☐ **WEISER, Joseph Emmanuel** ................ *paintings* <br> German 1847-1911 | | $715 | $2,640 |
| ☐ **WEISGERBER, Albert** ........................ *drawings* <br> German 1878-1915 | | | $220 |
| ☐ **WEISHAUPT, Viktor** .......................... *paintings* <br> German 1848-1905 | | | $935 |
| ☐ **WEISMAN, W. H.** ............................. *paintings* <br> American 19th/20th cent. | | $77 | $467 |
| ☐ **WEISS, Emile Georges** ........................ *paintings* <br> French b. 1861 | | | $990 |
| ☐ **WEISS, F.** ....................................... *paintings* <br> German 20th cent. | | $176 | $302 |
| ☐ **WEISS, George** ................................. *paintings* <br> French b. 1861 | | | $440 |
| ☐ **WEISS, Johann Baptist** ....................... *paintings* <br> German 1812-1879 | | | $935 |

| | | Current Price Range | |
|---|---|---|---|
| | | Low | High |
| ☐ **WEISS, Jose** ........................... *paintings* | | $165 | $3,300 |
| British 1859-1929 | | | |
| ☐ **WEISS, S.A.** ........................... *paintings* | | | $660 |
| American c. 1916 | | | |
| ☐ **WEISS (?), Ida** ........................... *paintings* | | | $1,100 |
| ☐ **WEISSE, Rudolph** ............................... *paintings* | | $9,350 | $17,600 |
| Czechoslovakian b. 1869 | | | |
| ☐ **WEISSENBRUCH, Jan (or Johannes)** ..... *paintings* | | $796 | $6,600 |
| Dutch 1824-1880 | | | |
| ☐ **WEISSENBRUCH, Jan Hendrik** | | | |
| **(or Hendrik Johannes)** ........................... *paintings* | | $660 | $18,700 |
| Dutch 1824-1903 ........................... *drawings* | | $522 | $4,675 |
| ☐ **WEISSENBRUCH, Willem** ................... *paintings* | | | $418 |
| Dutch | | | |
| ☐ **WEISSENBRUCH, Willem Johannes** ..... *paintings* | | | $330 |
| ☐ **WEISSMAN, W.H.** ........................... *paintings* | | | $220 |
| American 20th cent. | | | |
| ☐ **WEISZ, Adolf** ........................... *paintings* | | | $3,300 |
| Austrian b. 1838 | | | |
| ☐ **WEISZ, Adolphe** ............................... *paintings* | | | $2,200 |
| French b. 1868; ac. 1875-1900 ...................... *drawings* | | | $242 |
| ☐ **WEISZ, Eugen** ........................... *paintings* | | $577 | $852 |
| American 1890-1954 | | | |
| ☐ **WELBECK, G.A.** ........................... *paintings* | | | $440 |
| American 19th/20th cent. | | | |
| ☐ **WELCH, Ludmilla P.** ........................... *paintings* | | $165 | $990 |
| American 19th/20th cent. ........................... *drawings* | | | $192 |
| ☐ **WELCH, Mabel R.** ............................... *paintings* | | | $825 |
| American 19th/20th cent. ........................... *drawings* | | | $325 |
| ☐ **WELCH, Thaddeus** ........................... *paintings* | | $357 | $4,400 |
| American 1844-1919 ........................... *drawings* | | $632 | $1,210 |
| ☐ **WELCH, Thomas** ........................... *paintings* | | | $440 |
| ☐ **WELCH, William** ........................... *paintings* | | | $2,200 |
| American 1828-1887 | | | |
| ☐ **WELDON, Charles D.** ........................... *paintings* | | $2,750 | $7,975 |
| American 1844-1935 ........................... *drawings* | | $522 | $715 |
| ☐ **WELLER, H.F.** ........................... *paintings* | | | $660 |
| American | | | |
| ☐ **WELLESLEY, Sir Victor** ...................... *drawings* | | | $176 |
| British 20th cent. | | | |
| ☐ **WELLINGTON, J.** ............................... *paintings* | | | $198 |
| American 19th/20th cent. | | | |
| ☐ **WELLIVER, Neil** ............................... *paintings* | | $2,310 | $27,500 |
| American b. 1929 | | | |
| ☐ **WELLS, Betty** ........................... *drawings* | | | $247 |
| American 20th cent. | | | |
| ☐ **WELLS, George** ........................... *paintings* | | $275 | $550 |
| British 1842-1888 | | | |

|  | | Current Price Range | |
|---|---|---|---|
|  | | Low | High |
| ☐ **WELLS, John Sanderson** ....................... *paintings* | | $715 | $12,100 |
| British b. 1872 ...................................... *drawings* | | | $825 |
| ☐ **WELLS, Lynton** .................................. *paintings* | | | $9,900 |
| American b. 1940 | | | |
| ☐ **WELLS, Newton A.** ............................ *paintings* | | | $605 |
| ☐ **WELSCH, Feodor Charles** .................... *paintings* | | $1,210 | $2,860 |
| German ac. 1879-1892 | | | |
| ☐ **WENACA, Marion** ............................. *sculpture* | | | $440 |
| American 20th cent. | | | |
| ☐ **WENBAN, Sion** ................................. *paintings* | | $220 | $247 |
| American 1848-1897 | | | |
| ☐ **WENDEL, R.** ...................................... *paintings* | | | $522 |
| German 19th cent. | | | |
| ☐ **WENDEL, Theodore** ........................... *paintings* | | $1,760 | $40,700 |
| American 1857-1932 ................................. *drawings* | | | $5,000 |
| ☐ **WENDENLEFT** ................................... *paintings* | | | $275 |
| ☐ **WENDEROTH, Augustus** ..................... *paintings* | | | $1,595 |
| American b. 1825 | | | |
| ☐ **WENDEROTH, Frederick A.** ................ *paintings* | | | $1,650 |
| American 19th/20th cent. | | | |
| ☐ **WENDLEBERGER, H.D.H.** ................. *paintings* | | | $418 |
| ☐ **WENDLER, Friedrich Mariz** ................ *drawings* | | | $715 |
| German 1814-1872 | | | |
| ☐ **WENDT, William** ............................... *paintings* | | $660 | $11,550 |
| American 1865-1946 | | | |
| ☐ **WENGEROTH, Isabel S.** ...................... *paintings* | | | $385 |
| American 1875-after 1934 | | | |
| ☐ **WENGEROTH, Stow** ........................... *paintings* | | | $40 |
| American 1906-1978 .................................... *drawings* | | $605 | $605 |
| ☐ **WENGLEIN, Joseph** ........................... *paintings* | | $1,100 | $30,800 |
| German 1845-1919 ................................... *drawings* | | | $242 |
| ☐ **WENNINGER, Johann** ......................... *paintings* | | | $660 |
| ☐ **WENTWORTH, Cecile de** ..................... *paintings* | | | $275 |
| ☐ **WENTWORTH, Daniel F.** ..................... *paintings* | | $88 | $1,100 |
| American b. 1850 .................................... *drawings* | | $192 | $231 |
| ☐ **WENTWORTH, G.A.** ........................... *paintings* | | | $325 |
| ☐ **WENTWORTH, R.** .............................. *paintings* | | | $880 |
| American ac. 1870 | | | |
| ☐ **WENZELL, Albert Beck** ....................... *paintings* | | $55 | $440 |
| American 1864-1917 .................................... *drawings* | | $137 | $2,420 |
| ☐ **WENZLER, Sarah Wilhelmina** .............. *paintings* | | | $1,760 |
| American d. c. 1871 | | | |
| ☐ **WERBEL, Adolf** ................................. *paintings* | | | $3,025 |
| Austrian b. 1848 | | | |
| ☐ **WERENSKOLD, E.** .............................. *paintings* | | | $462 |
| ☐ **WERETSCHAGIN, Vassilij** ................. *paintings* | | $132 | $770 |
| Russian 1842-1904 | | | |
| ☐ **WERFF, Adriaen van der** ..................... *paintings* | | | $990 |
| Dutch 1659-1722 | | | |

| | | *Current Price Range* | |
|---|---|---|---|
| | | *Low* | *High* |
| ☐ **WERNER, A. von** ............................... *paintings* | | | $330 |
| ☐ **WERNER, Anton Alexander** ................ *paintings* | | $203 | $220 |
| German 1843-1915 | | | |
| ☐ **WERNER, B.** ....................................... *paintings* | | | $715 |
| ☐ **WERNER, Carl Friedrich Heinrich** ....... *paintings* | | $155 | $2,530 |
| German 1808-1894 ..................................... *drawings* | | $600 | $14,300 |
| ☐ **WERNER, S.** ....................................... *paintings* | | | $1,045 |
| American 20th cent. | | | |
| ☐ **WERNER-BEHN, Hans** ........................ *paintings* | | | $300 |
| American early 20th cent. | | | |
| ☐ **WERREN, W.** ..................................... *paintings* | | | $253 |
| American 19th cent. | | | |
| ☐ **WERTINFIELD, Joseph** ....................... *paintings* | | | $192 |
| American 20th cent. | | | |
| ☐ **WESCOTT, Paul** ................................ *paintings* | | $302 | $467 |
| American 1904-1970 | | | |
| ☐ **WESELY, A.** ....................................... *paintings* | | | $1,045 |
| American/English late 19th cent. | | | |
| ☐ **WESENDONCK, Otto** ........................... *sculpture* | | | $440 |
| ☐ **WESLEY, John** ................................... *paintings* | | $275 | $2,090 |
| American b. 1928 ..................................... *drawings* | | | $247 |
| ☐ **WESLEY, Paul** ................................... *paintings* | | | $330 |
| American 20th cent. | | | |
| ☐ **WESSEL, Herman H.** ........................... *drawings* | | | $247 |
| American 20th cent. | | | |
| ☐ **WESSELMANN, Tom** ........................... *paintings* | | $2,420 | $44,000 |
| American b. 1931 ..................................... *drawings* | | $385 | $19,500 |
| ..................................... *sculpture* | | $1,210 | $4,840 |
| ☐ **WESSLER, O.** ..................................... *paintings* | | | $1,320 |
| German 19th cent. | | | |
| ☐ **WEST, Benjamin** ............................... *paintings* | | $605 | $49,500 |
| American 1738-1820 ..................................... *drawings* | | $247 | $165,000 |
| ☐ **WEST, C.W.** ....................................... *paintings* | | | $1,100 |
| ☐ **WEST, Edward E.** ............................... *drawings* | | | $935 |
| ☐ **WEST, Gertrude** ............................... *paintings* | | | $192 |
| b. 1872 | | | |
| ☐ **WEST, H.T.** ....................................... *drawings* | | | $440 |
| ☐ **WEST, Levon** ................................... *drawings* | | | $385 |
| American | | | |
| ☐ **WEST, Peter B.** ................................... *paintings* | | $302 | $605 |
| American 1833-1913 | | | |
| ☐ **WEST, Richard W.** ............................... *paintings* | | | $550 |
| ☐ **WEST, William Edward** ....................... *paintings* | | | $770 |
| American | | | |
| ☐ **WESTALL** ........................................... *paintings* | | | $1,100 |
| ☐ **WESTALL, A.** ..................................... *paintings* | | | $550 |
| ☐ **WESTALL, C.** ..................................... *paintings* | | | $275 |
| ☐ **WESTALL, John** ................................... *paintings* | | $143 | $825 |
| English 19th cent. | | | |

| | | Current Price Range | |
|---|---|---|---|
| | | *Low* | *High* |
| ☐ **WESTALL, Richard** ............................ *paintings* | | $880 | $3,300 |
| English 1765-1836 ...................................... *drawings* | | | $1,320 |
| ☐ **WESTALL, T.** ...................................... *paintings* | | | $2,500 |
| ☐ **WESTALL, William** ............................ *paintings* | | $220 | $247 |
| English 1781-1850 | | | |
| ☐ **WESTCHILOFF, Constantin** ................ *paintings* | | $55 | $2,420 |
| Russian 20th cent. ...................................... *drawings* | | | $165 |
| ☐ **WESTCOTT, T.** .................................... *paintings* | | | $330 |
| English 19th/20th cent. | | | |
| ☐ **WESTENBERGER, Carl** ...................... *paintings* | | | $247 |
| German 20th cent. | | | |
| ☐ **WESTERBEEK, Cornelis** ...................... *paintings* | | $392 | $2,640 |
| Dutch 1844-1903 ........................................ *drawings* | | | $286 |
| ☐ **WESTERLUND, Mia** ............................ *paintings* | | | $1,430 |
| ................................................................ *drawings* | | | $385 |
| ☐ **WESTERMANN, Horace Clifford** ......... *drawings* | | $330 | $11,550 |
| American b. 1922 ...................................... *sculpture* | | $13,750 | $33,000 |
| ☐ **WESTMORE** ...................................... *paintings* | | | $550 |
| ☐ **WESTON, Morris** ............................... *paintings* | | $55 | $250 |
| American 19th/20th cent. | | | |
| ☐ **WESTPHALL, Friedrich** ...................... *paintings* | | | $1,320 |
| Danish 1804-1844 | | | |
| ☐ **WESTROTT, F.** ................................... *paintings* | | | $935 |
| European 19th cent. | | | |
| ☐ **WET, Hugh Oloff de** ......................... *sculpture* | | $700 | $1,540 |
| English 20th cent. | | | |
| ☐ **WET, Jacob Willemsz de** ................... *paintings* | | | $2,475 |
| Dutch 1610-1671 | | | |
| ☐ **WET, Jacob de** ................................... *paintings* | | | $2,200 |
| ☐ **WETERING DE ROOY,** | | | |
| **Johannes Embrosius van de** ................... *paintings* | | $302 | $330 |
| Dutch b. 1877 | | | |
| ☐ **WETHERBEE, Isaac Augustus** ............. *paintings* | | | $4,250 |
| American 1819-1904 | | | |
| ☐ **WETHERHILL, R.** ............................... *drawings* | | | $528 |
| ☐ **WETHERILL, Elisha Kent Kane** ........... *paintings* | | $88 | $660 |
| American 1874-1929 | | | |
| ☐ **WETTELAND, S.** .................................. *paintings* | | | $302 |
| ☐ **WEYAND, M.** ..................................... *paintings* | | | $330 |
| ☐ **WEYDEN, Harry van der** ..................... *paintings* | | $137 | $2,500 |
| American 1868-after 1935 | | | |
| ☐ **WEYER, Gabriel** ................................. *paintings* | | | $1,045 |
| German 1850-1640 | | | |
| ☐ **WEYL, Hans** ...................................... *drawings* | | | $2,750 |
| German 20th cent. | | | |
| ☐ **WEYL, Max** ....................................... *paintings* | | $200 | $3,960 |
| American 1837-1914 | | | |
| ☐ **WEYMANN, R.** ................................... *drawings* | | | $2,200 |
| German or Swiss 19th cent. | | | |

| | | | *Current Price Range* | |
| | | | Low | High |
|---|---|---|---|---|
| ☐ **WEYTS, Carolus Ludovicus** ............... *paintings* | | | | $5,000 |
| Belgian 1828-1875 | | | | |
| ☐ **WEYTS, Petrus** ................................. *paintings* | | | | $6,000 |
| Belgian 1799-1855 | | | | |
| ☐ **WHAITE, James** ............................. *paintings* | | | | $522 |
| English ac. 1867-1896 ............................... *drawings* | | | | $247 |
| ☐ **WHALEN, James T.** ........................... *paintings* | | | | $330 |
| English 19th cent. | | | | |
| ☐ **WHATLEY, Henry** ............................. *drawings* | | | $99 | $825 |
| ☐ **WHATS, J.W.** ................................. *paintings* | | | | $176 |
| English 19th cent. | | | | |
| ☐ **WHEATLEY, Edith Grace** ................... *paintings* | | | | $230 |
| British 20th cent. | | | | |
| ☐ **WHEATLEY, Francis** ........................... *paintings* | | | $1,320 | $12,000 |
| English 1747-1801 ................................ *drawings* | | | $687 | $7,700 |
| ☐ **WHEATLEY, G.H.** ........................... *paintings* | | | $247 | $440 |
| ☐ **WHEELER, Alfred** ............................. *paintings* | | | $660 | $6,270 |
| British 1851-1932 | | | | |
| ☐ **WHEELER, Candace** ........................... *paintings* | | | | $352 |
| ☐ **WHEELER, Charles Arthur** ................. *paintings* | | | | $330 |
| American b. 1881 | | | | |
| ☐ **WHEELER, Hughlette "Tex"** ................. *sculpture* | | | $660 | $2,750 |
| American 1901-1954 | | | | |
| ☐ **WHEELER, J.** ................................. *paintings* | | | | $1,375 |
| English 19th cent. | | | | |
| ☐ **WHEELER, John (of Bath)** ................... *paintings* | | | $770 | $16,500 |
| British 1821-1903 | | | | |
| ☐ **WHEELER, Robert P.** ........................... *paintings* | | | | $250 |
| American 20th cent. | | | | |
| ☐ **WHEELER, W.R.** ............................... *paintings* | | | | $275 |
| American b. 1832 | | | | |
| ☐ **WHEELER, Walter Herbert** ................. *paintings* | | | | $330 |
| ☐ **WHEELER, William (Sr.)** ..................... *paintings* | | | | $1,100 |
| American d. 1893 | | | | |
| ☐ **WHEELOCK, Lila Audubon** ................. *sculpture* | | | | $770 |
| American | | | | |
| ☐ **WHEELOCK, Walter W.** ..................... *paintings* | | | | $350 |
| American 19th cent. | | | | |
| ☐ **WHEELOCK, Warren** ........................ *paintings* | | | $110 | $550 |
| ☐ **WHEELRIGHT, W. H.** ...................... *paintings* | | | $550 | $605 |
| English 19th cent. | | | | |
| ☐ **WHEELWRIGHT, Rowland** ................. *paintings* | | | | $1,100 |
| ☐ **WHELAN, Thomas** ............................. *paintings* | | | | $825 |
| American 20th cent. | | | | |
| ☐ **WHELLER, James** ............................. *paintings* | | | | $424 |
| ☐ **WHICHELO, A.G.** ............................. *paintings* | | | | $4,180 |
| ☐ **WHIPPLE, Seth Arca** ........................ *paintings* | | | | $2,640 |
| American 1856-1901 | | | | |

|  | | Current Price Range | |
|---|---|---|---|
|  | | Low | High |
| ☐ **WHISTLER, James Abbott McNeill** ...... *paintings* | | $1,210 | $82,500 |
| American 1834-1903 .................................. *drawings* | | $1,320 | $85,250 |
| ☐ **WHITAKER, George William** .............. *paintings* | | $77 | $2,300 |
| American 1841-1916 | | | |
| ☐ **WHITAKER, William** ......................... *drawings* | | $6,600 | $10,500 |
| American b. 1943 | | | |
| ☐ **WHITCOMB, Jon** ............................... *paintings* | | | $440 |
| b. 1906 .................................................. *drawings* | | $275 | $467 |
| ☐ **WHITCOMBE, Thomas** ...................... *paintings* | | $12,100 | $12,650 |
| British c. 1760-c. 1824 | | | |
| ☐ **WHITE, Charles Henry** ...................... *paintings* | | | $880 |
| American b. 1878 | | | |
| ☐ **WHITE, Charles Wilbert** ..................... *drawings* | | $1,210 | $4,950 |
| American 1918-1980 | | | |
| ☐ **WHITE, Clarence Scott** ...................... *paintings* | | $220 | $440 |
| American b. 1872 ..................................... *drawings* | | | $192 |
| ☐ **WHITE, Edwin** .................................. *paintings* | | $44 | $2,970 |
| American 1817-1877 | | | |
| ☐ **WHITE, Fritz** ................................... *drawings* | | $3,000 | $3,500 |
| American b. 1930 .................................... *sculpture* | | $5,000 | $24,000 |
| ☐ **WHITE, Harold Durand** ...................... *drawings* | | | $275 |
| ☐ **WHITE, Henry Cook** .......................... *paintings* | | | $495 |
| American 1861-1934 ................................. *drawings* | | | $278 |
| ☐ **WHITE, John** ................................... *drawings* | | $300 | $495 |
| ☐ **WHITE, Juliet** ................................. *drawings* | | | $440 |
| American 20th cent. | | | |
| ☐ **WHITE, Orrin Augustine** .................... *paintings* | | $330 | $3,300 |
| American 1883-1969 ................................. *drawings* | | $275 | $330 |
| ☐ **WHITE, Robert** ................................ *paintings* | | | $176 |
| American 20th cent. | | | |
| ☐ **WHITE, Stanford** .............................. *drawings* | | | $1,870 |
| American 1853-1906 | | | |
| ☐ **WHITE, Thomas Gilbert** ..................... *paintings* | | | $412 |
| American b. 1877 | | | |
| ☐ **WHITE, Walter Charles Lewis** .............. *paintings* | | | $300 |
| Anglo/American 1876-1963 | | | |
| ☐ **WHITEHEAD, Walter** ......................... *paintings* | | | $330 |
| American 1874-1956 | | | |
| ☐ **WHITEMAN, Samuel Edwin** ................ *paintings* | | $330 | $935 |
| American 1860-1922 | | | |
| ☐ **WHITESIDE, Frank Reed** .................... *paintings* | | $121 | $330 |
| American 1866-1929 | | | |
| ☐ **WHITFORD, R.** ................................. *paintings* | | $2,530 | $6,600 |
| ☐ **WHITING, Henry W.** .......................... *paintings* | | $132 | $2,000 |
| American 19th cent. | | | |
| ☐ **WHITLEY, Thomas W.** ....................... *paintings* | | | $2,860 |
| Anglo/American ac. 1835-1863 | | | |
| ☐ **WHITMACK, Edgar Franklin** .............. *paintings* | | | $880 |

|  | | | Current Price Range | |
|---|---|---|---|---|
|  | | | *Low* | *High* |
| ☐ **WHITMAN, S. Edwin** .......................... *paintings* | | | $247 | $385 |
| American 1860-1922 | | | | |
| ☐ **WHITMORE, M. Coburn (Coby)** .......... *paintings* | | | $412 | $660 |
| b. 1913 ...................................................... *drawings* | | | | $44 |
| ☐ **WHITNEY, Gertrude Vanderbilt** .......... *sculpture* | | | $1,870 | $3,080 |
| American 1875-1942 | | | | |
| ☐ **WHITON(?), H.W.** .............................. *paintings* | | | | $247 |
| American 19th cent. | | | | |
| ☐ **WHITSIT, Jesse** ................................... *paintings* | | | | $192 |
| American 20th cent. | | | | |
| ☐ **WHITTAKER** ...................................... *paintings* | | | | $1,100 |
| American mid 19th cent. | | | | |
| ☐ **WHITTAKER, G.W.** ............................ *paintings* | | | | $528 |
| ☐ **WHITTAKER, John Barnard** .............. *paintings* | | | $70 | $2,860 |
| American b. 1836 | | | | |
| ☐ **WHITTAKER, L.** ................................. *paintings* | | | | $660 |
| American contemporary | | | | |
| ☐ **WHITTEMORE, William John** .............. *paintings* | | | $121 | $660 |
| American 1860-1955 .................................... *drawings* | | | | $220 |
| ☐ **WHITTLE, H.A.** .................................. *paintings* | | | | $1,320 |
| British 19th cent. | | | | |
| ☐ **WHITTLE, Thomas (Jr.)** ...................... *paintings* | | | $330 | $1,760 |
| British ac. 1865-1885 | | | | |
| ☐ **WHITTLE, Thomas (Sr.)** ...................... *paintings* | | | | $770 |
| British ac. 1854-1868 | | | | |
| ☐ **WHITTMACK, Edgar Franklin** ............ *paintings* | | | | $264 |
| American | | | | |
| ☐ **WHITTREDGE, Thomas Worthington** .. *paintings* | | | $1,045 | $308,000 |
| American 1820-1910 | | | | |
| ☐ **WHORF, John** ..................................... *paintings* | | | $475 | $3,850 |
| American 1903-1959 .................................... *drawings* | | | $137 | $3,630 |
| ☐ **WHYTE, Isiah** .................................... *paintings* | | | | $900 |
| ☐ **WHYTE, Raymond** ............................. *paintings* | | | | $330 |
| ☐ **WICAR, Jean Baptiste Joseph** .............. *drawings* | | | | $412 |
| ☐ **WICHERA, Raimund R.V.** ................... *paintings* | | | | $660 |
| Austrian b. 1862 | | | | |
| ☐ **WICHT, John von** .............................. *paintings* | | | $110 | $247 |
| 1888-1970 | | | | |
| ☐ **WICKES, E.M.** ................................... *paintings* | | | | $440 |
| ☐ **WICKS, Heppie En Earl** ..................... *paintings* | | | $77 | $247 |
| American b. 1869 | | | | |
| ☐ **WICKSTEED, C.F.** .............................. *paintings* | | | | $5,500 |
| ☐ **WIDDAS, Richard Dodd** ...................... *paintings* | | | $2,200 | $2,200 |
| English 1826-1885 ...................................... *drawings* | | | | $1,850 |
| ☐ **WIDFORSS, Gunnar Mauritz** .............. *drawings* | | | $242 | $3,080 |
| Swedish/American 1879-1934 | | | | |
| ☐ **WIDGERY, William** ............................. *paintings* | | | $302 | $1,650 |
| British 1822-1893 | | | | |
| ☐ **WIDMAN, Bruno** ................................. *paintings* | | | $1,320 | $1,320 |

| | | Current Price Range | |
|---|---|---|---|
| | | *Low* | *High* |
| ☐ **WIECZOREK, Max** .......................... *paintings* | | | $330 |
| ☐ **WIEGAND, Charles** .......................... *paintings* | | | $1,320 |
| American | | | |
| ☐ **WIEGAND, Charmion von** ................. *paintings* | | | $5,500 |
| contemporary ............................................. *drawings* | | | $1,210 |
| ☐ **WIEGAND, Gustav Adolph** ................. *paintings* | | $143 | $1,650 |
| German/American 1870-1957 | | | |
| ☐ **WIEGERT, Th.** ................................. *paintings* | | | $467 |
| German 19th/20th cent. | | | |
| ☐ **WIEGHORST, Olaf Carl** ..................... *paintings* | | $3,025 | $80,000 |
| American b. 1899 ..................................... *drawings* | | $550 | $5,000 |
| ...................................................... *sculpture* | | | $5,500 |
| ☐ **WIEHL, Franz** ................................. *paintings* | | | $286 |
| ☐ **WIELANDT, Manuel** .......................... *paintings* | | | $715 |
| German 1863-1922 | | | |
| ☐ **WIENGAREDT, A.B. de** ...................... *paintings* | | | $1,760 |
| Dutch 19th cent. | | | |
| ☐ **WIERINGA, Franciscus Gerardus** ......... *paintings* | | | $20,900 |
| Dutch 1758-1817 | | | |
| ☐ **WIERINGEN, Cornelis Claesz. van** ....... *paintings* | | | $8,800 |
| ☐ **WIERTZ, Antoine** ............................. *paintings* | | $330 | $385 |
| ☐ **WIERTZ, Antonie Joseph** .................... *drawings* | | | $247 |
| Belgian 1806-1865 | | | |
| ☐ **WIES, W.** ...................................... *paintings* | | | $220 |
| American School 19th/20th cent. | | | |
| ☐ **WIESELTHIER, Vally** ......................... *drawings* | | | $528 |
| ☐ **WIESMANN (?), Alfred** ....................... *paintings* | | | $770 |
| German (?) 20th cent. | | | |
| ☐ **WIESNER, A.** ................................... *paintings* | | | $357 |
| German 19th cent. | | | |
| ☐ **WIESSLER, William** .......................... *paintings* | | | $220 |
| American b. 1887 | | | |
| ☐ **WIGAND, Adeline Albright** ................. *paintings* | | | $220 |
| American d. 1944 | | | |
| ☐ **WIGAND, Balthasar** .......................... *drawings* | | $2,420 | $4,675 |
| Austrian 1771-1846 | | | |
| ☐ **WIGGINS, Carleton** | | | |
| **(or John Carleton)** ......................... *paintings* | | $174 | $2,750 |
| American 1848-1932 | | | |
| ☐ **WIGGINS, Guy Carleton** ..................... *paintings* | | $385 | $28,600 |
| American 1883-1962 ................................ *drawings* | | $165 | $1,017 |
| ☐ **WIGGINS, Sidney Miller** ..................... *paintings* | | $165 | $770 |
| American 1881-1940 | | | |
| ☐ **WIGHT, Moses** ................................. *paintings* | | $375 | $3,300 |
| American 1827-1895 | | | |
| ☐ **WIGHT, Mrs. Col. Edwin Liegh** ........... *paintings* | | | $1,150 |
| American late 19th cent. | | | |
| ☐ **WIJNGAERDT, Piet Theodorus van** ...... *drawings* | | | $1,430 |
| Dutch b. 1873 | | | |

| | | Current Price Range | |
|---|---|---|---|
| | | *Low* | *High* |
| ☐ **WIJNVELD, Barend** .......................... *paintings* | | | **$9,350** |
| Dutch 1820-1902 | | | |
| ☐ **WIKSTROM, Bror Anders** .................. *paintings* | | **$990** | **$1,210** |
| Swedish c. 1840-1909 | | | |
| ☐ **WILATCH, Micha** ............................ *paintings* | | **$176** | **$770** |
| French b. 1905 | | | |
| ☐ **WILBUR, Theodore E.** ........................ *paintings* | | | **$467** |
| American 19th cent. | | | |
| ☐ **WILCOX, Frank N.** ........................... *drawings* | | **$154** | **$352** |
| American b. 1887 | | | |
| ☐ **WILCOX, Lois** ................................. *paintings* | | | **$1,760** |
| American 20th cent. | | | |
| ☐ **WILCOX, W.H.** ............................... *paintings* | | **$220** | **$550** |
| American 19th cent. | | | |
| ☐ **WILD, Frank Percy** .......................... *paintings* | | | **$3,850** |
| English b. 1861 | | | |
| ☐ **WILD, H.** ..................................... *paintings* | | | **$200** |
| American late 19th cent. | | | |
| ☐ **WILDA, Charles** .............................. *paintings* | | **$2,200** | **$9,900** |
| Austrian 1854-1907 ................................ *drawings* | | | **$1,540** |
| ☐ **WILDE, Hamilton G.** ......................... *paintings* | | | **$308** |
| ☐ **WILDE, Samuel de** ........................... *drawings* | | **$110** | **$440** |
| British 1748-1832 | | | |
| ☐ **WILDENS, Jan** ............................... *paintings* | | | **$28,600** |
| Flemish 1586-1653 | | | |
| ☐ **WILDENS, Jeremias** .......................... *paintings* | | | **$7,150** |
| Flemish 1621-1653 | | | |
| ☐ **WILDER, Arthur B.** .......................... *paintings* | | **$44** | **$550** |
| American b. 1857 | | | |
| ☐ **WILDER, Tom** ................................ *paintings* | | | **$176** |
| American b. 1876 | | | |
| ☐ **WILDSTOSSER, A.** ........................... *paintings* | | | **$2,090** |
| German 19th cent. | | | |
| ☐ **WILE, Edith** ................................. *paintings* | | | **$192** |
| American 19th cent. | | | |
| ☐ **WILES, Gladys** ............................... *paintings* | | | **$385** |
| ☐ **WILES, Irving Ramsay** ....................... *paintings* | | **$440** | **$9,350** |
| American 1861-1948 ............................... *drawings* | | **$275** | **$3,520** |
| ☐ **WILES, Lemuel Maynard** ..................... *paintings* | | **$550** | **$12,000** |
| American 1826-1905 | | | |
| ☐ **WILES, M.** ................................... *paintings* | | | **$247** |
| American 20th cent. | | | |
| ☐ **WILEY, William** .............................. *drawings* | | **$825** | **$2,200** |
| ☐ **WILEY, William T.** ........................... *paintings* | | **$1,870** | **$14,300** |
| American b. 1937 ................................. *drawings* | | **$1,430** | **$6,500** |
| ☐ **WILFORD, Loran Frederick** ................ *paintings* | | **$302** | **$418** |
| American b. 1892 ................................. *drawings* | | | **$132** |
| ☐ **WILHELM, Heinrich** ......................... *paintings* | | | **$3,190** |
| German d. 1902 | | | |

| | Current Price Range | |
|---|---|---|
| | Low | High |
| ☐ **WILK, Joseph** ............ *paintings* | $462 | $2,200 |
| European | | |
| ☐ **WILKIE, Robert D.** ............ *paintings* | $1,600 | $9,500 |
| American 1828-1903 ............ *drawings* | | $275 |
| ☐ **WILKINSON, H.** ............ *paintings* | | $357 |
| ☐ **WILKINSON, J. Walter** ............ *paintings* | | $528 |
| American | | |
| ☐ **WILKINSON, Norman** ............ *paintings* | $385 | $825 |
| British 1878-1934 | | |
| ☐ **WILKINSON, R.** ............ *paintings* | | $687 |
| English | | |
| ☐ **WILKS, W.** ............ *paintings* | | $2,200 |
| British 19th cent. | | |
| ☐ **WILLAERTS, Abraham** ............ *paintings* | | $44,000 |
| Dutch 1603-1669 | | |
| ☐ **WILLAERTS, Adam** ............ *paintings* | $7,700 | $33,000 |
| Flemish 1577-1664 | | |
| ☐ **WILLAERTS, Cornelis** ............ *paintings* | | $1,100 |
| ☐ **WILLARD, Archibald M.** ............ *paintings* | $176 | $150,000 |
| American 1836/37-1918 | | |
| ☐ **WILLARD, Frank Henry** ............ *drawings* | $82 | $385 |
| 1893-1958 | | |
| ☐ **WILLARD, Harriet** ............ *drawings* | | $880 |
| English 19th cent. | | |
| ☐ **WILLCOCK, B.** ............ *paintings* | | $440 |
| ☐ **WILLE, Alb.** ............ *sculpture* | | $880 |
| ☐ **WILLE, Fritz Julius von** ............ *paintings* | $1,650 | $3,300 |
| German 1860-1941 | | |
| ☐ **WILLE, Johann Georg** ............ *drawings* | | $990 |
| German 1715-1808 | | |
| ☐ **WILLE, Pierre Alexandre** ............ *drawings* | $1,540 | $1,980 |
| French 1748-1821 | | |
| ☐ **WILLEBEECK, Peeter** ............ *paintings* | | $7,700 |
| Flemish ac. 1632-1647 | | |
| ☐ **WILLEMS, Florent** ............ *paintings* | $990 | $9,900 |
| Belgian 1823-1905 | | |
| ☐ **WILLETT, Arthur Reginald** ............ *drawings* | $150 | $550 |
| American b. 1868 | | |
| ☐ **WILLETT, J.** ............ *paintings* | | $412 |
| Continental 20th cent. | | |
| ☐ **WILLIAM, Graham** ............ *paintings* | $137 | $220 |
| Scottish b. 1892 | | |
| ☐ **WILLIAM, S.** ............ *paintings* | $275 | $301 |
| ☐ **WILLIAM, S.** ............ *paintings* | | $275 |
| English 19th cent. | | |
| ☐ **WILLIAMS, Abigail Osgood** ............ *paintings* | | $605 |
| American 1823-1913 | | |
| ☐ **WILLIAMS, Alfred W.** ............ *paintings* | $660 | $1,980 |
| English 19th cent. | | |

| | | *Current Price Range* | |
|---|---|---|---|
| | | *Low* | *High* |

☐ **WILLIAMS, Benjamin** .......................... *paintings* | | **$6,050**
British 1831-1923

☐ **WILLIAMS, C. D.** ............................. *drawings* | | **$330**
1875-1954

☐ **WILLIAMS, C.C.** ............................. *paintings* | | **$495**
American

☐ **WILLIAMS, C.P.** ............................. *paintings* | | **$200**
Canadian 19th cent.

☐ **WILLIAMS, David** ............................. *paintings* | | **$1,430**
American (Apache)

☐ **WILLIAMS, E.C.** ............................. *paintings* | **$770** | **$2,200**
English 1939-1889

☐ **WILLIAMS, Edward (Jr.)** ..................... *paintings* | | **$2,200**
English 1782-1855

☐ **WILLIAMS, Edward Charles** ............... *paintings* | **$605** | **$5,000**
English ac. 1839-1845

☐ **WILLIAMS, Edward K.** ........................ *paintings* | | **$1,100**
American 19th/20th cent.

☐ **WILLIAMS, Frederick Ballard** ............. *paintings* | **$220** | **$1,650**
American 1871-1956 .................................. *drawings* | | **$192**

☐ **WILLIAMS, Frederick Dickinson** .......... *paintings* | **$275** | **$6,050**
American 1829-1915 .................................. *drawings* | | **$220**

☐ **WILLIAMS, George Alfred** ................. *drawings* | **$90** | **$880**
American 1875-1932

☐ **WILLIAMS, George Augustus** ............. *paintings* | **$385** | **$2,750**
British 1814-1901

☐ **WILLIAMS, H.P.** ............................. *paintings* | | **$247**
British 19th cent.

☐ **WILLIAMS, Henry** ............................ *paintings* | | **$1,980**
American 1787-1830

☐ **WILLIAMS, J.F.** ............................. *paintings* | | **$385**
American d. 1879

☐ **WILLIAMS, James W.** ........................ *paintings* | | **$660**
English b. 1797

☐ **WILLIAMS, John Alonzo** ..................... *drawings* | | **$220**
American b. 1869

☐ **WILLIAMS, John Haynes** ..................... *paintings* | | **$1,045**
European

☐ **WILLIAMS, John Michael** ..................... *paintings* | | **$1,100**

☐ **WILLIAMS, John Scott** ........................ *paintings* | | **$132**
b. 1877 .............................................. *drawings* | | **$192**

☐ **WILLIAMS, M.C.** ............................. *paintings* | | **$715**
American 19th cent.

☐ **WILLIAMS, Mary Belle** ....................... *paintings* | **$82** | **$1,045**
American 19th/20th cent.

☐ **WILLIAMS, Mary E.** .......................... *drawings* | | **$660**
American late 19th cent.

☐ **WILLIAMS, May** ............................. *drawings* | | **$357**
American early 20th cent.

| | | Current Price Range | |
|---|---|---|---|
| | | Low | High |
| ☐ **WILLIAMS, Micah** ............................ *paintings* | | | **$9,900** |
| American 1782/83-1837 ............................ *drawings* | | | **$4,950** |
| ☐ **WILLIAMS, Mildred E.** ....................... *paintings* | | **$77** | **$400** |
| American b. 1892 | | | |
| ☐ **WILLIAMS, Mrs. F.M.** ........................ *paintings* | | | **$3,300** |
| 19th cent. | | | |
| ☐ **WILLIAMS, Penry** ............................ *paintings* | | **$1,650** | **$2,970** |
| English, d. Rome 1798-1885 | | | |
| ☐ **WILLIAMS, Richard** ........................... *paintings* | | | **$825** |
| ☐ **WILLIAMS, Ruskin** ........................... *paintings* | | | **$1,320** |
| American .................................................. *drawings* | | | **$302** |
| ☐ **WILLIAMS, Sam** ............................. *sculpture* | | | **$5,000** |
| English | | | |
| ☐ **WILLIAMS, T.D.** .............................. *paintings* | | | **$1,210** |
| American 19th cent. | | | |
| ☐ **WILLIAMS, Terrick** ........................... *paintings* | | | **$8,800** |
| English 1860-1936 ..................................... *drawings* | | | **$850** |
| ☐ **WILLIAMS, Virgil** ............................ *paintings* | | **$275** | **$2,860** |
| American 1830-1886 ................................... *drawings* | | | **$110** |
| ☐ **WILLIAMS, W.** ................................. *paintings* | | | **$935** |
| British 19th cent. | | | |
| ☐ **WILLIAMS, W.L.** .............................. *paintings* | | | **$850** |
| American 19th cent. | | | |
| ☐ **WILLIAMS, W.M.** ............................. *paintings* | | | **$550** |
| British 19th cent. | | | |
| ☐ **WILLIAMS, W.W.** ............................ *paintings* | | | **$440** |
| ☐ **WILLIAMS, Walter** ........................... *paintings* | | **$250** | **$4,400** |
| English 1835-1906 | | | |
| ☐ **WILLIAMS, Warren** ........................... *drawings* | | | **$302** |
| British 1863-1918 | | | |
| ☐ **WILLIAMS, Wheeler** ........................... *sculpture* | | **$1,320** | **$28,600** |
| American 1897-1972 | | | |
| ☐ **WILLIAMSON, Ada C.** ........................ *paintings* | | | **$192** |
| American 20th cent. | | | |
| ☐ **WILLIAMSON, Daniel Alexander** ......... *paintings* | | | **$500** |
| British 1822-1903 | | | |
| ☐ **WILLIAMSON, Francis John** ............... *paintings* | | | **$1,210** |
| British 1833-1920 | | | |
| ☐ **WILLIAMSON, J. Maynard** ................. *paintings* | | | **$605** |
| American b. 1892 | | | |
| ☐ **WILLIAMSON, John** ........................... *paintings* | | **$550** | **$7,700** |
| American 1826-1885 | | | |
| ☐ **WILLIAMSON, William H.** ................. *paintings* | | **$275** | **$715** |
| English 1820-1883 | | | |
| ☐ **WILLIARDSON, Dave** ........................ *drawings* | | | **$275** |
| contemporary | | | |
| ☐ **WILLIGEN, Claesz Jans van der** .......... *paintings* | | | **$3,300** |
| Dutch 1630-1676 | | | |
| ☐ **WILLINGHAUSEN** ............................ *drawings* | | | **$308** |

| | | Current Price Range | |
|---|---|---|---|
| | | Low | High |
| ☐ **WILLIOT, F.** ............................... *paintings* | | | **$1,100** |
| ☐ **WILLIOT, P.** ............................... *paintings* | | **$605** | **$4,400** |
| Belgian 19th cent. | | | |
| ☐ **WILLIS, Albert Paul** ............... *paintings* | | | **$440** |
| American 1867-1944 | | | |
| ☐ **WILLIS, Edmund Aylburton** ........... *paintings* | | **$247** | **$3,520** |
| American 1808-1899 | | | |
| ☐ **WILLIS, F.R.** ............................... *paintings* | | | **$1,100** |
| 19th cent. | | | |
| ☐ **WILLIS, Henry Brittan** ............ *paintings* | | **$350** | **$1,750** |
| English 1810-1884 ........................... *drawings* | | | **$300** |
| ☐ **WILLIS, J.** ............................... *paintings* | | **$137** | **$715** |
| 19th cent. | | | |
| ☐ **WILLIS, J.** ............................... *paintings* | | | **$715** |
| French 19th cent. | | | |
| ☐ **WILLIS, Thomas** ....................... *paintings* | | **$1,650** | **$4,000** |
| American 1850-1912 | | | |
| ☐ **WILLIS, Thornton** ..................... *paintings* | | **$1,540** | **$5,500** |
| American b. 1936 | | | |
| ☐ **WILLMORE, James Tilbitts** ........... *paintings* | | | **$1,430** |
| English 1800-1863 | | | |
| ☐ **WILLNER, Madge Stewart** ........... *paintings* | | | **$770** |
| American b. 1952 | | | |
| ☐ **WILLONBORN, H. A.** ..................... *paintings* | | | **$605** |
| ☐ **WILLOUGHBY, Robert** ................. *paintings* | | | **$880** |
| British 1768-1843 | | | |
| ☐ **WILLOUGHBY, William H.** ........... *paintings* | | | **$440** |
| English 19th cent. | | | |
| ☐ **WILLSON, B.** ............................... *paintings* | | | **$770** |
| American 19th cent. | | | |
| ☐ **WILLSON, James Mallory** ............ *paintings* | | | **$220** |
| American b. 1890 | | | |
| ☐ **WILMARTH, Chris** ..................... *drawings* | | | **$770** |
| ☐ **WILMARTH, Lemuel Everett** ........... *paintings* | | | **$7,150** |
| American 1835-1918 | | | |
| ☐ **WILMS, Peter Josef** ..................... *paintings* | | | **$5,500** |
| German 1814-92 | | | |
| ☐ **WILNER, Jean** ............................ *paintings* | | | **$467** |
| Haitian | | | |
| ☐ **WILS, Jan** ............................... *paintings* | | | **$4,620** |
| Dutch 1600-1666 | | | |
| ☐ **WILSCHER, A.** ............................ *paintings* | | | **$700** |
| ☐ **WILSON, Andrew** ..................... *paintings* | | | **$440** |
| Scottish 1780-1848 | | | |
| ☐ **WILSON, C.J.A** ............................ *drawings* | | | **$450** |
| b. 1880 | | | |
| ☐ **WILSON, C.L.** ............................ *paintings* | | | **$250** |
| ☐ **WILSON, Charles Theller** ........... *paintings* | | | **$247** |
| American 1855-1920 ........................... *drawings* | | | **$88** |

| | | Current Price Range | |
|---|---|---|---|
| | | *Low* | *High* |
| ☐ **WILSON, Douglas** ............................... *paintings* | | | **$880** |
| American 19th cent. | | | |
| ☐ **WILSON, Edwin Arthur** ....................... *paintings* | | | **$275** |
| b. 1886 | | | |
| ☐ **WILSON, F.** ....................................... *paintings* | | | **$412** |
| American 19th cent. | | | |
| ☐ **WILSON, F.H.** .................................... *paintings* | | | **$220** |
| English early 20th cent. | | | |
| ☐ **WILSON, Francis Vaux** ....................... *drawings* | **$88** | | **$176** |
| American | | | |
| ☐ **WILSON, G.B.** .................................... *paintings* | **$2,750** | | **$13,200** |
| British 19th cent. | | | |
| ☐ **WILSON, Gahan** ................................. *drawings* | | | **$330** |
| American 20th cent. | | | |
| ☐ **WILSON, Harriet** ................................ *drawings* | | | **$192** |
| American 20th cent. | | | |
| ☐ **WILSON, Jane** .................................... *paintings* | | | **$1,650** |
| American b. 1924 | | | |
| ☐ **WILSON, Jean** .................................... *paintings* | **$424** | | **$3,250** |
| 19th cent. | | | |
| ☐ **WILSON, John James** .......................... *paintings* | **$220** | | **$4,675** |
| Scottish 1818-1875 | | | |
| ☐ **WILSON, Lottie E.** .............................. *paintings* | | | **$302** |
| American 19th/20th cent. | | | |
| ☐ **WILSON, Lyons** .................................. *paintings* | | | **$247** |
| American b. 1892 | | | |
| ☐ **WILSON, Margaret Elizabeth** ............... *paintings* | | | **$440** |
| ☐ **WILSON, Mary Ann** ............................ *paintings* | | | **$137** |
| American 19th/20th cent. ............................. *drawings* | | | **$1,870** |
| ☐ **WILSON, Richard** ............................... *paintings* | **$200** | | **$7,150** |
| British 1714-1782 .................................... *drawings* | **$125** | | **$423** |
| ☐ **WILSON, Robert Burns** ....................... *drawings* | **$264** | | **$286** |
| American 1851-1916 | | | |
| ☐ **WILSON, Solomon** .............................. *paintings* | **$44** | | **$412** |
| Polish/American 1894/96-1974 ....................... *drawings* | | | **$60** |
| ☐ **WILSON, T.** ...................................... *paintings* | **$66** | | **$357** |
| American 19th/20th cent. | | | |
| ☐ **WILSON, Thomas Fairbairn** ................. *paintings* | | | **$7,425** |
| British ac. 1808-46 | | | |
| ☐ **WILSON, Thomas W.** .......................... *paintings* | | | **$440** |
| ☐ **WILSON, W.** ..................................... *paintings* | **$220** | | **$462** |
| English 19th cent. | | | |
| ☐ **WILSON, William J.** ........................... *paintings* | **$137** | | **$247** |
| American b. 1884 | | | |
| ☐ **WILT, Hans** ...................................... *drawings* | **$1,100** | | **$1,320** |
| Austrian 1867-1917 | | | |
| ☐ **WILT, Otto** ....................................... *paintings* | **$247** | | **$357** |
| German b. 1898 | | | |
| ☐ **WILTON, J.** ....................................... *paintings* | | | **$264** |

| | | Current Price Range | |
|---|---|---|---|
| | | Low | High |
| □ **WIMAR, Charles** ............................ *paintings* | | $13,200 | $18,700 |
| American 1828-1863 | | | |
| □ **WIMPERIS, Edmund Morison** .............. *drawings* | | | $275 |
| English 1835-1900 | | | |
| □ **WINANS, Walter** ................................ *sculpture* | | $275 | $412 |
| American | | | |
| □ **WINCHENBACK, L.A.** ........................ *paintings* | | | $2,750 |
| American | | | |
| □ **WINCHESTER, Mrs. B.** ....................... *paintings* | | | $357 |
| American 18th/19th cent. | | | |
| □ **WINCK, Johann Christian Thomas** ....... *paintings* | | | $11,000 |
| German 1738-1797 | | | |
| □ **WINDBERG** ...................................... *paintings* | | | $411 |
| 20th cent. | | | |
| □ **WINDMAYER, Anton** ......................... *paintings* | | | $9,350 |
| German 1840-1896 | | | |
| □ **WINDMAYER, Wilhelm Theodor** ......... *paintings* | | | $1,320 |
| German 1828-1883 | | | |
| □ **WINDRED, E.** ................................... *paintings* | | | $1,375 |
| 19th cent. | | | |
| □ **WINDT, Chris van der** ...................... *drawings* | | | $275 |
| Dutch b. 1877 | | | |
| □ **WINDT, Laurent van der** ..................... *paintings* | | | $1,540 |
| Dutch 1878-1916 | | | |
| □ **WINES, James** ................................. *sculpture* | | | $550 |
| American b. 1932 | | | |
| □ **WINFIELD, Rodney** ........................... *paintings* | | | $1,320 |
| American contemporary | | | |
| □ **WINGATE, Sir James Lawton** .............. *paintings* | | $550 | $1,100 |
| Scottish 1846-1924 | | | |
| □ **WINGERT, Edward Oswald** ................ *paintings* | | | $192 |
| American 1864-1934 | | | |
| □ **WINGFIELD, James Digman** ................ *paintings* | | $100 | $5,225 |
| English 1800-1872 | | | |
| □ **WINKLER, Fritz** ............................... *paintings* | | | $2,200 |
| German 1894-1964 | | | |
| □ **WINKLER, Olof** ............................... *paintings* | | | $1,870 |
| German b. 1843 | | | |
| □ **WINNER, William E.** ......................... *paintings* | | $121 | $7,150 |
| American c. 1815-1883 | | | |
| □ **WINOGRADOFF, Arssenievitch** ........... *paintings* | | $1,430 | $5,500 |
| Russian b. 1869 | | | |
| □ **WINS, E.** ........................................ *paintings* | | | $605 |
| British 19th cent. | | | |
| □ **WINSCOE, Christa** ............................ *sculpture* | | | $715 |
| □ **WINSOR, Helen A.** ........................... *paintings* | | | $990 |
| American 19th cent. | | | |
| □ **WINSTANLEY, H.** ............................. *paintings* | | | $522 |
| English 18th cent. | | | |

| | | Current Price Range | |
|---|---|---|---|
| | | *Low* | *High* |
| ☐ WINT, Peter de ................................... *drawings* <br> British 1784-1849 | | **$300** | **$1,980** |
| ☐ WINTER, Alice Beach .......................... *paintings* | | | **$275** |
| ☐ WINTER, Andrew ............................... *paintings* <br> American 1893-1958 ................................. *drawings* | | **$475** <br> **$88** | **$550** <br> **$400** |
| ☐ WINTER, Charles Allan ...................... *paintings* <br> American 1869-1942 ............................... *drawings* | | **$302** | **$4,400** <br> **$2,750** |
| ☐ WINTER, Fritz ................................... *paintings* <br> German 1905-1978 | | | **$1,650** |
| ☐ WINTER, H. ...................................... *paintings* <br> Continental 19th cent. | | | **$935** |
| ☐ WINTER, H.W.G. .............................. *paintings* | | | **$440** |
| ☐ WINTER, Heinrich ............................. *paintings* <br> German b. 1843 | | | **$275** |
| ☐ WINTER, Robert A. ........................... *paintings* <br> American contemporary | | | **$11,000** |
| ☐ WINTERHALTER, Franz Xaver ........... *paintings* <br> German 1806-1873 | | **$935** | **$66,000** |
| ☐ WINTHER, Frederik Julius August ....... *paintings* <br> Danish 1853-1916 | | | **$2,970** |
| ☐ WINTHUYSEN Y LOSADA, <br> Francisco Javier de ............................. *paintings* <br> Spanish b. 1874 | | | **$192** |
| ☐ WINTZ, Guillaume ............................. *paintings* | | **$2,420** | **$3,300** |
| ☐ WISBY, Jack ..................................... *paintings* <br> American 1870-1940 | | **$220** | **$1,210** |
| ☐ WISINGER, Olga Florian ..................... *paintings* <br> Austrian 1844-1926 | | **$4,400** | **$6,875** |
| ☐ WISSING, J.C. ................................... *drawings* | | | **$550** |
| ☐ WISSING, William ............................. *paintings* <br> Dutch 1653-1687 | | **$1,100** | **$3,300** |
| ☐ WISTEHUFF, Revere F. ....................... *paintings* <br> American 20th cent. | | **$605** | **$605** |
| ☐ WIT, Jakob de .................................. *drawings* <br> Dutch 1695-1754 | | **$200** | **$3,190** |
| ☐ WITHERINGTON, William Frederick ... *paintings* <br> British 1785-1865 | | **$385** | **$4,950** |
| ☐ WITHERS, John ................................. *drawings* | | | **$264** |
| ☐ WITHERS, M.N. ................................. *paintings* <br> English early 20th cent. | | | **$440** |
| ☐ WITHERSTINE, Donald F. ................... *paintings* <br> American 20th cent. | | | **$275** |
| ☐ WITHOLM, K. ................................... *paintings* | | **$225** | **$275** |
| ☐ WITHOOS, Matthias .......................... *paintings* <br> Dutch 1627-1703 | | **$110** | **$6,600** |
| ☐ WITHROW, Evelyn Almond ................ *paintings* <br> American 19th cent. | | | **$467** |
| ☐ WITKIN, Jerome ............................... *drawings* | | | **$440** |

| | | | Current Price Range | |
|---|---|---|---|---|
| | | | **Low** | **High** |
| ☐ **WITKOWSKI, Karl** ............................ | *paintings* | | $605 | $13,200 |
| American 1860-1910 ................................. | *drawings* | | $1,100 | $1,980 |
| ☐ **WITMAN, C.F.** .................................. | *paintings* | | | $1,000 |
| American 19th cent. | | | | |
| ☐ **WITMAN, Graeff** ............................. | *paintings* | | | $302 |
| ☐ **WITROWSKY** .................................. | *paintings* | | | $385 |
| ☐ **WITT, John Harrison** ....................... | *paintings* | | $467 | $2,750 |
| American 1840-1901 | | | | |
| ☐ **WITTE, Emanuel de** .......................... | *paintings* | | $15,400 | $55,000 |
| Dutch 1617/18-1692 | | | | |
| ☐ **WITTE, O.** ...................................... | *paintings* | | | $302 |
| ☐ **WITTE, Philippe de** .......................... | *paintings* | | | $440 |
| Dutch 1802-1876 | | | | |
| ☐ **WITTEL, Gaspard van** ....................... | *paintings* | | | $18,700 |
| Dutch 1653-1736 | | | | |
| ☐ **WITTKAMP, Johann Bernhard** ........... | *paintings* | | $880 | $2,475 |
| German 1820-1885 | | | | |
| ☐ **WIVEZ, W.** ..................................... | *paintings* | | | $495 |
| ☐ **WIX, O.** ......................................... | *drawings* | | | $330 |
| 19th/20th cent. | | | | |
| ☐ **WLERICK, Robert** ............................ | *sculpture* | | | $385 |
| French 1882-1944 | | | | |
| ☐ **WOBB, H.** ...................................... | *paintings* | | | $275 |
| American 19th cent. | | | | |
| ☐ **WOELFLE, Arthur William** ................ | *paintings* | | $132 | $9,350 |
| American 1873-1936 ............................... | *drawings* | | | $242 |
| ☐ **WOFFORD, Philip** ........................... | *paintings* | | | $1,320 |
| ☐ **WOHNER, Louis** .............................. | *paintings* | | $137 | $577 |
| German b. 1888 | | | | |
| ☐ **WOLCOTT, Harold** ........................... | *paintings* | | $55 | $660 |
| American 20th cent. | | | | |
| ☐ **WOLCOTT, Josiah** ............................ | *paintings* | | | $1,100 |
| ☐ **WOLCOTT, Roger A.** ......................... | *paintings* | | | $495 |
| American 20th cent. | | | | |
| ☐ **WOLCOTT, Roger H.** ......................... | *paintings* | | $357 | $385 |
| American 20th cent. | | | | |
| ☐ **WOLDEK, H.** ................................... | *paintings* | | | $500 |
| European 19th cent. | | | | |
| ☐ **WOLF, Chas. H.** ............................... | *drawings* | | | $30,000 |
| American | | | | |
| ☐ **WOLF, F.H.** .................................... | *paintings* | | | $605 |
| American 20th cent. | | | | |
| ☐ **WOLF, Franz** ................................... | *paintings* | | | $1,210 |
| Austrian 1795-1859 | | | | |
| ☐ **WOLF, Franz Xaver** .......................... | *paintings* | | $550 | $4,730 |
| Austrian b. 1896 | | | | |
| ☐ **WOLF, Georg** .................................. | *sculpture* | | | $632 |
| American b. 1858 | | | | |

| | Current Price Range | |
|---|---|---|
| | *Low* | *High* |

☐ **WOLF, J.** .................................... *paintings*     **$3,080**
German 19th cent.

☐ **WOLF, Joseph** .................................... *paintings*     **$4,400**

☐ **WOLF, M.** .................................... *sculpture*     **$1,540**
Russian late 19th cent.

☐ **WOLF, Wallace L. de** .................... *paintings*   **$1,045**    **$1,100**
American 1854-1930

☐ **WOLFE, Bryon B.** .......................... *drawings*   **$1,500**    **$6,500**
American 1904-1973

☐ **WOLFE, George** .......................... *drawings*     **$660**
English 1834-1890

☐ **WOLFE, Jack** .................................... *paintings*     **$550**
American 20th cent.

☐ **WOLFE, Peter** .......................... *drawings*     **$1,430**

☐ **WOLFE, Wayne** .................................... *paintings*   **$4,000**    **$30,000**
American contemporary

☐ **WOLFERS, Philippe** .......................... *sculpture*   **$1,320**    **$4,400**
Belgian 1858-1929

☐ **WOLFF, Gustave** .................................... *paintings*   **$319**    **$2,640**
German/American 1863-1935

☐ **WOLFLE, Inge** .................................... *paintings*   **$280**    **$1,320**
German b. 1928

☐ **WOLFROM, Friedrich Ernst** ............... *paintings*     **$2,750**
German b. 1857

☐ **WOLFSEN, Aleyda** .......................... *paintings*     **$4,180**

☐ **WOLLASTON, John** .......................... *paintings*   **$4,400**    **$13,200**
American ac. 1750-1767

☐ **WOLS,**
**(Alfred O Wolfgang SCHULTZE-**
**BATTMAN)** .................................... *drawings*   **$6,325**    **$14,300**
German 1913-1951

☐ **WOLSKI, Stanislaw Pomian** ................ *paintings*     **$6,050**
Polish 1859-94

☐ **WOLST, W.** .................................... *sculpture*     **$275**

☐ **WOLSTENHOLME, Dean (Jr.)** ............. *paintings*     **$800**
English 1798-1882

☐ **WOLSTENHOLME, Dean (Sr.)** ............. *paintings*   **$1,430**    **$22,000**
English 1757-1837

☐ **WOLTON, E.E.** .................................... *drawings*     **$330**
19th/20th cent.

☐ **WOLTZE, Berthold** .......................... *paintings*     **$440**

☐ **WOMBILL, T.W.** .......................... *paintings*     **$4,675**

☐ **WOMBRILL, William** .......................... *paintings*     **$2,750**

☐ **WONG, Mrs. Shu-Ping** .......................... *paintings*     **$275**
Chinese 19th cent.

☐ **WONNER, Paul** .................................... *drawings*   **$550**    **$3,520**
American b. 1924

☐ **WONTNER, William** .......................... *paintings*   **$2,090**    **$28,600**
British ac. 1879-1922

| | | Current Price Range | |
|---|---|---|---|
| | | Low | High |
| ☐ **WOOD, A.M.** ..................................... *paintings* | | $120 | $450 |
| American 19th/20th cent. | | | |
| ☐ **WOOD, Alexander W.** .......................... *paintings* | | $935 | $1,430 |
| American 19th cent. | | | |
| ☐ **WOOD, Carlos C.** ................................ *drawings* | | | $12,100 |
| English 1772-1856 | | | |
| ☐ **WOOD, Elsie Anna** ............................. *drawings* | | | $247 |
| English 20th cent. | | | |
| ☐ **WOOD, Ethelwyn A.** ........................... *paintings* | | | $770 |
| American | | | |
| ☐ **WOOD, Frank** ..................................... *paintings* | | | $495 |
| English 19th cent. | | | |
| ☐ **WOOD, Franklin Tyler** ......................... *drawings* | | | $550 |
| American 1887-1945 | | | |
| ☐ **WOOD, George Albert** .......................... *paintings* | | $300 | $412 |
| American b. 1840 | | | |
| ☐ **WOOD, George B.** ............................... *paintings* | | $330 | $2,400 |
| American 1832-1910 | | | |
| ☐ **WOOD, Grant** ..................................... *paintings* | | $1,540 | $1,375,000 |
| American 1892-1942 ................................... *drawings* | | $20,900 | $297,000 |
| ☐ **WOOD, Hunter** ................................... *paintings* | | $385 | $1,650 |
| American b. 1908 ..................................... *drawings* | | $290 | $330 |
| ☐ **WOOD, James F.** ................................ *paintings* | | | $220 |
| American 19th cent. | | | |
| ☐ **WOOD, James Longacre** ....................... *paintings* | | | $18,700 |
| American 1867-1938 | | | |
| ☐ **WOOD, Joe** ....................................... *paintings* | | | $264 |
| ☐ **WOOD, John** ..................................... *paintings* | | | $1,650 |
| British 1801-1870 | | | |
| ☐ **WOOD, Lawson** ................................. *drawings* | | | $300 |
| British 1878-1957 | | | |
| ☐ **WOOD, Lewis John** ............................. *drawings* | | | $412 |
| English 1813-1901 | | | |
| ☐ **WOOD, Ogden** ................................... *paintings* | | $66 | $825 |
| American 1851-1912 | | | |
| ☐ **WOOD, Robert** ................................... *paintings* | | $1,320 | $11,000 |
| American 1889-1979 | | | |
| ☐ **WOOD, Robert E.** .............................. *paintings* | | $275 | $17,000 |
| American b. 1926 ..................................... *drawings* | | $357 | $1,430 |
| ☐ **WOOD, Stanley** ................................. *drawings* | | | $19,800 |
| ☐ **WOOD, Stanley L.** ............................. *paintings* | | $825 | $2,750 |
| American 1860-1940 | | | |
| ☐ **WOOD, Thomas P.** ............................. *paintings* | | | $495 |
| English 19th cent. | | | |
| ☐ **WOOD, Thomas Waterman** .................. *paintings* | | $500 | $50,600 |
| American 1823-1903 ................................... *drawings* | | $302 | $27,500 |
| ☐ **WOOD, William R.C.** .......................... *paintings* | | $165 | $1,210 |
| American 1875-1915 | | | |

| | | | *Current Price Range* | |
|---|---|---|---|---|
| | | | Low | High |
| ☐ **WOOD, Worden** | ............................... | *paintings* | $200 | $440 |
| American 20th cent. | ............................... | *drawings* | $120 | $550 |
| ☐ **WOODBURN, A.** | ............................... | *drawings* | | $176 |
| American 20th cent. | | | | |
| ☐ **WOODBURY, Charles Herbert** | ............ | *paintings* | $125 | $3,520 |
| American 1864-1940 | ............................... | *drawings* | $33 | $4,180 |
| ☐ **WOODBURY, Marcia Oakes** | ............... | *paintings* | $275 | $577 |
| American 1865-1913 | | | | |
| ☐ **WOODCOCK, Hartwell L.** | ................. | *drawings* | $44 | $385 |
| American 1853-1929 | | | | |
| ☐ **WOODFORDE, Samuel** | ..................... | *paintings* | | $660 |
| ☐ **WOODHOUSE, William** | ..................... | *paintings* | $467 | $3,850 |
| ☐ **WOODMAN, P.E.** | ............................... | *paintings* | | $247 |
| British 19th cent. | | | | |
| ☐ **WOODMAN, T. H.** | ............................ | *drawings* | | $275 |
| English 19th cent. | | | | |
| ☐ **WOODRUFF, Daniel F.** | ..................... | *drawings* | | $1,760 |
| ☐ **WOODRUFF, G.L.** | ............................ | *paintings* | | $715 |
| American 19th cent. | | | | |
| ☐ **WOODS, Henry** | ............................... | *paintings* | | $1,320 |
| English 1846-1921 | | | | |
| ☐ **WOODS, Robb** | ............................... | *paintings* | $3,000 | $7,500 |
| American contemporary | | | | |
| ☐ **WOODS, W.H.** | ............................... | *paintings* | | $495 |
| ☐ **WOODSIDE, John Archibald** | ............... | *paintings* | $2,200 | $286,000 |
| American 1781-1852 | | | | |
| ☐ **WOODVILLE, Richard Caton (Jr.)** | ........ | *paintings* | $4,400 | $5,500 |
| British 1856-1927 | | | | |
| ☐ **WOODWARD, Ellsworth** | ..................... | *drawings* | $302 | $2,090 |
| American b. 1861 | | | | |
| ☐ **WOODWARD, Henry** | ..................... | *drawings* | | $660 |
| ☐ **WOODWARD, John Douglass** | ............... | *paintings* | $121 | $1,045 |
| American 1848-1924 | | | | |
| ☐ **WOODWARD, Laura** | ..................... | *paintings* | $150 | $462 |
| American 19th cent. | | | | |
| ☐ **WOODWARD, Mabel May** | ................... | *paintings* | $495 | $18,150 |
| American 1877-1945 | | | | |
| ☐ **WOODWARD, P.** | ............................... | *paintings* | | $375 |
| ☐ **WOODWARD, Robert Strong** | ............... | *paintings* | $440 | $2,310 |
| American b. 1885 | ............................... | *drawings* | | $385 |
| ☐ **WOODWARD, Stanley Wingate** | ............ | *paintings* | $82 | $3,300 |
| American 1890-1970 | | | | |
| ☐ **WOODWARD, Thomas** | ..................... | *paintings* | $4,950 | $6,050 |
| English 1801-1852 | | | | |
| ☐ **WOODWORTH, W.C.** | ..................... | *paintings* | | $250 |
| ☐ **WOOG, Raymond** | ............................ | *paintings* | | $4,675 |
| French b. 1875 | | | | |
| ☐ **WOOLF, Samuel Johnson** | ................. | *paintings* | $99 | $1,210 |
| American b. 1880 | | | | |

| | Current Price Range | |
|---|---|---|
| | Low | High |
| ☐ **WOOLLETT, Ely** ............................... *paintings* | | $495 |
| English 19th cent. | | |
| ☐ **WOOLLETT, Henry C.A.** ..................... *paintings* | $1,760 | $4,000 |
| British ac. 1851-1872 | | |
| ☐ **WOOLMER, Alfred Joseph** ................. *paintings* | $495 | $2,750 |
| English 1805-1892 | | |
| ☐ **WOOLMER, W.** ............................... *paintings* | | $1,430 |
| English 19th cent. | | |
| ☐ **WOOLNOTH, Charles N.** ..................... *drawings* | | $330 |
| ☐ **WOOLRYCH, F. Humphry W.** ............. *paintings* | $275 | $330 |
| American b. 1868 ....................................... *drawings* | | $220 |
| ☐ **WOOLSEY, W.** ................................. *paintings* | | $825 |
| ☐ **WOOSTER, A.C.** .............................. *paintings* | $522 | $767 |
| American 19th cent. | | |
| ☐ **WOOSTER, Austin C.** ......................... *paintings* | $660 | $6,050 |
| American ac. 1910 | | |
| ☐ **WOOTTON, Frank** ............................. *paintings* | | $715 |
| British 20th cent. | | |
| ☐ **WOOTTON, John** .............................. *paintings* | $4,400 | $77,000 |
| English c. 1686-1765 | | |
| ☐ **WOPFNER, Joseph** ............................ *paintings* | $825 | $23,100 |
| Austrian 1843-1927 | | |
| ☐ **WORES, Theodore** ............................. *paintings* | $440 | $3,575 |
| American 1859/60-1939 ............................. *drawings* | $220 | $605 |
| ☐ **WORLIDGE, Thomas** ......................... *paintings* | $176 | $2,640 |
| English 1700-1766 .................................... *drawings* | $165 | $385 |
| ☐ **WORMORWALD, E.** ........................... *paintings* | | $1,100 |
| Danish late 19th/early 20th cent. | | |
| ☐ **WORMS, Jules** ................................... *paintings* | $440 | $24,200 |
| French 1832-1924 ..................................... *drawings* | $302 | $1,540 |
| ☐ **WORMS, Roger** ................................ *paintings* | $220 | $330 |
| French b. 1907 | | |
| ☐ **WORMULLER, G.** ............................. *paintings* | | $770 |
| ☐ **WORRALL, C.A.** ............................... *paintings* | | $357 |
| English 19th cent. | | |
| ☐ **WORSDALE, James** ........................... *paintings* | | $3,850 |
| English d. 1767 | | |
| ☐ **WORSEY, Thomas** ............................. *paintings* | | $990 |
| ☐ **WORTHINGTON, W.F.** ...................... *paintings* | | $308 |
| ☐ **WORTLEY, Archibald James Stuart** ..... *paintings* | | $935 |
| English 1849-1905 ..................................... *drawings* | | $264 |
| ☐ **WOTRUBA, Fritz** ............................. *drawings* | $550 | $1,210 |
| German 1907-1975 ..................................... *sculpture* | | $15,400 |
| ☐ **WOU, Claes Claesz** ........................... *paintings* | $1,980 | $14,300 |
| Dutch c. 1592-1665 | | |
| ☐ **WOUTERMAERTENS, Edouard** .......... *paintings* | | $2,640 |
| Belgian 1819-1897 | | |
| ☐ **WOUTERS, G.J.** ............................... *paintings* | | $440 |
| Dutch 19th cent. | | |

| | | | Current Price Range | |
|---|---|---|---|---|
| | | | Low | High |
| ☐ **WOUTERS, J.** | *paintings* | | $165 | $440 |
| Dutch 19th cent. | | | | |
| ☐ **WOUTERS, K.** | *paintings* | | | $385 |
| Dutch 19th cent. | | | | |
| ☐ **WOUWERMAN, Pieter** | *paintings* | | $1,870 | $5,225 |
| Dutch 1623-1682 | | | | |
| ☐ **WOUWERMANS, Jan** | *paintings* | | $4,950 | $10,450 |
| Dutch 1629-1666 | | | | |
| ☐ **WOUWERMANS, Philips** | *paintings* | | $2,750 | $95,700 |
| Dutch 1619-1668 | | | | |
| ☐ **WRAY, Henry Russell** | *paintings* | | $160 | $352 |
| ☐ **WRENN, Charles J.** | *paintings* | | | $440 |
| American | | | | |
| ☐ **WRENN, Charles Lewis** | *paintings* | | | $220 |
| American b. 1880 | | | | |
| ☐ **WRIGHT** | *sculpture* | | | $302 |
| American 20th cent. | | | | |
| ☐ **WRIGHT, (of Liverpool)** | *paintings* | | | $2,970 |
| British 1735-1774 | | | | |
| ☐ **WRIGHT, Charles Lenox** | *paintings* | | | $495 |
| American b. 1876 | | | | |
| ☐ **WRIGHT, David** | *paintings* | | $8,500 | $10,000 |
| American contemporary | | | | |
| ☐ **WRIGHT, F.D.** | *drawings* | | | $264 |
| ☐ **WRIGHT, Frank Lloyd** | *drawings* | | $13,200 | $33,000 |
| American 1869-1959 | | | | |
| ☐ **WRIGHT, George** | *drawings* | | | $357 |
| Canadian 19th/20th cent. | | | | |
| ☐ **WRIGHT, George** | *paintings* | | $5,775 | $40,700 |
| American 1834-1934 | | | | |
| ☐ **WRIGHT, George** | *paintings* | | $1,045 | $12,100 |
| English 1860-1942 | | | | |
| ☐ **WRIGHT, George Frederick** | *paintings* | | | $192 |
| American 1828-1881 | | | | |
| ☐ **WRIGHT, George Hand** | *paintings* | | $6,050 | $31,900 |
| American 1872-1951 | *drawings* | | $247 | $2,750 |
| ☐ **WRIGHT, Gilbert S.** | *paintings* | | $1,650 | $16,500 |
| British ac. 1896-1900 | | | | |
| ☐ **WRIGHT, J.B.** | *paintings* | | | $308 |
| ☐ **WRIGHT, James Couper** | *drawings* | | $137 | $220 |
| Scottish/American b. 1906 | | | | |
| ☐ **WRIGHT, James Henry** | *paintings* | | $192 | $2,200 |
| American 1813-1883 | *drawings* | | | $275 |
| ☐ **WRIGHT, John Michael** | *paintings* | | | $3,300 |
| ☐ **WRIGHT, Joseph (of Derby)** | *paintings* | | | $1,100 |
| British 1734-1797 | | | | |
| ☐ **WRIGHT, Marion Lois** | *paintings* | | | $308 |
| ☐ **WRIGHT, Mason** | *paintings* | | | $275 |
| American 20th cent. | | | | |

|  | | | *Current Price Range* | |
|--|--|--|--|--|
|  | | | Low | High |
| ☐ **WRIGHT, Redmond Stephen** | ............... *paintings* | | $30 | $440 |
| American b. 1903 | ................................ *drawings* | | | $99 |
| ☐ **WRIGHT, Robert William** | ................... *paintings* | | $440 | $3,520 |
| British ac. 1871-1906 | | | | |
| ☐ **WRIGHT, Rufus** | ............... *paintings* | | $88 | $2,310 |
| American 1827/32-1895 | | | | |
| ☐ **WSSEL, Manuel** | .................................. *paintings* | | $1,320 | $7,700 |
| Spanish 19th cent. | | | | |
| ☐ **WUCHERER, Fritz** | ............................ *paintings* | | | $4,400 |
| Swiss b. 1873 | | | | |
| ☐ **WUDL, Tom** | ....................................... *paintings* | | | $1,650 |
| American b. 1948 | ...................................... *drawings* | | $660 | $1,320 |
| ☐ **WUERMER, Carl** | ............................... *paintings* | | $1,650 | $18,700 |
| American 1900-1983 | | | | |
| ☐ **WUERPEL, Edmund Henry** | ............... *paintings* | | $385 | $660 |
| American 1866-1958 | | | | |
| ☐ **WUERTZ, Emil** | ............................... *sculpture* | | | $935 |
| American 1856-1898 | | | | |
| ☐ **WUIRT, Walter** | ................................. *paintings* | | | $1,300 |
| American | | | | |
| ☐ **WULFFAERT, Andrianus** | ................... *paintings* | | | $2,530 |
| Belgian b. 1804 | | | | |
| ☐ **WULKOW, V.** | ..................................... *paintings* | | $440 | $2,200 |
| Russian (?) 19th/20th cent. | | | | |
| ☐ **WUN, Chung** | ....................................... *paintings* | | | $715 |
| Chinese 19th cent. | | | | |
| ☐ **WUNDER, George** | ............................. *drawings* | | | $275 |
| b. 1912 | | | | |
| ☐ **WUNDERLICH, G.** | ............................ *paintings* | | | $12,100 |
| ☐ **WUNDERLICH, Paul** | ......................... *paintings* | | $3,520 | $24,200 |
| German b. 1927 | ......................................... *drawings* | | $770 | $5,775 |
| ☐ **WUNECH, Maria** | ............................... *paintings* | | | $1,100 |
| ☐ **WUNNENBERG, Carl** | ......................... *paintings* | | $724 | $7,150 |
| German 1850-1929 | | | | |
| ☐ **WUNSCH, Marie** | ............................... *paintings* | | $770 | $3,850 |
| German 1860/62-1898 | | | | |
| ☐ **WURFFEL, Hans** | ............................... *paintings* | | | $302 |
| German b. 1884 | | | | |
| ☐ **WURZER, Johann Matthias** | .................. *paintings* | | | $2,200 |
| ☐ **WUST, Alexander** | ............................... *paintings* | | $330 | $990 |
| American 1837-1876 | | | | |
| ☐ **WUST, W.** | ....................................... *paintings* | | | $385 |
| ☐ **WUSTROW, L.** | ..................................... *sculpture* | | | $665 |
| ☐ **WYANT, Alexander Helwig** | .................. *paintings* | | $137 | $57,200 |
| American 1836-1892 | ................................. *drawings* | | $176 | $2,860 |
| ☐ **WYATT, Henry** | ................................. *paintings* | | | $2,090 |
| ☐ **WYATT, Matthew Digby** | ...................... *drawings* | | | $302 |
| British 1820-1877 | | | | |
| ☐ **WYCK, Jan** | ......................................... *paintings* | | | $1,980 |

| | | *Current Price Range* | |
|---|---|---|---|
| | | *Low* | *High* |
| ☐ **WYCK, Thomas** ................... *paintings* <br> Dutch 1616-1677 | | $4,950 | $15,400 |
| ☐ **WYCKOFF, H.** ................... *paintings* <br> American 19th cent. | | | $192 |
| ☐ **WYDEVELD, Arnoud** ................... *paintings* <br> Dutch/American ac. 1855-1862 | | $660 | $3,100 |
| ☐ **WYDINI, E.** ................... *paintings* | | | $275 |
| ☐ **WYDOOGEN, N.M.** ................... *paintings* <br> Dutch 19th cent. | | $495 | $522 |
| ☐ **WYETH, Andrew** ................... *paintings* <br> American b. 1917 ................... *drawings* | | $55,000 <br> $770 | $462,000 <br> $85,250 |
| ☐ **WYETH, Henriette** ................... *paintings* <br> American b. 1907 | | | $4,400 |
| ☐ **WYETH, James** ................... *paintings* <br> American b. 1946 ................... *drawings* | | $11,000 <br> $247 | $33,000 <br> $6,875 |
| ☐ **WYETH, John Allen** ................... *paintings* <br> American 20th cent. ................... *drawings* | | $88 | $412 <br> $55 |
| ☐ **WYETH, Newell Convers** ................... *paintings* <br> American 1882-1945 ................... *drawings* | | $2,200 <br> $110 | $30,250 <br> $4,675 |
| ☐ **WYGRZYWALSKI, Feliks K.** ................... *paintings* | | | $880 |
| ☐ **WYK, Henri van** ................... *paintings* <br> Dutch b. 1883 | | $330 | $1,760 |
| ☐ **WYLD, William** ................... *drawings* <br> English 1806-1889 | | $990 | $4,400 |
| ☐ **WYLIE, Robert** ................... *paintings* <br> English 1839-1877 | | | $1,650 |
| ☐ **WYLIE, S. S.** ................... *drawings* <br> American 19th cent. | | | $385 |
| ☐ **WYLLIE, William Lionel** ................... *paintings* <br> British 1851-1931 | | | $2,090 |
| ☐ **WYMAN, F.A.** ................... *paintings* <br> American 19th cent. | | | $41,800 |
| ☐ **WYNANTS, Jan** ................... *paintings* <br> Dutch c. 1630/35-1684 | | $44,000 | $60,500 |
| ☐ **WYNGAERDT, Anthonie Jacobus van** .. *paintings* <br> Dutch 1808-1887 | | $165 | $5,280 |
| ☐ **WYNGAERDT, Piet van** ................... *paintings* <br> Dutch 1875-1964 | | $110 | $330 |
| ☐ **WYNNE, Arthur** ................... *paintings* <br> British 19th cent. | | $351 | $440 |
| ☐ **WYNTRACK, Dirck** ................... *paintings* <br> Dutch before 1625-1678 | | | $3,300 |
| ☐ **WYON, E.W.** ................... *sculpture* | | | $302 |
| ☐ **WYSMAN, P.** ................... *paintings* | | | $440 |
| ☐ **WYSMULLER, Johan Hillebrand** ......... *paintings* <br> Dutch 1855-1925 | | $440 | $900 |
| ☐ **WYSOCKI, M.** ................... *paintings* <br> Polish 19th/20th cent. | | $110 | $412 |

| | | Current Price Range | |
|---|---|---|---|
| | | Low | High |
| ☐ **WYTSMAN, Rudolphe** ............... *paintings* | | | $275 |
| Dutch 1860-1927 | | | |
| ☐ **WYWIORSKI, Michal Gorstkin** ........... *paintings* | | | $6,600 |
| Polish 1861-1926 | | | |
| ☐ **XAVERY, Jacob** ............... *paintings* | | | $2,090 |
| ☐ **XCERON, Jean** ............... *paintings* | | $1,980 | $2,970 |
| American 1890-1967 ............... *drawings* | | | $302 |
| ☐ **XICARA, Ixquiac** ............... *paintings* | | | $880 |
| Guatemalan | | | |
| ☐ **XUAREZ, Nicolas Rodriguez** ............... *paintings* | | | $17,600 |
| Mexican 1667-1734 | | | |
| ☐ **YAKOULOFF, Georges** ............... *drawings* | | $880 | $1,210 |
| ☐ **YALE, Charlotte Lilla** ............... *paintings* | | | $192 |
| American 19th/20th cent. | | | |
| ☐ **YANKEL, Jacques** ............... *paintings* | | $154 | $286 |
| ☐ **YANYONG, Ding** ............... *drawings* | | $385 | $412 |
| 1902-1978 | | | |
| ☐ **YAO, C.J.** ............... *drawings* | | | $3,300 |
| contemporary | | | |
| ☐ **YARD, Sydney Janis** ............... *drawings* | | $191 | $1,320 |
| American 1855-1909 | | | |
| ☐ **YARNELL, A.** ............... *sculpture* | | $137 | $220 |
| American 20th cent. | | | |
| ☐ **YARNOLD, George B.** ............... *paintings* | | | $1,045 |
| English 19th cent. | | | |
| ☐ **YARNOLD, Joseph W.** ............... *paintings* | | $2,420 | $2,530 |
| British 19th cent. | | | |
| ☐ **YARROW, William Henry Kemble** ........ *drawings* | | | $550 |
| American b. 1891 | | | |
| ☐ **YATES, Cullen** ............... *paintings* | | $484 | $3,850 |
| American b. 1866 | | | |
| ☐ **YATES, Frederick** ............... *paintings* | | | $2,200 |
| British d. 1920 | | | |
| ☐ **YATES, H.J.** ............... *paintings* | | | $220 |
| British 20th cent. | | | |
| ☐ **YATES, Lieutenant Thomas** ............... *drawings* | | $577 | $935 |
| British 19th cent. | | | |
| ☐ **YATES, William Henry** ............... *paintings* | | $400 | $5,500 |
| American 1845-1934 | | | |
| ☐ **YDEMA, Egnatius** ............... *paintings* | | $165 | $330 |
| Dutch 1876-1937 | | | |
| ☐ **YEATS, Jack Butler** ............... *drawings* | | | $825 |
| Irish 1871-1957 | | | |
| ☐ **YECKLEY, Norman** ............... *paintings* | | | $302 |
| 19th/20th cent. | | | |
| ☐ **YEEND-KING, Henry John** ............... *paintings* | | $220 | $5,500 |
| English 1855-1924 | | | |
| ☐ **YEISER, Charles William** ............... *paintings* | | $330 | $467 |
| American | | | |

| | *Current Price Range* | |
|---|---|---|
| | *Low* | *High* |
| ☐ **YEKTAI, Manoucher** ............................ *paintings* | $77 | $1,980 |
| Iranian/American b. 1922 | | |
| ☐ **YELLAND, Raymond Dabb** .................. *paintings* | $247 | $1,870 |
| American 1848-1900 ................................ *drawings* | | $660 |
| ☐ **YENNAD, Aduasha** ............................ *paintings* | | $192 |
| American 20th cent. | | |
| ☐ **YENS, Karl Julius** ............................... *paintings* | $220 | $495 |
| American 1868-1945 | | |
| ☐ **YEOMANS, Thomas** ........................... *paintings* | $1,870 | $3,300 |
| ☐ **YEWELL, George Henry** ...................... *paintings* | $330 | $1,200 |
| American 1830-1923 | | |
| ☐ **YKENS, Frans** ..................................... *paintings* | | $49,500 |
| Flemish 1601-1693 | | |
| ☐ **YO QUA** .............................................. *paintings* | | $6,325 |
| ☐ **YOAKUM, Joseph** ............................... *drawings* | $825 | $935 |
| American 1886-1973 | | |
| ☐ **YOHN, Frederick Coffray** ..................... *paintings* | $825 | $1,100 |
| American 1875-1933 ................................ *drawings* | $99 | $121 |
| ☐ **YORKE, George Hoard** ........................ *paintings* | | $11,550 |
| British 19th cent. | | |
| ☐ **YORKE, William G.** ............................. *paintings* | $6,050 | $8,800 |
| American | | |
| ☐ **YORKE, William Howard** ...................... *paintings* | $2,300 | $15,950 |
| British ac.1858-after 1913 | | |
| ☐ **YOSHIDA, Matsugoro** ......................... *paintings* | | $275 |
| Japanese b. 1900 | | |
| ☐ **YOUCIEVITCH** ................................... *sculpture* | | $1,925 |
| 20th cent. | | |
| ☐ **YOUNG, August** ................................. *paintings* | $192 | $3,025 |
| American 1839-1913 | | |
| ☐ **YOUNG, B.S.** ..................................... *paintings* | $2,700 | $4,290 |
| American 19th cent. | | |
| ☐ **YOUNG, Charles Morris** ...................... *paintings* | $495 | $3,850 |
| American b. 1869 | | |
| ☐ **YOUNG, Edward** ................................. *paintings* | $1,100 | $1,540 |
| Austrian 1823-1882 | | |
| ☐ **YOUNG, Fred Grand** ........................... *paintings* | $220 | $495 |
| American 19th/20th cent. | | |
| ☐ **YOUNG, Harvey B.** ............................. *paintings* | $220 | $7,150 |
| American 1840-1901 ................................ *drawings* | $385 | $1,540 |
| ☐ **YOUNG, J.B.** ..................................... *paintings* | | $1,650 |
| British 19th cent. | | |
| ☐ **YOUNG, James Harvey** ....................... *paintings* | | $1,100 |
| American 1830-1901 | | |
| ☐ **YOUNG, John Chin** ............................. *drawings* | | $400 |
| American b. 1909 | | |
| ☐ **YOUNG, Lyman (Chic)** ........................ *drawings* | $192 | $825 |
| b. 1893 | | |

|  | | Current Price Range | |
|---|---|---|---|
|  | | Low | High |
| ☐ **YOUNG, Mahonri MacKintosh** ............. *drawings* | | $132 | $440 |
| American 1877-1957 ................................ *sculpture* | | $220 | $11,000 |
| ☐ **YOUNG, Peter** .................................... *paintings* | | $440 | $550 |
| ................................................. *drawings* | | | $286 |
| ☐ **YOUNG, Tobias** ................................ *paintings* | | | $4,180 |
| English d. 1824 | | | |
| ☐ **YOUNG, W.S.** ................................... *paintings* | | $187 | $1,870 |
| American 19th/20th cent. | | | |
| ☐ **YOUNG, William** ............................... *drawings* | | | $192 |
| British ac. 1874 | | | |
| ☐ **YOUNG-HUNTER, John** ..................... *paintings* | | $715 | $2,750 |
| American 1874-1955 | | | |
| ☐ **YOUNGERMAN, Jack** ........................ *paintings* | | $1,100 | $6,600 |
| American b. 1926 ................................... *drawings* | | $275 | $1,100 |
| ☐ **YOUNGMAN, Annie Mary** ................. *drawings* | | | $715 |
| English 1859/60-1919 | | | |
| ☐ **YOUNGMAN, F.T.** ............................ *paintings* | | | $660 |
| ☐ **YRRARAZAVAL, Ricardo** ................... *paintings* | | | $1,650 |
| b. Chile 1940 | | | |
| ☐ **YSANZ, Ulpiano Checa** ........................ *paintings* | | | $1,650 |
| ☐ **YSSELSTEYN, Adrianus van** ............... *paintings* | | | $2,530 |
| ☐ **YU-HO, Tseng** ................................... *drawings* | | | $440 |
| American 20th cent. | | | |
| ☐ **YUNKERS, Adja** ............................... *paintings* | | | $440 |
| Latvian/American b. 1900 ...................... *drawings* | | | $440 |
| ☐ **YUTZ, Carl** ....................................... *paintings* | | | $330 |
| German 19th cent. | | | |
| ☐ **YUYAHEOVA, Bevins** ....................... *drawings* | | $880 | $1,320 |
| American (Hopi) | | | |
| ☐ **YVARAL, Jean Pierre** | | | |
| **(Jean Pierre VASARELY)** ..................... *paintings* | | $550 | $3,520 |
| French b. 1934 ....................................... *drawings* | | | $605 |
| ☐ **YVON, Adolphe** ................................. *paintings* | | $11,000 | $27,500 |
| French 1817-1893 | | | |
| ☐ **ZAALBERG, K.A.** ............................. *paintings* | | | $275 |
| Dutch 20th cent. | | | |
| ☐ **ZABEHLICKY, A.** ............................. *paintings* | | $550 | $880 |
| German 19th cent. | | | |
| ☐ **ZABEHLICKY, Franz** ........................ *paintings* | | | $935 |
| German 19th cent. | | | |
| ☐ **ZABEHLICKY, L.** ............................. *paintings* | | $356 | $385 |
| European 19th/20th cent. | | | |
| ☐ **ZACH, Bruno (or ZACK)** ..................... *sculpture* | | $385 | $30,800 |
| Austrian early 20th cent. | | | |
| ☐ **ZACHAROV, F.** ................................. *paintings* | | | $440 |
| ☐ **ZACHINETTI, G.** .............................. *paintings* | | $2,100 | $2,640 |
| ☐ **ZACHO, Christian** ............................ *paintings* | | | $1,320 |
| Danish 1843-1913 ................................. *drawings* | | | $27 |
| ☐ **ZADIKOW, Arnold** ........................... *sculpture* | | | $550 |

| | | Current Price Range | |
|---|---|---|---|
| | | *Low* | *High* |
| ☐ **ZADKINE, Ossip** .................... *drawings* | | $247 | $3,520 |
| Russian/French 1890-1967 ............. *sculpture* | | $4,400 | $29,700 |
| ☐ **ZAGBAUM, R.F.** .................. *drawings* | | | $330 |
| ☐ **ZAHND, Johann** ................. *paintings* | | | $1,650 |
| Swiss 1854-1934 | | | |
| ☐ **ZAIS, Giuseppe** ................. *paintings* | | $2,475 | $11,000 |
| Italian 1709-1784 ..................... *drawings* | | $1,540 | $2,750 |
| ☐ **ZAJAC, Jack** ................... *sculpture* | | $577 | $3,100 |
| American b. 1929 | | | |
| ☐ **ZAK, Eugene** ................... *paintings* | | $220 | $3,520 |
| Polish 1884-1926 ..................... *drawings* | | $462 | $935 |
| ☐ **ZAKANYCH, Robert** ............. *paintings* | | $220 | $11,000 |
| American b. 1935 | | | |
| ☐ **ZALCE, Alfredo** ................ *paintings* | | $110 | $1,650 |
| Mexican b. 1908 ...................... *drawings* | | $302 | $1,650 |
| ☐ **ZALIOUK, Sacha** ................ *drawings* | | $660 | $2,090 |
| ☐ **ZAMACOIS Y ZABALA, Eduardo** ....... *paintings* | | $990 | $4,400 |
| Spanish 1842-1871 .................... *drawings* | | $191 | $605 |
| ☐ **ZAMAZAL, Jaroslav (called VERIS)** ...... *paintings* | | | $467 |
| Czechoslovakian b. 1900 | | | |
| ☐ **ZAMBONI, Dante** ............... *sculpture* | | | $3,520 |
| Italian b. 1905 | | | |
| ☐ **ZAMBRE, Etienne A.** ............. *paintings* | | | $275 |
| ☐ **ZAMORA, Jesus Maria** ........... *paintings* | | $1,980 | $6,325 |
| Colombian 1875-1949 | | | |
| ☐ **ZAMORA, Merced** ............... *paintings* | | | $13,200 |
| ☐ **ZAMPIGHI, Eugenio Eduardo** ............. *paintings* | | $528 | $12,100 |
| Italian 1859-1944 | | | |
| ☐ **ZANAZIO, G.** .................... *paintings* | | $308 | $715 |
| Italian 19th/20th cent. | | | |
| ☐ **ZANDOMENEGHI, Federigo** ............... *drawings* | | | $29,700 |
| Italian 1841-1917 | | | |
| ☐ **ZANDT, Thomas K. van** ............... *paintings* | | $330 | $852 |
| American ac. 1844-1845 | | | |
| ☐ **ZANETTI** ....................... *paintings* | | | $253 |
| Italian 19th/20th cent. | | | |
| ☐ **ZANETTI-ZELLA, Vettori** ............... *paintings* | | | $1,100 |
| Italian 1864-1945 .................... *drawings* | | | $150 |
| ☐ **ZANG, J.J.** ..................... *paintings* | | $1,100 | $4,950 |
| American 19th cent. | | | |
| ☐ **ZANIERI, Arturo** ................. *paintings* | | | $3,245 |
| Italian b. 1870 | | | |
| ☐ **ZANTHO, Darin** ................. *paintings* | | | $242 |
| American 20th cent. | | | |
| ☐ **ZAO-WOU-KI** .................... *paintings* | | $412 | $3,080 |
| Chinese/French 1921-after 1964 | | | |
| ☐ **ZAPATA, Antonio** ............... *paintings* | | | $2,200 |
| ☐ **ZAPKUS, Kestutis** ............... *paintings* | | $550 | $2,640 |
| Lithuanian/Amer. b. 1938 | | | |

| | Current Price Range | |
| --- | --- | --- |
| | Low | High |
| ☐ ZARAGOZA, Jose .............................. *paintings* | | $3,520 |
| ☐ ZAREMBSKI, M. .............................. *paintings* | | $800 |
| ☐ ZARRAGA, Angel .............................. *paintings* | $605 | $2,860 |
| Mexican 1886-1946 | | |
| ☐ ZATZKA, Hans .............................. *paintings* | $1,210 | $8,800 |
| Austrian b. 1859 | | |
| ☐ ZAVARO, Albert .............................. *paintings* | $44 | $191 |
| Spanish 20th cent. | | |
| ☐ ZAYAS, G. de .............................. *drawings* | $308 | $440 |
| ☐ ZBAUER, F.F. .............................. *paintings* | | $1,760 |
| German 19th cent. | | |
| ☐ ZDANEVITCH, Kiril .............................. *drawings* | $187 | $660 |
| Russian 1892-1970 | | |
| ☐ ZECCHI, Cesare .............................. *sculpture* | | $440 |
| ☐ ZEECK, J. .............................. *paintings* | | $411 |
| Portugese 19th/20th cent. | | |
| ☐ ZEFFIRELLI, Franco .............................. *drawings* | | $935 |
| Italian b. 1923 | | |
| ☐ ZEITTER, John Christian .............................. *paintings* | | $935 |
| British d. 1862 | | |
| ☐ ZELECHOWSKI, Gaspard .............................. *paintings* | | $330 |
| Polish b. 1863 | | |
| ☐ ZELLENBERG, F. .............................. *paintings* | | $935 |
| ☐ ZELLINSKY, C.L. .............................. *paintings* | $1,320 | $1,430 |
| ☐ ZELO, Giovanni .............................. *drawings* | | $330 |
| ☐ ZELONI, R. .............................. *paintings* | $385 | $1,540 |
| Italian 19th cent. | | |
| ☐ ZELTEA, Paul .............................. *drawings* | | $330 |
| ☐ ZELTNER, William .............................. *drawings* | | $275 |
| American 19th/20th cent. | | |
| ☐ ZENAZOO, G. .............................. *paintings* | | $522 |
| European 20th cent. | | |
| ☐ ZENISEK, Josef .............................. *paintings* | | $275 |
| Czechoslovakian b. 1855 | | |
| ☐ ZEPPENFELD, Victor .............................. *paintings* | | $357 |
| German 1834-1871 | | |
| ☐ ZERBE, Karl .............................. *paintings* | $88 | $990 |
| German/American 1903-1972 | | |
| ☐ ZERMATI, Jules .............................. *paintings* | $880 | $2,750 |
| Italian 19th/20th cent. | | |
| ☐ ZERVAS .............................. *paintings* | | $605 |
| American(?) 20th cent. | | |
| ☐ ZEWY, Karl .............................. *paintings* | $3,300 | $6,050 |
| Austrian 1855-1929 | | |
| ☐ ZHUKOV .............................. *paintings* | | $495 |
| Russian 19th cent. | | |
| ☐ ZICHY, G. .............................. *paintings* | | $275 |
| ☐ ZICHY, Mikhail .............................. *drawings* | | $1,980 |
| ☐ ZICK, C. .............................. *paintings* | | $495 |

| | | | Current Price Range | |
|---|---|---|---|---|
| | | | Low | High |

☐ **ZICK, Januarius Johann Rasso** ............ *paintings* | | $7,150
German 1730-1797

☐ **ZIEGLER** ............................... *paintings* | | $1,320
French 1804-1856

☐ **ZIEGLER, Eustace Paul** ...................... *paintings* | $990 | $14,300
American b. 1881 ..................................... *drawings* | | $4,400

☐ **ZIEM, Felix** ............................... *paintings* | $385 | $42,900
French 1821-1911 .............................. *drawings* | $1,540 | $3,960

☐ **ZIER, Francois Edouard** ...................... *paintings* | $1,155 | $2,090
French 1856-1924

☐ **ZIESENIS, Johann Georg** .............. *paintings* | | $880
German 1716-1776

☐ **ZIGLIARA, Eugene Louis** .............. *paintings* | $3,300 | $3,520
French 1873-1918

☐ **ZILLE, Heinrich** ............................ *drawings* | $137 | $3,300
German 1858/64-1929

☐ **ZIMM, A.L.** ................................. *paintings* | $192 | $253

☐ **ZIMMELE, Margaret Scully** ................ *paintings* | $165 | $577
American b. 1872

☐ **ZIMMER, Bernd** ............................... *paintings* | | $6,600
b. 1948

☐ **ZIMMER, Wilhelm Carl August** ........... *paintings* | $2,200 | $15,400
German 1853-1937

☐ **ZIMMERMAN, Albert August** .............. *paintings* | | $3,960
German 1808-1888

☐ **ZIMMERMAN, Ernst Karl Georg** ........ *paintings* | $2,640 | $6,050
German 1852-1901 ...................................... *drawings* | $82 | $90

☐ **ZIMMERMAN, Frederick Almond** ........ *paintings* | $99 | $715
American 1886-1976

☐ **ZIMMERMAN, William** ...................... *drawings* | | $412
American 20th cent.

☐ **ZIMMERMANN, Alfred** ...................... *paintings* | | $1,100
German 1854-1910

☐ **ZIMMERMANN, Carl** .......................... *paintings* | | $3,740
German 1863-1930

☐ **ZIMMERMANN, Reinhard Sebastian** .... *paintings* | $6,050 | $41,800
German 1815-1893

☐ **ZINGONI, Aurelio** ............................. *paintings* | $1,210 | $3,850
Italian 1853-1922

☐ **ZINI, Umberto** ................................. *paintings* | | $357
Italian 1878-1964

☐ **ZINK, R.** ...................................... *paintings* | | $11,000
French

☐ **ZINKEISEN, Anna** ............................ *paintings* | | $1,100
British b. 1901

☐ **ZINKEISEN, Doris** ............................ *paintings* | $385 | $825
English 20th cent.

☐ **ZINNOGGER, Leopold** ........................ *drawings* | $357 | $522
Austrian 1811-1872

|                                                      | Current Price Range |           |
|                                                      | Low      | High     |
|------------------------------------------------------|----------|----------|
| ☐ **ZINOVIEV, A.** ........................ *paintings* |          | $247     |
| ........................ *drawings*                   |          | $440     |
| ☐ **ZION, Ben** ........................ *paintings*   | $275     | $330     |
| American ........................ *drawings*          |          | $77      |
| ☐ **ZLIM, Felix** ........................ *paintings* |          | $242     |
| French 20th cent.                                    |          |          |
| ☐ **ZOBEL, Fernando** ............... *paintings*     | $209     | $357     |
| Spanish b. 1924                                      |          |          |
| ☐ **ZOCCHI, Emilio** ............... *paintings*      |          | $2,530   |
| Italian 1835-1920                                    |          |          |
| ☐ **ZOCCHI, Giuseppe** ............ *paintings*       |          | $4,070   |
| Italian 1711-1767                                    |          |          |
| ☐ **ZOCCHI, Guglielmo** ........... *paintings*       | $1,300   | $6,600   |
| Italian b. 1874                                      |          |          |
| ☐ **ZOCCHI, Silvio** ............... *paintings*      | $880     | $1,870   |
| Italian 19th cent.                                   |          |          |
| ☐ **ZOFF, Alfred** ........................ *paintings* |          | $1,430   |
| Austrian 1852-1927                                   |          |          |
| ☐ **ZOFFOLI, A.** ........................ *paintings* |          | $3,520   |
| Italian 19th cent.                                   |          |          |
| ☐ **ZOGBAUM, Rufus Fairchild** ......... *drawings*   | $770     | $1,540   |
| 1849-1925                                            |          |          |
| ☐ **ZOGBAUM, Wilfred M.** ............ *paintings*    |          | $4,180   |
| American 1915-1965 ........................ *drawings* |          | $330     |
| ☐ **ZOICK, Bruno** ............... *sculpture*        |          | $750     |
| ☐ **ZOLAN, Donald James** ............ *paintings*    |          | $220     |
| American contemporary                                |          |          |
| ☐ **ZOLLER, Josef Anton** ............ *drawings*     |          | $825     |
| Austrian 1730-1791                                   |          |          |
| ☐ **ZOMPINI, Gaetano** ............ *drawings*        | $605     | $880     |
| ☐ **ZOPF, Carl** ........................ *paintings* |          | $1,320   |
| German b. 1858                                       |          |          |
| ☐ **ZOPPI, Antonio** ............... *paintings*      | $400     | $1,430   |
| Italian 1860-1926                                    |          |          |
| ☐ **ZOPPI, Antonio** ............... *paintings*      |          | $1,210   |
| Italian 1826-1896                                    |          |          |
| ☐ **ZORACH, Marguerite** ............ *paintings*     | $660     | $3,080   |
| American 1887-1968 ............... *drawings*         | $132     | $770     |
| ☐ **ZORACH, William** ............ *paintings*        |          | $1,045   |
| Lithuanian/American 1887-1966 ......... *drawings*    | $192     | $2,640   |
| ........................ *sculpture*                 | $352     | $14,300  |
| ☐ **ZORN, Anders** ............ *paintings*           | $3,850   | $198,000 |
| Swedish 1860-1920 ........................ *drawings* | $770     | $3,850   |
| ☐ **ZOX, Larry** ........................ *paintings* | $275     | $3,520   |
| American b. 1936                                     |          |          |
| ☐ **ZRZAVY, Jan** ............... *paintings*         |          | $935     |
| Czechoslovakian b. 1890                              |          |          |
| ☐ **ZUBER BUHLER, Fritz** ......... *paintings*       | $3,960   | $57,750  |
| Swiss 1822-1896                                      |          |          |

|  | | Current Price Range | |
|---|---|---|---|
|  | | Low | High |
| ☐ **ZUBIAURRE, Valentin de** ............... *paintings* | | | $2,200 |
| Spanish b. 1879 | | | |
| ☐ **ZUBRITZKY, Lorand de** ............... *paintings* | | | $19,250 |
| Hungarian b. 1869 | | | |
| ☐ **ZUCCARELLI, Francesco** ............... *paintings* | | $4,500 | $33,000 |
| Italian 1701/02-1788 | | | |
| ☐ **ZUCCARO, Federico** ............... *drawings* | | | $1,100 |
| Italian 1540/43-1609 | | | |
| ☐ **ZUCCARO, Taddeo** ............... *paintings* | | | $3,850 |
| Italian 1529-1566 | | | |
| ☐ **ZUCCHI, Antonio** ............... *drawings* | | $825 | $1,045 |
| Italian 1726-1795 | | | |
| ☐ **ZUCCO, Francesco** ............... *paintings* | | | $7,700 |
| Italian c. 1570/1600-1627 | | | |
| ☐ **ZUCKER, Jacques** ............... *paintings* | | $132 | $247 |
| Polish/American b. 1900 ............... *drawings* | | $70 | $77 |
| ☐ **ZUFO, C. del** ............... *paintings* | | | $495 |
| Italian School early 20th cent. | | | |
| ☐ **ZUGEL, Heinrich Johann** ............... *paintings* | | $16,500 | $159,500 |
| German 1850-1941 | | | |
| ☐ **ZUILL, Alice E.** ............... *paintings* | | | $1,300 |
| American 19th cent. | | | |
| ☐ **ZULOAGA Y ZABALETA, Ignacio** ....... *paintings* | | $3,850 | $137,500 |
| Spanish 1870-1945 ............... *drawings* | | $495 | $1,320 |
| ☐ **ZUNEFF, V.** ............... *drawings* | | | $330 |
| American | | | |
| ☐ **ZUNIGA, Francisco** ............... *paintings* | | | $8,250 |
| Mexican b. 1913 ............... *drawings* | | $650 | $12,650 |
| ............... *sculpture* | | $1,760 | $126,500 |
| ☐ **ZURBARAN, Francisco de** ............... *paintings* | | $132,000 | $280,000 |
| ☐ **ZWAAN, Cornelisz C.** ............... *paintings* | | $750 | $2,475 |
| Dutch 1882-1964 | | | |
| ☐ **ZWADO,** | | | |
| **(Jan Waclaw ZOWADOWSKI)** ............... *paintings* | | | $1,100 |
| Polish b. 1891 | | | |
| ☐ **ZWARA, Jan** ............... *paintings* | | | $220 |
| American 20th cent. | | | |
| ☐ **ZWART, Petrus Antonius de** ............... *paintings* | | | $550 |
| Dutch 1880-1967 | | | |
| ☐ **ZWART, Willem de** ............... *paintings* | | $220 | $935 |
| Dutch 1862-1931 ............... *drawings* | | | $66 |
| ☐ **ZWENGAUER, Anton** ............... *paintings* | | $2,310 | $3,520 |
| German 1810-1884 | | | |
| ☐ **ZWERLING, Lisa** ............... *paintings* | | | $275 |
| American 20th cent. | | | |
| ☐ **ZWILLER, Marie Augustin** ............... *paintings* | | $1,100 | $4,400 |
| French 1850-1939 | | | |
| ☐ **ZYLINSKI, Andrew** ............... *paintings* | | | $800 |

# Museums

## Alabama
*Birmingham*
Birmingham Museum of Art

*Montgomery*
Montgomery Museum of Fine Arts

*Tuscaloosa*
Warner Collection of Gulf States
  Paper Corporation

## Alaska
*Anchorage*
Anchorage Historical and Fine
  Arts Museum

## Arizona
*Phoenix*
Phoenix Art Museum

*Tempe*
University Art Collections,
  Matthews Center, Arizona State

*Tucson*
Tucson Museum of Art
University of Arizona Museum
  of Art

## Arkansas
*Harrison*
Bryant Art Museum

*Little Rock*
Arkansas Arts Center

## California
*Berkeley*
University Art Museum, University
  of California, Berkeley

*La Jolla*
La Jolla Museum of Contemporary
  Art

*Los Angeles*
Los Angeles County Museum of Art

*Malibu*
J. Paul Getty Museum

*Pasadena*
Norton Simon Museum of Art

*San Diego*
Timken Art Gallery

*San Francisco*
M.H. de Young Memorial Museum
California Palace of the Legion
  of Honor
San Francisco Museum of Modern
  Art

*San Marino*
Huntington Library, Art Gallery
  and Botanical Gardens

*Santa Barbara*
Santa Barbara Museum of Art

## Colorado
*Colorado Springs*
Colorado Springs Fine Art Center

*Denver*
Denver Art Museum

## Connecticut
*Bridgeport*
Housatonic Museum of Art

*Farmington*
Hill-Stead Museum

*Hartford*
Wadsworth Atheneum

*New Britain*
New Britain Museum of
  American Art

*New Haven*
Yale University Art Gallery
Yale Center for British Art

*New London*
Lyman Allyn Museum

*Ridgefield*
Aldrich Museum of
  Contemporary Art

*Storrs*
William Benton Museum of Art,
   University of Connecticut

**Delaware**
*Wilmington*
Delaware Art Museum

*Winterthur*
Henry Francis du Pont Winterthur
   Museum

**District of Columbia**
*Washington*
Corcoran Gallery of Art
Hirshhorn Museum and Sculpture
   Garden
National Museum of American Art
National Gallery of Art
National Portrait Gallery
The Phillips Collection

**Florida**
*Coral Gables*
Lowe Art Museum, University
   of Miami
Metropolitan Museum and Art
   Centers, Inc.

*Jacksonville*
Cummer Gallery of Art

*Miami Beach*
Bass Museum of Art

*Orlando*
Loch Haven Art Center

*Palm Beach*
Society of the Four Arts Museum

*St. Petersburg*
Museum of Fine Arts

*Sarasota*
Ringling Museums of Art

*West Palm Beach*
Norton Gallery and School of Art

**Georgia**
*Athens*
Georgia Museum of Art

*Atlanta*
High Museum of Art

*Savannah*
Telfair Academy of Arts
   and Sciences

**Hawaii**
*Honolulu*
Contemporary Arts Center
   of Hawaii
Honolulu Academy of Arts

**Idaho**
*Boise*
Boise Gallery of Art

**Illinois**
*Champaign*
Krannert Art Museum, University
   of Illinois

*Chicago*
Art Institute of Chicago
Museum of Contemporary Art
Terra Art Museum

**Indiana**
*Bloomington*
Indiana University Art Museum

*Evansville*
Evansville Museum of Arts
   and Science

*Indianapolis*
Indianapolis Museum of Art

*South Bend*
Smite Museum of Art, University
   of Notre Dame

*Terre Haute*
Sheldon Swope Art Gallery

## Iowa
*Cedar Falls*
Gallery of Art, University of
  Northern Iowa

*Davenport*
Davenport Municipal Art Gallery

*Des Moines*
Des Moines Art Center

*Iowa City*
University of Iowa Museum of Art

*Mason City*
Charles H. MacNider Museum

## Kansas
*Lawrence*
Spencer Museum of Art,
  University of Kansas

*Wichita*
Edwin A. Ulrich Museum of Art,
  Wichita State University
Wichita Art Museum

## Kentucky
*Lexington*
University of Kentucky Art Museum

*Louisville*
J.B. Speed Art Museum

*Owensboro*
Owensboro Museum of Fine Art

## Louisiana
*Jennings*
Zigler Museum

*New Orleans*
New Orleans Museum of Art

*Shreveport*
R.W. Norton Art Gallery

## Maine
*Brunswick*
Bowdoin College Museum of Art

*Portland*
Portland Museum of Art

*Rockland*
William A. Farnsworth Library
  and Art Museum

*Waterville*
Colby College Museum of Art

## Maryland
*Baltimore*
Baltimore Museum of Art
Walters Art Gallery

## Massachusetts
*Andover*
Addison Gallery of American Art

*Boston*
Museum of Fine Arts
Isabella Stewart Gardener Museum

*Brockton*
Brockton Art Museum

*Cambridge*
Arthur M. Sackler Art Museum
Busch-Reisinger Museum
Fogg Art Museum

*Framingham*
Danforth Museum

*Northhampton*
Smith College Museum of Art

*Salem*
Peabody Museum of Salem

*Springfield*
Museum of Fine Arts

*Waltham*
Rose Art Museum,
  Brandeis University

*Wellesley*
Wellesley College Museum,
  Jewett Art Center

*Williamstown*
Sterling and Francine Clark
  Art Institute

*Worcester*
Worcester Art Museum

## Michigan
*Ann Arbor*
University of Michigan
  Museum of Art
*Detroit*
Detroit Institute of Arts
*Flint*
Flint Institute of Arts
*Grand Rapids*
Grand Rapids Art Museum

## Minnesota
*Duluth*
Tweed Museum of Art, University
  of Minnesota
*Minneapolis*
Minneapolis Institute of Arts
University Gallery, University of
  Minnesota
Walker Art Center
*St. Paul*
Minnesota Museum of Art

## Mississippi
*Laurel*
Lauren Rogers Memorial Library
  and Museum of Art

## Missouri
*Kansas City*
William Rockhill Nelson Gallery of
  Art and Mary Atkins Museum of
  Fine Art
*St. Louis*
St. Louis Art Museum

## Montana
*Billings*
Yellowstone Art Center
*Great Falls*
C.M. Russell Gallery

## Nebraska
*Lincoln*
Sheldon Memorial Art Gallery,
  University of Nebraska Art
  Gallery
*Omaha*
Joslyn Art Museum

## Nevada
*Las Vegas*
Las Vegas Art Museum

## New Hampshire
*Hanover*
Hood Museum of Art, Dartmouth
  College
*Manchester*
Currier Gallery of Art

## New Jersey
*Newark*
Newark Museum
*Princeton*
The Art Museum, Princeton
  University
*Trenton*
New Jersey State Museum

## New Mexico
*Albuquerque*
Jonson Gallery, University of New
  Mexico
*Santa Fe*
Museum of Fine Arts, Museum
  of New Mexico

## New York
*Buffalo*
Albright-Knox Art Gallery
*Canajoharie*
Canajoharie Library and
  Art Gallery

*Corning*
The Rockwell-Corning Museum

*Elmira*
Arnot Art Museum

*Glens Falls*
Hyde Collection

*Huntington*
Heckscher Museum

*Ithaca*
Herbert F. Johnson Museum
   of Art, Cornell University

*New York City*
The Frick Collection
Solomon R. Guggenheim Museum
Jewish Museum
Metropolitan Museum of Art
Museum of Modern Art
New York Historical Society
Whitney Museum of American Art
The Brooklyn Museum

*Rochester*
Memorial Art Gallery of the University
   of Rochester

*Syracuse*
Everson Museum of Art of Syracuse
   and Onondaga County

*Utica*
Munson-Williams-Proctor Institute,
   Museum of Art

**North Carolina**
*Charlotte*
Mint Museum

*Greensboro*
Weatherspoon Art Gallery

*Raleigh*
North Carolina Museum of Art

**Ohio**
*Akron*
Akron Art Museum

*Cincinnati*
Cincinnati Art Museum

Taft Museum

*Cleveland*
Cleveland Museum of Art

*Columbus*
Gallery of Fine Art,
   Ohio State University

*Dayton*
Dayton Art Institute

*Oberlin*
Allen Memorial Art Museum,
   Oberlin College

*Toledo*
Toledo Museum of Art

**Oklahoma**
*Norman*
Museum of Art, University of
   Oklahoma

*Oklahoma City*
National Cowboy Hall of Fame and
   Western Heritage Center
Oklahoma Museum of Art

*Tulsa*
Thomas Gilcrease Institute of
   American History and Art

**Oregon**
*Eugene*
Museum of Art, University
   of Oregon

*Portland*
Portland Art Museum

**Pennsylvania**
*Chadds Ford*
Brandywine River Museum

*Philadelphia*
Barnes Foundation
Pennsylvania Academy of the
   Fine Arts
Philadelphia Museum of Art

*Pittsburgh*
Museum of Art, Carnegie Institute

**Rhode Island**
*Providence*
Museum of Art, Rhode Island School
  of Design

**South Carolina**
*Greenville*
Greenville County Museum of Art
*Murrells Inlet*
Brookgreen Gardens

**South Dakota**
*Brookings*
South Dakota Memorial Art Gallery

**Tennessee**
*Chattanooga*
Hunter Museum of Art
*Memphis*
Memphis Brooks Museum of Art
Dixon Gallery and Gardens
*Nashville*
The Parthenon
Tennessee Botanical Gardens and
  Fine Arts Center, Inc.
Carl Van Vechten Gallery of
  Fine Arts, Fisk University

**Texas**
*Austin*
Archer M. Huntington Art Gallery,
  University of Texas at Austin
*Dallas*
Dallas Museum of Art
*El Paso*
El Paso Museum of Art
*Fort Worth*
Amon Carter Museum of Western Art
*Fort Worth Art Museum*
Kimbell Art Museum
*Houston*
The Houston Museum of Fine Arts

**Utah**
*Provo*
B.F. Larsen Gallery
Brigham Young University Art
  Museum
*Salt Lake City*
Utah Museum of Fine Arts,
  University of Utah
*Springville*
Springville Museum of Art

**Vermont**
*Bennington*
Bennington Museum
*Middlebury*
Johnson Gallery, Middlebury
  College
*Shelburne*
Shelburne Museum, Inc.

**Virginia**
*Charlottesville*
University of Virginia Art Museum
*Newport News*
Mariners Museum
*Norfolk*
Chrysler Museum
*Richmond*
Virginia Museum of Fine Arts
*Williamsburg*
Abby Aldrich Rockefeller Folk
  Art Center

**Washington**
*Pullman*
Museum of Art, Washington State
  University
*Seattle*
Seattle Art Museum
Henry Art Gallery, University of
  Washington
*Tacoma*
Tacoma Art Museum

**West Virginia**
*Huntington*
Huntington Galleries

**Wisconsin**
*Madison*
Elvehjem Museum of Art,
  University of Wisconsin-Madison
*Milwaukee*
Milwaukee Art Museum

**Wyoming**
*Cody*
Buffalo Bill Historical Center, The
  Whitney Gallery of Western Art
*Laramie*
Art Museum, University of
  Wyoming
*Rock Springs*
Community Fine Arts Center

# Publications*

**American Artist** (M)
1 Color Court
Marion, OH 43306

**American Collectors Journal** (T)
P.O. Box 407
Kewanee, IL 61443

**Americana** (M)
Subscription Office
205 West Center Street
Marion, OH 43302

**The Antiquarian** (T)
Box 798
Huntington, NY 11743

**The Antique Gazette** (T)
929 Davidson Drive
Nashville, TN 37205

**Antique Market Report** (M)
WEB Publications, Inc.
15100 West Kellogg
P.O. Box 12830
Wichita, KS 67277

**Antique Market Tabloid** (T)
10822 Childs Court
Silver Springs, MD 20901

**Antique Monthly** (T)
1305 Greensboro Avenue
P.O. Drawer 2
Tuscaloosa, AL 35402

**Antique Press** (T)
12403 N. Florida Avenue
Tampa, FL 33612

**The Antique Trader Weekly** (T)
P.O. Box 1050
Dubuque, IA 52001

**Antique Week** (T)
27 N. Jefferson
P.O. Box 90
Knightstown, IN 46148

**Antiques (The Magazine Antiques)**
(M)
980 Madison Avenue, 3rd Floor
New York, NY 10021

**Antiques & Collecting Hobbies** (M)
1006 South Michigan Avenue
Chicago, IL 60605

**Antiques and the Arts Weekly/
 The Newtown Bee** (T)
Newtown, CT 06470

**Antiques West** (T)
3315 Sacramento Street
San Francisco, CA 94118

**Art & Antiques** (M)
89 Fifth Avenue
New York, NY 10003

**Art & Auction** (M)
250 West 57th Street, Room 215
New York, NY 10019

**The Art/Antiques Investment
 Report** (N)
99 Wall Street
New York, NY 10005

**Art in America** (M)
980 Madison Avenue
New York, NY 10021

**ARTnews** (N)
P.O. Box 969
Farmingdale, NY 11737

---

*Key:* (J) - Journal, (M) - Magazine, (N) - Newsletter, (T) - Tabloid.

**The ARTnewsletter** (N)
5 West 37th Street
New York, NY 10018

**Art Today** (M)
WEB Publications, Inc.
15100 W. Kellogg
Wichita, KS 67235

**Artweek** (T)
1628 Telegraph Avenue
Oakland, CA 94612

**Art/World** (T)
1295 Madison Avenue
New York, NY 10128

**Avenues to Art** (M)
Big Pine, CA 93513

**Antiques & Fine Art** (M)
434 South First Street
San Jose, CA 95113

**Cape Cod Antiques Monthly** (T)
503 Rt. 6A
P.O. Box 340
E. Sandwich, MA 02537

**Collector** (T)
467 North Main Street
Pomono, CA 91768

**The Collector** (T)
Box 158
105 South Buchanan
Heyworth, IL 61745

**Collectors Journal** (T)
421 First Avenue, Box 601
Vinton, IA 52349

**Collector's News &**
  **The Antique Reporter** (T)
P.O. Box 156
506 Second Street
Grundy Center, IA 50638

**The Connoisseur** (M)
P.O. Box 10107
Des Moines, IA 50350

**Fine Art and Auction Review** (T)
2227 Granville Street
Vancouver, B.C. V6H 3G1

**Joel Sater's Antiques**
  **and Auction News** (T)
P.O. Box 500
Mount Joy, PA 17552

**Kovels on Antiques**
  **and Collectibles** (N)
P.O. Box 22200
Beachwood, OH 44122

**Leonard's Price Index**
  **of Art Auctions** (J)
30 Valentine Park
Newton, MA 02165

**Maine Antique Digest (M.A.D.)** (T)
P.O. Box 645
71 Main Street
Waldoboro, ME 04572

**Mass Bay Antiques** (T)
Circulation Department
2 Washington Street
Box 192
Ipswich, MA 01938

**midAtlantic Antiques Magazine** (T)
P.O. Box 908
Henderson, NC 27536

**New England Antiques Journal** (T)
4 Church Street
Ware, MA 01082

**The New York Almanac** (T)
P.O. Box 335
Lawrence, NY 11559

**New York-Pennsylvania Collector** (T)
Fishers, NY 14453

**Ohio Antique Review** (T)
P.O. Box 538
Worthington, OH 43085

**Renninger's Antique Guide** (T)
P.O. Box 495
Lafayette Hill, PA 19444

**Southern Antiques** (T)
P.O. Box 1550
Lake City, FL 32056

**Southwest Art** (M)
P.O. Box 13037
Houston, TX 77219-3037

**The Upper Canadian** (T)
P.O. Box 1171
Kingston, Ontario K7L 4Y8
Canada

**West Art** (T)
P.O. Box 6868
Auburn, CA 95604

**West Coast Peddler** (T)
P.O. Box 5134
Whittier, CA 90607

**Yesteryear** (T)
P.O. Box 2
Princeton, WI 54968

# Auction Houses

**Neal Alford Company**
4139 Magazine Street
New Orleans, Louisiana 70115
(504) 899-5329

**F.O. Bailey Auction Gallery**
141 Middle Street
Portland, Maine 04101
(207) 744-1479

**James R. Bakker**
370 Broadway
Cambridge, MA 02139
(617) 864-7067

**Frank H. Boos Gallery, Inc.**
420 Enterprise Court
Bloomfield Hills, Michigan 48013
(313) 332-1500

**Richard A. Bourne Co., Inc.**
Corporation Street
Hyannis, Massachusetts 02601
Mail: P.O. Box 141
Hyannis Port, Massachusetts 02647
(617) 775-0797

**Butterfield & Butterfield**
220 San Bruno Avenue
San Francisco, California 94103
(415) 673-1362

**Caropreso Gallery**
136 High Street
Lee, Massachusetts
(413) 243-3424

**Chase Gilmore Art Galleries**
724 West Washington
Chicago, IL 60606
(312) 648-1690

**Chicago Art Galleries, Inc.**
20 West Hubbard Street
Chicago, Illinois 60610
(312) 645-0686

**Christie, Manson & Woods
    International, Inc.**
502 Park Avenue
New York, New York 10022
(212) 546-1000

**Christie's East**
219 East 67th Street
New York, New York 10021
(212) 606-0400

**Jim Depew Galleries**
1860 Piedmont Road, NE
Atlanta, Georgia 30324
(404) 874-2286

**J.C. Devine, Inc.**
Auctioneers and Appraisers
P.O. Box 413, Savage Road
Milford, New Hampshire 03055
(603) 673-4967

**Douglas Auctioneers**
Route 5
South Deerfield, Massachusetts 01373
(413) 665-2877

**William Doyle Galleries**
175 East 87th Street
New York, New York 10128
(212) 427-2730

**Du Mouchelle Art Galleries**
409 E. Jefferson
Detroit, Michigan 48226
(313) 963-6255

**Dunning's Auction Service, Inc.**
P.O. Box 866
Elgin, IL 60121
(312) 741-3483

**Robert C. Eldred Co., Inc.**
Route 6A, Box 796
East Dennis, Massachusetts 02641
(617) 385-3116

**Fine Arts Co. of Philadelphia**
2317 Chestnut Street
Philadelphia, Pennsylvania 19103
(215) 564-3644

**Samuel T. Freeman & Co.**
1808 Chestnut Street
Philadelphia, Pennsylvania 19103
(215) 563-9275

**Garth's Auctions, Inc.**
2690 Stratford Road
P.O. Box 369
Delaware, Ohio 43105
(614) 362-4771

**Morton M. Goldberg Auction Galleries, Inc.**
215 N. Rampart Street
New Orleans, Louisiana 70112
(504) 529-5578

**Guernsey's**
136 East 73rd Street
New York, New York 10021
(212) 794-2280

**Hanzel Galleries**
1120 South Michigan Avenue
Chicago, Illinois 60605
(312) 922-6234

**Willis Henry Auctions**
22 Main Street
Marshfield, Massachusetts 02050
(617) 834-7774

**Leslie Hindman Auctioneers**
215 West Ohio Street
Chicago, Illinois 60610
(312) 670-0010

**F.B. Hubley & Co., Inc.**
364 Broadway
Cambridge, Massachusetts 02139
(617) 876-2030

**Iroquois Auction Gallery**
Box 66
Port Henry, New York 12974
(518) 546-7003

**James D. Julia**
RFD #1, Box 91
Fairfield, Maine 04937
(207) 453-9725

**Litchfield Auction Gallery**
Route 202
Litchfield, Connecticut 06759
(203) 567-4303

**Lubin Galleries**
30 West 26th Street
New York, New York 10010
(212) 924-3777

**Mapes Auctioneers and Appraisers**
1600 Vestal Parkway West
Vestal, New York 13850
(607) 754-9193

**Paul McInnis**
356 Exeter Road
Hampton Falls, New Hampshire 03844
(603) 778-8989

**Marc J. Matz Gallery**
366-B Broadway
Cambridge, Massachusetts 02139
(617) 661-6200

**Duane Merrill**
32 Beacon Street
S. Burlington, Vermont 05403
(802) 878-2625

**Milwaukee Auction Galleries**
4747 West Bradley Road
Milwaukee, Wisconsin 53223
(414) 355-5054

**Wayne Mock, Inc.**
Box 37
Tamworth, New Hampshire 03886
(603) 323-8749

**Phillips Son & Neale, Inc.**
406 East 79th Street
New York, New York 10021
(212) 570-4830

**Pioneer Auction of Amherst**
Jct. Rt. 116 and 63
N. Amherst, Massachusetts 01059
(413) 253-9914

**John C. Rosselle Co.**
Commercial Drive
Lakeville, Massachusetts 02346
(617) 947-2122

**Selkirk Galleries**
4166 Olive Street
St. Louis, Missouri 63108
(314) 533-1700

**Philip C. Shute Gallery**
50 Turnpike Street
West Bridgewater, Massachusetts 02379
(617) 588-0022

**Robert W. Skinner, Inc.**
Route 117
Bolton, Massachusetts 01740
(617) 779-5528

**C.G. Sloan & Company, Inc.**
919 E. Street, N.W.
Washington, D.C. 20004
(202) 628-1468

**Sotheby's, Inc.**
1334 York Avenue
New York, New York 10021
(212) 606-7000

**Sotheby's Arcade Auctions**
1334 York Avenue
New York, New York 10021
(212) 606-7409

**Stalker Gallery, Inc.**
2975 W. Maple Road
Troy, Michigan 48084
(303) 288-3820

**Texas Art Gallery**
1400 Main Street
Dallas, Texas 75202
(214) 747-8158

**Weschler's**
905 E. St., N.W.
Washington, D.C. 20004
(202) 628-1281

**Gustave White Auctioneers**
37 Bellevue Avenue
P.O. Box 59
Newport, Rhode Island 02840
(401) 847-4250

**Helen Winter Associates**
21 Cooke Street
Plainville, Connecticut 06062
(203) 793-2244

**Wolf's Auction Gallery**
13015 Larchmere Blvd.
Shaker Heights, Ohio 44120
(216) 231-3888

# Indexing Guidelines for Listing Artists' Last Names

These fundamental rules are based on the *Anglo-American Cataloguing Rules* revised in 1979 and published by the American Library Association.*

Try to ascertain how the artist signed his name, or the most common listing of the name, before turning to the general rules.

> *Ex.* The famous American cartoonist Al Capp is listed "CAPP, Al," and not by his given name, Alfred Gerald Caplin.

**English -** Names are listed under the prefix.

> *Ex.* DECAMP, Joseph Rodefer

**Dutch -** The listing is under the part of the name that follows the prefix unless the prefix is "ver."

> *Ex.* GOGH, Vincent van

**French -** Look under the prefix if it is an article (le, la, les) or a contraction of an article and a preposition (du, des, de le, del).

> *Ex.* LE SIDANER, Henri

> If the article and preposition are separate words, look under the part of the name following the preposition.

> *Ex.* LA PAGE, Raymond de

**German -** If the prefix is an article or a contraction of an article and a preposition, look under the prefix (Am, Aus'm, Vom, Zum, Zur). Otherwise, look under the name following the prefix.

> *Ex.* SCHWIND, Moritz Ludwig von

**Italian -** Modern names are catalogued under the prefix.

> *Ex.* DEL LUNGO, Isidoro

> Medieval names are listed under the name that follows the prefix.

> *Ex.* ROBBIA, Luca della

**Spanish -** If the prefix is an article only, look under the article.

> *Ex.* LAS HERAS, Manual Antonio

> Look for other Spanish names under the part following the prefix (de, del, de las).

**Exceptions -** There are exceptions to every rule. If you can't find a name where you think it should be, look under the variants.

> *Ex.* MEYER VON BREMEN, George

---

*Indexes of names in books published prior to 1979 may not conform to these rules.

# Atypical Highs

**BERNARD, Emile**      French 1868-1941      $181,500
*Les Quatre Saisons (recto) and Les Bucherons Miserables (verso): Double-Sided Four Panel Screen* (prov., exhib., lit., 11-14-84, Christie's, #513, each panel 69 x 25½ in., "peinture a la colle" on canvas).

**BLUM, Robert Frederick**      American 1857-1903      $473,000
*The Flower Market, Tokyo* (s. Blum, prov., exhib., lit., exec. c. 1891, 06-03-82, Christie's, #199, 31⅝ x 25⅜ in., oil on canvas).

**COOPER, Abraham**      British 1787-1868      $176,000
*The Arabian "Selim Pacha" With Arab Attendants In An Eastern Landscape* (mono., d. 1860, prov., from The Collection of Coral Petroleum, Inc., 05-22-85, Sotheby's, #3, 28 x 44 in., oil on canvas).

**DALBY, John**      British 1826-1853      $110,000
*Hunting Scenes: "The Middleton - Mounting At Covertside"; "Huntsman And Whipper In With Hounds Going To Draw"; "Full Cry, Crossing The Road";* and *"Crossing A Brook"* (a set of four, all s., 06-10-83, Christie's, #163, 9¼ x 15 in., oil on canvas).

**DAVIS, William M.**      American 1829-1920      $66,000
*Cider Making, Stony Brook* (inits. W.D., 10-22-82, Sotheby's, #3, 15½ x 24 in., oil on canvas).

**DECKER, Joseph**      German/American 1853-1924      $220,000
*Greenings* (s. Joseph Decker, 12-09-83, Christie's, #80, 9 x 11 in., oil on canvas).

**DUNNING, Robert Spear**      American 1829-1905      $187,000
*Cherries In Basket And Hat* (s. R.S. Dunning, d. 1866, also s. and d. verso, 10-24-84, Doyle, #36, 20 x 26½ in., oil on canvas).

**DUVENECK, Frank**      American 1848-1919      $85,250
*Flower Girl* (prov., lit., 05-30-85, Sotheby's, #140A, 24 x 19 in., oil on canvas).

**EICHHOLTZ, Jacob**      American 1776-1842      $44,000
*Mr. and Mrs. Longenecker* (p. 1820, a pair, prov., lit., 10-17-80, Sotheby's, #98, 30 x 25 in., oil on canvas.)

**PETO, John Frederick**      American 1854-1907      $460,000
*For The Track* (s. J.F. Peto, d. 95, 06-01-84, Christie's, #32, 43½ x 29⅞ in., oil on canvas).

**TACK, Augustus Vincent**      American b. 1870      $165,000
*Untitled* (framed by the artist, 10-30-84, Phillips, #1075, 31½ x 34 in., oil on canvas).